D1625095

ADVANCED MATHEMATICS

A PREPARATION FOR CALCULUS

Arthur F. Coxford

Joseph N. Payne

HARCOURT BRACE JOVANOVICH, INC.

New York   Chicago   San Francisco   Atlanta   Dallas

ABOUT THE AUTHORS

ARTHUR F. COXFORD
Associate Professor of Mathematics Education
University of Michigan
Ann Arbor, Michigan

JOSEPH N. PAYNE
Professor of Mathematics Education
University of Michigan
Ann Arbor, Michigan

ABOUT THE COVER
The cover design is adapted from a photograph by Marvin J. Neivert

PICTURE CREDITS
Chapter One Opening: Top left, Chris Reeberg-d.p.i.; background, center right, and bottom, Harbrace.

Chapter Two Opening: Top, Gregory K. Hunt; center, Harbrace; bottom, Eleutherian Mills Historical Library.

Chapter Three Opening: Top left and center left, Gregory K. Hunt; top right, Ewing Galloway; bottom, 3M Company.

Chapter Four Opening: Top, The Bettmann Archive; center left, Brown Brothers; center right, From "Mathematical Games" by Martin Gardner, © 1970, by Scientific American, Inc. All rights reserved; bottom, Fred Ward-Black Star.

Chapter Five Opening: Top, U.S. Forest Service; bottom, New York Daily News Photo.

Chapter Six Opening: Top left, Harbrace; right, Ray Atkeson-d.p.i.; bottom, U.S. Steel.

Chapter Seven Opening: Top, University of California; center, Ewing Galloway; bottom, Harbrace Art.

Chapter Eight Opening: Background, Ewing Galloway; top insert, Editorial Photocolor Archives; bottom insert, U.P.I.

Chapter Nine Opening: Top left, Authenticated News International; top right, Annan Photo Features; center left, Gregory K. Hunt; bottom, Harbrace.

Chapter Ten Opening: Top left, U.S. Air Force; top right, Howard Harrison; bottom, Frank Tartaglia.

Chapter Eleven Opening: Top right, U.P.I.; bottom, Gregory K. Hunt.

Chapter Twelve Opening: Top left, General Motors; top right, California Computer Products, Inc.; bottom, Pictorial Parade.

Chapter Thirteen Opening: Top, Charles Harbutt-Magnum; bottom right, Susan Feinberg-d.p.i.; bottom left, Gregory K. Hunt.

Chapter Fourteen Opening: Top left, Gregory K. Hunt; top right, Franz Kraus-d.p.i.; bottom, Hays—Monkmeyer.

ISBN 0-15-354082-6

Printed in the United States of America

Contents

CHAPTER 1

NUMBERS, RELATIONS, AND FUNCTIONS

Functions are basic to the study of mathematics as well as physics, chemistry, and biology. They are also found in everyday situations such as those shown here.

The oldest known subset of real numbers is the natural (counting) numbers. One particularly useful relationship involving natural numbers is called *mathematical induction*. The idea behind it is suggested by the row of dominoes shown at the bottom of the opposite page. If the first domino is knocked down and the dominoes are spaced as shown then all the dominoes will fall. Therefore, if each domino represented a natural number, what is true for one would be true for all the natural numbers. When would some of the dominoes not fall?

The rational numbers which are a subset of the set of real numbers are used in musical notation. A simple example is found on the keyboard of a piano. The rational number $\frac{440}{220} = \frac{2}{1}$ is the ratio of the frequencies of the two A's separated by an octave interval. All other intervals can also be expressed as rational numbers but the octave is the simplest.

You can set up a relationship between the dots on the maps and the cities they represent. This would represent a one-to-one correspondence. The rule which relates the dots to the cities is a *mapping*.

Sometimes it is necessary to use more than one function in order to get from point A to point B. By combining the functions in a specific order you get what is called a *composite function*. Looking at the picture of traffic in the upper left hand corner you can relate the number of people to the amount of pollution caused by motor vehicles by a composite function. The first function would map the set of people to the set of cars, buses, or trucks. Then the second function would map the set of cars to the amount of pollution produced by each car.

1–1   The Real Numbers

The six statements that you see are about **real numbers,** a set of numbers that is central in the mathematics of this book. Can you decide whether each statement is true or false? Each of the statements involves either a real number, a way to name a real number, or a subclassification of real numbers. (A "bar" over a digit means that the digit repeats indefinitely.)

You may find it hard to believe that **a** is true, but it is. Here is one way to show it.

EXAMPLE.   Show that

$$1 = 0.999 \cdots$$

Let $\qquad\qquad x = 0.999 \cdots \qquad$ **1**

Then $\qquad\quad 10x = 9.999 \cdots \qquad$ **2**

Subtract **1** from **2.**

$$9x = 9$$
$$x = 1$$

TRUE OR FALSE?

a. $1 = 0.999 \cdots$ or
   $1 = 0.\overline{9}$

b. $\frac{1}{3} = 0.3333 \cdots$ or
   $\frac{1}{3} = 0.\overline{3}$

c. $5.050050005 \cdots$ is a repeating decimal.

d. $\sqrt{2} = 1.414 \cdots$
   $= 1.4\overline{14}$

e. $1,\ 0.\overline{9},\ \frac{1}{3}$ are real numbers that are also rational numbers.

f. $\sqrt{2}$ and $5.050050005 \cdots$ are real numbers that are also irrational numbers.

The fact that **a** is true may surprise you. It says that 1 and $0.999 \cdots$ are names for the same number. This situation is a quirk of the decimal system and the fact that the decimal expression $0.999 \cdots$ never ends. In its most general interpretation it says that terminating decimals may be expressed as infinite repeating decimals. For example,

$$\tfrac{1}{8} = 0.125$$

but also

$$\tfrac{1}{8} = 0.1249999 \cdots$$

because $0.0009999 \cdots = 0.001$. (You should verify this.)

This discussion points out the not uncommon phenomenon in mathematics that there are various expressions which denote the same mathematical concept. The fact that $0.\overline{9} = 1$ should not be any more startling than the fact that $\frac{2}{3}$ is also named by $\frac{4}{6}, \frac{20}{30}$, and by as many more expressions as you care to write. In Chapter 5 you will study this phenomenon in more detail.

You can verify that **b** is true by dividing 1 by 3 or by a procedure similar to the one used in the example. **c** is false because one more zero is inserted each time a 5 occurs. Thus there can be no repeat. **d** is false because, as can be shown, $\sqrt{2}$ is irrational and irrational numbers never have a repeating decimal. **e** and **f** are true.

As the above discussion suggests, you may define the real numbers, denoted R, as the set of numbers that can be named with decimals. The set of real numbers in turn can be subclassified into two sets by the nature of the decimal expansions. Those whose decimal expansions are infinite and nonrepeating (such as $\sqrt{2}$, 5.050050005 ··· and π) are called **irrational numbers**. Those whose decimal expansions are terminating or repeating (such as $\frac{1}{8}$, $\frac{2}{3}$, 1, and 2,746) are called **rational numbers**. The set of irrational numbers is denoted "Ir" while "Q" (for "quotient" — see below) is used to denote the set of rational numbers. The union ($\cup$) of Ir and Q is the set of real numbers.

$$\text{Ir} \cup \text{Q} = \text{R}$$

Three useful subsets of Q, and therefore of R, can also be identified. Those rational numbers whose decimal expansion terminates at or before the ones place are called **integers**. The symbol "I" is used to identify the set of integers.

$$\text{I} = \{\cdots, -2, -1, 0, 1, 2, \cdots\}$$

When the set of negative integers is removed from the set I, the result is the set of **whole numbers** W.

$$\text{W} = \{0, 1, 2, 3, 4, 5, \cdots\}$$

The set of numbers obtained by removing zero from W is the set of **natural numbers** N.

$$\text{N} = \{1, 2, 3, 4, 5, \cdots\}$$

The diagram illustrates how the sets N, W, I, Q, Ir and R are related.

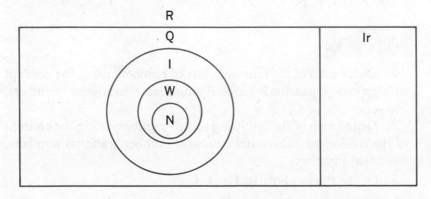

At times an alternate description of the set of rational numbers is useful. It is

$$Q = \left\{ \frac{r}{s} : r \in I \text{ and } s \in N \right\}.$$

("$r \in I$" is read "r is an element of set I")

Describing Q in this manner leads to expressions like

$$-\frac{2}{3}, \frac{1}{7}, \frac{10}{100}, \frac{471}{10}$$

to represent rational numbers. You should be able to demonstrate that a rational number expressed as $\frac{r}{s}$, $r \in I$, $s \in N$, is always expressible as a terminating or repeating infinite decimal (See Exercise 37.)

Now try these

▬ Check yourself on the symbolism of sets. Match each symbol in the column on the left with a phrase in the column on the right.

1. { }   a. is an element of
2. ∪   b. intersection
3. ∈   c. the set of all x such that
4. ∉   d. union
5. {x: }   e. is not an element of
6. ∩   f. the set
7. ⊆   g. is a subset of

▬ Classify each number as a member of N, W, I, Q, Ir, or R Some numbers may belong to more than one set.

8. 3   9. −3   10. $\sqrt{5}$ 11. $\frac{7}{3}$

Answers: 1. f.   2. d.   3. a.   4. e.   5. c.   6. b.   7. g.
8. R, Q, I, W, N.   9. R, I, Q.   10. R, Ir.   11. R, Q.

Checkpoint

1. Define each of the following sets of numbers using the concept of decimal expansion: rational numbers, irrational numbers, integers.

2. Define each of the following sets of numbers using the concept of the ratio of an integer and a natural number: rational numbers, irrational numbers.

3. Define the symbols R, Ir, Q, I, W, N.

Exercises

A ▬ Classify each number as a member of N, W, I, Q, Ir or R. Some numbers may belong to more than one set.

1. $\frac{7}{2}$ 2. $\sqrt{2}$ 3. 0   4. -17
5. 8   6. $0.101001\cdots$ 7. $0.\overline{101}$ 8. $-\sqrt{7}$
9. 1.31   10. 1235.78901   11. $1.0\overline{9}$ 12. $8.999\cdots$

▬ Say whether each statement is *True* or *False*.

13. $-5 \in W$ 14. $0 \in W$ 15. $R \subseteq Ir$
16. $N \subseteq I$ 17. $I \subseteq Ir$ 18. $W \subseteq Q$
19. $W \cup N \subseteq W$ 20. $W \cap N \subseteq N$ 21. $I \in Q$
22. $Ir \cap Q \subseteq R$ 23. $0 \in Ir$ 24. $Q \cup N = N$

B ▬ Give a fractional name for each rational number.

25. 1.25   26. 21.478   27. 0.1043

Example. $5.\overline{14}$, or $5.141414\cdots$
$5.\overline{14} = 5 + 0.\overline{14}$ Let $S = 0.\overline{14}$. Then, $100S = 14.\overline{14}$, and $100S - S = 14$. Thus, $99S = 14$, or $S = \frac{14}{99}$. $5.\overline{14} = 5 + \frac{14}{99}$, or $\frac{509}{99}$.

28. $2.\overline{45}$ 29. $0.00\overline{9}$ 30. $1.30\overline{9}$
31. $37.37\overline{141}$ 32. $0.0\overline{9}$ 33. $0.5\overline{0}$

▬ Show that the two expressions name the same number.

34. 0.001 and $0.000\overline{9}$ 35. 1.14 and $1.13\overline{9}$ 36. $2.\overline{0}$ and $1.\overline{9}$

C 37. Write an argument you would use with a classmate to convince him of the validity of the statement: *Every rational number expressed as a fraction $\frac{r}{s}$, $r \in I$, $s \in N$ can be expressed as a terminating decimal or as a repeating infinite decimal.* Hint: Consider the number of possible remainders when r is divided by s.

38. Examine each fraction. Which are usually associated with terminating decimal expressions? with infinite decimal expressions?

a. $\frac{1}{5}$ b. $\frac{1}{3}$ c. $\frac{1}{4}$ d. $\frac{1}{15}$
e. $\frac{1}{14}$ f. $\frac{1}{200}$ g. $\frac{1}{8}$ h. $\frac{1}{625}$

39. Factor each denominator of the fractions in Exercise 38. What do you notice about the factors of the denominators of the fractions expressible as terminating decimals? the others?

40. Generalize your observations of Exercise 39. Test the generalization several times. Argue that your generalization is valid.

1–2 Postulates, Definitions, and Proof

The fundamental operations defined on the real numbers are addition and multiplication. Each of these is an example of a **binary operation** because it associates every ordered pair of numbers with a unique number. For example "+" associates the pair (2, 3) with the number 5. The mathematical system consisting of R and the operations "+" and "×" has the following eleven properties which are called the **Field Postulates.** The Field Postulates are subdivided into three subcategories: I Addition, II Multiplication and III Addition and Multiplication. (In the material that follows new symbols are used. For example "$\forall a \in$ R, $\exists - a \in$ R" means "For each real number a there exists a real number $-a$". Think of the words "all" and "exists" when using the symbols "$\forall$" and "$\exists$".)

I <u>Addition</u>: a, b, $c \in$ R

Postulate 1 Any two numbers, a and b, have a unique sum, $a + b \in$ R. (Closure Property)

Postulate 2 $a + b = b + a$ (Commutative Property)

Postulate 3 $a + (b + c) = (a + b) + c$ (Associative Property)

Postulate 4 $\exists$ a number 0 such that $\forall a \in$ R, $a + 0 = a$. (Identity Property)

Postulate 5 $\forall a \in$ R, $\exists - a \in$ R such that $a + -a = 0$. (Inverse Property)

A rough translation of Postulate 4 is, "Some number is an identity number for every number." It can be shown that this identity number is unique. (See Theorem 1–2 on page 10.) Thus it can be given a name: *zero.*

Postulate 5 can be translated as "Every number has an opposite." Thus the symbol "$-a$" can be read "opposite of a". The terminology "negative of a" is also sometimes used for "$-a$" but this may lead to confusion when using negative numbers. For example the positive number $-(-3)$ is most accurately thought of as "the opposite of negative three." It can be shown that every number's opposite is unique. (See Exercise 6.) Therefore, $-a$ will be referred to as "*the* opposite of a" from now on.

Postulates 6–10 deal with the properties of real numbers that hold under the operation of multiplication. The same properties that hold under the operation of addition are true for multiplication, except that zero has no multiplicative inverse.

II Multiplication: $a, b, c \in R$

Postulate 6 Any two numbers, a and b, have a unique product, $a \cdot b \in R$.   (Closure Property)

Postulate 7 $a \cdot b = b \cdot a$ (Commutative Property)

Postulate 8 $a \cdot (b \cdot c) = (a \cdot b) \cdot c$ (Associative Property)

Postulate 9 $\exists$ a number 1 such that $\forall a \in R, a \cdot 1 = a$. (Identity Property)

Postulate 10 $\forall a \in R \ (a \neq 0), \exists \frac{1}{a} \in R$ such that $a \cdot \frac{1}{a} = 1$. (Inverse Property)

The number 1 in Postulate 9 is called *one*. The number $\frac{1}{a}$ in Postulate 10 is called the **reciprocal** of the number a. From what has preceded the following definitions can now be stated.

Definitions   To subtract b from a, add the opposite of b to a.

$$\forall a, b \in R \qquad a - b = a + (-b)$$

To divide a by b, multiply a by the reciprocal of b.

$$\forall a, b \in R, b \neq 0 \qquad a \div b = a \cdot \frac{1}{b}$$

The property that relates multiplication and addition is the **Distributive Property of Multiplication over Addition.**

III Addition and Multiplication

Postulate 11 $\forall a, b, c \in R, \ a(b + c) = ab + ac$ (Distributive Property)

Recall that "$a = b$" means that a and b name the same number or that a may be substituted for b in any expression involving b. "Equality" satisfies the following properties:

IV Equality

Postulate 12 $\forall a \in R$, $a = a$.

Postulate 13 $\forall a, b \in R$, "$a = b$" implies "$b = a$."

Postulate 14 $\forall a, b, c \in R$ "$a = b$ and $b = c$" implies "$a = c$."

The *Field Postulates* (I–III) and the *Equality Postulates* (IV) together can be used to prove many relationships that are familiar to you.

The proof of Theorem 1–1, which follows, is an example of a **direct proof.** This is the type you have used most often in the past. Recall that a **theorem** is any statement proved from postulates and definitions. Furthermore, once a theorem has been proved, it can be used in the proof of other theorems. Theorem 1–1 is proved using Postulates 2, 3, 4 and 5.

Theorem 1–1 (Law of Cancellation for Addition) For all real numbers, if $a + b = a + c$, then $b = c$.

Proof: By Postulate 5, $\exists -a$ such that $a + (-a) = 0$.

Adding $-a$ to both sides of $a + b = a + c$, you have

$$(-a) + (a + b) = (-a) + (a + c)$$

Then,	$[a + (-a)] + b = [a + (-a)] + c$	(Postulates 2 and 3.)
	$0 + b = 0 + c$	(Postulate 5.)
	$b + 0 = c + 0$	(Postulate 2.)
	$b = c$	(Postulate 4.)

Sometimes a proof can be done in two or more parts. An important instance of this occurs when a theorem uses the phrase "if and only if". Such theorems can always be interpreted as two theorems, one the converse of the other. The following Example illustrates a two part proof that results from a theorem in which the phrase "if and only if" is used.

EXAMPLE. Prove that $a - b = c$ if and only if (iff) $a = c + b$.

You may recall from your previous work with logic that "if p then q," "p only if q," and "q if p" all have the same meaning. If the p and q are interchanged in the above three formulas then the *converse* of the original statement is obtained. In the example a statement and its converse must each be proved since "p iff q" means "if p then q *and* if q then p."

Part 1: If $a - b = c$ then $a = c + b$.

  Proof:

$$a - b = c$$
$$a + (-b) = c \qquad \text{(Definition of Subtraction)}$$

Adding b to both sides,

$$[a + (-b)] + b = c + b.$$

Then,
$$a + [-b + b] = c + b \qquad \text{(Why?)}$$
$$a + 0 = c + b \qquad \text{(Why?)}$$
$$a = c + b \qquad \text{(Why?)}$$

Part 2: If $a = c + b$ then $a - b = c$.

  Proof:

$$a = c + b$$

Subtract b from both sides,

$$a + (-b) = [c + b] + (-b)$$
$$a - b = c + [b + (-b)] \qquad \text{(Why?)}$$
$$a - b = c + [b - b] \qquad \text{(Why?)}$$
$$a - b = c + 0 \qquad \text{(Why?)}$$
$$a - b = c. \qquad \text{(Why?)}$$

Therefore $a - b = c$ iff $a = c + b$.

As you can see, in a direct proof you reason directly toward your goal. Another type of proof that occurs frequently in more advanced mathematics is the **indirect proof.** For an indirect proof, it is sufficient to show that the opposite of your goal *is not true.* If there are only two possibilities, and the opposite of a statement is not true, then the statement is true.

The proof of Theorem 1–2, which follows, is an example of an indirect proof. You are trying to prove the uniqueness of zero. You assume zero is not unique and try to show that a contradiction results.

Theorem 1–2 (Uniqueness of zero) There is only one real number n such that $a + n = a$ for all a.

Proof: From Postulate 4 you know that there is one number, 0, that has the property of Theorem 1–2. Now suppose that there is some other real number n, $n \neq 0$, that also has that property. Then both "$a + 0 = a$" and "$a + n = a$" are true. Now since $n \in R$, Postulate 4 may be used. Thus,

$$n + 0 = n. \qquad \textbf{1}$$

Furthermore, using the assumption that $\forall a \in R$, $a + n = a$ and the fact that $0 \in R$, $0 + n = 0$.

From the Commutative Postulate,

$$n + 0 = 0 + n,$$

so

$$n + 0 = 0. \qquad \textbf{2}$$

Combining equations **1** and **2** gives

$$n = n + 0 = 0, \quad \text{or} \quad n = 0.$$

This contradicts the assumption that $n \neq 0$ is true. Thus, 0 is unique.

Exercises

A ▬ For each subset of R state which, if any, of the Field Postulates do not hold.

    1. N   **2.** W   **3.** I   **4.** Q   **5.** Ir

B   **6.** Prove: The opposite of a number is unique.

    7. Prove: $-0 = 0$. (*Hint:* By Postulate 4, $0 + 0 = 0$ and by Postulate 5 $0 + (-0) = 0$. Use the cancellation property.)

    8. Prove: $-(-a) = a$. (*Hint:* By Postulate 5, $-a + -(-a) = 0$ and $a + (-a) = 0$. Use the cancellation property.)

    9. Prove: $0 - a = -a$. (*Hint:* Use the definition of subtraction.)

    10. Prove: $-(a + b) = -a + (-b)$. (*Hint:* Prove that $(a + b) + [(-a) + (-b)] = 0$ and use the result of Exercise 6.)

    11. Prove: $-(a - b) = b + (-a)$.

    12. Prove: There is only one number having the property of Postulate 9. This is the *Uniqueness of One*.

    13. Prove the Cancellation Property for Multiplication:

$$\text{If } a \cdot b = a \cdot c \text{ and } a \neq 0, \text{ then } b = c$$

    14. Prove: The reciprocal of a ($\neq 0$) is unique. (See Exercise 6.)

C **15.** Prove: $a \cdot 0 = 0$. (*Hint:* $a \cdot 0 + 0 = a \cdot 0 = a(0 + 0) = a \cdot 0 + a \cdot 0$. Use the Cancellation Property for Addition on the first and last members.)

16. Prove: If $xy = 0$, then $x = 0$ *or* $y = 0$. (The compound sentence $x = 0$ *or* $y = 0$ is true if $x = 0$ is true, $y = 0$ is true, or both are true.)

17. Prove: $a \div b = c$ if and only if $a = c \cdot b$, $b \neq 0$.

1–3 Order Relations

The real numbers can be placed in a one-to-one correspondence with the points of a line. When this is done in the usual manner, the result appears like that below.

Notice that the real numbers are partitioned into three disjoint sets: numbers to the right of zero, zero, and numbers to the left of zero. Those numbers shown to the right of zero are positive numbers, and those shown to the left of zero are negative numbers. A number $x \in R$ is negative if and only if $-x$ is positive. For example, if $-2 = x$, then $-x = -(-2) = 2$, which is positive. The number 0 is neither positive nor negative.

The following assumptions are made about the real numbers and the idea of positiveness.

Order Postulates

Postulate 15 Some numbers are positive.

Postulate 16 For any number a, exactly one of the following three statements is true.

$$a = 0, a \text{ is positive, or } -a \text{ is positive.}$$

Postulate 17 The sum of two positive numbers is positive.

Postulate 18 The product of two positive numbers is positive.

Why these postulates and not some other ones? Experience has shown that these postulates, when combined with appropriate definitions, give a secure basis for understanding order relationships. Check to see that you find the Order Postulates reasonable.

Order among the real numbers is indicated by signs such as $<$, $>$, $\leq$, $\geq$, and $=$. Intuitively you know that $a < b$ is true whenever a is shown to the left of b on the real line. For example, $-2 < 5$ is true. The formal definition of "is less than" is based on the Order Postulates.

> **Definition** The symbol $<$ is defined by either of the two statements below.
>
> **i.** $a < b$ if and only if $b - a$ is positive
>
> **ii.** $a < b$ if and only if there is a positive real number x such that $a + x = b$.

(Show that i and ii are equivalent.)

EXAMPLE 1. Prove that $-2 < 5$ is a true statement.

You must find a positive number x such that
$$-2 + x = 5.$$

Since $$-2 + 7 = 5$$

and $$7 > 0$$

then $$-2 < 5.$$

EXAMPLE 2. Prove: $0 < a$ if and only if a is positive.

i. If a is positive, then $0 + a = a$, and by the definition of $<$, the sentence $0 < a$ is true.

ii. If $0 < a$, then there is a positive x such that $0 + x = a$. But $0 + x = x$, so $x = a$. Since x is positive, so is a.

The familiar relations denoted by

"$>$" (is greater than)

"$\leq$" (is less than or equal to)

and "$\geq$" (is greater than or equal to)

are defined in terms of $<$ as follows:

Definitions   **i.** $a > b$ if and only if $b < a$.

                 ii. $a \le b$ if and only if $a < b$ or $a = b$.

                 iii. $a \ge b$ if and only if $a > b$ or $a = b$.

Several familiar properties of inequality follow from the definition of $<$ and the Order Postulates.

Theorem 1–3 (The Trichotomy Property) $\forall a, b \in R$ exactly one of the following statements is true: $a < b$, $a = b$, or $b < a$.

Proof: $a < b$ if and only if $b - a$ is positive.

        $a = b$ if and only if $b - a = 0$.

        $b < a$ if and only if $a - b = -(b - a)$ is positive.

By Postulate 16, exactly one of the statements below is true.

    i. $b - a$ is positive.   **ii.** $b - a = 0$.   **iii.** $-(b - a)$ is positive.

Therefore, exactly one of $a < b$, $a = b$, $b < a$ is true, and the Trichotomy Property is proved.

Theorem 1–4 (The Transitive Property) $\forall a, b, c \in R$, if $a < b$ and $b < c$ then $a < c$.

Outline of Proof: $b - a$ and $c - b$ are positive. Thus $(b - a) + (c - b)$ is positive. Show that this means that $(c - a)$ is positive.

Theorem 1–5 (The Addition Property) $\forall a, b, c \in R$, if $a < b$ then $a + c < b + c$.

The proof is left for you, as is the proof of the following theorem.

Theorem 1–6 (The Multiplication Property) $\forall a, b \in R$ and all positive numbers $c \in R$, if $a < b$, then $ac < bc$.

Exercises

A ━━ Determine whether each statement 1–8 is true or false. If a statement is false, explain why it is false.

  1. $2 < 5$ **2.** $-5 < 0$ **3.** $7 < 6$ **4.** $-2 \leq -1$

  5. $-5 \leq -3$ **6.** $2 \geq 2$ **7.** $-3 \leq -5$ **8.** $-2 \geq 1$

  9. If $2 < 5$, why does it follow that $6 < 15$?

  10. If $-4 < 2$, why does it follow that $-1 < 5$?

  11. Given $x < 2$ and $2 < z$, what can you conclude about the order of x and z?

  12. Given $x, y \in R$, what can you conclude about x and y?

B   **13.** Prove Theorem 1–4.

  14. Prove Theorem 1–5.

  15. Prove the converse of Theorem 1–5.

  16. Prove Theorem 1–6.

  17. Prove the converse of Theorem 1–6.

  18. Is it true that if $a \leq b$ and $b \leq c$, then $a \leq c$? If not, produce a counterexample. If true, prove it.

C   **19.** Prove: $a < 0$ if and only if a is negative. (*Hint:* Show that $a < 0$ implies $-a$ is positive.)

  20. Assume that the product of two negative numbers is a positive number. Use this assumption to prove:

$$\text{If } a < b \text{ and } c \text{ is negative, then } ca > cb.$$

  21. Prove: If $x \leq y$ and $y \leq x$, then $x = y$.

1–4 Graphs

The real number line is a *geometric model* of the real numbers. A number line is illustrated below.

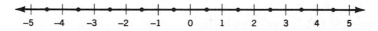

The great value of the real line is that it allows sets of numbers to be represented visually. A geometric representation of a set of real numbers by a set of points is called a **graph.** Some graphs of sets of real numbers are illustrated in Example 1.

EXAMPLE 1. Graph the sets of real numbers. Describe each set of points geometrically.

a. $\{r : r = -2 \; or \; r = 3\}$
b. $\{x : -1 \leq x\}$
c. $\{t : t < 5\}$
d. $\{y : -1 \leq y \leq 4\}$
e. $\{k : 3 < k \; or \; k < -2\}$

a.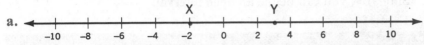

The graph of $\{r : r = -2 \; or \; r = 3\}$ is the set of 2 points $\{X, Y\}$.

b.

The graph of $\{x : -1 \leq x\}$ is a **ray** with its endpoint at -1.
The dot at -1 indicates that that point is included in the graph.

c.

The graph of $\{t : t < 5\}$ is a **half line** (a ray without the endpoint).
The "open circle" at 5 indicates that the point is not included in the graph.

d.

The graph of $\{y : -1 \leq y \leq 4\}$ is a **segment**. The points of the segment exclusive of the endpoints are between the endpoints. In a similar manner the real numbers corresponding to these points are between -1 and 4.

e.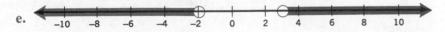

The graph of $\{k : 3 < k \; or \; k < -2\}$ is the union of two half-lines.

Not all the graphs of sets of real numbers can be represented by one of the common geometric figures: point, segment, ray, and half-line. In most cases, however, the graph will be the union of two or more such figures.

There are several sets of real numbers that, along with their graphs, are given special names. The first is the **closed interval.**

Definition The symbol $[a, b]$, where a and b are real numbers and $a < b$, denotes the set of real numbers x such that $a \leq x \leq b$ or the points of the segment whose endpoints have coordinates a and b. $[a, b]$ is a closed interval.

$$[a, b] = \{x : a \leq x \leq b, a, b, x \in \mathrm{R}\} \text{ or its graph.}$$

Similarly, you can define an **open interval.**

Definition The symbol $\langle a, b \rangle$, where $a, b \in \mathrm{R}$ and $a < b$, denotes the set $\{x : a < x < b, a, b, x \in \mathrm{R}\}$ or the graph of this set. $\langle a, b \rangle$ is an open interval.

An open interval is a segment without its endpoints. If one endpoint is included, an interval that is neither closed nor open is the result.

Definitions $[a, b\rangle = \langle a, b \rangle \cup \{a\}$
$\langle a, b] = \langle a, b \rangle \cup \{b\}$

EXAMPLE 2. Graph $[2, 3.5]$, $\langle 2, 3.5 \rangle$, $\langle 2, 3.5]$, and $[2, 3.5\rangle$. What is the set of real numbers associated with each interval?

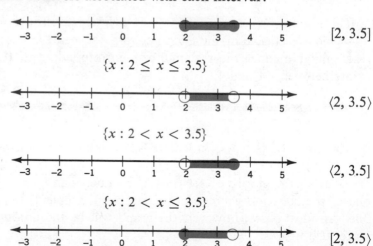

$$\{x : 2 \leq x \leq 3.5\}$$

$$\{x : 2 < x < 3.5\}$$

$$\{x : 2 < x \leq 3.5\}$$

$$\{x : 2 \leq x < 3.5\}$$

Graphs of sets of real numbers are also useful in depicting the solution set of an inequality.

EXAMPLE 3. Solve $5y - 2 > 2y - 8$ where the replacement set is R. Graph the solution set.

The field and order postulates of the real numbers imply that the following inequalities are equivalent to each other.

  ① $5y - 2 > 2y - 8$ (Given)
  ② $5y > 2y - 6$ (Addition of $+2$)
  ③ $3y > -6$ (Addition of $-2y$)
  ④ $y > -2$ (Multiplication by $\frac{1}{3}$)

Thus the solution set is

$$\{y : y > -2, y \in R\}$$

The graph is shown below.

Exercises

A — Graph each set of real numbers.

1. $\{a : a < -1\}$ **2.** $\{b : b \geq 2.5\}$
3. $\{c : c = -2 \text{ or } c = 0\}$ **4.** $\langle 0, 3 \rangle$
5. $\langle 0, 3]$ **6.** $[0, 3]$
7. $[\frac{2}{3}, \frac{7}{4} \rangle$ **8.** $\{d : \frac{2}{3} < d \leq 7\}$
9. $\{k : k \leq 5\}$ **10.** $\langle -2, 3 \rangle \cup [3, 4]$
11. $\langle -2, 3 \rangle \cap [1, 4]$ **12.** $[-2, 3] \cap [-4, 0]$
13. $[-2, 3] \cup [-4, 1]$
14. $\{v : v \in [1, 4] \text{ or } v \in [-4, -1]\}$
15. $\{r : r > -2\} \cap \{r : r < 3\}$ **16.** $\{u : u \leq 5 \text{ and } u \geq 5\}$
17. $\{p : p \geq 0, p \leq 5, p \in W\}$ **18.** $\{q : q \leq -1 \text{ and } q \geq 4\}$
19. $\{x : x \in [1, 3 \rangle \text{ or } x < -2\}$ **20.** $\{y : -3 < y \text{ and } y < 3\}$

— Find the solution set of each inequality if the replacement set is R. Graph each nonempty solution set.

21. $2y + 3 \leq 3y - 2$ **22.** $3y + 7 \geq 5y - 7$
23. $2t - 3 + t < -t + 5$ **24.** $4n > -n$
25. $-\frac{2}{3}n < n - 6$ **26.** $-2t + 5 < -2t - 5$

27. $-t + 5 < t - 5$ 　　　　　　　**28.** $-2(t + 4) > -t - 6$

29. $-39p < 0$ 　　　　　　　　　**30.** $p^2 > -2$

B ━━ Graph as many points of each of the following sets as you find convenient to do (that is, you should stop when points become too close together to show).

31. $\left\{\frac{1}{2}, \frac{1}{4}, \frac{1}{8}, \frac{1}{16}, \ldots, \frac{1}{2^n}, n \in N\right\}$

32. $\left\{1, \frac{1}{2}, \frac{1}{3}, \frac{1}{4}, \frac{1}{5}, \ldots, \frac{1}{n}, n \in N\right\}$

C **33.** $\left\{\frac{1}{2}, \frac{1}{2} + \frac{1}{4}, \frac{1}{2} + \frac{1}{4} + \frac{1}{8}, \ldots, \frac{1}{2} + \frac{1}{4} + \frac{1}{8} + \cdots + \frac{1}{2^n}, n \in N\right\}$

34. $\left\{1, 1 + \frac{1}{2}, 1 + \frac{1}{2} + \frac{1}{3}, \ldots, 1 + \frac{1}{2} + \frac{1}{3} + \cdots + \frac{1}{n}, n \in N\right\}$

1–5　Solving Inequalities

A type of inequality that often appears in working with intervals is one such as $-3 < 2x + 1 < 5$.

Notice that there are two "is less than" signs used in this sentence. The sentence $-3 < 2x + 1 < 5$ is a shorthand way of writing

$$-3 < 2x + 1 \quad and \quad 2x + 1 < 5,$$

which is a **compound inequality** connected by *and*. Thus the solution set will consist of those real numbers that make both inequalities true at the same time. Consequently, the solution of $-3 < 2x + 1 < 5$ is the *intersection* of the solution sets of $-3 < 2x + 1$ and $2x + 1 < 5$.

EXAMPLE 1. Find and graph the solution set of $-3 < 2x + 1 < 5$.

The number that x represents is in the solution set of this inequality, if and only if (iff)

x is in the solution set of $-3 < 2x + 1$	*and*	x is in the solution set of $2x + 1 < 5$.

$$
\begin{array}{ll}
-3 < 2x + 1 & \qquad 2x + 1 < 5 \\
-4 < 2x & \qquad 2x < 4 \\
-2 < x & \qquad x < 2
\end{array}
$$

Thus, the solution set of $-3 < 2x + 1$ is	*and*	The solution set of $2x + 1 < 5$ is
$\{x : -2 < x\}$.		$\{x : x < 2\}$.

18　　CHAPTER 1

The solution set of $-3 < 2x + 1 < 5$ is $\{x : -2 < x\} \cap \{x : x < 2\}$
or
$$\{x : -2 < x \ and \ x < 2\}$$
or
$$\{x : -2 < x < 2\}.$$
The graph is $\langle -2, 2 \rangle$.

Another type of inequality that deserves special mention is one
such as
$$x^2 + x - 6 < 0.$$
Since there is a second-degree term in the expression $x^2 + x - 6$ this
is called a **quadratic inequality**. The procedure for obtaining a solution
depends on the fact that the product of two real numbers is less than
zero if and only if one of the factors is negative and the other is positive.

EXAMPLE 2. Find and graph the solution set of
$$x^2 + x - 6 < 0.$$

First factor $x^2 + x - 6$ to obtain $(x + 3)(x - 2)$. The sentence
$(x + 3)(x - 2) < 0$ is true iff

$x + 3 < 0 \ and \ x - 2 > 0$ or $x + 3 > 0 \ and \ x - 2 < 0.$
$x < -3 \ and \ x > 2$ $x > -3 \ and \ x < 2$

This is clearly impossible,   The solution set is
and the solution set is $\emptyset$. $\{x : -3 < x < 2\}.$

The solution set of $x^2 + x - 6 < 0$, or $(x + 3)(x - 2) < 0$, is then
$$\emptyset \cup \{x : -3 < x < 2\} = \{x : -3 < x < 2\}.$$
The graph is the interval $\langle -3, 2 \rangle$.

Exercises

A ▬ Find the solution set of each inequality. Graph each nonempty
solution set.

    1. $4 < 3x - 2 < 5$ **2.** $0 < 5x + 4 < 6$
    3. $-7 < 2x - 3 < -1$ **4.** $4 > x + 4 > 2$

5. $4 - 2x < 3x + 1 < 7$

6. $5 < -x + 2 < 7$

7. $3x > 4$ *and* $x > 3x - 2$

8. $(x + 1)(x - 2) < 0$

9. $2 > \frac{2}{3}x - 1 > -1$

10. $\frac{1}{6} < \frac{2}{5}x < \frac{1}{3}$

Example. Find and graph the solution set of

$$(x + 3)(x - 2) > 0.$$

The sentence $(x + 3)(x - 2) > 0$ is true iff

$[x + 3 > 0 \ and \ x - 2 > 0]$ *or* $[x + 3 < 0 \ and \ x - 2 < 0]$ (Why?)

$\quad x + 3 > 0 \ and \ x - 2 > 0 \qquad\quad x + 3 < 0 \ and \ x - 2 < 0$

$\qquad x > -3 \ and \ x > 2 \qquad\qquad\quad x < -3 \ and \ x < 2$

The intersection of the solution sets of these inequalities is

$\qquad \{x : x > 2\}.$

The intersection of the solution sets
of these inequalities is

$\qquad \{x : x < -3\}.$

Thus the solution set of $(x + 3)(x - 2) > 0$ is

$$\{x : x > 2\} \cup \{x : x < -3\}.$$

The graph is

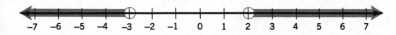

11. $(x - \frac{1}{2})(x + 2) > 0$

12. $x(x - 7) < 0$

13. $x^2 - 5x > 0$

14. $(x - \frac{1}{3})(2x - 4) < 0$

15. $(x - 1)(x - 1) < 0$

16. $(x - 2)(x - 2) > 0$

17. $(x - 1)(x - 1) \leq 0$

18. $(x - 2)(x - 2) \geq 0$

B **19.** $x^2 - 4x < 5$

20. $x^2 + 3x \geq -2$

21. $\frac{-x^2}{10} + \frac{7x}{10} < 1$

22. $(2x - 1)(3x + 2) \leq 0$

23. $16x^2 \leq 1$

24. $x^2 + x + 1 < 0$

25. $2x + 1 < 5 \ or \ 2x - 1 > 9$

26. $5x - 2 < 3 \ or \ -2 < 2x - 6 < 4$

27. $3x - 5 \leq 4 \ and \ -2x + 2 \leq -4$

28. $x^2 - 1 \geq 0 \ and \ 5 < 2x + 5 < 7$

C **29.** $(x - 1)(x - 2)(x - 3) < 0$

30. $(2x - 1)(x + 3)(x - 4) > 0$

31. $(3x - 1)(2x + 3)(x + 2) < 0$

32. $(4x - 6)(x)(x + 2) \geq 0$

33. For what value of k will the solution set of $3x - k < 2$ be $\{x : x < 4\}$?

34. For what value of k will the solution set of $x^2 + x + k < 0$ be $\{x : -3 < x < 2\}$?

35. How is the solution set of $x^2 - 3x + 2 < 0$ related to the solution set of $x^2 - 3x + 2 \geq 0$?

1-6   Mathematical Induction

Suppose that the following claim is made: For all natural numbers, n, the natural number $n^3 + 2n$ is divisible by 3. Is the claim true? Is it false? To find out you might begin by examining several cases.

$$n = 1: \quad 1^3 + 2 \cdot 1 = 3; \qquad 3 \text{ is divisible by 3.}$$
$$n = 2: \quad 2^3 + 2 \cdot 2 = 12; \qquad 12 \text{ is divisible by 3.}$$
$$n = 3: \quad 3^3 + 2 \cdot 3 = 33; \qquad 33 \text{ is divisible by 3.}$$

So far so good. Now check the statement for $n = 4$, $n = 5$, and $n = 6$. What are your results?

One thing is clear: You cannot possibly substantiate the claim for all natural numbers n. Only a finite number of instances could be checked. What you need, then, is a method of proof which verifies the claim for all natural numbers at once. The method of proof sought is **mathematical induction.**

Mathematical induction is based on simple characteristics of the natural numbers. They are stated in the **Axiom of Induction.**

Axiom of Induction: If T is a set of natural numbers with the properties

      i. $1 \in$ T and

      ii. $k \in$ T implies $k + 1 \in$ T,

then T is the set of natural numbers N.

The pair of conditions in the Axiom of Induction uniquely determine the set of natural numbers. Notice that both conditions must be satisfied for the Axiom of Induction to hold. The following example will help to illustrate the point.

For example, consider the following set T.

$$T = \{1, 2, 3\}$$

Clearly $1 \in T$, but it is not true that $k + 1 \in T$ every time $k \in T$, e.g., $3 \in T$ but $4 \notin T$. Thus $T \neq N$.

$$\text{Let } T = \{10, 11, 12, \cdots\}.$$

Clearly if $k \in T$, then $k + 1 \in T$ but $1 \notin T$. Thus, again, $T \neq N$.

The Theorem of Mathematical Induction follows directly.

Theorem 1–7   For every $n \in N$ let P_n be a statement which is either true or false. If

i. P_1 is true and

ii. whenever this statement is true for k, it is true for $k + 1$

then P_n is true for all $n \in N$.

Proof: Let T be the set of natural numbers for which P_n is true.

$$1 \in T \text{ because of i in Theorem 1–7.}$$

$$k + 1 \in T \text{ whenever } k \in T \text{ because of ii.}$$

Thus $T = N$ and P_n is true for all $n \in N$.

To apply the Theorem of Mathematical Induction you must do *two* things: You must verify that P_1 is true. You must also verify that P_{k+1} is true whenever P_k is true.

EXAMPLE 1.   For n a natural number, P_n is the statement:

$$n^3 + 2n \text{ is divisible by 3.}$$

Prove P_n true for all $n \in N$.

The proof is by mathematical induction.

i. *Verify that P_1 is true.*

$$P_1 : 1^3 + 2 \cdot 1 \text{ is divisible by 3.}$$

P_1 is clearly true since $1^3 + 2 \cdot 1 = 3$.

ii. *Verify that whenever P_n is true for a natural number, say $n = k$, then it is true for the next natural number, $n = k + 1$.*

To carry out this portion of the argument, you must assume that P_k is true for some $k \in N$. This assumption is the *induction hypothesis*.

Assume P_k is true; i.e., $k^3 + 2k$ is divisible by 3. Next show that P_k implies P_{k+1}, i.e., prove that P_{k+1} must also be true; i.e., $(k + 1)^3 + 2(k + 1)$ is divisible by 3. First notice that

$$
\begin{aligned}
(k + 1)^3 + 2(k + 1) &= k^3 + 3k^2 + 3k + 1 + 2k + 2 \\
&= (k^3 + 2k) + 3k^2 + 3k + 3 \\
&= P(k) + 3(k^2 + k + 1)
\end{aligned}
$$

The symbol $P(k)$ is used in the last line to stand for "$k^3 + 2k$". It should not be confused with the symbol P_k which stands for the sentence "$k^3 + 2k$ is divisible by 3". Similarly, $P(k + 1)$ stands for "$(k + 1)^3 + 2(k + 1)$".

Since $P(k)$ is divisible by 3 and $3(k^2 + k + 1)$ is divisible by 3, $P(k + 1)$ is also divisible by 3. Thus both conditions of the Theorem of Mathematical Induction are satisfied. You may thus conclude that $n^3 + 2n$ is divisible by 3 for *all* $n \in N$.

EXAMPLE 2. For n a natural number, P_n is the statement:

$$
1 + 2 + 3 + \cdots + n = \frac{n(n + 1)}{2}.
$$

Prove P_n true for all $n \in N$.

i. P_1 is true, since $\frac{1(1 + 1)}{2} = 1$.

ii. Induction hypothesis:

Assume P_k is true; i.e., $1 + 2 + \cdots + k = \frac{k(k + 1)}{2}$.

Prove that P_{k+1} follows from P_k.

The left hand side of P_{k+1} is $1 + 2 + 3 + \cdots + k + (k + 1)$. But this is the left side of P_k with $k + 1$ added. This suggests that a proof may be made by adding $(k + 1)$ to both sides of the true statement P_k.

Thus

$$
\begin{aligned}
1 + 2 + \cdots + k + (k + 1) &= \frac{k(k + 1)}{2} + (k + 1) \\
&= \frac{k(k + 1) + 2(k + 1)}{2} \\
&= \frac{(k + 1)(k + 2)}{2} \\
1 + 2 + \cdots + k + (k + 1) &= \frac{(k + 1)(k + 1 + 1)}{2}
\end{aligned}
$$

The last statement is P_{k+1}. Thus P_{k+1} follows from P_k.

By the Theorem of Mathematical Induction P_n is true for all $n \in N$.

EXAMPLE 3. For n a natural number, P_n is the statement:

$$(1 + p)^n \geq 1 + np, \quad p > -1.$$

Prove P_n true for all $n \in N$.

i. Verify P_1.

$$P_1 : (1 + p)^1 \geq 1 + 1 \cdot p$$

$$1 + p \geq 1 + p, \quad p > -1$$

Thus P_1 is true.

ii. Induction Hypothesis.

Assume P_k is true, i.e., $(1 + p)^k \geq 1 + kp$. Now prove that the truth of P_{k+1} follows from that of P_k. The left hand side of the statement P_{k+1} is $(1 + p)^{k+1} = (1 + p)(1 + p)^k$. The second factor in $(1 + p)(1 + p)^k$ is the left hand side of P_k. This suggests that you may be able to make the proof by beginning with P_k and multiplying by $(1 + p)$. You know that

$$(1 + p)^k \geq 1 + kp.$$

Since, $1 + p \geq 0$ then

$$(1 + p)(1 + p)^k \geq (1 + kp)(1 + p)$$

or $\qquad (1 + p)^{k+1} \geq 1 + kp + p + kp^2 = 1 + (k + 1)p + kp^2.$

Since $kp^2 \geq 0$

$$1 + (k + 1)p + kp^2 \geq 1 + (k + 1)p$$

Thus $\qquad (1 + p)^{k+1} \geq 1 + (k + 1)p + kp^2 \geq 1 + (k + 1)p$

or $\qquad (1 + p)^{k+1} \geq 1 + (k + 1)p$

But this is P_{k+1}! Thus the statement P_n is true for all $n \in N$.

It is important to realize that both parts of the Theorem of Mathematical Induction must be satisfied for P_n to be true for all natural numbers n. For example, suppose P_n is the statement

$$1 + 2 + 3 + \cdots + n = \frac{n(n + 1)}{2} + \frac{(n - 1)}{2}$$

P_1 is true since "$1 = \frac{1(1 + 1)}{2} + \frac{(1 - 1)}{2}$" is true.

In this case, however, you cannot conclude that whenever P_k is true, P_{k+1} is also true because there is no general way to produce P_{k+1} from P_k. Thus P_n is not true for all $n \in N$. The way to disprove this statement is to produce a counterexample, i.e., a natural number for which P_n is not true. P_3 is not true because

$$6 = 1 + 2 + 3 \neq \frac{3(3 + 1)}{2} + \frac{(3 - 1)}{2} = 6 + 1 = 7.$$

On the other hand suppose that P_n is the statement

$$1 + 2 + 3 + \cdots + n = \frac{n(n + 1)}{2} + 17.$$

Then you can show that *if* P_k is true, P_{k+1} must be true also. However, it is impossible to show that P_n is true for *any* n much less for $n = 1$.

Exercises

A ▬ In Exercises 1–12 P_n is given. Prove by Mathematical Induction that P_n is true for all $n \in N$.

1. $1 + 3 + 5 + \cdots + (2n - 1) = n^2$

2. $2 + 4 + 6 + \cdots + 2n = n(n + 1)$

3. $\frac{1}{1 \cdot 2} + \frac{1}{2 \cdot 3} + \cdots + \frac{1}{n(n + 1)} = \frac{n}{n + 1}$

4. $\frac{1}{2} + \frac{1}{2^2} + \cdots + \frac{1}{2^n} = \frac{2^n - 1}{2^n}$

5. $-\frac{1}{2} - \frac{1}{4} - \frac{1}{8} - \cdots - \frac{1}{2^n} = \frac{1 - (2)^n}{2^n}$

6. $(b_1 - b_2) + (b_2 - b_3) + \cdots + (b_n - b_{n+1}) = b_1 - b_{n+1}$

7. $5 + 5 \cdot \frac{1}{3} + 5 \cdot \frac{1}{3^2} + \cdots + 5 \frac{1}{3^{n-1}} = 5 \frac{1 - (\frac{1}{3})^n}{1 - \frac{1}{3}}$

8. $5 + 7 + 9 + \cdots + [5 + 2(n - 1)] = \frac{n(10 + 2n - 2)}{2}$

B   **9.** $a + aq^1 + aq^2 + \cdots + aq^{n-1} = a \frac{1 - q^n}{1 - q}$ $a, q \in R, q \neq 1$

10. $a + (a + d) + (a + 2d) + \cdots + [a + (n - 1)d] =$ ✓
$\frac{n[(2a + (n - 1)d]}{2}$ $a, d \in R$

11. $n^3 - n$ is divisible by 6

12. $1^2 + 2^2 + \cdots + n^2 = \frac{n(n + 1)(2n + 1)}{6}$

13. Prove that the sum of n positive integers is positive. (*Hint:* See Section 1–3, Postulate 17.)

14. Prove that the product of n positive integers is positive. (*Hint:* See Section 1–3, Postulate 18.)

15. Prove that if $x_0 < x_1, x_1 < x_2, x_2 < x_3, x_3 < x_4, \ldots, x_{n-1} < x_n$, then $x_0 < x_n$. (*Hint:* Use Theorem 1–4.)

16. Prove the general distributive law:

$$y(x_1 + x_2 + \cdots + x_n) = yx_1 + yx_2 + \cdots yx_n$$

(*Hint:* Use Postulate 11.)

17. Define a positive integral power for a real number x as follows:

    i. $x^1 = x$ **ii.** $x^{n+1} = x^n \cdot x$

Prove

    a. $x^n = x \cdot x \cdot \ldots x$ (n factors of x.)

    b. $(x \cdot y)^n = x^n \cdot y^n$

    c. $x^m \cdot x^n = x^{m+n}$ (*Hint:* Use induction on n, i.e., show that $x^m \cdot x^1 = x^{m+1}$ and that $x^m x^k = x^{m+k}$ implies that $x^m \times x^{k+1} = x^{m+(k+1)}$

    d. $(x^m)^n = x^{m \cdot n}$

18. If n is a positive integer, **n factorial,** written $n!$, is defined: $n! = 1 \cdot 2 \cdot 3 \cdot \ldots n$. **Zero factorial** is defined: $0! = 1$. If r is a positive integer or zero and if $0 \le r \le n$, the binomial coefficient $\binom{n}{r}$ is defined:

$$\binom{n}{r} = \frac{n!}{(n-r)!r!}$$

    a. Establish the law of Pascal's Triangle:

$$\binom{n+1}{r} = \binom{n}{r-1} + \binom{n}{r}$$

    b. Use the result of **a** to prove that $\binom{n}{r}$ is a positive integer.

1–7   Absolute Value

Let A and B be two points on a number line whose origin is at O. Suppose A is to the left of O and B is to the right of O as depicted in the diagram. Suppose further that segments AO and OB are congruent. Then A and B are the same distance from O. If, for example, the real number associated with A is -6, then the coordinate of B is 6. The distance of each from the origin is 6.

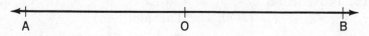

The concept of **absolute value** is used to designate the distance from the origin O of the point associated with the real number x. The absolute value of x is written $|x|$. Since distance is always nonnegative, $|x|$ is always positive or zero. Moreover, since a number x and its additive inverse $-x$ are the same distance from the origin, $|x| = |-x|$. In particular, then, $|-6| = |6| = 6$. These ideas are formalized in the next definition.

Definition For all $x \in R$

$$|x| = \begin{cases} x & \text{if } x \geq 0 \\ -x & \text{if } x < 0 \end{cases}$$

How would you interpret the inequality $|x| < 3$, $x \in R$? When you think in terms of distance from the origin, the interpretation is easy. The sentence $|x| < 3$ describes all those points whose distance from the origin is less than three. This set is shown graphically below.

The graph is the open interval $\langle -3, 3 \rangle$. This interval represents the following set.

$$\{x : -3 < x < 3\}$$

The equivalence of $\{x : |x| < 3\}$ and $\langle -3, 3 \rangle$ is an instance of the next theorem.

Theorem 1–8 For all $x, a \in R$, $a > 0$, $|x| < a$ if and only if $-a < x < a$, i.e., $|x| < a$ if and only if $x \in \langle -a, a \rangle$.

EXAMPLE 1. Express the following interval as an inequality involving an absolute value sign.

$$x \in \langle -2, 2 \rangle$$

Use Theorem 1–8. Since x is an element of an interval of the form $\langle -a, a \rangle$, then $|x| < a$ so $|x| < 2$.

Theorem 1–8 can also be used in solving inequalities involving absolute values.

EXAMPLE 2.   Find and graph the solution set of $|x - 3| < 2, x \in R$.

$$|x - 3| < 2 \text{ iff } -2 < x - 3 < 2$$
$$-2 < x - 3 < 2 \text{ iff } -2 < x - 3 \text{ and } x - 3 < 2$$
$$\text{iff} \quad 1 < x \qquad \text{and } x < 5$$
$$\text{iff} \qquad 1 < x < 5$$

The solution set is $\{x : 1 < x < 5\}$.

The midpoint of the interval $\langle 1, 5 \rangle$ is 3.   All those real numbers that make this inequality true are less than 2 units from 3.

Theorem 1-9   The set of points whose coordinates satisfy

$$|x - a| < b, \quad \forall a, b \in R, \quad b > 0$$

are those points which are less than b units from a.

Proof:

$$|x - a| < b \text{ iff } -b < x - a < b \qquad \text{(Theorem 1-8)}$$
$$\text{iff } -b + a < x < b + a$$
$$\text{or } x \in \langle -b + a, b + a \rangle$$

Distance is also useful in interpreting inequalities such as $|x| > 3$ or $|x - 3| > 2$.   In the first case the set of points must be more than three units from the origin.   In the second the set of points must be more than 2 units from 3.   The graphs are shown below.

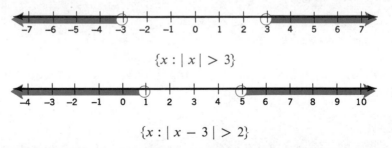

$$\{x : |x| > 3\}$$

$$\{x : |x - 3| > 2\}$$

It is clear then that $|x| > 3$ is equivalent to $x < -3 \text{ or } x > 3$, while $|x - 3| > 2$ is equivalent to $x - 3 < -2 \text{ or } x - 3 > 2$. So $x < 1$ or $x > 5$.

28   CHAPTER 1

Theorem 1–10 $\forall x, a \in \mathbf{R}, a > 0,$

$|x| > a$ if and only if $x < -a$ or $x > a$.

EXAMPLE 3. $|2x - 1| \geq 5$

$$2x - 1 \leq -5 \quad \text{or} \quad 2x - 1 \geq 5$$
$$2x \leq -4 \quad \text{or} \quad 2x \geq 6$$
$$x \leq -2 \quad \text{or} \quad x \geq 3$$

The solution set is $\{x : x \leq -2\} \cup \{x : x \geq 3\}$

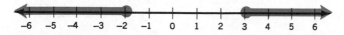

EXAMPLE 4. $|2x - 2| \leq 2 - x$

$$|2x - 2| \leq 2 - x \text{ iff}$$
$$-(2 - x) \leq 2x - 2 \leq 2 - x \text{ iff}$$
$$x - 2 \leq 2x - 2 \text{ and } 2x - 2 \leq 2 - x \text{ iff}$$
$$x \leq 2x \text{ and } 2x \leq 4 - x \text{ iff}$$
$$0 \leq x \text{ and } 3x \leq 4 \text{ iff}$$
$$0 \leq x \text{ and } x \leq \tfrac{4}{3}$$

The solution set is $\{x : x \geq 0\} \cap \{x : x \leq \tfrac{4}{3}\}$
Therefore $\{x : 0 \leq x \leq \tfrac{4}{3}\} = [0, \tfrac{4}{3}].$

Exercises

A ━━ Find and graph the solution set of each sentence. The replacement set for the variables is R.

1. $|x| \leq 2$ **2.** $|t| \geq 5$ **3.** $|r| < 3$
4. $|x + 1| < 3$ **5.** $|x - 1| > 2$ **6.** $|r - 3| \leq 4$
7. $|g + 4| \geq 2$ **8.** $|2 - y| < 3$ **9.** $|5 - r| < 2$
10. $|x - 5| = 4$ **11.** $|13 - (g + 2)| < 1$ **12.** $|3x - 1| < 5$

13. $|5x + 2| \leq 3$ **14.** $|2 - 4t| < 3$
B **15.** $|4 - 2(x - 1)| \leq 3$ **16.** $|3x - 2| \leq 2x - 1$
17. $|x + 5| \leq 3x - 3$ **18.** $|2x - 1| < 3x + 4$
19. $|\tfrac{r}{3} - 2| > r + 1$ **20.** $2|x - 1| < 4x - 2$
21. $\left|\tfrac{3y}{4} - \tfrac{1}{3}\right| > y + 1$ **22.** $|4 - x| < 2x$
23. $|x - (2x + 1)| < \tfrac{1}{2}x - 3$ **24.** $|y - 3| - \tfrac{y}{4} \geq 2$

C **25.** Prove: $|xy| = |x| \cdot |y|$ $x, y \in R$

26. Prove: $\left|\dfrac{x}{y}\right| = \dfrac{|x|}{|y|}$ $(y \neq 0)$ $x, y \in R$

27. Prove: $|x - y| = |y - x|$ $x, y \in R$

28. Prove: $xy \leq |xy|$ $x, y \in R$

29. Prove: $|x|^2 = x^2$ $x \in R$

30. Prove: $|x + y| \leq |x| + |y|$ $x, y \in R$ (*Hint:* This proof may be done by considering the following cases.

   a. $x \geq 0$ and $y \geq 0$ **b.** $x < 0$ and $y < 0$
   c. $x \geq 0$ and $y < 0$ **d.** $x < 0$ and $y \geq 0$)

31. Prove: $|x| - |y| \leq |x + y|$ $x, y \in R$ (*Hint:* You know $|(x + y) + (-y)| \leq |x + y| + |-y|$ by Exercise 30.)

32. Prove that

$$|x_1 \cdot x_2 \cdot \ldots x_n| = |x_1| \cdot |x_2| \ldots |x_n| \text{ for all } n \in N.$$

33. Prove the general triangle inequality: $|.x_1 + x_2 + \cdots + x_n| \leq |x_1| + |x_2| + \cdots + |x_n|$ (*Hint:* Use Exercise 30 and Mathematical Induction.)

34. Prove Theorem 1–8. (*Hint:* Show that $|x| < a$ is equivalent to ($x \geq 0$ and $x < a$) or ($x < 0$ and $-x < a$).)

1–8   Relations

In Figures 1–4 are shown four sets of points such that no three of the points in any set are collinear. You can verify that the number of lines l is related to the number of points p as follows:

p	2	3	4	5
l	1	3	6	10

How many lines would there be if there were 6 points? 7 points?

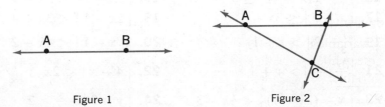

Figure 1   Figure 2

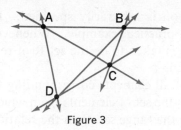
Figure 3

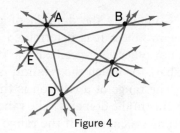
Figure 4

From your earlier experience with mathematical induction you can see that l is related to the number of points p by the formula

$$l = p\,\frac{(p-1)}{2}.$$

Each whole number replacement for p leads to a specific number of lines l. The set of ordered pairs (p, l) thus obtained is one way to describe the relation between the number of points, no three of which are collinear, and the number of lines determined by them. Such a pairing is a **relation.**

Definition   A <u>relation</u> is a set of ordered pairs.

In set notation the relation described above is

$$\left\{(p, l) : l = p\,\frac{(p-1)}{2}\right\}.$$

The set of replacements for p is called the **domain** of the relation. Since there can only be a whole number of points and since you need at least two points to determine a line the domain of the relation is $U = \{p : p \geq 2, p \in W\}$

If U is the set of replacement for p, you find the set of values of l to be

$$V = \{1, 3, 6, 10, 15, 21, 28, \ldots\}.$$

The set V is the **range** of the relation.

Definitions   The <u>domain</u> of a relation is the set of all its first elements, and the <u>range</u> of a relation is the set of all its second elements.

A variable associated with the domain is the <u>independent</u> variable, while a variable associated with the range is the <u>dependent</u> variable.

Commonly the domain of a relation is arbitrarily specified. In other instances it is determined by the practical example. Whenever it is not otherwise specified, the domain is taken to be the set R of real numbers for which the relation is defined.

The range of a relation is the set of all elements corresponding to elements in the domain. The **range set** is the set of elements from which the range is chosen. If the range equals the range set, then the relation is an **onto** relation. When the range does not equal the range set, then the relation is an **into** relation.

EXAMPLE 1. Let the relations T_1 and T_2 have domain = $\{1, 2, 3, 4\}$. Let the range set be P = $\{2, 5, 7\}$.

a. Let T_1 = $\{(1, 2), (2, 5), (3, 7), (4, 2)\}$.
Then the range of T_1 is V_1 = P. T_1 is an onto relation.

b. Let T_2 = $\{(1, 2), (2, 2), (3, 2), (4, 2)\}$.
The range of T_2 is V_2 = $\{2\} \neq$ P.
The relation T_2 is an into relation.

You have seen that a relation may be described by a set of ordered pairs. By specifying the domain you may describe a relation by a mathematical sentence in which the independent variable may be replaced by any member of the domain. In this book if a relation is described by a sentence in x and y, x is the independent variable unless otherwise stated. A third way in which a relation may be described is by a graph.

EXAMPLE 2. Graph the relation

$$T = \{(0, 5), (1, 3), (2, 1), (3, -1), (2, -3), (1, -5)\}.$$

The domain of T is usually associated with the points on the horizontal axis. The range is associated with the vertical axis. To locate (2, 1) you find the point on the perpendicular to the horizontal axis at 2 which is 1 unit above the horizontal. To locate (2, -3) you find the point on the perpendicular to the horizontal axis at 2 which is 3 units below the horizontal. The remaining points are plotted in the same way. The complete graph is shown at right.

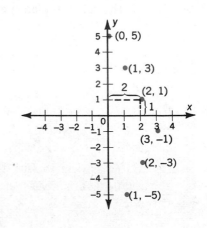

Checkpoint

1. What is a relation?
2. What is the domain of a relation?
3. What is the range of a relation?
4. What is the graph of a relation?
5. What are three ways used to describe a relation?
6. Can you think of any other way to describe a relation?

Exercises

A ━━ Find the range of each relation given the domain.

1. $y = 2x - 3$ $\qquad x \in \{-1, -2, -3, 0, 1, 2\}$
2. $y = \frac{1}{3}x + 1$ $\qquad x \in \{-1, -\frac{1}{2}, 0, \frac{1}{2}, 1, \frac{3}{2}, 2\}$
3. $y = x^2 - 2x + 1$ $\qquad x \in \{-1, 0, 1, 2, 3\}$
4. $r = 4(s + 2)$ $\qquad s \in \{-1, -\frac{3}{4}, -\frac{1}{2}, -\frac{1}{4}, 0, \frac{1}{4}, \frac{1}{2}, \frac{3}{4}, 1\}$
5. $z = \frac{2}{3}t - \frac{5}{3}t$ $\qquad t \in \{-3, -2, -1, 0, 1, 2, 3\}$
6. $q = \frac{1}{3}p$ $\qquad p \in \{-1, -\frac{2}{3}, -\frac{1}{3}, 0, \frac{1}{3}, \frac{2}{3}, 1\}$
7. $y = x^2$ $\qquad x \in \{0, 1, 2, 4, 8, 12\}$
8. $y = 2x - 1$ $\qquad x \in \{-5, -3, -1, 1, 3, 5\}$
9. $t > 2r$ $\qquad r \in \{-2, -1, 0, 1, 2\}$
10. $y < 2x - 3$ $\qquad x \in \{-1, 0, 2\}$
11. $y \leq 3x - 1$ $\qquad x \in \{-\frac{1}{3}, 0, \frac{1}{3}\}$
12. $y \geq \frac{5}{2}x$ $\qquad x \in \{0, 2, 4, 6\}$
13. $y = x$ $\qquad x \in \{-2, -1, 0, 1, 2\}$

━━ Given are a relation, its domain, and range set **P**. Is the relation onto or into?

14. $y = 2x - 3$, $x \in \{-1, -2, -3, 0, 1, 2\}$,
$P = \{-9, -7, -5, -3, -1, 1\}$
15. $y = \frac{1}{3}x + 1$, $x \in \{1, 2, 3, 4\}$, $P = \{1, 3, 4\}$
16. $y = |x|$, $x \in \{-4, -2, 0, 2, 4\}$, $P = \{0, 2, 4\}$
17. $y = x^2$, $x \in \{-4, -2, 1, 3\}$, $P = \{0, 1, 4, 9, 16\}$
18. $y = 2x$, $x \in N$, $P = N$
19. $y = 2x$, $x \in N$, $P = \{2, 4, 6, 8, \ldots\}$
20. $y = 2x + 1$, $x \in N$, $P = \{1, 3, 5, 7, \ldots\}$
21. $y = x^3$, $x \in \{0, 1, 2\}$, $P = \{-8, -1, 0, 1, 8\}$
22. $y = -x$, $x \in \{-1, 0, 1, 2\}$, $P = \{-2, -1, 0, 1\}$
23. $y = x$, $x \in Ir \cup Q$, $P = R$

Example. Graph the relation defined as follows:

$$\{(x, y) : y = x - 1\} \text{ and } x \in \{-3, -2, 0, 1, 2, 3\}$$

You must find the ordered pairs in the relation by finding the value or values of y associated with each x. The ordered pairs are $(-3, -4)$, $(-2, -3)$, $(-1, -2)$, $(0, -1)$, $(1, 0)$, $(2, 1)$, $(3, 2)$.

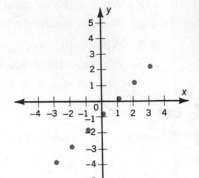

24. Graph the relations in
    a. Exercise 1.
    b. Exercise 3.
    c. Exercise 5.
    d. Exercise 7.
    e. Exercise 8.

Example. Graph the relation whose domain is $\{-1, 0, 1, 2\}$ and is defined by $y \leq x$.

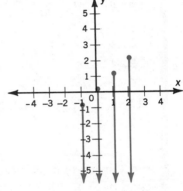

Although the domain contains only four numbers, the range is considered to be all those $y \in R$ such that $y \leq x$ for some $x \in \{-1, 0, 1, 2\}$. Thus for each x there is an infinite subset of real numbers that satisfy the inequality $y < x$. For $x = 2$, some of the ordered pairs in the relation are $(2, 2)$, $(2, 1.9)$, $(2, 0)$, $(2, -\sqrt{.2})$, $(2, -1000)$. The set of all points corresponding to ordered pairs with the first coordinate 2, are those points of the ray with endpoint $(2, 2)$ and perpendicular to the horizontal, or x axis. The complete graph is shown above. It is the union of four rays.

25. Graph the relations described in
    a. Exercise 9.　　b. Exercise 10.

B 26. Find the range and make a graph of the following relations:

$$y = |x| \qquad x \in \{-3, -2, -1, 0, 1, 2, 3\}$$

27. Find the range and make a graph of the following relation:

$$y = |x| \qquad x \in [-3, 3]$$

28. Repeat Exercises 26 and 27 for the relation $y = -|x|$.

34　　CHAPTER 1

29. Graph each relation where $x \in \{-4, -3, -2, -1, 0, 1, 2, 3, 4\}$.

    a. $y = |x - 1|$ **b.** $y = |x| - 1$ **c.** $y = x - 1$

Graph the relation described by $y < |x| - 1$ over the domain $\{x : -2 \leq x \leq 2, x \in I\}$.

C 30. Suppose that postage is 8 cents for the first ounce and 8 cents for each additional ounce.

    a. What is the domain of this postage relation? the range?

    b. Describe the relation geometrically.

31. Pick five classmates. Find the ordered pairs in the relation "is taller than." Let the domain and range be the five people.

32. Use the five classmates chosen in Exercise 31 and find the ordered pairs in the relation "is heavier than." Are the relations "is taller than" and "is heavier than" the same? Could they be?

1–9 Functions and Mappings

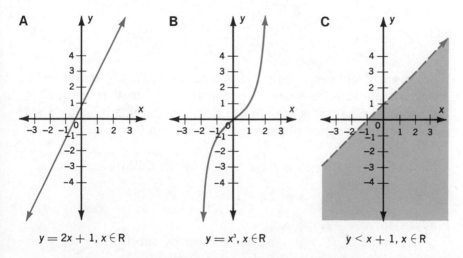

$y = 2x + 1, x \in R$ $y = x^3, x \in R$ $y < x + 1, x \in R$

    Each graph above is a geometric model of a relation. A and B, however, differ from C in one important respect. For each value of x in A and B there is exactly one element y in the respective ranges. An easy way to see this is to picture a line perpendicular to the x axis at its left-hand side; by sliding the line to the right, you can observe that for each x there is only one point in the graph of the relation. This is called the **vertical-line test** for a **function**.

Definition A function is a relation such that for every element of the domain there is one and only one element of the range.

For each domain element in C, $y < x + 1$, $x \in R$, there are infinitely many range elements. For example let $x = 3$.

Then

$$y < x + 1$$

So

$$y < 3 + 1$$
$$y < 4$$

So y assumes all real values less than 4. Verify that this is true for all values of x by the vertical-line test. Relation C is not a function.

When x is a domain element of a function f, then $f(x)$, read "f at x," is the corresponding range element. The function f is the set of ordered pairs of the form $(x, f(x))$. For example, if

$$f = \{(2, 3), (-4, 7)\},$$

then

$$f(2) = 3$$

and

$$f(-4) = 7.$$

When a set of ordered pairs (x, y) is a function, $f(x)$ is another name for y, an element in the range of the function. A function whose range is equal to its range set is an **onto** function. Similarly, a function whose range is a proper subset of its range set is an **into** function.

EXAMPLE. Let a function f be defined by the following equation.

$$y = 2x - 1 \qquad x \in R$$

Find $f(x)$ for $x = -2, 1, \frac{1}{2}, p$.

The value of $f(x)$ may be determined by substituting the corresponding value of x into the following equation.

$$f(x) = y = 2x - 1$$
$$f(-2) = 2(-2) - 1 = -4 - 1 = -5$$
$$f(1) = 2(1) - 1 = 2 - 1 = 1$$
$$f(\tfrac{1}{2}) = 2(\tfrac{1}{2}) - 1 = 1 - 1 = 0$$
$$f(p) = 2p - 1$$

Consider a function f with domain U = $\{0, 2, 4\}$ and range V = $\{1, 3, 5\}$. There are several ways you could associate $x \in$ U with $f(x) \in$ V. Here is one which lists x and its corresponding value of $f(x)$ in table form.

x	$f(x)$
0	1
2	3
4	5

Or

$$f = \{(0, 1), (2, 3), (4, 5)\}.$$

The same function may be shown as follows.

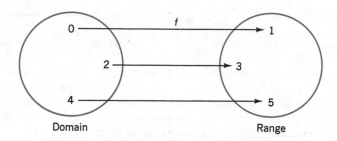

Domain   Range

The drawing suggests a rule or procedure by which the elements of U are associated with those in V. Rather than emphasizing the ordered pairs, the drawing focuses your attention on the rule. In the instance shown here, the rule is *Add 1 to each element of U, or*

$$f(x) = x + 1.$$

Such a rule is called a **mapping** of the elements of U onto the elements of V.

A mapping is commonly denoted

$$f : x \rightarrow f(x),$$

which is read "f maps x onto $f(x)$."

In this particular example, you would write

$$f : x \rightarrow x + 1,$$

or "f maps x onto $x + 1$."

In this book there will be no distinction made between mappings and relations. The function f may be thought of as either the set of ordered pairs $\{(x, y) : y = f(x)\}$ or as the rule that associates x with $f(x)$. Sometimes one interpretation may be more useful than the other, however.

Now try these

━━ Determine which mappings are functions.

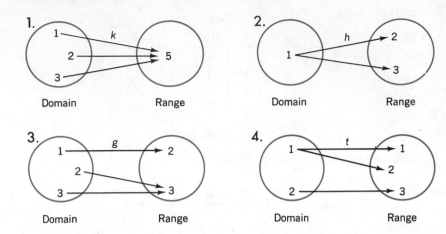

1.   2.

Domain   Range   Domain   Range

3.   4.

Domain   Range   Domain   Range

Answers: **1** and **3** are functions because there is exactly one element in the range
for each element in the domain. **2** and **4** are not functions. In each case
more than one element of the range corresponds to at least one element
in the domain. This is easily determined by noting that in **2** and in **4**
the element 1 has two arrows emanating from it.

Checkpoint

1. How does a function differ from a relation?

2. Would the following statement be acceptable as a definition
of the word *function?* The set f is a function if and only if (x, y_1)
and (x, y_2) are elements of f only when $y_1 = y_2$ is true.

3. Distinguish between a mapping and a function.

Exercises

A ━━ Let a mapping be defined by $f : x \rightarrow \frac{1}{2}x$, $x \in$ W.

1. What is the range of f?

2. Find $f(4)$.   **3.** Find $3f(2)$.

4. Find $f(2x)$.   **5.** Find $2f(x)$.

6. Does $f(3) + f(5) = f(3 + 5)$?

━━ Represent each relation as a mapping. Which are functions?

7. $y = x - 1$ U $= \{x : -3 \le x < 3, x \in$ I$\}$

8. $\{(1, 2), (2, 2), (3, 4), (4, 4)\}$

9. $\{(1, 2), (2, 2), (3, 4), (3, 5)\}$

10. $y = x^2$ $x \in \{-1, 0, 1\}$

11. $y = \sqrt{x}$ $x \in \{9, 4, 1, 0\}$

12. $y = \sqrt[3]{x}$ $x \in \{-8, 1, -1, 27\}$

13. $r = |t|$ $t \in \{1, \frac{1}{2}, -\frac{1}{2}, -\frac{1}{3}\} = U$

14. $r = |t|$ $r \in \{0, 1, 2\} = V$

15. $y < x + 1$ $U = \{x : 0 < x < 4, x \in I\}, y \in W$

16. $y > x + 1$ $U = \{x : -3 < x < 3, x \in I\},$
                         $y \in \{-5, -4, \ldots, 4, 5\}$

17. $f : x \rightarrow \frac{1}{2}x + 1$ $x \in \{2, 4, 6, 8\}$

18. $f : x \rightarrow -|x|$ $x \in \{\pm4, \pm2, 0\}$

B   **19.** In Exercises 7–18 graph each relation that is a function.

20. Let $f : x \rightarrow x^2 - 3$, $x \in \{\pm4, \pm3, \pm2, \pm10\}$. What is the range of f?

21. Let $g : y \rightarrow y + 1$, $y \in \{13, 6, 1, -2, -3\}$. What is the range of g?

22. Find the range of $g[f(x)]$ where g and f are defined as in Exercises 20 and 21.

C ▬▬ How many functions are there that map $x \in U$ onto $y \in V$ when

23. U and V each has one element?

24. U and V each has two elements?

25. U and V each has three elements?

26. U and V each has four elements?

27. U and V each has n elements ($n \in W$)?

28. A *linear function* is a function described by the equation $y = mx + b$, $m \neq 0$, $U = \{x : x \in R\}$.

     a. What geometric figure is the graph of a linear function?

     b. What is the significance of m?

     c. What is the significance of b?

29. The *absolute value function* is the function that maps each real number onto its absolute value. It is symbolized $f : x \rightarrow |x|$. Graph f for $x \in R$ and $-5 \leq x \leq 5$.

▬▬ Graph.

30. $f : x \rightarrow |x + 1|$, $U = \{x : -5 \leq x \leq 5, x \in R\}$

31. $g : x \rightarrow |x| + 1$, $U = \{x : -5 \leq x = 5, x \in R\}$

32. Does $f = g$ in Exercises 30 and 31?

█ The *greatest integer* function is the function that maps each real number onto the greatest integer not greater than the given real number. It is symbolized $f : x \rightarrow [x]$.

33. Graph $f : x \rightarrow [x]$ $U = \{x : -5 \le x \le 5, x \in R\}$.

34. Graph $g : x \rightarrow [x + 1]$ $U = \{x : -5 \le x \le 5, x \in R\}$.

35. Graph $h : x \rightarrow [x] + 1$ $U = \{x : -5 \le x \le 5, x \in R\}$.

36. Does $g = h$ in Exercises 34 and 35?

37. The *identity* function is the function that maps each real number onto itself. It is symbolized $I : x \rightarrow x$.
Graph $I : x \rightarrow x$, $U = \{x : -5 \le x \le 5, x \in R\}$

█ The *opposite* function is the function that maps each real number onto its additive inverse.

38. If O is the opposite function, complete $O : x \rightarrow \underline{\ ?\ }$.

39. Graph $O(x)$, $U = \{x : -5 \le x \le 5, x \in R\}$.

40. How are I and O related?

41. What would be the equivalent of the *opposite* function for multiplication?

42. Graph the function in Exercise 41 for the set $U = \{-10, -5, -3, -2, -1, 0, 1, 2, 3, 5, 10\}$.

43. Graph the function in Exercise 41 for the set $U = \{x : -5 \le x \le 5\}$.

1–10   Composition of Functions

Let f be a function mapping the elements of A onto those in B. Let g be a function mapping the elements of B onto those in C.

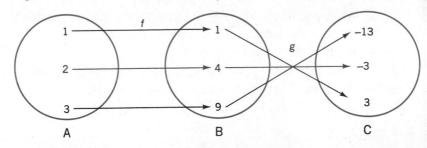

Notice that 1 maps onto 1, which in turn maps onto 3. Similarly, 2 maps onto 4, which maps onto -3, and 3 maps onto 9, which maps onto -13.

Thus, by applying f to the elements of A and then applying g to the elements in the range of f—that is, set B—the result is a mapping from A to C. This mapping is clearly a function. It is the **composition** of g with f and is denoted gf, which is read "g composition f." The function gf is the **composite function.** The mapping gf is pictured below.

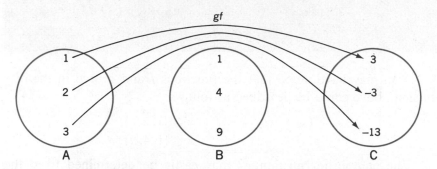

It may seem that the set B is of little consequence to the final mapping gf. This is far from the truth. In the example B was the range of f *and* the domain of g. Thus gf had domain A and range C because for each $x \in A$ there was an $f(x) \in B$ and finally a $g[f(x)]$ in C.

If the set B does not contain all the elements of the range of f nor all the elements of the domain of g, the domain of gf is lessened and so is its range. The next figure illustrates this situation.

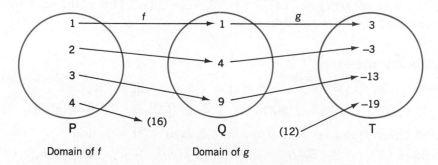

The domain of f is $\{1, 2, 3, 4\}$ and its range is $\{1, 4, 9, 16\}$. The domain of g is $\{1, 4, 9, 12\}$ and its range is $\{3, -3, -13, -19\}$. Since $f(4) = 16 \notin \{1, 4, 9, 12\}$, $g[f(4)]$ is not defined. Likewise since there is no $x \in \{1, 2, 3, 4\}$ such that $f(x) = 12$, there is no x in the domain of gf such that $g[f(x)] = -19$. Thus the domain of gf is $\{1, 2, 3\}$ and the range is $\{3, -3, -13\}$. The domain of gf is a subset of the domain of f and the range of gf is a subset of the range of g.

The following definition summarizes this discussion and gives the fundamental notation for gf.

Definition   Given two functions f and g, the function
$$gf : x \rightarrow g[f(x)]$$
is the <u>composite function</u>. The domain of gf is the set of all elements x in the domain of f for which $f(x)$ is in the domain of g. The operation of forming a composite of two functions is <u>composition</u>.

You may have noted that the functions f and g used in the discussion above could be described as follows:

$$f(x) = x^2 \qquad x \in \{1, 2, 3\}$$
$$g(x) = -2x + 5 \qquad x \in \{1, 4, 9\}$$

The composite function gf may easily be determined from the equations of f and g.

$$gf : x \rightarrow g[f(x)]$$

Thus

$$g[f(x)] = g[x^2] \text{ since } f(x) = x^2$$
$$= -2(x^2) + 5 \text{ since } g(x) = -2(x) + 5.$$

So

$$g[f(x)] = -2x^2 + 5 \qquad x \in \{1, 2, 3\}.$$

The range of $gf(x) = -2x^2 + 5$ is $\{3, -3, -13\}$. This is the set C of the example on the previous page.

Now try these

■ Given $f(x) = 3x - 1$ and $g(x) = x + 3$ for all $x \in R$, find

1. $g[f(x)]$.   **2.** $f[g(x)]$.   **3.** $f[f(x)]$.   **4.** $g[g(x)]$.

■ Given $f(x) = x^2 + 1$, $g(x) = x - 2$, $h(x) = 2x + 1$, find

5. gh.   **6.** fg.   **7.** $f(gh)$.   **8.** $(fg)h$.

Answers: **1.** $g[f(x)] = g[3x - 1] = [3x - 1] + 3 = 3x + 2$
2. $f[g(x)] = f[x + 3] = 3[x + 3] - 1 = 3x + 9 - 1 = 3x + 8$
3. $f[f(x)] = f[3x - 1] = 3[3x - 1] - 1 = 9x - 3 - 1 = 9x - 4$
4. $g[g(x)] = g[x + 3] = [x + 3] + 3 = x + 6$
5. $g[h(x)] = [2x + 1] - 2 = 2x - 1$
6. $f[g(x)] = [x - 2]^2 + 1 = x^2 - 4x + 4 + 1 = x^2 - 4x + 5$
7. $f[gh] = [2x - 1]^2 + 1 = 4x^2 - 4x + 1 + 1 = 4x^2 - 4x + 2$
8. $(fg)[h] = [2x + 1]^2 - 4[2x + 1] + 5 = 4x^2 + 4x + 1 - 8x - 4 + 5$
$$= 4x^2 - 4x + 2$$

Exercises

A

1. Which exercises in *Now try these* prove that composition of functions is not commutative?

2. Which exercises in *Now try these* show that composition of functions may be associative? (It is, in fact associative although the theorem to that effect is not proved in this book.)

━━ Draw a mapping diagram that pictures each composite function. Specify the domain and range of the composite function.

3. $f = \{(1, 2), (3, 4), (5, 6)\}$
$\, g = \{(4, 5), (2, 3), (6, 7)\}$
$\, gf = \underline{\ ?\ }$

4. $g = \{(-5, 1), (-2, 4), (0, 2)\}$
$\, h = \{(2, -1), (4, -3), (1, 5)\}$
$\, hg = \underline{\ ?\ }$

5. $h = \{(1, 2), (3, 5), (4, 7)\}$
$\, f = \{(2, 3), (5, 4), (7, 6)\}$
$\, fh = \underline{\ ?\ }$

6. $\_ = \{(a, b), (b, c), (c, d)\}$
$\, H = \{(d, c), (c, b), (b, a)\}$
$\, H\_ = \underline{\ ?\ }$

7. Given $A = \{1, 2, 3\}$ the domain of f, $B = \{4, 5, 6\}$ the range of f and domain of g, and $C = \{7, 8, 9\}$ the range of g. How many different composite functions may be represented by the symbol gf?

━━ Given $f(x) = 3x - 4$, $h(x) = x^2 + 3$, $g(x) = -2x + 1$, $x \in R$, find the following.

8. fh	**9.** hf	**10.** fg	**11.** gf
12. $h(fg)$	**13.** $g(fh)$	**14.** $fg(2)$	**15.** $f(gh(3))$
16. $hg(-5)$	**17.** hh	**18.** $f(hh)$	

B ━━ In Exercises 19–21, let $f : x \rightarrow ax + b$, $h : x \rightarrow cx + d$, $x \in R$.

19. What is the slope of the graph of f? of the graph of h?

20. Find fh and hf.

21. What is the slope of the graph of fh? the graph of hf? Compare them with the slopes found in Exercise 19. State the generalization.

━━ In Exercises 22–25, let $f(x) = \frac{1}{x}$, $x \in R$, $x \neq 0$.

22. Find $ff(2)$ **23.** Find $ff(-3)$ **24.** Find $ff(100)$

25. What function is ff?

━━ In Exercises 26–29, let $I : x \rightarrow x$ and $g : x \rightarrow x - 3$, $x \in R$.

26. Find $g[I]$ and $I[g]$.

27. Find a function f such that $gf = I$, $x \in R$.

28. Find a function h such that $hg = I$, $x \in R$.

29. Compare h and f of Exercises 27 and 28.

C **30.** Let $f(x) = 2x + 1$ and $g(x) = 3$. Find expressions for $f[g(x)]$ and $g[f(x)]$.

31. Let $f(x) = x^3$ and $g(x) = x^2$. Find expressions for $f[g(x)]$ and $g[f(x)]$.

32. Let $f(x) = x^m$ and $g(x) = x^n$. Find expressions for $f[g(x)]$ and $g[f(x)]$.

33. Let $f(x) = x^3$ and $g(x) = x^2$. Find expressions for $f \cdot g(x)$ and $g \cdot f(x)$ where $f \cdot g$ and $g \cdot f$ are products of f and g. (*i.e.*, $f \cdot g(x) = f(x) \cdot g(x)$) Compare with Exercise 31.

34. Let $f(x) = x^m$ and $g(x) = x^n$. Find an expression for the product $f \cdot g(x)$. Compare with Exercise 32.

━━ In Exercises 35–39, let $f(x) = x + 2$, $g(x) = x - 3$, and $h(x) = x^2$. Find expressions for each of these.

35. $g \cdot f(x)$ **36.** $(g \cdot f)[h(x)]$

37. $g[h(x)]$ **38.** $f[h(x)]$

39. $[gh \cdot fh](x)$ **40.** Compare Exercises 36 and 39.

41. Does $h[g \cdot f(x)] = [hg \cdot hf](x)$ for f, g, and h in Exercises 35–39?

1–11　Inverses of Functions

Suppose f is the function

$$f : x \rightarrow x - 5$$

and g is the function

$$g : x \rightarrow x + 5.$$

The effect of f is to decrease each number by 5. The effect of g is to increase each number by 5. Then f and g are inversely related in the sense that each undoes the effect of the other. If you apply f to a real number r, you map r onto $r - 5$. If you then apply g to $r - 5$, you map $r - 5$ onto $(r - 5) + 5$, or r. The effect of the composite function gf is to map r onto r, or

$$gf : r \rightarrow r.$$

A function that maps each domain element onto itself is an **identity function** I (see Section 1–9, Exercise 37). Thus, $gf = I$. Two identity functions with unequal domains are different functions. I will be referred to as the identity function, irrespective of the domain.

In symbols, you can see that gf evaluated at r is

$$g[f(r)] = g[r - 5] = (r - 5) + 5 = r. \qquad \text{(Domain of } f = R\text{)}$$

Similary,

$$f[g(r)] = f[r + 5] = (r + 5) - 5 = r. \qquad \text{(Domain of } g = R\text{)}$$

Thus,

$$gf = I = fg. \qquad \text{(Domain of } f = \text{Domain of } g\text{)}$$

If the domain of f does not equal the domain of g then $gf \neq fg$. Consider now the function h described by

$$h(x) = \frac{3x - 1}{2}.$$

Here h tells you to take a number x, triple it, subtract 1, and divide the result by 2. To construct the inversely related mapping you would take a number x, multiply it by 2, add 1, and divide the result by 3. The resulting mapping would be

$$g(x) = \frac{2x + 1}{3}.$$

To see that h and g are inversely related, find the composite functions hg and gh.

$$h[g(x)] = \frac{3\left(\dfrac{2x + 1}{3}\right) - 1}{2} = \frac{(2x + 1) - 1}{2} = x$$

and

$$g[h(x)] = \frac{2\left(\dfrac{3x - 1}{2}\right) + 1}{3} = \frac{(3x - 1) + 1}{3} = x.$$

In both cases the result is the identity I.

$$hg = I = gh$$

This discussion is summarized by the definition of **inverse** functions.

Definition If f and g are functions so related that $fg : x \to x$ for every element x in the domain of g and $gf : y \to y$ for every element y in the domain of f, then f and g are inverses of each other.

In the above definition, if f and g have the same domain, then $fg = I = gf$.

Depicting a function as a mapping clearly brings out the inverse relationship between two inverse functions. If f maps x onto y, that is $y = f(x)$, then g, the inverse of f, maps y onto x; that is $g(y) = x$. This is depicted by reversing the arrows.

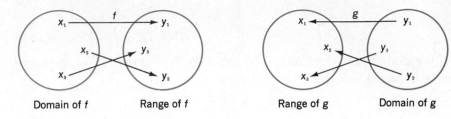

| Domain of f | Range of f | Range of g | Domain of g |

For *any* mapping you can reverse the arrows and obtain another mapping. If the original mapping was a function, it does not follow, however, that the inverse mapping is also a function. Consider the diagram below.

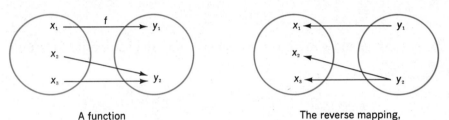

A function   The reverse mapping, Not a function.

Any function f that associates two different elements in its domain with *one* element in the range has an inverse mapping that is not a function. In the diagram above f maps x_2 and x_3 onto y_2. Thus, the inverse mapping associates y_2 with x_2 and x_3. This inverse mapping is not a function. You can conclude that not all inverses of functions are themselves functions.

By comparing the two diagrams you can see exactly what kinds of functions have inverses that are functions. The mapping must be *one-to-one*; that is for the inverse of f to be a function $x_1 \neq x_2$ if and only if $f(x_1) \neq f(x_2)$.

Frequently the inverse of f is denoted by f^{-1}.

EXAMPLE. Given $f = \{(0, 1), (2, -1)\}$ find f^{-1}.

$$f : 0 \rightarrow 1 \qquad \text{so} \qquad f^{-1} : 1 \rightarrow 0$$
$$f : 2 \rightarrow -1 \qquad \text{so} \qquad f^{-1} : -1 \rightarrow 2$$

Therefore $\qquad\qquad\qquad f^{-1} = \{(1, 0), (-1, 2)\}.$

Exercises

A ▬ In Exercises 1–5, suppose $f = \{(1, 2), (3, 4), (5, 6), (7, 8)\}$ and g is the inverse of f.

1. Construct a mapping diagram for f, for g.

2. What ordered pairs are in g?

3. How can the ordered pairs of g be obtained from those of f?

4. Repeat Exercises 1–3 for $f = \{(2, -\frac{1}{2}), (3, -\frac{1}{3}), (4, -\frac{1}{4})\}$.

5. Let f be a function with an inverse that is also a function. If

$$f = \{(x, y) : y = f(x), x \in R\}$$

then what is f^{-1}, the inverse of f (see Exercises 1–4).

▬ For each function find the inverse. If the inverse is not a function, explain why this is so.

Example 1. $g : x \to 2x \qquad g^{-1} : x \to \frac{1}{2}x$

Example 2. $f : x \to x^2$

f maps x onto the square of x, so $f : 2 \to 4$ and $f : -2 \to 4$. Since both 2 and -2 are mapped onto 4, the inverse would map 4 onto 2 and onto -2, and therefore is not a function.

6. $f : x \to 2x + 5$

7. $g : x \to \frac{1}{3}x$

8. $h : x \to \frac{1}{3}x - 1$

9. $G : r \to 2r + 1$

10. $F : t \to \frac{2}{3}t + \frac{1}{3}$

11. $H : x \to x^3$

12. $h : x \to x^3 - 8$

13. $f : x \to x^2 - 4$

14. $T : r \to \dfrac{4r + 5}{3}$

15. $H : y \to \frac{2}{5}y - 5$

16. In Exercises 6–15 show that the composite of the function and its inverse is the identity.

▬ Find an inverse of each of the following functions.

17. $x \to x + 3$

18. $x \to 5x - 7$

19. $x \to \dfrac{1}{x}, x \neq 0$

20. $x \to -x$

▬ Solve each of the following equations for x in terms of y and compare your answers with those obtained in Exercises 17–20.

21. $y = x + 3$

22. $y = 5x - 7$

23. $y = \dfrac{1}{x}, x \neq 0$

24. $y = -x$

25. On the basis of Exercises 17–24, describe a method that can be used to find the inverse of a function.

Find the inverses of the following using Exercise 25.

26. $f(x) = \frac{7}{2}x - 1$

27. $g(x) = x^3 + 27$

28. $h(x) = x^2 - 4$

B ━━ Consider $f = \{(0, 2), (1, 0), (2, -2), (3, -4)\}$.

29. Graph f.

30. Graph f^{-1}.

31. Graph $I : x \to x, \ x \in R$.

32. How are the graphs of f and f^{-1} related to that of I?

33. Repeat Exercises 29–32 for $f : x \to 3x - 4$ where

$$U = \{x : -4 \le x \le 4, \ x \in R\}.$$

34. Generalize the results of Exercises 29–33.

35. Use your generalization of Exercise 34 to graph

a. two points of the inverse of $f(x) = \frac{1}{3}x + 1, \ x \in R$.

b. the complete inverse of f.

C **36.** What function is its own inverse?

37. Prove that every linear function has an inverse.

1–12   Complex Numbers

The set of **complex numbers** includes and is defined in terms of real numbers. You are familiar with the **imaginary unit** i with the property $i^2 = -1$. You can also identify i as $\sqrt{-1}$.

> **Definitions**   For all $a, b \in R$, $a + bi$, $i = \sqrt{-1}$, is a complex number. a is the real part of the complex number, while b is the imaginary part. The set of complex numbers is denoted C.

If in a complex number $a + bi$ the real part is zero, then $a + bi$, or bi, is a **pure imaginary** number. Likewise if in $a + bi$, $b = 0$, then $a + bi$, or a is a real number. Thus C contains pure imaginaries and real numbers as subsets.

Equality of complex numbers is defined as follows in terms of the equality of real numbers.

Definition For all $a + bi$, $c + di \in C$, $\underline{a + bi = c + di}$ if and only if $a = c$ and $b = d$.

The fundamental operations of addition and multiplication of complex numbers are defined so that the familiar properties of these operations for real numbers continue to apply for the complex numbers.

Definitions Addition: $\forall a, b, c, d \in R$

$$(a + bi) + (c + di) = (a + c) + (b + d)i$$

Multiplication: $\forall a, b, c, d \in R$

$$(a + bi)(c + di) = ac - bd + (bc + ad)i$$

With these definitions, C is *closed* with respect to addition and multiplication. Moreover it can be shown that the operations of addition and multiplication of complex numbers are *commutative* and associative, that *multiplication distributes over addition*, and that the *identity* elements are $0 + 0i$ and $1 + 0i$ respectively. Finally for $a + bi$, $-a + (-bi)$ and $\dfrac{1}{a + bi}$ ($a + bi \neq 0$) are the *additive* and *multiplicative inverses*. You are asked to verify these statements in the exercises.

Subtraction and division are defined in terms of addition and multiplication.

Definitions Subtraction: $\forall z_1, z_2, z_3 \in C$,

$$z_1 - z_2 = z_3 \text{ if and only if } z_1 = z_3 + z_2.$$

Division: $\forall z_1, z_2, z_3 \in C, z_2 \neq 0$,

$$z_1 \div z_2 = z_3 \text{ if and only if } z_1 = z_3 \cdot z_2.$$

These definitions can be used to show that

$$z_1 - z_2 = z_1 + (-z_2)$$

and that

$$z_1 \div z_2 = z_1 \cdot \frac{1}{z_2}.$$

The methods are illustrated in the following two examples.

EXAMPLE 1. Given that $z_1 = a + bi$, $z_2 = c + di$ and $-z_2 = -c + (-di)$, show that $z_1 - z_2 = z_1 + (-z_2)$.

The sentence $z_1 - z_2 = z_3$ is true if and only if $z_1 = z_3 + z_2$ is true. Thus, $(a + bi) - (c + di) = x + iy = z_3$ if and only if

$$a + bi = x + yi + (c + di)$$
$$= (x + c) + (y + d)i.$$

(Definition of Addition of Complex Numbers)

Thus, $\qquad a = x + c$ implies $x = a - c = a + (-c)$

and $\qquad b = y + d$ implies $y = b - d = b + (-d)$

(Definition of Equality of Complex Numbers)

So, $\qquad z_1 - z_2 = x + yi = [a + (-c)] + [b + (-d)]i$
$$= a + bi + [-c + (-di)]$$
$$= (a + bi) + [-(c + di)]$$
$$= z_1 + (-z_2)$$

EXAMPLE 2. Given that $z_1 = a + bi$ and $z_2 = c + di \neq 0$, show that $z_1 \div z_2 = z_1 \cdot \dfrac{1}{z_2}$.

It is useful to keep all results in the form $A + Bi$ where A and B are real numbers. Initially show that

$$\frac{1}{z_2} = \frac{1}{c + di} = \frac{c}{c^2 + d^2} + \frac{-di}{c^2 + d^2}.$$

This is shown as follows.

$$\frac{1}{c + di} = \frac{1(c - di)}{(c + di)(c - di)} = \frac{c - di}{c^2 - d^2 i^2}$$
$$= \frac{c - di}{c^2 + d^2}$$
$$= \frac{c}{c^2 + d^2} + \frac{-di}{c^2 + d^2}$$

The number $c - di$ is the **conjugate** of $c + di$. Thus,

$$z_1 \cdot \frac{1}{z_2} = (a + bi) \frac{1}{c + di}$$
$$= (a + bi) \frac{c - di}{c^2 + d^2}$$
$$= \frac{(a + bi)(c - di)}{c^2 + d^2}$$
$$= \frac{(ac + bd)}{c^2 + d^2} + \frac{(bc - ad)i}{c^2 + d^2}$$

Turning to $z_1 \div z_2$, you know that the following holds.

$$z_1 \div z_2 = z_3 \text{ iff } z_1 = z_3 \cdot z_2$$

Thus,

$$(a + bi) \div (c + di) = x + yi \text{ iff}$$
$$a + bi = (x + yi)(c + di)$$
$$= (xc - yd) + (cy + dx)i$$

So $\qquad a = xc - yd$

and $\qquad b = xd + yc$ by the definition of equality.

Solving these equations for x and y, you find

$$x = \frac{ac + bd}{c^2 + d^2}$$

and

$$y = \frac{bc - ad}{c^2 + d^2}.$$

Thus,

$$x + yi = \frac{(ac + bd)}{c^2 + d^2} + \frac{(bc - ad)i}{c^2 + d^2}$$
$$= z_1 \cdot \frac{1}{z_2}.$$

Thus, to divide $a + bi$ by $c + di$ you can multiply $a + bi$ by $\frac{c - di}{c^2 + d^2}$, the multiplicative inverse of $c + di$.

Exercises

A ▬ Perform the indicated operation. Express the number in the form $a + bi$.

1. $(3 + 2i) - (4 - i)$
2. $(5 - 2i) + (3 + 7i)$
3. $(7 - i) - (7 + i)$
4. $(-2 + 3i) + (4 - 3i)$
5. $(2 - 3i) \cdot (-2 + i)$
6. $i(2 - 7i)$
7. $(1 + 5i)(5 - i)$
8. $(1 - i)^2$
9. $\dfrac{1 + i}{2 - i}$
10. $\dfrac{2 - i}{1 - i}$
11. $\dfrac{2(1 + i)}{i}$
12. $\dfrac{8 + 12i}{(2 + 2i)(2 - 2i)}$

B 13. $(3 + i)(3 - i)\left(\dfrac{2 + i}{10}\right)$
14. $\dfrac{1 + 2i}{3 - 4i} + \dfrac{2 - i}{5i}$
15. $\dfrac{2i}{(i - 1)(i - 2)(i - 3)}$
16. $\dfrac{3i}{1 + 2i} - \dfrac{4}{1 - 2i}$

17. Show that $1 + i$ and $1 - i$ satisfy $z^2 - 2z + 2 = 0$.

18. Show that the numbers $z = \dfrac{-1 \pm i\sqrt{2}}{3}$ satisfy the equation $3z^2 + 2z + 1 = 0$.

19. Prove that if $z_1 z_2 = 0$, then $z_1 = 0$ or $z_2 = 0$, $z_1, z_2 \in C$.

C **20.** Prove that if $z_1 z_2 \ldots z_n = 0$, then at least one of the complex numbers $z_1, z_2, \ldots, z_n$ is zero for all $n \in N$.

21. Establish the associative law of addition for complex numbers. Do the same for multiplication.

22. Establish the commutative law of addition for complex numbers. Do the same for multiplication.

23. Prove that multiplication distributes over addition for complex numbers.

1–13   Complex Numbers As Vectors

A complex number z written in the form $c + di$ is said to be in *standard form*. The standard form of $\dfrac{1}{a + bi}$ is $\dfrac{a}{a^2 + b^2} + \left(\dfrac{-b}{a^2 + b^2}\right) i$. An efficient way to compute the standard form of $\dfrac{1}{a + bi}$ is to multiply it by $\dfrac{a - bi}{a - bi}$. This is true because

$$\frac{1}{a + bi} = \frac{1}{a + bi} \cdot \frac{a - bi}{a - bi}$$

$$= \frac{a - bi}{(a^2 + b^2) + (ab - ab)i}$$

$$= \frac{a - bi}{a^2 + b^2}$$

$$= \frac{a}{a^2 + b^2} + \frac{-b}{a^2 + b^2} \, i.$$

For the complex number $a + bi$, $a - bi$ is the *conjugate*. The conjugate of z_1 is denoted $\bar{z}_1$ (read "z_1 conjugate"). The standard form of $\dfrac{1}{z_1}$ is $\dfrac{\bar{z}_1}{z_1 \bar{z}_1}$. This provides a simple algorithm for dividing z_2 by z_1; namely

$$z_2 \div z_1 = z_2 \cdot \frac{1}{z_1} = \frac{z_2}{z_1} \cdot \frac{\bar{z}_1}{\bar{z}_1}.$$

That is, multiply numerator and denominator by the conjugate of the denominator.

EXAMPLE 1. Write $\frac{2-3i}{1-2i}$ in standard form. The conjugate of $1 - 2i$ is $1 + 2i$. Thus

$$\frac{2-3i}{1-2i} = \frac{2-3i}{1-2i} \cdot \frac{1+2i}{1+2i}$$

$$= \frac{(2+6) + (4-3)i}{1+4}$$

$$= \frac{8+i}{5}.$$

For each ordered pair (a, b) of real numbers there is a unique complex number $a + bi$. Conversely, for each complex number $a + bi$, there is a unique ordered pair (a, b) of real numbers. Thus there is a one-to-one correspondence between the ordered pairs of real numbers and the complex numbers.

Furthermore, there is a one-to-one correspondence between the ordered pairs of real numbers and the points in a rectangular coordinate system. Finally, the complex numbers and the points in the plane are associated in a one-to-one fashion.

It is natural to use this association between complex numbers and points in the plane to represent complex numbers geometrically. Usually a complex number $z = a + bi$ is represented by the directed line segment or vector from the origin to the point (a, b). See the figure at the right. The 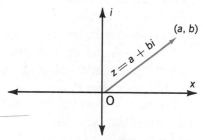 horizontal axis is the real axis and the vertical axis is the imaginary axis or the i axis. All real numbers are represented by points on the real axis; pure imaginaries by points on the i axis; and other complex numbers by points not on either axis. $z = 0 + 0i$ is the origin.

EXAMPLE 2. Show the geometric representation of z and $\bar{z}$ when

$$z = a + bi.$$

$z = a + bi$ is shown in the figure at the right. Then $\bar{z} = a - bi$, so it is a vector from 0 to $(a, -b)$. It is the reflection of the vector z in the real axis. See the figure at the right.

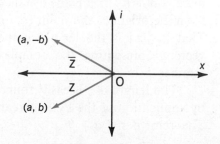

Given two complex numbers $z_1 = a + bi$ and $z_2 = c + di$; the sum $z_1 + z_2 = (a + c) + (b + d)i$. $z_1 + z_2$ is represented geometrically by the vector from the origin to $(a + c, b + d)$. The sum can be found geometrically by thinking of z_1 and z_2 as two sides of a parallelogram whose fourth vertex is $(a + c, b + d)$. Thus $z_1 + z_2$ is the diagonal from the origin to the fourth vertex.

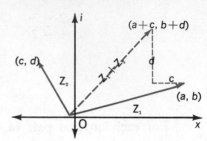

The same construction works for subtraction. $z_1 - z_2 = z_1 + (-z_2)$. Thus you construct the diagonal of the parallelogram with sides z_1 and $-z_2$. This is illustrated in the figure.

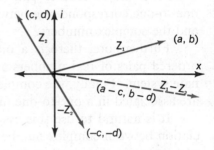

EXAMPLE 3. If $z_1 = 1 - 2i$, $z_2 = 2 + 3i$, exhibit $z_1 + z_2$ and $z_1 - z_2$ geometrically.

$z_1 + z_2$ is the diagonal of the parallelogram with sides z_1 and z_2. $z_1 + z_2 = 3 + i$, $z_1 - z_2 = z_1 + (-z_2)$, so $z_1 - z_2$ is the diagonal of the parallelogram with sides z_1 and $-z_2$.

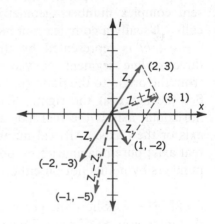

Recall that the absolute value of a real number x, $|x|$, is the distance from the origin to the point x. In a similar manner, the absolute value of a complex number $z = a + bi$, $|z|$, is the distance from the origin to the point (a, b). That is, $|z|$ is the length of the vector representing the complex number z.

The length of z is easily found by application of the Pythagorean Theorem: if $z = a + bi$

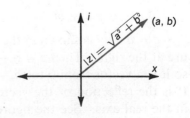

$$|z| = \sqrt{a^2 + b^2}.$$

This discussion is summarized by the next definition.

Definition Let $z = a + bi$. The absolute value of z, $|z|$, is defined

$$|z| = \sqrt{a^2 + b^2}.$$

EXAMPLE 4. If $z = 5 + 12i$, find $|z|$.

$$\begin{aligned} |z| &= \sqrt{5^2 + 12^2} \\ &= \sqrt{25 + 144} \\ &= \sqrt{169} \\ &= 13 \end{aligned}$$

EXAMPLE 5. Prove: $|z| = |\bar{z}|$
Let $z = a + bi$. Then $\bar{z} = a - bi$.

$$|z| = \sqrt{a^2 + b^2} \qquad \begin{aligned} |\bar{z}| &= \sqrt{a^2 + (-b)^2} \\ &= \sqrt{a^2 + b^2} \end{aligned}$$

Thus $|z| = |\bar{z}|$.

Exercises

A ━━ In Exercises 1–7 find the sum and difference of z_1 and z_2. Exhibit all numbers geometrically.

1. $z_1 = -3 + i$ $\qquad z_2 = 1 + 3i$

2. $z_1 = 4 + 2i$ $\qquad z_2 = 4 - 2i$

3. $z_1 = 3 - 4i$ $\qquad z_2 = -3 - 4i$

4. $z_1 = -2 + 3i$ $\qquad z_2 = -2 + 3i$

5. $z_1 = 2$ $\qquad z_2 = 4i$

6. $z_1 = -3$ $\qquad z_2 = 2$

7. $z_1 = 3i$ $\qquad z_2 = 2i$

8. Find the absolute value of z_1 in each Exercise 1–7.

9. Find the conjugate of each number z_2 in Exercises 1–7.

10. Prove: $z_1 + \bar{z}_1$ is twice the real part of z_1.

━━ Compute each quotient in Exercises 11–14.

11. $\dfrac{2 + 3i}{1 - 2i}$ $\qquad\qquad$ **12.** $\dfrac{2 - 3i}{2 + 3i}$

13. $\dfrac{5 - i}{-3 - 4i}$ $\qquad\qquad$ **14.** $\dfrac{1 + i}{-2 + 6i}$

15. Prove: $\bar{z} = z$ if and only if z is a real number.

16. Prove: $\bar{\bar{z}} = z$.

17. Prove: $|z| = |\bar{z}|$.

B **18.** Prove: $|z| = \sqrt{z \cdot \overline{z}}$ or $|z|^2 = z \cdot \overline{z}$.

19. Prove: $\overline{z_1 + z_2} = \overline{z}_1 + \overline{z}_2$. (In words: the conjugate of the sum is the sum of the conjugates.)

20. Prove: $\overline{z_1 - z_2} = \overline{z}_1 - \overline{z}_2$.

21. Prove: $\overline{z_1 z_2} = \overline{z}_1 \cdot \overline{z}_2$.

22. Prove that $z_1 - \overline{z}_1$ is twice the imaginary part of z_1.

C **23.** Prove: $|z_1 \cdot z_2| = |z_1| \cdot |z_2|$. (*Hint:* $|z_1 \cdot z_2|^2 = z_1 z_2 \cdot \overline{z_1 z_2}$. Simplify this by using Exercise 21 and the commutativity of multiplication of complex numbers.)

24. Prove: $|z_1 \cdot z_2 \cdots z_n| = |z_1| \cdot |z_2| \cdots |z_n|$ for $n \in N$. (*Hint:* Use Exercise 23 and mathematical induction.)

25. Prove: **a.** $|z| \geq$ the absolute value of the real part of z.
b. $|z| \geq$ the absolute value of the imaginary part of z.

26. Prove: $|z_1 + z_2| \leq |z_1| + |z_2|$.
(*Hint:* $|z_1 + z_2|^2 = (z_1 + z_2)(\overline{z}_1 + \overline{z}_2)$.) Expand this. Then use Exercise 10. Use 25a and Example 5.

27. Prove: $\overline{z_1 \cdot z_2 \cdots z_n} = \overline{z}_1 \cdot \overline{z}_2 \cdots \overline{z}_n$ for all $n \in N$. (*Hint:* Use mathematical induction and Exercise 21.)

CHAPTER OBJECTIVES AND REVIEW

Objective: *To know the meaning of the important mathematical terms of this chapter.*

1. Here are many of the mathematical terms used in this chapter. Be sure that you know them thoroughly and can use them correctly.

real numbers (*2*)	distributive property (*7*)
irrational numbers (*3*)	direct proof (*8*)
rational numbers (*3*)	theorem (*8*)
integers (*3*)	indirect proof (*9*)
whole numbers (*3*)	graph (*14*)
natural numbers (*3*)	ray (*15*)
binary operation (*6*)	half line (*15*)
Field Postulates (*6*)	segment (*15*)
closure (*6*)	closed interval (*15*)
commutative property (*6*)	open interval (*16*)
associative property (*6*)	compound inequality (*18*)
identity (*6*)	quadratic inequality (*19*)
inverse (*6*)	mathematical induction (*21*)
reciprocal (*7*)	n factorial (*26*)

zero factorial (26)
absolute value (27)
relation (31)
domain (31)
range (31)
independent variable (31)
dependent variable (31)
range set (32)
onto relation (32)
into relation (32)
vertical-line test (35)
function (35)
onto function (36)

into function (36)
mapping (37)
composition (41)
composite function (41)
identity function (44)
inverse functions (45)
complex numbers (48)
imaginary unit i (48)
real part (48)
imaginary part (48)
pure imaginary number (48)
equality of complex numbers (48)
conjugate (50)

Objective: *To identify numbers as natural, whole, integer, rational, irrational, real, imaginary, or complex.*

━━ Place each number in as many categories as appropriate.

2. $3i$ **3.** $14\frac{2}{7}$ **4.** 0 **5.** $2 + 6i$

6. $0.010020003000004\ldots$ **7.** $1.15\overline{6132}$ **8.** $\sqrt{3}$

Objective: *To translate repeating and terminating decimal expansions into fractions and vice-versa.*

━━ In Exercises 9–12 translate the fraction into a decimal expansion or vice-versa.

9. $\frac{2}{7}$ **10.** $0.\overline{127}$

11. 0.195 **12.** $\frac{11}{40}$

Objective: *To cite the field postulate, postulate of equality or order, theorem, or definition which justifies an algebraic manipulation or statement of relation.*

━━ Cite an appropriate definition, postulate, or theorem in each of Exercises 13–21.

13. $2x + 4x = 6x$ **14.** $-5 < -3$

15. $2 - 7 = 2 + (-7)$ **16.** $0.\overline{9} = 1$ so $1 = 0.\overline{9}$

17. $2 + (3 + 5) = (3 + 5) + 2$

18. $(5 + 6i) + (0 + 0i) = 5 + 6i$

19. $\frac{3}{4}(\frac{4}{3} \cdot \frac{5}{2}) = (\frac{3}{4} \cdot \frac{4}{3}) \cdot \frac{5}{2}$

20. $5 + 3x = 2 - x$ implies that $3x = -3 - x$

21. The sum of two complex numbers is a complex number.

Objective: *To use the properties of order relations and real numbers to solve inequalities.*

━━━ Solve the following inequalities.

22. $5 < 2x + 3 \le 9$

23. $(x - 3)(x + 2) \ge 0$

24. $|x + 1| < 4$

25. $|x| > 10$

Objective: *To graph the solution set of an inequality and describe it using open and closed intervals.*

26. Graph the solution sets of Exercises 22–25.

27. Describe in geometric terms the graphs of the solution sets in Exercise 26.

28. Write inequality statements describing

    a. $\langle -2, 3 \rangle$ **b.** $[-2, 3 \rangle$ **c.** $[-2, 3]$ **d.** $\langle -a, a \rangle$

Objective: *To identify relations and functions, their domains and ranges and determine which have inverses that are functions.*

29. If $\{2, 4, 6, 8, 10\}$ is the domain of the relation $y = \frac{1}{2}x - 3$, what is the range?

━━━ Which of the following relations are functions? Which of the functions have inverses that are functions? In each case the domain is R.

30. $y = x$ **31.** $y = \sqrt{x}$ **32.** $3x + 2y = 7$ **33.** $y = x^3$

34. $y < x$ **35.** $y = x^2$ **36.** $xy = 25$

Objective: *To give a composite mapping for two mappings.*

━━━ Find fg and gf for the given mappings.

37. $f : x \longrightarrow x - 5$
    $g : x \longrightarrow 2x + 1$

38. $f : x \longrightarrow x^2$
    $g : x \longrightarrow 3 - x$

39. $f : x \longrightarrow \frac{1}{x} \ x \ne 0$
    $g : x \longrightarrow \frac{1}{2}x - 3$

40. $f : x \longrightarrow x^3$
    $g : x \longrightarrow x^{\frac{1}{3}}$

Objective: *To perform the fundamental operations on complex numbers.*

41. $(2 - 3i) + (4i - 1)$

42. $(2 - 3i) \div (4i - 1)$

43. $(2 - 3i) - (4i - 1)$

44. $(2 - 3i) \cdot (4i - 1)$

45. If $z = 4 - 2i$ then find $\bar{z}$.

46. Find the multiplicative inverse of $5 + 9i$. Express it in the form $A + Bi$, where A and B are real numbers.

Objective: *To explain and apply mathematical induction.*

47. In your own words explain the idea of mathematical induction.

48. Use mathematical induction to prove P_n true for all $n \in N$.

    a. P_n is "$4 + 8 + 12 + \cdots + 4n = 2n(n + 1)$."

    b. P_n is "$1 + 5 + 9 + \cdots + (4n - 3) = n(2n - 1)$."

    c. P_n is "$1 + 6 + 6^2 + \cdots + 6^{n-1} = \frac{1}{5}(6^n - 1)$."

Objective: *To prove selected theorems.*

CHAPTER TEST

1. Express the number $0.\overline{2}$ as a fraction.

2. Prove $(a + b) - c = a + (b - c)$ for real numbers a, b, and c.

3. Use mathematical induction to prove that the sum of the first n even numbers is $n(n + 1)$, $n \in N$.

4. If x is a real number and $-x$ is negative, what can you conclude about x and why?

5. What is a simpler way of describing each of the following sets?

    a. $[a, b\rangle \cup \langle a, b]$ **b.** $[a, b\rangle \cap \langle a, b]$

6. Solve for x, $-2 > |x + 2|$. Graph the solution set.

7. Define "absolute value."

━━━ Draw an example of each of the following on the real line.

8. segment   **9.** half line

10. ray   **11.** open interval

12. For each graph in 8–11 write an inequality describing the graph.

━━━ If $f : x \longrightarrow x + \frac{1}{2}$ and $h : x \longrightarrow 2x - 3$ find

13. fh **14.** hf **15.** f^{-1} **16.** h^{-1}

17. Produce an example of an infinite decimal which names an irrational number.

18. Find the multiplicative inverse of $\frac{1}{i}$. Write it in $A + Bi$ form with $A, B \in R$.

CHAPTER 2
CIRCULAR FUNCTIONS

The real number line can be used to measure many aspects of the physical world. A good example is provided by the points of a path (straight or otherwise). By placing the points of the real number line into correspondence with the points of a path, you can define a relation. In this chapter you will see how the real number line can be related to a circular path to produce the *circular functions*, which are the basis for the modern mathematical development of trigonometry.

The horse engine at the bottom of the opposite page illustrates an important feature of circular functions. Such functions are *periodic*. To see what is meant by this, compare the number of times the horses walk around the circle with the path that they cover. Assuming that the horses walk at a constant rate the same paths will recur at regular intervals. A somewhat similar situation holds true with circular functions, as you will see in this chapter. Other examples of periodic events, are ocean tides and the rotation of the earth.

The idea of periodicity can also be seen in the architectural design of the Marin County Civic Center designed by Frank Lloyd Wright. This is pictured at the top of the opposite page. The patterns are intended to give a feeling of serenity.

Sometimes you may want to repeat a pattern a little to the left or right of the original one in order to make the total effect more interesting. The patterns are then said to be "out of phase" with each other. Songs that are sung as rounds illustrate this mathematical idea of *phase*. One familiar example, Frère Jacques, is shown. In this chapter you will see that the graphs of trigonometric functions sometimes "overlap" in a similar way.

2-1 Distance and Circles

The length of a segment on the real number line with endpoints at a and b is $|b - a|$ or $|a - b|$.

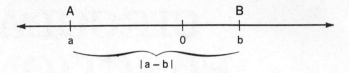

In the figure above, point A has the coordinate a and point B has the coordinate b. The measure of segment $\overline{AB}$ (its length) can be denoted either as $|\overline{AB}|$ or as AB. In this book the notation AB will be used. So, $AB = |b - a| = |a - b|$.

In the coordinate plane, each point has two coordinates. Generalize the formula $AB = |b - a| = |a - b|$ to two dimensions to determine the length of $\overline{PQ}$.

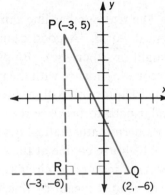

Choose a point R so that $\overline{QR}$ and $\overline{PR}$ are parallel to the x and y axes. In the drawing, R was chosen so that $\overline{QR}$ is parallel to the x axis. The coordinates of R are $(-3, -6)$ since each point on $\overline{PR}$ has a first coordinate -3 and each point on $\overline{QR}$ has a second coordinate -6.

Since $\triangle PQR$ is a right triangle, you may apply the Pythagorean Theorem.

$$(PQ)^2 = (PR)^2 + (QR)^2$$

Segments parallel to a coordinate axis may be measured by the formula for segments on the real line.

$$PR = |5 - (-6)| = 11 \qquad QR = |-3 - 2| = 5$$

Thus,

$$(PQ)^2 = 11^2 + 5^2$$

and

$$PQ = \sqrt{11^2 + 5^2} = \sqrt{146}$$

The same procedure may be applied to any segment in the plane. Assign P and Q the coordinates $P(x_1, y_1)$ and $Q(x_2, y_2)$.

$$PQ = \sqrt{(|x_1 - x_2|)^2 + (|y_1 - y_2|)^2}$$

Since $\forall x \in R$, $|x|^2 = x^2$, as you have shown, you may write more simply as follows.

$$PQ = \sqrt{(x_1 - x_2)^2 + (y_1 - y_2)^2} \qquad \textbf{1}$$

Formula **1** gives the measure of any segment PQ in the coordinate plane. Since the measure of the segment is also the distance between P and Q, formula **1** is called the **distance formula.**

One of the simplest applications of the distance formula is its use in finding the equation of a circle. A circle is the set of all points in a plane at a distance r from the center. Thus, if $P(x, y)$ are coordinates of any point of the circle with center $C(h, k)$ and radius r, by the distance formula

$$r = CP = \sqrt{(x - h)^2 + (y - k)^2}.$$

Squaring both sides you obtain

$$r^2 = (x - h)^2 + (y - k)^2. \qquad \textbf{2}$$

It is a simple matter to show that any point satisfying equation **2** is on the circle with center $C(h, k)$ and radius r.

Theorem 2–1   The equation of a circle with radius r and center at (h, k) is $(x - h)^2 + (y - k)^2 = r^2$.

Exercises

A ━━ Calculate the distance determined by each pair of points.

Example. $P(2, -7)$; $Q(-5, 1)$
Apply the distance formula $PQ = \sqrt{(x_1 - x_2)^2 + (y_1 - y_2)^2}$.
Let $(2, -7) = (x_1, y_1)$ and $(-5, 1) = (x_2, y_2)$.

$$\begin{aligned} PQ &= \sqrt{(2 - (-5))^2 + (-7 - 1)^2} \\ &= \sqrt{(7)^2 + (8)^2} \\ &= \sqrt{49 + 64} \\ &= \sqrt{113} \end{aligned}$$

If you let $(-5, 1) = (x_1, y_1)$ and $(2, -7) = (x_2, y_2)$ the result would be the same as above. Verify this.

1. $P(0, 1)$; $Q(0, -5)$ **2.** $A(-3, 0)$; $B(-7, 0)$

3. $D(2, -3)$; $E(2, 5)$ **4.** $C(-2, 5)$; $D(-8, 5)$

5. $T(5, 1)$; $R(2, -3)$ **6.** $P(-1, 3)$; $Q(5, -8)$

7. $A(-5, 2)$; $D(7, -3)$ **8.** $Q(4, 3)$; $R(2, 1)$

9. $M(\frac{1}{2}, \frac{2}{3})$; $N(-\frac{1}{2}, -\frac{7}{3})$ **10.** $U(0, 0)$; $V(-4, 3)$

11. $P(1, -7)$; $Q(3, 1)$ **12.** $A(1003, 104)$; $B(1000, 108)$

13. $H(x + 2, y - 3)$; $J(x - 2, y)$ **14.** $P(a + b, a - b)$; $Q(a - b, a + b)$ $b > 0$

15. $K(2a, a)$; $L(0, 0)$ **16.** $A(x, y)$; $B(-x, -y)$

▬ Find the equation of each circle with center C and radius r.

Example. $C(0, 0)$; $r = 1$

$$1^2 = (x - 0)^2 + (y - 0)^2$$
$$1 = x^2 + y^2$$

A circle with radius 1 is called a *unit circle.*

17. $C(2, -5)$; $r = 3$ **18.** $C(1, 3)$; $r = 4$

19. $C(-5, -1)$; $r = 7$ **20.** $C(-2, 1)$; $r = 2$

21. $C(\frac{2}{3}, -\frac{1}{3})$; $r = \frac{1}{2}$ **22.** $C(-\frac{1}{4}, \frac{1}{5})$; $r = 1$

B   **23.** Find the equation of the circle with center $(1, 2)$ which passes through the point $(-3, 7)$.

24. For what values of k is $(-3, -5)$ ten units from $(5, k)$?

25. For what values of h is $(1, 3)$ thirteen units from $(h, -2)$?

26. Demonstrate that if R is a circle with center $C(h, k)$ and radius r, and if $P(x, y)$ satisfies $(x - h)^2 + (y - k)^2 = r^2$, then P is on circle R.

27. Find the length of the sides of the triangle PQR for the points $P(2, 1)$, $Q(3, -4)$, and $R(3, 0)$.

C   **28.** Find the equation of the circle for which $P(-3, 4)$ and Q $(-3, -2)$ are ends of a diameter.

29. Find the equation of the set of points that are the same distance from $P(4, 1)$ and $Q(-1, -4)$.

30. Show that $(x - h)^2 + (y - k)^2 = r^2$ can be written in the form $x^2 + y^2 + Ax + By + C = 0$. Express A, B, and C in terms of h, k, and r.

31. Given that $x^2 + y^2 - 6x - 4y - 3 = 0$ is the equation of a circle, find the center and radius. (*Hint:* Complete the square for $x^2 - 6x + y^2 - 4y$.)

32. What is the graph of each of the following equations?

$$(x - h)^2 + (y - k)^2 = 0$$
$$(x - h)^2 + (y - k)^2 = -1$$

2–2 The Wrapping Function

Consider a circle with center at the origin and a radius of one unit. Such a circle is called a **unit circle.** Let the axes be labeled u and v. If $P(u, v)$ is any point on the unit circle, then

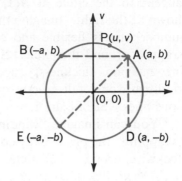

$$u^2 + v^2 = 1.$$

Now suppose $A(a, b)$ is a point on the unit circle. Then

$$a^2 + b^2 = 1.$$

However, $(-a)^2 + (b)^2 = 1$ is true also, so $B = (-a, b)$ is a point on the circle. That is, whenever $A(a, b)$ is on the circle, then $B(-a, b)$ is on the circle. A curve that has this property is said to be *symmetric with respect to the vertical axis.*

There are also two other points that must be on the circle if $A(a, b)$ is on it. These are $D(a, -b)$ and $E(-a, -b)$. This follows because

$$a^2 + (-b)^2 = a^2 + b^2 = 1$$

and

$$(-a)^2 + (-b)^2 = a^2 + b^2 = 1.$$

A curve that contains $D(a, -b)$ whenever it contains $A(a, b)$ is said to be *symmetric with respect to the horizontal axis.* Similarly, if $E(-a, -b)$ is on a curve whenever $A(a, b)$ is on it, then the curve is *symmetric with respect to the origin.*

Notice that if any one of the points $A(a, b)$, $B(-a, b)$, $D(a, -b)$, or $E(-a, -b)$ is on the unit circle, then all of them are on it. For what point $A(a, b)$ does it follow that $B = E$? that $E = D$?

You know from geometry that the circumference of a circle of radius r is $C = 2\pi r$. If $r = 1$, then $C = 2\pi$. Thus, for the unit circle with its center at the origin, the circumference is 2π units. This means that if a string were wrapped around the circle exactly once the string would be 2π units long when straightened. If the string were wrapped only part way around the circle, its length would be some fraction of 2π. Clearly the string could also be wrapped around the circle several times. In that case the length would be some real-number multiple of 2π.

Now consider a unit circle with center $C(0, 0)$ and a number line tangent to the circle at $A(1, 0)$, as shown at the right. Imagine that the number line is flexible and can be wrapped around the circle. Since a line has no thickness, successive windings would fall exactly on previous ones. See Figure 1.

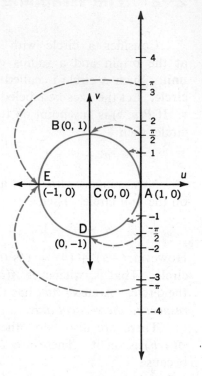

You can imagine "winding" or "wrapping" the positive ray counterclockwise around the circle. The point $\frac{\pi}{2}$ of the number line would fall on the point $B(0, 1)$ of the unit circle. This happens because the arc AB is one-fourth of the circle and thus is $\frac{1}{4} \times 2\pi = \frac{\pi}{2}$ units long.

By similar reasoning you can conclude that π is paired with $E(-1, 0)$, $\frac{3\pi}{2}$ with $D(0, -1)$, and 2π with $A(1, 0)$. In considering real numbers greater than 2π, you can

Figure 1

see that these numbers are paired with points on the circle that already are paired with real numbers between 0 and 2π. Thus each $x \in R$, $x \geq 0$, is paired with one point $P(u, v)$ on the circle, but $P(u, v)$ corresponds to an infinite set of real numbers. If $P(u, v)$ is paired with $x \in R$, then $P(u, v)$ is also paired with $x + 2\pi$, $x + 4\pi$, $x + 6\pi$, and, in general, with $x + 2n\pi$, $n \in W$. For example, if 3 is paired with $P(u, v)$, then $3 + 2\pi$ and $3 + 4\pi$ are two other real numbers that are paired with $P(u, v)$.

By wrapping the negative ray clockwise around the unit circle, you pair $-\frac{\pi}{2}$ with $D(0, -1)$, $-\pi$ with $C(-1, 0)$, $-\frac{3\pi}{2}$ with $B(0, 1)$, and -2π with $A(1, 0)$. If $x \in R$, $x < 0$, is paired with $P(u, v)$, then $x - 2\pi$, $x - 4\pi$, and, in general, $x - 2n\pi$, $n \in W$, are each paired with $P(u, v)$.

Thus, the wrapping procedure defines a function, the **wrapping function** W. W maps the real numbers onto the points of the unit circle.

From the above discussion what would the inverse of the wrapping function be? Is it a function?

66   CHAPTER 2

Suppose W is as follows

$$W : x \rightarrow (a, b),$$

as shown in the figure at the right. It then follows from the symmetry of the circle that

$$W : -x \rightarrow (a, -b).$$

Similarly, (see figures below)

$$W : x + \pi \rightarrow (-a, -b) \text{ and}$$
$$W : -x + \pi \rightarrow (-a, b).$$

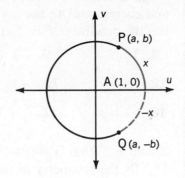

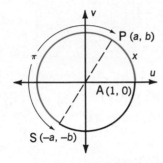
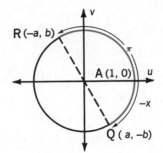

Exercises

A ━━ Suppose $W : 2 \rightarrow (u, v)$.

1. Name five positive real numbers besides 2 that map onto this same point under the wrapping function.

2. Name five negative real numbers that map onto the same point under W.

━━ Suppose $W : -3 \rightarrow (a, b)$.

3. Name four negative numbers besides -3 that W maps onto (a, b).

4. Name four positive numbers that W maps onto (a, b).

━━ Let $W : \frac{2\pi}{3} \rightarrow (r, s)$.

5. Write an expression that names all the other positive real numbers that map onto (r, s).

6. Write an expression that names all the negative real numbers that map onto (r, s).

7. Combine the results of Exercises 5 and 6 into one expression that names all the real numbers that map onto (r, s).

In Exercises 8–19 let P be the point that lies on the unit circle and corresponds to the x value below for the function W. Identify the quadrant of P. Let $\pi \approx 3.142$ if necessary.

8. 1

9. −1

10. $6\pi - \frac{4\pi}{3}$

11. 6

12. −3

13. −5

14. $\frac{1004\pi}{3}$

15. $-\frac{7\pi}{6}$

16. $\frac{7\pi}{6} + \pi$

17. $\frac{\pi}{3} + 13\pi$

18. $-\frac{4\pi}{3} + \frac{\pi}{2}$

19. $\frac{15\pi}{2}$

Example. What is $W(x - \pi)$ if $W : x \to (\frac{3}{5}, \frac{4}{5})$?

By the symmetry of the circle, you can see that the following is true.

$$W(x - \pi) = (-\tfrac{3}{5}, -\tfrac{4}{5})$$

or

$$W : x - \pi \to (-\tfrac{3}{5}, -\tfrac{4}{5})$$

20. Let $W : x \to (\frac{12}{13}, \frac{5}{13})$. What is
   a. $W(-x)$?
   b. $W(x + \pi)$?
   c. $W(x + 2\pi)$?
   d. $W(-x + \pi)$?

21. Let $W : x \to (-\frac{3}{5}, \frac{4}{5})$. What is
   a. $W(x + \pi)$?
   b. $W(-x)$?
   c. $W(\pi - x)$?
   d. $W(2\pi + x)$?

22. Let $W : x \to \left(\frac{\sqrt{3}}{2}, -\frac{1}{2}\right)$. What is
   a. $W(2\pi + x)$?
   b. $W(x + \pi)$?
   c. $W(\pi - x)$?
   d. $W(-x)$?

23. Let $W : x \to \left(-\frac{\sqrt{13}}{14}, -\frac{1}{14}\right)$. What is
   a. $W(\pi - x)$?
   b. $W(x + 2\pi)$?
   c. $W(x + \pi)$?
   d. $W(-x)$?

24. Let $W : \frac{3\pi}{4} \to \left(-\frac{\sqrt{2}}{2}, \frac{\sqrt{2}}{2}\right)$. What is
   a. $W\left(\frac{\pi}{4}\right)$?
   b. $W\left(-\frac{3\pi}{4}\right)$?
   c. $W\left(\frac{7\pi}{4}\right)$?
   d. $W\left(\frac{5\pi}{4}\right)$?

25. Let $W : \frac{\pi}{3} \to \left(\frac{1}{2}, \frac{\sqrt{3}}{2}\right)$. What is
   a. $W\left(\frac{4\pi}{3}\right)$?
   b. $W\left(-\frac{\pi}{3}\right)$?
   c. $W\left(-\frac{4\pi}{3}\right)$?
   d. $W\left(\frac{2\pi}{3}\right)$?

B *Example.* Find the coordinates of $P(u, v)$, when

$$W : \frac{\pi}{4} \to (u, v).$$

Subsequently find $W\left(-\frac{\pi}{4}\right)$, $W\left(\frac{5\pi}{4}\right)$, and $W\left(\frac{3\pi}{4}\right)$.

Refer to the figure at right. Since $\frac{\pi}{4}$ is one-eighth the distance around the circle, $P(u, v)$ is the midpoint of the arc AB. Thus $\overset{\frown}{AP} = \overset{\frown}{PB} = \frac{\pi}{4}$. Since the arcs are equal, so are their chords: $AP = PB$ (Why?). By the distance formula,

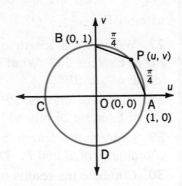

$$\sqrt{u^2 + (v - 1)^2} = PB = AP = \sqrt{(u - 1)^2 + v^2}.$$
$$u^2 + v^2 - 2v + 1 = u^2 - 2u + 1 + v^2$$
$$-2v = -2u$$
$$u = v.$$

But $u^2 + v^2 = 1$, and thus

$$u^2 + u^2 = 2u^2$$
$$= 1.$$
$$u^2 = \tfrac{1}{2}$$
$$u = \frac{1}{\sqrt{2}} = \frac{\sqrt{2}}{2} = v$$

It follows that

$$W : \frac{\pi}{4} \to \left(\frac{\sqrt{2}}{2}, \frac{\sqrt{2}}{2}\right).$$

By the symmetry of the circle,

$$W : -\frac{\pi}{4} \to \left(\frac{\sqrt{2}}{2}, -\frac{\sqrt{2}}{2}\right).$$

Since $\frac{5\pi}{4} = \pi + \frac{\pi}{4}$,

$$W : \frac{\pi}{4} + \pi \to \left(-\frac{\sqrt{2}}{2}, -\frac{\sqrt{2}}{2}\right).$$

Finally, since $\frac{3\pi}{4} = -\frac{\pi}{4} + \pi$,

$$W : -\frac{\pi}{4} + \pi \to \left(-\frac{\sqrt{2}}{2}, \frac{\sqrt{2}}{2}\right).$$

26. Let the coordinates of the point that corresponds to $\frac{\pi}{6}$ be $P(u, v)$. What are the coordinates of $W\left(-\frac{\pi}{6}\right) = Q$?

27. What is the length of arc PQ in Exercise 26? What is the length of arc BP?

28. How are chords $\overline{BP}$ and $\overline{PQ}$ of Exercise 26 related?

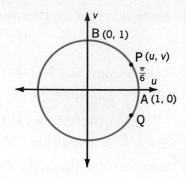

29. Express the length of $\overline{BP}$ of Exercise 26 in terms of the coordinates of B and P. Do the same for $\overline{PQ}$.

30. Combine the results of Exercises 28–29 to write an equation. Simplify this equation by squaring both sides. Use the fact that $u^2 + v^2 = 1$ to simplify the resulting expression.

31. Find u and v when

$$W\left(\frac{\pi}{6}\right) = (u, v).$$

━━ Use the result of Exercise 31 to find the value of the wrapping function at each of the given values.

32. $W\left(-\frac{\pi}{6}\right)$ **33.** $W\left(\frac{5\pi}{6}\right)$ **34.** $W\left(\frac{7\pi}{6}\right)$

C **35.** Place the square ABCD as shown in the figure. Imagine a number line with its origin at $O(1, 0)$ which is wrapped counterclockwise around the square. Each point of the number line maps onto a single point on the square. This wrapping defines a function mapping non-negative real numbers onto points of the square. Call it T. For example $T : 2 \rightarrow (0, 1)$. Find the image under T of each of the following.

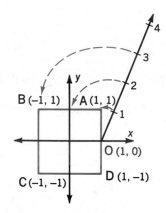

    a. 3   **b.** 4   **c.** 5

    d. 6   **e.** 7   **f.** 8

    g. $2\frac{1}{2}$ **h.** 100   **i.** 2000

36. Define two new functions "soon" and "tusoon". Let T be the wrapping function of Exercise 35 which maps x onto $P(u, v)$ on the square. Then

$$\text{soon} = \{(x, v) : v = \text{soon } x\}$$
$$\text{tusoon} = \{(x, u) : u = \text{tusoon } x\}$$

Find the values of "soon" and "tusoon" for x as follows:

a. 0   **b.** 1   **c.** 3   **d.** $5\frac{1}{2}$

e. $6.\overline{9}$ **f.** 8   **g.** 100   **h.** 2000

37. Complete the following.

a. For $0 \leq x \leq 1$ tusoon $x =$ ___ while ___ $\leq$ soon $x \leq$ ___.

b. For $1 < x \leq 3$ soon $x =$ ___ while ___ $\leq$ tusoon $x <$ ___.

c. For $3 < x \leq 5$ tusoon $x =$ ___ while ___ $\leq$ soon $x <$ ___.

d. For $5 < x \leq 7$ soon $x =$ ___ while ___ $<$ tusoon $x \leq$ ___.

e. For $7 < x \leq 8$ tusoon $x =$ ___ while ___ $<$ soon $x \leq$ ___.

38. Use the results of Exercises 36 and 37 to graph the following two functions.

$$y = \text{soon } x, \quad 0 \leq x \leq 8$$

and

$$y = \text{tusoon } x, \quad 0 \leq x \leq 8$$

2–3   The Sine and Cosine Functions

The pairing of real numbers with points on the unit circle by the wrapping function W allows you to define two new functions. The first of these functions maps each real number x onto the *first coordinate* of $W(x) = (u, v)$ and is called the **cosine function** (abbreviated cos). The second function maps each real number x onto the *second coordinate* of $W(x) = (u, v)$ and is called the **sine function** (abbreviated sin). These functions are called **circular functions.**

Definition   Let W be the wrapping function that maps $x \in R$ onto the point $P(u, v)$ that is x units from $(1, 0)$ along the circle $u^2 + v^2 = 1$. Then the cosine and sine functions are

$$\cos = \{(x, u) : u = \cos x\}$$

and

$$\sin = \{(x, v) : v = \sin x\}.$$

The definition is illustrated at the right. If x is the positive or negative length of an arc along the circle from $A(1, 0)$, then the coordinates of the corresponding point P are $(\cos x, \sin x)$.

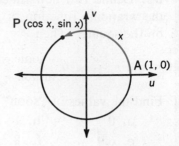

A fundamental property of the sine and cosine functions follows immediately from the definition.

Theorem 2–2 $\forall x \in R$

$$\sin^2 x + \cos^2 x = 1$$

Notice that $\sin^2 x$ is commonly used to represent $(\sin x)^2$. Similarly $\cos^2 x$ means $(\cos x)^2$. The proof of Theorem 2–2 is left to you.

You saw that the symmetry of the circle led to the fact that

if $W : x \rightarrow (u, v)$, then $W : -x \rightarrow (u, -v)$.

Restating this relationship in terms of the $\cos x$ and $\sin x$ you have

Theorem 2–3 $\forall x \in R$

$$\cos (-x) = \cos x$$
$$\sin (-x) = -\sin x$$

By further appealing to the symmetry of the circle, you can express $\cos (\pi - x)$ and $\cos (\pi + x)$ in terms of $\cos x$ or $\sin (\pi - x)$ and $\sin (\pi + x)$ in terms of $\sin x$. These are left for you to do in the exercises.

Note that $\cos (0) = 1$ and $\sin (0) = 0$ because $W : 0 \rightarrow (1, 0)$. Now let $0 < x < \frac{\pi}{2}$. Here

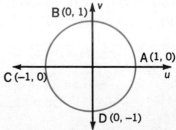

$$W : x \rightarrow (\cos x, \sin x),$$

and $(\cos x, \sin x)$ is a point in Quadrant I.

Thus $\cos x > 0$ and $\sin x > 0$ when $0 < x < \frac{\pi}{2}$, because any point in Quadrant I has positive coordinates.

By similar reasoning you can show that the figure below is an accurate representation of the signs of $\cos x$ and $\sin x$ for all $x \in R$ such that $0 \leq x < 2\pi$. When $x \in R$ is associated with a point $P(\cos x, \sin x)$ that is in a certain quadrant, it is conventional to say that *x is in that quadrant.*

How can you determine the sign of $\cos x$ and $\sin x$ when $x \in R$ and $x > 2\pi$ or $x < 0$?

Quadrant II $\quad x = \frac{\pi}{2}: \cos x = 0, \sin x = 1 \quad$ Quadrant I

$\frac{\pi}{2} < x < \pi$ $\qquad\qquad\qquad\qquad$ $0 < x < \frac{\pi}{2}$

$\cos x < 0$ $\qquad\qquad\qquad\qquad$ $\cos x > 0$

$\sin x > 0$ $\qquad\qquad\qquad\qquad$ $\sin x > 0$

$x = \pi: \cos x = -1, \sin x = 0 \mid x = 0: \cos x = 1, \sin x = 0$

$\pi < x < \frac{3\pi}{2}$ $\qquad\qquad\qquad$ $\frac{3\pi}{2} < x < 2\pi$

$\cos x < 0$ $\qquad\qquad\qquad\qquad$ $\cos x > 0$

$\sin x < 0$ $\qquad\qquad\qquad\qquad$ $\sin x < 0$

Quadrant III $\quad x = \frac{3\pi}{2}: \cos x = 0, \sin x = -1 \quad$ Quadrant IV

Theorem 2–4 $\forall x \in R$ and $\forall n \in W$

$$\cos (x \pm 2n\pi) = \cos x$$
$$\sin (x \pm 2n\pi) = \sin x$$

This theorem follows from the fact that the wrapping function W pairs x and $x \pm 2n\pi$ with the same point on the unit circle.

EXAMPLE 1. Determine the quadrant in which x lies and the signs of $\cos x$ and $\sin x$ if $x = \frac{21\pi}{4}$.

$$x = \frac{21\pi}{4} = 5\pi + \frac{\pi}{4} = 4\pi + \frac{5\pi}{4}$$

Since $\frac{5\pi}{4}$ is in Quadrant III, so is $\frac{21\pi}{4}$. Applying Theorem 2–4,

$$\cos (\tfrac{5}{4}\pi + 4\pi) = \cos \frac{5\pi}{4} \quad \text{and} \quad \sin (\tfrac{5}{4}\pi + 4\pi) = \sin \frac{5\pi}{4}.$$

Thus, since $\frac{5\pi}{4}$ is in Quadrant III,

$$\cos \frac{5\pi}{4} < 0 \quad \text{and} \quad \sin \frac{5\pi}{4} < 0.$$

Consequently, $\cos \frac{21\pi}{4} < 0$ and $\sin \frac{21\pi}{4} < 0$.

EXAMPLE 2. Determine the quadrant in which x lies and the signs of $\cos x$ and $\sin x$.

$$x = -\frac{16\pi}{3} = -5\pi - \frac{\pi}{3}$$

$$= -4\pi - \frac{4\pi}{3}$$

$$= -4\pi - \left(2\pi - \frac{2\pi}{3}\right)$$

$$= -6\pi + \frac{2\pi}{3}$$

Since $\frac{2\pi}{3}$ is in Quadrant II, so is $-\frac{16\pi}{3}$. Thus,

$$\cos\left(-\frac{16\pi}{3}\right) = \cos\left(-6\pi + \frac{2\pi}{3}\right) = \cos\frac{2\pi}{3} < 0.$$

Similarly, $\sin\left(-\frac{16\pi}{3}\right) = \sin\frac{2\pi}{3}$, so $\sin\left(-\frac{16\pi}{3}\right) > 0$.

Exercises

A ■■ In Exercises 1–15 determine the quadrant in which x lies. Then determine the signs of $\cos x$ and $\sin x$. Use the approximation $\pi \approx 3.142$ if necessary.

1. $x = 3$

2. $x = 4$

3. $x = 5$

4. $x = \frac{9\pi}{4}$

5. $x = -\frac{9\pi}{4}$

6. $x = \frac{100\pi}{3}$

7. $x = -\frac{19\pi}{4}$

8. $x = \frac{35\pi}{6}$

9. $x = -\frac{19\pi}{6}$

10. $x = -\frac{99\pi}{4}$

11. $x = -3$

12. $x = -5$

13. $x = -\frac{14\pi}{3}$

14. $x = -\frac{11\pi}{3}$

15. $x = \frac{22\pi}{5}$

■■ In Exercises 16–23 determine the other circular function, given one circular function and the quadrant in which x lies.

Example. $\sin x = -\frac{3}{5}$, x in Quadrant IV
By Theorem 2-2, $\sin^2 x + \cos^2 x = 1$.

$$(-\tfrac{3}{5})^2 + \cos^2 x = 1$$

$$\cos^2 x = 1 - \tfrac{9}{25} = \tfrac{16}{25}$$

Since x is in Quadrant IV, $\cos x > 0$, so $\cos x = \frac{4}{5}$.

16. $\sin x = \frac{12}{13}$, x in Quadrant II

17. $\cos x = \frac{12}{13}$, x in Quadrant IV

18. $\sin x = -\frac{4}{5}$, x in Quadrant III

19. $\cos x = \frac{3}{5}$, x in Quadrant I

20. $\cos x = -\frac{2\sqrt{2}}{3}$, x in Quadrant II

21. $\sin x = -\frac{1}{\sqrt{5}}$, x in Quadrant IV

22. $\cos x = \frac{\sqrt{15}}{4}$, x in Quadrant IV

23. $\sin x = \frac{\sqrt{17}}{3\sqrt{2}}$, x in Quadrant I

━━ Use the unit circle to find the following.

Example. $\sin \frac{\pi}{2}$.

The real number $\frac{\pi}{2}$ maps onto $(0, 1)$ on the unit circle, so $\sin \frac{\pi}{2} = 1$.

24. $\cos \frac{\pi}{2}$ **25.** $\sin 0$ **26.** $\cos 0$

27. $\cos \pi$ **28.** $\sin \pi$ **29.** $\sin \frac{3\pi}{2}$

30. $\cos \frac{3\pi}{2}$ **31.** $\sin 2\pi$ **32.** $\cos 2\pi$

33. Use the symmetry of the unit circle to
    a. express $\cos (\pi - x)$ in terms of $\cos x$.
    b. express $\cos (\pi + x)$ in terms of $\cos x$.

34. Use the symmetry of the unit circle to
    a. express $\sin (\pi - x)$ in terms of $\sin x$.
    b. express $\sin (\pi + x)$ in terms of $\sin x$.

B   **35.** Prove that for each $x \in R$, $|\sin x| \leq 1$.

    36. Prove that for each $x \in R$, $|\cos x| \leq 1$.

    37. A function f is *odd* if and only if $f(-x) = -f(x)$. What theorem of this section insures that sin is odd?

    38. A function f is *even* if and only if $f(-x) = f(x)$. What theorem of this section insures that cos is even?

C ━━ Refer to the figure at the right for Exercises 39–41.

    39. $BP = PA$. Explain.

    40. Use the distance formula and the fact that $BP = PA$ to show that $\cos \frac{\pi}{4} = \sin \frac{\pi}{4}$.

    41. Use Exercise 40 and
        $\cos^2 x + \sin^2 x = 1$
    to find $\cos \frac{\pi}{4}$ and $\sin \frac{\pi}{4}$.

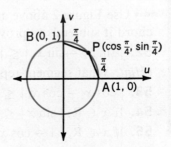

━━ Use the results of Exercises 33, 34 and 39–41 and Theorems 2–3 and 2–4 to find the values of the following.

42. $\sin -\dfrac{\pi}{4}$ and $\cos -\dfrac{\pi}{4}$

43. $\sin \dfrac{7\pi}{4}$ and $\cos \dfrac{7\pi}{4}$

44. $\sin \dfrac{3\pi}{4}$ and $\cos \dfrac{3\pi}{4}$

45. $\sin \dfrac{5\pi}{4}$ and $\cos \dfrac{15\pi}{4}$

━━ Refer to Figure 1 below for Exercises 46–48.

46. Express the coordinates of Q in terms of $\cos \dfrac{\pi}{6}$ and $\sin \dfrac{\pi}{6}$.

47. $BP = PQ$. Explain.

48. Use the distance formula and the relation

$$\cos^2 x + \sin^2 x = 1$$

to find the values of $\cos \dfrac{\pi}{6}$ and $\sin \dfrac{\pi}{6}$.

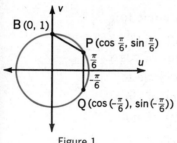

Figure 1

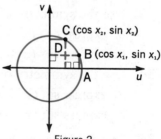

Figure 2

━━ Use the results of Exercises 33, 34, 46–48 and Theorems 2–3 and 2–4 to find the values of the following.

49. $\sin \dfrac{7\pi}{6}$ and $\cos \dfrac{7\pi}{6}$

50. $\sin \dfrac{5\pi}{6}$ and $\cos \dfrac{5\pi}{6}$

51. $\sin \dfrac{11\pi}{6}$ and $\cos \dfrac{11\pi}{6}$

━━ Use Figure 2 above and the fact that an arc is longer than the chord it subtends to prove the statements in Exercises 52–55.

52. $|\sin x_2 - \sin x_1| \le |x_2 - x_1|$, $x_1, x_2 \in R$
(*Hint:* What segment represents $|\sin x_2 - \sin x_1|$?)

53. $|\cos x_2 - \cos x_1| \le |x_2 - x_1|$

54. If $x \in R$, $|\sin x| \le |x|$ (*Hint:* Use Exercise 52.)

55. If $x \in R$, $|1 - \cos x| \le |x|$ (*Hint:* Use Exercise 53.)

76   CHAPTER 2

2–4 Values of sin x and cos x

In the table below are values you have found in the examples, exercises, and discussions of Sections 2–2 and 2–3.

x	$\cos x$	$\sin x$
0	1	0
$\dfrac{\pi}{6}$	$\dfrac{\sqrt{3}}{2}$	$\dfrac{1}{2}$
$\dfrac{\pi}{4}$	$\dfrac{\sqrt{2}}{2}$	$\dfrac{\sqrt{2}}{2}$
$\dfrac{\pi}{3}$		
$\dfrac{\pi}{2}$	0	1
$\dfrac{2\pi}{3}$		
$\dfrac{3\pi}{4}$	$-\dfrac{\sqrt{2}}{2}$	$\dfrac{\sqrt{2}}{2}$
$\dfrac{5\pi}{6}$	$-\dfrac{\sqrt{3}}{2}$	$\dfrac{1}{2}$
π	-1	0
$\dfrac{7\pi}{6}$	$-\dfrac{\sqrt{3}}{2}$	$-\dfrac{1}{2}$
$\dfrac{5\pi}{4}$	$-\dfrac{\sqrt{2}}{2}$	$-\dfrac{\sqrt{2}}{2}$
$\dfrac{4\pi}{3}$		
$\dfrac{3\pi}{2}$	0	-1
$\dfrac{5\pi}{3}$		
$\dfrac{7\pi}{4}$	$\dfrac{\sqrt{2}}{2}$	$-\dfrac{\sqrt{2}}{2}$
$\dfrac{11\pi}{6}$	$\dfrac{\sqrt{3}}{2}$	$-\dfrac{1}{2}$
2π	1	0

The values of $\cos x$ and $\sin x$ for $x \in \left\{\dfrac{\pi}{3}, \dfrac{2\pi}{3}, \dfrac{4\pi}{3}, \dfrac{5\pi}{3}\right\}$ are obtained in this section. For that reason you will find the next theorem useful.

Theorem 2–5 $\forall x \in R$

$$\cos\left(\frac{\pi}{2} + x\right) = -\sin x \qquad \sin\left(\frac{\pi}{2} + x\right) = \cos x$$

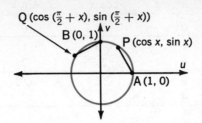

$Q\left(\cos\left(\frac{\pi}{2} + x\right), \sin\left(\frac{\pi}{2} + x\right)\right)$

$B(0, 1)$

$P(\cos x, \sin x)$

$A(1, 0)$

Proof: Refer to the figure above. The arc AP has length x, and the arc AQ has length $\frac{\pi}{2} + x$. Since

$$\widehat{AQ} = \widehat{AB} + \widehat{BQ}$$

and $\widehat{AB}$ is $\frac{\pi}{2}$ units, arc BQ is x units long, thus $\overline{BQ} = \overline{AP}$. (Why?)

$$(BQ)^2 = \cos^2\left(\frac{\pi}{2} + x\right) + \left(\sin\left(\frac{\pi}{2} + x\right) - 1\right)^2$$

$$= \cos^2\left(\frac{\pi}{2} + x\right) + \sin^2\left(\frac{\pi}{2} + x\right) - 2\sin\left(\frac{\pi}{2} + x\right) + 1$$

$$= \qquad\qquad 1 \qquad\qquad\qquad - 2\sin\left(\frac{\pi}{2} + x\right) + 1$$

$$= 2 - 2\sin\left(\frac{\pi}{2} + x\right)$$

$$(AP)^2 = (\cos x - 1)^2 + \sin^2 x$$

$$= \cos^2 x - 2\cos x + 1 + \sin^2 x$$

$$= (\cos^2 x + \sin^2 x) - 2\cos x + 1$$

$$= \qquad 1 \qquad\qquad - 2\cos x + 1$$

$$= 2 - 2\cos x$$

Since $BQ = AP$, $(BQ)^2 = (PA)^2$, so

$$2 - 2\sin\left(\frac{\pi}{2} + x\right) = 2 - 2\cos x$$

or

$$\sin\left(\frac{\pi}{2} + x\right) = \cos x.$$

You can now use $\cos^2 x + \sin^2 x = 1$.

$$\sin^2 \left(\frac{\pi}{2} + x\right) + \cos^2 \left(\frac{\pi}{2} + x\right) = 1$$

$$\cos^2 \left(\frac{\pi}{2} + x\right) = 1 - \sin^2 \left(\frac{\pi}{2} + x\right)$$

$$= 1 - \cos^2 x. \quad \text{(Why?)}$$

$$= \sin^2 x \quad \text{(Why?)}$$

$$\cos \left(\frac{\pi}{2} + x\right) = \sin x \text{ or } -\sin x \quad \text{(Why?)}$$

Thus, if x is in Quadrant I, then $\frac{\pi}{2} + x$ is in Quadrant II, and

$$\cos \left(\frac{\pi}{2} + x\right) = -\sin x.$$

Similarly, whatever quadrant x is in, $\frac{\pi}{2} + x$ is in the next quadrant. In each case the signs of $\sin x$ and $\cos \left(\frac{\pi}{2} + x\right)$ are opposites. Thus,

$$\forall x \in \mathbf{R} \qquad \cos \left(\frac{\pi}{2} + x\right) = -\sin x.$$

Since $\frac{2\pi}{3} = \frac{\pi}{2} + \frac{\pi}{6}$, by Theorem 2–5,

$$\sin \frac{2\pi}{3} = \cos \frac{\pi}{6} = \frac{\sqrt{3}}{2}$$

and

$$\cos \frac{2\pi}{3} = -\sin \frac{\pi}{6} = -\tfrac{1}{2}.$$

The table below summarizes many facts on $\sin x$ and $\cos x$.

1. $\forall x \in \mathbf{R} \quad \sin^2 x + \cos^2 x = 1\}$ **Theorem 2-2**

2. $\forall x \in \mathbf{R} \quad \begin{aligned} &\sin(-x) = -\sin x \\ &\cos(-x) = \cos x \end{aligned} \Big\}$ **Theorem 2-3**

3. $\forall x \in \mathbf{R} \quad \begin{aligned} &\cos(\pi + x) = -\cos x \\ &\cos(\pi - x) = -\cos x \end{aligned} \Big\}$ See Exercise 33, Section 2–3

4. $\forall x \in \mathbf{R} \quad \begin{aligned} &\sin(\pi + x) = -\sin x \\ &\sin(\pi - x) = \sin x \end{aligned} \Big\}$ See Exercise 34, Section 2–3

5. $\forall x \in \mathbf{R} \quad n \in \mathbf{W} \quad \begin{aligned} &\cos(x \pm 2n\pi) = \cos x \\ &\sin(x \pm 2n\pi) = \sin x \end{aligned} \Big\}$ **Theorem 2-4**

6. $\forall x \in \mathbf{R} \quad \begin{aligned} &\sin \left(\frac{\pi}{2} + x\right) = \cos x \\[1em] &\cos \left(\frac{\pi}{2} + x\right) = -\sin x \end{aligned} \Bigg\}$ **Theorem 2-5**

Exercises

A   **1.** Complete the table on page 77 by adding values for

$$x \in \left\{ \frac{\pi}{3}, \frac{2\pi}{3}, \frac{4\pi}{3}, \frac{5\pi}{3} \right\}.$$

Make a copy of the complete table and keep it for further reference. You should memorize the entries, also.

▬ Use your table to determine whether each of the following is true or false.

2. $2 \sin \frac{\pi}{6} \cos \frac{\pi}{6} = \sin \frac{\pi}{3}$

3. $\sin \frac{2\pi}{3} \cos \frac{2\pi}{3} = \sin \frac{4\pi}{3}$

4. $\sin \frac{\pi}{4} \cos \frac{\pi}{4} + \cos \frac{\pi}{4} \sin \frac{\pi}{4} = 1$

5. $2 \sin \frac{3\pi}{4} \cos \frac{3\pi}{4} = -1$

6. $\sin \frac{\pi}{6} \cos \frac{\pi}{3} + \cos \frac{\pi}{2} \sin \frac{\pi}{3} = 1$

7. $\cos^2 \frac{5\pi}{6} - \sin^2 \frac{5\pi}{6} = \cos \frac{5\pi}{6}$

8. $\cos^2 \frac{5\pi}{4} - \sin^2 \frac{5\pi}{4} = 1$

9. $\cos \frac{4\pi}{3} \cos \frac{2\pi}{3} - \sin \frac{4\pi}{3} \sin \frac{2\pi}{3} = 1$

10. $\cos \frac{11\pi}{6} \cos \frac{5\pi}{6} + \sin \frac{11\pi}{6} \sin \frac{5\pi}{6} = 1$

11. $\cos^2 \frac{\pi}{6} - \sin^2 \frac{\pi}{6} = \frac{1}{2}$

▬ In Exercises 12–23 find a real number x, $0 \le x \le \frac{\pi}{2}$, for which $\pm\sin x$ or $\pm\cos x$ is equal to the given number. Often there is more than one correct answer.

Example. $\cos \frac{4\pi}{5}$

Since

$$\frac{4\pi}{5} = \pi - \frac{\pi}{5}, \qquad\qquad \cos \frac{4\pi}{5} = \cos \left(\pi - \frac{\pi}{5} \right)$$

$$= -\cos \frac{\pi}{5}$$

Since

$$\frac{4\pi}{5} = \frac{\pi}{2} + \frac{3\pi}{10}, \qquad\qquad \cos \frac{4\pi}{5} = \cos \left(\frac{\pi}{2} + \frac{3\pi}{10} \right)$$

$$= -\sin \frac{3\pi}{10}$$

12. $\cos \left(-\frac{\pi}{7} \right)$

13. $\sin \left(-\frac{\pi}{8} \right)$

14. $\cos \left(\frac{11\pi}{10} \right)$

15. $\sin \left(\frac{10\pi}{9} \right)$

16. $\cos\left(\frac{7\pi}{8}\right)$

17. $\sin\left(\frac{7\pi}{8}\right)$

18. $\cos\left(\frac{\pi}{5} + 7\pi\right)$

19. $\sin\left(\frac{\pi}{7} + 8\pi\right)$

20. $\sin\left(\frac{4\pi}{7}\right)$

21. $\cos\left(\frac{19\pi}{3}\right)$

22. $\sin\left(-\frac{19\pi}{3}\right)$

23. $\sin\left(\frac{4n+1}{2}\pi\right), n \in W$

B **24.** Find an expression for $\sin\left(\frac{\pi}{2} - x\right)$ in terms of cos x.

25. Find an expression for $\sin\left(x - \frac{\pi}{2}\right)$ in terms of cos x.

26. Find an expression for $\cos\left(\frac{\pi}{2} - x\right)$ in terms of sin x.

27. Find an expression for $\cos\left(x - \frac{\pi}{2}\right)$ in terms of sin x.

28. Find an expression for $\sin(x - \pi)$ in terms of sin x.

29. Find an expression for $\cos(x - \pi)$ in terms of cos x.

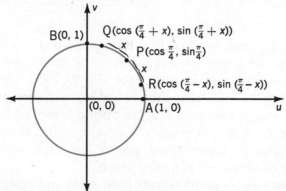

C ▬▬ Refer to the figure above. Let $x \in R$ and $0 < x < \frac{\pi}{4}$. Let A, B, P, Q and R have coordinates as indicated.

30. Show that $BQ = AR$.

31. Use Exercise 30, the distance formula, and the relation

$$\sin^2 x + \cos^2 x = 1$$

to show that

a. $\sin\left(\frac{\pi}{4} - x\right) = \cos\left(\frac{\pi}{4} + x\right).$

b. $\cos\left(\frac{\pi}{4} - x\right) = \sin\left(\frac{\pi}{4} + x\right).$

32. Does the result of Exercise 31 hold when $x > \frac{\pi}{4}$? $x < 0$? $x = \frac{\pi}{4}$? Explain in detail.

2–5   Graphs of The Sine and Cosine Functions

You know by Theorem 2–4 that $\forall x \in R$ and $n \in W$

$$\cos (x \pm 2n\pi) = \cos x \qquad \text{and} \qquad \sin (x \pm 2n\pi) = \sin x.$$

You can use Theorem 2–4 to find $\cos r$ and $\sin r$ for every real number r.

Suppose you divide the real number r by 2π. The result is a quotient $n \in I$ and a remainder x such that $0 \le x < 2\pi$. That is,

$$r \div 2\pi = n + \frac{x}{2\pi}, \quad n \in I. \tag{1}$$

Multiplying both sides of **1** by 2π, you obtain

$$r = 2\pi n + x, \qquad 0 \le x < 2\pi. \tag{2}$$

Equation **2** holds for any real number r. It says in essence that any real number is an integral multiple of 2π plus a remainder x, $0 \le x < 2\pi$. Since $I = \{-n\} \cup \{n\}$, $n \in W$, **2** can be written

$$r = \pm 2n\pi + x, \qquad 0 \le x < 2\pi, \qquad n \in W.$$

Since every real number can be expressed $r = \pm 2n\pi + x$, the graphs of $y = \sin x$ and $y = \cos x$ for $x \in R$ are determined by the graphs of $y = \sin x$ and $y = \cos x$ for $x \in [0, 2\pi)$. On each other interval that is 2π units long and has a left endpoint of $\pm 2n\pi$, the graphs of $y = \sin x$ and $y = \cos x$ are carbon copies of the graphs on $[0, 2\pi)$. Thus it suffices to graph $y = \sin x$, $x \in [0, 2\pi)$ and $y = \cos x$, $x \in [0, 2\pi)$ and to repeat these graphs on each interval $[\pm 2n\pi, \pm 2(n + 1)\pi)$ to obtain the complete graph.

A function whose graph repeats itself again and again is a **periodic function.**

Definition   If f is a function with domain R and if there is a number $p > 0$ such that

$$\forall x \in R \qquad f(x + p) = f(x)$$

then f is a periodic function. If p is the smallest positive number with this property, then p is the period of f.

The number 2π is the smallest positive p such that

$$\sin (x + p) = \sin x \qquad \text{and} \qquad \cos (x + p) = \cos x.$$

Thus the sine and cosine functions have the *period* 2π.

The figure below shows a graph of $y = \sin x$. The dots correspond to known pairs $(x, \sin x)$ from Exercise 1 of Section 2–4.

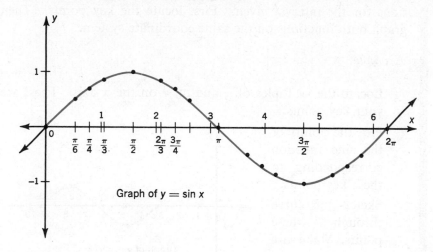

Graph of $y = \sin x$

The red portion of the graph is the graph on the interval $[0, 2\pi)$. Any interval of length 2π could be used in a repetitive fashion to construct the entire curve. Such an interval is called a **cycle** of the curve. Any interval $[x, x + 2\pi)$, $x \in R$, will determine a cycle.

The cosine function is graphed below. The red portion corresponds to the interval $[0, 2\pi)$. Again a cycle is the graph over an interval $[x, x + 2\pi)$, $x \in R$.

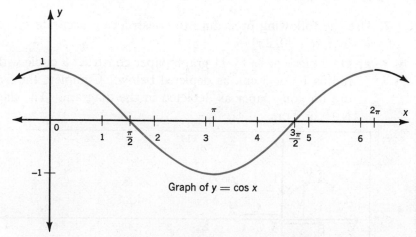

Graph of $y = \cos x$

Compare the graph of the cosine on $\left[-\frac{\pi}{2}, \frac{3\pi}{2}\right)$ with that of the sine on $[0, 2\pi)$. These two cycles are identical. It appears that the graph of $y = \cos x$ is the graph of $y = \sin x$ shifted $\frac{\pi}{2}$ units to the left.

CIRCULAR FUNCTIONS 83

Exercises

A ■— In Exercises 1–6 sketch the graphs of the sine and cosine functions for the interval given. First locate the key points. Then graph both functions on the same coordinate system.

Example. $x \in \left[\frac{\pi}{2}, 3\pi\right]$.

① Locate the multiples of $\frac{\pi}{2}$ and of π on the x axis. These are your key points.

② Plot the points of the sine function corresponding to these key points.

③ Sketch the curve through these points. Make sure it has the general shape of the sine curve.

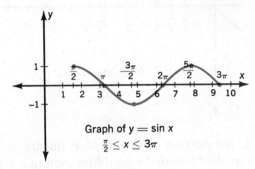

Graph of $y = \sin x$

$\frac{\pi}{2} \leq x \leq 3\pi$

④ Repeat the procedure for the cosine function.

1. $\left[-\frac{3\pi}{2}, \frac{3\pi}{2}\right]$ 2. $[3\pi, 6\pi]$ 3. $[-5\pi, -\pi]$

4. $\left[-\frac{3\pi}{4}, 3\pi\right]$ 5. $\left[\frac{8\pi}{3}, 5\pi\right]$ 6. $\left[-\frac{17\pi}{6}, -\frac{\pi}{6}\right]$

7. Use the following procedure to construct an accurate graph of $y = \sin x$, $x \in [0, 2\pi]$.

    a. On a piece of $8\frac{1}{2}$ by 11 graph paper construct a circle with radius $1''$ or 3 cm. as depicted below. Complete the figure on your paper as depicted in the diagram. The unit is $1''$ or 3 cm.

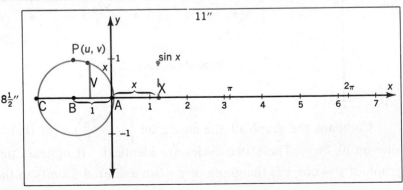

b. Sin x is the second coordinate of $P(u, v)$ where $P(u, v)$ is x units along the circle from A. Thus $\sin x$ is the perpendicular distance from $\overline{AC}$ to $P(u, v)$. Find the point on the x axis at x, which is the fourth vertex of the rectangle $PBX\_$. This point is the graph of $(x, \sin x)$.

c. Repeat this process for as many values of x as necessary to construct an accurate graph. You should plot at least 30 points.

8. Construct an accurate graph of $y = \cos x$, $0 \le x \le 2\pi$ by using the graph you constructed in Exercise 7. Do this by copying $y = \sin x$ for $x \in \left[\dfrac{\pi}{2}, \dfrac{5\pi}{2}\right]$ on the interval $[0, 2\pi]$.

B ━━ In Exercises 9–18 use the accurate graphs you constructed in Exercises 7 and 8 to give a reasonable estimate to the value of $x \in [0, 2\pi]$ that satisfies each of the following statements. Some statements may be satisfied by no x.

9. $\cos x = \sin x$ **10.** $\cos x = -\sin x$

11. $\sin x < \cos x$ **12.** $\sin x - \cos x = 0$

13. $\sin x + \cos x = 0$ **14.** $\sin x + \cos x = 1$

15. $\sin x - \cos x = -1$ **16.** $|\sin x + \cos x| = 1$

17. $\sin x \cdot \cos x > 1$ **18.** $\sin x \cdot \cos x < 0$

C   **19.** Sketch the graph of $y = |\sin x|$, $x \in [0, 2\pi]$.

    20. Sketch the graph of $y = 1 + \cos x$, $x \in [0, 2\pi]$.

    21. Sketch the graph of $y = 1 + |\cos x|$, $x \in [0, 2\pi]$.

    22. Sketch the graph of $y = 2 \sin x$, $x \in [0, 2\pi]$.

    23. Explain how you might sketch the graph of $y = \sin x + \cos x$, given the graphs of the sine and cosine functions. Can you sketch the graph without calculating any values of the sine or cosine functions?

    24. Sketch the graph of $y = \sin x + \cos x$, $x \in [0, 2\pi]$.

    25. Sketch the graph of $y = x + \sin x$, $x \in [0, 2\pi]$.

    26. Sketch the graph of $y = x + \cos x$, $x \in [0, 2\pi]$.

    27. Imagine a record player with a tall spindle and a vertical rod clamped to the outer edge of the moving turntable. With the turntable revolving slowly what appears to happen to the distance between the rod and the central spindle? Make a graph of this situation. (*Hint:* Show the number of revolutions of the turntable on the horizontal axis and the apparent distance between the rod and spindle on the vertical axis.)

2–6 Amplitude and Period

If f is a function and if there exists $M \in R$ such that $f(x) \leq M$ for all x in the domain of f, then f is **bounded above** by M, or M is an **upper bound** of f. Similarly, m is a **lower bound** of f, or f is **bounded below** by m, if and only if $f(x) \geq m$ for all x in the domain of f. The smallest upper bound of a function f is the **least upper bound** (l.u.b.) while the largest lower bound of f is the **greatest lower bound** (g.l.b.).

Since 1 is the maximum value of $\sin x$ and $\cos x$, $x \in R$, 1 is the least upper bound for the sine and cosine functions. Likewise, -1 is the greatest lower bound of the sine and cosine functions.

If M and m are the least upper and greatest lower bounds of a periodic function f, then

$$\tfrac{1}{2}(M - m)$$

is the **amplitude** of the function f.

EXAMPLE 1. Find the amplitude of $y = \sin x$ and $y = \cos x$, $x \in R$.

The amplitude is $\tfrac{1}{2}(M - m)$. Thus, the amplitude of $\cos x$ is $\tfrac{1}{2}[1 - (-1)] = 1$, and the amplitude of $\sin x$ is $\tfrac{1}{2}[1 - (-1)] = 1$.

Graphed below are

$$y = \sin x \qquad x \in [0, 2\pi] \qquad\qquad\qquad 1$$
$$y = 2 \sin x \qquad x \in [0, 2\pi]. \qquad\qquad\qquad 2$$

The functional values of **2** are each twice those of **1**. The amplitude of $y = 2 \sin x$ is $\tfrac{1}{2}[2 - (-2)] = 2$. The period of $y = 2 \sin x$ is 2π.

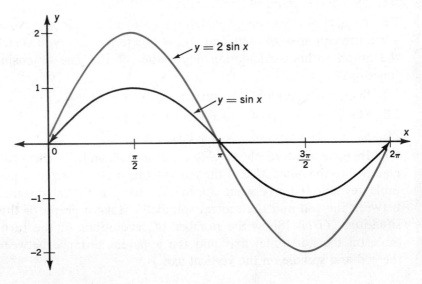

In general, the graph of $y = A \sin x$ is a sine curve with amplitude $|A|$ and period 2π.

The same situation occurs for the cosine function. In summary:

1. The graph of $y = A \sin x$ is a sine curve with amplitude $|A|$ and period 2π.
2. The graph of $y = A \cos x$ is a cosine curve with amplitude $|A|$ and period 2π.

Now consider the functions described by

$$y = \cos x$$

and

$$y = \cos (2x)$$

x	$2x$	$\cos 2x$
0	0	1
$\dfrac{\pi}{6}$	$\dfrac{\pi}{3}$	$\dfrac{1}{2}$
$\dfrac{\pi}{4}$	$\dfrac{\pi}{2}$	0
$\dfrac{\pi}{3}$	$\dfrac{2\pi}{3}$	$-\dfrac{1}{2}$
$\dfrac{\pi}{2}$	π	-1
$\dfrac{2\pi}{3}$	$\dfrac{4\pi}{3}$	$-\dfrac{1}{2}$
$\dfrac{3\pi}{4}$	$\dfrac{3\pi}{2}$	0
$\dfrac{5\pi}{6}$	$\dfrac{5\pi}{3}$	$\dfrac{1}{2}$
π	2π	1

x	$2x$	$\cos 2x$
$\dfrac{7\pi}{6}$	$\dfrac{7\pi}{3}$	$\dfrac{1}{2}$
$\dfrac{5\pi}{4}$	$\dfrac{5\pi}{2}$	0
$\dfrac{4\pi}{3}$	$\dfrac{8\pi}{8}$	$-\dfrac{1}{2}$
$\dfrac{3\pi}{2}$	3π	-1
$\dfrac{5\pi}{3}$	$\dfrac{10\pi}{3}$	$-\dfrac{1}{2}$
$\dfrac{7\pi}{4}$	$\dfrac{7\pi}{2}$	0
$\dfrac{11\pi}{6}$	$\dfrac{11\pi}{3}$	$\dfrac{1}{2}$
2π	4π	1

Notice that when x is π, then $2x$ is 2π. Thus, $y = \cos (2x)$ forms a complete cycle on the interval $[0, \pi]$ and on $[\pi, 2\pi]$. There are 2 periods of $y = \cos (2x)$ for every one of $y = \cos x$. Consequently each period is one-half as long. The period of $y = \cos (2x)$ is $\frac{1}{2}(2\pi) = \pi$.

■ Find the coordinates of the
  a. maxima
  b. minima
  c. points with y coordinates equal to zero
for each function on its period beginning with $x = 0$.

9. $g : x \rightarrow 2 \sin x$ **10.** $h : x \rightarrow -2 \sin x$
11. $f(x) = \frac{4}{5} \cos (2x)$ **12.** $y = \frac{4}{5} \cos (-2x)$
13. $h(x) = 5 \sin \left(\frac{2}{3}x\right)$ **14.** $g : x \rightarrow -5 \sin \left(-\frac{2}{3}x\right)$
15. $y = \cos \left(\frac{4}{5}x\right)$ **16.** $f : x \rightarrow -8 \cos (4x)$

■ Sketch the graph of one period of the function in each of the following exercises.

Example. $y = -2 \cos \frac{1}{2}x$.

The amplitude is $|-2| = 2$ and the period is $\frac{2\pi}{\frac{1}{2}} = 4\pi$. The maximum value occurs at 2π. The minimum values occur at the endpoints of $[0, 4\pi]$.

The curve crosses the x axis at the quarter and three-quarter points of $[0, 4\pi]$, or at π and 3π.

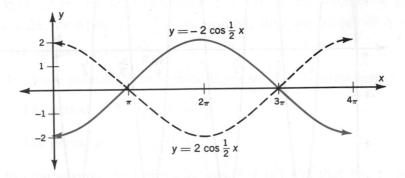

17. Exercise 9.   **18.** Exercise 10.
19. Exercise 11.   **20.** Exercise 12.
21. Exercise 13.   **22.** Exercise 14.
23. Exercise 15.   **24.** Exercise 16.

■ Write an equation describing a sine function with the given characteristics.

25. Amplitude 3 and period π
26. Amplitude $\frac{1}{2}$ and period 3π
27. Amplitude 12 and period 2
28. Amplitude $\frac{2}{3}$ and period $\frac{1}{2}$

B **29.** Amplitude 4, minimum $\left(\frac{\pi}{4}, -4\right)$

30. Amplitude $\frac{2}{5}$, maximum $\left(\frac{3\pi}{4}, \frac{2}{5}\right)$

31. Amplitude 7, contains $\left(\frac{2\pi}{3}, 0\right)$

32. Maximum $(\pi, 4)$, period 4π

33. Maximum $\left(\frac{15\pi}{4}, 2\right)$, minimum $\left(\frac{5\pi}{4}, -2\right)$

34. Maximum $\left(\frac{7\pi}{4}, 5\right)$, contains $\left(\frac{7\pi}{2}, 0\right)$

C **35.** Show that

$$y = A \sin x, \qquad A > 0$$

and

$$y = -A \sin x, \qquad A > 0$$

have the same amplitude.

36. a. Graph $y = 2 \sin x$ and $y = 3 \cos x$ on the interval $[-2\pi, 2\pi]$. Use the same coordinate system to graph both curves.

b. Graph $y = 2 \sin x + 3 \cos x$, $x \in [-2\pi, 2\pi]$ by adding the coordinates in **a.**

c. What is the maximum and minimum value of $y = 2 \sin x + 3 \cos x$?

d. What is the amplitude of $y = 2 \sin x + 3 \cos x$?

━━ The reciprocal of the period of a periodic function is the **frequency** of the function. The *frequency* represents the number of cycles completed by a function over an interval one unit long. What is the frequency of each of the following?

37. $y = \sin 2\pi x$ **38.** $y = \sin \left(\frac{1}{2}x\right)$

39. $y = \cos 120\pi x$ **40.** $y = -4 \cos 80x$

41. $y = 30 \sin 40\pi x$ **42.** $y = -20 \cos (-20\pi x)$

43. $y = \cos x + \sin x$ **44.** $y = 3 \cos 2x + 3 \sin 2x$

45. $y = \cos 2x + \sin 2x$

46. The voltage drop across the terminals of an ordinary electrical outlet can be described by an equation

$$E = A \sin Bt.$$

Write the equation with amplitude 155 and frequency 60 cycles per second. Draw the graph over two periods.

2–7   Phase Shift

Suppose you wished to graph $y = 3 \sin \left(2x - \frac{\pi}{2}\right)$. From the equation it follows that

1. the amplitude is 3,
2. the period is $\frac{2\pi}{2} = \pi$, and
3. the graph is a sine curve like the graph of $y = 3 \sin (2x)$.

Suppose further that you wanted to graph $y = 3 \sin \left(2x - \frac{\pi}{2}\right)$ over an interval π units long (the period) such that y is 0 when x is either endpoint of the interval.

To find an x so that y is 0, you must find an x such that $3 \sin \left(2x - \frac{\pi}{2}\right)$ is 0.   The expression $3 \sin \left(2x - \frac{\pi}{2}\right)$ is 0 when $\sin \left(2x - \frac{\pi}{2}\right)$ is 0, and the sine function is 0 when its domain value is 0. Thus, $\sin \left(2x - \frac{\pi}{2}\right) = 0$ when

$$2x - \frac{\pi}{2} = 0.$$

Solving, you find $x = \frac{\pi}{4}$.

The left-hand endpoint of the interval is $\frac{\pi}{4}$. If x is the left-hand endpoint, then certainly $x + \pi$ is the right-hand endpoint, so the right-hand endpoint is $\frac{\pi}{4} + \pi = \frac{5\pi}{4}$. You should verify that

$$0 = y = \sin \left(2 \cdot \frac{5\pi}{4} - \frac{\pi}{2}\right).$$

How is the graph of $y = 3 \sin \left(2x - \frac{\pi}{2}\right)$ related to the graph of $y = 3 \sin (2x)$? The graph of $y = 3 \sin (2x)$ has amplitude 3, period π and completes a cycle on $[0, \pi]$ such that $y = 0$ at both endpoints. Likewise, the graph of $y = 3 \sin \left(2x - \frac{\pi}{2}\right)$ has amplitude 3, period π and completes a similar cycle on the interval $\left[\frac{\pi}{4}, \frac{5\pi}{4}\right]$. Thus the graph of $y = 3 \sin \left(2x - \frac{\pi}{2}\right)$ is similar to that of $y = 3 \sin (2x)$ in all respects except for the endpoints of a fundamental interval. If the graph of $y = 3 \sin 2x$ is moved $\frac{\pi}{4}$ units to the right along the x axis, then it coincides with the graph of $y = 3 \sin \left(2x - \frac{\pi}{2}\right)$. The number $\frac{\pi}{4}$ is the **phase shift** of the curve $y = 3 \sin \left(2x - \frac{\pi}{2}\right)$.

The graph of each function is shown below. Notice that the graph of $y = 3 \sin \left(2x - \frac{\pi}{2}\right)$ is always $\frac{\pi}{4}$ units ahead of the graph of $y = 3 \sin (2x)$. This is the effect of the phase shift.

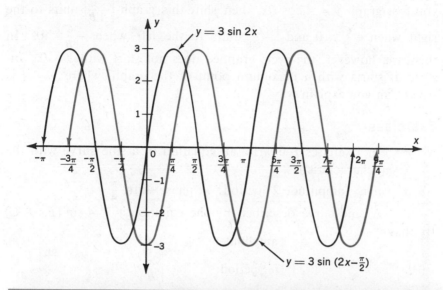

$y = 3 \sin 2x$

$y = 3 \sin \left(2x - \frac{\pi}{2}\right)$

Definition The <u>phase shift</u> of a function $y = A \sin (Bx + C)$ is the number of units that the graph of $y = A \sin Bx$ must be shifted along the x axis so that it coincides with the graph of $y = A \sin (Bx + C)$.

Consider the general equation

$$y = A \sin (Bx + C) \qquad A, B \neq 0.$$

To find the phase shift, find the value of x such that

$$0 = y = A \sin (Bx + C).$$

That value of x is found by solving $Bx + C = 0$. (Why?). But $Bx + C = 0$ when $x = -\frac{C}{B}$. Thus, $-\frac{C}{B}$ is the phase shift of $y = A \sin (Bx + C)$. When $-\frac{C}{B} > 0$, the shift is $\left|-\frac{C}{B}\right|$ units to the right; and the graph can be sketched by shifting the graph of $y = A \sin Bx$ $\left|-\frac{C}{B}\right|$ units to the *right*. Similarly when $-\frac{C}{B} < 0$, the graph of $y = A \sin (Bx + C)$ is similar to the graph of $y = A \sin Bx$, but is shifted $\left|-\frac{C}{B}\right|$ units to the *left*.

A similar analysis is valid for the cosine curve

$$y = A \cos (Bx + C) \qquad A, B \neq 0.$$

$-\frac{C}{B}$ is the phase shift. To obtain the graph of $y = A \cos (Bx + C)$, you first graph $y = A \cos Bx$, then shift this graph $\left| -\frac{C}{B} \right|$ units to the right when $-\frac{C}{B} > 0$ and $\left| -\frac{C}{B} \right|$ units to the left when $-\frac{C}{B} < 0$. In this case, however, the cycle graphed does not start with $y = 0$. Instead, it starts with a maximum point of the graph, where $y = A$ is true. Can you explain why?

Exercises

A ━━ For Exercises 1–6 write an equation of a sine curve with the given characteristics.

Example. amplitude 2; period: π; phase shift: $\frac{\pi}{4}$

A sine curve described by the equation $y = A \sin (Bx + C)$ has

amplitude:	$\|A\|$
period:	$\left\| \frac{2\pi}{B} \right\|$
phase shift:	$-\frac{C}{B}$.

The conditions tell you that the amplitude must be 2, so $A = 2$ or $A = -2$. Since the period is to be π, $B = 2$ or $B = -2$. If the phase shift is to be $\frac{\pi}{4}$, then $-\frac{C}{2} = \frac{\pi}{4}$ or $\frac{-C}{-2} = \frac{\pi}{4}$, so $C = -\frac{\pi}{2}$ or $C = \frac{\pi}{2}$.

The possible equations for the sine curve are as follows.

1. $y = 2 \sin \left(2x - \frac{\pi}{2} \right)$ 2. $y = -2 \sin \left(2x - \frac{\pi}{2} \right)$

3. $y = 2 \sin \left(-2x + \frac{\pi}{2} \right)$ 4. $y = -2 \sin \left(-2x + \frac{\pi}{2} \right)$

Equations 3 and 4 are equivalent to equations 2 and 1, respectively. (Why?) Thus, there are two sine curves satisfying the given characteristics.

1. Amplitude: 5; period: 2π; phase shift: $\frac{\pi}{3}$

2. Amplitude: 3; period: $\frac{2\pi}{3}$; phase shift: $\frac{\pi}{3}$

3. Amplitude: $\frac{2}{3}$; period: $\frac{\pi}{4}$; phase shift: $-\frac{\pi}{8}$

4. Amplitude: 17; period: 4π; phase shift: $\frac{\pi}{4}$

5. Amplitude: 7; period: $\frac{3\pi}{2}$; phase shift: $-\frac{\pi}{4}$

6. Amplitude: $\frac{1}{2}$; period: $\frac{5\pi}{4}$; phase shift: $-\frac{5}{8}$

━━ For Exercises 7–12 write an equation of a cosine curve with the given characteristics.

7. Amplitude: 3; period: π; phase shift: $\frac{2\pi}{3}$

8. Amplitude: 6; period: $\frac{2\pi}{3}$; phase shift: $-\frac{5}{8}$

9. Amplitude: 100; period: 3π; phase shift: $-\pi$

10. Amplitude: $\frac{1}{5}$; period: $\frac{\pi}{5}$; phase shift: 2

11. Amplitude: $\frac{7}{3}$; period: $\frac{5\pi}{6}$; phase shift: -1

12. Amplitude: 1; period: $\frac{3\pi}{4}$; phase shift: $\frac{3\pi}{2}$

━━ Identify the amplitude, period, and phase shift of each function in Exercises 13–28. Sketch the graph of each.

Example. $y = 2 \cos (3x + \pi)$

The amplitude is $|2| = 2$. The period is $\frac{2\pi}{3}$. The phase shift is $-\frac{\pi}{3}$. The graph of $y = 2 \cos (3x + \pi)$ is shifted $\frac{\pi}{3}$ units to left of the graph of $y = 2 \cos 3x$.

To construct the graph, it is useful to sketch the graph of $y = 2 \cos 3x$ initially. This graph can be used to approximate the required graph.

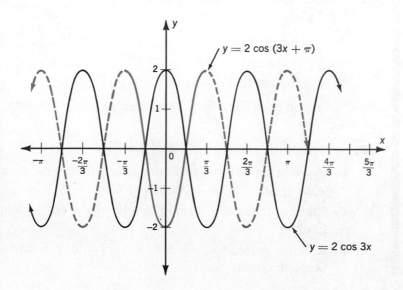

13. $y = -3 \sin \left(x - \dfrac{\pi}{4}\right)$

14. $y = \cos (3x + \pi)$

15. $y = \dfrac{2}{3} \sin \left(\dfrac{1}{2}x + \dfrac{\pi}{5}\right)$

16. $y = \cos \left(2x - \dfrac{\pi}{3}\right)$

17. $y = -\sin \left(\dfrac{2}{3}x - \pi\right)$

18. $y = 4 \cos \left(\dfrac{1}{3}x + \pi\right)$

19. $y = 2 \sin \left(-2x + \dfrac{\pi}{2}\right)$

20. $y = -\dfrac{1}{2} \cos (-4\pi x - 2\pi)$

B 21. $y = 3 \sin (2\pi x + \pi)$

22. $y = 4 \cos \left(\dfrac{\pi}{2} x - \pi\right)$

23. $y = 2 \sin \left(\pi x - \dfrac{\pi}{2}\right)$

24. $y = \cos (4\pi x + \pi)$

25. $y = -3 \sin (4x + 2)$

26. $y = -2 \cos (6x - 4)$

27. $y = 5 \sin (x - 3)$

28. $y = -5 \cos (x + 4)$

C 29. Verify that the equations

$$y = 2 \sin \left(3x - \dfrac{\pi}{2}\right)$$

and

$$y = -2 \sin \left(-3x + \dfrac{\pi}{2}\right)$$

have the same graphs.

30. Verify that the equations

$$y = -3 \sin (-5x + \pi)$$

and

$$y = 3 \sin (5x - \pi)$$

have the same graphs.

31. You are given the following equations.

    i. $y = 3 \cos (2x - \pi)$

    ii. $y = -3 \cos (2x - \pi)$

    iii. $y = 3 \cos (-2x + \pi)$

    iv. $y = -3 \cos (-2x + \pi)$

Find pairs of equations with the same graphs. Explain your choices.

32. a. Sketch the graph of $y = \sin \left(x + \dfrac{\pi}{2}\right)$.

    b. If $y = A \sin (Bx + C)$ has the same graph, and $A, B \neq 1$, what are the values of A, B, and C?

    c. Are the graphs of $y = \sin \left(x + \dfrac{\pi}{2}\right)$ and $y = \cos x$ identical? Explain.

    d. Are the graphs of $y = \cos \left(x - \dfrac{\pi}{2}\right)$ and $y = \sin x$ identical? Explain.

2–8 Tangent and Co-Functions

The sine and cosine functions are the fundamental circular functions. Given these functions four other circular functions can be defined. They are the **tangent** (tan), **cotangent** (cot), **secant** (sec), and **cosecant** (csc).

Definitions Let $x \in$ R.

$$\tan x = \left\{ (x, y) : y = \frac{\sin x}{\cos x}, \ \cos x \neq 0 \right\}$$

$$\cot x = \left\{ (x, y) : y = \frac{\cos x}{\sin x}, \ \sin x \neq 0 \right\}$$

$$\sec x = \left\{ (x, y) : y = \frac{1}{\cos x}, \ \cos x \neq 0 \right\}$$

$$\csc x = \left\{ (x, y) : y = \frac{1}{\sin x}, \ \sin x \neq 0 \right\}$$

Notice that the tangent and cotangent functions are *reciprocals* of each other.

$$\frac{1}{\tan x} = \frac{1}{\dfrac{\sin x}{\cos x}}$$

$$= \frac{\cos x}{\sin x}$$

$$= \cot x$$

Thus, tan x and cot x are called **reciprocal functions.**

By definition sec x and cos x are also reciprocal functions as are sin x and csc x. The reciprocal relation between these pairs of functions provides a way of determining the domain, range and graph of each function.

First consider the secant function, $\sec x = \dfrac{1}{\cos x}$, $\cos x \neq 0$. The value of cos x is 0 for $x \in \left\{ (2n + 1) \dfrac{\pi}{2}, n \in \text{I} \right\}$, so sec x is *not defined* for $x \in \left\{ \cdots -\dfrac{5\pi}{2}, -\dfrac{3\pi}{2}, -\dfrac{\pi}{2}, \dfrac{\pi}{2}, \dfrac{3\pi}{2}, \dfrac{5\pi}{2}, \cdots \right\}$. Sec x is defined for all other real numbers x. Thus the domain of sec x is R with the set $\left\{ (2n + 1) \dfrac{\pi}{2}, n \in \text{I} \right\}$ deleted.

The range of sec x can also be defined by considering the range of cos x as follows.

For all $x \in R$ such that $\cos x \neq 0$, $-1 \leq \cos x < 0$ is true or $0 < \cos x \leq 1$ is true. Dividing each term of the first expression by $\cos x < 0$, you obtain

$$-\frac{1}{\cos x} \geq 1.$$

Similarly, by dividing each term of $0 < \cos x \leq 1$ by $\cos x > 0$,

$$1 \leq \frac{1}{\cos x}.$$

Thus, since $\sec x = \dfrac{1}{\cos x}$, you have

$$\sec x \leq -1 \qquad\qquad \text{(for negative } \cos x)$$

or

$$\sec x \geq 1 \qquad\qquad \text{(for positive } \cos x)$$

It follows that the range of $\sec x$ is

$$V = \{y : y \leq -1 \ or \ y \geq 1, y \in R\}.$$

The graph of the secant function can be sketched by first sketching the graph of $y = \cos x$ and then estimating the reciprocals of $\cos x$. The dotted vertical lines have equations $x = (2n + 1)\frac{\pi}{2}$, $n \in I$, and correspond to the values of x for which $y = \sec x$ is not defined.

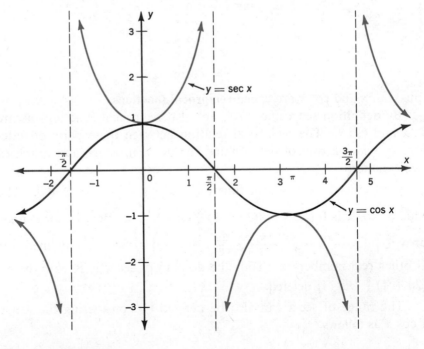

Similarly, you can verify that the domain of the cosecant functions is R with the set $\{n\pi, n \in I\}$ deleted. The range is

$$V = \{y : y \leq -1 \text{ or } y \geq 1, y \in R\}.$$

The graph is shown below.

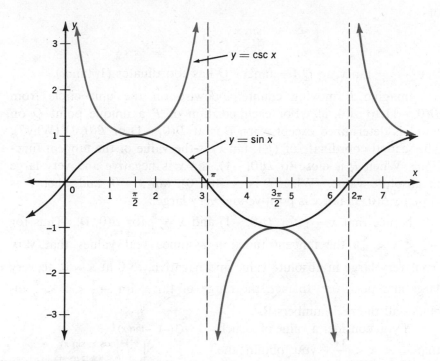

A sketch of the graph of the tangent function could be obtained in a manner similar to that used for sec x and csc x, but is fairly cumbersome in this case. The unit circle and similar triangles provide a satisfactory alternative.

Let $P(\cos x, \sin x)$ be a point on the unit circle in the first or fourth quadrant as at right. Let $\overline{PR}$ be perpendicular to the u axis at R, and let the line $u = 1$ be tangent to the circle at $A(1, 0)$. Let $\overrightarrow{OP}$ intersect $u = 1$ in Q.

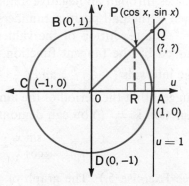

Now $\triangle OPR$ is similar to $\triangle OQA$ (Why?). Thus the following holds.

$$\frac{PR}{OR} = \frac{QA}{OA}$$

Since P has coordinates $(\cos x, \sin x)$, $PR = \sin x$ and $OR = \cos x$.
Thus $\dfrac{PR}{OR} = \dfrac{\sin x}{\cos x}$. Also $OA = 1$. It follows that

$$\frac{PR}{OR} = \frac{\sin x}{\cos x} = \frac{QA}{1}$$

or

$$\frac{\sin x}{\cos x} = QA.$$

But $\dfrac{\sin x}{\cos x} = \tan x$, so $QA = \tan x$. Q has coordinates $(1, \tan x)$.

Imagine P moving counterclockwise on the unit circle from $D(0, -1)$ to $B(0, 1)$. For each position of P a unique point Q on $u = 1$ is determined except when P is at $D(0, -1)$ or $B(0, 1)$ (Why?). The second coordinate of $Q(1, \tan x)$ is the value of the tangent function. When P is close to $D(0, -1)$, $\tan x$ is negative and very large in absolute value. When P is at $A(1, 0)$, $\tan x = 0$, and when P is close to $B(0, 1)$ $\tan x$ is positive and very large.

Notice that $x = \dfrac{\pi}{2}$ for $D(0, -1)$ and $x = \dfrac{\pi}{2}$ for $B(0, 1)$. Thus for $-\dfrac{\pi}{2} < x < \dfrac{\pi}{2}$, the tangent function assumes real values that vary from very large in absolute value and negative, to 0 at $x = 0$, to very large and positive. In fact, the range of $\tan x$ for $-\dfrac{\pi}{2} < x < \dfrac{\pi}{2}$ includes all the real numbers R.

If you consider a value of x such that $\dfrac{\pi}{2} < x < \dfrac{3\pi}{2}$, you obtain the same range for $\tan x$. (See the figure at right.) Can you explain why, as x increases from $\dfrac{\pi}{2}$ to $\dfrac{3\pi}{2}$, $\tan x$ passes through all negative numbers, then 0, then all positive numbers?

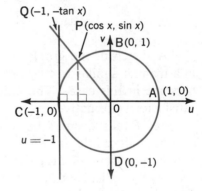

The repetition of the values assumed by the tangent function over the intervals $\left\langle -\dfrac{\pi}{2}, \dfrac{\pi}{2} \right\rangle$ and $\left\langle \dfrac{\pi}{2}, \dfrac{3\pi}{2} \right\rangle$ suggest that the period of the tangent function is π. (You can demonstrate this by showing that

$$\frac{\sin x}{\cos x} = \frac{\sin(x + \pi)}{\cos(x + \pi)}.$$

See Exercise 5.) The graph of $y = \tan x$ is sketched by repeating the graph over the interval $\left\langle -\dfrac{\pi}{2}, \dfrac{\pi}{2} \right\rangle$.

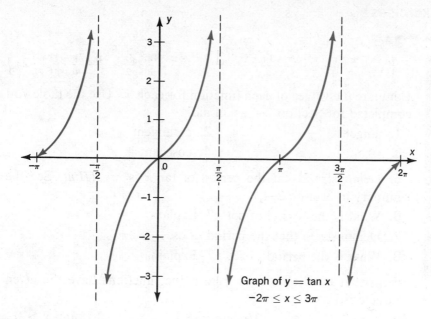

Graph of $y = \tan x$
$-2\pi \le x \le 3\pi$

Since $\cot x = \dfrac{1}{\tan x}$, each value of the cotangent function is the reciprocal of the corresponding value of the tangent function. Notice
that the values of x for which $y = \cot x$ is undefined are the same as
the values of x for which $\tan x = 0$. What are these values of x?

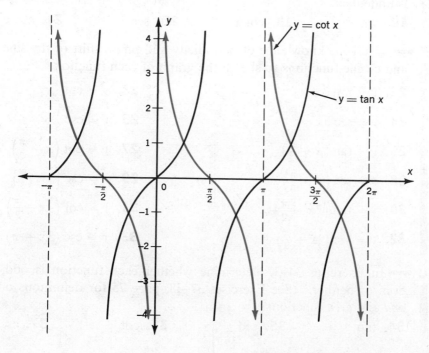

$y = \cot x$

$y = \tan x$

Exercises

A — Let

$$x \in \left\{0, \frac{\pi}{6}, \frac{\pi}{4}, \frac{\pi}{3}, \frac{\pi}{2}, \frac{2\pi}{3}, \frac{3\pi}{4}, \frac{5\pi}{6}, \pi, \frac{7\pi}{6}, \frac{5\pi}{4}, \frac{4\pi}{3}, \frac{3\pi}{2}, \frac{5\pi}{3}, \frac{7\pi}{4}, \frac{11\pi}{6}, 2\pi\right\}$$

Compute the values of each function for each x. Use the table you completed for Section 2–4 as an aid.

1. tangent **2.** cotangent

3. secant **4.** cosecant

5. Demonstrate that the period of $\tan x$ is π. (*Hint:* See the summary in Section 2–4.)

6. What is the period of $\cot x$? Explain.

7. Demonstrate that the period of $\csc x$ is 2π.

8. What is the period of $\sec x$? Explain.

— In what quadrants does x lie if the functions have the given characteristics?

9. $\sec x \geq 1$ **10.** $\csc x \geq 1$ **11.** $\tan x > 0$

12. $\cot x > 0$ **13.** $\sec x \leq -1$ **14.** $\csc x \leq -1$

15. $\tan x < 0$ **16.** $\cot x < 0$ **17.** $\sin x < 0$

— State the values of x $(-2\pi \leq x \leq 2\pi)$ for which each function is undefined.

18. $\tan x$ **19.** $\cot x$ **20.** $\sec x$ **21.** $\csc x$

B — Use your knowledge of periodicity and phase shift of the sine and cosine functions to sketch the graph of each function.

22. $y = \tan 2x$ **23.** $y = \cot \frac{1}{2}x$

24. $y = \sec 3x$ **25.** $y = \csc \frac{1}{3}x$

26. $y = \tan\left(x + \frac{\pi}{2}\right)$ **27.** $y = \cot\left(x - \frac{\pi}{2}\right)$

28. $y = \sec\left(x - \frac{\pi}{4}\right)$ **29.** $y = \csc\left(x + \frac{\pi}{3}\right)$

30. $y = \tan\left(2x - \frac{\pi}{2}\right)$ **31.** $y = \cot\left(\frac{1}{3}x - \frac{\pi}{2}\right)$

32. $y = \sec\left(\frac{1}{2}x + \frac{\pi}{4}\right)$ **33.** $y = \csc\left(3x + \pi\right)$

C — In Exercises 34–37 determine whether each function is odd, even or neither. (See Exercises 37–38, page 75 for definitions of *odd* and *even* functions.)

34. tan **35.** sec **36.** cot **37.** csc

38. How is the graph of $y = -\tan x$ related to the graph of $y = \cot\left(x + \frac{\pi}{2}\right)$? Explain your answer. (See summary, Section 2–4.)

39. How is the graph of $y = -\cot x$ related to the graph of $y = \tan\left(x + \frac{\pi}{2}\right)$? Explain.

40. Prove $|\tan x| \geq |\sin x|$, $\forall x \in$ R for which $\tan x$ is defined.

41. Prove $|\cot x| \geq |\cos x|$, $\forall x \in$ R for which $\cot x$ is defined.

42. Prove $|\sec x| \geq |\tan x|$, $\forall x \in$ R for which $\sec x$ and $\tan x$ are defined.

43. Prove $|\cot x| \leq |\csc x|$, $\forall x \in$ R for which $\cot x$ and $\csc x$ are defined.

2–9 Identities

An equation such as $x^2 + 3x + 2 = (x + 2)(x + 1)$ that is true for all allowable real or complex replacements of x is an **identity** over the given replacement set. You can demonstrate that this equation is an identity by performing the indicated multiplication $(x + 2)(x + 1)$. The product is $x^2 + 3x + 2$. Hence, both sides of the equation represent the same real or complex number, irrespective of the value of x.

There are identities involving circular functions, the most fundamental of which is

$$\sin^2 x + \cos^2 x = 1, x \in \text{R}.$$

Other identities are simply the definitions.

$$\tan x = \frac{\sin x}{\cos x}, \; x \in \text{R}, \cos x \neq 0$$

$$\cot x = \frac{1}{\tan x}, \; x \in \text{R}, \tan x \neq 0$$

$$\sec x = \frac{1}{\cos x}, \; x \in \text{R}, \cos x \neq 0$$

$$\csc x = \frac{1}{\sin x}, \; x \in \text{R}, \sin x \neq 0$$

Several other identities were listed in the summary of Section 2–4. You should review them now.

To prove that an equation is an identity, you can manipulate *either* side of the equation until it is identical to the other side.

EXAMPLE 1. Prove $\sin^4 x - \cos^4 x = \sin^2 x - \cos^2 x$ is an identity.

Notice first that $\sin^4 x - \cos^4 x$ is the difference of two squares and consequently may be factored.

$$\sin^4 x - \cos^4 x = (\sin^2 x + \cos^2 x)(\sin^2 x - \cos^2 x)$$

You can use $\sin^2 x + \cos^2 x = 1$, $\forall x \in R$.

$$\begin{aligned}\sin^4 x - \cos^4 x &= (\sin^2 x + \cos^2 x)(\sin^2 x - \cos^2 x) \\ &= 1\,(\sin^2 x - \cos^2 x) \\ &= \sin^2 x - \cos^2 x\end{aligned}$$

Consequently the identity is proved.

You could attack the same equation somewhat differently.

$$\begin{aligned}\sin^2 x - \cos^2 x &= 1 \cdot (\sin^2 x - \cos^2 x) \\ &= (\sin^2 x + \cos^2 x)(\sin^2 x - \cos^2 x) \\ &= \sin^4 x - \cos^4 x.\end{aligned}$$

Again the identity is proved.

EXAMPLE 2. Prove the identity $\sin x = \tan x \cdot \cos x$.

$$\begin{aligned}\tan x \cdot \cos x &= \frac{\sin x}{\cos x} \cdot \cos x \\ &= \sin x \cdot \frac{\cos x}{\cos x} \\ &= \sin x\end{aligned}$$

Notice that the substitution $\frac{\cos x}{\cos x} = 1$ was made in the next-to-last step. This is permitted because you assume that the replacements for x in the original equation are exactly those for which each expression is defined. Since the original equation contains $\tan x$, you assume that $\cos x \neq 0$. In that case, $\frac{\cos x}{\cos x}$ is equal to 1.

EXAMPLE 3. Prove the identity $1 + \cot^2 x = \csc^2 x$.

$$\begin{aligned}1 + \cot^2 x &= 1 + \frac{\cos^2 x}{\sin^2 x} \\ &= \frac{\sin^2 x}{\sin^2 x} + \frac{\cos^2 x}{\sin^2 x} \\ &= \frac{\sin^2 x + \cos^2 x}{\sin^2 x} \\ &= \frac{1}{\sin^2 x} \\ &= \csc^2 x.\end{aligned}$$

Consequently, $1 + \cot^2 x = \csc^2 x$.

EXAMPLE 4. Express $\cos x$ in terms of $\sin x$.

Start with $\sin^2 x + \cos^2 x = 1$, and rewrite it as $\cos^2 x = 1 - \sin^2 x$. Since $\cos x > 0$ for x in Quadrants I and IV, and $\cos x < 0$ for x in Quadrants II and III,

$$\cos x = \sqrt{1 - \sin^2 x}, \qquad x \text{ in Quadrants I and IV}$$

and

$$\cos x = -\sqrt{1 - \sin^2 x}, \quad x \text{ in Quadrants II and III.}$$

EXAMPLE 5. Prove the identity $\dfrac{\csc x}{1 - \csc x} = \dfrac{\sec x}{\tan x - \sec x}$.

The procedure used to prove this identity is somewhat different from that illustrated previously. The tactic is to change both the left side and the right side to the same expression.

Left side	Right side
$\dfrac{\csc x}{1 - \csc x} = \dfrac{\dfrac{1}{\sin x}}{1 - \dfrac{1}{\sin x}}$	$\dfrac{\sec x}{\tan x - \sec x} = \dfrac{\dfrac{1}{\cos x}}{\dfrac{\sin x}{\cos x} - \dfrac{1}{\cos x}}$
$= \dfrac{\dfrac{1}{\sin x}}{\dfrac{\sin x - 1}{\sin x}}$	$= \dfrac{1}{\sin x - 1}$
$= \dfrac{1}{\sin x - 1}$	

Consequently, $\dfrac{\csc x}{1 - \csc x} = \dfrac{\sec x}{\tan x - \sec x}$

Exercises

A — Prove that each of the following equations is an identity.

1. $\tan x = \sin x \cdot \sec x$

2. $\cot x = \cos x \cdot \csc x$

3. $\tan^2 x = \dfrac{1 - \cos^2 x}{\cos^2 x}$

4. $\cot^2 x = \csc^2 x - 1$

5. $1 + \tan^2 x = \sec^2 x$

6. $\sec^2 x = \dfrac{\sin^2 x + \cos^2 x}{\cos^2 x}$

7. $\csc^4 x - \cot^4 x = \csc^2 x + \cot^2 x$

8. $\sec^4 x - \tan^4 x = \tan^2 x + \sec^2 x$

9. $(1 - \tan x)^2 = \sec^2 x - 2 \tan x$

10. $(1 - \sin^2 x)(1 + \tan^2 x) = 1$

11. $\dfrac{\cos^2 x}{\sin x} + \sin x = \csc x$

12. $\tan x + \cot x = \sec x \cdot \csc x$

13. $\dfrac{\tan x}{1 - \cos^2 x} = \sec x \cdot \csc x$

14. $\dfrac{\cot x}{\cos x} + \dfrac{\sec x}{\cot x} = \sec^2 x \cdot \csc x$

15. $2 \sin^2 x - 1 = 1 - 2 \cos^2 x$

16. $\csc x = \dfrac{\cot x}{\cos x}$

B **17.** Express $\tan x$ in terms of

    a. $\sin x$ **b.** $\cos x$ **c.** $\sec x$

18. Express $\cos x$ in terms of

    a. $\sin x$ **b.** $\tan x$ **c.** $\sec x$

19. Express $\cot x$ in terms of

    a. $\cos x$ **b.** $\tan x$

20. Express $\sin x$ in terms of

    a. $\cos x$ **b.** $\sec x$

In Exercises 21–32 change the first expression into the second.

21. $\dfrac{\cos x - \sin x}{\cos x}$, $1 - \tan x$

22. $\dfrac{1 + \sin x - \sin^2 x}{\cos x}$, $\cos x + \tan x$

23. $\tan x (\tan x + \cot x)$, $\sec^2 x$

24. $(\sec x - \tan x)(\sec x + \tan x)$, $\sin^2 x + \cos^2 x$

C **25.** $\dfrac{\cos x + 1}{\sin^3 x}$, $\dfrac{\csc x}{1 - \cos x}$

26. $\dfrac{\sin x}{1 - \cos x}$, $\csc x + \cot x$

27. $\dfrac{\tan x}{\sec x} + \dfrac{\cot x}{\csc x}$, $\sin x + \cos x$

28. $\dfrac{\sin x}{\csc x - 1} + \dfrac{\sin x}{\csc x + 1}$, $2 \tan^2 x$

29. $\dfrac{\sin^3 x + \cos^3 x}{1 - 2 \cos^2 x}$, $\dfrac{\sec x - \sin x}{\tan x - 1}$

30. $\dfrac{1 - 2 \sin x - 3 \sin^2 x}{\cos^2 x}$, $\dfrac{1 - 3 \sin x}{1 - \sin x}$

31. $\dfrac{\sin x}{1 - \cos x}$, $\sqrt{\dfrac{1 + \cos x}{1 - \cos x}}$, x in Quadrants I or II

32. $\sqrt{\dfrac{\csc x + 1}{\csc x - 1}}$, $\dfrac{1 + \sin x}{\cos x}$, x in Quadrants I or IV

33. Show $\cos\left(x + \dfrac{3\pi}{2}\right) = \sin x$. (*Hint:* See summary, Section 2–4.)

CHAPTER OBJECTIVES AND REVIEW

Objective: *To know the meaning of the important mathematical terms of this chapter.*

1. Here are many of the mathematical terms used in this chapter. Be sure that you know them thoroughly and can use them correctly.

distance formula *(63)*   greatest lower bound *(86)*
unit circle *(65)*   amplitude *(86)*
wrapping function *(66)*   frequency *(91)*
cosine function *(71)*   phase shift *(92)*
sine function *(71)*   tangent *(97)*
circular functions *(71)*   cotangent *(97)*
periodic function *(82)*   secant *(97)*
upper bound *(86)*   cosecant *(97)*
lower bound *(86)*   reciprocal functions *(97)*
least upper bound *(86)*   identity *(103)*

Objective: *To state the distance formula and to use it to find the distance between two points.*

2. If $P(s, t)$ and $Q(u, v)$, what is PQ?

▬ Find the distance between the given points.

3. $A(-2, -5)$, $B(1, -7)$ **4.** $R(-3, \frac{1}{2})$, $S(\frac{1}{2}, -3)$

5. $M(-7, 5)$, $N(-7, -10)$

6. $A(1, 3)$, $B(6, 2)$, $C(8, 5)$, $D(3, 6)$ are the vertices of a quadrilateral. What kind of a quadrilateral is it? Explain.

Objective: *To describe a wrapping and to apply it.*

7. Describe as clearly as you can the wrapping function W.

8. Suppose the square with vertices

$A(1, 1)$, $B(-1, 1)$, $C(-1, -1)$, $D(1, -1)$

is wrapped counterclockwise with a number line with zero at $T(1, 0)$.

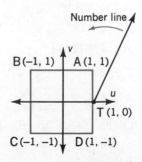

   a. Describe this "wrapping" function.

   b. Suppose $W : 2\frac{1}{2} \rightarrow (u, v)$. Name four real numbers besides $2\frac{1}{2}$ that map onto this same point under the wrapping function.

Objective: *To define the six circular functions.*

9. Define the functions sine and cosine.

10. Define the functions tangent and cotangent.   Note the restrictions on the domain.

11. Define the functions secant and cosecant.   Note the restrictions on the domain.

12. Describe precisely the range of each circular function.

Objective: *To deduce the following five identities using the definitions of sine and cosine and the geometry of the circle.*

■ Prove the following.

13. $\forall x \in R,\ \sin^2 x + \cos^2 x = 1$

14. $\forall x \in R,\ n \in W,\ \sin (x \pm 2n\pi) = \sin x$

15. $\forall x \in R,\ n \in W,\ \cos (x \pm 2n\pi) = \cos x$

16. $\forall x \in R,\ \cos (-x) = \cos x$

17. $\forall x \in R,\ \sin (-x) = -\sin x$

Objective: *To sketch the graphs of the six circular functions.*

■ Sketch the graph of each function.

18. $y = \cos x$ **19.** $y = \sin x$

20. $y = \tan x$ **21.** $y = \cot x$

22. $y = \csc x$ **23.** $y = \sec x$

Objective: *Given an equation $y = A \sin (Bx + C)$ or $y = A \cos (Bx + C)$, to determine the **a.** amplitude, **b.** the period, and **c.** the phase shift and be able to sketch the graph.*

■ Find the amplitude, period and phase shift of each function. Sketch the graph.

24. $y = -3 \sin x$ **25.** $y = \frac{1}{2} \cos x$

26. $y = 2 \sin (4x)$ **27.** $y = -4 \cos (-2x)$

28. $y = \frac{1}{2} \sin \left(x - \frac{\pi}{2} \right)$ **29.** $y = 3 \cos (x + \pi)$

30. $y = \frac{5}{2} \sin \left(2x - \frac{\pi}{2} \right)$ **31.** $y = -2 \cos (4x + \pi)$

32. Given $y = A \sin (Bx + C)$, identify the following.

    a. amplitude

    b. period

    c. phase shift

Objective: *To use fundamental identities and definitions to verify identities.*

▬ Prove that each equation is an identity.

33. $\sin^2 x = \dfrac{\sec^2 x - 1}{\sec^2 x}$

34. $\tan x = \cos x \cdot \sin x \cdot (1 + \tan^2 x)$

35. $\sec x + \tan x = (1 + \sin x) \sec x$

36. $(1 - \cot x)^2 = \csc^2 x - 2 \cot x$

37. $\tan (-x) = -\tan x$

38. $\sec (-x) = \sec x$

CHAPTER TEST ▬▬▬▬▬▬▬▬▬▬

1. Find the lengths of the sides of $\triangle ABC$ where $A(2, 5)$, $B(-3, -2)$, $C(-1, 6)$.

2. $\sin 0.48 \approx 0.4617$. Find

    a. $\sin (-0.48)$ **b.** $\cos \left(\dfrac{\pi}{2} + 0.48\right)$ **c.** $\cos (0.48)$

3. Compute $\sin \dfrac{\pi}{3} \cdot \cos \dfrac{\pi}{6}$.

4. Sketch a graph of

    a. $y = \sin x$ $0 \leq x \leq 4\pi$
    b. $y = \cos x$ $0 \leq x \leq 4\pi$

5. In your own words define a periodic function and the period of a periodic function.

6. What is the period of $y = \sin Bx$? of $y = \cos Bx$?

7. a. What is the amplitude of a function?
    b. What is the amplitude of $y = A \sin x$? of $y = A \cos x$?

8. Sketch a graph of $y = 2 \sin 4x$.

9. Sketch the graph of $y = -2 \cos \left(2x - \dfrac{\pi}{2}\right)$.

10. Sketch the graph of $y = \tan x$, $0 \leq x \leq 2\pi$.

11. For $0 \leq x \leq 2\pi$ what is the range of

    a. $y = \sec x$?   **b.** $y = \csc x$?   **c.** $y = \cot x$?

12. Using $\sin^2 x + \cos^2 x = 1$ and the definitions of $\tan x$, $\cot x$, $\sec x$ and $\csc x$ find expressions for the following.

    a. $\tan^2 x$ in terms of $\sec x$.
    b. $\cot^2 x$ in terms of $\csc x$.
    c. $\sec^2 x$ in terms of $\sin x$ and $\cos x$.
    d. $\csc^2 x$ in terms of $\sin x$ and $\cos x$.

CHAPTER 3
TRIGONOMETRY

Angles and triangles are part of everyday life. You cannot construct a building, a piece of furniture or paint a painting without taking into consideration the angles at which lines and planes meet. It is thus easy to understand why the trigonometry of triangles, which is treated in this chapter and the next, was developed many years before the trigonometry of real numbers which you learned about in Chapter 2.

The John Hancock building pictured at the upper left of the opposite page uses 90 degree angles as well as acute and obtuse angles as part of its basic architectural design.

The Nathan Moore house designed by Frank Lloyd Wright pictured in the center left hand corner uses the same angle repeatedly to give the house a distinctive look. Many ski houses or houses built in areas where there are heavy snowfalls use roofs of similar shape in order to avoid roof damage. The steep angle allows the melting snow to slide harmlessly off.

On the other hand the Leaning Tower of Pisa may be the only building ever to have become famous precisely because it stands at an angle not intended by its architect. If you can imagine a perpendicular dropped from the top of the tower to the ground you could construct a triangle with the tower as one side. This triangle could then be used to find the height of the tower or the height of the top of the tower from the ground.

Angles even have to be taken into consideration in the construction of athletic fields. For example, the Astrodome in Texas uses artificial turf to cover the ground. If the turf is not brushed at the correct angle it will become slippery and cause accidents.

3-1 Angles and Rotation

In geometry you learned that an angle was the union of two rays with a common endpoint. This definition was appropriate for the needs of geometry, because you were seldom interested in angles larger than a straight angle. Now, however, a more general definition is needed.

Think of a ray in a plane and imagine that this ray is rotated about its endpoint to some position in the same plane. The result is an angle. The point is the **vertex** of the angle, the initial position of the rotating ray is the **initial side** of the angle, and the final position of the ray is the **terminal side** of the angle.

Illustrated in Figure 1 at right is the angle formed by rotating a ray in a counter-clockwise direction about O from its initial position $\overrightarrow{OA}$ to its terminal position $\overrightarrow{OB}$. The curved arrow, shown in color, indicates the magnitude and direction of rotation in moving counterclockwise from $\overrightarrow{OA}$ to $\overrightarrow{OB}$. The magnitude and

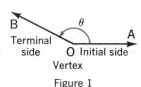

Figure 1

direction of rotation is the measure of the angle, represented by the Greek letter θ (theta).

If the ray does not rotate at all, as in Figure 2, the initial side and terminal side of the angle coincide, and the measure of the angle is 0°. If the ray makes one complete rotation in the counterclockwise direction, as in Figure 3, again the initial and terminal sides coincide, but the measure of the angle is 360°.

Figure 2   Figure 3

If the ray completes more than one complete counterclockwise rotation, the measure of the angle is greater than 360°.

A ray can be rotated in either a counterclockwise or clockwise direction to form an angle with any real number measure.

The measure of an angle formed by a counterclockwise rotation is indicated by a positive number.
The measure of an angle formed by a clockwise rotation is indicated by a negative number.

Thus $m\angle AOB$ is 45° while $m\angle CDE$ is −45° in the figure below.

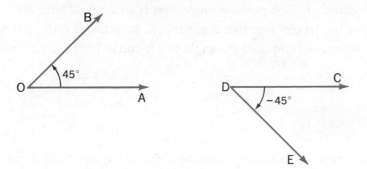

When the vertex of an angle is at the origin of a coordinate system and its initial side coincides with the positive x axis, the angle is in **standard position.** Angle AOB in the figure at the right is in standard position.

For such an angle, there are eight possible ways for the terminal side to lie. The terminal side may coincide with either the positive or negative x or y axis. This accounts for four of the possibilities. In these cases the angle is called a **quadrantal angle.** The other four

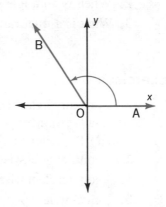

possibilities are for the terminal side to lie in one of the four quadrants. An angle in standard position is said to be *in* the quadrant in which its terminal side lies. Angle AOB above is in quadrant II.

Suppose $P(x, y)$ is a point in one of the four quadrants. Then the positive x axis and the ray $\overrightarrow{OP}$ determine an angle with positive measure. If θ is the measure of $\angle POA$ such that $0 \le \theta < 360°$, then $\theta + n \cdot 360°$, $n \in W$, is the measure of an angle in standard position with terminal side $\overrightarrow{OP}$ for each n. Angles with the same terminal side are said to be **coterminal angles.** Notice that there are also infinitely many coterminal angles with terminal side $\overrightarrow{OP}$ and having negative measures. What is an expression for the measure of these angles?

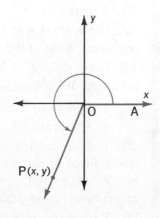

Now try these

1. Find the smallest positive angle that is coterminal with 860°.
2. Give the largest negative angle that is coterminal with 225°.
3. In what quadrant does the angle you found in Exercise 1 terminate?

Answers: **1.** 140°   **2.** −135°   **3.** Quadrant II.

Checkpoint

1. How does the definition for angle in trigonometry differ from the definition you used in geometry?
2. When is an angle said to be in standard position?
3. What is a quadrantal angle? List their degree measures.

Exercises

A ━━ Sketch an angle AOB in standard position, with $\overrightarrow{OB}$ horizontal, that results from the following rotations. Determine the measure of each. ("$\frac{1}{3}$ clockwise" denotes $\frac{1}{3}$ of a complete revolution.)

1. $\frac{1}{4}$ counterclockwise
2. $\frac{1}{2}$ counterclockwise
3. $\frac{3}{4}$ counterclockwise
4. 1 counterclockwise
5. $\frac{1}{4}$ clockwise
6. $\frac{1}{2}$ clockwise
7. $\frac{1}{6}$ clockwise
8. $\frac{1}{8}$ counterclockwise
9. $\frac{5}{12}$ counterclockwise
10. $\frac{3}{10}$ clockwise
11. $\frac{4}{5}$ counterclockwise
12. $\frac{3}{2}$ clockwise
13. $\frac{17}{12}$ counterclockwise
14. $\frac{7}{6}$ clockwise
15. $\frac{2}{3}$ clockwise
16. $\frac{4}{3}$ counterclockwise

17. Let θ, $0° < \theta < 360°$, be the measure of $\angle AOB$ in standard position. What is the measure of one negative coterminal angle?

18. Let θ, $0° < \theta < 360°$, be the measure of $\angle AOB$ in standard position. What are the limits on θ if the terminal side lies in

   a. Quadrant I   **b.** Quadrant II

   c. Quadrant III   **d.** Quadrant IV

19. For all angles in standard position with measure $\theta > 0°$ which lie in Quadrant I, θ is between $n \cdot 360°$ and $90° + n \cdot 360°$, $n \in W$ or $n \cdot 360° < \theta < 90° + n \cdot 360°$, $n \in W$. Find similar expressions for angles in Quadrants II, III, and IV.

20. Repeat Exercise 19 for $\theta < 0°$.

■ Use your results for Exercise 19 and 20 to find the quadrant in which the terminal side of an angle in standard position lies if its measure is the following.

21. 41°   **22.** −420°   **23.** 1000°   **24.** −290°

25. 451°   **26.** −539°   **27.** −2000°   **28.** 181°

29. 359°   **30.** −719°   **31.** 495°   **32.** 380°

■ The angle at right is in standard position. Its terminal side contains the point $A(-2, 4)$.

33. Plot the following points and see if they are on the terminal side of the angle. $B(-4, 8)$, $C(-6, 12)$, $D(-8, 16)$ $E(-10, 15)$.

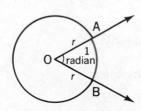

34. Use the distance formula to find the measure of $\overline{AO}$, $\overline{BO}$, $\overline{CO}$ and $\overline{DO}$.

35. Let r represent in turn the distance from each of A, B, C, and D to O. Find $\frac{x}{r}$, $\frac{y}{r}$, and $\frac{y}{x}$ for each point.

36. For any point $P(x, y)$ on the terminal side of the angle, what is the value of $\frac{x}{r}$, $\frac{y}{r}$, $\frac{y}{x}$?

37. Draw an angle in standard position with $A(3, -4)$ on its terminal side. Repeat Exercises 33–36 but use the points $B(6, -8)$, $C(8, -12)$, and $D(10, -16)$.

3–2   Angles Measured in Radians

It is often convenient in mathematics to use a unit of angular measure called a **radian.** An angle of one radian, that is the unit angle for radian measure, is an angle with its vertex at the center of a circle that subtends an arc of the circle the same length as the radius of the circle. In the figure at right, the radius of the circle is r, $(OA = OB = r)$, and the length of arc AB, shown in color, is r. Thus the radian measure of $\angle AOB$ is 1 radian.

EXAMPLE 1. Suppose $\overparen{AB}$ measures 7 units and the radius r of circle O is 3 units. What is the radian measure of $\angle AOB$?

The radius of the circle is 3. For every 3 units of arc length, an angle of one radian is determined. Since $\overparen{AB}$ has length 7, the angle AOB has measure $\frac{7}{3}$ or $2\frac{1}{3}$ radians.

> **Definition** A <u>radian</u> is the measure of an angle that intercepts an arc equal in length to the radius of a circle whose center is the vertex of the angle.

EXAMPLE 2. How many radians are there in one complete revolution of a ray?

Let the ray be $\overrightarrow{OA}$ and consider a circle of radius r with center O. Since $\overrightarrow{OA}$ has made one complete revolution about O, the arc intercepted by the angle is the circle. The measure of the distance around the circle is $C = 2\pi r$. To find the number of radians in $2\pi r$ units of arc, you divide by r. Why? Consequently there are 2π radians in one revolution of a ray.

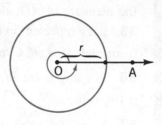

In Example 2 you found there were 2π radians in one counterclockwise revolution of a ray. In degrees, the same angle measures 360°. Thus

$$2\pi \text{ radians} = 360° \qquad\qquad 1$$

or

$$\pi \text{ radians} = 180° \qquad\qquad 2$$

Equation 2 is used to find the number of radians in one degree and the number of degrees in one radian. Dividing each member of 2 by 180, you find

$$1° = \frac{\pi}{180}. \qquad\qquad 3$$

Similarly
$$1 \text{ radian} = \frac{180°}{\pi} \qquad\qquad 4$$

Consequently
$$1° \approx 0.0174533 \text{ radians}$$

and
$$1 \text{ radian} \approx 57° \ 17' \ 44.8''$$

In indicating the measure of an angle you should feel free to use either degrees or radians. In writing 25 degrees you should use the degree symbol, °; for example, 25°. When writing the measure of an angle in radians, no additional symbol is required. For example, if $m\angle A = 1.5$, then the 1.5 is interpreted to be 1.5 radians.

Notice that the rotation of a ray needed to produce an angle measuring 3° is significantly less than that needed to produce an angle of 3 (radians).

EXAMPLE 3. Find the approximate number of

a. radians in 3° **b.** degrees in 3 radians

From Example 2
$1° \approx 0.0174533$ radians
$3° \approx 0.0523599$ radians

From Example 2
1 radian $\approx 57° \, 17' \, 44.8''$
3 radians $\approx 171° \, 53' \, 14.4''$

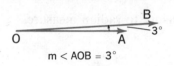

m < AOB = 3°

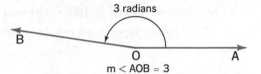

m < AOB = 3

The full importance of radian measure of angles will become clear to you in the next few sections. For now it must suffice to say that radians provide an important link between angular measure and linear measure. That is, if the circle used to determine the radian measure of an angle is a unit circle, then the radian measure of the angle *and* the measure of the arc intercepted by that angle are expressed using the same number. This is illustrated in the figure below. $\overset{\frown}{AB}$ is x units long *and* $m\angle BOA = x$.

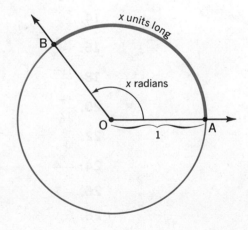

Now try these

━━ Change the following degree measures to radian measures. (Leave results in terms of π.)

1. 45°   **2.** 30°   **3.** 105°

━━ Change the following radian measures to degree measures.

4. 3π **5.** $\dfrac{5\pi}{6}$ **6.** 2

Answers: **1.** $\dfrac{\pi}{4}$ **2.** $\dfrac{\pi}{6}$ **3.** $\dfrac{7\pi}{12}$ **4.** 540°   **5.** 150°   **6.** $\dfrac{360}{\pi}$

Checkpoint

1. When the measure of an angle is stated in radians, conversion to degrees may be accomplished, if desired, by using the relation π radians = 180°. Explain why.

2. Explain how to change degree measure to radian measure.

Exercises

A ━━ Change each degree measure to radian measure. (Leave results in terms of π.)

1. 60°   **2.** 90°   **3.** −180°

4. 270°   **5.** −30°   **6.** −72°

7. 135°   **8.** −75°   **9.** 330°

10. 495°   **11.** −210°   **12.** −690°

━━ Change each radian measure to a degree measure.

13. $\dfrac{\pi}{6}$ **14.** $\dfrac{\pi}{3}$

15. $\dfrac{\pi}{2}$ **16.** $-\dfrac{3\pi}{2}$

17. $-\dfrac{4\pi}{3}$ **18.** $\dfrac{11\pi}{6}$

19. $-\dfrac{4\pi}{5}$ **20.** $\dfrac{5\pi}{12}$

21. -3π **22.** $\dfrac{4\pi}{3}$

23. $\dfrac{17\pi}{5}$ **24.** −4

25. −1   **26.** −7

27. $\dfrac{13\pi}{2}$ **28.** 6

B **29.** What part of a revolution does the minute hand of a clock make in 6 minutes?

30. Through how many degrees does the minute hand of a clock rotate in 6 minutes?

31. Through how many radians does the minute hand of a clock rotate in 6 minutes?

32. If the minute hand of a clock is 4 inches long, how far does the tip travel in 6 minutes?

33. Repeat Exercises 29–32 for the following.

    a. 15 minutes   **b.** 32 minutes

    c. 45 minutes   **d.** 50 minutes

34. Assume the hour hand of a clock is two inches long. What part of a revolution does it make in 6 minutes?

35. Through how many degrees does the hour hand of the clock in Exercise 34 rotate in 6 minutes?

36. Through how many radians does the hour hand of the clock in Exercise 34 rotate in 6 minutes?

37. How far does the tip of the hour hand in Exercise 34 travel in 6 minutes?

38. How far will a fly sitting on the outer rim of a wheel travel in one minute if the wheel has a radius of 1 foot and is turning at 10 revolutions per second?

39. The radius of a wheel of a car is 12 inches. Find the number of revolutions the wheel makes in 1 second if the car is traveling 60 mph (60 mph = 88 ft/sec).

40. Repeat Exercise 39 when the radius of the wheel of the car is 10 inches.

C **41.** Let O be the center of a circle of radius r. If $\angle AOB$ intercepts an arc s units long, what is the radian measure of $\angle AOB$?

42. A plane region bounded by an arc of a circle and the sides of a central angle is a *circular sector*. Given a circle with radius r intercepting an arc of measure s, derive a formula for the area K of a circular sector in terms of r and s.

43. Write a definition of "degree" similar to that given for radian.

44. David said to his classmate Brian that a radian and a degree were each measures of angles. Is David right? Explain your position.

3–3   The Trigonometric Functions

Let $P(x, y)$ be r units, $r \neq 0$, from the origin on the terminal side of an angle in standard position.   Let θ indicate the measure of the angle.   By the distance formula, $r = \sqrt{x^2 + y^2}$.   For a given angle of measure θ the ratios $\frac{x}{r}, \frac{y}{r},$ and $\frac{y}{x}$ are independent of the point $P(x, y)$. These ratios are three basic relationships of **trigonometry.** The distance $r = \sqrt{x^2 + y^2}$ is the measure of the **radius vector** of the point P.   The triangle formed by drawing a perpendicular from P to the x axis is called a **reference triangle.**

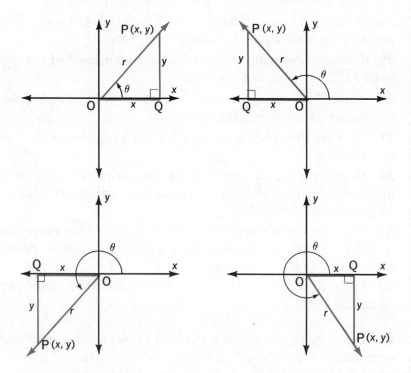

For any angle with measure θ and point $P(x, y)$ on its terminal side you have the following definitions.

$$\text{sine } \theta \text{ (abbreviated sin } \theta) = \frac{y}{r}, \qquad r = \sqrt{x^2 + y^2}$$

$$\text{cosine } \theta \text{ (abbreviated cos } \theta) = \frac{x}{r}, \qquad r = \sqrt{x^2 + y^2}$$

$$\text{tangent } \theta \text{ (abbreviated tan } \theta) = \frac{y}{x}, \qquad x \neq 0$$

You can easily demonstrate that the sine, cosine and tangent ratios are constant for a given angle of measure θ.

In the figure $m\angle POQ = \theta$ and $P_1(x_1, y_1)$, $P_2(x_2, y_2)$, and $P_3(x_3, y_3)$ are points on the terminal side of $\angle POQ$. The triangles P_1OQ_1, P_2OQ_2, and P_3OQ_3 are similar. (Why?) Since the corresponding sides of similar triangles are proportional, you can state the following.

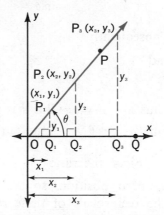

$$\sin \theta = \frac{y_1}{r_1} = \frac{y_2}{r_2} = \frac{y_3}{r_3}$$

$$\cos \theta = \frac{x_1}{r_1} = \frac{x_2}{r_2} = \frac{x_3}{r_3}$$

$$\tan \theta = \frac{y_1}{x_1} = \frac{y_2}{x_2} = \frac{y_3}{x_3}$$

For a given angle with measure θ, $\sin \theta$ has one and only one value; hence the set of ordered pairs $(\theta, \sin \theta)$ is a function. The first member of each ordered pair is the measure of an angle, the second member is the ratio $\frac{y}{r}$. Similar reasoning allows you to conclude that the cosine and tangent relations are also functions. Each of these functions is called a **trigonometric function.**

The domains of the sine and cosine functions are measures of angles, and these measures may be any real number. Therefore the domain of the sine and cosine functions is the set of real numbers. The domain of the tangent function is a subset of the real numbers, for certain members must be excluded. These excluded real numbers are the measures of angles whose terminal sides coincide with the positive or negative y axis. Explain why.

EXAMPLE 1. Sketch the angle whose terminal side contains the point $P(-5, -12)$. In which quadrant is the angle? Use the reference triangle to find the sine, cosine, and tangent of θ where θ is the measure of the angle.

The angle and the reference triangle are shown at the right. θ lies in Quadrant III. By the distance formula, you find

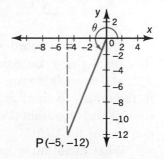

$$r = \sqrt{(-5)^2 + (-12)^2}$$
$$= \sqrt{25 + 144}$$
$$= \sqrt{169} = 13.$$

Thus, $\sin \theta = \frac{y}{r} = -\frac{12}{13}$; $\cos \theta = \frac{x}{r} = -\frac{5}{13}$; $\tan \theta = \frac{y}{x} = \frac{12}{5}$

EXAMPLE 2. Given $\sin \theta = \frac{1}{2}$, θ in Quadrant I. Find $\cos \theta$ and $\tan \theta$.

$$\sin \theta = \frac{y}{r} \qquad \text{and} \qquad r = \sqrt{x^2 + y^2}.$$

Consequently

$$2 = \sqrt{x^2 + 1}$$

and

$$4 = x^2 + 1$$

or

$$3 = x^2.$$

Thus $x = \pm\sqrt{3}$. But θ is in Quadrant I, so $x > 0$. Thus $x = \sqrt{3}$. Finally: $\cos \theta = \frac{\sqrt{3}}{2}$ and $\tan \theta = \frac{1}{\sqrt{3}} = \frac{\sqrt{3}}{3}$.

Since the ratios $\frac{y}{r}$, $\frac{x}{r}$, $\frac{y}{x}$, $x \neq 0$ are constant for each angle in standard position, so are their reciprocals when they are defined. The reciprocals of these ratios are three other trigonometric functions for any angle with measure θ and point $P(x, y)$ in its terminal side.

$$\text{cosecant } \theta \text{ (abbreviated csc } \theta) = \frac{r}{y}, \qquad y \neq 0$$

$$\text{secant } \theta \text{ (abbreviated sec } \theta) = \frac{r}{x}, \qquad x \neq 0$$

$$\text{cotangent } \theta \text{ (abbreviated cot } \theta) = \frac{x}{y}, \qquad y \neq 0$$

EXAMPLE 3. Let $P(2, -3)$ be a point on the terminal side of an angle in standard position which has measure θ. Find the values of the six trigonometric functions. In what quadrant does θ lie?

$$x = 2 \qquad \text{and} \qquad y = -3$$

By the distance formula $r = \sqrt{2^2 + (-3)^2} = \sqrt{4 + 9} = \sqrt{13}$. Consequently,

$$\sin \theta = -\frac{3}{\sqrt{13}}, \qquad \cos \theta = \frac{2}{\sqrt{13}}, \qquad \tan \theta = -\frac{3}{2}$$

$$\csc \theta = -\frac{\sqrt{13}}{3}, \qquad \sec \theta = \frac{\sqrt{13}}{2}, \qquad \cot \theta = -\frac{2}{3}.$$

Since the x coordinate of P is positive and the y coordinate is negative, $P(2, -3)$ is in Quadrant IV. An angle is in the same quadrant as its terminal side, so θ is in Quadrant IV. The angle is graphed at the right.

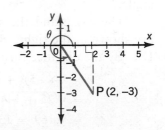

What quadrant would $P(2, 3)$ be in? What quadrant would $P(-2, 3)$ be in? $P(-2, -3)$?

1. What is a reference triangle? How is it used?

2. Define the following trigonometric functions: sine, cosine, tangent, cotangent, secant, and cosecant.

Exercises

A ━━ Find the six trigonometric functions of θ when θ is the measure of an angle in standard position whose terminal side contains the given point. Leave answers in radical form when radicals occur.

1. $(5, 3)$ 2. $(-5, 3)$
3. $(-5, -3)$ 4. $(5, -3)$
5. $(1, -8)$ 6. $(3, 4)$
7. $(-6, 8)$ 8. $(-1, -2)$
9. $(0, 4)$ 10. $(-3, 0)$
11. $(2, 0)$ 12. $(0, -1)$
13. $(12, 5)$ 14. $(1, -3)$
15. $(-\sqrt{2}, \sqrt{2})$ 16. $(-\sqrt{3}, -1)$

B ━━ Find the five other trigonometric functions of θ when the terminal side of the angle is in the indicated quadrant.

17. $\tan \theta = \frac{2}{5}$ θ is in Quadrant I.
18. $\sin \theta = \frac{2}{3}$ θ is in Quadrant II.
19. $\cos \theta = \frac{\sqrt{3}}{2}$ θ is in Quadrant IV.
20. $\tan \theta = 1$ θ is in Quadrant III.
21. $\sin \theta = -\frac{5}{13}$ θ is in Quadrant IV.
22. $\cos \theta = -\frac{5}{13}$ θ is in Quadrant III.
23. $\cos \theta = -\frac{2}{5}$ θ is in Quadrant II.
24. $\sin \theta = \frac{1}{5}$ θ is in Quadrant I.

25. Make a table showing the sign of the trigonometric functions sine, cosine, and tangent when θ is in Quadrant I, II, III, or IV.

26. $\sin \theta = \frac{u}{v}$, θ is in Quadrant II. Find the trigonometric functions $\tan \theta$ and $\cos \theta$ in terms of u and v.

27. $\tan \theta = \frac{u}{v}$, θ is in Quadrant III. Find the trigonometric functions $\sin \theta$ and $\cos \theta$ in terms of u and v.

28. $\cos \theta = \frac{u}{v}$, θ is in Quadrant IV. Find the trigonometric functions $\sin \theta$ and $\tan \theta$ in terms of u and v.

3–4   Trigonometric and Circular Functions

How trigonometric functions (Section 3–3) and circular functions (Chapter 2) are related is explained below through the example of the sine function.

Recall that the circular function sine was defined to be the second coordinate of a point on the unit circle with center at the origin. If $P(x, y)$ was t units from the point $A(1, 0)$ along the circle, then $y =$ sin t. (See the figure at the right.)

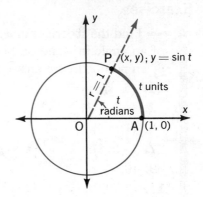

Now consider the ray OP and the measure of the angle POA in *radians*. Since the radius of the unit circle is 1, the measure of $\angle POA$ is t radians. (Why?) Consequently the value of the *trigonometric function* sin t is by definition $\frac{y}{1}$ or y.

Thus the value of the circular function sin t, $t \in$ R, is the same as the value of the trigonometric function sin t when t *is the radian measure* of the angle POA and the radius vector r is 1. But, for a given angle of measure t, the ratio $\frac{y}{r}$ is constant for all points $P(x, y)$ on the terminal side of the angle. Consequently the trigonometric function "sine" is identical to the circular function sine when the independent variable is interpreted as the radian measure of an angle in standard position. That is, if $(t, \sin t)$ is in either function, then it is in the other also.

Using similar reasoning you can conclude that each trigonometric function is equal to the circular function of the same name.

If the independent variable of a trigonometric function happens to be the degree measure of angle, then the relationship

$$1° = \frac{\pi}{180} \text{ radians}$$

allows you to convert degrees to radians. Thus even when degree measure is used to measure angles, you can equate the ordered pairs of trigonometric and circular functions. For example, the ordered pair $(30°, \sin 30°)$ corresponds to the ordered pair $\left(\frac{\pi}{6}, \sin \frac{\pi}{6}\right)$, where the last pair is an element of the sine function whether it be considered circular or trigonometric.

EXAMPLE 1. Show that the identity $\sin(-\theta) = -\sin\theta$ is valid when θ is the measure of an angle. Draw the reference triangles and show that they are similar.

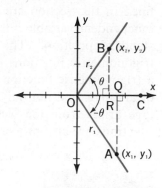

Let $-\theta$ be the measure of $\angle AOC$ in Quadrant IV. Let $\angle BOC$ be an angle in standard position with measure θ ($\theta > 0°$ and θ in Quadrant I). The reference triangles are similar, and thus $\left|\frac{y_2}{r_2}\right| = \left|\frac{y_1}{r_1}\right|$.

Since y_2 is in Quadrant I and y_1 is in Quadrant IV, y_2 and y_1 are opposite in sign. r_1 and r_2 are positive by definition of the radius vector. Thus $-\frac{y_2}{r_2} = \frac{y_1}{r_1}$ or $-\sin\theta = \sin(-\theta)$. A similar argument shows that if θ is in Quadrant I, II, or III, the relationship remains true. Thus

$$\forall\ \theta \in R \qquad \sin(-\theta) = -\sin\theta.$$

Notice that the argument is independent of the unit used to measure the angle. It may be radians or degrees. Thus the identity is valid for the sine function whether it is thought of as a trigonometric or as a circular function, and whether θ is in degrees or radians.

The properties of the circular functions may be used to specify the domain and range of the trigonometric functions. This is illustrated for the tangent function in the next example.

EXAMPLE 2. Specify the range and domain of the trigonometric function tangent. For what real numbers is tangent undefined when θ is in radians? in degrees?

The range of the circular-function tangent is R. Thus the same is true of the trigonometric-function tangent.

If θ is in radians, $\tan\theta$ is undefined for $\pm\frac{\pi}{2}$, $\pm\frac{3\pi}{2}$, $\pm\frac{5\pi}{2}$, $\cdots$ or

$$\left\{\theta : \theta = \frac{\pi}{2} \pm n\pi, n \in W\right\}.$$

In terms of degree measure, $\tan\theta$ is undefined for $\pm90°$, $\pm270°$, $\pm450°$ $\cdots$ or

$$\forall\ \theta \in \{90° \pm n \cdot 180°, n \in W\}.$$

The domain in each case is the rest of the real numbers, as follows.

$$R - \left\{\frac{\pi}{2} + n\pi, n \in W\right\} \qquad \text{or} \qquad R - \{90° \pm n \cdot 180°, n \in W\}$$

In summary, you could say that the trigonometric functions defined in this section are the circular functions of Chapter 2 with the independent variable interpreted as the radian measure of an angle in standard position. The advantage of this interpretation is that the trigonometric functions find valuable applications in triangles. Also a trigonometric function is defined for any point on the terminal side of an angle and not only for points on the unit circle. A final advantage arises from the fact that the properties you found for circular functions are also properties of trigonometric functions.

Checkpoint

▬ Specify the domain and range of each trigonometric function. Express the domain in terms of real numbers interpreted both as degree measure and as radian measure of angles.

1. sine   2. cosine   3. cotangent
4. cosecant   5. secant   6. tangent

Exercises

A ▬ Each of the following identities is valid for trigonometric as well as circular functions. Each is expressed in radians. Translate each to a statement in degrees and draw a figure showing the angles and the reference triangles. Assume for convenience that θ is an angle in Quadrant I.

1. $\cos(-\theta) = \cos\theta$
2. $\cos(\pi - \theta) = -\cos\theta$
3. $\cos(\pi + \theta) = -\cos\theta$
4. $\sin(\pi + \theta) = -\sin\theta$
5. $\sin(\pi - \theta) = \sin\theta$
6. $\sin\left(\frac{\pi}{2} + \theta\right) = \cos\theta$
7. $\cos\left(\frac{\pi}{2} + \theta\right) = -\sin\theta$
8. $\cos(\theta \pm 2n\pi) = \cos\theta, \ n \in W$
9. $\sin(\theta \pm 2n\pi) = \sin\theta, \ n \in W$
10. $\sin\left(\theta + \frac{\pi}{4}\right) = \cos\left(\theta - \frac{\pi}{4}\right)$
11. $\sin\left(\theta - \frac{\pi}{4}\right) = -\cos\left(\theta + \frac{\pi}{4}\right)$

126   CHAPTER 3

B **12.** Use the table on page 77 to help you complete the table below. Assume x in that table is a radian measure of an angle. Leave a cell blank when the function is undefined. Keep your copy for use later. Leave entries in radical form.

	sin θ	cos θ	tan θ	csc θ	sec θ	cot θ
0°						
30°						
45°						
60°						
90°						
120°						
135°						
150°						
180°						
210°						
225°						
240°						
270°						
300°						
315°						
330°						
360°						

Use the result of Example 1 and Exercise 1 to express each of the following.

13. tan $(-\theta)$ in terms of tan θ.

14. sec $(-\theta)$ in terms of sec θ.

15. csc $(-\theta)$ in terms of csc θ.

16. cot $(-\theta)$ in terms of cot θ.

17. Use Exercises 3 and 4 to write an equivalent expression for tan $(\pi + \theta)$.

18. Use Exercises 2 and 5 to write an expression equivalent to tan $(\pi - \theta)$.

3–5 Trigonometric Functions and Triangles

The trigonometric functions may also be defined for the acute angles of a right triangle. Consider the right triangle ABC and the acute angle A with measure θ in the figure at the left below. Place a coordinate system with origin at A and positive x axis coinciding with side $\overrightarrow{AC}$ of $\angle BAC$ as in the figure at the right below. Let B have coordinates (x, y).

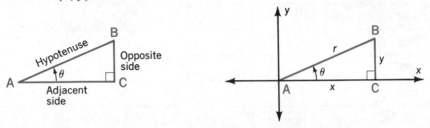

Now it is clear by comparing the two figures above that the definitions for right triangles are as follows.

$$\sin \theta = \frac{y}{r} = \frac{\text{side opposite } A}{\text{hypotenuse}}$$

$$\cos \theta = \frac{x}{r} = \frac{\text{side adjacent } \theta}{\text{hypotenuse}}$$

$$\tan \theta = \frac{y}{x} = \frac{\text{side opposite } \theta}{\text{side adjacent } \theta}$$

Often when working with right triangles, the letter denoting the vertex of the angle replaces the customary symbol θ. Thus to denote the sine of the acute angle at A, you would write $\sin A$.

The table on pages 692–696 gives the sine, cosine, and tangent function values of $0°$ to $90°$ to the nearest ten-thousandth. The table can be used to solve right triangles.

The following example will illustrate the use of trigonometric functions in solving triangles.

EXAMPLE 1. If c, the length of the hypotenuse, is 100 feet and A (the measure of $\angle A$) is $29° 50'$ ($50'$ is read "50 minutes") find the length of the side opposite angle A.

Make a sketch of the right triangle and note the given information.

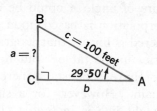 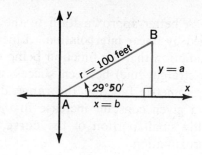

If you use the *right triangle definitions* make a sketch like the one at the left above. If you use the *coordinate-system definitions* place $\angle A$ in standard position as at the right above.

In either case by definition

$$\sin A = \frac{a}{c} = \frac{a}{100}.$$

From the table, $\qquad \sin 29° \ 50' \approx 0.4975.$

Thus, $\qquad\qquad\qquad \frac{a}{100} \approx 0.4975$

$$a \approx 49.75 \text{ feet}$$

EXAMPLE 2. Given the figure at the right with the lengths of sides as indicated. Find, to the nearest whole number, the length of $\overline{AC}$. Then find, to the nearest 10 minutes, the measure of angle A.

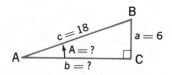

From the Pythagorean Theorem,

$$18^2 = 6^2 + b^2$$
$$324 - 36 = b^2$$
$$288 = b^2.$$

Thus $b \approx 17$, because $17^2 = 289$.

By definition $\qquad \sin A = \frac{6}{18} = \frac{1}{3} \approx 0.3333.$

From the table $\qquad\quad \sin 19° \ 20' = 0.3311$
$$\sin 19° \ 30' = 0.3338.$$

Thus

$$\sin A (\approx 0.3333) \text{ is nearly } \sin 19° \ 30'.$$

Consequently

$$A \approx 19° \ 30' \text{ (to the nearest 10 minutes).}$$

A better approximation to the measure of angle A could be obtained by **linear interpolation.** Linear interpolation is based upon the assumption that the function being considered is linear (that its graph is a straight line) between successive entries in the table. But for a trigonometric function the range does not have a constant increase for a given constant increase in the domain. However, for a sufficiently small portion of the curve, a straight line is in fact a close approximation.

To avoid errors, you may arrange your work as is demonstrated below.

$$y \left\{ \begin{array}{l} 19°\ 20' \\ \underline{\quad ? \quad} \\ 19°\ 30' \end{array} \right\} 10 \qquad\qquad .0022 \left. \begin{array}{l} 0.3311 \\ 0.3333 \\ 0.3338 \end{array} \right\} .0027$$

You then write the following proportion and solve for y.

$$\frac{y}{10} \approx \frac{.0022}{.0027}$$

$$y \approx 8'$$

Then,

$$\sin A \approx 19°\ 20' + 8'$$
$$\approx 19°\ 28'$$

The trigonometric functions are useful in calculating lengths which are not amenable to direct measurement. Very often these applications depend on an *angle of elevation* or an *angle of depression.* An example of each of these angles is represented by Figure 1 and Figure 2 below.

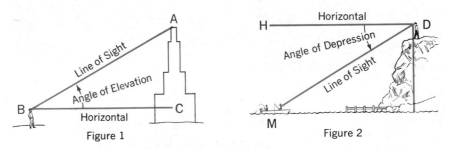

Figure 1   Figure 2

In each case the angle in question is determined by the horizontal and the line of sight.

It is important to remember that the height of the individual doing the sighting is a factor in determining the sides of the triangle used for calculation. The next example illustrates this point.

EXAMPLE 3. A man 6 feet tall stands 15 feet from a building. If the angle of elevation to the top of the building is 75°, how far is the top of the building from the ground?

Refer to Figure 1 on the previous page.

$$BC = 15', \quad \angle B \text{ is } 75°$$

The height of the building is $AC + 6$ feet. (Why?)

By definition

$$\tan 75° = \frac{AC}{15}$$

From the table on page 693,

$$\tan 75° \approx 3.7321$$

Consequently,

$$3.7321 \approx \frac{AC}{15}$$

$$15(3.7321) \approx AC$$

$$55.98 \approx AC$$

To the nearest foot

$$AC = 56.$$

$AC + 6 = 62$ feet is the approximate height of the building.

Now try these

▬ In the Exercises below, a, b, and c respectively represent the lengths of the sides opposite angles A, B, and C, where C is a right angle. What trigonometric function, or other means, would you use to find:

1. b, given a and A

2. b, given a and B

3. a, given c and A

4. a, given c and B

5. c, given b and B

6. c, given a and b

7. c, given b and A

8. a, given c and b

Answers: **1.** tangent   **2.** cosine   **3.** sine   **4.** cosine   **5.** sine
6. $c^2 = a^2 + b^2$ **7.** cos   **8.** $c^2 = a^2 + b^2$

Checkpoint

▬ Given a right triangle with right angle at C, answer the following.

1. Is it true that $\sin B = \frac{b}{c}$? What does $\cos A$ equal?

2. Is it true that $\cos B = \frac{a}{c}$? What does $\sin A$ equal? Then is $\sin A$ equal to $\cos B$?

Exercises

A ━━ Use the table on pages 692–696 to find each of the following.

1. sin 67°   **2.** cos 41°   **3.** tan 14°

4. sin 23° 40′   **5.** cos 71° 30′   **6.** tan 88° 50′

━━ Use the table to find θ for each of the following.

7. sin θ = .9730   **8.** cos θ = .9730   **9.** tan θ = 2.0353

10. sin θ = .0523   **11.** cos θ = .5299   **12.** tan θ = .2065

━━ Use the table and linear interpolation to find θ to the nearest minute for each of the following.

13. sin θ = .2520   **14.** cos θ = .2520   **15.** tan θ = 2.0000

16. sin θ = .9080   **17.** cos θ = .7780   **18.** tan θ = 1.0029

B **19.** A regular pentagon is inscribed in a circle whose diameter is 24 inches. Find the length of its side.

20. From a point 100 feet from the base of a tower, the angle of elevation to its top is 38°. Find its height.

21. If the diameter of the earth is taken as 7912 miles, what is the distance of the furthest point of the surface visible from the summit of a mountain 1 mile in height? (Assume the earth is a perfect sphere.)

22. From the top of a lighthouse 133 feet above the sea, the angle of depression of a buoy is 18° 30′. Find the horizontal distance from the buoy.

23. Use the data in Exercise 22 to find the line-of-sight distance from the top of the house to the buoy.

24. The furthest point of the earth's surface visible from a mountain top is 80 miles distant. Find the height of the mountain if the earth's diameter is 7912 miles.

25. How far from the foot of a pole 80 feet high must a 6-foot person stand so that the angle of elevation of the top of the pole is 10°?

26. From the top of a tower, the angle of depression to a point 1000 feet from the base is 21°. Find the height of the tower.

27. Find the length of the side of a regular hexagon inscribed in a circle whose radius is 10 inches.

C **28.** In the table on pages 692–696 sin 36° = cos 54°, sin 19° = cos 71° and sin 84° = cos 6°. Explain this phenomenon in terms of an identity given in Exercises 1–11 of Section 3–4.

3-6   Reduction Formulas

The Table of values for the trigonometric functions includes only the measures of angles for $0° \leq \theta \leq 90°$. Suppose you were faced with finding the sine of θ where θ is greater than $90°$, what would you do? Clearly you would like to express $\sin \theta$ in terms of an angle between $0°$ and $90°$ so you could use the table.

The identities given in Section 2-4 and again in the Exercises of Section 3-4 provide the necessary tools to solve this problem. They are restated here for your convenience.

In degrees	In radians
1. a. $\sin(-\theta) = -\sin \theta$	$\sin(-\theta) = -\sin \theta$
b. $\cos(-\theta) = \cos \theta$	$\cos(-\theta) = \cos \theta$
c. $\tan(-\theta) = -\tan \theta$	$\tan(-\theta) = -\tan \theta$
2. a. $\sin(180° - \theta) = \sin \theta$	$\sin(\pi - \theta) = \sin \theta$
b. $\cos(180° - \theta) = -\cos \theta$	$\cos(\pi - \theta) = -\cos \theta$
c. $\tan(180° - \theta) = -\tan \theta$	$\tan(\pi - \theta) = -\tan \theta$
3. a. $\sin(180° + \theta) = -\sin \theta$	$\sin(\pi + \theta) = -\sin \theta$
b. $\cos(180° + \theta) = -\cos \theta$	$\cos(\pi + \theta) = -\cos \theta$
c. $\tan(180° + \theta) = \tan \theta$	$\tan(\pi + \theta) = \tan \theta$
4. a. $\sin(90° + \theta) = \cos \theta$	$\sin\left(\dfrac{\pi}{2} + \theta\right) = \cos \theta$
b. $\cos(90° + \theta) = -\sin \theta$	$\cos\left(\dfrac{\pi}{2} + \theta\right) = -\sin \theta$
c. $\tan(90° + \theta) = -\cot \theta$	$\tan\left(\dfrac{\pi}{2} + \theta\right) = -\cot \theta$

There are two other sets of three identities needed to complete the relationships most often used. They can be derived by using the Sets 1-4 given above.

5. a. $\sin(360° - \theta) = -\sin \theta$	$\sin(2\pi - \theta) = -\sin \theta$
b. $\cos(360° - \theta) = \cos \theta$	$\cos(2\pi - \theta) = \cos \theta$
c. $\tan(360° - \theta) = -\tan \theta$	$\tan(2\pi - \theta) = -\tan \theta$

Proof of 5a:

$$\begin{aligned}
\sin(360° - \theta) &= \sin\{180° + (180° - \theta)\} \\
&= -\sin(180° - \theta) \qquad \text{by 3a} \\
&= -\sin \theta \qquad\qquad\quad \text{by 2a}
\end{aligned}$$

The proofs of 5b and 5c are left for you to do.

6. a. $\sin (90° - \theta) = \cos \theta$ $\sin \left(\dfrac{\pi}{2} - \theta \right) = \cos \theta$

b. $\cos (90° - \theta) = \sin \theta$ $\cos \left(\dfrac{\pi}{2} - \theta \right) = \sin \theta$

c. $\tan (90° - \theta) = \cot \theta$ $\tan \left(\dfrac{\pi}{2} - \theta \right) = \cot \theta$

Proof of 6b: $\cos (90° - \theta) = \cos \{180° - (90 + \theta)\}$

$$= -\cos (90° + \theta) \qquad \text{by 2b}$$
$$= - [-\sin \theta] \qquad \text{by 4b}$$
$$= \sin \theta$$

The proofs of 6a and 6c are left for you to do.

EXAMPLE 1.   Find the value of cos 205° 10′.

205° 10′ is not in the table but
$$205° \ 10' = 180° + 25° \ 10'$$
So cos 205° 10′ $= \cos (180° + 25° \ 10')$
$$= -\cos 25° \ 10' \qquad \text{By 3b.}$$
$$= -0.9051 \qquad \text{By the table.}$$

EXAMPLE 2.   Find the value of tan 123° 50′.

a. $123° \ 50' = 180° - 56° \ 10'$
So tan 123° 50′ $= \tan (180° - 56° \ 10')$
$$= -\tan 56° \ 10' \qquad \text{By 2c.}$$
$$= -1.4919 \qquad \text{By the table.}$$

b. $123° \ 50' = 90° + 33° \ 50'$
So tan 123° 50′ $= \tan (90° + 33° \ 50')$
$$= -\cot 33° \ 50' \qquad \text{By 4c.}$$
$$= -1.4919 \qquad \text{By the table.}$$

Now try these

■■■ Find the value of each of the following.
1. tan 225°   **2.** cos 220°   **3.** sin 233°
4. Express cos 310° as the sine of an acute angle.

Answers: **1.** 1   **2.** −.7660   **3.** −.7986   **4.** sin 40°

Checkpoint

How do you find sine, cosine, or tangent of θ where $\theta > 90°$?

Exercises

A ▬ Express each of the following in the form $(180° - \theta)$.

1. $101° \, 10'$ **2.** $179° \, 50'$ **3.** $141° \, 30'$

4. $120° \, 20'$ **5.** $161° \, 40'$ **6.** $97° \, 25'$

▬ Express each of the following in the form $(180° + \theta)$.

7. $183° \, 20'$ **8.** $265° \, 50'$ **9.** $224° \, 50'$

▬ Express each of the following in the form $(360° - \theta)$.

10. $285° \, 40'$ **11.** $331° \, 10'$ **12.** $359° \, 30'$

13. $270° \, 10'$ **14.** $300° \, 50'$ **15.** $345° \, 20'$

▬ Express each of the following in the form $(90° + \theta)$.

16. $142° \, 10'$ **17.** $96° \, 5'$ **18.** $179° \, 30'$

▬ Express each of the following in the form $(90° - \theta)$.

19. $38° \, 20'$ **20.** $97° \, 30'$ **21.** $1° \, 10'$

▬ Find the value of each of the following.

22. $\sin 165°$ **23.** $\cos \frac{7\pi}{6}$ **24.** $\tan 92°$

25. $\sin 281°$ **26.** $\cos \left(-\frac{\pi}{4}\right)$ **27.** $\tan 265°$

28. $\sin \frac{4\pi}{3}$ **29.** $\cos 335°$ **30.** $\tan 271°$

B **31.** Find reduction formulas for $\sin (270° - \theta)$, $\cos (270° - \theta)$ and $\tan (270° - \theta)$ by using the relation $270° - \theta = [360 - (90° + \theta)]$ and the formulas of this section.

32. Repeat Exercise 31 for $\sin (270° + \theta)$, $\cos (270° + \theta)$ and $\tan (270° + \theta)$.

3–7   Sum and Difference Identities for Cosine

In Section 3–4 you saw that circular functions and trigonometric functions were related by means of the radian measure of angles. Moreover every fact that can be proved for circular functions is also true for trigonometric functions whether the independent variable represents degree or radian measure of an angle. In this Section two identities are derived using the definition of circular functions. In light of the previous comments, these identities are valid for trigonometric functions also.

The first identity relates the cosine of the sum of two numbers (or the sum of the measure of two angles) to the sine and cosine of the numbers individually. For example:

$$\cos\left(\frac{\pi}{3}\right) = \frac{1}{2} \quad \cos\left(\frac{\pi}{6}\right) = \frac{\sqrt{3}}{2}$$

and

$$\cos\left(\frac{\pi}{3} + \frac{\pi}{6}\right) = \cos\frac{\pi}{2} = 0.$$

Clearly

$$\frac{1}{2} + \frac{\sqrt{3}}{2} \neq 0$$

and so,

$$\cos\left(\frac{\pi}{3} + \frac{\pi}{6}\right) \neq \cos\frac{\pi}{3} + \cos\frac{\pi}{6}.$$

But

$$\cos\frac{\pi}{3}\cdot\cos\frac{\pi}{6} = \frac{1}{2}\cdot\frac{\sqrt{3}}{2}$$

and

$$\sin\frac{\pi}{3}\cdot\sin\frac{\pi}{6} = \frac{\sqrt{3}}{2}\cdot\frac{1}{2}.$$

Thus

$$\cos\left(\frac{\pi}{3} + \frac{\pi}{6}\right) = \cos\frac{\pi}{3}\cdot\cos\frac{\pi}{6} - \sin\frac{\pi}{3}\cdot\sin\frac{\pi}{6}$$
$$= \frac{1}{2}\cdot\frac{\sqrt{3}}{2} - \frac{\sqrt{3}}{2}\cdot\frac{1}{2} = 0.$$

Letting the Greek letters α (alpha) and β (beta) represent real numbers (or measures of angles), the last statement can be written as follows.

$$\cos(\alpha + \beta) = \cos\alpha\cdot\cos\beta - \sin\alpha\cdot\sin\beta$$

Theorem 3–1 (The Addition Identity for the Cosine Function)
If α and β are any real numbers (measures of angles)

$$\cos(\alpha + \beta) = \cos\alpha\cos\beta - \sin\alpha\sin\beta$$

Proof: Consider the unit circle at the right. The points P, Q and R have coordinates as indicated in the figure at the right.

The measure of $\overset{\frown}{QA}$ and $\overset{\frown}{PR}$ is β. The measure of $\overset{\frown}{AP} = \alpha$. Thus the measure of $\overset{\frown}{QAP} = \alpha + \beta = \overset{\frown}{APR}$. Consequently the chords $\overline{PQ}$ and $\overline{RA}$ have the same measure: $PQ = RA$.

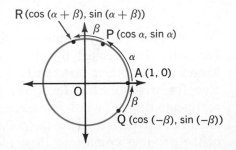

R $(\cos(\alpha + \beta), \sin(\alpha + \beta))$
P $(\cos\alpha, \sin\alpha)$
A $(1, 0)$
Q $(\cos(-\beta), \sin(-\beta))$

The distance formula is now used to express PQ and RA in terms of the coordinates of P, Q, and R.

$$PQ = RA$$

$$\sqrt{[\cos \alpha - \cos (-\beta)]^2 + [\sin \alpha - \sin (-\beta)]^2} = \sqrt{[\cos (\alpha + \beta) - 1]^2 + [\sin (\alpha + \beta) - 0]^2}$$

$$\cos^2 \alpha - 2 \cos \alpha \cos (-\beta) + \cos^2 (-\beta) + \sin^2 \alpha - 2 \sin \alpha \sin (-\beta) + \sin^2 (-\beta)$$
$$= \cos^2 (\alpha + \beta) - 2 \cos (\alpha + \beta) + 1 + \sin^2 (\alpha + \beta) \qquad \mathbf{1}$$

The fundamental identity $\sin^2 x + \cos^2 x = 1$ is used to simplify the left and right members of Equation 1.

$$\cos^2 \alpha + \sin^2 \alpha = 1$$
$$\cos^2 (-\beta) + \sin^2 (-\beta) = 1$$
$$\cos^2 (\alpha + \beta) + \sin^2 (\alpha + \beta) = 1$$

Thus

$$-2 \cos \alpha \cos (-\beta) - 2 \sin \alpha \sin (-\beta) + 2 = -2 \cos (\alpha + \beta) + 2 \qquad \mathbf{2}$$

Subtracting 2 from both members of **2** and dividing by -2, you obtain

$$\cos \alpha \cos (-\beta) + \sin \alpha \sin (-\beta) = \cos (\alpha + \beta). \qquad \mathbf{3}$$

You can now use the identities

$$\cos (-x) = \cos x$$

and

$$\sin (-x) = -\sin x$$

to simplify **3**. The result is

$$\cos (\alpha + \beta) = \cos \alpha \cos \beta - \sin \alpha \sin \beta.$$

EXAMPLE 1. Find the exact value of $\cos 75°$.

$$75° = 30° + 45°,$$

thus, $\cos 75° = \cos (30° + 45°) = \cos 30° \cos 45° - \sin 30° \sin 45°$

$$\cos 30° = \frac{\sqrt{3}}{2}, \quad \cos 45° = \frac{\sqrt{2}}{2}, \quad \sin 30° = \frac{1}{2} \quad \text{and} \quad \sin 45° = \frac{\sqrt{2}}{2}$$

Consequently
$$\cos 75° = \frac{\sqrt{3}}{2} \cdot \frac{\sqrt{2}}{2} - \frac{1}{2} \cdot \frac{\sqrt{2}}{2}$$

$$= \frac{\sqrt{2}}{2} \left(\frac{\sqrt{3} - 1}{2} \right)$$

$$= \frac{\sqrt{2}}{4} (\sqrt{3} - 1)$$

An identity for the $\cos (\alpha - \beta)$ follows easily from Theorem 3–1.

(The Subtraction Identity for the Cosine Function)   If α and β are any real numbers (measures of angles)

$$\cos (\alpha - \beta) = \cos \alpha \cos \beta + \sin \alpha \sin \beta.$$

Proof: From Theorem 3–1.

$$\cos (\alpha + \beta) = \cos \alpha \cos \beta - \sin \alpha \sin \beta.$$

Notice that $(\alpha - \beta) = [\alpha + (-\beta)].$

Consequently

$$\cos (\alpha - \beta) = \cos [\alpha + (-\beta)]$$
$$= \cos \alpha \cos (-\beta) - \sin \alpha \sin (-\beta).$$

by Theorem 3–1.

Then $\cos (\alpha - \beta) = \cos \alpha \cos \beta + \sin \alpha \sin \beta.$

The last step follows from the fact that $\cos (-x) = \cos x$ and $\sin (-x) = -\sin x$.

EXAMPLE 2.   Prove the following reduction formula.

$$\cos \left(\frac{\pi}{2} - x \right) = \sin x$$

Proof: $$\cos \left(\frac{\pi}{2} - x \right) = \cos \frac{\pi}{2} \cos x + \sin \frac{\pi}{2} \cdot \sin x$$
$$= 0 \cdot \cos x + 1 \cdot \sin x$$
$$= \sin x.$$

The remainder of the reduction formulas for the cosine function given in Section 3–6 can be verified in a similar manner.

Now try these

1. Verify the reduction formula $\cos (180° - x) = -\cos x$.

2. Find $\cos 15°$. Does your result agree with the entry in the Table of Values of Trigonometric Functions?

Answers: **1.** $\cos (x - y) = \cos x \cos y + \sin x \sin y$
$\cos (180° - x) = \cos 180° \cos x + \sin 180° \sin x$
$= -1 \cos x + 0 \sin x = -\cos x$

2. $\cos 15° = .966$; yes.

Exercises

A ━━ Use either Theorem 3–1 or 3–2 to find the value of the following.

1. $\cos 105°$
2. $\cos \dfrac{5\pi}{12}$
3. $\cos 195°$
4. $\cos \dfrac{19\pi}{12}$

5. $\cos 15°$
6. $\cos \dfrac{11\pi}{12}$
7. $\cos 255°$
8. $\cos \left(-\dfrac{\pi}{12}\right)$

Use either Theorem 3–1 or 3–2 to verify each identity.

9. $\cos \left(\dfrac{\pi}{2} + \theta\right) = -\sin \theta$
10. $\cos (360° - \theta) = \cos \theta$

11. $\cos (180° - \theta) = -\cos \theta$
12. $\cos \left(\dfrac{3\pi}{2} - \theta\right) = -\sin \theta$

13. $\cos (\pi + \theta) = -\cos \theta$
14. $\cos \left(\dfrac{3\pi}{2} + \theta\right) = \sin \theta$

B ━━ Let α and β be the measure of two first quadrant angles. Find $\cos (\alpha + \beta)$ given the following information.

15. $\cos \alpha = \frac{3}{5}$, $\sin \beta = \frac{3}{5}$
16. $\cos \alpha = \frac{5}{13}$, $\cos \beta = \frac{35}{37}$

17. $\sin \alpha = \frac{8}{17}$, $\tan \beta = \frac{7}{24}$
18. $\tan \alpha = \frac{4}{3}$, $\cot \beta = \frac{5}{12}$

19. $\sec \alpha = \frac{29}{21}$, $\sec \beta = \frac{5}{3}$
20. $\cot \alpha = \frac{12}{5}$, $\tan \beta = \frac{60}{11}$

21. Find $\cos (\alpha - \beta)$ given the data in Exercises 15–20.

C **22.** Prove: $\cos 3x \cos 5x - \sin 3x \underline{\sin} 5x = \cos 8x$.

23. Prove: $\cos 3x \cos 5x + \sin 3x \sin 5x = \cos 2x$.

24. Prove: $\cos (\alpha + \beta) + \cos (\alpha - \beta) = 2 \cos \alpha \cos \beta$.

25. Prove: $\cos (\alpha - \beta) - \cos (\alpha + \beta) = 2 \sin \alpha \sin \beta$.

26. Prove: $\cos \left(\dfrac{\pi}{2} + \alpha - \beta\right) = \cos \alpha \sin \beta - \sin \alpha \cos \beta$.

27. Derive an identity for $\cos (\alpha + \beta + \theta)$ in terms of sines and cosines of α, β, and θ.

28. Assume the angles whose measures are α, β, and $\alpha + \beta$ are positive acute angles as shown at the right. Use this figure to prove $\cos (\alpha + \beta) = \cos \alpha \cos \beta - \sin \alpha \sin \beta$.

(*Hint:*
$$\cos (\alpha + \beta) = \frac{OB}{OA}$$
$$= \frac{OC - BC}{OA}$$
$$= \frac{OC}{OA} - \frac{BC}{OA}.$$

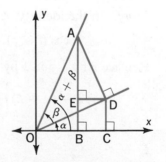

What is $\cos \alpha$ in $\triangle ODC$? What is $\sin \alpha$ in $\triangle AED$?)

29. Is the proof for Exercise 28 as general as the previous one? (Theorem 3–1) Why or why not?

3–8 Sum and Difference Identities for Sine and Tangent

The difference identity for the cosine function can be used to derive an identity for $\sin(\alpha + \beta)$. One additional fact must be recalled first, namely:

$$\sin\left(\frac{\pi}{2} - \theta\right) = \cos\theta. \qquad 1$$

The identity stated in 1 can be verified as follows:

Recall (Example 2, Section 3–7) that

$$\cos\left(\frac{\pi}{2} - x\right) = \sin x. \qquad 2$$

Replace x in 2 by $\left(\frac{\pi}{2} - \theta\right)$.

Thus

$$\cos\left[\frac{\pi}{2} - \left(\frac{\pi}{2} - \theta\right)\right] = \sin\left(\frac{\pi}{2} - \theta\right)$$

or

$$\cos\theta = \sin\left(\frac{\pi}{2} - \theta\right)$$

which is the identity stated in 1.

Now you can prove the following theorem.

Theorem 3–3 (The Addition Identity for the Sine Function)
If α and β are any real numbers (measures of angles)

$$\sin(\alpha + \beta) = \sin\alpha\cos\beta + \cos\alpha\sin\beta.$$

Proof: In the identity, $r, s \in R$,

$$\cos(r - s) = \cos r\cos s + \sin r\sin s.$$

Replace r by $\frac{\pi}{2}$ and s by $(\alpha + \beta)$. Thus

$$\cos\left[\frac{\pi}{2} - (\alpha + \beta)\right] = \cos\left[\left(\frac{\pi}{2} - \alpha\right) - \beta\right]$$

$$= \cos\left(\frac{\pi}{2} - \alpha\right)\cos\beta + \sin\left(\frac{\pi}{2} - \alpha\right)\sin\beta$$

$$= \sin\alpha\cos\beta + \cos\alpha\sin\beta.$$

But $\cos\left[\frac{\pi}{2} - (\alpha + \beta)\right] = \sin(\alpha + \beta)$ (Why?)

Thus $\sin(\alpha + \beta) = \sin\alpha\cos\beta + \cos\alpha\sin\beta.$ \qquad 3

Replacing β in 3 by $-\beta$ and using the identities

$$\sin(-x) = -\sin x$$
$$\cos(-x) = \cos x$$

you have

$$\sin(\alpha - \beta) = \sin \alpha \cos \beta - \cos \alpha \sin \beta$$

thus proving the next theorem.

Theorem 3–4 (The Subtraction Identity for the Sine Function)
If α and β are any real numbers (measures of angles)

$$\sin(\alpha - \beta) = \sin \alpha \cos \beta - \cos \alpha \sin \beta.$$

Theorems 3–3 and 3–4 have the same type of applications as their counterparts for the cosine function.

EXAMPLE 1. Find the value of $\sin 75°$.

$75° = 45° + 30°$ and $\sin 45° = \frac{\sqrt{2}}{2}$, $\cos 45° = \frac{\sqrt{2}}{2}$, $\sin 30° = \frac{1}{2}$, and $\cos 30° = \frac{\sqrt{3}}{2}$.

Thus

$$\begin{aligned}
\sin 75° &= \sin(45° + 30°) \\
&= \sin 45° \cdot \cos 30° + \cos 45° \cdot \sin 30° \\
&= \frac{\sqrt{2}}{2} \cdot \frac{\sqrt{3}}{2} + \frac{\sqrt{2}}{2} \cdot \frac{1}{2} \\
&= \frac{\sqrt{2}}{4}(\sqrt{3} + 1).
\end{aligned}$$

By definition $\tan \theta = \frac{\sin \theta}{\cos \theta}$, $\forall\ \theta \in \mathbf{R}$, $\cos \theta \neq 0$. Consequently

$$\begin{aligned}
\tan(\alpha + \beta) &= \frac{\sin(\alpha + \beta)}{\cos(\alpha + \beta)}, \quad \cos(\alpha + \beta) \neq 0 \\
&= \frac{\sin \alpha \cos \beta + \cos \alpha \sin \beta}{\cos \alpha \cos \beta - \sin \alpha \sin \beta} \qquad \text{(Why?)} \\
&= \frac{\dfrac{\sin \alpha \cos \beta}{\cos \alpha \cos \beta} + \dfrac{\cos \alpha \sin \beta}{\cos \alpha \cos \beta}}{\dfrac{\cos \alpha \cos \beta}{\cos \alpha \cos \beta} - \dfrac{\sin \alpha \sin \beta}{\cos \alpha \cos \beta}} \\
&= \frac{\tan \alpha + \tan \beta}{1 - \tan \alpha \tan \beta}.
\end{aligned}$$

This argument proves the following theorem.

Theorem 3–5 (The Addition Identity for the Tangent Function) If $\alpha, \beta \in R$ and $\cos\alpha$, $\cos\beta$, $\cos(\alpha+\beta) \neq 0$, then

$$\tan(\alpha+\beta) = \frac{\tan\alpha + \tan\beta}{1 - \tan\alpha\tan\beta}.$$

Using the identity $\tan(-x) = -\tan x$, you can prove the following theorem.

Theorem 3–6 (The Subtraction Identity for the Tangent Function) If $\alpha, \beta \in R$ and $\cos\alpha$, $\cos(-\beta)$, $\cos(\alpha-\beta) \neq 0$, then

$$\tan(\alpha-\beta) = \frac{\tan\alpha - \tan\beta}{1 + \tan\alpha\tan\beta}.$$

EXAMPLE 2. Find the value of tan 75°.

$$75° = 45° + 30°$$
$$\tan 45° = 1$$
$$\tan 30° = \frac{\sqrt{3}}{3}$$

From Theorem 3–5

$$\tan 75° = \tan(45° + 30°)$$
$$= \frac{\tan 45° + \tan 30°}{1 - \tan 45° \tan 30°}$$
$$= \frac{1 + \frac{\sqrt{3}}{3}}{1 - 1\cdot\frac{\sqrt{3}}{3}}$$
$$= \frac{3 + \sqrt{3}}{3 - \sqrt{3}}$$

Now try these

1. Using functions of 45° and 30° and theorems of this section, find sin 15°.

2. Use the tables to find $\sin(\alpha - \beta)$ and $\cos(\alpha - \beta)$ if $\alpha = 45°$ and $\beta = 30°$.

Answers: **1.** sin 15° = .2588   **2.** .2588; .9659

Checkpoint

In your own words state the sum and difference identities for sine and tangent.

Exercises

A ▬▬ Use the theorems of this section to find the following.

1. $\sin 105°$ **2.** $\sin \dfrac{5\pi}{12}$ **3.** $\sin 30°$ **4.** $\sin \dfrac{11\pi}{12}$

5. $\tan 105°$ **6.** $\tan \dfrac{5\pi}{12}$ **7.** $\tan 30°$ **8.** $\tan \dfrac{11\pi}{12}$

9. $\sin 195°$ **10.** $\sin \dfrac{19\pi}{12}$ **11.** $\sin 255°$ **12.** $\sin \left(-\dfrac{\pi}{12}\right)$

13. $\tan 195°$ **14.** $\tan \dfrac{19\pi}{12}$ **15.** $\tan 255°$ **16.** $\tan \left(-\dfrac{\pi}{12}\right)$

▬▬ Verify the following identities.

17. $\sin \left(\dfrac{\pi}{2} + x\right) = \cos x$ **18.** $\tan (90° + \theta) = -\cot \theta$

19. $\sin (180° + \theta) = -\sin \theta$ **20.** $\tan \left(\dfrac{\pi}{2} - x\right) = \cot x$

21. $\sin (\pi - \theta) = \sin \theta$ **22.** $\sin (270° + x) = -\cos x$

23. $\tan (180° + \theta) = \tan \theta$ (Is Theorem 3–5 applicable?)

24. $\sin \left(\dfrac{3\pi}{2} - \theta\right) = -\cos \theta$ **25.** $\tan \left(\dfrac{3\pi}{2} + \theta\right) = -\cot \theta$

26. $\tan (\pi - \theta) = -\tan \theta$ (Is Theorem 3–6 applicable?)

27. $\tan (270° - x) = \cot x$

B ▬▬ Verify that each of the following statements is true.

28. $2 \sin^2 150° = 1 - \cos 300°$ **29.** $\tan \dfrac{\pi}{3} = \sqrt{\dfrac{1 - \cos \frac{2\pi}{3}}{1 + \cos \frac{2\pi}{3}}}$

30. $\cos 330° = \sqrt{\dfrac{1 + \cos 660°}{2}}$ **31.** $\tan \dfrac{3\pi}{4} = \dfrac{\sin \frac{3\pi}{2}}{1 + \cos \frac{3\pi}{2}}$

32. $\tan 240° = \dfrac{2 \tan 120°}{1 - \tan^2 120°}$ **33.** $\cos \dfrac{2\pi}{3} = \cos^2 \dfrac{\pi}{3} - \sin^2 \dfrac{\pi}{3}$

▬▬ Prove the following statements are identities

34. $\sin (\alpha + \beta) - \sin (\alpha - \beta) = 2 \cos \alpha \sin \beta$.

35. $\sin (\alpha + \beta) + \sin (\alpha - \beta) = 2 \sin \alpha \cos \beta$.

36. $\cot (\alpha + \beta) = \dfrac{\cot \alpha \cot \beta - 1}{\cot \alpha + \cot \beta}$.

For what values of α and β is each statement true?

37. $\cot(-\alpha) = -\cot\alpha$

38. $\cot(\alpha - \beta) = \dfrac{\cot\alpha\cot\beta + 1}{\cot\beta - \cot\alpha}$

39. $\sin(\alpha + \beta) \cdot \sin(\alpha - \beta) = \sin^2\alpha - \sin^2\beta$

40. $\cos(\alpha + \beta) \cdot \cos(\alpha - \beta) = \cos^2\alpha - \sin^2\beta$

41. $\sin(\alpha + \beta) \cdot \sin(\alpha - \beta) = \cos^2\beta - \cos^2\alpha$

42. $\cos(\alpha + \beta) \cdot \cos(\alpha - \beta) = \cos^2\beta - \sin^2\alpha$

43. $\sec(\alpha + \beta) = \dfrac{\sec\alpha\sec\beta\csc\alpha\csc\beta}{\csc\alpha\csc\beta - \sec\alpha\sec\beta}$

44. $\sec(\alpha - \beta) = \dfrac{\sec\alpha\sec\beta\csc\alpha\csc\beta}{\csc\alpha\csc\beta + \sec\alpha\sec\beta}$

3–9   Double- and Half-Angle Identities

Here is a set of identities which relate the trigonometric functions of an angle to those of twice or half of the angle. Reasonably enough these are called the **double-** and **half-angle** formulas. In general their derivations are accomplished by appropriate substitutions in the angle sum identities.

Theorem 3–7   (The Double-Angle Identity for Sine)   If θ is a real number (measure of an angle), then

$$\sin(2\theta) = 2\sin\theta\cos\theta.$$

Proof: $\sin(\alpha + \beta) = \sin\alpha\cos\beta + \cos\alpha\sin\beta$.
  Letting $\alpha = \beta = \theta$, you have

$$\begin{aligned}
\sin(\theta + \theta) &= \sin(2\theta) \\
&= \sin\theta\cos\theta + \sin\theta\cos\theta \\
&= 2\sin\theta\cos\theta.
\end{aligned}$$

Theorem 3–8   (The Double-Angle Identity for Cosine)   If θ is a real number (measure of an angle), then

$$\begin{aligned}
\cos 2\theta &= \cos^2\theta - \sin^2\theta \\
&= 2\cos^2\theta - 1 \\
&= 1 - 2\sin^2\theta.
\end{aligned}$$

Proof: $\cos(\alpha + \beta) = \cos\alpha\cos\beta - \sin\alpha\sin\beta.$

Let $\alpha = \beta = \theta.$ Then $\cos(\theta + \theta) = \cos(2\theta) = \cos^2\theta - \sin^2\theta.$ Since $\sin^2\theta + \cos^2\theta = 1$ for all $\theta \in R,$

$$\begin{aligned}\cos(2\theta) &= \cos^2\theta - \sin^2\theta\\ &= \cos^2\theta - (1 - \cos^2\theta)\\ &= 2\cos^2\theta - 1\end{aligned}$$

and

$$\begin{aligned}\cos(2\theta) &= (1 - \sin^2\theta) - \sin^2\theta\\ &= 1 - 2\sin^2\theta.\end{aligned}$$

In a similar fashion you can prove the following.

Theorem 3–9 (The Double-Angle Identity for Tangent) If $\theta \in R, \cos\theta \neq 0, \cos 2\theta \neq 0,$ then

$$\tan(2\theta) = \frac{2\tan\theta}{1 - \tan^2\theta}.$$

EXAMPLE 1. Given $\sin\theta = \dfrac{2}{\sqrt{5}}, 0 < \theta < \dfrac{\pi}{2}.$ Find the following.

a. $\cos 2\theta,$ b. $\sin 2\theta,$ c. $\tan 2\theta.$

Since $\sin^2\theta + \cos^2\theta = 1,$ then $\frac{4}{5} + \cos^2\theta = 1$ and $\cos\theta = \dfrac{1}{\sqrt{5}}$ $\left(\text{because } 0 < \theta < \dfrac{\pi}{2}\right).$ It follows that $\tan\theta = \frac{2}{1}.$ (Why?)

a. $\cos 2\theta = \cos^2\theta - \sin^2\theta$

     $= \frac{1}{5} - \frac{4}{5} = -\frac{3}{5}$

b. $\sin 2\theta = 2\sin\theta\cos\theta$

     $= 2 \cdot \dfrac{2}{\sqrt{5}} \cdot \dfrac{1}{\sqrt{5}} = \dfrac{4}{5}$

c. $\tan 2\theta = \dfrac{2\tan\theta}{1 - \tan^2\theta} = \dfrac{4}{1 - 4} = -\dfrac{4}{3}$

The half-angle identities are derived from

1      $\cos 2\theta = 1 - 2\sin^2\theta$ *and* $\cos 2\theta = 2\cos^2\theta - 1$ 2

     Substitute $\dfrac{\alpha}{2}$ for $\theta.$ Substitute $\dfrac{\alpha}{2}$ for $\theta.$

     $\cos\alpha = 1 - 2\sin^2\dfrac{\alpha}{2}$

or $\dfrac{\cos\alpha - 1}{-2} = \sin^2\dfrac{\alpha}{2}$ $\cos\alpha = 2\cos^2\dfrac{\alpha}{2} - 1$

or $\sin^2\dfrac{\alpha}{2} = \dfrac{1 - \cos\alpha}{2}$ *or* $\dfrac{\cos\alpha + 1}{2} = \cos^2\dfrac{\alpha}{2}$

and $\sin\dfrac{\alpha}{2} = \pm\sqrt{\dfrac{1 - \cos\alpha}{2}}$ *or* $\cos\dfrac{\alpha}{2} = \pm\sqrt{\dfrac{1 + \cos\alpha}{2}}$

The "+" is used when $\frac{\alpha}{2}$ is in Quadrant I or II, otherwise the "−" is used.

The "+" is used when $\frac{\alpha}{2}$ is in Quadrant I or IV, otherwise the "−" is used.

By definition $\tan \theta = \dfrac{\sin \theta}{\cos \theta}$.

Thus

$$\tan \frac{\alpha}{2} = \pm \sqrt{\frac{1 - \cos \alpha}{1 + \cos \alpha}} \qquad (\cos \alpha \neq -1)$$

the "+" being used when $\frac{\alpha}{2}$ is in Quadrant I or III, otherwise the "−" is used. In summary, you have the following theorem.

Theorem 3–10 (The Half-Angle Identities) If α is a real number (measure of an angle). Then

$$\text{i. } \sin \frac{\alpha}{2} = \pm \sqrt{\frac{1 - \cos \alpha}{2}}.$$

$$\text{ii. } \cos \frac{\alpha}{2} = \pm \sqrt{\frac{\cos \alpha + 1}{2}}.$$

$$\text{iii. } \tan \frac{\alpha}{2} = \pm \sqrt{\frac{1 - \cos \alpha}{1 + \cos \alpha}}.$$

EXAMPLE 2. Given $\cos \frac{\pi}{4} = \frac{\sqrt{2}}{2}$, find the following.

a. $\sin \frac{\pi}{8}$ b. $\cos \frac{\pi}{8}$ c. $\tan \frac{\pi}{8}$

$\frac{\pi}{8}$ is the measure of an angle in Quadrant I. Consequently "+" is used in each identity of Theorem 3–10.

$$\text{a. } \sin \frac{\pi}{8} = \sqrt{\frac{1 - \frac{\sqrt{2}}{2}}{2}} = \sqrt{\frac{2 - \sqrt{2}}{4}} = \frac{\sqrt{2 - \sqrt{2}}}{2}$$

$$\text{b. } \cos \frac{\pi}{8} = \sqrt{\frac{1 + \frac{\sqrt{2}}{2}}{2}} = \sqrt{\frac{2 + \sqrt{2}}{4}} = \frac{\sqrt{2 + \sqrt{2}}}{2}$$

$$\text{c. } \tan \frac{\pi}{8} = \sqrt{\frac{1 - \frac{\sqrt{2}}{2}}{1 + \frac{\sqrt{2}}{2}}} = \sqrt{\frac{2 - \sqrt{2}}{2 + \sqrt{2}}}$$

Now try these

━━━ Use the half or double angle identities to find each of the following.

1. $\sin \frac{\pi}{8}$ **2.** $\cos \frac{\pi}{8}$ **3.** $\tan \frac{\pi}{8}$

━━━ If $0 < \theta < \frac{\pi}{2}$, in what quadrant is

4. $\frac{1}{2}\theta$?   **5.** 2θ?

Answers: **1.** .383   **2.** .924   **3.** .414   **4.** Quadrant I.   **5.** Quadrant I or II.

Checkpoint

━━━ Explain the method for deriving double and half-angle formulas.

Exercises

A ━━━ Use the half- or double-angle identities to find each of the following.

1. $\sin \frac{\pi}{12}$ **2.** $\cos \frac{\pi}{12}$ **3.** $\tan \frac{\pi}{12}$

4. $\sin \frac{7\pi}{12}$ **5.** $\cos \frac{7\pi}{12}$ **6.** $\tan \frac{7\pi}{12}$

7. $\sin \frac{3\pi}{8}$ **8.** $\cos \frac{3\pi}{8}$ **9.** $\tan \frac{3\pi}{8}$

10. $\sin \frac{11\pi}{12}$ **11.** $\cos \frac{11\pi}{12}$ **12.** $\tan \frac{11\pi}{12}$

13. $\sin \frac{5\pi}{24}$ **14.** $\cos \frac{3\pi}{16}$ **15.** $\tan \frac{\pi}{16}$

16. If $\frac{\pi}{2} < \theta < \pi$, in what quadrant is each of the following?

     a. $\frac{1}{2}\theta$ **b.** 2θ

17. If $\pi < \theta < \frac{3\pi}{2}$, in what quadrant is each of the following?

     a. $\frac{1}{2}\theta$ **b.** 2θ

18. If $\frac{3\pi}{2} < \theta < 2\pi$, in what quadrant is each of the following?

     a. $\frac{1}{2}\theta$ **b.** 2θ

━━━ Let $P(-5, -12)$ be on the terminal side of an angle in standard position with measure θ. Find each of the following.

19. $\sin \theta$ **20.** $\cos \theta$ **21.** $\tan \theta$ **22.** $\sin \frac{1}{2}\theta$

23. $\cos \frac{1}{2}\theta$ **24.** $\sin 2\theta$ **25.** $\cos 2\theta$ **26.** $\tan 2\theta$

▬ Let $P(3, -4)$ be on the terminal side of an angle in standard position with measure α. Find each of the following.

27. $\sin \frac{1}{2}\alpha$ **28.** $\cos \frac{1}{2}\alpha$ **29.** $\tan \frac{1}{2}\alpha$

30. $\sin 2\alpha$ **31.** $\cos 2\alpha$ **32.** $\tan 2\alpha$

B ▬ Prove each of the following identities.

33. $\csc 2\theta = \dfrac{\sec \theta \csc \theta}{2}$ **34.** $\sec 2\theta = \dfrac{\sec^2 \theta}{2 - \sec^2 \theta}$

35. $\sec 2\theta = \dfrac{\csc^2 \theta}{\csc^2 \theta - 2}$ **36.** $\sec 2\theta = \dfrac{\sec^2 \theta \cdot \csc^2 \theta}{\csc^2 \theta - \sec^2 \theta}$

37. $\cot 2\theta = \dfrac{1 + \cos 4\theta}{\sin 4\theta}$ **38.** $\sec \frac{1}{2}\theta = \pm\dfrac{\sqrt{2 + 2\cos \theta}}{1 + \cos \theta}$

39. $\csc \frac{1}{2}\theta = \pm\dfrac{\sqrt{2 - 2\cos \theta}}{1 - \cos \theta}$ **40.** $\csc \frac{1}{2}\theta = \pm\dfrac{\sqrt{2 + 2\cos \theta}}{\sin \theta}$

41. $\tan \frac{1}{2}\theta = \dfrac{\sin \theta}{1 + \cos \theta}$ **42.** $\tan \frac{1}{2}\theta = \dfrac{1 - \cos \theta}{\sin \theta}$

C   **43.** $\cos 3\alpha = 4 \cos^3 \alpha - 3 \cos \alpha$

44. $\sin 3\alpha = 3 \sin \alpha - 4 \sin^3 \alpha$

45. $\cos 4\alpha = 8 \cos^4 \alpha - 8 \cos^2 \alpha + 1$

46. $\sin 4\alpha = 4 \sin \alpha \cdot \cos \alpha \, (2 \cos^2 \alpha - 1)$

3–10   Sum and Product Identities

The final set of identities discussed in this chapter provides a means to convert products of certain trigonometric functions into sums and conversely. As was true in the derivation of the half and double angle identities, the major tools are the sum and difference identities for the sine and cosine functions.

Theorem 3–11 (The Sum-Product Identities for Sine and Cosine) If α, β are real numbers (measures of angles), then

i. $\sin (\alpha + \beta) + \sin (\alpha - \beta) = 2 \sin \alpha \cos \beta.$
ii. $\sin (\alpha + \beta) - \sin (\alpha - \beta) = 2 \cos \alpha \sin \beta.$
iii. $\cos (\alpha + \beta) + \cos (\alpha - \beta) = 2 \cos \alpha \cos \beta.$
iv. $\cos (\alpha + \beta) - \cos (\alpha - \beta) = -2 \sin \alpha \sin \beta.$

To prove Theorem 3–11 begin with the sum and difference identities and add or subtract as indicated in the left members of i–iv.

EXAMPLE 1. Convert the product $2 \cos 7x \cos 2x$ to a sum.
Using Identity [iii] of Theorem 3–11

$$7x = \alpha \qquad \text{and} \qquad 2x = \beta$$

Consequently $\qquad 2 \cos 7x \cos 2x = \cos 9x + \cos 5x.$

The sum-product identities may be converted to an equivalent form by making the substitution of variables.

$$x = \alpha + \beta$$
$$y = \alpha - \beta$$

Solving these for α and β you find

$$\alpha = \frac{x + y}{2}$$
$$\beta = \frac{x - y}{2}$$

Making the appropriate substitutions in Theorem 3–11, you get alternate forms of Identities [i–iv.].

v. $\qquad \sin x + \sin y = 2 \sin \dfrac{x + y}{2} \cdot \cos \dfrac{x - y}{2}$

vi. $\qquad \sin x - \sin y = 2 \cos \dfrac{x + y}{2} \cdot \sin \dfrac{x - y}{2}$

vii. $\qquad \cos x + \cos y = 2 \cos \dfrac{x + y}{2} \cdot \cos \dfrac{x - y}{2}$

viii. $\qquad \cos x - \cos y = -2 \sin \dfrac{x + y}{2} \cdot \sin \dfrac{x - y}{2}$

EXAMPLE 2. Express $\sin \dfrac{17\pi}{12} - \sin \dfrac{11\pi}{12}$ as a product. Use Identity [i.].

$$\sin \frac{17\pi}{12} - \sin \frac{11\pi}{12} = 2 \cos \frac{\dfrac{17\pi}{12} + \dfrac{11\pi}{12}}{2} \cdot \sin \frac{\dfrac{17\pi}{12} - \dfrac{11\pi}{12}}{2}$$

$$= 2 \cos \frac{28\pi}{24} \cdot \sin \frac{6\pi}{24}$$

$$= 2 \cos \frac{7\pi}{6} \cdot \sin \frac{\pi}{4}$$

EXAMPLE 3. Express $\cos 61° + \cos 73°$ as a product. Use Identity viii.

$$\cos 61° + \cos 73° = 2 \cos \frac{61° + 73°}{2} \cos \frac{61° - 73°}{2}$$

$$= 2 \cos 67° \cdot \cos (-6°)$$

$$= 2 \cos 67° \cdot \cos 6° \quad \text{(Why?)}$$

EXAMPLE 4. Prove the following identity.

$$\frac{\sin 5t + \sin 3t}{\cos 5t - \cos 3t} = \cot(-t)$$

$$\frac{\sin 5t + \sin 3t}{\cos 5t - \cos 3t} = \frac{2 \sin 4t \cos t}{-2 \sin 4t \sin t}$$

$$= \frac{\cos t}{-\sin t}$$

$$= -\cot t$$

$$= \cot(-t)$$

Now try these

1. Express the product $\sin \frac{\pi}{3} \cos \frac{\pi}{4}$ as a sum of trigonometric functional values.

2. Express the difference $\cos \frac{\pi}{3} - \cos \frac{\pi}{4}$ as a product of trigonometric functional values.

Answers: **1.** $\frac{1}{2} \sin \frac{7\pi}{12} + \frac{1}{2} \sin \frac{\pi}{12}$ **2.** $-2 \sin \frac{7\pi}{24} \sin \frac{\pi}{24}$

Exercises

A ▬ Write each of the following products as a sum.

1. $2 \sin 3x \cos x$ **2.** $2 \cos 11t \sin 5t$

3. $2 \cos 5x \cos 2x$ **4.** $-2 \sin 7v \sin 5v$

5. $\sin 10x \sin 4x$ **6.** $\sin 15t \cos(-3t)$

7. $\cos 8x \sin 4x$ **8.** $\cos 3t \cos 5t$

▬ Write each of the following sums as a product.

9. $\cos 51° - \cos 23°$ **10.** $\sin \frac{\pi}{8} + \sin \frac{\pi}{16}$

11. $\sin 131° - \sin 43°$ **12.** $\cos \frac{5\pi}{7} + \cos \frac{3\pi}{7}$

13. $\sin \frac{\pi}{3} + \sin \frac{\pi}{4}$ **14.** $\sin \left(x - \frac{\pi}{2}\right) - \sin \left(x + \frac{\pi}{2}\right)$

15. $\cos \frac{1}{4} + \cos \frac{3}{4}$ **16.** $\cos(-3t) - \cos(5t)$

B ▬ Prove each of the following identities.

17. $\frac{\cos 7t + \cos 5t}{\sin 7t - \sin 5t} = \frac{\csc t}{\sec t}$ **18.** $\frac{\sin 3t + \sin t}{\sin 3t - \sin t} = \frac{2}{1 - \tan^2 t}$

19. $\frac{\sin 4x + \sin 2x}{\cos 4x + \cos 2x} = \frac{1}{\cot 3x}$ **20.** $\frac{\sin 3x + \sin x}{\cos 3x - \cos x} = -\frac{\csc x}{\sec x}$

21. $\frac{\sin 3x - \sin x}{\cos 3x + \cos x} = \tan x$ **22.** $\frac{\cos 9x + \cos 5x}{\sin 9x - \sin 5x} = \frac{1 - \tan^2 x}{2 \tan x}$

CHAPTER OBJECTIVES AND REVIEW

Objective: *To know the meaning of the important mathematical terms of this chapter.*

1. Here are many of the mathematical terms used in this chapter. Be sure that you know them thoroughly and can use them correctly.

vertex (*112*)
initial side (*112*)
terminal side (*112*)
standard position (*113*)
quadrantal angle (*113*)
coterminal angles (*113*)
radian (*115*)
radius vector (*120*)
reference triangle (*120*)
trigonometric functions (*121*)
linear interpolation (*130*)
double-angle formula (*144*)
half-angle formula (*144*)

Objective: *To sketch an angle in standard position given its measure.*

2. Identify the following for the angle AOB.
a. Initial side
b. Vertex
c. Terminal side
d. Direction of rotation
e. If $\theta = m\angle AOB$, is θ positive or negative?

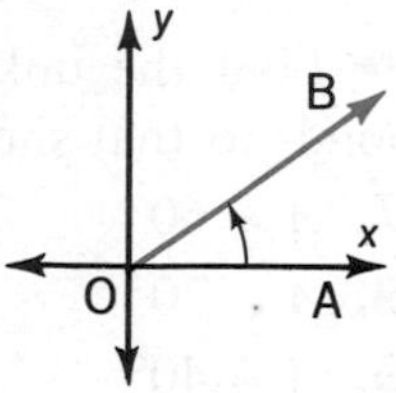

Sketch an angle AOB of measure θ in standard position for

3. $\theta = 120°$.
4. $\theta = -120°$.
5. $\theta = 170°$.
6. $\theta = -300°$.
7. $P(2, -1)$ is on $\overrightarrow{OB}$.
8. $P(-2, -3)$ is on $\overrightarrow{OB}$.
9. Explain what it means for two angles to be "coterminal."

Objective: *To define radian.*

10. Define radian in your own words.

Objective: *Given an angle measured in radians or in degrees, to convert one to the other.*

11. What is the basic relationship relating radians and degrees?

Convert the following degrees to radians.

12. 120° **13.** −60° **14.** 52° **15.** 385°

Convert the following radians to degrees.

16. $\frac{\pi}{2}$ **17.** $\frac{-11\pi}{6}$ **18.** $\frac{2\pi}{9}$ **19.** $3\frac{1}{2}\pi$

Objective: *To define the trigonometric functions in terms of the radius vector r and the coordinates of P(x, y) on the terminal side of an angle of measure θ.*

▬ Define each of the following trigonometric functions.

20. $\sin \theta$ **21.** $\cos \theta$ **22.** $\tan \theta$

23. $\cot \theta$ **24.** $\sec \theta$ **25.** $\csc \theta$

Objective: *To describe the relationship between trigonometric functions and circular functions.*

26. How are trigonometric functions related to circular functions? Include in your discussion comments on the differences in definitions and in domains.

Objective: *To use the trigonometric functions to solve acute right triangles.*

▬ Find the unknown parts of the triangle. Notation used corresponds to that shown in the figure at the right.

27. $A = 60°$ $a = 3$ $b = \underline{\ ?\ }$

28. $A = 70°$ $a = 3$ $c = \underline{\ ?\ }$

29. $A = 40°$ $b = 3$ $c = \underline{\ ?\ }$

30. $a = 3$ $b = 5$ $A = \underline{\ ?\ }$

31. $a = 1$ $b = 2$ $c = \underline{\ ?\ }$

32. The angle of elevation to the top of a hill from a point 300 yards from its base is 42°. Find the height of the hill to the nearest ten yards.

33. From an airplane 2 miles higher than the control tower of the airfield, the angle of depression to the control tower is 17°. Find the ground distance to the tower. Express the ground distance to the nearest half mile.

Objective: *To cite and apply the sum and difference identities for sine and cosine.*

▬ Complete each identity.

34. $\sin (\alpha + \beta) = \underline{\ ?\ }$ **35.** $\sin (\alpha - \beta) = \underline{\ ?\ }$

36. $\cos (\alpha - \beta) = \underline{\ ?\ }$ **37.** $\cos (\alpha + \beta) = \underline{\ ?\ }$

▬ Use the identities in 34–37 to complete the following.

38. $\sin (\pi - \alpha) = \underline{\ ?\ }$ **39.** $\cos (\pi + \alpha) = \underline{\ ?\ }$

40. $\sin 2\alpha = \sin (\alpha + \alpha) = \underline{\ ?\ }$ **41.** $\cos 2\alpha = \cos (\alpha + \alpha) = \underline{\ ?\ }$

CHAPTER TEST

1. Make a sketch of an angle of measure $-50°$ in standard position.
    a. What is the direction of rotation?
    b. In what quadrant is the angle?
    c. Label the initial and terminal sides.

2. Angle AOB has measure $-145°$ and is in standard position. List the measures of three angles coterminal to $\angle AOB$. Include at least one positive measure and one negative measure.

3. Change the following degree measures to radian measures.
    a. $72°$ b. $-480°$ c. $10°$

4. Change the following radian measures to degree measures.
    a. $\frac{5\pi}{18}$ b. $\frac{-15\pi}{4}$ c. 2

5. Given $P(x, y)$ with $r = OP$. Define each of the following trigonometric functions in terms of x, y and r. See the figure.
    a. $\sin \theta$ b. $\cos \theta$
    c. $\tan \theta$ d. $\cot \theta$
    e. $\sec \theta$ f. $\csc \theta$

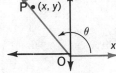

6. Complete each of the following identities.
    a. $\sin^2 \theta + \cos^2 \theta =$ _____.
    b. $\sin (\alpha + \beta) =$ _____.
    c. $\sin (\alpha - \beta) =$ _____.
    d. $\cos (\alpha + \beta) =$ _____.   e. $\cos (\alpha - \beta) =$ _____.

7. Prove that $\sin (\pi - \theta) = \sin \theta$.

8. Find the exact value of $\cos (15°)$ without tables.

9. Find the exact value of $\sin \frac{\pi}{8}$ without tables.

10. Find the exact value of $\tan 75°$ without tables.

11. A forest ranger spots a fire while on lookout in his 150 foot tower. The angle of depression is $4°$. How far from the base of the tower is the fire?

12. Convert the product $2 \cos 9x \sin 3x$ to a sum or difference.

13. Use the tables to find approximate values for the following.
    a. $\sin (139°)$ b. $\tan (193°)$
    c. $\cos (-21°)$ d. $\tan (311°)$

14. A hunter spies a mountain goat on a cliff 250 feet higher than his position. If the angle of elevation is $20°$, what is the distance from the man to the goat?

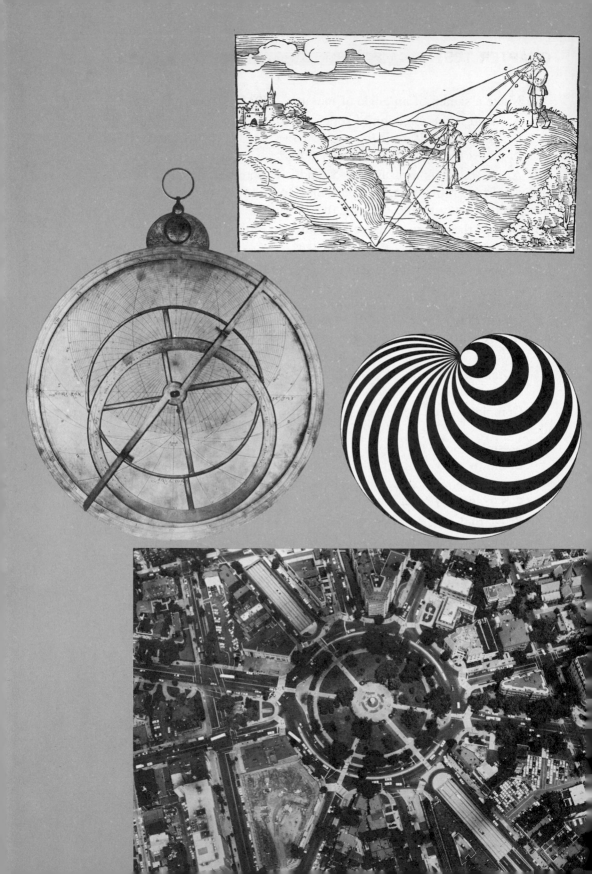

CHAPTER 4
APPLYING TRIGONOMETRY

Now that you have studied the basic concepts of trigonometry, you will find that there are many situations in which your knowledge can be applied. Sometimes you may want to find the distance between two places which is not directly measurable. A combination of trigonometry and surveyor's instruments is useful.

The surveyors pictured at the top of the opposite page are finding the distance across a river by using similar triangles and special measuring equipment. The picture at the center left on the opposite page shows a surveyor's instrument, called an astrolabe, that dates from 1575. This instrument is used for finding the location of planets and stars.

At other times your problem might involve describing how to go from one place to another that is not in sight.

In the aerial view of Washington D.C., pictured at the bottom of the opposite page, notice that all the streets radiate from the center of the picture. To describe where a particular house or building is located you could first choose one of the radiating streets as a "reference street" and then describe any other street by the counterclockwise angle that it forms with the reference street. Then by knowing the distance from the angle's vertex to any point on the street you could describe exactly where a particular house is located. This is the basic idea behind *polar coordinates*—to locate a position by using both a distance along a line and the angle formed by that line and some reference line.

Polar coordinates are also useful in graphing certain shapes that are difficult to graph using rectangular coordinates. An example is the *cardioid*, the heart-shaped figure that appears opposite as a piece of Op art. You will find other examples of polar graphs in this chapter.

4-1   Law of Sines

In Section 3–5 you learned to use trigonometric functions to solve right triangles. Trigonometry is also useful in solving triangles which contain no right angle. A major relation used in such cases is the **Law of Sines.** The following example illustrates the Law of Sines.

EXAMPLE 1.   John wishes to determine the width of Perch Lake from point A to point B. The measures of sides and angles of $\triangle ABC$ are as given in the figure. To the nearest foot, how far is it from A to B?

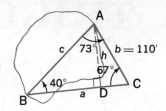

John's first thought is to construct a perpendicular from A to $\overline{BC}$. He does this, but notes that he cannot measure it directly. He notices that

$$\sin B = \frac{h}{c} \quad (\text{in } \triangle ADB)$$

and

$$\sin C = \frac{h}{b} \quad (\text{in } \triangle ADC).$$

Thus

$$h = c \sin B = b \sin C$$

or

$$\frac{b}{\sin B} = \frac{c}{\sin C}. \qquad \qquad 1$$

Since the measures of $\angle B$, $\angle C$, and b are known to John, he uses **1** to calculate the distance c from A to B as follows.

$$\frac{110}{\sin 40°} = \frac{c}{\sin 67°} \qquad \text{and} \qquad \frac{110 \cdot \sin 67°}{\sin 40°} = c$$

Thus

$$c = \frac{110(0.9205)}{0.6428} \qquad \text{(from the table).}$$

Consequently

$$c \approx 158' \text{ to the nearest foot.}$$

In Example 1 you saw part of the Law of Sines used to determine the distance from A to B. In complete form the Law of Sines is stated as follows.

Theorem 4–1 (The Law of Sines) In any triangle, the measures of the sides are proportional to the sines of the measures of the angles opposite them. In $\triangle ABC$,

$$\frac{a}{\sin A} = \frac{b}{\sin B} = \frac{c}{\sin C}.$$

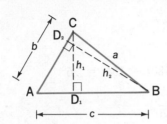
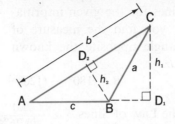

Proof: Consider two cases.

Case 1:

Each angle of $\triangle ABC$ is an acute angle. h_1 and h_2 are the measures of the altitudes from C and B respectively.

In right triangles ACD_1 and BCD_1, $\frac{h_1}{b} = \sin A$ and $\frac{h_1}{a} = \sin B$.

Thus $\qquad \dfrac{b}{\sin B} = \dfrac{a}{\sin A} \qquad$ **i.**

In right triangles ABD_2 and CBD_2, $\frac{h_2}{c} = \sin A$ and $\frac{h_2}{a} = \sin C$.

Thus $\qquad \dfrac{a}{\sin A} = \dfrac{c}{\sin C} \qquad$ **ii.**

Case 2:

$\angle B$ in $\triangle ABC$ is obtuse. h_1 and h_2 are the measures of the altitudes from C and B respectively.

In right triangles ACD_1 and BCD_1, $\frac{h_1}{b} = \sin A$ and $\frac{h_1}{a} = \sin (180 - B)$. Since you know $\sin (180 - B) = \sin B$, it follows

that $\qquad \dfrac{b}{\sin B} = \dfrac{a}{\sin A} \qquad$ **iii.**

In right triangles ABD_2 and CBD_2, $\frac{h_2}{c} = \sin A$ and $\frac{h_2}{a} = \sin C$.

Thus $\qquad \dfrac{a}{\sin A} = \dfrac{c}{\sin C} \qquad$ **iv.**

Consequently

$$\frac{a}{\sin A} = \frac{b}{\sin B} = \frac{c}{\sin C}$$

for acute angled triangles.

Consequently

$$\frac{a}{\sin A} = \frac{b}{\sin B} = \frac{c}{\sin C}$$

for triangles with an obtuse angle.

The two arguments establish the Law of Sines for acute and obtuse triangles. Demonstrate that it is also valid for right triangles.

EXAMPLE 2. If, in $\triangle ABC$, $A = 34°$, $C = 120°$ and $b = 200$ feet, how long are sides BC and AB?

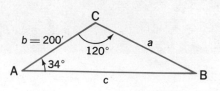

In order to apply the Law of Sines for the given information, you find the measure of the angle opposite the known side b.

$$B = 180° - (120° + 34) = 180° - 154° = 26°$$

By the Law of Sines

$$\frac{200}{\sin 26°} = \frac{c}{\sin 120°}.$$

Solving for c,

$$c = \frac{200 \sin 120°}{\sin 26°}$$

$$= \frac{200 \sin 60°}{\sin 26°} \qquad \text{(Why?)}$$

$$\approx \frac{200(.8660)}{.4384}$$

$$\approx 395 \text{ feet}$$

Now try these

1. If in $\triangle ABC$, $\angle C = 90°$, is the Law of Sines valid?

2. Solve $\triangle ABC$, given $\angle B = 40°$, $\angle C = 45°$ and $BC = 10$.

Answers: **1.** The Law of Sines is applicable to all triangles.
2. $\angle A = 95°$, $b = 6.452$, $c = 7.098$

Checkpoint

What data must be known about a triangle in order to use the Law of Sines to solve it?

Exercises

A ━ Solve each triangle. As is customary, a, b, and c refer to the measures of the sides opposite angles A, B, and C, respectively.

1. $A = 71°$, $B = 42°$, $c = 15$ **2.** $A = 71°$, $a = 20$, $C = 62°$

3. $B = 41°$, $C = 130°$, $a = 10$ **4.** $A = 65°$, $a = 30$, $b = 20$

5. $C = 50° 20'$, $B = 39° 40'$, $c = 25$

6. $A = 90°$, $B = 40°$, $b = 12$

7. $a = 15$, $b = 20$, $B = 100°$

8. $a = 12$, $B = 110°$, $C = 35°$

— Prove that each identity is true for any triangle ABC.

9. $\dfrac{a}{b} = \dfrac{\sin A}{\sin B}$

10. $\dfrac{a - b}{b} = \dfrac{\sin A - \sin B}{\sin B}$

B 11. Two light houses at points A and B on the coast of Maine are 40 miles apart. Each has visual contact with a freighter at point C. If $\angle CAB$ measures 20° 30′ and $\angle CBA$ measures 115°, how far is the freighter from A? from B?

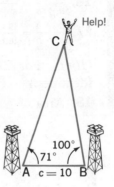
Help!

12. Two ranger stations located 10 miles apart receive a distress call from a camper. Electronic equipment allows them to determine that the camper is at an angle of 71° from the first station and 100° from the second, each angle having as one side the line of the stations. Which station is closer to the camper? How far away is it?

13. To find the height of a tree standing at point C across the Huron River from point A, a base line 200 feet long is established on one side of the river. The measure of $\angle BAC$ was found to be 53° and that of $\angle CBA$ was 74° 10′. The angle of elevation of the top of the tree from A measures 12°. What is the height of the tree? See the figure at the left below.

14. What is the length of a side of a regular octagon if a diagonal is 15 inches long? See the figure at the right below.

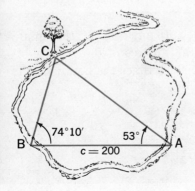

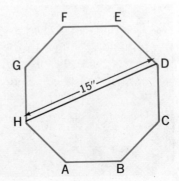

15. A tower 80 feet high stands on a cliff. From the top and bottom of the tower, the angles of depression to a ship are 18° and 14° respectively.

    a. What is the distance of the ship from the foot of the tower?

    b. What is the distance of the ship from the foot of the cliff?

    c. How high is the cliff?

C ▬ Prove that each identity is true for any triangle *ABC*.

16. $\dfrac{a - b}{a + b} = \dfrac{\sin A - \sin B}{\sin A + \sin B}$

17. $\dfrac{a + b}{a - b} = \dfrac{\tan \frac{1}{2}(A + B)}{\tan \frac{1}{2}(A - B)}$

(*Hint:* For Exercise 17, use Exercise 16 and the Sum-Product Identities.)

18. Area of $\triangle ABC = \frac{1}{2}a \cdot b \sin C$.

4–2   Law of Cosines

The Law of Sines may be used to solve any triangle for which you are given

    1. two angles and any one side.

The Law of Sines is of no use when you are given

    2. three sides, or

    3. two sides and their included angle.

For data as given in 2 and 3 the **Law of Cosines** is required.

Theorem 4–2 (The Law of Cosines) In any triangle, the square of a side is equal to the sum of the squares of the other sides minus twice the product of these sides times the cosine of the measure of their included angle. In $\triangle ABC$

$$a^2 = b^2 + c^2 - 2\,bc \cos A$$

$$b^2 = a^2 + c^2 - 2\,ac \cos B$$

$$c^2 = a^2 + b^2 - 2\,ab \cos C.$$

Proof: There are two cases to consider: 1. $\triangle ABC$ is acute, and 2. $\triangle ABC$ is obtuse. Only the proof of 2 is given.

Suppose $\triangle ABC$ is obtuse and $\overline{CD} \perp \overline{AD}$.

In $\triangle CDB$,

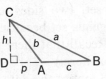

$$a^2 = h^2 + (c + p)^2$$
$$= h^2 + c^2 + 2cp + p^2. \qquad \textbf{1}$$

In $\triangle CAD$

$$h^2 = b^2 - p^2. \qquad \textbf{2}$$

Substituting for h^2 in **1**

$$a^2 = b^2 + c^2 + 2cp. \qquad \textbf{3}$$

The measure of $\angle CAD$ is θ, and $\cos \theta = \frac{p}{b}$ from which $p = b \cos \theta$. Notice that $\angle CAD$ is a supplement to $\angle A$; hence

$$\cos \theta = \cos (180° - A) = -\cos A,$$

from which

$$p = -b \cos A.$$

Substituting for p in **3**,

$$a^2 = b^2 + c^2 - 2bc \cos A.$$

EXAMPLE 1. Given $\triangle ABC$ with $A = 40°$, $b = 10$, $c = 20$. Solve the triangle.

From the Law of Cosines

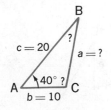

$$\begin{aligned}
a^2 &= b^2 + c^2 - 2b \cdot c \cos A \\
&= (10)^2 + (20)^2 - 2 \cdot 10 \cdot 20 \cdot (0.7660) \\
&= 100 + 400 - 400(0.7660) \\
&= 500 - 306.4 \\
&= 193.6 \\
a &= \sqrt{193.6} \approx 13.9
\end{aligned}$$

B may be found by using the Law of Sines:

$$\sin B = \frac{b \sin A}{a}$$

and

$$C = 180° - (A + B).$$

Carry out the details and compare your results with $B \approx 27° 30'$, $C \approx 112° 30'$.

Notice that in applying either the Law of Cosines or the Law of Sines the data must include three parts of the triangle. Three types of data sets were indicated at the beginning of this section. A fourth data set, two sides and an angle opposite either side, is called the **ambiguous set** because there may be two, one, or no triangle satisfying it. (Recall that there is no SSA congruence theorem. The situation is similar here.)

Suppose the data set includes A, b and a. The situations pictured below may result for $A < 90°$ and for $A \geq 90°$.

$A < 90°$

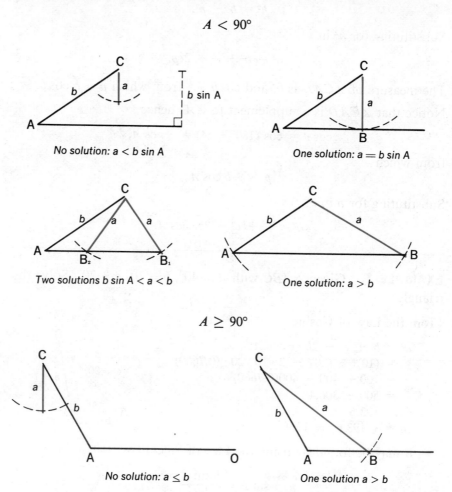

No solution: $a < b \sin A$

One solution: $a = b \sin A$

Two solutions $b \sin A < a < b$

One solution: $a > b$

$A \geq 90°$

No solution: $a \leq b$

One solution $a > b$

The Law of Sines may be used to solve the triangle for which the data set is ambiguous, but first you must determine whether a solution exists. The following example will illustrate the case where there are two solutions.

EXAMPLE 2. Given $\triangle ABC$ with $A = 30°$, $a = 15$, $b = 20$, find B and c.

$$\sin 30° = \tfrac{1}{2} \quad \text{and} \quad b \sin 30° = 10$$

Hence

$$b \sin 30° < a < b \qquad (10 < 15 < 20)$$

and there are two solutions.

Solution 1

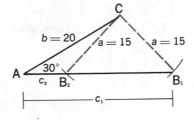

$$\frac{a}{\sin 30°} = \frac{b}{\sin B_1} \quad \text{or} \quad \frac{15}{\tfrac{1}{2}} = \frac{20}{\sin B_1}$$

Thus, $\sin B_1 = \tfrac{10}{15} = \tfrac{2}{3}$,
and $B_1 \approx 41° 50'$.
The measure of $\angle ACB_1 \approx 108° 10'$
and

$$
\begin{aligned}
c &\approx \frac{\sin (108° \ 10') \cdot 15}{\sin 30°} \\
&\approx \sin (71° \ 50') \cdot 30 \\
&\approx (0.9502) \cdot 30 \\
&\approx 28.5.
\end{aligned}
$$

Solution 2

Since $\angle AB_2C$ and $\angle CB_2B_1$ are supplementary and $\angle CB_2B_1 = \angle CB_1B_2$, the measure of $\angle AB_2C$ is $138° 10'$. The measure of $\angle ACB_2 = 180° - (30° + 138° \ 10') = 11° \ 50'$.

Consequently

$$\frac{c}{\sin C} = \frac{a}{\sin A}$$

or

$$c = \frac{\sin (11° \ 50') \cdot 15}{\sin 30°}$$

$$
\begin{aligned}
c &\approx (0.2051)(30) \\
&\approx 6.2
\end{aligned}
$$

Now try these

1. In $\angle ABC$ it is given that $a = 6$, $b = 4$, and $c = 5$. Find the approximate measure of the angles.

2. The lengths of the sides of a triangle are 8, 9, and 13. Without using tables, determine whether the largest angle is acute or obtuse.

Answers: **1.** $A \approx 82° \ 49'$ $B \approx 41° \ 25'$ $C \approx 55° \ 46'$
2. The largest angle is obtuse. (cos θ is negative.)

1. State the Law of Cosines.

2. State the information that must be given in order to solve a triangle by the Law of Sines.

3. State the information that must be given to solve a triangle by the Law of Cosines.

4. The various possibilities of three given parts in a triangle are
   a. *AAA*   b. *ASA*
   c. *SSA*   d. *AAS*
   e. *SAS*   f. *SSS*.

Which of these do not give unique solutions? Why?

Exercises

A ▬ Use the Law of Cosines to solve each of the following.

1. In $\triangle ABC$, $a = 5$, $b = 8$, $C = 40°$. Find c.
2. In $\triangle ABC$, $b = 7$, $c = 10$, $A = 51°$. Find a.
3. In $\triangle ABC$, $a = 10$, $c = 15$, $B = 171°$. Find b.
4. In $\triangle ABC$, $a = 3$, $b = 7$, $c = 5$. Find A, B, and C.
5. In $\triangle ABC$, $b = 9$, $c = 11$, $A = 123°$. Find a.
6. In $\triangle ABC$, $a = 8$, $b = 6$, $C = 60°$. Find c.
7. In $\triangle ABC$, $a = 9$, $c = 5$, $B = 120°$. Find b.
8. In $\triangle ABC$, $a = 1$, $b = 2$, $c = 2$. Find A, B, and C.

▬ Indicate whether a solution exists and if so the number of solutions for each set of data. Do not solve.

9. $a = 2$, $b = 3$, $c = 6$
10. $C = 17°$, $a = 10$, $c = 11$
11. $B = 71°$, $a = 5$, $c = 275$
12. $A = 20°$, $a = 7$, $b = 20$
13. $A = 41°$, $B = 160°$, $a = 10$
14. $C = 30°$, $b = 10$, $c = 4$
15. $A = 60°$, $b = 2$, $a = \sqrt{3}$
16. $A = 90°$, $a = 20$, $b = 19$
17. $B = 140°$, $a = 3$, $b = 2$
18. $C = 120°$, $b = 14$, $c = 13$

B **19.** Two steamships leave the same port simultaneously, one traveling 10 knots and the other 8 knots. At the end of two hours they are 15 nautical miles apart. What was the measure of the angle between their courses? (Express the measure of angle to the nearest 10′. 1 knot = 1 nautical mile per hour.) See the figure below.

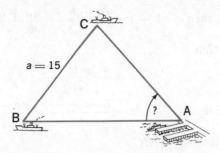

20. Two jet aircraft leave an airport at the same time. The course of the first is 160° east of north while the course of the second is 70° west of north. If the first travels 500 mph and the second 600 mph, what is the distance between them at the end of 3 hours? See the figure below.

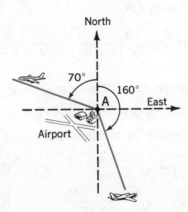

21. A man hikes 6 miles due north, then turns to the right and hikes 9 miles. If the angle determined by his initial course and his final position measures 40°, through how many degrees did he turn when he turned to the right? If the angle determined by his initial course and his final position is 60°, through how many degrees did he turn when he turned to the right?

22. The radius of a circle is 20 inches, and two radii OX and OY form an angle which measures 115°. How long is the chord XY?

23. Two sides and a diagonal of a parallelogram measure 7, 9, and 15 respectively. Find the measures of the angles of the parallelogram.

24. Show that if

$$t = \frac{a^2 + b^2 - c^2}{2ab}$$

then $\quad 1 + t = \frac{(a + b + c)(a + b - c)}{2ab}$

25. Show that if

$$t = \frac{a^2 + b^2 - c^2}{2ab}$$

then $\quad 1 - t = \frac{(-a + b + c)(a - b + c)}{2ab}$

26. Show that in $\triangle ABC$

$$1 + \cos C = \frac{(a + b + c)(a + b - c)}{2ab}$$

27. Show that in $\triangle ABC$

$$1 - \cos C = \frac{(-a + b + c)(a - b + c)}{2ab}$$

28. Show that in $\triangle ABC$

$$\tan \frac{C}{2} = \sqrt{\frac{(-a + b + c)(a - b + c)}{(a + b + c)(a + b - c)}}$$

C **29.** The *semiperimeter* s of a triangle with sides measuring a, b, and c is defined by $s = \frac{a + b + c}{2}$. Let $p = \sqrt{\frac{(s - a)(s - b)(s - c)}{s}}$ and use Exercises 26–28 to show that

i. $\sin \left(\frac{C}{2}\right) = \sqrt{\frac{(s - a)(s - b)}{ab}}$. **ii.** $\cos \left(\frac{C}{2}\right) = \sqrt{\frac{s(s - c)}{ab}}$.

iii. $\tan \left(\frac{C}{2}\right) = \sqrt{\frac{(s - a)(s - b)}{s(s - c)}}$. **iv.** $\tan \left(\frac{C}{2}\right) = \frac{p}{s - c}$.

30. Prove that the sum of the squares of the diagonals of a parallelogram is equal to the sum of the squares of the lengths of the four sides.

31. Show that in $\triangle ABC$

$$\sin C = \frac{2}{ab} \sqrt{s(s - a)(s - b)(s - c)}.$$

$$\left(Hint: \quad \sin C = 2 \sin \left(\frac{C}{2}\right) \cdot \cos \left(\frac{C}{2}\right).\right)$$

4-3 Area

You will recall that if K represents the area of a triangle, then the area formula is

$$K = \tfrac{1}{2}b \cdot h \qquad\qquad \mathbf{1}$$

where b and h are measures of one side and the altitude to that side. Formula **1** may be used to obtain other expressions for the area when given specific sets of data.

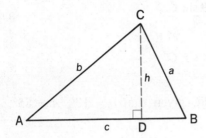 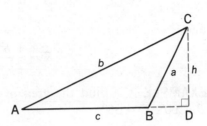

Data Set I: Given the measures of two sides and the included angle. Suppose you are given A, b and c. There are two cases to consider: $\triangle ABC$ is acute or $\triangle ABC$ is obtuse. In either case the area K is

$$K = \tfrac{1}{2}ch. \qquad\qquad \mathbf{2}$$

But $h = b \sin A$ in either case; hence

$$K = \tfrac{1}{2}cb \sin A. \qquad\qquad \mathbf{3}$$

Similarly

$$K = \tfrac{1}{2}ab \sin C \qquad\qquad \mathbf{4}$$

and

$$K = \tfrac{1}{2}ac \sin B. \qquad\qquad \mathbf{5}$$

Formulas **3–5** may be used to calculate the area of any triangle given two sides and their included angle.

EXAMPLE 1. Find the area of $\triangle ABC$ given that $B = 40°$, $a = 5'$, $c = 10'$. From formula **5**

$$K = \tfrac{1}{2}ac \sin B.$$

Consequently

$$
\begin{aligned}
K &= \tfrac{1}{2} \cdot 5 \cdot 10 \sin 40° \\
&= \tfrac{1}{2} \cdot 5 \cdot 10 \cdot (0.6428) \\
&= \tfrac{1}{2} \cdot 5 \cdot 6.428 \\
&= 5 \cdot 3.214 \\
&= 16.070 \approx 16 \text{ sq. ft.}
\end{aligned}
$$

Data Set II: Given the measures of one side and the angles. Suppose you know A, B and c. Then from formula 3

$$K = \tfrac{1}{2}bc \sin A. \qquad\qquad 6$$

But by the Law of Sines $\dfrac{b}{\sin B} = \dfrac{c}{\sin C}$ or $b = \dfrac{c \sin B}{\sin C}$.

Substituting in 6 you find

$$K = \frac{1}{2}\,\frac{c^2 \sin A \sin B}{\sin C}. \qquad\qquad 7$$

Similarly

$$K = \frac{1}{2}\,\frac{a^2 \sin B \sin C}{\sin A} \qquad\qquad 8$$

and

$$K = \frac{1}{2}\,\frac{b^2 \sin A \sin C}{\sin B}. \qquad\qquad 9$$

EXAMPLE 2.   Find the area of $\triangle ABC$ given that $a = 10'$, $A = 85°$, $B = 60°$, $C = 35°$.

From formula 8

$$K = \frac{1}{2}\,\frac{a^2 \sin B \sin C}{\sin A}$$

$$= \frac{1}{2}\,\frac{10^2(.8660)(.5736)}{(.9962)}$$

$$= 24.93$$

$$\approx 25 \text{ feet.}$$

Data Set III: Given the measures of the three sides. Suppose you are given a, b, and c. Let the *semiperimeter* s be defined by

$$s = \frac{a + b + c}{2}.$$

By formula 4

$$K = \tfrac{1}{2}ab \sin C \qquad\qquad 10$$

and by Exercise 31, Section 4–2

$$\sin C = \frac{2}{ab}\sqrt{s(s - a)(s - b)(s - c)}. \qquad\qquad 11$$

Substituting 11 in 10, you find

$$K = \tfrac{1}{2}ab\left(\frac{2}{ab}\right)\sqrt{s(s - a)(s - b)(s - c)}$$

$$= \sqrt{s(s - a)(s - b)(s - c)}. \qquad\qquad 12$$

Formula 12 is known as **Heron's Formula.**   (Also known as Hero's Formula.)

EXAMPLE 3. Find the area of $\triangle ABC$ if $a = 7$, $b = 8$, $c = 9$.

$$s = \frac{7 + 8 + 9}{2}$$
$$= 12$$

From **12**

$$K = \sqrt{12(12 - 7)(12 - 8)(12 - 9)}$$
$$= \sqrt{12(5)(4)(3)}$$
$$= 12\sqrt{5}.$$

Now try these

1. In $\triangle ABC$, $b = 281$, $c = 358$, and $A = 32° 20'$. Find K.

2. In $\triangle ABC$, $a = 496$, $b = 564$, and $c = 632$. Find K.

3. In $\triangle ABC$, $A = 29° 40'$, $B = 78° 50'$, $a = 69.7$. Find K.

Answers: **1.** $K \approx 26{,}900$ (sq. units)   **2.** $K \approx 134{,}000$ (sq. units)
     3. $K \approx 4570$ (sq. units)

Checkpoint

How do you find the area of a triangle when two sides and the angle opposite one of them are known?

Exercises

A — **1–12.** Find the area of the triangle or triangles (if any) satisfying the data sets in Exercises 7–18, Section 4–2.

13. Given: $K = 100$, $A = 36°$, $B = 74°$. Find b.

14. Given: $K = 50$, $A = 30°$, $b = 10$. Find c.

15. Given: $K = 50$, $a = 20$, $b = 10$, $C > 90°$. Find C.

16. The adjacent sides of a parallelogram measure 12 and 18 inches. If one angle measures 45°, find its area.

17. The sides of a rhombus measure 10 feet and one diagonal is 12 feet. Find the area.

18. The diagonals of a parallelogram have measures 60 and 40, and form an angle which measures 60°. Find the area.

B **19.** Find a formula for the area of an isosceles triangle with base b and base angles measuring θ. (Use formula **9**, page 168.)

20. In $\triangle ABC$ express the length h of the altitude to $\overline{AB}$ in terms of the lengths of the sides of the triangle. (Use formula **12**.)

21. Find an expression for the radius r of a circle inscribed in a triangle in terms of the area K and the semiperimeter s.

22. Given: $\triangle ABC$, circle O an escribed circle to $\triangle ABC$. Find an expression for the radius r of circle O in terms of K, s and the lengths of the sides of $\triangle ABC$. See figure below. (*Hint:* Area $\triangle ABC$ = Area $\triangle OCA$ + Area $\triangle OAB$ − Area $\triangle OBC$)

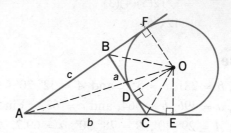

23. Show that the radius R of a circle circumscribed about a triangle ABC is given by

$$R = \frac{a}{2 \sin A} = \frac{b}{2 \sin B} = \frac{c}{2 \sin C}.$$

24. Use the results from Exercise 23 and

$$K = \frac{bc \sin A}{2}$$

to show that

$$R = \frac{abc}{4K}.$$

━━ Prove that in any $\triangle ABC$ each of the following is true.

25. $a \cos B + b \cos A = c$.

26. $a \cos B - b \cos A = \dfrac{a^2 - b^2}{c}$.   (The equation for Exercise 25 is useful.)

27. $2Rr = \dfrac{abc}{a + b + c}$. r is the radius of a circle inscribed in a triangle. (See Exercise 21.) R is the radius of a circle circumscribed about a triangle. (See Exercise 24.)

28. $K = \frac{1}{2}a^2 \dfrac{\sin B \sin C}{\sin (B + C)}$.

29. $K = ab \sin \left(\dfrac{C}{2}\right) \cos \left(\dfrac{C}{2}\right)$.   (See Exercises 29 and 31, Section 4–2.)

4-4 Finding Angles

If you were asked to find the values of x for which $\cos x = 2$, you would respond that the solution set is the empty set because the range of $\cos x$ is $\{-1 \le y \le 1\}$. However if asked to find the values of x for which $\cos x = \frac{\sqrt{2}}{2}$ you should respond that the solution set has infinitely many members. Why is this so?

You know $\cos \frac{\pi}{4} = \frac{\sqrt{2}}{2}$ and $\cos \left(-\frac{\pi}{4}\right) = \frac{\sqrt{2}}{2}$. Thus $\frac{\pi}{4}$ and $-\frac{\pi}{4}$ are elements of the solution set of $\cos x = \frac{\sqrt{2}}{2}$. You also know that $\cos (\theta \pm 2n\pi) = \cos \theta, n \in W, \theta \in R$.

Thus $\cos \left(\frac{\pi}{4} \pm 2n\pi\right) = \cos \frac{\pi}{4} = \frac{\sqrt{2}}{2}$ and $\cos \left(-\frac{\pi}{4} \pm 2n\pi\right) = \cos \left(-\frac{\pi}{4}\right) = \frac{\sqrt{2}}{2}$. It follows that the solution set of $\cos x = \frac{\sqrt{2}}{2}$ is the following.

$$\left\{ x : x = \frac{\pi}{4} \pm 2n\pi \quad \text{or} \quad x = -\frac{\pi}{4} \pm 2n\pi, \, n \in W \right\}$$

This infinite set is denoted **arc cos** $\left(\frac{\sqrt{2}}{2}\right)$ or **cos**$^{-1}\left(\frac{\sqrt{2}}{2}\right)$. Either expression may be read "the set of real numbers whose cosine is $\frac{\sqrt{2}}{2}$" or "arc cosine $\frac{\sqrt{2}}{2}$." If you think of x as representing the measure of an angle, then arc cos $\frac{\sqrt{2}}{2}$ is thought of as "the set of angle measures whose cosine is $\frac{\sqrt{2}}{2}$."

It should be noted that $\cos^{-1} \frac{\sqrt{2}}{2} \ne \left(\cos \frac{\sqrt{2}}{2}\right)^{-1}$. In the former expression the "-1" is part of the symbol for "arc cos." In the latter, the "-1" is an exponent and $\left(\cos \frac{\sqrt{2}}{2}\right)^{-1} = \frac{1}{\cos \frac{\sqrt{2}}{2}}$.

> In general, **arc cos x** is the set of real numbers y such that **$\cos y = x$.** In other words $y \in$ arc cos x if and only if $\cos y = x$.

The sets **arc sin x, arc tan x, arc cot x, arc sec x,** and **arc csc x** are defined in a similar manner.

EXAMPLE 1. Identify the members of the set arc $\tan \frac{\sqrt{3}}{3}$.

y is an element of arc $\tan \frac{\sqrt{3}}{3}$ if and only if $\tan y = \frac{\sqrt{3}}{3}$. Since $\tan \frac{\pi}{6} = \frac{\sqrt{3}}{3}$ and $\tan \frac{7\pi}{6} = \frac{\sqrt{3}}{3}$, $\frac{\pi}{6}$ and $\frac{7\pi}{6}$ are elements of arc $\tan \frac{\sqrt{3}}{3}$.

Since the tangent function is periodic with period π,

$$\tan\left(\frac{\pi}{6} \pm n\pi\right) = \frac{\sqrt{3}}{3}, \ n \in W.$$

When $n = 1$, $\frac{\pi}{6} + 1 \cdot \pi = \frac{7\pi}{6}$. Thus

$$\text{arc } \tan \frac{\sqrt{3}}{3} = \left\{ y : y = \frac{\pi}{6} \pm n\pi, \ n \in W \right\}$$

or

$$\text{arc } \tan \frac{\sqrt{3}}{3} = \{ y : y = 30° \pm n \cdot 180°, \ n \in W \} \qquad \text{(Why?)}$$

The key to identifying all the members of a set like arc $\sin x$ or arc $\cot x$ is to find the real numbers y such that $0 \leq y < 2\pi$ (or $0° \leq y < 360°$) and then use the period of the function to determine the remaining members.

An expression like "$\sin\left(\text{arc } \cos \frac{\sqrt{2}}{2}\right)$", read "sine arc cosine $\frac{\sqrt{2}}{2}$", or read as "the sine of a number whose cosine is $\frac{\sqrt{2}}{2}$" may sometimes be misinterpreted. $\text{Sin}\left(\text{arc } \cos \frac{\sqrt{2}}{2}\right)$ is used to denote the values of the sines of all numbers x for which $\cos x = \frac{\sqrt{2}}{2}$ is true. Even though there are infinitely many such x, usually there are only one or two values of an expression such as $\sin\left(\text{arc } \cos \frac{\sqrt{2}}{2}\right)$.

EXAMPLE 2. Evaluate $\sin\left(\text{arc } \cos \frac{\sqrt{2}}{2}\right)$.

You saw previously that

$$\text{arc } \cos \frac{\sqrt{2}}{2} = \left\{ x : x = \frac{\pi}{4} \pm 2n\pi \ \text{ or } \ x = \frac{-\pi}{4} \pm 2n\pi, \ n \in W \right\}.$$

Thus

$$\sin\left(\text{arc } \cos \frac{\sqrt{2}}{2}\right) = \sin\left(\frac{\pi}{4} \pm 2n\pi\right) \ \text{ or } \ \sin\left(\frac{-\pi}{4} \pm 2n\pi\right), \ n \in W$$

$$= \sin \frac{\pi}{4} \ \text{ or } \ \sin\left(\frac{-\pi}{4}\right) \qquad \text{(Why?)}$$

$$= \frac{\sqrt{2}}{2} \ \text{ or } \ \frac{-\sqrt{2}}{2}.$$

You may find it convenient to think of expressions such as arc tan 1 as sets of measures of angles. Then arc tan 1 is the set of measures of angles whose tangent is 1. Thinking this way can help you to evaluate expressions such as sec (arc tan 1) by drawing a figure. This is illustrated in Example 3.

EXAMPLE 3. Evaluate

$$\text{sec (arc tan 1)}.$$

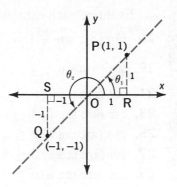

Arc tan 1 is the set of measures of angles whose tangent is 1. Thus $\tan \theta = 1$ and θ is the measure of an angle in Quadrant I or III. Also the points $P(1, 1)$ and $Q(-1, -1)$ are on the terminal sides of these angles. Complete the right triangles POR and QOS as shown in the figure. Since

$$\sec \theta = \frac{r}{x}, \qquad \sec \theta_1 = \frac{\sqrt{2}}{1},$$

and

$$\sec \theta_2 = \frac{\sqrt{2}}{-1}.$$

Hence

$$\text{sec (arc tan 1)} = \frac{\sqrt{2}}{1} \text{ or } \frac{-\sqrt{2}}{1}.$$

EXAMPLE 4. Find $\sin (\text{arc cos } \frac{5}{13})$.

If $\cos \theta = \frac{5}{13}$, then θ is the measure of an angle in Quadrant I or IV. Also $r = 13$ and $x = 5$, and applying the Pythagorean Theorem $y = 12$.

Thus, for the drawing,

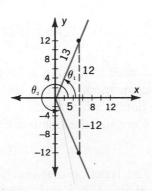

$$\sin \left(\text{arc cos } \frac{5}{13} \right) = \frac{12}{13} \text{ or } \frac{-12}{13}.$$

Exercises

A — Find the members of each of the following sets.

1. arc tan (-1) **2.** arc sin (-1) **3.** arc cos (-1)
4. arc sin 0   **5.** arc cos $\frac{1}{2}$ **6.** arc tan $\sqrt{3}$

7. arc cot $\sqrt{3}$ **8.** arc sec (-2) **9.** arc csc $\frac{2\sqrt{3}}{3}$

10. arc sin $(-\frac{1}{2})$ **11.** arc csc 1 **12.** arc cot 0

13. arc sin (0.6428)

14. arc sin $\frac{\sqrt{3}}{2} \cap$ arc cos $\left(\frac{-1}{2}\right)$

15. arc tan $(-1) \cup$ arc csc (-2)

▬ Evaluate each expression.

16. $\tan\left(\text{arc sin } \frac{-3}{5}\right)$ **17.** $\sin(\text{arc sin } \frac{4}{5})$ **18.** $\cos(\text{arc sec } 4)$

19. $\sec\left(\text{arc sin } \frac{-7}{25}\right)$ **20.** $\csc(\text{arc tan } \frac{1}{3})$

21. $\cot(\text{arc csc } \frac{25}{24})$ **22.** $\sin(\text{arc cos } \frac{1}{3})$

23. $\csc(\text{arc tan } [-4])$ **24.** $\cos(\text{arc cot } [-4])$

25. $\tan(\text{arc sin } u)\ 0 \le u < 1$ **26.** $\cos(\text{arc tan } u)\ u > 0$

27. $\sin(\text{arc cos } u)\ 0 \le u < 1$ **28.** $\cot(\text{arc cos } u)\ 0 \le u < 1$

29. $\sec(\text{arc tan } u)\ u \ge 0$ **30.** $\csc(\text{arc cos } u)\ 0 \le u < 1$

B Evaluate each expression.

31. $\cos(\text{arc sin } \frac{3}{5} + \text{arc tan } \frac{12}{13})$ [*Hint:* What is $\cos(\alpha + \beta)$?]

32. $\sin(\text{arc cos } \frac{3}{5} + \text{arc sec } 3)$

33. $\sin(2 \text{ arc sin } \frac{4}{5})$ [*Hint:* What is $\sin 2\theta$?]

34. $\cos(2 \text{ arc cot } \frac{5}{13})$

35. $\tan(2 \text{ arc sin } \frac{7}{25})$

36. $\tan(\frac{1}{2} \text{ arc cos } \frac{1}{2})$ [*Hint:* What is $\tan(\frac{1}{2}\theta)$?]

4–5 Inverse Circular Functions

Recall that if f is a function which maps the elements of U onto the elements of V, then the inverse of f is a relation g which may or may not be a function.

Consider the sine function:

$$\{(x, y) : y = \sin x\}.$$

The sine function maps each real number onto a unique real number y such that $-1 \le y \le 1$. The mapping which is the inverse of the sine function is

$$\{(x, y) : x = \sin y\}$$

or

$$\{(x, y) : y \in \text{arc sin } x\}.$$

Since arc sin x for each x such that $-1 \le x \le 1$ is an infinite set, the inverse of the sine function is not a function; it is a relation. By restricting the range of this relation to the set $\left\{\frac{-\pi}{2} \le y \le \frac{\pi}{2}\right\}$, you can pair each number x, $-1 \le x \le 1$, with a unique number y. The resulting mapping is a function.

The unique number y such that

$$y \in \text{arc sin } x, \quad \frac{-\pi}{2} \le y \le \frac{\pi}{2},$$

is called the **principal value of arc sin x** and is denoted as follows.

$$y = \textbf{Arc sin } x$$

The capital "A" on Arc denotes the principal value. The Arc sin function is

$$\{(x, y) : y = \text{Arc sin } x, \ |x| \le 1, \ x \in R\}.$$

The graphs of $y = \sin x$, $y = \text{arc sin } x$ and $y = \text{Arc sin } x$ are shown in the next figure, Arc sin x being shown in color.

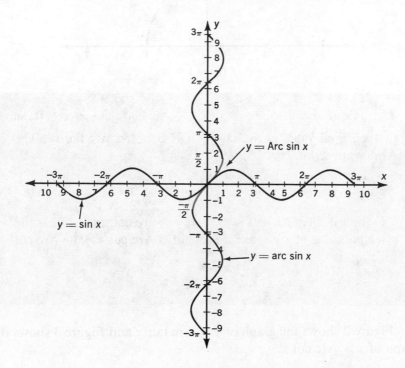

The graph of the function described by $y =$ Arc cos x is shown
below in Figure 1.

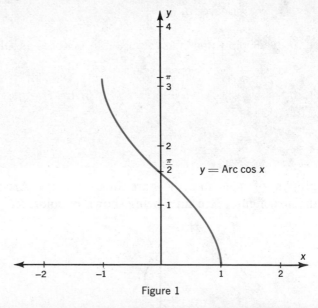

Figure 1

Figure 2 shows the graph of $y =$ Arc tan x and Figure 3 shows the
graph of $y =$ Arc cot x.

The graph of $y = \text{Arc tan } x$ is shown below.

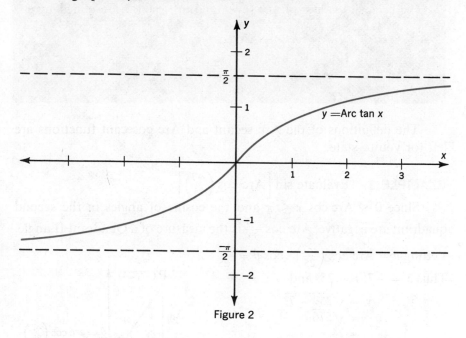

Figure 2

The graph of $y = \text{Arc cot } x$ is shown below.

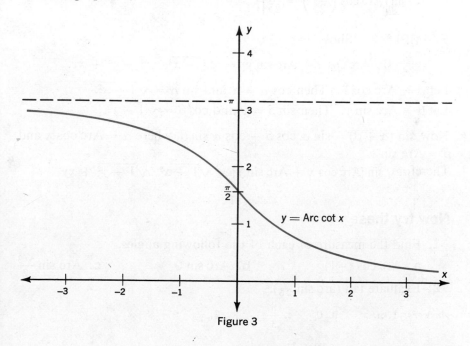

Figure 3

The **principal values of arc sec** x and **arc csc** x are defined by

$$\text{Arc sec } x = \text{Arc cos } \frac{1}{x}, \quad |x| \geq 1$$

$$\text{Arc csc } x = \text{Arc sin } \frac{1}{x}, \quad |x| \geq 1$$

The definitions of the Arc secant and Arc cosecant functions are left for you to state.

EXAMPLE 1. Evaluate $\sin\left[\text{Arc cos }\left(\frac{-7}{25}\right)\right]$.

Since $0 \leq \text{Arc cos } x \leq \pi$ and the cosine of angles in the second quadrant are negative, $\text{Arc cos } \frac{-7}{25}$ is the measure of a Quadrant II angle.

Letting $\theta = \text{Arc cos }\left(\frac{-7}{25}\right)$, $\cos \theta = \frac{-7}{25}$.

Thus $x = -7$, $r = 25$, and

$$y = \sqrt{25^2 - 7^2}$$
$$= \sqrt{576}$$
$$= 24.$$

Thus $\sin \theta = \frac{24}{25}$, and

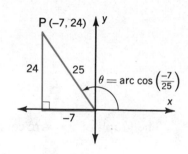

$$\sin\left[\text{Arc cos }\left(\frac{-7}{25}\right)\right] = \frac{24}{25}.$$

EXAMPLE 2. Show that

$$\sin\left[\text{Arc cos } x + \text{Arc sin } y\right] = \sqrt{1 - x^2} \cdot \sqrt{1 - y^2} + xy.$$

Let $\alpha = \text{Arc cos } x$. Then $\cos \alpha = x$ and $\sin \alpha = \sqrt{1 - x^2}$.
Let $\beta = \text{Arc sin } y$. Then $\sin \beta = y$ and $\cos \beta = \sqrt{1 - y^2}$.

Now $\sin(\alpha + \beta) = \sin \alpha \cos \beta + \cos \alpha \sin \beta$, where $\alpha = \text{Arc cos } x$ and $\beta = \text{Arc sin } y$.
Therefore, $\sin\left[\text{Arc cos } x + \text{Arc sin } y\right] = \sqrt{1 - x^2} \cdot \sqrt{1 - y^2} + xy$.

Now try these

1. Find the measure of each of the following angles.

  a. Arc cos (-1) **b.** Arc sin 0 **c.** Arc sin $\frac{\sqrt{3}}{2}$

2. Evaluate $\tan\left(\text{arc sin } \frac{7}{25}\right)$.

Answers: **1. a.** π **b.** 0 **c.** $\dfrac{\pi}{3}$ **2.** $\frac{7}{24}$

Checkpoint

1. How are the cosine and arc cosine functions related? Explain.

2. What is meant by the Principal Value of arc sin x? of arc cos x? of arc tan x?

Exercises

A ▬ Find the measure of each of the following angles.

1. Arc sin $\left(\frac{-\sqrt{2}}{2}\right)$ **2.** Arc cos $\frac{-4}{5}$ **3.** Arc tan (0.6009)

4. Arc cot (-1) **5.** Arc csc $\frac{2\sqrt{3}}{3}$ **6.** Arc sec (-2)

7. Arc sin $\left(\frac{1}{2}\right)$ **8.** Arc tan $\left(\frac{-\sqrt{3}}{3}\right)$ **9.** Arc cos 0.9272

▬ Evaluate each expression.

10. $\sin\left(\text{Arc cos }\frac{1}{3}\right)$ **11.** $\tan\left(\text{Arc tan }4\right)$

12. $\sin\left[\text{Arc tan }(-3)\right]$ **13.** $\sec\left(\text{Arc sin }\frac{1}{2}\right)$

14. $\csc\left[\text{Arc tan }(-4)\right]$ **15.** $\cot\left(\text{Arc cos }\frac{2}{3}\right)$

16. $\tan\left(\text{Arc sin }\frac{4}{7}\right)$ **17.** $\sin\left[\text{Arc cot }\left(\frac{-3}{4}\right)\right]$

18. $\cos\left[\text{Arc sin }(-\frac{1}{5})\right]$ **19.** $\cot\left[\text{Arc cos }\left(\frac{-11}{61}\right)\right]$

20. $\cos\left[\text{Arc tan }\left(\frac{-12}{5}\right)\right]$ **21.** $\sec\left(\text{Arc csc }4\right)$

B **22.** Sketch the graph of $y = \text{Arc sec } x$.

23. Sketch the graph of $y = \text{Arc csc } x$.

24. Show that Arc cot $x = \frac{\pi}{2} - \text{Arc tan } x$.

25. Show that $\cos(\text{Arc sin } u) = \sqrt{1 - u^2}$, $|u| \leq 1$.

26. Show that Arc tan $\frac{1}{2}$ + Arc tan $\frac{1}{3} = \frac{\pi}{4}$.

▬ Evaluate each of the following.

27. $\sin\left[\text{Arc cos }\frac{4}{5} + \frac{\pi}{2}\right]$

28. $\cos\left[\text{Arc cos }(-\frac{1}{2}) - \text{Arc sin }(\frac{3}{5})\right]$

29. $\sin\left[\text{Arc cos }(\frac{1}{2}) - \text{Arc sin }\frac{5}{13}\right]$

30. $\tan\left[\text{Arc sin }\frac{1}{\sqrt{10}} + \text{Arc cos }\left(\frac{-4}{5}\right)\right]$

31. $\cos\left[\text{Arc tan }\left(\frac{-4}{3}\right) - \text{Arc sin }(\frac{11}{61})\right]$

32. $\cot\left[\text{Arc cot }(\frac{2}{3}) + \text{Arc cot }(\frac{1}{3})\right]$

33. $\sin\left[2 \text{ Arc } \tan\left(\frac{-8}{15}\right)\right]$

34. $\cos\left[2 \text{ Arc } \sin\left(\frac{-4}{5}\right)\right]$

35. $\tan\left[2 \text{ Arc } \cot\left(\frac{24}{7}\right)\right]$

36. $\sin\left[\frac{1}{2} \text{ Arc } \tan\left(\frac{3}{5}\right)\right]$

37. $\cos\left[\frac{1}{2} \text{ Arc } \sin\left(\frac{-15}{17}\right)\right]$

38. $\tan\left[\frac{1}{2} \text{ Arc } \sec\left(\frac{-13}{5}\right)\right]$

C Prove each statement in the exercises below.

39. $\tan\left[\text{Arc } \tan a + \text{Arc } \tan 1\right] = \dfrac{1+a}{1-a}$

40. $\tan\left[\text{Arc } \tan b - \text{Arc } \tan a\right] = \dfrac{b-a}{1+ab}$

41. $\tan\left[\text{Arc } \cos a + \text{Arc } \sin b\right] = \dfrac{\sqrt{1-a^2}\cdot\sqrt{1-b^2}+ab}{a\sqrt{1-b^2}-b\sqrt{1-a^2}}$

42. $\sin\left[\text{Arc } \sin x + \text{Arc } \sin y\right] = x\sqrt{1-y^2}+y\sqrt{1-x^2}$

43. $\text{Arc } \sin \frac{3}{5} + \text{Arc } \cos \frac{5}{13} = \text{Arc } \sin \frac{63}{65}$

44. $\text{Arc } \tan\left(\frac{-3}{4}\right) + \text{Arc } \sin\left(\frac{-7}{25}\right) = \text{Arc } \cos \frac{3}{5}$

45. $2 \text{ Arc } \tan \frac{1}{3} + \text{Arc } \tan \frac{1}{7} = \dfrac{\pi}{4}$

46. $4 \text{ Arc } \tan \frac{1}{5} - \text{Arc } \tan (-5) = \dfrac{\pi}{2}$

47. $\text{Arc } \cos x + \text{Arc } \sin x = \dfrac{\pi}{2}$

48. $\text{Arc } \tan \frac{7}{4} + \text{Arc } \tan \frac{4}{7} = \dfrac{\pi}{2}$

4–6 Equations Involving Trigonometric Functions

Recall that an equation which is true for all replacements of the independent variable for which the statement is defined is an identity. An equation which is not an identity is a **conditional equation.** For example, $\sin \theta = \frac{1}{2}$ is a conditional equation. The solution set is

$$\left\{\theta : \theta = \frac{\pi}{6} \pm 2n\pi \quad or \quad \theta = \frac{5\pi}{6} \pm 2n\pi, \ n \in W\right\}.$$

Notice that the solution set is infinite.

A variety of techniques may be used to find the solution set of a conditional equation involving trigonometric (or circular) functions. You may need to use algebraic techniques such as factoring, or you may use a trigonometric identity. The symbol "$\vee$" will mean *or* and the symbol "$\wedge$" will mean *and* in the logical sense.

EXAMPLE 1. Solve $\sin 2x = 0$.

You know

$$\sin 2x = 2 \sin x \cos x.$$

Thus

$\sin 2x = 0$ is equivalent to (has the same solution set as)

$$2 \sin x \cos x = 0.$$

Consequently

$$\sin x = 0 \lor \cos x = 0.$$

When

$$\sin x = 0, \; x \in \{0 \pm n\pi\} = \text{arc sin } 0.$$

When

$$\cos x = 0, \; x \in \left\{\frac{\pi}{2} \pm n\pi\right\} = \text{arc cos } 0.$$

Thus the solution set of $\sin 2x = 0$ is

$$\left\{x : x = \pm n\pi \lor x = \frac{\pi}{2} \pm n\pi, \; n \in W\right\}.$$

In this section $n \in W$ will be omitted in specifying solution sets, for you know that n represents a whole number.

EXAMPLE 2. Solve $\sin 2x = 4 \sin x$.

In this example you can use an identity, and then factor. Notice that the solution set of one of the factors is ϕ.

$$\sin 2x = 4 \sin x \qquad \text{iff}$$
$$\sin 2x - 4 \sin x = 0 \qquad \text{iff}$$
$$2 \sin x \cos x - 4 \sin x = 0 \qquad \text{iff}$$
$$2 \sin x(\cos x - 2) = 0 \qquad \text{iff}$$
$$2 \sin x = 0 \qquad \lor \qquad \cos x - 2 = 0$$

Since $\sin 0 = \sin \pi = 0$,
the solution set of $2 \sin x = 0$ is

$$\{x : x = \pm n\pi\} = \text{arc sin } 0.$$

The solution set of $\cos x - 2 = 0$ is ϕ, because the range of $\cos x$ is $\{y : |y| \leq 1\}$. The solution set of $\sin 2x = 4 \sin x$ is

$$\{x : x = \pm n\pi\} \cup \phi = \{x : x = \pm n\pi\}.$$

EXAMPLE 3. Solve $\sin^2 x - \cos^2 x = 0$.

In this example you can use an alternative form of the identity $\sin^2 x + \cos^2 x = 1$, substitute and then factor in order to solve the trigonometric equation.

From

$$\sin^2 x + \cos^2 x = 1,$$

it follows that

$$\cos^2 x = 1 - \sin^2 x.$$

Thus

$$\sin^2 x - \cos^2 x = 0 \qquad \text{iff}$$

$$\sin^2 x - (1 - \sin^2 x) = 0 \qquad \text{iff}$$

$$2\sin^2 x - 1 = 0 \qquad \text{iff}$$

$$\sin^2 x = \tfrac{1}{2} \qquad \text{iff}$$

$$\sin x = \frac{1}{\sqrt{2}} \ \lor \ \sin x = -\frac{1}{\sqrt{2}} \cdot$$

First, each part of the *or* statement will be solved and then the two solutions will be combined and simplified to form the final solution. The solution set of $\sin x = \dfrac{1}{\sqrt{2}}$ is

$$\left\{ x : x = \frac{\pi}{4} \pm 2n\pi \ \lor \ x = \frac{3\pi}{4} \pm 2n\pi \right\} = \text{arc sin } \frac{1}{\sqrt{2}} \cdot$$

The solution set of $\sin x = \dfrac{-1}{\sqrt{2}}$ is

$$\left\{ x : x = \frac{5\pi}{4} \pm 2n\pi \ \lor \ x = \frac{7\pi}{4} \pm 2n\pi \right\} = \text{arc sin } \frac{-1}{\sqrt{2}} \cdot$$

The solution set of $\sin^2 x - \cos^2 x = 0$ is

$$\left\{ x : x = \frac{\pi}{4} \pm 2n\pi \ \lor \ x = \frac{3\pi}{4} + 2n\pi \right\}$$

$$\cup \left\{ x : x = \frac{5\pi}{4} \pm 2n\pi \ \lor \ x = \frac{7\pi}{4} \pm 2n\pi \right\} \cdot$$

This can be written more compactly as

$$\left\{ x : x = \frac{\pi}{4} \pm \frac{n\pi}{2} \right\} \cdot$$

Why is this true?

EXAMPLE 4. Solve $2 \sin^2 x - \cos x - 1 = 0$.

Use the identity

$$\sin^2 x + \cos^2 x = 1$$

in the following form.

$\sin^2 x = 1 - \cos^2 x$	iff
$2 \sin^2 x - \cos x - 1 = 0$	iff
$2(1 - \cos^2 x) - \cos x - 1 = 0$	iff
$-2 \cos^2 x - \cos x + 1 = 0$	iff
$2 \cos^2 x + \cos x - 1 = 0$	iff
$(2 \cos x - 1)(\cos x + 1) = 0$	iff
$(2 \cos x - 1 = 0) \vee (\cos x + 1 = 0)$	iff
$(\cos x = \frac{1}{2}) \vee (\cos x = -1)$	

The solution sets are

a. $\cos x = \frac{1}{2}$ $\left\{ x : x = \frac{\pi}{3} \pm 2n\pi \vee x = \frac{5\pi}{3} \pm 2n\pi \right\} = \text{arc cos } \frac{1}{2}$.

b. $\cos x = -1$ $\{ x : x = \pi \pm 2n\pi \} = \text{arc cos } (-1)$.

The solution set of $2 \sin^2 x - \cos x - 1 = 0$ is

$$\left\{ x : x = \frac{\pi}{3} \pm 2n\pi \vee x = \frac{5\pi}{3} \pm 2n\pi \vee x = \pi \pm 2n\pi \right\}.$$

When the solution set of an equation is not readily identified explicitly, the *arc-trigonometric* notation is used.

EXAMPLE 5. Solve $\tan^2 x = 5$.

$\tan^2 x = 5$	iff
$\tan x = \sqrt{5} \vee \tan x = -\sqrt{5}$	iff
$\tan x \approx 2.2361 \vee \tan x = -2.2361$	

The solution set of $\tan x \approx 2.2361$ is

$$\{ x : x \in \text{arc tan } 2.2361 \}.$$

The solution set of $\tan x \approx -2.2361$ is

$$\{ x : x \in \text{arc tan } (-2.2361) \}.$$

The solution set of $\tan^2 x = 5$ is most easily denoted as:

$$\{ x : x \in \text{arc tan } 2.2361 \vee x \in \text{arc tan } (-2.2361) \}$$

Exercises

A ━━ Solve each of the following equations.

1. $2 \sin x + \sqrt{3} = 0$

2. $\sqrt{3} \cot x + 1 = 0$

3. $\sqrt{2} \cos x - 1 = 0$

4. $2 \tan x - 4 = 0$

5. $\sqrt{3} \sec x + 2 = 0$

6. $3 \cos x - 1 = 0$

7. $4 \sin^2 x = 1$

8. $6 \cos^2 x + 5 \cos x + 1 = 0$

9. $3 \sin^2 x - \cos^2 x = 0$

10. $2 \tan^2 x - 3 \sec x + 3 = 0$

11. $2 \tan x - 2 \cot x = -3$

12. $\sqrt{3} \csc^2 x + 2 \csc x = 0$

13. $\cos 2x + \sin x = 1$

14. $\sin 2x + \cos x = 0$

15. $4 \tan x + \sin 2x = 0$

16. $\sin 2x = 2 \sin x$

B **17.** $\tan 2x \cot x - 3 = 0$

18. $\cos^2 x + \cos 2x = \frac{5}{4}$

19. $\cos^2 x - \cos 2x = \dfrac{-3}{4}$

20. $\tan x + \tan 2x = 0$

21. $\sin 2x \sin x + \cos 2x \cos x = 1$

22. $\cos x = \cos 2x$

23. $\sin \left(\frac{\pi}{4} + x \right) - \sin \left(\frac{\pi}{4} - x \right) = \frac{\sqrt{2}}{2}$

24. $\cos \left(\frac{\pi}{4} + x \right) + \cos \left(\frac{\pi}{4} - x \right) = 1$

25. $\sin 2x \cos x - \cos 2x \sin x = \dfrac{-\sqrt{3}}{2}$

26. $|\sin x| = \frac{1}{2}$

27. $\cos 2x + 3 \cos x - 1 = 0$

28. $\cos 2x + \cos x = 0$

29. $\sin^2 x - \cos^2 x - \cos x - 1 = 0$

30. $\cos 3x + \cos x = 0$

31. $\sin 3x + \sin x = 0$

32. $\sin 2x + \cos 3x = 0$

C **33.** $\sin x + \sin 2x + \sin 3x = 0$
(Use the Sum-Product Identities.)
34. $\cos x - \cos 3x - \cos 5x = 0$
35. $\sin x + \sin 2x - \sin 4x = 0$

4–7 Trigonometric Inequalities

Just as there are equations involving the trigonometric functions, inequalities may contain trigonometric functions. The methods of solution are the same as used in solving any inequality. Likewise the solution set usually is the union of intervals of real numbers.

EXAMPLE 1. Solve $\sin x > \frac{1}{2}$, $0 \leq x \leq 2\pi$.

A graph of $y = \sin x$ is useful in visualizing the solution set. The portion of the graph in color represents the ordered pairs $(x, \sin x)$ for which $\sin x > \frac{1}{2}$. Since $\sin \frac{\pi}{6} = \frac{1}{2}$ and $\sin \frac{5\pi}{6} = \frac{1}{2}$, the set

$$\left\{ x : \frac{\pi}{6} < x < \frac{5\pi}{6}, \ x \in R \right\}$$

is the solution set of the inequality $\sin x > \frac{1}{2}$, $0 \leq x \leq 2\pi$.

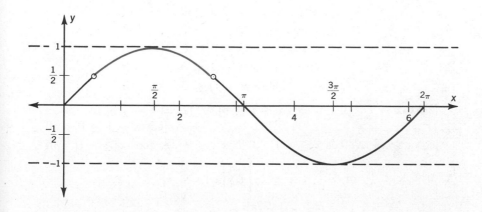

If you wanted the solution of $\sin x > \frac{1}{2}$, $x \in R$ it could be obtained by adding $\pm 2n\pi$ to $\frac{\pi}{6}$ and $\frac{5\pi}{6}$. (Explain why.) Thus, in this case the solution set is

$$\left\{ x : \frac{\pi}{6} \pm 2n\pi < x < \frac{5\pi}{6} \pm 2n\pi, \ x \in R \right\}.$$

APPLYING TRIGONOMETRY   185

EXAMPLE 2. Solve $\sin 2x > 0$, $0 \le x \le 2\pi$.

The identity $\sin 2x = 2 \sin x \cos x$ is useful here.

$$\sin 2x > 0 \qquad \text{iff}$$
$$2 \sin x \cos x > 0 \qquad \text{iff}$$
$$\sin x > 0 \wedge \cos x > 0 \quad \text{or} \quad \sin x < 0 \wedge \cos x < 0$$

The solution set is the union of the following sets.

$$\{x : 0 < x < \pi\} \cap \left\{x : 0 < x < \frac{\pi}{2} \quad \vee \quad \frac{3\pi}{2} < x < 2\pi\right\}$$

and

$$\{x : \pi < x < 2\pi\} \cap \left\{x : \frac{\pi}{2} < x < \frac{3\pi}{2}\right\}$$

That union is

$$\left\{x : 0 < x < \frac{\pi}{2}\right\} \cup \left\{x : \pi < x < \frac{3\pi}{2}\right\}$$

$$= \left\{x : 0 < x < \frac{\pi}{2} \quad \text{or} \quad \pi < x < \frac{3\pi}{2}\right\}.$$

EXAMPLE 3. Solve $2 \sin^2 x - \cos x - 1 \ge 0$.

Again the use of the identity $\sin^2 x + \cos^2 x = 1$ in the form

$$\sin^2 x = 1 - \cos^2 x$$

is helpful.

$$2 \sin^2 x - \cos x - 1 \ge 0 \qquad \text{iff}$$
$$2(1 - \cos^2 x) - \cos x - 1 \ge 0 \qquad \text{iff}$$
$$-2 \cos^2 x - \cos x + 1 \ge 0 \qquad \text{iff}$$
$$2 \cos^2 x + \cos x - 1 \le 0 \qquad \text{iff}$$
$$(2 \cos x - 1)(\cos x + 1) \le 0 \qquad \text{iff}$$

$$[2 \cos x - 1 \ge 0] \wedge [\cos x + 1 \le 0] \quad \vee \quad [2 \cos x - 1 \le 0]$$
$$\wedge [\cos x + 1 \ge 0] \qquad \text{iff}$$
$$[\cos x \ge \tfrac{1}{2}] \wedge [\cos x \le -1] \quad \vee \quad [\cos x \le \tfrac{1}{2}] \wedge [\cos x \ge -1] \qquad \text{iff}$$

$$\left\{x : 0 \le x \le \frac{\pi}{3} \quad \text{or} \quad \frac{5\pi}{3} \le x \le 2\pi\right\} \cap \{x : x = \pi\}$$

$$\cup \left\{x : \frac{\pi}{3} \le x \le \frac{5\pi}{3}\right\} \cap \{x : 0 \le x \le 2\pi\}$$

$$= \phi \cup \left\{x : \frac{\pi}{3} \le x \le \frac{5\pi}{3}\right\} = \left\{x : \frac{\pi}{3} \le x \le \frac{5\pi}{3}\right\}.$$

Consequently the solution set of $2 \sin^2 x - \cos x - 1 \ge 0$ is

$$\left\{x : \frac{\pi}{3} \le x \le \frac{5\pi}{3}\right\} \quad \text{or} \quad \left[\frac{\pi}{3}, \frac{5\pi}{3}\right].$$

Exercises

A ━━ Find the solution set of each inequality over $0 \le x \le 2\pi$.

1. $2 \sin x + \sqrt{3} \le 0$

2. $\sqrt{2} \cos x - 1 > 0$

3. $\tan x - 2 \le 0$

4. $\sqrt{3} \cot x - 1 \le 0$

5. $\tan x - 2 > -1$

6. $\sqrt{3} \sec x + 2 \ge 0$

7. $| \sin x | \le \frac{1}{2}$

8. $| \cos x | \ge \frac{3}{2}$

9. $\sin^2 x - \cos^2 x \ge 0$

10. $\cos 2x + \sin x \le 1$

B **11.** $\sin 2x \ge 2 \sin x$

12. $\frac{\tan x}{\tan 2x} + 1 > 0$

13. $2 \cos^2 x > 1$

14. $2 \sin^2 x + 3 \sin x - 2 \ge 0$

15. $2 \sin^2 x + \cos x \ge 1$

16. $\tan^2 x + \sec x + 1 \ge 0$

17. $\cot^2 x - \csc x + 1 > 0$

18. $\cos x + \cos 2x > 0$

C **19.** $\cos x \le \sin x$

20. $\cos 3x + \cos x < 0$

21. $\sin 2x < \dfrac{2 \sin x}{\sec x}$

22. $\sin x \cos x \tan x < 0$

4–8 Complex Numbers in Polar Form

In Figure 1 below, the horizontal axis is the **real axis** and the vertical axis is the **imaginary axis.** The complex number $a + bi$ is represented by the point (a, b) or by the vector from the origin to (a, b). The *absolute value* of $a + bi$, or r, denoted $| a + bi |$ or r, is the length of the vector determined by (a, b).

$$r = | a + bi | = \sqrt{a^2 + b^2}$$

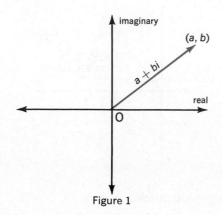

Figure 1

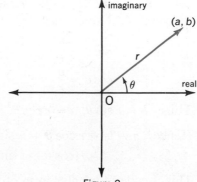

Figure 2

Each complex number can be represented graphically by a vector as shown in Figure 2. This vector along with the positive real axis, determines an angle in standard position. The measure of this angle is the **argument** of the complex number; it is usually denoted by the Greek letter "θ":

$$\text{argument } a + bi = \theta.$$

θ can be found by using any of the trigonometric functions, but since a and b are known, and $\tan \theta = \frac{b}{a}$, θ is defined by

$$\theta = \text{Arc} \tan \frac{b}{a}, \ a > 0 \qquad \theta = \pi + \text{Arc} \tan \frac{b}{a}, \ a < 0$$

$$\left(\text{Recall } \frac{-\pi}{2} \leq \text{Arc} \tan x \leq \frac{\pi}{2}, \text{ thus } \frac{\pi}{2} \leq \pi + \text{Arc} \tan x \leq \frac{3\pi}{2}, \text{ and thus } \frac{-\pi}{2} \leq \theta \leq \frac{3\pi}{2}. \right)$$

EXAMPLE 1. Let $z = -2\sqrt{3} + 2i$. Find $r = |z|$ and θ. Graph $-2\sqrt{3} + 2i$.

$$|z| = \sqrt{(-2\sqrt{3})^2 + 2^2}$$
$$= \sqrt{16}$$
$$= 4$$

Since $-2\sqrt{3} = a < 0$,

$$\theta = \pi + \text{Arc} \tan \frac{2}{-2\sqrt{3}}$$
$$= \pi + \left(\frac{-\pi}{6} \right)$$
$$= \frac{5\pi}{6} = 150°.$$

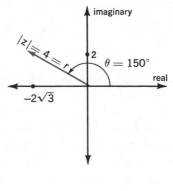

The graph is shown at the right.

Let $a + bi$ be a complex number with absolute value r and argument θ. Notice that

$$\sin \theta = \frac{b}{r}$$
$$\cos \theta = \frac{a}{r}.$$

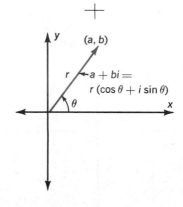

Thus $b = r \sin \theta$, $a = r \cos \theta$.

Hence $a + bi = r \cos \theta + ir \sin \theta$
$$= r(\cos \theta + i \sin \theta).$$

This is called the **polar form** of the complex number $a + bi$.

188   CHAPTER 4

EXAMPLE 2. Express $3 - i\sqrt{3}$ in polar form.

$$\theta = \text{Arc tan } \frac{-\sqrt{3}}{3} = -30°$$

$$r = \sqrt{3^2 + (\sqrt{3})^2} = \sqrt{12} = 2\sqrt{3}$$

Consequently

$$3 - i\sqrt{3} = 2\sqrt{3} \, (\cos (-30°) + i \sin (-30°)).$$

Since $360° - 30° = 330°$, you could write

$$3 - i\sqrt{3} = 2\sqrt{3} \, (\cos 330° + i \sin 330°).$$

Theorem 4–3   If z_1 and z_2 are complex numbers and

$$z_1 = r_1(\cos \theta_1 + i \sin \theta_1), \qquad z_2 = r_2(\cos \theta_2 + i \sin \theta_2)$$

then

$$z_1 \cdot z_2 = r_1 r_2 \big(\cos (\theta_1 + \theta_2) + i \sin (\theta_1 + \theta_2)\big).$$

Proof: $z_1 \cdot z_2 = r_1(\cos \theta_1 + i \sin \theta_1) \cdot r_2(\cos \theta_2 + i \sin \theta_2)$

$$= r_1 r_2 \cos \theta_1 \cos \theta_2 + r_1 r_2 i \cos \theta_1 \sin \theta_2 + r_1 r_2 i \sin \theta_1 \cos \theta_2 + r_1 r_2 \cdot i^2 \sin \theta_1 \sin \theta_2$$

$$= r_1 r_2 \, [\cos \theta_1 \cos \theta_2 + i^2 \sin \theta_1 \sin \theta_2] + r_1 r_2 i \, [\sin \theta_1 \cos \theta_2 + \cos \theta_1 \sin \theta_2]$$

$$= r_1 r_2 \, [\cos \theta_1 \cos \theta_2 - \sin \theta_1 \sin \theta_2] + i r_1 r_2 \sin (\theta_1 + \theta_2)$$

$$= r_1 r_2 \, [\cos (\theta_1 + \theta_2) + i \sin (\theta_1 + \theta_2)]$$

EXAMPLE 3.   Find $z_1 \cdot z_2$ when $z_1 = 2(\cos 40° + i \sin 40°)$ and $z_2 = 4(\cos 60° + i \sin 60°)$.   Write the product in $a + bi$ form.

$$z_1 \cdot z_2 = 2(\cos 40° + i \sin 40°) \cdot 4(\cos 60° + i \sin 60°)$$

$$= 2 \cdot 4(\cos (40° + 60°) + i \sin (40° + 60°))$$

$$= 8 \, (\cos 100° + i \sin 100°)$$

$$= 8(-\cos 80° + i \sin 80°)$$

$$= 8(-0.1736 + 0.9848i)$$

$$= -1.3888 + 7.8784i = a + bi$$

EXAMPLE 4. If $z = r(\cos \theta + i \sin \theta)$, then show that the conjugate of z, denoted $\bar{z}$, is $\bar{z} = r(\cos(-\theta) + i \sin(-\theta))$.

The conjugate, $\bar{z}$, of $a + bi$ is $a - bi$, thus

$$\bar{z} = r(\cos \theta - i \sin \theta)$$
$$= r(\cos(-\theta) - i \sin \theta) \quad \text{(Why?)}$$
$$= r(\cos(-\theta) + i \sin(-\theta)). \quad \text{(Why?)}$$

Theorem 4-4 If $z_1 = r_1(\cos \theta_1 + i \sin \theta_1)$

and

$$z_2 = r_2(\cos \theta_2 + i \sin \theta_2) \neq 0 + 0i,$$

then

$$\frac{z_1}{z_2} = \frac{r_1}{r_2}(\cos(\theta_1 - \theta_2) + i \sin(\theta_1 - \theta_2)).$$

You know that $\frac{z_1}{z_2} = \frac{z_1 \cdot \bar{z}_2}{z_2 \cdot \bar{z}_2}$. Express z_1, z_2, and $\bar{z}_2$ in polar form and use Theorem 4-3. The results are immediate.

Now try these

1. Express each of the following in polar form.

  a. $2 + 2i$ **b.** $-3i$ **c.** $1 - \sqrt{3}i$

2. What is the absolute value of a complex number expressed in polar form?

3. Suppose you are given a complex number in the following polar form, $r(\cos \theta + i \sin \theta)$. Express x and y in terms of r and θ.

Answers: **1. a.** $2\sqrt{2}(\cos 45° + i \sin 45°)$ **b.** $3(\cos 270° + i \sin 270°)$
     c. $2(\cos(-60°) + i \sin(-60°))$ or $2(\cos 300° + i \sin 300°)$
     2. r **3.** $x = r \cos \theta, \ y = r \sin \theta$

Exercises

A ▬ Graph each number on the complex plane. Find the polar form of each number.

  1. $4 + 4i$ **2.** $-1 + \sqrt{3}i$ **3.** $\frac{1}{2} - \frac{\sqrt{3}}{2}i$

  4. $-1 - 2i$ **5.** $-1 + 0i$ **6.** $0 + i$

  7. $0 - i$ **8.** $1 + 0i$ **9.** $0.9945 + 0.1045i$

  10. $-0.9336 + 0.3584i$

  11. $0.6428 - 0.7660i$

  12. $-2 - 3i$

Express each number in the form $a + bi$.

13. $\frac{1}{2}\left(\cos\frac{\pi}{3} + i\sin\frac{\pi}{3}\right)$

14. $2\left(\cos\frac{\pi}{2} + i\sin\frac{\pi}{2}\right)$

15. $4\left(\cos\frac{11\pi}{6} + i\sin\frac{11\pi}{6}\right)$

16. $3\left(\cos\frac{5\pi}{4} + i\sin\frac{5\pi}{4}\right)$

17. $\cos\left(\frac{-\pi}{2}\right) + i\sin\left(\frac{-\pi}{2}\right)$

18. $17(\cos\pi + i\sin\pi)$

19. $8\left(\cos\frac{\pi}{12} + i\sin\frac{\pi}{12}\right)$

20. $r(\cos\theta + i\sin\theta)$

B **21.** What is the polar form of any complex numbers whose graph is on the real axis?

22. What is the polar form of any complex numbers whose graph is on the imaginary axis?

23. Write out the details of the proof of Theorem 4–4.

24. Prove, using polar form, that $\frac{z}{z} = 1$ whenever $z \neq 0 + 0i$.

Find $z_1 \cdot z_2$ and $\frac{z_1}{z_2}$ in Exercises 25–30.

25. $z_1 = 3(\cos 80° + i\sin 80°)$, $z_2 = \frac{1}{2}(\cos 40° + i\sin 40°)$

26. $z_1 = 5\left(\cos\frac{2\pi}{3} + i\sin\frac{2\pi}{3}\right)$, $z_2 = 4\left(\cos\frac{3\pi}{4} + i\sin\frac{3\pi}{4}\right)$

27. $z_1 = 2(\cos 135° + i\sin 135°)$, $z_2 = \frac{2}{3}(\cos 150° + i\sin 150°)$

28. $z_1 = 3\left(\cos\frac{\pi}{2} + i\sin\frac{\pi}{2}\right)$, $z_2 = \left(\cos\frac{\pi}{2} + i\sin\left(\frac{-\pi}{2}\right)\right)$

29. $z_1 = 1 - i$, $z_2 = -i$

30. $z_1 = 5i$, $z_2 = 2 - 3i$

31. Draw a graph of $r_1(\cos\theta_1 + i\sin\theta_1)$ and of $r_2(\cos\theta_2 + i\sin\theta_2)$. Draw a graph of their product. Of their quotient.

32. How are the graphs of z and $\bar{z}$ related?

C **33.** Show that for $z \neq 0$,

$$\frac{1}{z} = \frac{1}{r}(\cos\theta - i\sin\theta) = \frac{1}{r^2} \cdot \bar{z}.$$

34. Show that $z^2 = [r(\cos\theta + i\sin\theta)]^2 = r^2(\cos 2\theta + i\sin 2\theta)$.

35. Show that $\frac{z}{\bar{z}} = \cos 2\theta + i\sin 2\theta$, $z \neq 0 + 0i$.

36. What is $\frac{\bar{z}}{z}$, if $z \neq 0 + 0i$?

37. Prove that the quotient of two complex numbers with the same argument is real.

38. Addition of complex numbers in polar form is more difficult than addition in rectangular form. Is this statement true for multiplication? Why or why not?

4–9 De Moivre's Theorem, Roots and Powers

Suppose $\quad z = r(\cos \theta + i \sin \theta)$.

Then $\qquad z^2 = [r(\cos \theta + i \sin \theta)]^2$

$$= r^2[\cos^2 \theta + 2i \sin \theta \cos \theta - \sin^2 \theta]$$
$$= r^2[\cos^2 \theta - \sin^2 \theta + i2 \sin \theta \cos \theta]$$
$$= r^2(\cos 2\theta + i \sin 2\theta)$$

Notice that the square of z is the product of the square of $r = |z|$ and the cosine of twice θ plus i times the sine of twice θ. This example illustrates a most remarkable theorem called **De Moivre's Theorem.**

Theorem 4–5 (De Moivre's Theorem). If $z = r(\cos \theta + i \sin \theta)$ and n is an integer, then

$$z^n = r^n(\cos n\theta + i \sin n\theta).$$

Proof: The proof is in two parts. (If $n = 0$, the proof is trivial.)

Part 1: n is a natural number. The proof is by *Mathematical Induction.*

Let P_n be the statement $z^n = r^n(\cos n\theta + i \sin n\theta)$.

a. P_1 is $z^1 = r^1(\cos (1 \cdot \theta) + i \sin (1 \cdot \theta))$.
P_1 is true because

$$z = r(\cos \theta + i \sin \theta)$$
$$= r^1(\cos (1 \cdot \theta) + i \sin (1 \cdot \theta)).$$

b. Assume P_n is true for $k \in$ N:

$$z^k = r^k(\cos (k\theta) + i \sin (k\theta)).$$

You must show that P_{k+1} is true.

$$z^{k+1} = z^k \cdot z^1$$
$$= r^k(\cos k\theta + i \sin k\theta) \cdot r(\cos \theta + i \sin \theta) \qquad \text{(Why?)}$$
$$= r^k \cdot r(\cos (k\theta + \theta) + i \sin (k\theta + \theta)) \qquad \text{(by Theorem 4–3)}$$
$$z^{k+1} = r^{k+1}(\cos [(k + 1)\theta] + i \sin [(k + 1)\theta]).$$

Thus P_{k+1} is true whenever P_k is true and, by the Principle of Mathematical Induction,

P_n is true for all natural numbers.

Part 2: $-n$ is a negative integer.

$$z^{-n} = \frac{1}{z^n}$$

$$= \frac{1}{r^n(\cos (n\theta) + i \sin (n\theta))} \qquad \text{by } Part\ 1$$

$$= \frac{1}{r^n(\cos n\theta + i \sin n\theta)} \cdot \frac{\cos (-n\theta) + i \sin (-n\theta)}{\cos (-n\theta) + i \sin (-n\theta)}$$

$$= \frac{r^{-n}(\cos (-n\theta) + i \sin (-n\theta))}{\cos (n\theta - n\theta) + i \sin (n\theta - n\theta)}$$

$$= r^{-n}(\cos (-n\theta) + i \sin (-n\theta))$$

Combining the results of Parts 1 and 2, you have proved De Moivre's Theorem.

The formula in De Moivre's Theorem is one of the most remarkable and useful relations in elementary mathematics.

EXAMPLE 1.   Derive identities for $\cos 3\theta$ and $\sin 3\theta$.

Let $(\cos \theta + i \sin \theta) = u + vi$; $u = \cos \theta$, $v = \sin \theta$. Then

$$(\cos \theta + i \sin \theta)^3 = \cos 3\theta + i \sin 3\theta,$$

and

$$(u + vi)^3 = u^3 + 3iu^2v + 3uv^2i^2 + v^3i^3 \qquad \text{(by The Binomial Theorem)}$$
$$= u^3 - 3uv^2 + i(3u^2v - v^3) \qquad\qquad \text{(Why?)}$$

Thus, substituting $u = \cos \theta$ and $v = \sin \theta$

$$\cos 3\theta + i \sin 3\theta = \cos^3 \theta - 3 \cos \theta \sin^2 \theta + i(3 \cos^2 \theta \sin \theta - \sin^3 \theta)$$

Two complex numbers are equal if and only if their real parts and imaginary parts are equal. Hence,

$$\cos 3\theta = \cos^3 \theta - 3 \cos \theta \sin^2 \theta$$
$$= \cos^3 \theta - 3 \cos \theta(1 - \cos^2 \theta)$$
$$= 4 \cos^3 \theta - 3 \cos \theta$$

and

$$\sin 3\theta = 3 \cos^2 \theta \sin \theta - \sin^3 \theta$$
$$= 3[1 - \sin^2 \theta] \sin \theta - \sin^3 \theta$$
$$= 3 \sin \theta - 4 \sin^3 \theta.$$

The key idea in the solution of Example 1 is that a single equation with two complex numbers is equivalent to a pair of equations with real numbers. A similar procedure may be used to derive identities for $\sin n\theta$ and $\cos n\theta$, $n \in I$.

De Moivre's Theorem can be used to find roots of complex numbers. The following example is an illustration of this.

EXAMPLE 2. Find the cube roots of $-6i$.

If $r(\cos \theta + i \sin \theta)$ is a cube root of $-6i = 6\left(\cos \frac{3\pi}{2} + i \sin \frac{3\pi}{2}\right)$,

then

$$[r(\cos \theta + i \sin \theta)]^3 = 6\left(\cos \frac{3\pi}{2} + i \sin \frac{3\pi}{2}\right)$$

or

$$r^3(\cos 3\theta + i \sin 3\theta) = 6\left(\cos \frac{3\pi}{2} + i \sin \frac{3\pi}{2}\right). \qquad\qquad 1$$

Complex numbers are equal if and only if their absolute values are equal and their arguments differ by $\pm 2n\pi$, $n \in W$. Thus **1** is equivalent to

$$r^3 = 6 \qquad\qquad 2$$

and

$$3\theta = \frac{3\pi}{2} \pm 2n\pi, \ n \in W. \qquad\qquad 3$$

From **2** and **3** you find,

$$r = \sqrt[3]{6} \qquad\qquad 4$$

and

$$\theta = \frac{\pi}{2} \pm \frac{2n\pi}{3}, \ n \in W. \qquad\qquad 5$$

Therefore the cube roots of $-6i$ are

$$\sqrt[3]{6}\left[\cos\left(\frac{\pi}{2} \pm \frac{2n\pi}{3}\right) + i \sin\left(\frac{\pi}{2} \pm \frac{2n\pi}{3}\right)\right]. \qquad\qquad 6$$

Substituting $n = 0, 1, 2, 3$, etc. in **6**, you find the cube roots to be

$$\sqrt[3]{6}\left(\cos \frac{\pi}{2} + i \sin \frac{\pi}{2}\right) = \sqrt[3]{6}\,(0 + i) \qquad\qquad 7$$

$$\sqrt[3]{6}\left(\cos \frac{7\pi}{6} + i \sin \frac{7\pi}{6}\right) = \sqrt[3]{6}\left(-\frac{1}{2} - i\frac{3}{2}\right) \qquad\qquad 8$$

$$\sqrt[3]{6}\left(\cos \frac{11\pi}{6} + i \sin \frac{11\pi}{6}\right) = \sqrt[3]{6}\left(-\frac{3}{2} + i\frac{1}{2}\right) \qquad\qquad 9$$

$$\sqrt[3]{6}\left(\cos \frac{5\pi}{2} + i \sin \frac{5\pi}{2}\right) = \sqrt[3]{6}\,(0 + i) \qquad\qquad 10$$

Notice that roots **7** and **10** are identical. All others found by substituting $n \geq 4$ in 6 will be identical to one of **7–9**. There are n roots of any complex number, one corresponding to each of the whole numbers $0, 1, 2, 3, \ldots, n - 1$.

Theorem 4–6 If $n \in N$, then the n roots of $z = r(\cos \theta + i \sin \theta)$ are given by

$$\sqrt[n]{r} \left[\cos \left(\frac{\theta}{n} \pm \frac{2k\pi}{n} \right) + i \sin \left(\frac{\theta}{n} \pm \frac{2k\pi}{n} \right) \right]$$

$$k = 0, 1, 2, 3, \ldots, n - 1.$$

Now try these

1. Use De Moivre's Theorem to evaluate each of the following expressions of complex numbers.

a. $(-2 - 2i)^5$

b. $-i^7$

c. $(3 - 5i)^{-3}$

d. $[2(\cos 30° + i \sin 30°)]^2$

2. Using De Moivre's Theorem, find the three cube roots of 8.

Answers: **1. a.** $128 + 128i$ **b.** i **c.** $\dfrac{(-99 + 5i)}{19652}$ **d.** $4(\cos 60° + i \sin 60°)$

2. When $k = 0$, the root is $2(\cos 0° + i \sin 0°)$, or 2.
   When $k = 1$, the root is $2(\cos 120° + i \sin 120°)$, or $-1 + i\sqrt{3}$.
   When $k = 2$, the root is $2(\cos 240° + i \sin 240°)$, or $-1 - i\sqrt{3}$.

Exercises

A ▬▬ Use De Moivre's Theorem to evaluate each expression. Write your result in polar form and in $a + bi$ form.

1. $(1 - i)^3$

2. $(1 + i)^{-4}$

3. $(i)^4$

4. $(1 - 3i)^5$

5. $(-1 + \sqrt{3}i)^{-5}$

6. $(-\sqrt{3} - i)^3$

7. $(-i)^{-5}$

8. $(2 - 2\sqrt{3}i)^2$

▬▬ Express each root in polar form. Plot the roots required in each exercise in the complex plane.

9. The fourth roots of 1

10. The cube roots of i

11. The cube roots of -1

12. The sixth roots of -1

13. The cube roots of $-1 + \sqrt{3}i$

14. The twelfth roots of 1

15. The square roots of i

16. The fifth roots of $1 - \sqrt{3}i$

B **17.** Use the procedure of Example 1 to derive identities for $\cos 4\theta$ and $\sin 4\theta$ in terms of $\sin \theta$ and $\cos \theta$.

18. Solve $z^3 = i^2$.   **19.** Solve $z^3 = (1 + i)^2$.

20. Solve $z^3 = (1 + \sqrt{3}i)^2$. (Leave answers in polar form.)

21. Show that the three cube roots of 1 are 1, ω, and ω^2 where $\omega = \cos \frac{2\pi}{3} + i \sin \frac{2\pi}{3}$.

22. Show that the four fourth roots of 1 are 1, ω, ω^2, and ω^3 where $\omega = \cos \frac{\pi}{2} + i \sin \frac{\pi}{2}$.

23. Show that $[r(\cos \theta + i \sin \theta)]^{-n}$, $n \in W$ is

$$r^{-n}(\cos n\theta - i \sin n\theta)$$

C **24.** Show that $z^{\frac{p}{q}} = [r(\cos \theta + i \sin \theta)]^{\frac{p}{q}}$, $q \in N$, $p \in I$ is

$$r^{\frac{p}{q}}\left(\cos \frac{p}{q}(\theta \pm 2n\pi) + i \sin \frac{p}{q}(\theta \pm 2n\pi)\right) \quad n = 0, 1, 2, 3, \ldots, q - 1.$$

—— Use the results of Exercise 24 to find each of the following.

25. The 3 values of $(1)^{\frac{2}{3}}$ **26.** The 3 values of $i^{\frac{2}{3}}$

27. The 4 values of $1^{\frac{3}{4}}$ **28.** The 3 values of $(-1)^{\frac{2}{3}}$

29. The 4 values of $i^{\frac{3}{4}}$ **30.** The 3 values of $(-i)^{\frac{2}{3}}$

4–10   Polar Coordinates

Each point P in the plane is on the terminal side of an angle in standard position, and it is a unique distance from the origin. The terminal side of the angle is determined by the measure θ of the angle. The distance of the point P from the origin is denoted by r. The ordered pair of numbers (r, θ) is called the **polar coordinates** of P. See Figure 1 below.

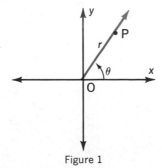

Figure 1

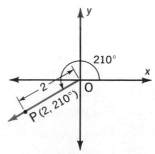

Figure 2

EXAMPLE 1. Plot the point P with polar coordinates (2, 210°).

Draw the terminal side of the angle in standard position which measures 210°. Find the point on this ray 2 units from 0. See Figure 2.

You should observe that the polar coordinates of P given in Example 1 are not unique. The same point has polar coordinates (2,570°), (2,930°), (2, −150°) and in general, (2,210° ± n · 360°), $n \in$ W. Using radian measure P is $\left(2, \frac{7\pi}{6} \pm 2n\pi\right)$, $n \in$ W.

There is still another way to identify the same point. This way makes use of −r and the *convention* associated with it. When the first coordinate of a polar pair is negative, it is interpreted to mean the point | r | units from the origin on the ray opposite to the terminal side of the angle with measure θ. Thus (−2, 30°) is the same point as (2, 210°). This is shown in the figure at the right.

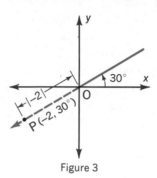

Figure 3

The polar coordinates of $P(2, 210°)$ may be given as any member of

$\{(r, \theta) : r = 2$ and $\theta = 210 \pm 2n\pi$ or $r = -2$ and $\theta = 30° \pm 2n\pi, n \in$ W$\}$

In general, if r is a real number and $\overrightarrow{OQ}$ is the terminal side of an angle in standard position with measure θ, then (r, θ) are the polar coordinates of a point P | r | units from O and on

a. $\overrightarrow{OQ}$ if $r > 0$

b. the ray opposite to $\overrightarrow{OQ}$ if $r < 0$

c. 0 if $r = 0$ ($\forall \theta \in$ R)

The vertex 0 of the angle in standard position is the pole. The initial side of the angle is the polar axis. Notice that it is not necessary to have a rectangular coordinate system on the plane in order to have polar coordinates. All that is necessary is the **pole,** the **polar axis,** the direction of rotation which will give positive θ, and the conventions **a, b,** and **c** above. See the figure at the right.

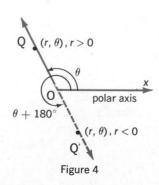

Figure 4

APPLYING TRIGONOMETRY   197

However, there are useful relations between polar and rectangular coordinates of a point. These are illustrated in the figure at the right.

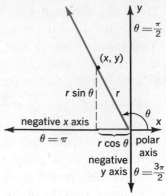

$$(x, y) = (r \cos \theta, r \sin \theta)$$

or

$$x = r \cos \theta, \ y = r \sin \theta \qquad \mathbf{1}$$

The equations in **1** allow you to convert from polar coordinates to rectangular coordinates.

Similarly, the following equations permit you to convert from rectangular coordinates.

Figure 5

$$r = \sqrt{x^2 + y^2} \qquad \qquad \mathbf{2}$$

$$\theta = \text{Arc tan} \frac{y}{x} \qquad x > 0 \qquad \mathbf{3}$$

$$\theta = \pi + \text{Arc tan} \frac{y}{x}, \qquad x < 0 \qquad \mathbf{4}$$

EXAMPLE 2. **a.** Find the rectangular coordinates of (3, 150°).

b. Find polar coordinates of (−2, −2) for $r > 0$ and for $r < 0$.

a. By Equation **1**

$$x = r \cos \theta \qquad\qquad y = r \sin \theta$$
$$= 3 \cos 150° \qquad\qquad = 3 \sin 150°$$
$$= 3\left(-\frac{\sqrt{3}}{2}\right) \qquad\qquad = 3\left(\frac{1}{2}\right)$$
$$= \frac{-3\sqrt{3}}{2}. \qquad\qquad = \frac{3}{2}.$$

b. From **2**, you have

$$|r| = \sqrt{(-2)^2 + (-2)^2}$$
$$= \sqrt{8}$$
$$= 2\sqrt{2}.$$

Since $x < 0$, from **4** you have

$$\theta = \pi + \text{Arc tan} \frac{-2}{-2}$$
$$= \pi + \frac{\pi}{4}$$
$$= \frac{5\pi}{4}.$$

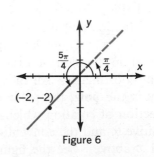

Figure 6

Consequently, for $r > 0$, polar coordinates are $\left(2\sqrt{2}, \frac{5\pi}{4}\right)$ or $(2\sqrt{2}, 225°)$. For $r < 0$, polar coordinates are $\left(-2\sqrt{2}, \frac{\pi}{4}\right)$ or $(-2\sqrt{2}, 45°)$. (See Figure 6.)

Now try these

1. Find the polar coordinates for $r > 0$ and $r < 0$ for the point whose rectangular coordinates are $(5, -5\sqrt{3})$.

2. Find the rectangular coordinates for the point whose polar coordinates are $(-10, 60°)$.

Answers: **1.** $(10, -60°)$ and $(-10, 120°)$ **2.** $(-5, -5\sqrt{3})$

Exercises

A — Find polar coordinates a for $r > 0$ and b for $r < 0$ for each point given in rectangular coordinates.

1. $(1, 1)$ **2.** $(0, 4)$ **3.** $(-9, 0)$ **4.** $(-1, 1)$
5. $(1, -\sqrt{3})$ **6.** $(-1, -\sqrt{3})$ **7.** $(-4, 8)$ **8.** $(0, -1)$

— Find rectangular coordinates for each point given in polar coordinates.

9. $(-2, 90°)$ **10.** $\left(4, \frac{3\pi}{4}\right)$ **11.** $\left(-1, \frac{7\pi}{6}\right)$ **12.** $\left(1, \frac{7\pi}{6}\right)$
13. $\left(3, \frac{-2\pi}{3}\right)$ **14.** $\left(-\frac{3}{2}, \frac{-\pi}{4}\right)$ **15.** $\left(5, \frac{3\pi}{2}\right)$ **16.** $\left(-9, \frac{13\pi}{3}\right)$

— Use the relations $x = r \cos \theta$ and $y = r \sin \theta$ to transform each equation into an equation in polar coordinates.

17. $x = 3$ **18.** $y = -4$ **19.** $2x - y = 3$
20. $y = x$ **21.** $x^2 + y^2 = 16$ **22.** $xy = a^2$
23. $x^2 + y^2 + 4x = 0$ **24.** $x^2 + y^2 + 2y = 0$ **25.** $y^2 = 4x$

B Use the relations 2–4 on page 198 to transform each equation into an equation in rectangular coordinates.

26. $r = 4$ **27.** $\theta = 0°$ **28.** $\theta = \frac{\pi}{4}$
29. $r = -4$ **30.** $r = 2 \sin \theta + 2 \cos \theta$ **31.** $r \sin \theta = 6$

C **32.** $r = 4 \sec \theta$ **33.** $r = 5 \csc \theta$ **34.** $r^2 - 3r + 2 = 0$
35. Prove that if a point (x_1, y_1) has polar coordinates (r, θ) and if (x_2, y_2) has polar coordinates $(r, -\theta)$, then $x_1 = x_2$ and $y_1 = -y_2$.

APPLYING TRIGONOMETRY   199

4–11 Graphs of Polar Equations

Equations in polar coordinates are **polar equations.** In a plane, the set of points (r, θ) which satisfy a polar equation is a **polar graph.** Some of the polar graphs are quite beautiful as you will see.

EXAMPLE 1. Graph $r = 5$.

The polar graph of $r = 5$ is the set of all points with polar coordinates $(5, \theta)$. Thus, the graph is the set of all points 5 units from the pole. The graph is clearly a circle. See Figure 1. What is the equation of the same circle in rectangular coordinates? What is the polar graph of $r = -5$?

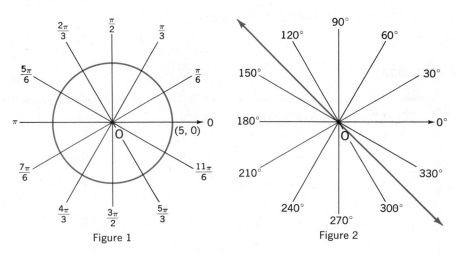

Figure 1   Figure 2

EXAMPLE 2. Sketch the polar graph of $\theta = 140°$.

The graph is all those points $(r, 140°)$ with second coordinate of $140°$ and first coordinate $r \in R$. The graph is a line through the pole. See Figure 2. What is the equation of the same line in rectangular coordinates?

EXAMPLE 3. Sketch the graph of $r = 3 \cos \theta$.

The best procedure here is to make a table of values (r, θ). For convenience the values of θ which are multiples of $\frac{\pi}{6}$ $(60°)$ are used. These points are plotted in color on the coordinate system. Recall that a point $\left(\frac{-3}{2}, \frac{2\pi}{3}\right)$ is $\frac{3}{2}$ unit on the ray opposite to the terminal side of the angle measuring $\frac{2\pi}{3}$; i.e., $\left(\frac{3}{2}, \frac{5\pi}{3}\right)$.

Do you see that the points in the graph corresponding to (r, θ), $\pi \le \theta \le 2\pi$ are exactly the same points as those corresponding to $(r, \theta), 0 \le \theta < \pi$? Thus the entire graph could be sketched by plotting only the points in the set $\{(r, \theta) : 0 \le \theta < \pi, r = 3 \cos \theta\}$.

θ	r
0	3
$\dfrac{\pi}{6}$	$\dfrac{3\sqrt{3}}{2}$
$\dfrac{\pi}{3}$	$\dfrac{3}{2}$
$\dfrac{\pi}{2}$	0
$\dfrac{2\pi}{3}$	$\dfrac{-3}{2}$
$\dfrac{5\pi}{6}$	$\dfrac{-3\sqrt{3}}{2}$
π	-3
$\dfrac{7\pi}{6}$	$\dfrac{-3\sqrt{3}}{2}$
$\dfrac{4\pi}{3}$	$\dfrac{-3}{2}$
$\dfrac{3\pi}{2}$	0
$\dfrac{5\pi}{3}$	$\dfrac{3}{2}$
$\dfrac{11\pi}{6}$	$\dfrac{3\sqrt{3}}{2}$
2π	3

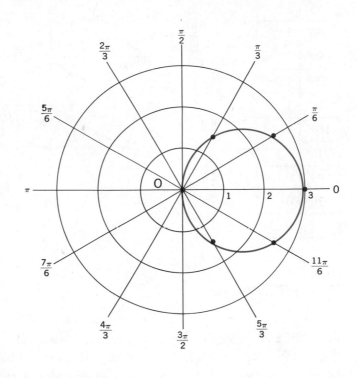

The graph is a circle. What is the equation of the same circle in rectangular coordinates? How do the following circles differ from the circle $r = \cos \theta$?

    a. $r = 6 \cos \theta$
    b. $r = \frac{3}{2} \cos \theta$
    c. $3r = 12 \cos \theta$

EXAMPLE 4. Sketch the polar graph of $r = \sin\theta + 1$.

Again, make a table of values of (r, θ). The points corresponding to the pairs in the table are plotted below. The curve is called a cardioid. (Can you guess why?)

θ	r
0	1
30°	1.5
60°	1.866
90°	2
120°	1.866
150°	1.5
180°	1
210°	0.5
240°	0.134
270°	0
300°	0.134
330°	0.5
360°	1

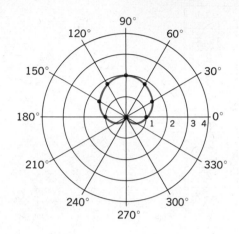

EXAMPLE 5. Sketch the polar graph of $r = \sin 2\theta$.

A table of values is valuable again. Because the equation involves 2θ, it is useful to consider values of θ at intervals of 15° $\left(\text{or } \dfrac{\pi}{12}\right)$.

θ	2θ	r
0	0	0
15°	30°	0.5
30°	60°	0.866
45°	90°	1
60°	120°	0.866
75°	150°	0.5
90°	180°	0

θ	2θ	r	
105°	210°	−0.5	
120°	240°	−0.866	
135°	270°	−1	2
150°	300°	−0.866	
165°	330°	−0.5	
180°	360°	0	
195°	390°	0.5	
210°	420°	0.866	
225°	450°	1	3
240°	480°	0.866	
255°	510°	0.5	
270°	540°	0	
285°	570°	−0.5	
300°	600°	−0.866	
315°	630°	−1	4
330°	660°	−0.866	
345°	690°	−0.5	
360°	720°	0	

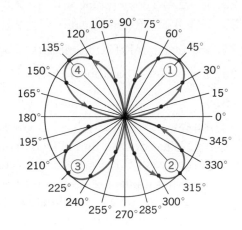

The graph is shown in the figure. It is called a *four-leaved rose*. Each branch (petal) is identified with a number. The values in the table which produce that branch are similarly designated. The arrowheads on the graph indicate the path a point A would follow with θ increasing from 0° to 360°.

Exercises

A ▬ Sketch the polar graph of each equation.

1. $r = -3$ **2.** $r = 1$ **3.** $\theta = 75°$

4. $\theta = \dfrac{-\pi}{3}$ **5.** $r = \cos\theta$ **6.** $r = 2\sin\theta$

7. $r = -3\cos\theta$ **8.** $r = -4\sin\theta$ **9.** $r\cos\theta = 2$

10. $r = 1 + \cos\theta$ (cardioid)   **11.** $r = \sin\theta - 1$ (cardioid)

12. $r = \cos \theta - 1$ (cardioid) **13.** $r = 2 \sin 3\theta$ (3-leaved rose)
14. $r = 3 \cos 3\theta$ (3-leaved rose) **15.** $r = \cos 2\theta$ (4-leaved rose)
16. $r = \sin 5\theta$ (5-leaved rose) **17.** $r = \cos 4\theta$ (8-leaved rose)

B **18.** $r = 2 + \cos \theta$ (limaçon) **19.** $r = 2 + \sin \theta$ (limaçon)
20. $r = 2 + 3 \cos \theta$ (limaçon) **21.** $r = 1 - 2 \sin \theta$ (limaçon)
22. $r^2 = 4 \sin 2\theta$ (lemniscate) **23.** $r^2 = 4 \cos 2\theta$ (lemniscate)

C **24.** $r = 2\theta$ (spiral of Archimedes) **25.** $r\theta = 3$ (hyperbolic spiral)

26. $r = \dfrac{4}{1 - \cos \theta}$ (parabola) **27.** $r = \dfrac{2}{1 - \frac{1}{2}\cos \theta}$ (ellipse)

28. $r = \dfrac{16}{1 - 4 \cos \theta}$ (hyperbola)

29. Graph $r = \sin \theta + 1$ and $r = \sin \theta - 1$ on the same coordinate system. What do you find is true about the graphs?

30. Graph each curve $r = \sin \theta - 1$ and $r = \cos \theta + 1$.
   a. What points are common to each?
   b. Do the polar coordinates of these points satisfy each equation simultaneously?
   c. In Exercise 29 you found $r = \sin \theta - 1$ and $r = \sin \theta + 1$ had the same graph. Do the points of intersection found in **a** satisfy $r = \sin \theta + 1$ and $r = \cos \theta + 1$ simultaneously?

31. Prove the theorem: the polar equations
   1. $r = f(\theta)$ 2. $-r = f(\theta + \pi)$ and
   3. $r = f(\theta + 2\pi)$ have the same graph.

32. Use Exercise 31 to explain your answer to Exercise 30c.

CHAPTER OBJECTIVES AND REVIEW

Objective: *To know the meaning of the important mathematical terms of this chapter.*

1. Here are many of the mathematical terms used in this chapter. Be sure that you know them thoroughly and can use them correctly.

Law of Sines (*156*) imaginary axis (*187*)
Law of Cosines (*160*) argument (*188*)
ambiguous case (*162*) polar form (*188*)
Hero(n)'s Formula (*168*) De Moivre's Theorem (*192*)
inverse circular function (*174*) polar coordinates (*196*)
principal value of an inverse pole (*197*)
   trigonometric function (*175*) polar axis (*197*)
conditional equation (*180*) polar equations (*200*)
real axis (*187*) polar graph (*200*)

Objective: *To cite the Law of Sines and use it to solve triangles.*

2. State the Law of Sines in your own words.

━━ Where appropriate use the Law of Sines to find the measure of the required angle or side of $\triangle ABC$. Express results to nearest unit.

3. $A = 15°$, $a = 4$, $C = 37°$. Find c.

4. $A = 15°$, $a = 4$, $C = 37°$. Find b.

5. $A = 15°$, $a = 4$, $b = 8$. Find B.

6. $A = 15°$, $a = 4$, $b = 8$. Find C.

Objective: *To cite the Law of Cosines and use it to solve triangles.*

7. State the Law of Cosines in your own words.

━━ Find the required angle or side of $\triangle ABC$.

8. $A = 20°$, $b = 5$, $c = 3$. Find a.

9. $a = 3$, $b = 4$, $c = 6$. Find B.

10. $C = 115°$, $a = 5$, $b = 7$. Find c.

Objective: *To use trigonometric relations to calculate the area of triangles given data other than the base and altitude.*

━━ Find the area of $\triangle ABC$.

11. $A = 25°$, $b = 6$, $c = 8$.   **12.** $A = 25°$, $B = 73°$, $c = 15$.

13. $a = 6$, $b = 7$, $c = 8$.

Objective: *To explain the meaning of the symbols arc tan x, arc cos x, Arc tan x, etc. and evaluate expressions involving such symbols.*

14. Explain what the symbol arc sin x means. How do you think about it when working a problem?

15. How do Arc tan x and arc tan x differ? Explain.

━━ Find the members of each set.

16. arc tan $\left(\frac{1}{2}\right)$ **17.** arc cos $\left(\frac{-\sqrt{3}}{3}\right)$

18. arc sin (-1) **19.** arc sin (0) $\cup$ arc cos (0)

20. Arc tan $\left(\frac{-\sqrt{3}}{1}\right)$ **21.** Arc cos $\left(\frac{1}{2}\right)$

━━ Evaluate each expression.

22. tan (arc cos $\frac{4}{5}$)   **23.** sin (arc sin $\frac{1}{3}$)

24. cos (arc tan $\frac{5}{12}$)   **25.** sin (arc cos u) $0 \le u < 1$

26. cos (Arc tan $-\frac{5}{12}$)   **27.** tan (Arc sin u) $0 \le u < 1$

Objective: *To graph the inverse circular functions Arc sin x, Arc cos x and Arc tan x.*

▬ Graph each function. Identify the domain.

28. $y = $ Arc sin x **29.** $y = $ Arc cos x **30.** $y = $ Arc tan x

Objective: *To solve equations and inequalities which involve circular functions.*

▬ Find the solution set for each open sentence.

31. $2 \sin x - \sqrt{3} = 0$ **32.** $\tan 2x = -\frac{1}{2}$

33. $2 \sin x \cos x = \frac{1}{2}$ **34.** $\cos^2 x - \sin^2 x = \frac{\sqrt{2}}{2}$

35. $2 \sin x - \sqrt{3} < 0$ **36.** $2 \sin x \cos x \le \frac{\sqrt{2}}{2}$

Objective: *To express a complex number a + bi in polar form and perform the operations multiplication, division, raising to a power and root taking using the polar form.*

▬ Express each complex number in polar form.

37. $2 + 1i$

38. $-2 + i$

39. $-3 - \sqrt{3}i$

40. Explain how you would multiply two complex numbers of the form $r_1(\cos \theta_1 + i \sin \theta_1)$ and $r_2(\cos \theta_2 + i \sin \theta_2)$.

41. How would you divide the numbers in Exercise 40?

42. Calculate $(2 - 2i)^7$.

43. Find the 5 roots of $-\sqrt{3} + i$.

44. State De Moivre's Theorem.

Objective: *To convert from rectangular to polar coordinates and vice-versa and graph equations in polar coordinates.*

▬ Find the polar coordinates of the following.

45. $(-6, 6)$ **46.** $(3, 0)$ **47.** $(2, -1)$

▬ Find the rectangular coordinates of the following.

48. $(-3, 270°)$ **49.** $\left(5, \frac{2\pi}{3}\right)$ **50.** $(-1, -60°)$

▬ Sketch the graph of each curve on a polar coordinate system.

51. $r = 5$ **52.** $\theta = -21°$

53. $r = 2 + \sin \theta$ **54.** $r = -\frac{1}{2} + \cos \theta$

CHAPTER TEST ▮▮▮▮▮▮▮▮▮▮▮

1. Find b if $A = 43°$, $B = 17°$, and $a = 100$.

2. Find A if $a = 40$, $b = 64$, and $c = 36$.

3. Find the area of the triangle in Exercise 1.

4. Find the area of the triangle in Exercise 2.

5. Two towns are 38,500 feet apart. Art, in one town, hears a thunder clap 8 seconds after the flash of lightening. If the angle of elevation of the flash were 75° and sound travels at 1100 feet per second, how long should it take Joe, in the other town, to hear the thunder?

▬ Evaluate each of the following expressions.

6. $\sin\left(\text{arc tan } \frac{-2}{3}\right)$

7. $\tan\left(\text{arc cos } \frac{1}{-5}\right)$

8. $\cos\left(\text{Arc sin } \frac{5}{8}\right)$

9. Arc sin $\frac{\sqrt{2}}{2}$

▬ Solve each of the following.

10. $\tan x = 1$

11. $2\cos^2 x - 1 = 0$

12. $1 - 2\sin^2 x < 0$

13. Find the four fourth roots of $-1 + i\sqrt{3}$.

14. Graph $r = \sin\theta - 2$.

CHAPTER 5

SEQUENCES, SERIES, AND LIMITS

Every time that a basket is made in a basketball game the score of the team making the basket increases by one or two points and the new score appears almost immediately on the scoreboard. In the picture shown opposite the score is tied with three seconds remaining in the game. In the next few moments one of the "99's" will change to "101", the tie will be broken, and the game will be over.

If the successive scores of the winning team were printed out in a row they might look like this:

$$\{2, 4, 6, 7, 9, \cdots, 97, 99, 101\}.$$

Such a listing is an example of a *sequence*.

Both this chapter and the next are based upon this concept. However, unlike the one shown above, most of the sequences to be considered are to a certain extent, predictable; that is a rule exists that enables you to find the value of any term in the sequence. For example, "double the number of the term" is a rule for any term in a sequence of positive even integers arranged in increasing order.

You will also see in this chapter that some sequences are *bounded* while others are not. For example, finite sequences (as well as some infinite ones) are bounded even when the number of terms is very large. To show what is meant by this, if you were to construct a sequence consisting of all of the heights of all of the trees that have ever existed on earth up to the present moment, the finite sequence that you constructed would be bounded since no tree would have a height greater than, say, one mile. (You could in this case safely pick smaller numbers such as one half mile.)

You will see in this chapter and the next how certain types of bounded sequences are related to another important concept, that of *limit*. This latter concept is the basis for the study of calculus.

5–1 Sequences

The concept of *limit* is fundamental in mathematics. Without it many areas of knowledge, such as physics and engineering, would not exist except in rudimentary form. The use of limits is virtually unavoidable when studying those aspects of nature that are continuous (such as temperatures and velocities). Limits are needed even in some areas of knowledge, such as statistics, that deal mainly with non-continuous (discrete) phenomena. To provide you with the background that will best illuminate the concept of limit, an important and related concept is developed first, *sequences*.

During a nine-hole golf match between two millionaires, the first millionaire suggested the following wager:

> The first hole shall be worth one dollar to the winner, and each succeeding hole shall be worth twice as much as the hole immediately preceding it.

What was each of the nine holes worth?

To solve this problem set up a one-to-one correspondence between the holes and their dollar values, one dollar to the first with the value of each succeeding hole double the prior one. The following correspondence results.

Hole number	1	2	3	4	5	6	7	8	9
Dollar value	1	2	4	8	16	32	64	128	256

Consequently, the dollar value of each hole is given by one member of the ordered set of numbers: 1, 2, 4, 8, 16, 32, 64, 128, 256. The set of numbers 1, 2, 4, 8, $\cdots$, 256, in the order given is a **finite sequence** because its members are in a one-to-one correspondence with the subset $\{1, 2, 3, 4, \cdots, 9\}$ of the positive integers.

Suppose that there were a golf hole for every positive integer and that the wager remained the same. The wager, then would constitute the ordered set of numbers

$$1, 2, 4, 8, 16, 32, \cdots .$$

Such a set is an **infinite sequence** since it can be put in a one-to-one correspondence with the set of positive integers

$$\{1, 2, 3, \cdots\}.$$

The three dots indicate that the numbers continue in the same pattern indefinitely. Following are the basic definitions you will need.

Definitions A sequence is an ordered set of numbers which is the range of a function whose domain is the positive integers or a subset thereof. If the domain is the positive integers the sequence is an infinite sequence. If the domain is a subset, $1, 2, 3, \cdots, k$, of the positive integers, then it is a finite sequence.

The members of the sequence are terms of the sequence. The term corresponding to the positive integer n is the nth term of the sequence and is denoted by a symbol such as b_n. The sequence whose nth term is b_n is denoted $\{b_n\}$.

Each term of the sequence for the millionaire golf game can be expressed as a power of 2:

Hole number	1	2	3	4	5	6	7	8	$\cdots$	n
	$\updownarrow$	$\updownarrow$	$\updownarrow$	$\updownarrow$	$\updownarrow$	$\updownarrow$	$\updownarrow$	$\updownarrow$		$\updownarrow$
Dollar value	2^0	2^1	2^2	2^3	2^4	2^5	2^6	2^7	$\cdots$	2^{n-1}

If b_n denotes the nth term of this sequence, then b_n, $n \in \{1, 2, 3, \cdots\}$, is given by the formula

$$b_n = 2^{n-1}.$$

The sequence is $\{2^{n-1}\}$.

A general expression for the nth term of a sequence permits the calculation of any specific term of the sequence.

EXAMPLE 1. Calculate the fourth and the eleventh terms of the sequence 2^{n-1}.

The nth term is $\qquad b_n = 2^{n-1}.$

Thus the 4th term is $\qquad b_4 = 2^{4-1}$
$\qquad\qquad\qquad\qquad\quad = 2^3$
$\qquad\qquad\qquad\qquad\quad = 8.$

The 11th term is $\qquad b_{11} = 2^{11-1}$
$\qquad\qquad\qquad\qquad\quad = 2^{10}$
$\qquad\qquad\qquad\qquad\quad = 1024.$

Not all sequences possess a pattern expressible in terms of a formula. The sequence

$$3, 3.1, 3.14, 3.141, 3.1415, 3.14159, 3.141592, \cdots$$

of rational approximations to π is such a sequence.

Examination of the sequence $\frac{1}{1}, \frac{1}{3}, \frac{1}{6}, \cdots$ suggests that the fourth term might be $\frac{1}{10}$ since the denominators appear to increase by 2, by 3, etc. Replacing n in the expression

$$\frac{1}{-n^3 + \frac{13}{2}n^2 - \frac{21}{2}n + 6}$$

by 1, 2, and 3, respectively, you obtain the first three terms of the sequence above. Moreover, replacing n by 4 gives $\frac{1}{4}$, not $\frac{1}{10}$ as was suggested by the apparent pattern. This example illustrates that a sequence is not necessarily determined by specifying some of its terms. (Incidentally, a general term which gives a fourth term of $\frac{1}{10}$ is $\frac{1}{\frac{1}{2}n^2 + \frac{1}{2}n}$. Check this!)

Although not every sequence can be described by a formula, the sequences in this course will usually be described by a formula.

There are two common ways used to describe a sequence:

1. Stating the general term. For example:

$$b_n = 2^n - 3 \qquad n \in \{1, 2, 3, \cdots\}.$$

2. Giving the first term, b_1, and stating the relationship between each term and its successor. For example:

$$b_1 = -1,$$
$$b_{n+1} = b_n + 2^n \qquad n \in \{1, 2, 3, \cdots\}.$$

When the second procedure is used to define a sequence, the sequence is said to be defined **recursively** or by means of a **recursion formula.**

The use of a recursive definition to find the terms of a sequence is demonstrated in the following example.

EXAMPLE 2. Let b_n be defined as follows:

$$b_1 = -1$$
$$b_{n+1} = b_n + 2^n \qquad n \in \{1, 2, 3, \cdots\}$$

a. Find the first seven terms of $\{b_n\}$.
b. Find an expression for the nth term of $\{b_n\}$.

a.
$$b_1 = -1$$
$$b_2 = b_1 + 2^1 = -1 + 2 = 1$$
$$b_3 = b_2 + 2^2 = 1 + 4 = 5$$
$$b_4 = b_3 + 2^3 = 5 + 8 = 13$$
$$b_5 = b_4 + 2^4 = 13 + 16 = 29$$
$$b_6 = b_5 + 2^5 = 29 + 32 = 61$$
$$b_7 = b_6 + 2^6 = 61 + 64 = 125$$

b.

$$b_n = b_{n-1} + 2^{n-1}$$
$$= b_{n-2} + 2^{n-2} + 2^{n-1}$$
$$= b_{n-3} + 2^{n-3} + 2^{n-2} + 2^{n-1}$$
$$\vdots$$
$$= b_1 + 2^1 + 2^2 + \cdots + 2^{n-2} + 2^{n-1}$$
$$b_n = -1 + 2^1 + 2^2 + \cdots + 2^{n-2} + 2^{n-1}$$

To find a simple expression for b_n, do the following:

$$2(b_n + 1) = 2^2 + 2^3 + \cdots + 2^{n-1} + 2^n \qquad \mathbf{1}$$
$$(b_n + 1) = 2^1 + 2^2 + 2^3 + \cdots + 2^{n-1} \qquad \mathbf{2}$$

Subtracting **2** from **1**

$$2b_n + 2 - b_n - 1 = -2^1 + 2^n$$

or

$$b_n = 2^n - 3.$$

Now try these

━━ Write the first three terms of the sequence with the given general term.

1. $a_n = 3n$ **2.** $a_n = n^3$ **3.** $a_n = 3^n$ **4.** $a_n = 3$ **5.** $a_n = \sin\left(\frac{\pi n}{2}\right)$

Answers: **1.** 3, 6, 9   **2.** 1, 8, 27   **3.** 3, 9, 27   **4.** 3, 3, 3   **5.** 1, 0, −1

Checkpoint

1. If the range of a function is to be a sequence, what restrictions must be imposed on the domain of the function?

2. Name three ways in which a sequence may be described. What are the advantages and disadvantages of each way?

Exercises

A ━━ Each sequence below is defined recursively. Write the first six terms of each.

1. $b_1 = 5, b_{n+1} = b_n - 2$ **2.** $b_1 = 1, b_{n+1} = b_n + 2^{n-1}$

3. $b_1 = 3, b_{n+1} = 2b_n$ **4.** $b_1 = 4, b_{n+1} = (-3)b_n$

5. $a_1 = 4, a_{n+1} = (-1)^n a_n$ **6.** $a_1 = \frac{1}{2}, a_{n+1} = (-1)^{n-1} a_n$

7. $c_1 = 1, c_{n+1} = (2c_n)^{n-1}$ **8.** $c_1 = 2, c_{n+1} = (c_n - 2)^2$

9. $d_1 = 5, d_{n+1} = \frac{1}{n} d_n$ **10.** $d_1 = 1, d_2 = 1, d_{n+1} = d_n + d_{n-1}$

The general term of a sequence is given. Write the first five terms of the sequence.

11. $a_n = \dfrac{4}{n}$ **12.** $b_n = 2n - 1$ **13.** $c_k = 3k^2$

14. $d_k = k(k - 1)$ **15.** $a_t = 2t - 1$ **16.** $b_t = |2t| - 3$

17. $c_t = |2t - 3|$ **18.** $d_n = \dfrac{n}{2n - 1}$ **19.** $a_k = \dfrac{k + 2}{2k + 3}$

20. $b_k = \cos\dfrac{k\pi}{2}$ **21.** $c_t = \cos^2\dfrac{t\pi}{2}$ **22.** $d_t = (i)^t (i = \sqrt{-1})$

Give **a.** the general term and **b.** the recursive definition of each sequence.

23. $1, 2, 3, 4, \cdots$ **24.** $1, 3, 5, 7, 9, \cdots$

25. $\dfrac{3}{1}, \dfrac{3}{1 \cdot 2}, \dfrac{3}{1 \cdot 2 \cdot 3}, \dfrac{3}{1 \cdot 2 \cdot 3 \cdot 4}, \cdots$ **26.** $1, \frac{1}{2}, \frac{1}{4}, \frac{1}{8}, \cdots$

27. $1, -1, 1, -1, \cdots$ **28.** $-3, 2, 7, 12, \cdots$

B Use the following definition in Exercises 29–33.

> An <u>arithmetic sequence</u> is a sequence with general term: $a_n = a_1 + d(n - 1)$ where a_1 is the first term and d is a constant.

29. Let $a_1 = 2$, $d = 3$. Find a_2, a_3, a_4 and a_5.

30. Let $a_1 = 5$, $d = -2$. Find a_2, a_3, a_4 and a_5.

31. If $a_n = 1 - 3(n - 1)$, find the 6th term of the sequence.

32. Prove: If $a_n = a_1 + d(n - 1)$ then $a_{k+1} - a_k = d$.

33. Write a recursive definition of the arithmetic sequence with $a_n = a_1 + d(n - 1)$.

Use the following definition in Exercises 34–38.

> A <u>geometric sequence</u> is a sequence with general term $a_n = a_1 \cdot r^{n-1}$ where a_1 is the first term and r is a constant.

34. Let $a_1 = 2$, $r = 3$. Find a_2, a_3, a_4, and a_5.

35. Let $a_1 = 5$, $r = \frac{1}{3}$. Find a_2, a_3, a_4, and a_5.

36. Let $a_1 = 3$, $r = \frac{1}{2}$. Find a_2, a_3, a_4, and a_5.

37. If $a_n = \frac{2}{3}(\frac{1}{2})^{n-1}$, find the 6th term of the sequence.

38. Prove: If $a_n = a_1 r^{n-1}$, then $\dfrac{a_{k+1}}{a_k} = r$.

C **39.** Three sequences are defined below. Show that the first three terms of each are identical, but that the fourth terms are different.

a. $a_n = \dfrac{1}{n}$ 　　　　 **b.** $b_n = \dfrac{1}{n^3 - 6n^2 + 12n - 6}$

c. $c_n = \begin{cases} -\dfrac{1}{n} & \text{for } n \text{ a multiple of 4} \\ \dfrac{1}{n} & \text{otherwise} \end{cases}$

━━ Given $a_n = 3n$. Since $(n - 1)(n - 2)(n - 3) \cdots (n - k)$ equals 0 for $n \in \{1, 2, 3, \cdots k\}$, a second sequence identical to the first for k terms can be written by adding $(n - 1)(n - 2)(n - 3) \cdots (n - k)$ to the general term $3n$. That is, $a_n = 3n$ defines the sequence 3, 6, 9, 12, 15, $\cdots$, while $b_n = 3n + (n - 1)(n - 2)(n - 3)$ gives the sequence 3, 6, 9, 18, 39, $\cdots$. $\{a_n\}$ and $\{b_n\}$ are identical for three terms, but differ for all terms thereafter.

40. Write a general term for a sequence whose first four terms are 2, 4, 8, 16, but whose fifth term is not 32.

41. Write the general term of a sequence whose first three terms are $\frac{1}{2}, \frac{2}{3}, \frac{3}{4}$, and whose fourth term is the following.

　　a. $\frac{4}{5}$ 　　　　 **b.** $\frac{4}{11}$ 　　　　 **c.** $\frac{1}{2}$

5–2　Graphing Sequences

Finite sequences are not as useful in mathematics as are infinite sequences. There are many interesting theorems dealing with infinite sequences, and much of advanced analysis is based on these theorems. For reasons such as these, finite sequences will not be studied further. From this point forward "sequence" will mean "infinite sequence." So that you no longer have to concern yourself with finite sequences, the following convention is adopted for associating a finite sequence with an infinite sequence.

With the finite sequence

$$a_n, n \in \{1, 2, 3, \cdots, k\}$$

associate the infinite sequence

$$b_n = \begin{cases} a_n, n \in \{1, 2, 3, \cdots, k\} \\ 0, n > k. \end{cases}$$

For example, the finite sequence $\left\{1, \frac{1}{2}, \frac{1}{3}, \cdots, \frac{1}{k}\right\}$ is associated with the sequence $\left\{1, \frac{1}{2}, \frac{1}{3}, \cdots, \frac{1}{k}, 0, 0, 0, \cdots\right\}$.

A sequence $\{a_n\}$ is the range of a function that maps the positive integers into a set (possibly the same set) of numbers such as C or R. A sequence may be represented geometrically by plotting the points $(1, a_1)$, $(2, a_2)$, $(3, a_3)$, $\cdots$ in a coordinate plane. However, the usual procedure is to associate each term of the sequence with a point on a number line. The following graph shows the first seven terms of the sequence $\{a_n\} = \left\{\dfrac{n}{n+1}\right\}$. The rest of the terms lie between $\frac{7}{8}$ and 1. a_{11}, a_{23} and a_{47} are shown.

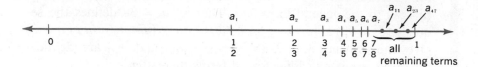

It is not possible to graph all of the terms of an infinite sequence. An adequate graph must depict accurately enough points corresponding to terms of the sequence to enable you to visualize easily the location of the remaining points.

EXAMPLE 1. Graph $\{b_n\} = \left\{(-1)^n \cdot \dfrac{1}{n}\right\}$.

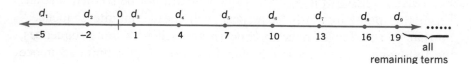

EXAMPLE 2. Graph $\{d_n\} = \{3n - 8\}$.

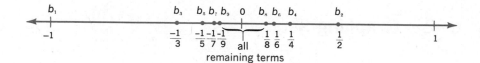

EXAMPLE 3. Graph $\{a_n\} = \{(-1)^n 3\}$.

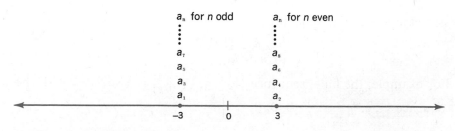

216   CHAPTER 5

EXAMPLE 4. Graph $\{c_n\} = \{9(\frac{2}{3})^{n-1}\}$.

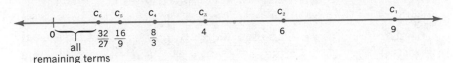

The notion of interval, first introduced in Chapter 1, is useful in describing the graph of a sequence. For example, in the graph of $\{a_n\} = \{\frac{n}{n+1}\}$ the points corresponding to $1, 2, \cdots, 7$ were located. The remaining points were shown to lie between $\frac{7}{8}$ and 1. That is to say for $n > 7$

$$a_n \in \langle \tfrac{7}{8}, 1 \rangle.$$

Similarly, in Example 1, for $n > 10$

$$b_n \in \langle -\tfrac{1}{9}, \tfrac{1}{8} \rangle.$$

In Example 4, for $n > 6$

$$c_n \in \langle 0, \tfrac{32}{27} \rangle.$$

The remaining points of $\{d_n\} = \{3n - 8\}$ of Example 2 can be located in an open interval also, if the notion of open interval is extended slightly. The extension needed is to include *half-lines* as open intervals, that is, the half-line $\{x : x > a, \quad a, x \in R\}$.

> **Definition**
>
> $$\{x : x > a, \quad a, x \in R\} = \langle a, \infty \rangle$$
>
> is an open interval with no right end.
>
> Also,
>
> $$\{x : x < a, \quad a, x \in R\} = \langle -\infty, a \rangle$$
>
> is an open interval with no left end.

Now the remaining points in the graph of $\{d_n\} = \{3n - 8\}$ in Example 2 lie in an open interval, namely for $n > 9$,

$$d_n \in \langle 19, \infty \rangle.$$

Open intervals are useful in designating a set of points that lie within a given distance from one point. Suppose the point is 3 and the distance is 2. The interval $\langle 1, 5 \rangle$ is the set of all points within two units of 3. The open interval $\langle 1, 5 \rangle$ is the **neighborhood of** 3 **with radius** 2. Notice that 3 is the midpoint of $\langle 1, 5 \rangle$.

Definition Given a point M on a line; any open interval with M as midpoint is a <u>neighborhood of M</u>. If $\langle a, b \rangle$ is a neighborhood of M, then the <u>radius</u> of $\langle a, b \rangle$ is $\dfrac{b - a}{2}$ $(a < b)$.

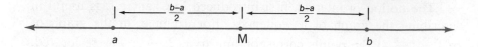

Now try these

━━ Find an open interval that includes all the terms of the indicated sequence.

1. $\{a_n\} = \left\{\dfrac{1}{n + 1}\right\}$ **2.** $\{a_n\} = \{n + 1\}$ **3.** $\{a_n\} = \left\{\cos \dfrac{\pi n}{2}\right\}$

Answers: **1.** $\langle 0, \frac{3}{4} \rangle$ **2.** $\langle 1\frac{7}{8}, \infty \rangle$ **3.** $\langle -1.1, 1.05 \rangle$ Note: These intervals, or any other set of open intervals, can be replaced by open intervals that are more restrictive. The new set of intervals can be similarly replaced by an even more restrictive set and so on indefinitely.

Checkpoint

1. How do graphs of sequences differ from graphs of other functions?

2. What is meant by a neighborhood of a point on a line? Explain your answer.

Exercises

A ━━ In Exercises 1–9 graph between five and ten terms of each sequence on a number line. When possible produce an open interval in which the remaining points lie.

1. $\{a_n\} = \{2n - 5\}$ **2.** $\{a_n\} = \left\{\dfrac{n + 1}{n}\right\}$ **3.** $\{a_n\} = \left\{\dfrac{1}{2n - 1}\right\}$

4. $\{b_n\} = \left\{(\tfrac{3}{4})^{n-1}\right\}$ **5.** $\{b_n\} = \left\{(-1)^{n-1}\right\}$ **6.** $\{b_n\} = \left\{6 - \dfrac{2}{n}\right\}$

7. $\{c_n\} = \left\{(\tfrac{3}{2})^n\right\}$ **8.** $\{c_n\} = \left\{\dfrac{(-1)^n}{n}\right\}$ **9.** $\{c_n\} = \left\{-3 + \dfrac{3}{n^2}\right\}$

10. For each Exercise 1–9 determine, if possible, an open interval which includes all the terms of the sequence for $n > 100$, but excludes those terms for $n \le 100$. For $n > 1000$, but excludes those terms for $n \le 1000$.

■ In Exercises 11–16 show graphically and express algebraically using inequalities the neighborhood of M with radius r.

11. $M = 5, r = 3$ **12.** $M = \frac{3}{2}, r = 1$ **13.** $M = 0, r = \frac{5}{2}$

14. $M = -2, r = 3$ **15.** $M = -\frac{3}{4}, r = \frac{3}{2}$ **16.** $M = t, r = p$

B   **17.** Find a neighborhood about $M = 1$ such that all the terms of $\left\{\frac{n+1}{n}\right\}$ for $n \geq 10$ lie in that neighborhood, but the preceding terms lie outside the neighborhood.

18. Repeat Exercise 17 for the sequence $\{1 + (\frac{1}{2})^n\}$.

19. Repeat Exercise 17 for the sequence $\{(-1)^n\}$. What happens here?

5–3 "Is Close To"

Examine the graph of the sequence $\{a_n\} = \left\{\frac{1}{2n}\right\}$.

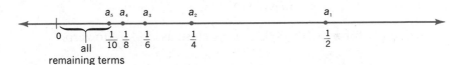

Notice first that each term of $\{a_n\}$ appears to be smaller than its predecessor, that is, the sequence is decreasing. This can be verified by proving that $a_m < a_n$ $(m > n)$. In particular, prove that

$$\frac{1}{2m} < \frac{1}{2n} \qquad \text{whenever } m > n.$$

The proof follows. $m > n$ $m, n \in N$

Thus

$$\frac{1}{2mn} \cdot m > \frac{1}{2mn} \cdot n \qquad \left(\frac{1}{2mn} > 0\right)$$

or

$$\frac{1}{2n} > \frac{1}{2m}.$$

So the terms of $\{a_n\}$ are decreasing.

Look again at the graph. It appears that if n is large enough, then a_n "is close to" zero. For example, if $n = 500$, then $a_{500} = \frac{1}{1000}$ is close to zero. In fact, it is within one one thousandth of a unit of zero. Moreover, since each succeeding term of $\{a_n\}$ is smaller than the preceding terms, all the terms of $\{a_n\}$ for $n > 500$ are closer than one one thousandth of a unit to zero.

How large would you have to choose n to be so that all the terms of $\{a_n\}$ from that n on would be as close as one one millionth of a unit to zero? The answer to this question may be found as follows.

If a_n is to be as close as one one millionth of a unit from zero, then a_n must be less than $\frac{1}{1,000,000}$ for some $n \in N$. This can be expressed in the inequality

$$\frac{1}{2n} < \frac{1}{1,000,000}. \qquad\qquad \textbf{1}$$

How large must n be? Multiply both sides of **1** by $n \cdot 1,000,000$ getting

$$500,000 < n. \qquad\qquad \textbf{2}$$

Thus it *appears* that n larger than 500,000 will make a_n as close as $\frac{1}{1,000,000}$ to zero. To verify this, reverse the steps **1** and **2**, that is, let

$$n > 500,000.$$

Then

$$\frac{1}{1,000,000} > \frac{1}{2n},$$

or

$$\frac{1}{1,000,000} > a_n.$$

Consequently for $n > 500,000$, a_n is as close as $\frac{1}{1,000,000}$ to zero.

EXAMPLE. Let $\{b_n\} = \left\{\frac{n-1}{n+1}\right\}$.

a. Show that $b_n < b_{n+1}$ for $n \in N$.
b. Find $M \in N$ so that b_n is as close to 1 as $\frac{1}{50}$ for all $n \geq M$.

a.
$$b_n = \frac{n-1}{n+1} \qquad b_{n+1} = \frac{n}{n+2}$$

As is often the case when trying to prove an inequality, you begin with the inequality you are trying to prove and see if you can reduce it by reversible operations to an inequality known to be true. The sequence in reverse order constitutes a proof:

$$b_n < b_{n+1}$$

iff
$$\frac{n-1}{n+1} < \frac{n}{n+2}$$

iff $\qquad (n-1)(n+2) < n(n+1)$

(Both $(n+1)$ and $(n+2) > 0$.)

iff $\qquad n^2 + n - 2 < n^2 + n$
iff $\qquad\qquad -2 < 0$

Thus $b_n < b_{n+1}$ for $n \in N$.

b. You want to find an $M \in \mathbb{N}$ (M is a fixed number) so that b_n is within $\frac{1}{50}$ of a unit of 1. Since each $b_n < 1$ (why?), this condition may be expressed as follows.

$$1 - b_n < \tfrac{1}{50}$$

or
$$1 - \tfrac{1}{50} < b_n$$

So solve for n as follows.

$$b_n > \tfrac{49}{50}$$

iff
$$\frac{n-1}{n+1} > \frac{49}{50}$$

iff
$$50(n-1) > 49(n+1)$$

iff
$$50n - 50 > 49n + 49$$

iff
$$n > 99$$

Working backwards in this derivation from $n > 99$ to $b_n > \frac{49}{50}$ constitutes a proof of the statement: For $n \geq 100$, b_n is as close as $\frac{1}{50}$ to 1. Thus M can be chosen to be 100 (or any larger number). A quick computation will show you that $b_{100} = \frac{99}{101}$ which is within $\frac{2}{101}$ of 1. This is just slightly less than $\frac{1}{50}$.

Checkpoint

In the discussion of the sequence $\{a_n\} = \left\{\frac{1}{2n}\right\}$, you found that you could get as close as $\frac{1}{1,000,000}$ to zero. Could you get closer to zero than this for some $n \in \mathbb{N}$? How close can you get?

Exercises

A
1. Let $\{a_n\} = \left\{\frac{1}{n}\right\}$.
   a. Show that $a_n > a_{n+1}$ for $n \in \mathbb{N}$.
   b. Find $M \in \mathbb{N}$ so that a_n is as close to 0 as $\frac{1}{200}$ for all $n \geq M$.
2. Let $\{b_n\} = \left\{\frac{n}{n+1}\right\}$.
   a. Show that $b_n < b_{n+1}$ for $n \in \mathbb{N}$.
   b. Find $M \in \mathbb{N}$ so that b_n is as close to 1 as $\frac{1}{500}$ for all $n \geq M$.
3. Let $\{c_n\} = \left\{\frac{1}{2^n}\right\}$.
   a. Show that $c_n > c_{n+1}$ for $n \in \mathbb{N}$.
   b. Find $M \in \mathbb{N}$ so that c_n is as close to 0 as $\frac{1}{1000}$ for all $n \geq M$. As close to 0 as $\frac{1}{1,000,000}$.

4. Let $\{a_n\} = \left\{\dfrac{2n}{4n+1}\right\}$.

    a. Show that $a_n < a_{n+1}$ for $n \in N$.

    b. Find $M \in N$ so that a_n is as close to $\frac{1}{2}$ as $\frac{1}{100}$ for all $n \geq M$.

    c. Find $M \in N$ so that a_n is as close to $\frac{1}{2}$ as $\frac{1}{500}$ for all $n \geq M$.

    d. Does the M found in **c** suffice to solve **b**? Explain.

5. Let $\{a_n\} = \left\{-\dfrac{1}{n}\right\}$.

    a. Show that $a_n < a_{n+1}$ for $n \in N$.

    b. Find an $M \in N$ so that a_n is as close to 0 as $\frac{1}{100}$ for all $n \geq M$.

B **6.** Let $\{d_n\} = \left\{-\dfrac{(n-1)}{n}\right\}$.

    a. Show that $d_n > d_{n+1}$ for $n \in N$.

    b. Find an $M \in N$ so that d_n is as close to -1 as $\frac{1}{500}$ for all $n \geq M$.

7. Let $\{c_n\} = \dfrac{n}{3n+1}$.

    a. Show that $c_n < c_{n+1}$ for $n \in N$.

    b. Find an $M \in N$ so that c_n is as close to $\frac{1}{3}$ as $\frac{1}{50}$ for all $n \geq M$.

8. Let $\{b_n\} = \left\{\dfrac{2n-1}{2n+1}\right\}$.

    a. Show that $b_n < b_{n+1}$ for $n \in N$.

    b. Find an $M \in N$ so that b_n is as close to 1 as $\dfrac{1}{20,000}$ for all $n \geq M$.

C **9.** Let $\{a_n\} = \left\{\dfrac{1}{5n}\right\}$.

    a. Show that $a_n > a_{n+1}$ for $n \in N$.

    b. Find an $M \in N$ so that a_n is as close to 0 as $k > 0$ for all $n \geq M$.

5–4 Neighborhoods and Sequences

In the previous section you learned how to find an $M \in N$ so that the terms of a sequence $\{a_n\}$ for $n \geq M$ were within a specified distance of some given number. The sequences with which you worked had all positive or all negative terms—never a mixture of positive and negative terms. The methods you learned in the last section will now be extended to a more general method which can always be used. The idea of neighborhood is central to this method. An example will clarify the idea.

EXAMPLE 1. Consider the sequence $\{a_n\} = \left\{\dfrac{n+2}{n+3}\right\}$ and the neighborhood of 1 with radius $\frac{1}{10}$; that is, $\langle 0.9, 1.1 \rangle$.

Which terms of $\left\{\dfrac{n+2}{n+3}\right\}$ lie in $\langle 0.9, 1.1 \rangle$? That is, how large must n be so that a_n is within $\frac{1}{10}$ of 1? For a term a_n to be in $\langle 0.9, 1.1 \rangle$, a_n must be between 0.9 and 1.1. That is, the compound inequality

$$0.9 < \frac{n+2}{n+3} < 1.1$$

must be true. Consequently the question can be answered by solving the compound inequality

$$0.9 < \frac{n+2}{n+3} \quad and \quad \frac{n+2}{n+3} < 1.1.$$

The solutions to these two simple inequalities follow.

$0.9 < \dfrac{n+2}{n+3}$	$\dfrac{n+2}{n+3} < 1.1$
iff $9 < \dfrac{10n+20}{n+3}$	iff $\dfrac{10n+20}{n+3} < 11$
iff $9n + 27 < 10n + 20$	iff $10n + 20 < 11n + 33$
iff $7 < n$	iff $-13 < n$

The solution set of $7 < n$ is $\{n : n > 7, n \in \mathbf{N}\}$.
The solution set of $-13 < n$ is $\{n : n > -13, n \in \mathbf{N}\}$.
Consequently the solution set of $7 < n$ *and* $-13 < n$ is

$$\{n : n > 7, n \in \mathbf{N}\} \cap \{n : n > -13, n \in \mathbf{N}\}$$

or $$\{n : n > 7, n \in \mathbf{N}\}.$$

Hence, for all $n > 7$, a_n is in $\langle 0.9, 1.1 \rangle$. That is, if you choose M to be 8, then $a_n \in \langle 0.9, 1.1 \rangle$ for all $n \geq M = 8$. This situation is shown in the graph below.

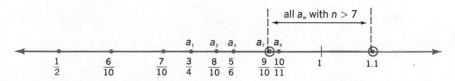

Table 1 contains similar information for other neighborhoods of 1 and the sequence $\left\{\dfrac{n+2}{n+3}\right\}$. The entries in the last column name the first term of the sequence that lies in the given neighborhood. For example, the last entry in the last row shows that a_{99998} and all succeeding terms of $\left\{\dfrac{n+2}{n+3}\right\}$ lie in the neighborhood $\langle 0.99999, 1.00001 \rangle$ of 1. In this case M could be 99998.

Neighborhood of One	Radius of Neighborhood	First Term of $\{a_n\}$ in the Neighborhood
$\langle 0.9, 1.1 \rangle$	$\dfrac{1}{10}$	a_8
$\langle 0.99, 1.01 \rangle$	$\dfrac{1}{100}$	a_{98}
$\langle 0.999, 1.001 \rangle$	$\dfrac{1}{1000}$	a_{998}
$\langle 0.9999, 1.0001 \rangle$	$\dfrac{1}{10,000}$	a_{9998}
$\langle 0.99999, 1.00001 \rangle$	$\dfrac{1}{100,000}$	a_{99998}

Table 1

The next example illustrates how using neighborhoods facilitates finding M when the sequence has both positive and negative terms. In this instance notice that both parts of the compound inequality play a vital role.

EXAMPLE 2. Find an $M \in N$ so that for $n \geq M$ the terms of $\{b_n\} = \left\{\dfrac{(-1)^n}{n}\right\}$ are in the neighborhood of 0 with radius $\dfrac{1}{1000}$, i.e., within $\dfrac{1}{1000}$ of 0.

$M \in N$ is obtained by solving the compound inequality

$$-0.001 < \frac{(-1)^n}{n} < .001. \qquad \text{That is,}$$

$-.001 < \dfrac{(-1)^n}{n}$	*and*	$\dfrac{(-1)^n}{n} < .001.$
$-.001 < \dfrac{(-1)^n}{n}$ iff		$\dfrac{(-1)^n}{n} < .001$ iff
$-1 < \dfrac{(-1)^n}{n}1000$ iff		$\dfrac{(-1)^n}{n}1000 < 1$ iff
$-n < (-1)^n 1000$ iff		$(-1)^n 1000 < n$
$n > (-1)^{n+1}1000$		

If n is even, $(-1)^{n+1} = -1$, and $n > -1 \cdot 1000$ for all n. If n is odd, $(-1)^{n+1} = 1$, and $n > 1 \cdot 1000$ when $n \geq 1001$.

If n is odd, $(-1)^n = -1$, and $-1 \cdot 1000 < n$ for all n. If n is even, $(-1)^n = 1$, and $1 \cdot 1000 < n$ when $n > 1001$.

If $n \geq 1001$, then the conditions $n > 1001$ (n even) and $n \geq 1001$ (n odd) are both satisfied. Consequently b_{1001} and all succeeding terms are in $\langle -0.001, 0.001 \rangle$.

In the same manner it can be shown that the entries in Table 2 are accurate. Again it is clear that *most* (all but a finite number) of the terms of $\frac{(-1)^n}{n}$ are close to 0. Considering the neighborhood $\langle -0.000001, 0.000001 \rangle$, all but 1,000,000 of the terms are in the interval. In fact, no matter how small you make the radius of the neighborhood about 0, you could still prove that only a finite number of the terms of $\frac{(-1)^n}{n}$ lie outside the neighborhood.

However, there are neighborhoods of points which contain only a finite number of terms of a sequence.

Neighborhood of Zero	Radius of Neighborhood	First Term in Neighborhood
$\langle -0.01, 0.01 \rangle$	$\dfrac{1}{100}$	b_{101}
$\langle -0.0001, 0.0001 \rangle$	$\dfrac{1}{10,000}$	b_{10001}
$\langle -0.00001, 0.00001 \rangle$	$\dfrac{1}{100,000}$	$b_{100,001}$
$\langle -0.000001, 0.000001 \rangle$	$\dfrac{1}{1,000,000}$	$b_{1,000,001}$

Table 2

EXAMPLE 3. How many terms of the sequence $\{c_n\} = \left\{\dfrac{24}{n}\right\}$ lie in the neighborhood $\langle \frac{1}{2}, \frac{3}{2} \rangle$?

$$\frac{1}{2} < \frac{24}{n} < \frac{3}{2}$$

$$\frac{1}{2} < \frac{24}{n} \qquad and \qquad \frac{24}{n} < \frac{3}{2}$$

$$\frac{1}{2} < \frac{24}{n} \quad \text{iff} \qquad \qquad \frac{24}{n} < \frac{3}{2} \quad \text{iff}$$

$$n < 48 \qquad \qquad \qquad 48 < 3n \quad \text{iff}$$

$$16 < n$$

The solution of the compound inequality is $16 < n < 48$. Hence for $n \in \{17, 18, \cdots, 46, 47\}$ c_n lies in $\langle \frac{1}{2}, \frac{3}{2} \rangle$. There are 31 terms of $\{c_n\}$ in this neighborhood.

There are neighborhoods of points which contain an infinite subset of the terms of a sequence, but another infinite subset of the sequence lies outside the neighborhood. For example, the neighborhood $\langle \frac{1}{2}, \frac{3}{2} \rangle$ contains an infinite number of the terms of $(-1)^n$. An infinite number also lie outside $\langle \frac{1}{2}, \frac{3}{2} \rangle$, namely all those terms for odd n.

Exercises

A ━━ In Exercises 1–10 find the terms for each sequence which are in the neighborhood of radius r about m.

1. $\{a_n\} = \left\{\dfrac{n}{n+1}\right\}$, $r = \frac{1}{2}$, $m = 1$

2. $\{a_n\} = \left\{\dfrac{n}{n+1}\right\}$, $r = \frac{1}{1000}$, $m = 1$

3. $\{b_n\} = \{6(\frac{2}{3})^{n-1}\}$, $r = \frac{1}{2}$, $m = 1$

4. $\{b_n\} = \{6(\frac{2}{3})^{n-1}\}$, $r = \frac{1}{100}$, $m = \frac{2}{100}$

5. $\{c_n\} = \{2n - 3\}$, $r = 5$, $m = 2$

6. $\{c_n\} = \{2n - 3\}$, $r = 2$, $m = \frac{9}{10}$

7. $\{d_n\} = \left\{(-1)^n \dfrac{n}{n+1}\right\}$, $r = \frac{3}{4}$, $m = 0$

8. $\{d_n\} = \left\{(-1)^n \dfrac{n}{n+1}\right\}$, $r = \frac{1}{10}$, $m = 1$

9. $\{e_n\} = \left\{\dfrac{2n}{n+5}\right\}$, $r = \frac{1}{4}$, $m = 1\frac{1}{4}$

10. $\{e_n\} = \left\{\dfrac{2n}{n+5}\right\}$, $r = \frac{1}{100}$, $m = 2$

11. Given $\dfrac{n-1}{2n} < \dfrac{1}{10}$. Justify each step in the following argument. What statement does the argument prove?

a. $\dfrac{10n - 10}{2n} < 1$ iff

b. $10n - 10 < 2n$ iff

c. $-10 < -8n$ iff

d. $5 > 4n$ iff

e. $\frac{5}{4} > n$

In Exercises 12–17 you are given $\{a_n\} = \left\{\dfrac{1}{2n-1}\right\}$. In each exercise for the given neighborhood of 0, what is the first term within the neighborhood? How many terms lie outside it?

12. $\langle -1, 1 \rangle$ **13.** $\langle -\frac{1}{2}, \frac{1}{2} \rangle$ **14.** $\langle -\frac{1}{10}, \frac{1}{10} \rangle$ **15.** $\langle -\frac{1}{1000}, \frac{1}{1000} \rangle$

16. $\left\langle -\dfrac{1}{1,000,000}, \dfrac{1}{1,000,000} \right\rangle$ **17.** $\langle -R, R \rangle$ where $R > 0$

B **18.** Given $\{a_n\} = \left\{\dfrac{7n + 13}{3n}\right\}$. Which terms of $\{a_n\}$ are

a. greater than 2?   **b.** less than $\frac{8}{3}$?

c. in $\langle 2, 2\frac{2}{3} \rangle$?   **d.** in $\langle \frac{13}{6}, \frac{15}{6} \rangle$?

5–5 The Limit of a Sequence

What does it mean to say that "a sequence has a limit"? Here are some examples that will help you build an intuitive basis for the definition.

Examples of Sequences

1. $\{a_n\} = \left\{\frac{1}{n}\right\}$ or $1, \frac{1}{2}, \frac{1}{3}, \frac{1}{4}, \frac{1}{5}, \frac{1}{6}, \frac{1}{7}, \cdots, \frac{1}{n}, \cdots$

2. $\{b_n\} = \{3n - 5\}$ or $-2, 1, 4, 7, 10, 13, \cdots, 3n - 5, \cdots$

3. $\{c_n\} = \left\{\frac{(-1)^n}{n}\right\}$ or $-1, \frac{1}{2}, -\frac{1}{3}, \frac{1}{4}, -\frac{1}{5}, \frac{1}{6}, \cdots, \frac{(-1)^n}{n}, \cdots$

4. $\{d_n\} = \left\{\frac{3n + 1}{n}\right\}$ or $4, \frac{7}{2}, \frac{10}{3}, \frac{13}{4}, \frac{16}{5}, \frac{19}{6}, \cdots, \frac{3n + 1}{n}, \cdots$

5. $\{e_n\} = \left\{(-1)^n \frac{2n + 1}{n}\right\}$ or $-3, \ 2\frac{1}{2}, \ -2\frac{1}{3}, \ 2\frac{1}{4}, \ -2\frac{1}{5}, \ 2\frac{1}{6}, \cdots,$ $(-1)^n \frac{2n + 1}{n}, \cdots$

EXAMPLE 1. The terms of sequence **1** are very small for large values of n. The terms are clustered very close to zero for large n, but zero is not a term of the sequence. Zero is the limit of the sequence. The sequence is said to converge to zero.

EXAMPLE 2. Each term in sequence **2** is three greater than its predecessor. For large values of n, the terms are large. There is no number about which the terms of the sequence cluster. This sequence has no limit; it is said to diverge.

EXAMPLE 3. Sequence **3** is similar to sequence **1**. The terms are close to zero for large values of n, but unlike sequence **1,** there are terms to the right and to the left of zero. This sequence converges to zero.

EXAMPLE 4. The terms of sequence **4** are very close to 3 for large values of n. To see this rewrite each term: $4, 3\frac{1}{2}, 3\frac{1}{3}, 3\frac{1}{4}, 3\frac{1}{5}, 3\frac{1}{6}, 3\frac{1}{7}, \cdots, 3 + \frac{1}{n}, \cdots$. Since the terms are close to 3, the sequence has a limit of 3.

EXAMPLE 5. The terms of sequence **5** which correspond to even numbers are close to 2. The terms corresponding to odd numbers are close to -2. Consequently there is *not* a unique single number about which the terms cluster. The sequence has no limit. Therefore it is said to diverge.

The discussion of the examples suggests the following ideas:

a. Some sequences have limits; some do not.

b. If a sequence has a limit, then the limit is a unique number.

c. If a sequence has a limit, then most of the terms are close to the limit.

It is sometimes difficult to determine the limit of a sequence. You can make a guess as to the identity of the limit based upon an examination of the given sequence and then try to confirm (or refute) your guess. To confirm or refute your guess you need to know the mathematical meaning of the phrase "most of the terms are very close to the limit". The definition follows.

Definition A sequence $\{a_n\}$ has a limit A (or a sequence $\{a_n\}$ converges to A) if for every neighborhood of A a positive integer M can be found such that a_n is in the neighborhood for all $n \geq M$. If a sequence has a limit, it is a convergent sequence. If a sequence has no limit, it is a divergent sequence.

The notation $\{a_n\} \longrightarrow A$ is read: "The sequence $\{a_n\}$ converges to A" or "The limit of $\{a_n\}$ is A." Notice that one refers to *the* limit of a sequence, although there is nothing concerning uniqueness in the definition. (Definitions generally do not concern themselves with the number of objects being defined, nor even with the matter of whether the object defined exists.) It can be shown that it is indeed correct to refer to *the* limit of a sequence, that is, that the limit of a sequence *is* unique if it exists at all.

The definition of a convergent sequence is the basis of a challenge to any person who claims that a certain number is a limit of a given sequence. It says that if you claim that A is the limit, then, when challenged with a neighborhood of A, you can always find a number M such that all the terms of the sequence that correspond to positive integers greater than or equal to M will lie in that neighborhood. The following example illustrates this idea.

EXAMPLE 6.

Given: $\{a_n\} = \left\{\dfrac{1}{n}\right\}$.

Claim: The limit of this sequence is 0, that is $\{a_n\} \longrightarrow 0$.

Challenge: Given the neighborhood $\langle -.01, .01 \rangle$, find M such that for all $n \geq M \quad a_n \in \langle -0.01, 0.01 \rangle$.

Accepting the challenge you have the following.

$$-\frac{1}{100} < \frac{1}{n} < \frac{1}{100} \qquad \text{if and only if}$$

$$-\frac{1}{100} < \frac{1}{n} \qquad and \qquad \frac{1}{n} < \frac{1}{100}.$$

$$-\frac{1}{100} < \frac{1}{n} \qquad\qquad \frac{1}{n} < \frac{1}{100} \text{ iff}$$

is always true $100 < n$

because $n > 0$.

Hence if M is chosen to be 101, then all terms from a_{101} on are in the neighborhood

$$\langle -0.01, 0.01 \rangle.$$

The challenge is successfully met.

But the challenger may not stop. He may say; "I'm going to choose a smaller neighborhood such as $\langle -0.000001, 0.000001 \rangle$ or $\langle -10^{-17}, 10^{-17} \rangle$". These challenges can be successfully met by using the procedure above. $M = 1{,}000{,}001$ and $M = 10^{17} + 1$ will suffice. (Check this.)

However, no matter how many such challenges you meet, you will not have proved that 0 is the limit of $\left\{\frac{1}{n}\right\}$ because the definition requires you to show that an M can be found for *every* neighborhood. How can this be done? The answer lies in the use of a **general neighborhood**.

Definition   The <u>general neighborhood</u> of A is $\langle A - \epsilon, A + \epsilon \rangle$ where ϵ is a variable whose replacement set is the set of positive real numbers.

Both ϵ and $\in$ are forms of the Greek letter *epsilon*. $\in$ will continue to be used in the sense of "is a member of" while ϵ will be used to stand for any positive number.

The general neighborhood of 0 is $\langle 0 - \epsilon, 0 + \epsilon \rangle = \langle -\epsilon, \epsilon \rangle$. You can *prove* that $\left\{\frac{1}{n}\right\} \longrightarrow 0$ by showing that you can find an M when the challenge neighborhood is the general neighborhood. This means that "most of the terms are close to 0" no matter who defines "is close to" because the real number ϵ in the definition of a general neighborhood can be as small as or smaller than any positive real number. The proof is given in Example 7.

EXAMPLE 7.

Given: $\{a_n\} = \left\{\frac{1}{n}\right\}$.

Claim: The limit of this sequence is 0.

Challenge: Find M, given the neighborhood $\langle-\epsilon, \epsilon\rangle$, ϵ a positive real number.

Accepting the challenge:

$$-\epsilon < \frac{1}{n} < \epsilon \quad \text{iff}$$

$$-\epsilon < \frac{1}{n} \qquad \text{and} \qquad \frac{1}{n} < \epsilon.$$

$-\epsilon < \dfrac{1}{n}$	$\dfrac{1}{n} < \epsilon \quad$ iff
is always true	$\dfrac{1}{\epsilon} < n.$
because $n > 0.$	

So choose M to be any integer greater than $\frac{1}{\epsilon}$. Therefore, the terms a_n for which $n \geq M > \frac{1}{\epsilon}$ are in the neighborhood $\langle-\epsilon, \epsilon\rangle$ because $n \geq M > \frac{1}{\epsilon}$ implies $\epsilon > \frac{1}{n}$. Also $-\epsilon < \frac{1}{n}$ for all $n \geq M$.

What has been done in this example is to show that for all values of ϵ there exists an M, namely, any number greater than $\frac{1}{\epsilon}$, such that all terms a_n with $n \geq M$ lie in the neighborhood $\langle-\epsilon, \epsilon\rangle$. Hence it has been *proved* that $\{a_n\} \longrightarrow 0$. For any neighborhood selected by a challenger, you can now find an appropriate M.

The following table lists some challenge neighborhoods, the corresponding values of $\frac{1}{\epsilon}$ and a value of M that would satisfy the condition that all the terms of the sequence corresponding to positive integers greater than or equal to M will lie in the neighborhood

$$\langle-\epsilon, \epsilon\rangle.$$

Challenge neighborhood	$\langle-10^{-6}, 10^{-6}\rangle$	$\langle-\frac{3}{4}, \frac{3}{4}\rangle$	$\langle-10^{-10}, 10^{-10}\rangle$	$\langle-\frac{1}{450}, \frac{1}{450}\rangle$
$\dfrac{1}{\epsilon}$	10^6	$\dfrac{4}{3}$	10^{10}	450
$M > \dfrac{1}{\epsilon}$	$10^6 + 1$	2	$10^{10} + 1$	451

The following examples prove that the suggested limits of the sequences in Examples 3 and 4 are actually the limits.

EXAMPLE 8. Prove: $\{c_n\} = \left\{\frac{(-1)^n}{n}\right\} \longrightarrow 0$

Challenge: Given $\langle -\epsilon, \epsilon \rangle$, find an M such that for $n \geq M \ c_n \in \langle -\epsilon, \epsilon \rangle$.

This requires the solution of the following compound inequality.

$$-\epsilon < \frac{(-1)^n}{n} < \epsilon$$

or

$$-\epsilon < \frac{(-1)^n}{n} \qquad \text{and} \qquad \frac{(-1)^n}{n} < \epsilon.$$

$$-\epsilon < \frac{(-1)^n}{n} \ \text{ iff} \qquad\qquad \frac{(-1)^n}{n} < \epsilon \ \text{ iff}$$

$$-n < \frac{(-1)^n}{\epsilon} \ \text{ iff} \qquad\qquad \frac{(-1)^n}{\epsilon} < n$$

$$n > \frac{(-1)^{n+1}}{\epsilon}$$

If n is even, $(-1)^{n+1} = -1$ If n is odd, $(-1)^n = -1$

and $n > -\frac{1}{\epsilon}$.   and $-\frac{1}{\epsilon} < n$.

If n is odd, $(-1)^{n+1} = 1$ If n is even, $(-1)^n = 1$

and $n > \frac{1}{\epsilon}$.   and $\frac{1}{\epsilon} < n$.

So, whether n is even or odd, choose $M > \frac{1}{\epsilon}$. Thus, for all $n \geq M$, a_n is in $\langle -\epsilon, \epsilon \rangle$ and 0 is the limit.

EXAMPLE 9. Prove: $\{d_n\} = \left\{\frac{3n + 1}{n}\right\} \longrightarrow 3$

Challenge: Given $\langle 3 - \epsilon, 3 + \epsilon \rangle$, find an M such that for $n \geq M$, $d_n \in \langle 3 - \epsilon, 3 + \epsilon \rangle$. This requires solving this compound inequality.

$$3 - \epsilon < \frac{3n + 1}{n} < 3 + \epsilon$$

or $$3 - \epsilon < \frac{3n + 1}{n} \qquad \text{and} \qquad \frac{3n + 1}{n} < 3 + \epsilon.$$

$$3 - \epsilon < \frac{3n + 1}{n} \ \text{ iff} \qquad\qquad \frac{3n + 1}{n} < 3 + \epsilon \qquad \text{iff}$$

$$3n - \epsilon n < 3n + 1 \ \ \text{iff} \qquad\qquad 3n + 1 < 3n + \epsilon n \quad \text{iff}$$

$$-\epsilon n < 1 \qquad\qquad \text{iff} \qquad\qquad\qquad 1 < \epsilon n \qquad\qquad \text{iff}$$

$$-n < \frac{1}{\epsilon} \qquad\qquad\qquad\qquad\qquad \frac{1}{\epsilon} < n$$

which is true for all
positive integers n.

So choose $M > \frac{1}{\epsilon}$. Consequently for all $n \geq M > \frac{1}{\epsilon}$, d_n is in

$$\langle 3 - \epsilon, 3 + \epsilon \rangle$$

and 3 is the limit of the sequence.

Checkpoint

If you wish to use the definition of *limit of a sequence* to show that a number A is the limit of a certain sequence $\{a_n\}$ you must be able to respond to challenges involving neighborhoods. What are you required to do when challenged with a particular neighborhood, such as $\langle A - \frac{1}{2}, A + \frac{1}{2} \rangle$? Why is it necessary for you to consider the challenge of a general neighborhood? How do you respond to this general challenge? What have you shown when you have successfully responded to the challenge of a general neighborhood?

Exercises

A **1.** Why in the proof that $\left\{ \frac{3n + 1}{n} \right\} \longrightarrow 3$ was the general neighborhood $\langle 3 - \epsilon, 3 + \epsilon \rangle$ used rather than $\langle -\epsilon, \epsilon \rangle$?

In Exercises 2–9 the claim is made that A is the limit of $\{a_n\}$. What is the general neighborhood of A for the given value of A?

2. $A = 2$ **3.** $A = -1$ **4.** $A = 0$ **5.** $A = -\frac{2}{3}$ **6.** $A = \frac{1}{4}$
7. $A = 100$ **8.** $A = -50$ **9.** $A = p$ (p a real number)

In Exercises 10–15, what appears to be the limit of each sequence?

10. $a_n = \frac{2n + 5}{3n}$ **11.** $a_n = \frac{2n - 11}{n}$

12. $a_n = \frac{4 - n}{n}$ **13.** $a_n = \frac{n^2 + 4}{3n^2}$

14. $a_n = \frac{3n^2}{n^2 + 1}$ **15.** $a_n = \left(\frac{2}{3} \right)^n$

16. The limit of $\{a_n\} = \left\{ \frac{2n + 1}{3n - 2} \right\}$ appears to be $\frac{2}{3}$. Find an M such that for all $n \geq M$, a_n is in the given neighborhood.

  a. $\langle \frac{2}{3} - \frac{1}{3}, \frac{2}{3} + \frac{1}{3} \rangle$ **b.** $\langle \frac{2}{3} - 0.01, \frac{2}{3} + 0.01 \rangle$
  c. $\langle \frac{2}{3} - 10^{-6}, \frac{2}{3} + 10^{-6} \rangle$ **d.** $\langle \frac{2}{3} - \epsilon, \frac{2}{3} + \epsilon \rangle$

B **17.** Prove: $\{a_n\} = \left\{ \frac{\frac{1}{2}n + 1}{n} \right\} \longrightarrow \frac{1}{2}$

18. Prove: $\{b_n\} = \left\{ \frac{6n - 2}{4n} \right\} \longrightarrow \frac{3}{2}$

19. Prove: $\{c_n\} = \left\{ \frac{-2n}{5n + 2} \right\} \longrightarrow \frac{-2}{5}$

C **20.** Prove: $\{d_n\} = \left\{ \frac{3n^2}{n^2 + 1} \right\} \longrightarrow 3$

21. Prove that 1 is not the limit of $\{a_n\} = \left\{ \frac{n - 1}{2n + 1} \right\}$ by finding a neighborhood of 1 which does *not* contain all terms of $\{a_n\}$ for $n \geq M$.

5–6   Convergent Sequences: Examples

Most of the sequences considered in the previous section had general terms of the form

$$\frac{\text{linear expression in } n}{\text{linear expression in } n}.$$

Here you consider sequences with general terms involving quadratic expressions and others which involve powers of real numbers. The purpose is to illustrate how such expressions are handled in the solution of the inequalities arising in limit proofs.

EXAMPLE 1.   Given: $\{a_n\} = \left\{\dfrac{2n^2 + 1}{n^2 + 1}\right\}.$ Prove: $\left\{\dfrac{2n^2 + 1}{n^2 + 1}\right\} \longrightarrow 2.$

Proof: The general neighborhood of 2 is $\langle 2 - \epsilon, 2 + \epsilon \rangle$. For 2 to be the limit, an M must be found such that $2 - \epsilon < a_n < 2 + \epsilon$ when $n \geq M$. This requires the solution of the compound inequality

$$2 - \epsilon < \frac{2n^2 + 1}{n^2 + 1} < 2 + \epsilon$$

or

$$2 - \epsilon < \frac{2n^2 + 1}{n^2 + 1} \qquad and \qquad \frac{2n^2 + 1}{n^2 + 1} < 2 + \epsilon.$$

The first step in solving either inequality is to divide $2n^2 + 1$ by $n^2 + 1$. You get the following

$$\frac{2n^2 + 1}{n^2 + 1} = 2 - \frac{1}{n^2 + 1}.$$

The inequalities now proceed as follows.

	$2 - \epsilon < 2 + \dfrac{-1}{n^2 + 1}$	*and*	$2 + \dfrac{-1}{n^2 + 1} < 2 + \epsilon$
iff	$-\epsilon < \dfrac{-1}{n^2 + 1}$	iff	$\dfrac{-1}{n^2 + 1} < \epsilon$
iff	$n^2 + 1 > \dfrac{-1}{-\epsilon}$	Since	$\dfrac{-1}{n^2 + 1} < 0$ and $0 < \epsilon,$
iff	$n^2 > \dfrac{1}{\epsilon} - 1$		$\dfrac{-1}{n^2 + 1} < \epsilon$
iff	$n > \sqrt{\dfrac{1}{\epsilon} - 1}$		is true for all $n \in \mathbb{N}.$

Thus choose $M > \sqrt{\dfrac{1}{\epsilon} - 1}.$ Then for all $n \geq M$, a_n is in

$$\langle 2 - \epsilon, 2 + \epsilon \rangle.$$

The following table shows possible choices of M for particular values of ϵ.

ϵ	$\dfrac{1}{10}$	$\dfrac{1}{100}$	$\dfrac{1}{500}$	$\dfrac{1}{10,000}$
$\sqrt{\dfrac{1}{\epsilon} - 1}$	$\sqrt{9}$	$\sqrt{99}$	$\sqrt{499}$	$\sqrt{9,999}$
M	4	11	25	200

Notice that the choices of M given in the table are not the smallest choices possible. In fact, when $\epsilon = \dfrac{1}{10,000}$, the smallest possible choice of M is 100. Choosing an M larger than necessary is perfectly legal because the definition does *not* specify that M should be as small as possible. All that is required is that there be some M which works. Consequently, any $M > \sqrt{\dfrac{1}{\epsilon} - 1}$ is satisfactory.

EXAMPLE 2. Given: $\{a_n\} = \{(\tfrac{2}{3})^n\}$
Prove: $\{(\tfrac{2}{3})^n\} \longrightarrow 0$

Proof:

$$-\epsilon < (\tfrac{2}{3})^n < \epsilon \quad \text{iff}$$

$$-\epsilon < (\tfrac{2}{3})^n \qquad\qquad and \qquad\qquad (\tfrac{2}{3})^n < \epsilon.$$

Since $(\tfrac{2}{3})^n > 0$ and $-\epsilon$ is negative, $-\epsilon < (\tfrac{2}{3})^n$ for all positive integers n.

(Taking logarithms of both sides),

$$n \log (\tfrac{2}{3}) < \log \epsilon \qquad \text{iff}$$

$$(\text{since } \log (\tfrac{2}{3}) < 0)$$

$$n > \frac{\log \epsilon}{\log (\tfrac{2}{3})}.$$

Consequently, M should be chosen greater than $\dfrac{\log \epsilon}{\log (\tfrac{2}{3})}$. Then for all $n \geq M$, a_n will lie in $\langle -\epsilon, \epsilon \rangle$.

Possible values of M for selected replacements of ϵ are shown in the following table. As above, the value of M chosen is not necessarily the least one possible. For the table below the approximation $\log (\tfrac{2}{3}) \approx -0.176$ is used.

ϵ	$\dfrac{1}{100}$	$\dfrac{1}{10,000}$	10^{-8}	10^{-16}
$\dfrac{\log \epsilon}{\log (\tfrac{2}{3})}$	$\dfrac{-2}{-.176}$	$\dfrac{-4}{-.176}$	$\dfrac{-8}{-.176}$	$\dfrac{-16}{-.176}$
M	12	25	50	92

EXAMPLE 3. Given: $\{a_n\} = \left\{\dfrac{\sqrt{n+1}}{n}\right\}$. Prove: $\left\{\dfrac{\sqrt{n+1}}{n}\right\} \longrightarrow 0$

Proof: $\qquad -\epsilon < \dfrac{\sqrt{n+1}}{n} < \epsilon$ iff

$$-\epsilon < \dfrac{\sqrt{n+1}}{n} \qquad\qquad and \qquad\qquad \dfrac{\sqrt{n+1}}{n} < \epsilon$$

Since $\dfrac{\sqrt{n+1}}{n}$ is positive for all n and $-\epsilon$ is negative, $-\epsilon < \dfrac{\sqrt{n+1}}{n}$ is true for all n.

(Since $\dfrac{\sqrt{n+1}}{n}$ and ϵ are positive, the inequality remains valid when both terms are squared.)

So, $\qquad \dfrac{n+1}{n^2} < \epsilon^2$ iff

$$\dfrac{1}{\epsilon^2} < \dfrac{n^2}{n+1}.$$

Now $\dfrac{n^2}{n+1} \geq \dfrac{n}{2}$ for all n as you can easily show.

Thus, if $\dfrac{1}{\epsilon^2} < \dfrac{n}{2}$ it is also true that $\dfrac{1}{\epsilon^2} < \dfrac{n^2}{n+1}$.

Therefore it is sufficient to solve:

$$\dfrac{1}{\epsilon^2} < \dfrac{n}{2} \quad\text{iff}$$

$$\dfrac{2}{\epsilon^2} < n.$$

Consequently, choosing $M > \dfrac{2}{\epsilon^2}$ will suffice to insure that a_n is in $\langle -\epsilon, \epsilon \rangle$ for all $n \geq M$.

To prove that the M determined is satisfactory, note that the steps in the derivation are reversible.

For all $n \geq M$ $\qquad\qquad n > \dfrac{2}{\epsilon^2} \qquad\qquad$ because $M > \dfrac{2}{\epsilon^2}$.

So $\qquad\qquad\qquad\qquad \dfrac{n}{2} > \dfrac{1}{\epsilon^2}$

But, for all n $\qquad\qquad \dfrac{n^2}{n+1} \leq \dfrac{n}{2}.$ $\qquad$ (This is the key step.)

So $\qquad\qquad\qquad\qquad \dfrac{n^2}{n+1} > \dfrac{1}{\epsilon^2} \qquad$ by transitivity of inequality

and $\qquad\qquad\qquad\qquad \dfrac{n+1}{n^2} < \epsilon^2.$

Thus $\qquad\qquad\qquad\qquad \dfrac{\sqrt{n+1}}{n} < \epsilon \qquad$ since all terms are positive.

Finally $-\epsilon < \dfrac{\sqrt{n+1}}{n}$ $\forall$ n. Therefore $-\epsilon < \dfrac{\sqrt{n+1}}{n} < \epsilon$ $\forall$ $n \geq M$.

The key idea in the strategy is to find an expression involving n $\left(\text{in this case } \frac{n}{2}\right)$ which is less than or equal to the complex expression $\left(\frac{n^2}{n+1}\right)$ and to solve the new inequality $\left(\frac{n}{2} > \frac{1}{\epsilon^2}\right)$ to determine M.

You may wonder why, in finding an M which implies $\frac{\sqrt{n+1}}{n} < \epsilon$ for all $n \geq M$, you did not solve the inequality $\frac{1}{\epsilon^2} < \frac{n^2}{n+1}$. You could have $\left(\text{the solution is } n > \frac{1}{2\epsilon} + \frac{\sqrt{1+4\epsilon}}{2\epsilon}\right)$, but the preference was to simplify the situation by solving an inequality, $\frac{n}{2} > \frac{1}{\epsilon^2}$, whose solution would also provide a satisfactory M.

The strategies illustrated in Examples 1, 2, and 3 are typical. General terms involving quadratic expressions usually lead to a solution involving a square root of an expression in ϵ. Similarly, when $a_n = (r)^n$, the solution usually involves logarithms.

Now try these

1. Find an M which proves that $\{a_n\} = \left\{\frac{3n^2 + 2}{4n^2}\right\} \longrightarrow \frac{3}{4}$.

2. Find an M which proves that $\{c_n\} = \{(\frac{4}{5})^n\} \longrightarrow 0$.

Answers: **1.** Choose $M > \sqrt{\dfrac{1}{2\epsilon}}$ **2.** Choose $M > \dfrac{\log \epsilon}{\log \frac{4}{5}}$

Exercises

A **1.** Prove: $\{a_n\} = \left\{\frac{2n^2 + 1}{3n^2}\right\} \longrightarrow \frac{2}{3}$

2. Prove: $\{b_n\} = \left\{\frac{1 - 3n^2}{n^2}\right\} \longrightarrow -3$

3. Prove: $\{c_n\} = \{(\frac{3}{4})^n\} \longrightarrow 0$

4. Prove: $\{d_n\} = \{1 - (\frac{1}{2})^n\} \longrightarrow 1$

5. Prove: $\{e_n\} = \left\{\frac{3}{\sqrt{n+2}}\right\} \longrightarrow 0$

6. Prove: $\{f_n\} = \left\{\frac{4}{(\sqrt{n+3})^2}\right\} \longrightarrow 0$

B **7.** Prove: $\{g_n\} = \left\{\frac{\sqrt{n+2}}{n}\right\} \longrightarrow 0$

8. Prove: $\{h_n\} = \left\{\sqrt{\frac{n+2}{n}}\right\} \longrightarrow 1$

9. Prove: $\{k_n\} = \left\{\frac{2}{n^3 + 5}\right\} \longrightarrow 0$

10. Prove: $\{l_n\} = \left\{\frac{2n}{n+1} - \frac{n+1}{2n}\right\} \longrightarrow \frac{3}{2}$

11. Prove: $\{m_n\} = \left\{\frac{1}{\sqrt{n^2 + 1}}\right\} \longrightarrow 0$

12. Prove: $\{p_n\} = \left\{\frac{(-1)^n}{n^2}\right\} \longrightarrow 0$

5–7   Completeness and Monotone Sequences

Let A ⊆ R. A can be represented geometrically by a set of points on a number line.

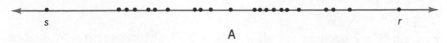

If there is a number $r \in R$ such that for each $x \in A$, x is less than or equal to r, then the subset A of R is said to be **bounded above** by r. Similarly, if there is a number $s \in R$ such that for each $x \in A$, x is greater than or equal to s, then A is **bounded below** by s. Possible positions for r and s are shown in the diagram above. (You may at this point wish to compare the above concepts with the upper and lower bounds of a function discussed in Section 2–6.)

If a set A ⊆ R is bounded above and bounded below it is said to be **bounded.** Geometrically a bounded set is one that is entirely contained in a closed interval. For example, A ⊆ $[s, r]$ above.

Given a set A ⊆ R with an upper bound r, it is clear that r is not unique. Any real number p such that $r < p$ is also an upper bound. Now it may happen that there is no upper bound of A that is smaller than r.

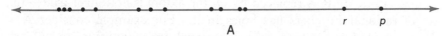

If so, then r is the **least upper bound.**

> **Definition**   Let A ⊆ R be bounded above. If the number r_0 is an upper bound of A and no number smaller than r_0 is an upper bound, then r_0 is the <u>least upper bound</u> of A, that is, r_0 = l.u.b.A (least upper bound A).

Greatest lower bound is defined in a similar manner.

> **Definition**   Let A ⊆ R be bounded below. If the number s_0 is a lower bound of A and no number greater than s_0 is a lower bound, then s_0 is the <u>greatest lower bound</u> of A, that is, s_0 = g.l.b.A (greatest lower bound A).

EXAMPLE. Let A = [3, 7], let B = ⟨3, 7⟩. Find **a.** l.u.b.A, **b.** g.l.b.A, **c.** l.u.b.B, and **d.** g.l.b.B.

a. l.u.b.A = 7 because for all $x \in A$, $x \le 7$. Moreover if $p < 7$, then p is not an upper bound of A. (Why?) Notice that l.u.b.A = 7 is an element of A.

b. g.l.b.A = 3.

c. l.u.b.B = 7 because for all $x \in B$, $x \le 7$. Moreover if $p < 7$, then p is not an upper bound of B because there exists a number $p_1 = \dfrac{p+7}{2}$ which is in B and which is greater than p. Notice that l.u.b.B = 7 is not an element of B.

d. g.l.b.B = 3.

You may be wondering about the reason for studying least upper bounds and greatest lower bounds, etc. The reason is found in the next axiom.

> **Least Upper Bound Axiom:** If A is any nonempty subset of R that is bounded above, then A has a least upper bound in R.

This axiom says, roughly, that the set of real numbers, R, has no "holes" in it. If R is replaced by Q, the axiom is no longer true—the set of rational numbers has holes in it. For example consider A = {1, 1.4, 1.41, 1.414, 1.4141, · · ·} of rational approximations to $\sqrt{2}$. A, as a subset of Q, has no least upper bound *in* Q, ($\sqrt{2}$ is irrational). But A, as a subset of R, has a least upper bound *in* R. Thus the significance of the axiom is that *all* sets in R which are bounded above have least upper bounds *in R*. In this sense the reals are *complete*. The axiom is one way of stating the **completeness property** of the reals.

You should be able to prove the next theorem.

> **Theorem 5–1** If A is any nonempty subset of R that is bounded below, then A has a greatest lower bound in R.

Proof Hint: Let B be the set of $-x$ where $x \in A$. Apply the Axiom to B.

The completeness property stated in the Axiom is applicable to sequences which are made up of real numbers. One especially useful result is true about bounded **monotone** sequences. The definition of a monotone sequence follows.

Definition Let $\{a_n\}$ be a sequence of real numbers. If $a_1 \leq a_2 \leq a_3 \leq \cdots \leq a_n \leq \cdots$, then $\{a_n\}$ is nondecreasing. If $a_1 \geq a_2 \geq a_3 \geq \cdots \geq a_n \geq \cdots$, then $\{a_n\}$ is nonincreasing. A monotone sequence is one which is either nondecreasing or nonincreasing (or both).

The major result about sequences follows.

Theorem 5-2 A nondecreasing sequence which is bounded above has a limit.

Proof: Let $\{a_n\}$ be the sequence. Then $A = \{a_n\}$ is a nonempty set of real numbers which is bounded above. Thus by the axiom A has a l.u.b.;

$$\text{l.u.b.} A = r_0.$$

The task now is to prove $\{a_n\} \longrightarrow r_0$. Consider the neighborhood $\langle r_0 - \epsilon, r_0 + \epsilon \rangle$, $\epsilon > 0$. Since $\epsilon > 0$ and l.u.b.$A = r_0$, $r_0 - \epsilon$ is *not* an upper bound of A. Thus for some $M \in N$, $a_m > r_0 - \epsilon$. But since $a_m \leq a_n$ for all $n \geq M$, $a_n > r_0 - \epsilon$ for all $n \geq M$. Since $a_n \leq r_0$ for all $n \in N$ (why?) it follows that

$$a_n \in \langle r_0 - \epsilon, r_0 + \epsilon \rangle \quad \text{for all } n \geq M.$$

Thus $\{a_n\} \longrightarrow r_0$.

Theorem 5-2 is useful because it provides a way to determine if a nondecreasing sequence has a limit, even when you do not know what the value of the limit is. For example,

$$\left\{ 2 - \frac{1}{2^{n-1}} \right\}$$

has a limit because it is nondecreasing and bounded above. The limit is 2.

The theorem for nonincreasing sequences similar to Theorem 5-2 is left for you to prove.

Theorem 5-3 A nonincreasing sequence which is bounded below has a limit.

Now try these

1. Let $A = [5, 8\rangle$.
   a. Find l.u.b.A b. Find g.l.b.A
   c. Is l.u.b.A an element of A?
   d. Is g.l.b.A an element of A?

2. Suppose $B = \{n\}$. a. Does B have a greatest lower bound? If so what is it? b. Does B have a least upper bound? If so what is it?

3. Suppose $C = \{x : x^2 < 2\}$. Does C have a least upper bound? If so what is it?

Answers: **1a.** 8 **b.** 5 **c.** No **d.** Yes   **2a.** g.l.b.$B = 1$ **b.** No l.u.b.
        3. l.u.b.$C = \sqrt{2}$

Checkpoint

1. What is meant by saying that the set of real numbers is "complete"? that the set of rational numbers is not complete?

2. How might you define an *increasing sequence*? In what way would your definition differ from that of a *nondecreasing sequence*?

3. Would Theorem 5–2 be true if the adjective "nondecreasing" were omitted? Why or why not?

4. Would Theorem 5–2 be true if the phrase "which is bounded above" were omitted. Why or why not?

Exercises

A 1. When is a sequence both nonincreasing and nondecreasing?

2. Make a drawing which may be used to show geometrically the reasoning used to prove Theorem 5–2.

3. Is a nondecreasing sequence $\{a_n\}$ which is bounded above by r bounded? If so, what is its g.l.b.?

4. Prove: A bounded monotone sequence has a limit.

— Determine whether or not each sequence is monotone.

5. $\{\sin n\pi\}$ 6. $\{\cos n\pi\}$

7. $\left\{\dfrac{1}{1 + n^2}\right\}$ 8. $\{2n + (-1)^n\}$

9. $\{\tan n\}$ 10. $\left\{\dfrac{3n + 1}{n}\right\}$

11. $\left\{\sin \dfrac{n\pi}{2}\right\}$ 12. $a_1 = 1$
                                                      $a_2 = 1$
                                                      $a_{n+1} = a_n + a_{n-1},\ n = 3, 4, \cdots$

13. Which of the sequences in Exercises 5–12 are bounded? Explain your answer.

14. Which of the sequences in Exercises 5–12 have a limit?

15. Construct an example of a sequence which is bounded but has no limit.

16. Construct an example of a monotone sequence which has no limit.

B **17.** Prove Theorem 5–1.

■ **18.** Prove Theorem 5–3.

C ▬ Use the following definition in Exercises 19–21.

> **Definition** A sequence $\{a_n\}$ diverges to infinity if for any real number $p > 0$ there is an $M \in \mathbf{N}$ such that $a_n \geq p$ for all $n \geq M$.

19. Give three examples of sequences which diverge to infinity.

20. Give an example of a sequence which is not monotone and diverges to infinity.

21. Prove: A nondecreasing sequence which is not bounded above diverges to infinity.

5–8 Series and Their Sums

In the millionaire golf match mentioned in Section 5–1, the finite sequence of dollar values of the bet was

$$1, 2, 4, 8, 16, 32, 64, 128, 256.$$

If the millionaire who proposed the bet lost each hole, his loss in dollars would be

$$1 + 2 + 4 + 8 + 16 + 32 + 64 + 128 + 256.$$

This indicated sum is called a **series.**

> **Definition** A series is an indicated sum of the terms of a sequence.

EXAMPLE 1. Given the arithmetic sequence (see the definition above Exercise 29, Section 5–1)

$$a, a + d, a + 2d, \cdots, a + (n - 1)d$$

the related arithmetic series is

$$a + (a + d) + (a + 2d) + \cdots + [a + (n - 1)d].$$

EXAMPLE 2. Given the geometric sequence (see the definition above Exercise 34, Section 5–1)

$$a, ar, ar^2, ar^3, \cdots, ar^{n-1},$$

the related geometric series is

$$a + ar + ar^2 + ar^3 + \cdots + ar^{n-1}.$$

The following definition can now be stated.

Definition A <u>harmonic</u> <u>sequence</u> is a sequence whose terms are reciprocals of the terms of an arithmetic sequence.

EXAMPLE 3. Given the harmonic sequence

$$\frac{1}{a}, \frac{1}{a + d}, \frac{1}{a + 2d}, \cdots, \frac{1}{a + (n - 1)d}$$

the related harmonic series is

$$\frac{1}{a} + \frac{1}{a + d} + \frac{1}{a + 2d} + \cdots + \frac{1}{a + (n - 1)d}.$$

If a series has a finite number of terms it has a sum and it is easy to determine the standard name for the sum. For example,

$$3 + 5 + 7 = 15.$$

If there are infinitely many terms in a series, the task is not so simple. *Not all infinite series have sums.* For those that do, the "sum" is not always easily identified. For example, given the infinite series

$$\frac{1}{2} + \frac{1}{4} + \frac{1}{8} + \frac{1}{16} + \cdots + \frac{1}{2^n} + \cdots$$

it is not at all clear that

$$\frac{1}{2} + \frac{1}{4} + \frac{1}{8} + \frac{1}{16} + \cdots + \frac{1}{2^n} + \cdots = 1.$$

The next example illustrates the ideas used in defining the "sum of an infinite series." A key idea used in that definition is partial sum.

EXAMPLE 4. Consider the infinite series $\frac{1}{2} + \frac{1}{4} + \frac{1}{8} + \cdots + \frac{1}{2^n} + \cdots$. The partial sums for this series are

$$S_1 = \frac{1}{2} \qquad\qquad\qquad = \frac{1}{2}$$

$$S_2 = \frac{1}{2} + \frac{1}{4} \qquad\qquad = \frac{3}{4}$$

$$S_3 = \frac{1}{2} + \frac{1}{4} + \frac{1}{8} \qquad = \frac{7}{8}$$

$$S_4 = \frac{1}{2} + \frac{1}{4} + \frac{1}{8} + \frac{1}{16} \qquad = \frac{15}{16}$$

$$\vdots \qquad\qquad\qquad\qquad \vdots$$

$$S_n = \frac{1}{2} + \frac{1}{4} + \frac{1}{8} + \quad\cdot\quad\cdot\quad\cdot\quad + \frac{1}{2^n} = \frac{2^n - 1}{2^n}$$

$$\vdots \qquad\qquad\qquad\qquad \vdots$$

The sequence of partial sums is

$$\frac{1}{2}, \frac{3}{4}, \frac{7}{8}, \frac{15}{16}, \frac{31}{32}, \ldots, \frac{2^n - 1}{2^n}, \ldots,$$

where the general term is $\frac{2^n - 1}{2^n}$. The sequence of partial sums $\left\{\frac{2^n - 1}{2^n}\right\}$ can be shown to converge to 1. And 1 is the number that was indicated to be the sum of $\frac{1}{2} + \frac{1}{4} + \frac{1}{8} + \cdots$. The relationship between the sum of an infinite series and the limit of the sequence of partial sums is not a casual one. It is taken to be the definition of the **sum of an infinite series.**

Finite and infinite series are often indicated by using the Greek letter $\sum$ (sigma). For example, the sum

$$a_1 + a_2 + a_3 + \cdots + a_n$$

can be written

$$\sum_{i=1}^{n} a_i$$

which is read "the sum of a_i from $i = 1$ to $i = n$." The infinite series

$$a_1 + a_2 + a_3 + \cdots$$

can be written

$$\sum_{i=1}^{\infty} a_i$$

which is read "the sum of a_i beginning with $i = 1$ and increasing without bound." Note that i denotes natural numbers only.

EXAMPLE 5. Express the series $\sum_{i=1}^{5} (2i - 3)$ as an *indicated* sum.

$$\sum_{i=1}^{5} (2i - 3) = [2(1) - 3] + [2(2) - 3] + [2(3) - 3]$$
$$+ [2(4) - 3] + [2(5) - 3]$$
$$= -1 + 1 + 3 + 5 + 7$$

EXAMPLE 6. Find the sum of the series $\sum_{i=1}^{4} i$.

$$\sum_{i=1}^{4} = 1 + 2 + 3 + 4 = 10$$

EXAMPLE 7. Determine whether the geometric series $\sum_{i=1}^{\infty} \frac{2}{3}(\frac{2}{3})^{i-1}$ has a sum, and if it does, specify it.

$$\sum_{i=1}^{\infty} \frac{2}{3}(\tfrac{2}{3})^{i-1} = \tfrac{2}{3} + \tfrac{4}{9} + \tfrac{8}{27} + \cdots + (\tfrac{2}{3})^n + \cdots$$

The nth partial sum is $S_n = \frac{2}{3} + \frac{2}{3}(\frac{2}{3}) + \frac{2}{3}(\frac{2}{3})^2 + \cdots + \frac{2}{3}(\frac{2}{3})^{n-1}$. In order to find the limit of the sequence of partial sums, a simpler expression is needed for S_n. This can be found as follows.

$$S_n = \tfrac{2}{3} + \tfrac{2}{3}(\tfrac{2}{3}) + \tfrac{2}{3}(\tfrac{2}{3})^2 + \cdots + \tfrac{2}{3}(\tfrac{2}{3})^{n-1}$$
$$\tfrac{2}{3}S_n = \tfrac{2}{3}(\tfrac{2}{3}) + \tfrac{2}{3}(\tfrac{2}{3})^2 + \cdots + \tfrac{2}{3}(\tfrac{2}{3})^{n-1} + \tfrac{2}{3}(\tfrac{2}{3})^n$$

Thus $$S_n - \tfrac{2}{3}S_n = \tfrac{2}{3} - \tfrac{2}{3}(\tfrac{2}{3})^n = \tfrac{2}{3}(1 - (\tfrac{2}{3})^n)$$

So $$S_n = \frac{\tfrac{2}{3}(1 - (\tfrac{2}{3})^n)}{1 - (\tfrac{2}{3})} = \frac{\tfrac{2}{3}(1 - (\tfrac{2}{3})^n)}{\tfrac{1}{3}} = 2(1 - (\tfrac{2}{3})^n)$$

Thus the sequence of partial sums is $\{S_n\} = \{2[1 - (\tfrac{2}{3})^n]\}$. If $\sum_{i=1}^{\infty} \tfrac{2}{3} \cdot (\tfrac{2}{3})^{i-1}$ is to have a sum, $\{S_n\}$ must have a limit. You can prove easily that $\{2[1 - (\tfrac{2}{3})^n]\}$ has a limit of 2. By the definition

$$\sum_{i=1}^{\infty} \tfrac{2}{3}(\tfrac{2}{3})^{i-1} = 2.$$

Two major ideas for determining whether an infinite series has a sum are illustrated in Example 7.

1. An expression for the partial sum S_n must be found.

2. The sequence $\{S_n\}$ must be shown either to converge or diverge.

Very often **1** is more difficult than **2**.

In the case of a geometric series,

$$\sum_{i=1}^{\infty} ar^{i-1} = a + ar^1 + ar^2 + \cdots,$$

the expression for the partial sum S_n may be found in a manner similar to that used in Example 7 when $r \neq 1$.

$$S_n = a + ar + ar^2 + \cdots + ar^{n-1}$$
$$rS_n = \qquad ar + ar^2 + \cdots + ar^{n-1} + ar^n$$
$$S_n - rS_n = a + 0 + 0 + \cdots + \quad 0 \quad - ar^n$$
$$S_n = \frac{a - ar^n}{1 - r}, \quad r \neq 1$$
$$S_n = a \cdot n \text{ when } r = 1$$

In other cases, an expression for S_n may not be easy to determine. For example, given $\sum_{i=1}^{\infty} 2i = 2 + 4 + 6 + \cdots$, the partial sums are as follows:

$$
\begin{aligned}
S_1 &= 2 && = 2 \\
S_2 &= 2 + 4 && = 6 \\
S_3 &= 2 + 4 + 6 && = 12 \\
&\;\;\vdots && \;\;\vdots
\end{aligned}
$$

$$S_n = 2 + 4 + 6 + 8 + \cdots + 2n = ?$$

In such cases look for a pattern such as $S_1 = 1 \cdot 2$, $S_2 = 2 \cdot 3$, $S_3 = 3 \cdot 4$, $S_4 = 4 \cdot 5$, $\cdots$, $S_n = n \cdot (n + 1)$. When you are quite sure the pattern is right, prove it correct by using mathematical induction. Then you may use the expression for S_n to decide whether the sequence $\{S_n\}$ converges or diverges. For $\{S_n\} = n(n + 1)$ it is clear that there is no limit because the sequence is monotone and unbounded. Check this.

Now try these

━━ Use the summation sign (Σ) to write each series.

1. $|x_3| + |x_4| + |x_5| + |x_6|$ **2.** $e^1 - e^2 + e^3 - e^4 + e^5$

Answers: **1.** $\displaystyle\sum_{i=3}^{6} |x_i|$ **2.** $\displaystyle\sum_{i=1}^{5} (-1)^{i+1} e^i$

Checkpoint

1. How does a series differ from a sequence?

2. How is the concept of *partial sum* used to define the sum of an infinite series?

3. Define *convergent series. divergent series.*

Exercises

A ━━ In Exercises 1–4 classify each series as harmonic, geometric, or arithmetic.

1. $\displaystyle\sum_{i=1}^{\infty} 4 - 2i$ **2.** $\displaystyle\sum_{i=1}^{\infty} \frac{1}{i}$ **3.** $\displaystyle\sum_{i=1}^{\infty} \frac{1}{2}i$ **4.** $\displaystyle\sum_{i=1}^{\infty} \frac{1}{1 + (i-1)}$

5. Prove by mathematical induction that

$$S_n = \tfrac{1}{2} + \tfrac{1}{4} + \tfrac{1}{8} + \cdots + \frac{1}{2^n} = \frac{2^n - 1}{2^n}.$$

6. Prove that the sum of the infinite series for which the nth partial sum is given in Exercise 5 is 1, i.e., $\left\{ \dfrac{2^n - 1}{2^n} \right\} \longrightarrow 1$.

7. Prove: $S_n = \tfrac{2}{3} + \tfrac{2}{3}(\tfrac{2}{3})^1 + \tfrac{2}{3}(\tfrac{2}{3})^2 + \cdots + \tfrac{2}{3}(\tfrac{2}{3})^{n-1} = 2[1 - (\tfrac{2}{3})^n]$.

8. Prove: $\{2 - 2(\tfrac{2}{3})^n\} \longrightarrow 2$.

9. Prove by mathematical induction that

$$S_n = a + ar + \cdots + ar^{n-1} = a\frac{(1 - r^n)}{1 - r}, r \neq 1, \quad \text{for all } M \in \mathbf{N}.$$

10. Given the arithmetic series $\displaystyle\sum_{i=1}^{\infty} a + d(i-1)$. Write an expression for S_n by adding

$$S_n = a + (a + d) + (a + 2d) + \cdots + a + d(n-2) + a + d(n-1)$$

and

$$S_n = a + d(n-1) + a + d(n-2) + a + d(n-3) + \cdots + a + d + a$$

term-by-term and solving the resulting equation for S_n.

In Exercises 11–16 write each series in expanded form.

11. $\displaystyle\sum_{n=1}^{5} |2 - n|$ **12.** $\displaystyle\sum_{i=1}^{4} (-1)^i i^2$ **13.** $\displaystyle\sum_{n=1}^{3} (-1)^n (n^2 - n)$

14. $\displaystyle\sum_{i=3}^{5} (2i - 9)$ **15.** $\displaystyle\sum_{i=0}^{4} \left(\frac{1}{i+1}\right)$ **16.** $\displaystyle\sum_{n=3}^{7} a_n$

In Exercises 17–20 use the summation sign to write each series.

17. $3 + 8 + 13 + 18$ **18.** $8 - 2 + \frac{1}{2} - \frac{1}{8}$

19. $a_1^2 + a_2^2 + a_3^2 + a_4^2$ **20.** $a_1 b_1 + a_2 b_2 + a_3 b_3$

B In Exercises 21–23 do the two expressions name the same series?

21. $\displaystyle\sum_{n=1}^{4} \frac{n+3}{n+1}$ and $\displaystyle\sum_{n=3}^{6} \frac{n+1}{n-1}$

22. $\displaystyle\sum_{k=5}^{8} \frac{k-3}{k-1}$ and $\displaystyle\sum_{k=1}^{4} \frac{k+1}{k+8}$

23. $\displaystyle\sum_{i=1}^{5} \frac{i}{i+1}$ and $\displaystyle\sum_{i=4}^{8} \frac{i-3}{i-1}$

In Exercises 24–26 find the sum of each geometric series. Prove that your result is correct.

24. $\displaystyle\sum_{i=1}^{\infty} 3(\tfrac{4}{5})^{i-1}$ **25.** $\displaystyle\sum_{i=1}^{\infty} 5(-\tfrac{1}{3})^{i-1}$ **26.** $\displaystyle\sum_{i=1}^{\infty} (\tfrac{9}{10})^{i-1}$

C ▬ Here is a recursive definition of the summation sign.

$$\sum_{i=1}^{1} a_i = a_1$$

$$\sum_{i=1}^{n+1} a_i = \left(\sum_{i=1}^{n} a_i\right) + a_{n+1}$$

Use this definition to prove each statement. (Use mathematical induction.)

27. $\displaystyle\sum_{i=1}^{n} c \cdot a_i = c \sum_{i=1}^{n} a_i$

28. $\displaystyle\sum_{i=1}^{n} c = cn$

29. $\displaystyle\sum_{i=1}^{n} (a_i + b_i) = \sum_{i=1}^{n} a_i + \sum_{i=1}^{n} b_i$

30. $\displaystyle\sum_{i=1}^{n} (a_i + b_i)^2 = \sum_{i=1}^{n} a_i^2 + 2 \sum_{i=1}^{n} a_i b_i + \sum_{i=1}^{n} b_i^2$

31. $\displaystyle\sum_{i=1}^{n} (a_i + c) = \sum_{i=1}^{n} a_i + cn$

32. $\displaystyle\sum_{i=1}^{n} c(a_i + b_i^2) = c \sum_{i=1}^{n} a_i + c \sum_{i=1}^{n} b_i^2$

5–9   Limits of Special Sequences

In this section you will examine some special convergent sequences. The limits of these special sequences will be quite useful in the next section.

EXAMPLE 1.   Prove: $\left\{\frac{1}{n^a}\right\} \longrightarrow 0$ where a is any positive real number.

Proof: Given the general neighborhood $\langle -\epsilon, \epsilon \rangle$ of 0, $\epsilon > 0$, you must show that there exists an M such that

$$\frac{1}{n^a} \in \langle -\epsilon, \epsilon \rangle \quad \text{for all } n \geq M.$$

Now,
$$-\epsilon < \frac{1}{n^a} < \epsilon \quad \text{iff}$$

$-\epsilon < \dfrac{1}{n^a}$ *and* $\dfrac{1}{n^a} < \epsilon.$

Since $-\epsilon$ is negative

and $\frac{1}{n^a}$ is always

positive, $-\epsilon < \frac{1}{n^a}$ is

true for all n.

$\dfrac{1}{n^a} < \epsilon$ iff

$\dfrac{1}{\epsilon} < n^a$ iff

$\left(\dfrac{1}{\epsilon}\right)^{\frac{1}{a}} < n.$

Since $-\epsilon < \frac{1}{n^a}$ is true for all n and thus for $n \geq M > \left(\frac{1}{\epsilon}\right)^{\frac{1}{a}}$, and $\frac{1}{n^a} < \epsilon$ is true for all $n \geq M > \left(\frac{1}{\epsilon}\right)^{\frac{1}{a}}$, $\frac{1}{n^a}$ is in $\langle -\epsilon, \epsilon \rangle$ for all $n > M$. Therefore $\left\{\frac{1}{n^a}\right\} \longrightarrow 0$ for all positive real a.

Often in books on mathematics, an alternate procedure is used to indicate that the terms of a sequence are in an open interval. The method uses absolute values.

For the sequence $\left\{\frac{1}{n^a}\right\}$ in Example 1, the general neighborhood is $\langle -\epsilon, \epsilon \rangle$ about 0, the proposed limit. For $\frac{1}{n^a}$ to be in $\langle -\epsilon, \epsilon \rangle$, the distance from $\frac{1}{n^a}$ to 0 must be less than ϵ units. The distance between two points a and b on a number line is given by the absolute value of the difference in their coordinates. Thus

$$|a - b|$$

is the distance between a and b.

In particular, then, the distance $\frac{1}{n^a}$ and 0 can be written

$$\left| \frac{1}{n^a} - 0 \right|.$$

If you want $\frac{1}{n^a}$ to be in the neighborhood $\langle -\epsilon, \epsilon \rangle$, the distance between $\frac{1}{n^a}$ and 0 must be less than ϵ. Thus

$$\left| \frac{1}{n^a} - 0 \right| < \epsilon, \epsilon > 0$$

expresses the fact that the distance between $\frac{1}{n^a}$ and 0 is less than ϵ, or that $\frac{1}{n^a}$ is in $\langle -\epsilon, \epsilon \rangle$.

In general, for $\{a_n\}$ to converge to A, it must be the case that

$$| a_n - A | < \epsilon$$

for all $n \geq M$, where ϵ is the radius of the general neighborhood about A.

In summary the following statements are equivalent:

1. $| a_n - A | < \epsilon, \epsilon > 0$
2. $A - \epsilon < a_n < A + \epsilon, \epsilon > 0$
3. $a_n \in \langle A - \epsilon, A + \epsilon \rangle, \epsilon > 0$

Any one of these three equivalent statements may be used in constructing limit proofs.

EXAMPLE 2. Let $\{a_n\} = \{c\}$. That is each term of the sequence is the same: $\{c\} = c, c, c, \cdots, c, \cdots$.
Prove $\{c\} \longrightarrow c$.

The proof is especially simple if you use the absolute value notation for a neighborhood. You must show that for every $\epsilon > 0$ there is an M such that

$$| a_n - c | < \epsilon \quad \text{for all } n \geq M.$$

Proof: Since $a_n = c$ for all n,

$$\begin{aligned} | a_n - c | &= | c - c | \\ &= 0 \end{aligned}$$

which is less than ϵ by the definition of ϵ. Thus you may choose $M = 1$ or any other positive integer.

EXAMPLE 3. Prove $\{r^n\} \longrightarrow 0$ when $|r| < 1$.

Using the absolute value notation for neighborhoods, you must show that for every $\epsilon > 0$ there is an $M \in \mathbf{N}$ such that for all $n \geq M$

$$|r^n - 0| < \epsilon.$$

Proof: Recall that

$$(1 + p)^n \geq 1 + np \quad (p \geq 0, n \in \mathbf{N}).$$

Since $|r| < 1$, then $p > 0$ can be found such that $|r| = \dfrac{1}{1 + p}$. Thus

$$\frac{1}{|r|^n} = (1 + p)^n \geq 1 + np > np.$$

So

$$|r|^n < \frac{1}{np}.$$

Since you wish $|r|^n$ to be less than ϵ, it will suffice if ϵ is greater than $\dfrac{1}{np}$. Therefore choose $M > \dfrac{1}{\epsilon p}$.

Thus $n \geq M > \dfrac{1}{\epsilon p}$ implies $\epsilon > \dfrac{1}{np} > |r|^n$ for all $n \geq M$. But $|r^n - 0| = |r|^n$ and so $|r^n - 0| < \epsilon$ for all $n \geq M > \dfrac{1}{\epsilon p}$.

Why in Example 3 was the restriction $|r| < 1$ necessary? In the proof the condition was used in the second step. That is, since $|r| < 1$, $|r| = \dfrac{1}{1 + p}$ with $p > 0$. It is essential that p be positive since otherwise $|r|^n$ would not be smaller than $\dfrac{1}{np}$ for any $n \in \mathbf{N}$. If $|r|$ were greater than one, the resulting sequence has no limit (see Exercise 19, Section 5–7).

If $|r| = 1$, the proof given is not valid. (Why?) However, if $|r| = 1$, then $r = 1$ or -1. If $r = 1$, then $r^n = 1$ for all n and $\{r^n\} \longrightarrow 1$ by Example 2.

If $r = -1$, the sequence $\{r^n\}$ is

$$-1, 1, -1, 1, \cdots.$$

It is easily seen that this sequence does not converge by applying an alternate definition of convergence which can be shown to be equivalent to the definition given in Section 5–5.

Alternate Definition of Convergence of a Sequence A sequence $\{a_n\}$ converges to A if for any neighborhood $\langle A - \epsilon, A + \epsilon \rangle$ of A at most a finite number of terms of $\{a_n\}$ lie outside $\langle A - \epsilon, A + \epsilon \rangle$.

The usefulness of this equivalent definition is that you need find only *one* neighborhood about the proposed limit outside of which an infinite number of terms lie in order to conclude that the sequence does not have that number as its limit. The obvious possibilities for the limit of

$$-1, 1, -1, 1, -1, \cdots$$

are -1 and 1. For any other number a neighborhood can always be chosen which contains *no* terms of the sequence. Suppose 1 is chosen as the prospective limit. Then choose a neighborhood, say $\langle 1 - \frac{1}{2}, 1 + \frac{1}{2} \rangle$ or $\langle \frac{1}{2}, \frac{3}{2} \rangle$. Obviously all $a_n = (-1)^n$ for *n even* lie in $\langle \frac{1}{2}, \frac{3}{2} \rangle$. But all $a_n = (-1)^n$ for *n odd* lie outside $\langle \frac{1}{2}, \frac{3}{2} \rangle$. Consequently $\{(-1)^n\}$ does not converge to 1. Similarly $\{(-1)^n\}$ does not converge to -1. Therefore it is a divergent sequence.

The major results of this section are summarized as theorems.

Theorem 5–4   Any sequence $\{b_n\} = \frac{1}{n^a}$ with $a > 0$ and $a \in R$ converges to zero.

For example: $\left\{\frac{1}{n^{\frac{1}{2}}}\right\} \longrightarrow 0$

Theorem 5–5   Any sequence $\{c\}$ of constants c converges to c.

For example: $\{5\} \longrightarrow 5$

Theorem 5–6   If $|r| < 1$, then $\{r^n\}$ converges to 0.

For example: $\{(-\frac{9}{10})^n\} \longrightarrow 0$

Now try these

1. Translate into an inequality involving absolute value:
   a. a_n is in $\langle -3, 3 \rangle$.   **b.** a_n is in $\langle 2.1, 3.5 \rangle$.
2. Find an M such that for all $n \geq M$ the inequality is true.
   a. $\left| \frac{3}{n} \right| < \frac{1}{10}$ **b.** $|a_n^* - 2| < \frac{1}{1000}$; $a_n = 2$

Answers: **1. a.** $|a_n - 0| < 3$ **b.** $|a_n - 2.8| < 0.7$
   2. a. 31 will do, or any larger number.   **b.** Any value for M will do.

Exercises

A ▬ In Exercises 1–8 translate each neighborhood statement into an inequality involving absolute value. a_n is in

1. $\langle -2, 2 \rangle$.

2. $\langle -.001, .001 \rangle$.

3. $\langle 1.5, 2.5 \rangle$.

4. $\langle -2.5, -1.5 \rangle$.

5. $\langle .99, 1.01 \rangle$.

6. $\langle 2, 3 \rangle$.

7. $\langle 1 - \epsilon, 1 + \epsilon \rangle$.

8. $\langle -\frac{2}{3} - \epsilon, -\frac{2}{3} + \epsilon \rangle$.

▬ In Exercises 9–16, translate each inequality involving absolute values into the corresponding neighborhood statement.

9. $|a_n - 0| < .5$

10. $|a_n - 2| < .001$

11. $|a_n + 1| < .1$

12. $|a_n - \frac{1}{3}| < \frac{1}{3}$

13. $|a_n| < \epsilon$

14. $|a_n + \frac{2}{3}| < \epsilon$

15. $|a_n - .9| < \epsilon$

16. $|a_n - .01| < .0001$

In Exercises 17–21, let a_n be the general term of a sequence. Find an M such that for all $n \geq M$ the inequality is true.

17. $a_n = \frac{2}{n}$; $|a_n - 0| < \frac{1}{2}$

18. $a_n = \frac{(-1^n)2}{n}$; $|a_n - 0| < \frac{1}{100}$

19. $a_n = 3$; $|a_n - 3| < 10^{-6}$

20. $a_n = \frac{1}{n^{\frac{1}{3}}}$; $|a_n - 0| < \frac{1}{100}$

21. $a_n = (\frac{9}{10})^n$; $|a_n - 0| < \frac{1}{10}$

▬ Specify the limit and the theorem which justifies it.

22. $\{100\}$ **23.** $\{\frac{1}{n^{.99}}\}$ **24.** $\{(.99)^n\}$

25. $\{-5\}$ **26.** $\{(-\frac{1}{3})^n\}$ **27.** $\{\frac{1}{n^{\frac{1}{3}}}\}$

B **28.** In your own words, explain why the two definitions of convergence for sequences are equivalent.

29. Prove: If $\{a_n\} = \{\frac{n}{n+1}\}$ then $\{a_n\} \longrightarrow 1$.

5-10   Operations with Sequences

When you add, subtract, multiply, or divide two numbers, you associate the pair of numbers with a sum, difference, product or quotient. You can perform the same operations on sequences. To do this you need to specify exactly what you mean by the sum, difference, product or quotient of two sequences:

> **Definitions**   Given any two sequences $\{a_n\}$ and $\{b_n\}$, then
> **a.** the sum of $\{a_n\}$ and $\{b_n\}$ is the sequence with nth term $a_n + b_n$; that is $\{a_n\} + \{b_n\} = \{a_n + b_n\}$.
> **b.** the difference of $\{a_n\}$ and $\{b_n\}$ is the sequence with nth term $a_n - b_n$; that is $\{a_n\} - \{b_n\} = \{a_n - b_n\}$.
> **c.** the product of $\{a_n\}$ and $\{b_n\}$ is the sequence with nth term $a_n b_n$; that is $\{a_n\} \times \{b_n\} = \{a_n \times b_n\}$.
>   Given any two sequences $\{a_n\}$ and $\{b_n\}$ with $b_n = 0$ for no n, then
> **d.** the quotient of $\{a_n\}$ and $\{b_n\}$ is the sequence with nth term $\frac{a_n}{b_n}$; that is $\{a_n\} \div \{b_n\} = \left\{\frac{a_n}{b_n}\right\}$.

Suppose $\{a_n\}$ and $\{b_n\}$ are defined as follows.

Sequence	First seven terms
$\{a_n\} = \left\{\dfrac{n+1}{n}\right\}$	$\dfrac{2}{1}, \dfrac{3}{2}, \dfrac{4}{3}, \dfrac{5}{4}, \dfrac{6}{5}, \dfrac{7}{6}, \dfrac{8}{7}$
$\{b_n\} = \left\{\dfrac{3n+2}{2n}\right\}$	$\dfrac{5}{2}, \dfrac{8}{4}, \dfrac{11}{6}, \dfrac{14}{8}, \dfrac{17}{10}, \dfrac{20}{12}, \dfrac{23}{14}$

Using the definition above gives these results.

Sequence	First seven terms
$\{a_n + b_n\} = \left\{\dfrac{5n+4}{2n}\right\}$	$\dfrac{9}{2}, \dfrac{14}{4}, \dfrac{19}{6}, \dfrac{24}{8}, \dfrac{29}{10}, \dfrac{34}{12}, \dfrac{39}{14}$
$\{a_n - b_n\} = \left\{-\dfrac{n}{2n}\right\}$	$-\dfrac{1}{2}, -\dfrac{1}{2}, -\dfrac{1}{2}, -\dfrac{1}{2}, -\dfrac{1}{2}, -\dfrac{1}{2}, -\dfrac{1}{2}$
$\{a_n \cdot b_n\} = \left\{\dfrac{3n^2 + 5n + 2}{2n^2}\right\}$	$5, 3, \dfrac{44}{18}, \dfrac{35}{16}, \dfrac{51}{25}, \dfrac{70}{36}, \dfrac{92}{49}$
$\left\{\dfrac{a_n}{b_n}\right\} = \left\{\dfrac{2n+2}{3n+2}\right\}$	$\dfrac{4}{5}, \dfrac{6}{8}, \dfrac{8}{11}, \dfrac{10}{14}, \dfrac{12}{17}, \dfrac{14}{20}, \dfrac{16}{23}$

Careful inspection suggests (and it can be proved) that:

$$\left\{\frac{n+1}{n}\right\} \longrightarrow 1 \qquad \text{and} \qquad \left\{\frac{3n+2}{2n}\right\} \longrightarrow \frac{3}{2}.$$

Also, $\qquad \{a_n + b_n\} = \left\{\frac{5n+4}{2n}\right\} \longrightarrow \frac{5}{2} = 1 + \frac{3}{2},$

$$\{a_n - b_n\} = \left\{\frac{-n}{2n}\right\} \longrightarrow -\frac{1}{2} = 1 - \frac{3}{2},$$

$$\{a_n \cdot b_n\} = \frac{3n^2 + 5n + 2}{2n^2} \longrightarrow \frac{3}{2} = 1 \times \frac{3}{2}, \quad \text{and}$$

$$\left\{\frac{a_n}{b_n}\right\} = \left\{\frac{2n+2}{3n+2}\right\} \longrightarrow \frac{2}{3} = 1 \div \frac{3}{2}$$

Notice that the expression at the right in each statement is the sum, the difference, the product, or the quotient of the limits of $\{a_n\}$ and $\{b_n\}$. The generalization is true and is stated in the theorems following:

Theorem 5–7   If $\{a_n\} \longrightarrow A$ and $\{b_n\} \longrightarrow B$, then
 a. $\{a_n + b_n\} \longrightarrow A + B$.
 b. $\{a_n - b_n\} \longrightarrow A - B$.
 c. $\{a_n \cdot b_n\} \longrightarrow A \cdot B$.

As is generally the case for division you have to be more careful.

Theorem 5–8   If $\{a_n\} \longrightarrow A$ and $\{b_n\} \longrightarrow B$ (B ≠ 0) and no b_n is 0, then $\left\{\frac{a_n}{b_n}\right\} \longrightarrow \frac{A}{B}$.

The proofs of these theorems are omitted.   Applications of the theorems make use of the theorems of Section 5–9.

EXAMPLE 1.   Find the limit, if it exists, of $\left\{\frac{7n+5}{5n}\right\}$.

$$\frac{7n+5}{5n} = \frac{7n}{5n} + \frac{5}{5n}$$

$$= \frac{7}{5} + \frac{1}{n}$$

Thus $\qquad \left\{\frac{7n+5}{5n}\right\} = \left\{\frac{7}{5}\right\} + \left\{\frac{1}{n}\right\}$

Since $\left\{\frac{7}{5}\right\} \longrightarrow \frac{7}{5}$ (Theorem 5–5) and $\left\{\frac{1}{n}\right\} \longrightarrow 0$ (Theorem 5–4),

then

$$\left\{\frac{7n + 5}{5n}\right\} \longrightarrow \frac{7}{5} + 0 = \frac{7}{5} \qquad \text{(Theorem 5–7a).}$$

A notation which is often used in place of $\left\{\frac{7n + 5}{5n}\right\} \longrightarrow \frac{7}{5}$ is the following

$$\lim_{n \to \infty} \frac{7n + 5}{5n} = \frac{7}{5}$$

which is read: "the limit of $\frac{7n + 5}{5n}$ as n increases without bound is $\frac{7}{5}$."
Using this notation, Theorem 5–7a would read:

If $\lim_{n \to \infty} a_n = A$ and $\lim_{n \to \infty} b_n = B$, then $\lim_{n \to \infty} (a_n + b_n) = A + B$.

This notation will be used when it is appropriate.

EXAMPLE 2. Find the limit of $\left\{\frac{6n^2 - 3n + 8}{2n^2}\right\}$ if it exists.

METHOD I $\qquad \dfrac{6n^2 - 3n + 8}{2n^2} = \dfrac{3n^2}{n^2} - \dfrac{3n}{2n^2} + \dfrac{4}{n^2}$

$$= 3 - \frac{3}{2} \cdot \frac{1}{n} + 4 \cdot \frac{1}{n^2}$$

Thus $\qquad \displaystyle\lim_{n \to \infty} \frac{6n^2 - 3n + 8}{2n^2} = \lim_{n \to \infty} 3 - \lim_{n \to \infty} \frac{3}{2} \cdot \frac{1}{n} + \lim_{n \to \infty} 4 \cdot \frac{1}{n^2}$

$$= 3 - \tfrac{3}{2} \cdot 0 + 4 \cdot 0$$

$$= 3.$$

METHOD II Multiply by $\dfrac{n^{-2}}{n^{-2}}$:

$$\frac{n^{-2}}{n^{-2}} \cdot \frac{6n^2 - 3n + 8}{2n^2} = \frac{6 - \dfrac{3}{n} + \dfrac{8}{n^2}}{2}$$

Then $\qquad \displaystyle\lim_{n \to \infty} \frac{6n^2 - 3n + 8}{2n^2} = \frac{\displaystyle\lim_{n \to \infty} \left(6 - \frac{3}{n} + \frac{8}{n^2}\right)}{\displaystyle\lim_{n \to \infty} 2}$

$$= \frac{6 - 0 + 0}{2}$$

$$= 3.$$

The second method uses Theorem 5–8 in combination with Theorem 5–7.

EXAMPLE 3. Find $\lim\limits_{n\to\infty} \dfrac{n^3+n}{n^2}$, if it exists.

$$\frac{n^3+n}{n^2} = \frac{n^3}{n^2} + \frac{n}{n^2} = n + \frac{1}{n}$$

It is clear that $\{n\}$ does not converge, that is, $\{n\}$ is a divergent sequence. Since every term of $\left\{\dfrac{n^3+n}{n^2}\right\}$ is greater than the corresponding term of $\{n\}$, it also follows that $\left\{\dfrac{n^3+n}{n^2}\right\}$ does not converge.

The reasoning used in Example 3 can be formalized as a test for divergence.

Comparison Test for Divergence: If $\{a_n\}$ and $\{b_n\}$ are two sequences such that $a_n \leq b_n$ for all n or for all n greater than a fixed natural number n_0 and $\{a_n\}$ diverges, then $\{b_n\}$ diverges.

Some examples of divergent sequences are:
1. $\{n+c\}$ and $\{-n+c\}$ where c is a real number
2. $\left\{\dfrac{n}{c}\right\}$ and $\left\{\dfrac{-n}{c}\right\}$ where c is a nonzero real number
3. $\{r^n\}$ where r is a real and $|r| > 1$
4. $\{n^p\}$ where p is real and positive.

EXAMPLE 4. Use the comparison test to show that $\{2n-3\}$ diverges.

METHOD I
$$2n-3 \geq n \quad \text{iff} \quad 2n \geq n+3$$
$$\text{iff} \quad n \geq 3$$

Thus for all $n \geq 3$, $2n-3 \geq n$. Since $\{n\}$ diverges, $\{2n-3\}$ diverges by the comparison test.

METHOD II
$$2n-3 \geq n-3 \quad \text{iff} \quad 2n \geq n$$
$$\text{iff} \quad n \geq 0$$

Thus for all $n > 0$, $2n-3 > n-3$ and $\{2n-3\}$ diverges by comparison with $\{n-3\}$.

Checkpoint

1. How do you define the sum of two sequences $\{a_n\}$ and $\{b_n\}$?
2. If $\{a_n\}$ and $\{b_n\}$ each converges does their sum converge? If so, to what number?

Exercises

A ▬▬ Use the theorems of this section to determine whether the sequence converges or diverges. If it converges, specify the limit.

1. $\left\{\dfrac{5n+21}{21n}\right\}$

2. $\left\{\dfrac{3+2n}{6n}\right\}$

3. $\left\{\dfrac{6-2n}{4n}\right\}$

4. $\left\{\dfrac{n+1}{n}+\dfrac{n}{2}\right\}$

5. $\left\{\dfrac{7n^2-2n}{5n^2}\right\}$

6. $\left\{\dfrac{7n^2+2n}{5n}\right\}$

7. $\left\{\left(\dfrac{2n+1}{n}\right)\left(5+\dfrac{7}{n}\right)\right\}$

8. $\left\{\dfrac{n^3}{n^2+10}\right\}$

9. $\left\{\left[2+\dfrac{1}{n}\right]^4\right\}$

10. $\left\{\dfrac{n+1}{n}\right\}$

11. $\left\{\dfrac{3n^2+2n+1}{6n^2+3n+2}\right\}$

12. $\left\{\dfrac{n^2+n}{n^2-2}\right\}$

13. $\left\{\dfrac{(n+1)(n+2)(n+3)}{3n^3}\right\}$

14. $\left\{\left(\dfrac{2n}{n}\right)\left(\dfrac{7}{10}\right)^n\right\}$

15. $\left\{5\left(\dfrac{n+1}{n}\right)\left(\dfrac{n}{n+1}\right)\right\}$

B **16.** Suppose $\{a_n\}$ and $\{b_n\}$ are two divergent sequences.

    a. Is $\{a_n+b_n\}$ always, sometimes, or never convergent (cite examples).

    b. Is $\{a_n \cdot b_n\}$ always, sometimes, or never convergent (cite examples).

    c. Is $\left\{\dfrac{a_n}{b_n}\right\}$ always, sometimes, or never convergent (cite examples).

17. Suppose $\{a_n\}$ is convergent and $\{b_n\}$ is divergent.

    a. Is $\{a_n+b_n\}$ always, sometimes, or never convergent (cite examples).

    b. Is $\{a_n \cdot b_n\}$ always, sometimes, or never convergent (cite examples).

    c. Is $\left\{\dfrac{a_n}{b_n}\right\}$ always, sometimes, or never convergent (cite examples).

18. a. Suppose $\{a_n\}$ and $\{b_n\}$ converge to the same number. What can you conclude, if anything, about the convergence of $\{a_n-b_n\}$?

    b. Suppose $\{a_n-b_n\}$ converges to zero. Does this mean that $\{a_n\}$ and $\{b_n\}$ converge to the same number? Explain.

CHAPTER OBJECTIVES AND REVIEW ▰▰▰▰▰▰

Objective: *To know the meaning of the important mathematical terms of this chapter.*

1. Here are many of the mathematical terms used in this chapter. Be sure that you know them thoroughly and can use them correctly.

infinite sequence (*211*)   general neighborhood (*229*)
finite sequence (*211*)   completeness property (*238*)
neighborhood (*218*)   monotone sequence (*239*)
convergent sequence (*228*)   series (*241*)
divergent sequence (*228*)   sum of an infinite series (*243*)

Objective: *To define a sequence and find any term or terms of the sequence given an expression for the nth term or a recursively stated relationship.*

2. Write a definition of a sequence which expresses what you think it is. Compare your definition with that given on p. 211.

▬ Find the first five terms of each sequence and one additional term as specified.

3. $a_n = \frac{2}{3} + n$; 15th term.

4. $b_n = \dfrac{2}{n+3}$; 25th term.

5. $a_1 = b,\ a_n = \frac{1}{10} a_{n-1}$; 10th term.

6. $b_n = (\frac{1}{2})^n + 10$; 10th term.

7. $c_1 = -2,\ c_n = -1c_{n-1}$; 20th term.

8. Write an expression for the nth term of the sequence.
  a. In Exercise 5.
  b. In Exercise 7.
  c. $a_1 = 2,\ a_n = 2a_{n-1}$
  d. $b_1 = -\frac{1}{2},\ b_n = -1b_{n-1}$

Objective: *To graph several terms of a sequence and identify an open interval in which the remaining terms lie.*

▬ Graph five terms of each sequence. Find an open interval containing the remaining terms but not containing the first five terms.

9. $\{a_n\} = \{-3 + 2n\}$

10. $\{b_n\} = \left\{ \dfrac{9^{n-1}}{10} \right\}$

11. $\{c_n\} = \{(0.9)^{n-1}\}$

12. $\{d_n\} = \{(-0.5)^n\}$

Objective: *To find all terms of a sequence which lie in a given neighborhood.*

■ For the given sequence and neighborhood identify all the terms of the sequence lying in the neighborhood.

13. $\{a_n\} = \{-3 + 2n\}$; $\langle 23, 47 \rangle$

14. $\{b_n\} = \left\{\frac{4n}{10}\right\}$; $\langle 0, 23 \rangle$

15. $\{c_n\} = \left\{\frac{2n - 1}{n}\right\}$; $\langle 1.8, 2.2 \rangle$

16. $\{d_n\} = \left\{\left(\frac{-2}{3}\right)^n\right\}$; $\langle -0.001, 0.001 \rangle$

17. $\{c_n\} = \left\{\frac{1}{3n}\right\}$; $\langle -\epsilon, \epsilon \rangle$, $\epsilon > 0$

Objective: *To apply the definition of the limit of a sequence to prove or disprove the claim that L is the limit of $\{a_n\}$.*

■ In each Exercise 18–21 the number L is claimed to be the limit of the sequence $\{a_n\}$. If you agree, prove you are correct. If you disagree produce a neighborhood of L which does not contain an infinite subset of $\{a_n\}$.

18. $\left\{\frac{2n}{n + 1}\right\}$; $L = 2$

19. $\left\{\frac{73}{n}\right\}$; $L = 0$

20. $\{2n - 49\}$; $L = 63$

21. $\left\{\frac{n - 3}{4n}\right\}$; $L = \frac{1}{2}$

22. State in your own words what it means to say $\{a_n\}$ has L as a limit.

Objective: *To find the least upper and greatest lower bounds of a sequence, and use these concepts to explain the completeness property of the real numbers.*

23. a. Which of the sequences in Exercises 18–21 are bounded?
　　b. Find l.u.b. and g.l.b. for the bounded sequences.
24. a. State in your own words the least upper bound axiom.
　　b. Explain what is meant by saying that the real numbers are complete.
25. Given $\{a_n\} = \left\{-1 + \frac{1}{n}\right\}$.

　　a. Is $\{a_n\}$ bounded? Illustrate.
　　b. Is $\{a_n\}$ monotone? Explain.
　　c. Does $\{a_n\}$ have a limit? Explain.

Objective: *To use the limit theorems for sequences (Theorems 5–7 and 5–8) to find limits of sequences.*

━━━ Find the limit (when possible) of each sequence.

26. $\{a_n\} = \left\{\dfrac{6n^2 + n - 1}{3n + 1}\right\}$

27. $\{b_n\} = \left\{\dfrac{n^3 + 17n^2 - 3n + 1}{43n^3 + 1}\right\}$

28. $\displaystyle\lim_{n\to\infty} \left[\left(\dfrac{2}{3}\right)^n \cdot \dfrac{n + 1}{4n - 3}\right]$

29. $\displaystyle\lim_{n\to\infty} \dfrac{(n - 1)(n - 2)(n - 3)}{3n^3}$

Objective: *To define the sum of an infinite series and find such sums.*

30. State your personal definition of the sum of a series. Compare your definition with the one given in the text book.

━━━ Write the first five addends in each series.

31. $\displaystyle\sum_{i=1}^{\infty} 4 + 2i$

32. $\displaystyle\sum_{i=1}^{\infty} -3\left(\dfrac{i}{5}\right)$

33. $\displaystyle\sum_{i=1}^{\infty} \left| -4 + \tfrac{1}{2}i \right|$

34. $\displaystyle\sum_{i=1}^{\infty} \left(\tfrac{3}{4}\right)^{i-1}$

━━━ Find the sum of each series.

35. $\displaystyle\sum_{i=1}^{\infty} 2\left(\tfrac{3}{4}\right)^{i-1}$

36. $\displaystyle\sum_{i=1}^{\infty} 2\left(\dfrac{-3}{4}\right)^{i-1}$

CHAPTER TEST ━━━━━━━━━━━━━━

1. Find the first seven terms of the sequence with nth term:

$$b_n = (-1)^n \frac{1}{2n}$$

What is b_{100}? b_{101}?

2. Find the first seven terms of the sequence defined as follows:

$$a_1 = 3, \; a_n = 2a_{n-1} - 1.$$

3. Let $c_n = 2^n + 1$. What are the first seven terms? Compare $\{c_n\}$ with $\{a_n\}$ of Exercise 2.

4. Graph $\{b_n\} = \left\{\frac{(-1)^n}{2n}\right\}$ on the number line. What is the apparent limit?

5. Graph $\{c_n\} = \{2^n + 1\}$ on the number line. Does there appear to be a limit?

6. Find an M so that all the terms of $\{a_n\} = \left\{\frac{(-1)^n}{2n}\right\}$ for $n \geq M$ lie inside the neighborhood $\langle -0.001, 0.001 \rangle$, $\langle -\epsilon, \epsilon \rangle$, $\epsilon > 0$.

7. What appears to be the limit of $\{b_n\} = \left\{\frac{2n + 1}{n - 2}\right\}$? Prove that your guess is correct by using the definition of limit of a sequence.

8. Construct a proof demonstrating that $\lim\limits_{n \to \infty} \dfrac{3}{n^2} = 0$.

9. Produce an example of a monotone sequence that is bounded; that is unbounded. Which of these sequences has a limit? Explain.

━━ Use the limit theorems to find the limit of each sequence.

10. $\{a_n\} = \left\{\dfrac{n - 3}{(n + 3)(n)}\right\}$

11. $\{b_n\} = \left\{\dfrac{2 \cdot (n - 5)}{3n}\right\}$

12. $\{c_n\} = \left\{(\frac{4}{5})^n \cdot \left(23 - \frac{1}{n}\right)\right\}$

━━ Write out at least five addends in each series.

13. $\displaystyle\sum_{i=1}^{\infty} \frac{(-1)^i}{3i}$

14. $\displaystyle\sum_{i=1}^{\infty} (2i - 3)$

15. Find the sum of the geometric series.

$$\sum_{i=1}^{\infty} (\tfrac{4}{5})^{i-1}$$

CHAPTER 6

FUNCTIONS AND LIMITS

Nature and Nature's laws lay hid in night;
God said, Let Newton be! and all was light.

Alexander Pope (1688–1744)

All of Nature's laws, contrary to the above couplet were not entirely "hid in night" before the time of Newton. However, there were many that were because much of the mathematics necessary for an understanding of Nature's laws had not been created until Newton's time. In this chapter you will begin your study of the *derived function*, one of the mathematical tools developed by both Newton and his contemporary, Leibniz. So many of the laws of nature depend upon this function and others related to it that without it the scientific study of the world around us would be impossible.

The skier pictured opposite leaves the earth along a path that is tangent to the earth's surface. Many of the physical aspects of his flight such as his velocity and the angle at which his skies are tangent to the earth can be analyzed using the derived function. In this chapter you will consider one of these applications, the slope of a line tangent to a curve.

The laws of nature that are often the easiest to handle mathematically are those that involve *continuous functions*. Even a small discontinuity, such as a break in the filament of a light bulb, may be a great practical and mathematical disadvantage.

Continuous curves are used in the designs of buildings, paintings, etc. The suspension bridge shown on the opposite page is an illustration of the use of continuous curves in engineering.

6–1 Sequences and Functions

In Chapter 5 a *sequence* was defined as the range of a function whose domain is the positive integers. Thus, if $\{a_n\} = \left\{\frac{n+1}{n}\right\}$ then $\{a_n\} = \{2, \frac{3}{2}, \frac{4}{3}, \frac{5}{4}, \cdots\}$. In order to develop an understanding of the *limit of a function* it is helpful to change this point of view slightly. For the purpose of this chapter, a sequence $\{a_n\}$ will be regarded as a *function* (not simply the range of a function). The set $\{1, 2, 3, \cdots\}$ of replacements for n is the *domain* of the function; the set $\{a_1, a_2, a_3, \cdots\}$ is its *range*.

In the previous chapter you graphed many sequences on a co-ordinatized line. In Figure 1 the sequence with general term

$$a_n = \frac{n+1}{n}$$

is graphed on a coordinatized line.

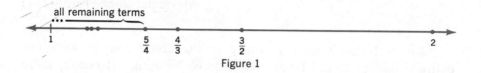

Figure 1

A sequence can just as easily be graphed in a coordinatized plane, if the sequence is defined as a function. In fact this is the standard practice for functions. Figure 2 shows the two dimensional graph of the first five terms of the sequence with general term $a_n = \frac{n+1}{n}$. As you know, $\lim_{n\to\infty} \frac{n+1}{n} = 1$. In the graph you can see that the points (n, a_n) are very close to the line $y = 1$ for large n.

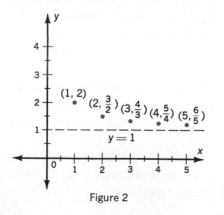

Figure 2

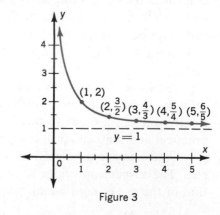

Figure 3

Suppose the domain of the function $a_n : n \longrightarrow \dfrac{n+1}{n}$ is extended to include all real numbers greater than 0. Then the graph of the function will resemble the one shown in Figure 3.

When the domain of a function is the set of real numbers or an interval of reals, the function is called a **function of a real variable.** These functions and their limits are the major concern of this chapter.

Recall that a sequence $\{a_n\}$ has a limit A if and only if for every $\epsilon > 0$, there is a natural number M such that for all $n \geq M$, $a_n \in \langle A - \epsilon, A + \epsilon \rangle$. The statement $n \geq M$ can be equivalently represented by the statement $n \in [M, +\infty)$ $\quad n, M \in \{1, 2, 3, \cdots\}$, where $[M, +\infty)$ is the set of all real numbers greater than or equal to M. (See Figure 4.)

> **Definition** $\displaystyle \lim_{n \to \infty} a_n = A$ iff for every $\epsilon > 0$, there is an M such that for all $n \in [M, +\infty)$ $a_n \in \langle A - \epsilon, A + \epsilon \rangle$.

The sequence graphed happens to alternate on either side of A. Since the graph is given in two dimensions, the neighborhood of A, $\langle A - \epsilon, A + \epsilon \rangle$ is located on the y axis rather than on the x axis as in Chapter 5. The dotted horizontal lines $y = A + \epsilon$ and $y = A - \epsilon$ are determined by the end points of the neighborhood. Notice that for a_n to be in $\langle A - \epsilon, A + \epsilon \rangle$, a_n must be in the region between $y = A + \epsilon$ and $y = A - \epsilon$.

The interval $[M, +\infty)$ is located on the x axis. All of the terms of $\{a_n\}$ are between $y = A + \epsilon$ and $y = A - \epsilon$ for $n \geq 7$. Thus $M = 7$ (or any larger natural number). The region for which $a_n \in \langle A - \epsilon, A + \epsilon \rangle$ when $n \in [M, +\infty)$ is shaded. If there is such a region for *every* $\epsilon > 0$, then the limit of $\{a_n\}$ is A.

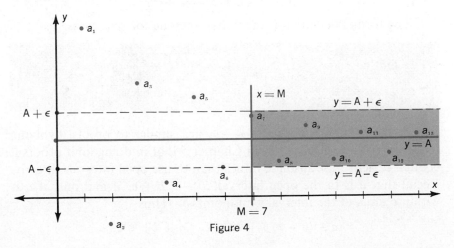

Figure 4

The situation for functions of a real variable is analogous. For the limit of $f(x)$ to be L, to each $\epsilon > 0$, there must be an x_0 (like M) such that $f(x) \in \langle L - \epsilon, L + \epsilon \rangle$ whenever $x \in \langle x_0, +\infty \rangle$. The major differences here are that x may be replaced by any real number in the interval $\langle x_0, +\infty \rangle$ and that x must assume a value greater than x_0 *but not equal to x_0.*

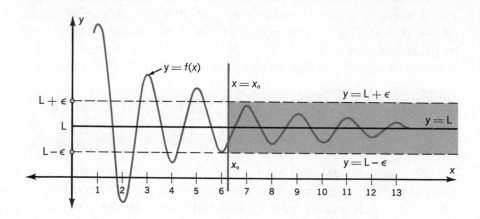

In the figure above each $f(x)$ for $x > x_0$ is in the shaded region bounded by $y = L + \epsilon$, $x = x_0$ and $y = L - \epsilon$. If such a shaded region can be found for each $\epsilon > 0$ chosen, then the limit of $f(x)$ as x increases without bound exists, and is L. This is symbolized in the following way.

$$\lim_{x \to \infty} f(x) = L$$

or

$$f(x) \longrightarrow L \text{ as } x \longrightarrow +\infty.$$

The formal definition is much like the one for sequences.

Definition $\lim\limits_{x \to +\infty} f(x) = L$ if and only if for each $\epsilon > 0$ there is an x_0 such that $f(x) \in \langle L - \epsilon, L + \epsilon \rangle$ whenever $x \in \langle x_0, +\infty \rangle$.

Proofs that $f(x) \longrightarrow L$ as $x \longrightarrow +\infty$ are similar to proofs involving sequences. You will recall from Chapter 5 that in doing limit proofs it is often easier to use absolute values than to use open intervals directly. Recall that a is in the open interval $\langle b - c, b + c \rangle$ if and only if a is within c units of the interval's midpoint, b. Thus

$$a \in \langle b - c, b + c \rangle \text{ iff } |a - b| < c.$$

EXAMPLE 1. Prove: $\lim\limits_{x \to \infty} f(x) = 1$ where $f(x) = \dfrac{x+1}{x}$ and $x > 0$.

Proof: Using absolute values, an x_0 must be found such that $\left| \dfrac{x+1}{x} - 1 \right| < \epsilon$ whenever $x > x_0$.

But

$$\left| \frac{x+1}{x} - 1 \right| < \epsilon \quad \text{iff}$$

$$\left| \frac{x+1}{x} - \frac{x}{x} \right| < \epsilon \quad \text{iff}$$

$$\left| \frac{1}{x} \right| < \epsilon \quad \text{iff}$$

$$\frac{1}{|x|} < \epsilon \quad \text{iff}$$

$$\frac{1}{\epsilon} < |x| \quad \text{iff}$$

$$\frac{1}{\epsilon} < x \quad \text{(since } x > 0\text{).}$$

Consequently, choose

$$x_0 = \frac{1}{\epsilon}.$$

It follows that if

$$x > x_0 = \frac{1}{\epsilon},$$

then

$$\left| \frac{x+1}{x} - 1 \right| < \epsilon$$

and

$$\lim\limits_{x \to \infty} \frac{x+1}{x} = 1.$$

Unlike sequences, a function of a real variable may have the set of negative real numbers for its domain. In such a case you may be asked to find the limit of the function as $|x|$ increases without bound. Since x is negative, $|x| \longrightarrow +\infty$ is equivalent to $x \longrightarrow -\infty$. This possibility may be handled by applying the next definition.

Definition $\lim\limits_{x \to -\infty} f(x) = L$ if and only if for each $\epsilon > 0$ there is an x_0 such that $f(x) \in \langle L - \epsilon, L + \epsilon \rangle$ whenever $x \in \langle -\infty, x_0 \rangle$.

EXAMPLE 2. Prove: $\lim\limits_{x \to -\infty} f(x) = 1$ where $f(x) = \frac{x+1}{x}$, $x < 0$

Proof:

$$\left| \frac{x+1}{x} - 1 \right| < \epsilon \quad \text{iff}$$

$$\left| \frac{x+1-x}{x} \right| < \epsilon \quad \text{iff}$$

$$\left| \frac{1}{x} \right| < \epsilon \quad \text{iff}$$

$$\frac{1}{|x|} < \epsilon \quad \text{iff}$$

$$\frac{1}{\epsilon} < |x| \quad \text{iff}$$

$$\frac{1}{\epsilon} < -x \quad (\text{since } x < 0) \quad \text{iff}$$

$$-\frac{1}{\epsilon} > x \quad (\text{multiplying both sides by } -1).$$

Consequently choose $x_0 = -\frac{1}{\epsilon}$. It follows that if $x < x_0 = -\frac{1}{\epsilon}$, then $\left| \frac{x+1}{x} - 1 \right| < \epsilon$ and $\lim\limits_{x \to -\infty} \frac{x+1}{x} = 1$.

Checkpoint

1. How does a function of a real variable differ from a sequence?
2. Name two differences between the limit of a sequence $A = \lim\limits_{n \to \infty} a_n$ and the limit of a function $L = \lim\limits_{x \to \infty} f(x)$.

Exercises

A — Graph each sequence and the associated function of a real variable. What appears to be the limit of each as $n \longrightarrow +\infty$ or as $x \longrightarrow +\infty$?

1. $a_n = \frac{n-1}{n}$, $f(x) = \frac{x-1}{x}$
2. $a_n = \frac{1}{n}$, $f(x) = \frac{1}{x}$
3. $a_n = \frac{2n^2 + 2n + 1}{n^2}$, $f(x) = \frac{2x^2 + 2x + 1}{x^2}$
4. $a_n = \frac{1-n}{n}$, $f(x) = \frac{1-x}{x}$
5. $a_n = 3, f(x) = 3$
6. $a_n = (\frac{1}{2})^{n-1}, f(x) = (\frac{1}{2})^{x-1}$
7. For Exercises 1–5 what does $\lim\limits_{x \to -\infty} f(x)$ appear to be?

B ━━ For each function in Exercises 8–11 find an x_0 so that all values of the function for $x \in \langle x_0, +\infty \rangle$ will be in the neighborhood of radius $\frac{1}{10}$ about the given limit L. Construct a graph for each.

8. $f(x) = \dfrac{1}{x}$, $L = 0$ **9.** $f(x) = \dfrac{3x + 2}{x}$, $L = 3$

10. $f(x) = \dfrac{3 - 2x}{3x}$, $L = -\frac{2}{3}$ **11.** $f(x) = \dfrac{3x}{5x + 1}$, $L = \frac{3}{5}$

12. Repeat Exercises 8–11 for a radius of $\frac{1}{100}$.

C **13.** Explain in your own words why the definitions of $\lim\limits_{x \to +\infty} f(x)$ and $\lim\limits_{x \to -\infty} f(x)$ are special cases of the following definition:

> $\lim\limits_{x \to \infty} f(x) = L$ if and only if for each $\epsilon > 0$ there is an x_0 such that $f(x) \in \langle L - \epsilon, L + \epsilon \rangle$ whenever $|x| > |x_0|$.

━━ Prove each of the following statements.

14. $\lim\limits_{x \to +\infty} \dfrac{1}{x} = 0$ **15.** $\lim\limits_{x \to -\infty} \dfrac{1}{x} = 0$

16. $\lim\limits_{x \to +\infty} \dfrac{-2x + 1}{x} = -2$ **17.** $\lim\limits_{x \to +\infty} \dfrac{3x}{5x + 1} = \dfrac{3}{5}$

18. $\lim\limits_{x \to -\infty} 2 = 2$ **19.** $\lim\limits_{x \to +\infty} \dfrac{-x^2 + 2x}{2x^2} = -\dfrac{1}{2}$

20. $\lim\limits_{x \to \infty} \dfrac{x + 3}{x + 2} = 1$ **21.** $\lim\limits_{x \to \infty} \dfrac{2(x^2 - 1)}{(x - 1)(x + 1)} = 2$

22. $\lim\limits_{x \to \infty} \dfrac{x + 1}{x^2 - 1} = 0$ **23.** $\lim\limits_{x \to \infty} \dfrac{-3x + 4}{-5x} = \dfrac{3}{5}$

24. $\lim\limits_{x \to \infty} \dfrac{1}{x} = 0$ **25.** $\lim\limits_{x \to \infty} \dfrac{1}{x^2} = 0$

6–2   Limit of a Function at a Point $x = a$

In the previous section you studied the limit of a function $f(x)$ as $x \longrightarrow +\infty$ and as $x \longrightarrow -\infty$. In this section the meaning of "the limit of $f(x)$ as x approaches a" is discussed.

The symbolism is the same as used previously. Thus "$\lim\limits_{x \to a} f(x) = L$" means "$L$ is the limit of the function $f(x)$ as x approaches a." The intuitive idea is similar: $\lim\limits_{x \to a} f(x) = L$ means that $f(x)$ is quite close to L when x is close to but not equal to a.

Let $y = f(x)$ have a graph as shown in the diagram below. Notice that a neighborhood of L and the horizontal lines determined by its endpoints have been indicated. Also a neighborhood of a, $\langle a - \delta, a + \delta \rangle$, and the vertical lines determined by its endpoints are indicated. (δ is the Greek letter delta.) The shaded region is the intersection of the points between $y = L + \epsilon$ and $y = L - \epsilon$ and those between $x = a + \delta$ and $x = a - \delta$.

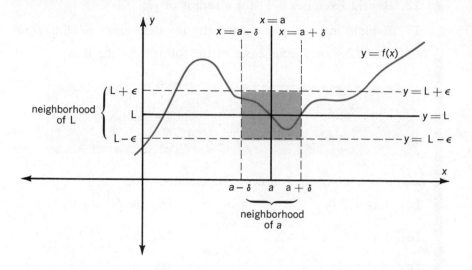

The function is said to **have a limit L as x approaches a** if and only if for every neighborhood of L a neighborhood of a can be found so that every value of the function corresponding to an $x(x \neq a)$ in the neighborhood of a lies in the neighborhood of the limit L. In graphical terms, every point of the curve between $x = a - \delta$ and $x = a + \delta$ ($x \neq a$) must also be between $y = L + \epsilon$ and $y = L - \epsilon$, that is, in the shaded region. To visualize the effect of making ϵ smaller, think of the lines $y = L + \epsilon$ and $y = L - \epsilon$ each moving close to $y = L$. If the lines $x = a - \delta$ and $x = a + \delta$ can each be moved close to $x = a$ so that the points of the graph remain in the shaded rectangular region, then L is the limit of $f(x)$ as x approaches a. These ideas are formalized in the next definition.

Definition $\lim\limits_{x \to a} f(x) = L$ if and only if for each $\epsilon > 0$ there is a $\delta > 0$ such that $f(x) \in \langle L - \epsilon, L + \epsilon \rangle$ whenever $x \in \langle a - \delta, a + \delta \rangle$ and $x \neq a$. If $\lim\limits_{x \to a} f(x) = L$, then $f(x)$ is said to have a limit at $x = a$.

Notice that $f(x)$ need not be defined at $x = a$ for $\lim_{x \to a} f(x)$ to exist. All that need be true is for all the x in $\langle a - \delta, a + \delta \rangle$ *other than* $x = a$ to correspond to values of the function which are in $\langle L - \epsilon, L + \epsilon \rangle$. Reasoning in the same manner, if $f(x)$ is defined at $x = a, f(a)$ does not necessarily have to equal the limit L.

There are many examples of functions which do not have a limit at $x = a$. One of these follows.

EXAMPLE 1. Consider the function $f(x)$ defined as follows:

$$f(x) = \begin{cases} x + 2 & \text{for } x < 1 \\ 4 & \text{for } x = 1 \\ x + 4 & \text{for } x > 1 \end{cases}$$

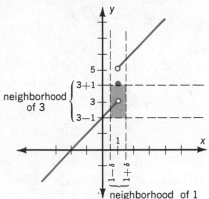

Show that it does not have a limit.

The possibilities for L appear to be any number between and including 3 and 5. However, none of these is the limit. Suppose you claimed $\lim_{x \to 1} f(x)$ was 3, and you were asked to find δ given that $\epsilon = 1$.

It is impossible to find an appropriate δ, for it is clear from the diagram that for those x between 1 and $1 + \delta, f(x)$ is not in the shaded region. This is true no matter how small δ is chosen to be.

The same type of situation occurs when 5 is claimed to be the limit. Here, however, the $f(x)$ corresponding to x between $1 - \delta$ and 1 are outside the shaded region when ϵ is chosen to be any number less than 2.

All other possible values for the limit lead to the same conclusion, namely, that there is always at least one $\epsilon > 0$ for which there is no neighborhood of 1 all of whose members not equal to 1 correspond to values of the function in $\langle L - \epsilon, L + \epsilon \rangle$. Consequently $\lim_{x \to 1} f(x)$ does not exist.

Even though $\lim_{x \to 1} f(x)$ does not exist for the function of Example 1, two *one-sided limits* do exist. Considering only those values of x which are less than 1, then the limit of $f(x)$ as x approaches 1 exists, and is equal to 3. This is true because the values of $f(x)$ for $x \in \langle 1 - \delta, 1 \rangle$ lie in the shaded region. Analytically this means that for a given $\epsilon > 0$, there is a $\delta > 0$ such that $f(x) \in \langle 3 - \epsilon, 3 + \epsilon \rangle$ whenever $x \in \langle 1 - \delta, 1 \rangle$ *and* $x < 1$. Since all values of x are less than 1, $f(x)$ is said to have a limit 3 *as x approaches 1 from the left.* In symbols: $\lim_{x \to 1^-} f(x) = 3.$

It is clear that the function of Example 1 also has a *one-sided* limit at $x = 1$ when x is restricted to values greater than 1. In this case, however, the limit is 5. The limit is denoted

$$\lim_{x \to 1^+} f(x) = 5.$$

Definition **a.** $f(x)$ has the limit L as x approaches a from the right, written

$$\lim_{x \to a^+} f(x) = L,$$

if and only if to each $\epsilon > 0$ there is a $\delta > 0$ such that $f(x) \in \langle L - \epsilon, L + \epsilon \rangle$ whenever $x \in \langle a, a + \delta \rangle$.

b. $f(x)$ has the limit L as x approaches a from the left, written

$$\lim_{x \to a^-} f(x) = L$$

if and only if to each $\epsilon > 0$ there is a $\delta > 0$ such that $f(x) \in \langle L - \epsilon, L + \epsilon \rangle$ whenever $x \in \langle a - \delta, a \rangle$.

EXAMPLE 2. Graph the following.

$$f(x) = \begin{cases} \dfrac{x^2 + x}{x} & \text{for } x \neq 0 \\ 5 & \text{for } x = 0 \end{cases}$$

By inspection determine $\lim_{x \to 0} f(x)$, $\lim_{x \to 0^+} f(x)$ and $\lim_{x \to 0^-} f(x)$.
The graph is shown at the right.
By inspection

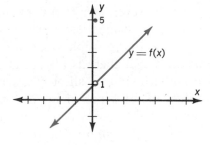

$$\lim_{x \to 0} f(x) = 1,$$

$$\lim_{x \to 0^+} f(x) = 1,$$

$$\lim_{x \to 0^-} f(x) = 1$$

Notice that $f(0) = 5$ and is not equal to $\lim_{x \to 0} f(x)$. Also note that the limit from the left and the limit from the right equal $\lim_{x \to 0} f(x)$.

Whenever a limit at a point exists, it is equal to the right and left hand limits. Also, whenever the right and left hand limits at a point both exist and are equal, the limit exists and is equal to the common value of the right and left hand limits. The proof of this statement is left for you to do in the exercises.

Exercises

In Exercises 1–9 use the given L and ϵ to find a neighborhood of a (if possible) so that $f(x) \in \langle L - \epsilon, L + \epsilon \rangle$ when $x \in \langle a - \delta, a + \delta \rangle$.

1. $f(x) = x + 3$ $L = 5, a = 2, \epsilon = \frac{1}{10}$

2. $f(x) = 2x - 3$ $L = -3, a = 0, \epsilon = \frac{1}{100}$

3. $f(x) = 3x + 2$ $L = 8, a = 2, \epsilon = \frac{1}{100}$

4. $f(x) = \frac{2}{3}x - 1$ $L = 0, a = 3, \epsilon = \frac{1}{100}$

5. $f(x) = \begin{cases} x - 2 & \text{for } x < 2 \\ -1 & \text{for } x = 2 \\ x - 4 & \text{for } x > 2 \end{cases}$ $L = 0, a = 2, \epsilon = \frac{1}{2}$

6. $f(x) = \begin{cases} x - 2 & \text{for } x < 2 \\ -1 & \text{for } x = 2 \\ x - 4 & \text{for } x > 2 \end{cases}$ $L = -2, a = 2, \epsilon = \frac{1}{2}$

7. $f(x) = \begin{cases} x - 2 & \text{for } x < 2 \\ -1 & \text{for } x = 2 \\ x - 4 & \text{for } x > 2 \end{cases}$ $L = -1, a = 2, \epsilon = \frac{1}{2}$

8. $f(x) = \begin{cases} x + 2 & \text{for } x < 2 \\ 2x & \text{for } x \geq 2 \end{cases}$ $L = 4, a = 2, \epsilon = \frac{1}{100}$

9. $f(x) = x^2$, $L = 1$, $a = 1$, $\epsilon = \frac{1}{100}$ (*Hint:* Restrict δ to values less than 1. Then $|x + 1| < 3$.)

In Exercises 10–13 find $\lim\limits_{x \to a} f(x)$, $\lim\limits_{x \to a^+} f(x)$ and $\lim\limits_{x \to a^-} f(x)$ (if possible) for the given function at the given point a. A graph will be of assistance.

10. $f(x) = \begin{cases} 1 & \text{for } x > 0 \\ 0 & \text{for } x = 0 \\ -1 & \text{for } x < 0 \end{cases}$ $a = 0$

11. $f(x) = \begin{cases} |x| & \text{for } x \neq 0 \\ 5 & \text{for } x = 0 \end{cases}$ $a = 0$

12. $f(x) = \begin{cases} \dfrac{2x^2 + x}{x} & \text{for } x \neq 0 \\ \text{undefined} & \text{for } x = 0 \end{cases}$ $a = 0$

13. $f(x) = \begin{cases} x - 2 & \text{for } x < 2 \\ -1 & \text{for } x = 2 \\ x - 4 & \text{for } x > 2 \end{cases}$ $a = 2$

14. Consider the following definition of the limit of a function at a point a.

> **Definition** $\lim_{x \to a} f(x) = L$ if and only if $f(x)$ can be found as close as you please to L provided x is sufficiently close to a.

Compare this definition with the definition as given in the text. What are the strengths and weaknesses of each?

C **15.** Explain in your own words why "$\lim_{x \to a} f(x) = L$" is equivalent to "$\lim_{x \to a^-} f(x) = L$ and $\lim_{x \to a^+} f(x) = L$."

6–3 Limit Theorems and Polynomials

Constructing a proof of $\lim_{x \to a} f(x) = L$ in accordance with the definition given in Section 6–2 can be quite complicated even for the simplest functions.

EXAMPLE 1. Prove $\lim_{x \to 2} x^2 = 4$.

Let $\epsilon > 0$ be given. Thus a δ must be found so that

$$x \in \langle 2 - \delta, 2 + \delta \rangle$$

and $x \neq 2$ implies $x^2 \in \langle 4 - \epsilon, 4 + \epsilon \rangle$. Restating these conditions using absolute values, you have

$$0 < |x - 2| < \delta \text{ implies } |x^2 - 4| < \epsilon. \qquad 1$$

That is, it must be shown that

$$|x^2 - 4| = |(x + 2)(x - 2)| = |x + 2| \cdot |x - 2|$$

is as small as you please when x is sufficiently near 2. The second factor, $|x - 2|$, is certainly small if x is near 2; and the first factor, $|x + 2|$ is near 4 when x is near 2. To make this precise, first require $\delta \leq 1$. (There is nothing special about 1. Another positive number could be used and not change the nature of the argument. The details would be different, however.) If x is within a distance less than δ of 2, then certainly $|x - 2| < \delta \leq 1$.

Thus you have the following.

$$|x - 2| < 1 \qquad \text{iff}$$
$$-1 < x - 2 < 1 \qquad \text{iff}$$
$$3 < x + 2 < 5$$

Thus certainly

$$|x + 2| < 5.$$

Hence $|x^2 - 4|$ will be less than ϵ if simultaneously

$$|x + 2| < 5 \qquad\qquad\qquad\qquad\qquad\qquad \textbf{2}$$

and

$$|x - 2| < \frac{\epsilon}{5} \qquad\qquad\qquad\qquad\qquad\qquad \textbf{3}$$

because you want

$$|x^2 - 4| = |x + 2| \cdot |x - 2| < 5 \cdot \frac{\epsilon}{5} = \epsilon.$$

Since $\delta \leq 1$, choose δ to be the smaller of 1 and $\frac{\epsilon}{5}$. That is, choose $\delta = \frac{\epsilon}{5}$ for $\epsilon \leq 5$ and choose $\delta = 1$ otherwise. This will force both inequalities **2** and **3** to be true. The proof is complete.

It would be tedious to prove each limit that you encountered in this manner, using only the definition. Several theorems follow which simplify matters considerably, but their proofs will not be given.

Theorem 6–1 If $f(x)$ is equal to a constant k, then $\lim_{x \to a} f(x)$ exists and $\lim_{x \to a} f(x) = k$.

Theorem 6–2 If $f(x) = x^m$ where m is a positive real number, $\lim_{x \to a} x^m = a^m$.

EXAMPLE 2. Evaluate the following two limits.

a. $\lim_{x \to 2} 3$ **b.** $\lim_{x \to 2} x^4$

a. $\lim_{x \to 2} 3 = 3$ by Theorem 6–1

b. $\lim_{x \to 2} x^4 = 2^4 = 16$ by Theorem 6–2

The next two theorems indicate how the limit of the sum, difference, product, and quotient of two functions may be found.

Theorem 6–3   If $\lim_{x \to a} f(x) = L$ and $\lim_{x \to a} g(x) = M$, then

i. $\lim_{x \to a} [f(x) + g(x)] = L + M$,

ii. $\lim_{x \to a} [f(x) - g(x)] = L - M$, and

iii. $\lim_{x \to a} [f(x) \cdot g(x)] = L \cdot M$.

Parts **i** and **iii** extend to the sum and product of any finite number of functions.

Theorem 6–4   If $\lim_{x \to a} f(x) = L$ and $\lim_{x \to a} g(x) = M$, $M \neq 0$
$g(x) \neq 0$, then

$$\lim_{x \to a} \frac{f(x)}{g(x)} = \frac{L}{M}.$$

These theorems are particularly useful in finding limits of polynomial functions. An expression of the form

$$a_0 x^n + a_1 x^{n-1} + a_2 x^{n-2} + \cdots + a_{n-1} x + a_n,$$

where n denotes a nonnegative integer, is a **polynomial in x.** If x is a variable with domain D, then any polynomial in x defines a **polynomial function** whose domain is D. The value of the polynomial function is found by replacing x by a member of the domain D.

EXAMPLE 3.   Let $P(x) = 3x^2 + 2x + 1$. What is $P(x)$ at $x = 2$?

$$P(2) = 3(2)^2 + 2(2) + 1 = 3 \cdot 4 + 4 + 1 = 17.$$

Evaluate $\lim_{x \to 2} P(x)$.

Employing Theorems 6–1, 6–2, and 6–3i and iii,

$$\lim_{x \to 2} (3x^2 + 2x + 1) = \lim_{x \to 2} 3x^2 + \lim_{x \to 2} 2x + \lim_{x \to 2} 1$$

(Theorem 6–3i)

$$= 3 \cdot \lim_{x \to 2} x^2 + 2 \lim_{x \to 2} x + 1$$

(Theorems 6–1 and 6–3iii)

$$= 3 \cdot 4 + 2 \cdot 2 + 1$$

(Theorem 6–2)

$$= 17.$$

Every polynomial is a sum of the products of constants and positive integral powers of the variable. Obviously the value of $P(x)$ at $x = a$ is defined and a finite number for any finite number a. By Theorems 6–1 to 6–3 the limit of a polynomial function $P(x)$, as x approaches a finite number a, is the value of the function at $x = a$. That is

$$\lim_{x \to a} P(x) = P(a)$$

where $P(x)$ is a polynomial function.

One of the reasons for studying polynomial functions is that they are an excellent example of a function that is *continuous*. An intuitive way to describe *continuity on an interval* is to say that if you can trace the graph of a function with your pencil without the pencil tip leaving the paper, then the function is continuous on that interval. (Polynomial functions are noteworthy for being continuous on *any* interval.) Before considering a precise definition of continuity on an interval, it is necessary to define continuity *at a point*.

Definition A function $f(x)$ is <u>continuous at $x = a$</u> if and only if the three conditions following are satisfied:

    i. $f(x)$ is defined at $x = a$,

    ii. $\lim_{x \to a} f(x)$ exists, and

    iii. $\lim_{x \to a} f(x) = f(a)$.

A function which fails to satisfy one or more of conditions **i.**, **ii.**, or **iii.**, at $x = a$ is said to be <u>discontinous at $x = a$</u>. A function is said to be <u>continuous on an interval</u> if and only if it is continuous at each point of the interval.

It is important to realize that although it is natural to think of continuity in connection with intervals, continuity is fundamentally a property that a function has or does not have at a particular *point*.

EXAMPLE 4. Let $f(x) = 4$ for all real x. Show that $f(x)$ is continuous at $x = 7$.

Since 7 is a real number, $f(x)$ is defined at $x = 7$. By Theorem 6–1, $\lim_{x \to 7} f(x)$ exists and $\lim_{x \to 7} f(x) = 4$. Since $f(7) = 4 = \lim_{x \to 7} f(x)$, conditions **i–iii** are satisfied. Thus $f(x) = 4$ is continuous at $x = 7$.

Discontinuities will be discussed in more detail in the next section.

1. What are the advantages and disadvantages of proving that a conjecture concerning a particular limit is correct

  a. using the definition of a limit? **b.** using the limit theorems?

2. Is every function that has a limit at $x = a$ continuous at $x = a$? Explain.

Exercises

A ▬ In Exercises 1–14 find the indicated limit (if possible).

1. $\lim\limits_{x\to3} (2x^2 - 5x + 1)$ **2.** $\lim\limits_{x\to2} (-3x^2 + 1)$

3. $\lim\limits_{x\to-2} (x^2 + 2x - 3)$ **4.** $\lim\limits_{x\to-3} (-\frac{1}{3}x^2 - 2x + 8)$

5. $\lim\limits_{x\to-2} \left(\dfrac{3x^2 - 5}{2x + 17}\right)$ **6.** $\lim\limits_{x\to-1} \left(\dfrac{x^2 - 1}{x}\right)$

7. $\lim\limits_{x\to-1} \left(\dfrac{x}{x^2 - 1}\right)$ **8.** $\lim\limits_{x\to1} \left[\dfrac{(x - 2)(x + 1)}{x^2 - x - 2}\right]$

9. $\lim\limits_{x\to3} (x^5 - 240)$ **10.** $\lim\limits_{x\to3} [x(x + 1)(x + 2)]$

11. $\lim\limits_{x\to4} (3x^2 - 5x)$ **12.** $\lim\limits_{x\to-5} \left(\dfrac{1}{x}\right)$

13. $\lim\limits_{x\to1} \left(\dfrac{4x^2 - 1}{5x + 2}\right)$ **14.** $\lim\limits_{x\to2} \dfrac{3x}{4x - 7}$

B   Each function is discontinuous at the point $x = a$. Determine which of the conditions which define continuity are not satisfied. Graph each function over the given interval.

15. $f(x) = \begin{cases} \dfrac{2x^2 + x}{x} & \text{for } x \neq 0 \\ 0 & \text{for } x = 0 \end{cases}$ $a = 0,\ [-2, 2]$

16. $f(x) = \begin{cases} \dfrac{1}{x} & \text{for } x \neq 0 \\ \text{undefined} & \text{for } x = 0 \end{cases}$ $a = 0,\ [-2, 2]$

17. $f(x) = \begin{cases} x^2 + 2 & \text{for } x < 0 \\ 4 & \text{for } x = 0 \\ x + 2 & \text{for } x > 0 \end{cases}$ $a = 0,\ [-2, 2]$

18. $f(x) = \begin{cases} 2x - 3 & \text{for } x < 2 \\ 1 & \text{for } x = 2 \\ -x & \text{for } x > 2 \end{cases}$ $a = 2,\ [0, 4]$

━━ Use the pattern of proof in Example 1 to find the required limit and to prove that it is the limit by direct use of the definition.

19. $\lim_{x \to 2} 3x$

20. $\lim_{x \to 2} \frac{1}{x}$

21. $\lim_{x \to 1} x^2 + 2$

22. $\lim_{x \to 2} \frac{3x + 1}{2x}$

23. Prove: $\lim_{x \to a} k = k$ (Theorem 6–1).

24. Prove: $\lim_{x \to a} x^m = a^m$, m a positive integer (Theorem 6–2).

6–4   Rational Functions and Discontinuities

An expression of the form

$$\frac{P(x)}{Q(x)}$$

where $P(x)$ and $Q(x)$ are polynomials is a rational expression in x. If x is a variable with domain D then a rational expression in x defines a rational function with domain D.   A value of a rational function $R(x)$ at $x = a$ can be found by substituting a for x in $R(x)$.

EXAMPLE 1.   Let $P(x) = 2x^2 + 3x$, $Q(x) = x + 5$.   What is the rational function

$$R(x) = \frac{P(x)}{Q(x)} \, ?$$

$$R(x) = \frac{2x^2 + 3x}{x + 5}$$

Find the value of $R(x)$ at $x = -2$.

$$R(-2) = \frac{2(-2)^2 + 3(-2)}{(-2) + 5}$$

$$= \frac{2 \cdot 4 - 6}{3}$$

$$= \tfrac{2}{3}$$

Whereas polynomial functions are always continuous at every finite point, a rational function may be *discontinuous* at one or more points.   There are essentially two types of discontinuities for rational functions: (1) removable discontinuities and (2) discontinuities associated with the nonexistence of at least one one-sided limit.

EXAMPLE 2. (A removable discontinuity.)

Consider the function defined by the following equation. (See Figure 5 below.)

$$f(x) = \frac{x^2 - x}{x - 1}, \quad x \in R$$

Since

$$x - 1 = 0 \quad \text{when } x = 1,$$

$f(x)$ is not defined for $x = 1$. Thus $f(x)$ is not continuous at $x = 1$. On the other hand,

$$\lim_{x \to 1} \frac{x^2 - x}{x - 1} = 1.$$

To see this, factor the numerator of $\frac{x^2 - x}{x - 1}$.

Since

$$x^2 - x = x(x - 1)$$

then

$$\frac{x^2 - x}{x - 1} = \frac{x(x - 1)}{x - 1}.$$

In determining the value of $\lim_{x \to 1} \frac{x(x - 1)}{x - 1}$, *x can never be equal to one.*
Thus $x - 1$ is never equal to zero. Moreover under these restrictions $\frac{x - 1}{x - 1}$ *always* equals 1. ($x \neq 1$)

Thus

$$\lim_{x \to 1} \frac{x(x - 1)}{x - 1} = \lim_{x \to 1} x = 1.$$

Consequently, $f(x) = \frac{x^2 - x}{x - 1}$ has a removable discontinuity at $x = 1$. The discontinuity can be removed by *defining* $f(x) = 1$, for $x = 1$. In the graph, the discontinuity can be thought of as a hole! By defining $f(x) = 1$ when $x = 1$, the hole is filled and the resulting function is continuous at every finite point. (The reason that this approach works, of course, is that

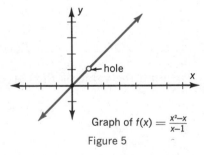

Graph of $f(x) = \frac{x^2-x}{x-1}$

Figure 5

it is permissible to define $f(1)$ any way you please since there exists no prior definition of $f(1)$ with which to be in conflict.)

There is a general procedure implicit in Example 2. If both the numerator and denominator of a rational function $R(x) = \frac{P(x)}{Q(x)}$ approach 0 as $x \longrightarrow a$, then you may be able to factor out the common terms and find the limit of the new function.

280   CHAPTER 6

EXAMPLE 3. (At least one one-sided limit fails to exist.)
Consider the function

$$f(x) = \frac{1}{x-1} \qquad x \in R.$$

$f(x)$ is not defined at $x = 1$ because division by zero is not defined. Hence, $f(x)$ is discontinuous at $x = 1$. Notice that $x - 1$ cannot be factored out. So the discontinuity is not removable.

However, the question remains: What happens to $f(x) = \frac{1}{x-1}$ as $x \longrightarrow 1$, but is not equal to 1? Considering first values of $x > 1$, it is clear that $x - 1$ is very small and positive for values of x very close to 1. Since $x - 1$ is *small* and *positive*, $f(x) = \frac{1}{x-1}$ is *large* and *positive* when x is close to 1. In fact $\frac{1}{x-1}$ can be made larger than any predetermined large real number by taking x close enough to 1. This is illustrated below.

x	$\dfrac{1}{x-1}$
1.2	5
1.1	10
1.05	20
1.01	100
1.001	1000

Thus the one-sided limit

$$\lim_{x \to 1+} \frac{1}{x-1}$$

does not exist; it equals no *finite real number*.

Since $f(x) = \frac{1}{x-1}$ increases without bound as $x \longrightarrow 1^+$, it is convenient to have a simple manner to indicate such a state of affairs. The statement "$\lim_{x \to 1+} \frac{1}{x-1} = +\infty$" is used to indicate this. In general, the statement

$$\lim_{x \to a^+} f(x) = +\infty \quad (\text{or} -\infty)$$

means that as $x \longrightarrow a^+$, the function assumes values larger (smaller) than a preassigned real number M.

In a similar manner, $\lim_{x \to 1^-} \frac{1}{x-1} = -\infty$, for when x is less than 1 and close to 1, $\frac{1}{x-1}$ is negative and large in absolute value. Consequently, $\frac{1}{x-1}$ decreases without bound as $x \longrightarrow 1^-$.

The line $x = 1$ is an *asymptote* for the function $f(x) = \frac{1}{x-1}$. An **asymptote** is a line that the graph of a function approaches as the variable x nears a fixed point a or tends to $+\infty$ or $-\infty$. A rational function $R(x) = \frac{P(x)}{Q(x)}$ has a *vertical asymptote* at a point a where $P(a) \neq 0$ and $Q(a) = 0$. For $f(x) = \frac{1}{x-1}$, the line $x = 1$ is a vertical asymptote.

$R(x) = \frac{P(x)}{Q(x)}$ has a *horizontal asymptote* $y = b$ whenever $\lim\limits_{x \to +\infty} R(x) = b$ or $\lim\limits_{x \to -\infty} R(x) = b$. For $f(x) = \frac{1}{x-1}$, $\lim\limits_{x \to +\infty} \frac{1}{x-1} = 0$. Thus $y = 0$ is an horizontal asymptote for $f(x)$.

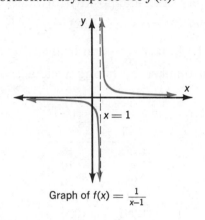

Graph of $f(x) = \frac{1}{x-1}$

Checkpoint

1. Are there any rational functions with
    a. no points of discontinuity?
    b. two points of discontinuity?
    c. five points of discontinuity?
2. How are removable discontinuities removed?
3. Distinguish between the meanings of **a** and **b** below.
    a. $\lim\limits_{x \to \infty} f(x) = 6$
    b. $\lim\limits_{x \to 6^+} f(x) = \infty$.

Exercises

A ▬▬ In Exercises 1–4 evaluate each rational function at the point specified.

1. $f(x) = \frac{x^2 - 2x}{x^2 + 2}$ $x = 3$ **2.** $f(x) = \frac{-2x^3 + 3x}{x - 4}$ $x = -2$

3. $f(x) = \frac{1}{x^3 + 2x^2 + 1}$ $x = -2$ **4.** $f(x) = \frac{-(x + 2)(x - 1)}{(-x + 1)(x - 3)}$ $x = \frac{1}{2}$

In Exercises 5–14 determine the real number(s) if any for which each function is undefined.

5. $f(x) = \dfrac{x}{x^2 - x - 2}$

6. $f(x) = \dfrac{1}{x^2 + 2x - 2}$

7. $f(x) = \dfrac{x^2 + 2x - 1}{x}$

8. $f(x) = \dfrac{(x - 2)(x - 1)(x - 3)}{x(x + 2)(x + 1)}$

9. $f(x) = \dfrac{x^3 - 1}{(x - 1)(x^2 + x + 1)}$

10. $f(x) = \dfrac{x - 2}{x^2 + 2}$

11. $f(x) = \dfrac{x^2 + 2}{x - 2}$

12. $f(x) = \dfrac{(x + 1)}{x^3 + 1}$

13. $f(x) = \dfrac{1}{x^4 + 1}$

14. $f(x) = \dfrac{x(x - 1)}{x(x - 1)}$

B   In Exercises 15–26 find the indicated limit. When an indicated limit does not exist, find the two one-sided limits. Use the notation $\lim\limits_{x \to a^+} f(x) = +\infty(-\infty)$ and $\lim\limits_{x \to a^-} f(x) = +\infty(-\infty)$.

15. $\lim\limits_{x \to 2} \dfrac{(2x - x^2)}{2 - x}$

16. $\lim\limits_{x \to -1} \left(\dfrac{x^2 + 4x + 3}{x^2 - x - 2} \right)$

17. $\lim\limits_{x \to 5} \dfrac{x^2 - 25}{x^2 - 4x - 5}$

18. $\lim\limits_{x \to -1} \dfrac{x}{x + 1}$

19. $\lim\limits_{x \to 2} \dfrac{x^2 - 4x + 4}{x - 2}$

20. $\lim\limits_{x \to 2} \dfrac{x - 2}{x^2 - 4x + 4}$

21. $\lim\limits_{x \to -4} \dfrac{x}{x^2 + 16}$

22. $\lim\limits_{x \to -3} \dfrac{x + 3}{(x + 3)(x^2 + 6x + 9)}$

23. $\lim\limits_{x \to 3} \dfrac{x + 3}{(x - 3)^2}$

24. $\lim\limits_{x \to 0} \dfrac{2}{x^2 - 2x}$

25. $\lim\limits_{x \to 2} \dfrac{2}{x^2 - 2x}$

26. $\lim\limits_{x \to 1} \dfrac{2}{x^2 - 2x}$

In Exercises 27–30 find the horizontal asymptotes using the limits: $\lim\limits_{x \to +\infty} f(x)$ and $\lim\limits_{x \to -\infty} f(x)$.

27. $f(x) = \dfrac{2x + 3}{x}$

28. $f(x) = \dfrac{2x + 3}{x^2 - 4}$

29. $f(x) = \dfrac{3x^2 - 2x}{x^2}$

30. $f(x) = \dfrac{3x^2 - 2x}{4x^2 + 4x + 1}$

31. Find all vertical asymptotes for the functions given in Exercises 27–30.

C   In Exercises 32–42 you are given that $f(x) = \dfrac{x + 1}{x(x + 1)(x - 2)}$.

32. What type of discontinuity does $f(x)$ have at $x = -1$, at $x = 0$, at $x = 2$?

33. Does $f(x)$ have any vertical asymptotes? If so identify them.

Find the following limits.

34. $\lim\limits_{x \to -\infty} f(x)$

35. $\lim\limits_{x \to -1^-} f(x)$

36. $\lim\limits_{x \to -1^+} f(x)$

37. $\lim_{x \to 0^-} f(x)$ **38.** $\lim_{x \to 0^+} f(x)$ **39.** $\lim_{x \to 2^-} f(x)$

40. $\lim_{x \to 2^+} f(x)$ **41.** $\lim_{x \to +\infty} f(x)$

42. Sketch the graph of $f(x)$.

▬ A rational function $R(x) = \dfrac{P(x)}{Q(x)}$ for which $\lim_{x \to a} P(x) = 0$ and $\lim_{x \to a} Q(x) = 0$ is said to be **indeterminate at** $x = a$ because $\lim_{x \to a} R(x) = \lim_{x \to a} \dfrac{P(x)}{Q(x)} = \dfrac{0}{0}$. The symbol "$\dfrac{0}{0}$" has no meaning and does not in itself imply anything about the limit of $R(x)$. It happens that the true limit may be any finite real number or $P(x)$ may increase or decrease without bound. Find the limit (if possible) of each indeterminate form.

43. $\lim_{x \to 1} \dfrac{x - 1}{x - 1}$ **44.** $\lim_{x \to 0} \dfrac{x}{x^2}$ **45.** $\lim_{x \to 2} \dfrac{(x - 2)^2}{x - 2}$

46. $\lim_{x \to 0} \dfrac{17x}{x}$ **47.** $\lim_{x \to 1} \dfrac{x - 1}{1 - x}$

▬ Find a rational function $R(x)$ whose numerator and denominator tend to zero as x approaches a but such that $\lim_{x \to a} R(x)$ equals each of the following.

48. -4 **49.** 1000 **50.** 0 **51.** $-\infty$ **52.** a

▬ Very often $\lim_{x \to +\infty} \dfrac{P(x)}{Q(x)}$ appears to have the form $\dfrac{\infty}{\infty}$ because $\lim_{x \to +\infty} P(x) = \infty$ and $\lim_{x \to +\infty} Q(x) = \infty$. For example, if

$$P(x) = 3x$$

and

$$Q(x) = x^2,$$

then

$$\lim_{x \to +\infty} \dfrac{P(x)}{Q(x)}$$

has the form

$$\dfrac{\infty}{\infty}.$$

This is an indeterminate form similar to the form $\dfrac{0}{0}$. Again the function $\dfrac{P(x)}{Q(x)}$ may have any finite number as its limit as $x \longrightarrow +\infty$ or it may increase or decrease without bound. Find the true limits of each indeterminate form.

53. $\lim_{x \to +\infty} \dfrac{3x}{x^2}$ **54.** $\lim_{x \to +\infty} \dfrac{3x^2}{x^2}$ **55.** $\lim_{x \to +\infty} \dfrac{3x^3}{x^2}$

56. $\lim_{x \to +\infty} \dfrac{-3x^3}{x^2}$ **57.** $\lim_{x \to +\infty} \dfrac{2x^2 + 2x^1}{5x^2}$

6–5 The Derived Function: An Application of Limits

Previous sections were devoted to limits of functions as $x \longrightarrow a$, $x \longrightarrow +\infty$, or $x \longrightarrow -\infty$. Here a new function $f'(x)$ is derived from a function $f(x)$ by using limits. The discussion will be restricted to real-valued functions of a real variable x which are defined in a neighborhood of the particular value of x under consideration.

> **Definition**   Given a function $y = f(x)$. $f(x)$ is said to have a derived function at x if and only if the following limit exists and is finite; the function $f'(x)$ defined by the limit is called the derived function of $f(x)$:
>
> $$f'(x) = \lim_{h \to 0} \frac{f(x + h) - f(x)}{h}$$

The expression $\dfrac{f(x + h) - f(x)}{h}$ can be interpreted as the *slope* of a line passing through two points on the graph of the function $f(x)$. The geometric interpretation of the *limit* of this expression as $h \longrightarrow 0$ is important and will be considered in the next section.

For any particular value of x, the limit in the definition of $f'(x)$ will be a number; that is, the value of the derived function at that value of x.

EXAMPLE 1.   Find the derived function of $f(x) = x^2 + 1$ at $x = 2$.

The $\lim\limits_{h \to 0} \dfrac{f(2 + h) - f(2)}{h}$ must be evaluated.

$$f(2 + h) = (2 + h)^2 + 1$$
$$f(2) = (2)^2 + 1$$
$$f(2 + h) - f(2) = (2 + h)^2 + 1 - [(2)^2 + 1]$$
$$= 4 + 4h + h^2 + 1 - 4 - 1$$
$$= 4h + h^2$$

Consequently, $\quad \dfrac{f(2 + h) - f(2)}{h} = \dfrac{4h + h^2}{h} = 4 + h$

since h is not equal to 0.   So $f'(2) = \lim\limits_{h \to 0} (4 + h) = 4$.   The derived function of $f(x) = x^2 + 1$ at $x = 2$ is equal to 4:

$$f'(2) = 4.$$

EXAMPLE 2. Find the derived function of $f(x) = \frac{1}{x}$ at $x = 3$.

Since
$$f'(3) = \lim_{h \to 0} \frac{f(3 + h) - f(3)}{h}$$

and
$$f(3 + h) = \frac{1}{3 + h}$$

$$f(3) = \tfrac{1}{3}$$

$$f(3 + h) - f(3) = \frac{1}{3 + h} - \frac{1}{3}$$

$$= \frac{3 - (3 + h)}{(3 + h) \cdot 3},$$

and
$$\frac{f(3 + h) - f(3)}{h} = \frac{-h}{h \cdot (3 + h) \cdot 3}$$

$$= \frac{-1}{3(3 + h)},$$

then
$$f'(3) = \lim_{h \to 0} \frac{-1}{3(3 + h)}$$

$$= \frac{-1}{3^2} = -\frac{1}{9}$$

so
$$f'(3) = -\tfrac{1}{9}.$$

A general expression for $f'(x)$ can be derived in a similar manner. All that need be done is substitute a symbol like x_0 for the particular value of x. Evaluation of the resulting expression at $x = a$ gives the value of the derived function at $x = a$ (when it exists).

EXAMPLE 3. Find the derived function of $f(x) = x^2 + 1$ at a general point $x = x_0$.

$$f(x_0) = x_0^2 + 1$$
$$f(x_0 + h) = (x_0 + h)^2 + 1$$
$$= x_0^2 + 2hx_0 + h^2 + 1$$

So
$$f(x_0 + h) - f(x_0) = x_0^2 + 2hx_0 + h^2 + 1 - x_0^2 - 1$$
$$= 2hx_0 + h^2.$$

Then
$$\frac{f(x_0 + h) - f(x_0)}{h} = \frac{2hx_0 + h^2}{h}$$

$$= 2x_0 + h$$
$$f'(x_0) = \lim_{h \to 0} (2x_0 + h) = 2x_0.$$

Thus $f'(x_0) = 2x_0$ when $f(x) = x^2 + 1$. Since $2x_0$ is defined for all x_0 which are finite, the subscript is dropped and the derived function $f'(x)$ for $f(x) = x^2 + 1$ is

$$f'(x) = 2x$$

for any real number x.

For example, $f'(2) = 2 \cdot 2 = 4$, which is the same as the result in Example 1.

EXAMPLE 4. Find the derived function of $f(x) = \dfrac{1}{x}$, $x \neq 0$.

$$f(x_0 + h) = \frac{1}{x_0 + h}, \ f(x_0) = \frac{1}{x_0} \ \text{and}$$

$$f(x_0 + h) - f(x_0) = \frac{1}{x_0 + h} - \frac{1}{x_0}$$

$$= \frac{x_0 - x_0 - h}{(x_0 + h)x_0}$$

So

$$\frac{f(x_0 + h) - f(x_0)}{h} = \frac{-h}{h \cdot (x_0 + h) \cdot x_0} \ \text{and}$$

$$f'(x_0) = \lim_{h \to 0} \frac{-1}{(x_0 + h)x_0} = -\frac{1}{x_0{}^2}.$$

Thus

$$f'(x) = -\frac{1}{x^2}, \ x \neq 0.$$

If $x = 3$, $f'(x) = -\dfrac{1}{3^2} = -\dfrac{1}{9}$ which corresponds to the result of Example 2.

Checkpoint

How is the derived function obtained from a given function $f(x)$?

Exercises

A ▬▬ Use the definition of derived function at $x = a$ to find the indicated values.

1. $f'(3)$ where $f(x) = 2x + 5$

2. $f'(2)$ where $f(x) = x^2 + x$

3. $f'(0)$ where $f(x) = x^2 - 2$

4. $f'(7)$ where $f(x) = 4x - 17$

5. $f'(-1)$ where $f(x) = \dfrac{1}{x - 1}$

6. $f'(2)$ where $f(x) = -x^2$

7. $f'(-3)$ where $f(x) = -5x + 6$

8. $f'(2)$ where $f(x) = -\dfrac{1}{x}$ $(x \neq 0)$

9. $f'(-2)$ where $f(x) = -x^2 + x$

10. $f'(a)$ where $f(x) = x + 2x^2$

B — Use the definition to find the derived function of $f(x)$ at a general point.

11. $f(x) = 3x^2 - 1$ **12.** $f(x) = \dfrac{1}{x+1}$ $(x \neq -1)$

13. $f(x) = x^2 - 3x$ **14.** $f(x) = \dfrac{-1}{x^2}$

15. $f(x) = x^3$ **16.** $f(x) = \dfrac{x}{x+1}$ $(x \neq -1)$

C The *one-sided* derived function at a point is defined in a manner similar to the one-sided limit at a point. That is, the right (left) derived function of $f(x)$ at $x = a$ is the one-sided limit

$$\lim_{h \to 0^+} \frac{f(a+h) - f(a)}{h} \qquad \left(\lim_{h \to 0^-} \frac{f(a+h) - f(a)}{h} \right).$$

17. Find the right and left derived functions at $x = 2$ of the following function.

$$f(x) = \begin{cases} x + 2 & \text{for } x < 2 \\ 2x & \text{for } x \geq 2 \end{cases}$$

18. Find the right and left derived functions at $x = 0$ of the following function.

$$f(x) = \begin{cases} -x & \text{for } x \leq 0 \\ x & \text{for } x > 0 \end{cases}$$

19. Find the right and left derived functions at $x = 1$ of the following function.

$$f(x) = \begin{cases} x^2 & \text{for } x < 1 \\ 3x - 2 & \text{for } x \geq 1 \end{cases}$$

20. Explain in your own words why a function has a derived function at a point if and only if the right and left derived functions are equal at the point.

21. Explain why a function is continuous at a point $x = x_0$ whenever the derived function at $x = x_0$ exists. (*Hint:* consider $f(x_0 + h) - f(x_0) = h \cdot \dfrac{f(x_0 + h) - f(x_0)}{h}$ and take limits of both sides.)

6-6   Geometric Interpretation of the Derived Function

Let $y = f(x)$ have a graph as seen at right. Let $x = a$ be a point for which $f(a)$ exists and let $f'(a)$ exist. The y coordinate of point B is $f(a)$.

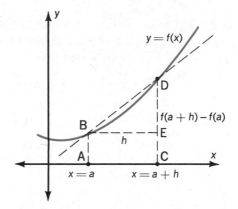

Let h be a real number, either positive or negative. Then $a + h$ is a point on the x axis and $f(a + h)$ is the y coordinate of point D. Consequently, $f(a + h) - f(a)$ is the difference in the y coordinates of points D and B and may be positive or negative. Its absolute value is depicted in the diagram as DE, the difference in the lengths of $\overline{CD}$ and $\overline{AB}$. Notice that the length of the segment BE is $|h|$.

The ratio

$$\frac{f(a + h) - f(a)}{h}$$

is the *slope* of the line determined by B and D. Such a line is a *secant* line. Now think of h taking on values close to 0. For each h the ratio $\frac{f(a + h) - f(a)}{h}$ is the slope of the corresponding secant line. When h is very close to 0, the points B and D are each on the graph of $y = f(x)$ and are very close together. Consequently, for small h, the secant line through B and D is very close to the line *tangent* to $f(x)$ at $x = a$.

Since the secant lines through B approach the line tangent to $f(x)$ at $x = a$, the slopes of the secant lines approach the slope of the tangent line. Since the slope of each secant line is given by

$$\frac{f(a + h) - f(a)}{h},$$

the slope of the tangent is given by

$$\lim_{h \to 0} \frac{f(a + h) - f(a)}{h}.$$

That is by the derived function of $f(x)$ evaluated at $x = a$.

The following is a statement of the geometric interpretation of $f'(a)$ and summarizes the above discussion.

EXAMPLE 1. A line with equation $f(x) = 3x - 5$ has slope 3 at $x = 6$ because the slope is the coefficient of x when the equation is in the form $f(x) = mx + b$. Verify that $f'(6) = 3$ also.

$$\frac{f(6 + h) - f(6)}{h} = \frac{3(6 + h) - 5 - (3 \cdot 6 - 5)}{h}$$

$$= \frac{18 + 3h - 5 - 18 + 5}{h}$$

$$= \frac{3h}{h}$$

$$= 3.$$

$$f'(6) = \lim_{h \to 0} 3 = 3$$

Notice that in this example $f'(x)$ does not depend on x, that is, $f'(x) = 3$ for all x. Hence, the slope of $f(x) = 3x - 5$ is 3 for all x. This is as it should be because the slope of a line is constant.

EXAMPLE 2. Find the slope of the tangent to $f(x) = x^2$ at $x = 1$.

$$f'(1) = \lim_{h \to 0} \frac{(1 + h)^2 - 1^2}{h}$$

$$= \lim_{h \to 0} \frac{2h + h^2}{h}$$

$$= \lim_{h \to 0} (2 + h)$$

$$= 2$$

Thus the tangent at $x = 1$ has the slope of 2.

Checkpoint

How do you interpret the derived function geometrically?

Exercises

A ▬▬ Find the slope of the tangent to the graph of the function at the given point.

1. $f(x) = \frac{2}{3}x - 1$ at $x = 5$ **2.** $f(x) = \frac{1}{x}$ at $x = 2$

3. $f(x) = -x^2$ at $x = 4$ **4.** $f(x) = \frac{1}{x - 1}$ at $x = 0$

5. $f(x) = 2x^2 + 3x$ at $x = 1$

6. $f(x) = 5$ at $x = 100$

7. $f(x) = 3x - x^2$ at $x = 0$

8. $f(x) = -x^2 + 4x - 1$ at $x = 1$

B — For Exercises 9–12 sketch a graph of the function. Estimate the slope of the line tangent at $x = a$. Find that slope and compare with your estimate.

9. $f(x) = x^2$ at $x = 3$

10. $f(x) = \dfrac{1}{x}$ at $x = -2$

11. $f(x) = x^2 - 2x$ at $x = 1$

12. $f(x) = 4x + 2$ at $x = -1$

13. What is the slope of a line that passes through points B and D if their coordinates are:

    a. $B(x_1, y_1)$, $D(x_2, y_2)$?

    b. $B(x, y_1)$, $D(x + h, y_2)$?

    c. $B(x, f(x))$, $D(x + h, f(x + h))$?

    d. $B(x + h, f(x + h))$, $D(x, f(x))$?

14. The expression

$$\lim_{h \to 0} \frac{f(a + h) - f(a)}{h}$$

may or may not exist at a. What is the geometric interpretation if it does not exist?

C — For a quadratic function

$$f(x) = ax^2 + bx + c \quad (a \neq 0),$$

the value of $f(x)$ at $x = -\dfrac{b}{2a}$ is the maximum or minimum value of the function. For each function find $f'(x)$ at $x = -\dfrac{b}{2a}$.

15. $f(x) = x^2$

16. $f(x) = -x^2 + 2x$

17. $f(x) = 2x^2 + x - 1$

18. $f(x) = -3x^2 + x - 5$

19. $f(x) = ax^2 + bx + c$

20. Generalize the results of Exercises 15–19.

21. Even though $f(x) = \dfrac{1}{x}$ is not defined at $x = 0$, for all $x \neq 0$ the function is defined. Find $f'(x)$ and discuss what happens to $f'(x)$ for x close to 0. What does this mean geometrically?

6–7   Rules for Finding $f'(x)$

The derived function for most functions can be written down by application of simple rules. Several of these rules are given in this section. Their use will allow you to determine the slope of a line tangent to a given curve quickly — a skill which will be useful in later chapters. The rules are stated as theorems, not all of which will be proved.

Theorem 6–5   If $f(x) = k$, k a constant, then $f'(x) = 0$.

Theorem 6–6   The derived function of the product of a constant k and a function $f(x)$ is the product of k and $f'(x)$.

EXAMPLE 1.   Find $f'(x)$ when

a. $f(x) = 17$

b. $f(x) = 4(x^2 + 1)$

a. If $f(x) = 17$, $f'(x) = 0$ by Theorem 6–5. This agrees with intuition because the line $f(x) = 17$ is horizontal and its slope is therefore 0.
b. Think of $f(x)$ as the product of 4 and $(x^2 + 1)$. The derived function for $x^2 + 1$ is $2x$ (Example 3 Section 6–5). Thus by Theorem 6–6,

$$f'(x) = 4 \cdot 2x$$
$$= 8x.$$

The next theorem states the general form of $f'(x)$ when $f(x)$ is a positive integral power of x.

Theorem 6–7   If $f(x) = x^m$ where m is a positive integer, then $f'(x) = mx^{m-1}$.

Proof: For Theorem 6–7 to be true, $\lim_{h \to 0} \dfrac{(x + h)^m - x^m}{h}$ must be mx^{m-1}. This can be shown by using the binomial formula to expand $(x + h)^m$. $(x + h)^m = x^m + mx^{m-1}h + $ (terms with powers of h greater than 1 such as h^2, h^3, h^4, $\cdots$). Thus $\dfrac{(x + h)^m - x^m}{h} = mx^{m-1} + $ (terms with powers of h greater than 0 such as h, h^2, h^3, $\cdots$). Each of the terms other than mx^{m-1} tends to zero as $h \longrightarrow 0$. Consequently: $f'(x) = mx^{m-1}$.

EXAMPLE 2. Find $f'(x)$ if $f(x) = x^5$.

By Theorem 6-7 $\qquad\qquad\qquad f'(x) = 5x^4.$

> **Theorem 6-8** If
>
> $$f(x) = f_1(x) + f_2(x) + \cdots + f_n(x),$$
>
> and $f'_n(x)$ exists for all n
>
> then $\qquad\qquad f'(x) = f'_1(x) + f'_2(x) + \cdots + f'_n(x).$

Theorems 6-5 through 6-8 combine to provide a means of determining the derived function of any polynomial function. The next example will illustrate this point.

EXAMPLE 3. Find $f'(x)$ when $f(x) = 2x^4 + 3x^2 + 7x + 2$.
By Theorem 6-8, $f'(x)$ may be found by finding the derived function of each addend in $2x^4 + 3x^2 + 7x + 2$. By Theorems 6-5, 6-6, and 6-7, the derived functions of the addends are $2 \cdot 4 \cdot x^3$, $3 \cdot 2 \cdot x$, 7 and 0. Thus by Theorem 6-8, $f'(x) = 8x^3 + 6x + 7$. Thus, for polynomial functions the next theorem is true.

> **Theorem 6-9** If
>
> $$f(x) = a_0 x^n + a_1 x^{n-1} + a_2 x^{n-2} + \cdots + a_{n-1} x + a_n$$
>
> then
>
> $$f'(x) = n a_0 x^{n-1} + (n-1) a_1 x^{n-2} + (n-2) a_2 x^{n-3} + \cdots + a_{n-1}.$$

EXAMPLE 4. Find $f'(x)$ when $f(x) = 2x^5 + 3x - 1$.

$$f'(x) = 2 \cdot 5x^4 + 3$$
$$= 10x^4 + 3$$

EXAMPLE 5. What is the slope of the tangent to the graph of $f(x) = 4x^3 + 2x$ at $x = 2$?

$$f'(x) = 12x^2 + 2$$
$$f'(2) = 12 \cdot 4 + 2$$
$$= 50$$

Previously it was found that if $f(x) = \frac{1}{x}$, $f'(x) = -\frac{1}{x^2}$. This is a special case of the following theorem.

Theorem 6–10 If $f(x) = \frac{1}{x^m}$, m a positive integer, $x \neq 0$, then

$$f'(x) = \frac{-m}{x^{m+1}}.$$

Proof: The difference

$$f(x + h) - f(x) = \frac{1}{(x + h)^m} - \frac{1}{x^m}$$

$$= \frac{x^m - (x + h)^m}{(x + h)^m \cdot x^m}$$

$$= \frac{x^m - \left(x^m + mx^{m-1}h + \dfrac{m(m - 1)}{2}x^{m-2}h^2 + \cdots + h^m\right)}{(x + h)^m \cdot x^m}$$

$$= \frac{-mx^{m-1}h - \dfrac{m(m - 1)}{2}x^{m-2}h^2 - \cdots - h^m}{(x + h)^m \cdot x^m}$$

The quotient $\dfrac{f(x + h) - f(x)}{h}$ is

$$\frac{-mx^{m-1}h - \dfrac{m(m - 1)}{2}x^{m-2}h^2 - \cdots - h^m}{h \cdot (x + h)^m \cdot x^m}$$

$$= \frac{-mx^{m-1} - \dfrac{m(m - 1)}{2}x^{m-2}h - \cdots - h^{m-1}}{(x + h)^m \cdot x^m}$$

Now as $h \longrightarrow 0$, the numerator approaches $-mx^{m-1}$ because all other addends approach zero. The denominator $(x + h)^m \cdot x^m \longrightarrow x^m \cdot x^m$ as $h \longrightarrow 0$. Thus

$$\lim_{h \to 0} \frac{f(x + h) - f(x)}{h} = \frac{-mx^{m-1}}{x^m \cdot x^m}$$

$$= \frac{-m}{x^m \cdot x^m \cdot x^{-m} \cdot x^1}$$

$$= \frac{-m}{x^{m+1}}$$

Now try these

— Find $f'(x)$ for each $f(x)$.

1. $f(x) = x^2$ **2.** $f(x) = 6x^2$ **3.** $f(x) = 6 + x^2$ **4.** $f(x) = \dfrac{6}{x^2}$

Answers: **1.** $2x$ **2.** $12x$ **3.** $2x$ **4.** $\dfrac{-12}{x^3}$

Exercises

A ▬ Find $f'(x)$ for each $f(x)$.

1. $f(x) = x^7$

2. $f(x) = 13x^4$

3. $f(x) = 4$

4. $f(x) = 3x^2 + 2$

5. $f(x) = \frac{1}{x^{100}}$

6. $f(x) = \frac{7}{x^5}$

7. $f(x) = 5x^{10} + x^5 - 2x^2 + 1$

8. $f(x) = x^5 - x^4 + x^2 - x + 1$

9. $f(x) = 12x^{-3}$

10. $f(x) = \frac{1}{x^4} - \frac{2}{x^2} + x$

B Use the point-slope form of the equation of a line to determine the equation of the line tangent to $f(x)$ at $x = a$. (Point-Slope form: $y - y_1 = m(x - x_1)$, m is the slope, point (x_1, y_1) is on the line.)

11. $f(x) = \frac{1}{2}x^2 + 2x$, $x = 3$

12. $f(x) = -\frac{1}{2}x^2 + 2x$, $x = 1$

13. $f(x) = 2x + 3$, $x = 1$

14. $f(x) = x^3 - x$, $x = -1$

15. $f(x) = \frac{1}{x^2}$, $x = 3$

16. $f(x) = \frac{20}{x^2}$, $x = -2$

C **17.** Prove Theorem 6–5.

18. Prove Theorem 6–6.

19. Suppose $f(x)$ and $g(x)$ have derived functions $f'(x)$ and $g'(x)$.

Let $p(x) = f(x) \cdot g(x)$. Show that $p'(x) = f(x) \cdot g'(x) + g(x)f'(x)$

Hint: $\dfrac{p(x + h) - p(x)}{h} = \dfrac{f(x + h) \cdot g(x + h) - f(x)g(x)}{h}$

$$= \frac{f(x + h)g(x + h) - f(x + h)g(x) + f(x + h)g(x) - f(x)g(x)}{h}$$

Simplify the last statement and consider $\lim\limits_{h \to 0} \dfrac{p(x + h) - p(x)}{h}$.

▬ Use the above rule to find the derived function of

20. $x^2 \cdot x^4$.

21. $x^2 \cdot \frac{1}{x^4}$.

22. $(x^2 + 1)(x^3 - 2)$.

CHAPTER OBJECTIVES AND REVIEW ▬▬▬▬

Objective: *To know the meaning of the important mathematical terms of this chapter.*

1. Here are many of the mathematical terms used in this chapter. Be sure that you know them thoroughly and can use them correctly.

function of a real variable (*265*)	discontinuous function (*279*)
polynomial in x (*276*)	asymptote (*282*)
polynomial function (*276*)	indeterminate function (*284*)
continuous function (*277*)	derived function (*285*)

Objective: *To illustrate geometrically the nature of a function when it has a limit and the definition of a limit of a function.*

▬ In Exercises 2–6 draw the graph of a function $f(x)$ that has a limit of 2 for each condition.

2. $x \longrightarrow +\infty$ **3.** $x \longrightarrow -\infty$

4. $x \longrightarrow 5^-$ **5.** $x \longrightarrow 5^+$

6. $x \longrightarrow 5$

7. Draw a graph of a function which has no finite limit at $x = -3$.

8. Draw a diagram geometrically illustrating the conditions needed to insure $\lim_{x \to 3} f(x) = -1$.

Objective: *To cite and use theorems about limits to calculate limits of functions.*

▬ In Exercises 9–13 complete the statement of each limit theorem. $\lim_{x \to a} f(x) = M, \lim_{x \to a} g(x) = N$.

9. $\lim_{x \to a} c =$ _____   **10.** $\lim_{x \to a} x^n =$ _____

11. $\lim_{x \to a} [f(x) \pm g(x)] =$ _____   **12.** $\lim_{x \to a} [f(x) \cdot g(x)] =$ _____

13. $\lim_{x \to a} \dfrac{f(x)}{g(x)} =$ _____

▬ Use the limit theorems in Exercises 9–13 to demonstrate the truth of each statement.

14. $\lim_{x \to 1} (2 \cdot x^2) = 2$ **15.** $\lim_{x \to -3} (x^2 - 2x) = 15$

16. $\lim_{x \to 1} \dfrac{x + 1}{x + 2} = \dfrac{2}{3}$ **17.** $\lim_{x \to +\infty} \dfrac{x + 1}{x} = 1$

Objective: *To define continuity of a function and discontinuity of a function at a point. To describe and illustrate a removable discontinuity and a nonremovable discontinuity.*

18. Given a function f and a point $x = a$ what three conditions must be true for f to be continuous at $x = a$?

19. In light of Exercise 18, when is a function f discontinuous at a point $x = a$?

▬ Draw a diagram illustrating each of the following instances of a discontinuous function.

20. A removable discontinuity at $x = a$.

21. A discontinuity at $x = a$ which is not removable.

Objective: *To define and use the derived function and its geometric interpretation.*

22. State the definition of $f'(x)$.

23. Use the definition of $f'(x)$ to calculate $f'(a)$ when $f(x) = x^2 - x$.

24. What is the geometric interpretation of the derived function evaluated at a point? Draw a diagram illustrating this interpretation.

▬ What is the derived function for each f in Exercises 25–28?

25. $f(x) = x^3$

26. $f(x) = 7x^3 - 2x$

27. $f(x) = \dfrac{3}{x^4}$

28. $f(x) = ax^4 - 2x^3 + 3x$

29. Find the equation of the line tangent to $f(x) = x^3 - 2x$ at the point $(1, -1)$.

CHAPTER TEST ▬▬▬▬▬▬▬▬▬▬

▬ Given $f(x) = x^2 - 2$. In questions 1–4 answer each question about $f(x)$.

1. What is $\lim\limits_{x \to 2} f(x)$?

2. What are $\lim\limits_{x \to 2^-} f(x)$ and $\lim\limits_{x \to 2^+} f(x)$?

3. Is $f(x)$ continuous at $x = 2$? Explain.

4. Draw a diagram illustrating geometrically the fact that the limit of $f(x)$ as x nears 2 is 2.

▬ Evaluate each limit in questions 5–10.

5. $\lim\limits_{x \to 1} x^5 - 2x^3 + x$

6. $\lim\limits_{x \to -3} \dfrac{x-3}{2x^2}$

7. $\lim\limits_{x \to 0} \dfrac{x^2 + x}{x}$

8. $\lim\limits_{x \to \infty} \dfrac{2x}{x^2}$

9. $\lim\limits_{x \to 2^+} \dfrac{4}{x-2}$

10. $\lim\limits_{x \to 2^-} \dfrac{4}{x-2}$

11. If $f(x) = 3x^2 - x + 1$, then use the definition of $f'(x)$ to calculate $f'(x)$.

12. Draw a diagram illustrating and explain the geometric significance of $f'(a)$.

▬ Find $f'(x)$ for each function of questions 13–15.

13. $f(x) = 4x^4 + 3x^2 - 2x + 1$

14. $f(x) = 3$

15. $f(x) = 4x - 5$

EEG

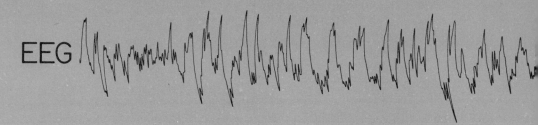

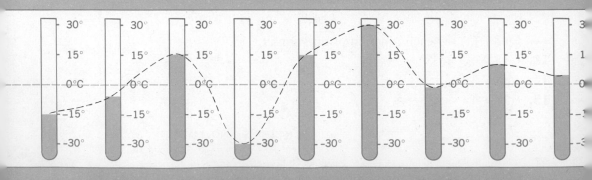

CHAPTER 7

ALGEBRAIC FUNCTIONS

In previous chapters you have studied different types of functions such as algebraic, exponential, and logarithmic functions. In this chapter you will study the set of functions called *polynomial functions*. What makes this set of functions particularly nice to study is the fact that all polynomial functions are continuous. This property will allow you to systematically and easily determine certain special values of these curves. Certain critical values, such as *relative maximum and minimum points*, are very useful in sketching the curves.

Relative maximum and minimum points occur naturally in the topography of the earth. Looking at a specific region you can determine its highest and lowest points. These points would be called *relative* maximum and minimum points because outside the chosen region you can probably find higher and lower points.

Tides in an area also have relative maximum and minimum values. The tides at the lobster pier in Friendship Maine, pictured on the opposite page, range from a minimum of eight feet to a maximum of twelve feet.

Medical science uses the idea of maxima and minima of graphs to help better understand how the human body functions. Pictured on the opposite page is an electroencephalogram, that is a graph of brain waves. This graph was taken while the person was asleep. The values of the relative maximum and minimum points can tell you whether or not the person was dreaming.

Other useful points to have when plotting a graph are the points at which it crosses the x axis. The x values of these points are called *real zeros*. If you let the line representing a reading of $0°$ be the x axis then the graph of the temperature readings pictured on the opposite page would have five real zeros.

7–1 Polynomial Functions

Suppose that you are given a symbol x and a set of numbers A. Many different expressions in x can be generated by a finite number of arithmetic operations upon x and the members of A. For example, $3 \cdot \pi \cdot x \cdot x + \sqrt{2}$. If the only operations permitted are multiplication, addition, and subtraction, the resulting expressions in x are polynomials in x *over the set* A, where A is either the set of integers, the set of rational numbers, the set of real numbers, or the set of complex numbers. Since each of these sets is closed with respect to the operations of multiplication, addition, and subtraction, the coefficients of the polynomials are in set A also.

EXAMPLE 1.

$16x^3 + 4x - 2$	Polynomial over the integers.
$2x^2 + \frac{13}{2}$	Polynomial over the rational numbers.
$\sqrt{2}x^{100} + x^{50} - \pi$	Polynomial over the real numbers.
$2ix^3 + 4$	Polynomial over the complex numbers.

If you are also permitted to use the operation of division to generate expressions in x, the resulting expressions are **rational expressions** in x *over the set* A.

EXAMPLE 2.

$\dfrac{x^2 + 2}{x + 1}$	Rational expression over the integers.
$\dfrac{\frac{x^3}{3} + 2x}{\frac{14}{5}x^4}$	Rational expression over the rationals.
$\dfrac{x^5 + x^4 + x^3}{\sqrt{2}x^3}$	Rational expression over the real numbers.
$\dfrac{\frac{3}{2}x + 2i}{\frac{9}{4}x^3 - 3i^3}$	Rational expression over the complex numbers.

Notice that all polynomial expressions are also rational expressions. Why?

If you may also use extraction of roots as an operation in generating expressions, the result is an **algebraic expression.** The following example illustrates the idea.

EXAMPLE 3.

$\dfrac{5\sqrt[3]{x}}{\sqrt{x+1}} - 2\sqrt[3]{x}$ Algebraic expression over the integers.

$\frac{1}{3}\sqrt{x} + 2\sqrt[4]{x}$ Algebraic expression over the rationals.

$\sqrt{3}\sqrt[3]{x^2} + \pi$ Algebraic expression over the real numbers.

$3 + 2i^3\sqrt{x}$ Algebraic expression over the complex numbers.

The set of algebraic expressions includes rational and polynomial expressions. Why?

> **A <u>polynomial</u> in the symbol x over the real numbers R is an algebraic expression that can be written**
>
> $$a_n x^n + a_{n-1}x^{n-1} + a_{n-2}x^{n-2} + \cdots + a_1 x + a_0$$
>
> **where n is a nonnegative integer, the coefficients a_i are in R, and $a_n \neq 0$. The number n is said to be the <u>degree</u> of the polynomial, and a_n is called the <u>leading</u> coefficient.**
>
> **If x is a variable whose domain is the set of real numbers R, then the association denoted by**
>
> $$f : x \longrightarrow a_n x^n + a_{n-1}x^{n-1} + \cdots + a_1 x + a_0$$
>
> **or**
>
> $$f(x) = a_n x^n + a_{n-1}x^{n-1} + \cdots + a_1 x + a_0$$
>
> **is called a <u>polynomial function</u>. The range of a polynomial function is $\{y : y = f(x), x \in R\}$.**

It is important to note that the range may be all of R or a subset of R. The degree of a polynomial function is the same as that of its defining polynomial.

EXAMPLE 4.

$f : x \longrightarrow x^5 + 2x^3 + x$ Polynomial function of degree 5.

$g(x) = 2x^3 + 1$ Polynomial function of degree 3.

$h(x) = \sqrt{x} + x^3$ Not a polynomial function. (Why?)

$r(x) = \frac{3}{2}ix^2 + 2$ Not a polynomial function. (Why?)

You are already familiar with the properties of three common polynomial functions. These are the polynomial functions of degrees 0, 1, and 2. They are commonly called the *constant*, *linear*, and *quadratic* functions.

Properties of the Constant Function

The **constant function** associates with every element x of its domain the number c. The range of the function is the single number c, and hence the graph of the function is either a line parallel to the x axis when $c \neq 0$ or the x axis itself when $c = 0$. The point at which the graph of a function intersects the y axis is called the **y intercept** of the function. The y intercept is the point $(0, f(0))$. The y intercept for the constant

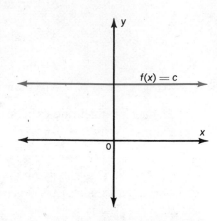

function is $(0, c)$. The slope of the graph of $f(x) = c$ is 0 at every point.

Of course, the constant function $f(x) = c$, $c \neq 0$, is just the polynomial function $f(x) = a_0 = c$ and hence the degree is 0. If, however, $c = 0$, then $f(x) = 0$ is *not* a polynomial function (Why?) and has no degree associated with it. Nevertheless, it is common practice to call $f(x) = 0$ the **zero polynomial**. You can conclude that every line with zero slope is associated with a polynomial function of degree 0 or with the zero polynomial.

Properties of the Linear Function

The graph of the **linear function** $f(x) = mx + b$, $m \neq 0$, is a line with slope m and y intercept $(0, b)$. The graph intersects the x axis at the point with x coordinate $-\dfrac{b}{m}$.

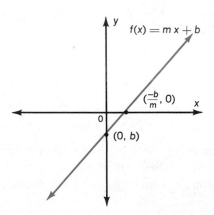

If the graph of a function and the x axis have any points in common, these points are called the **real zeros** of the function. Otherwise the zeros are imaginary. Stated more formally, the set of *zeros* of a function f is the set of all x in the domain of f for which $f(x) = 0$. The zeros of a function are found by setting $f(x)$ equal to 0 and solving the resulting equation for x.

For example, the zeros of the linear function

$$f(x) = 4x - 3$$

are found by solving

$$0 = 4x - 3$$
$$3 = 4x$$
$$\tfrac{3}{4} = x.$$

Hence the set of zeros of $f(x) = 4x - 3$ is

$$\left\{\tfrac{3}{4}\right\}.$$

In other words the line, $4x - 3$, crosses the x axis at $x = \tfrac{3}{4}$.

Properties of the Quadratic Function

The graph of the **quadratic function**

$$f(x) = ax^2 + bx + c, \qquad a \neq 0,$$

is a *parabola.* The y intercept is $(0, c)$.

The following two cases will be considered, the first when a is greater than zero, the second when a is less than zero. If $a > 0$, the parabola is *concave upward* (opens upward).

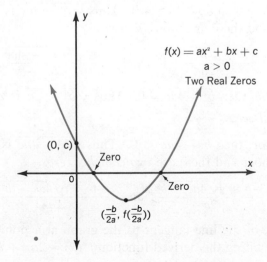

$f(x) = ax^2 + bx + c$
$a > 0$
Two Real Zeros

$(0, c)$

Zero

Zero

$\left(\frac{-b}{2a}, f\left(\frac{-b}{2a}\right)\right)$

If $a < 0$, the parabola is *concave downward* (opens downward).

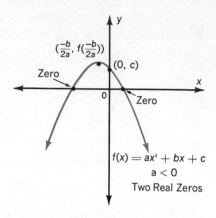

The **axis of symmetry** is the line with equation $x = -\dfrac{b}{2a}$. The **turning point** (maximum or minimum) is the point common to the axis of symmetry and the parabola. The y coordinate of this point is $f\left(-\dfrac{b}{2a}\right)$. (See Section 6–6, Exercises 15–21.) The zeros (if any) are found by applying the **quadratic formula.**

$$x = \frac{-b \pm \sqrt{b^2 - 4ac}}{2a}$$

The nature of the zeros of a quadratic function can be determined by examing the **discriminant,**

$$b^2 - 4ac.$$

① If $b^2 > 4ac$, then $b^2 - 4ac > 0$. Thus $\sqrt{b^2 - 4ac}$ is a positive real number and there are *two real zeros*.

$$\frac{-b + \sqrt{b^2 - 4ac}}{2a} \quad \text{and} \quad \frac{-b - \sqrt{b^2 - 4ac}}{2a}$$

② If $b^2 = 4ac$, then $b^2 - 4ac = 0$. Thus $\sqrt{b^2 - 4ac}$ is zero and there is *one real zero*: $-\dfrac{b}{2a}$

③ If $b^2 < 4ac$, then $b^2 - 4ac < 0$. Thus $\sqrt{b^2 - 4ac}$ is a pure imaginary number and there are *two complex zeros*.

$$\frac{-b + i\sqrt{4ac - b^2}}{2a} \quad \text{and} \quad \frac{-b - i\sqrt{4ac - b^2}}{2a}$$

The slope of the line tangent to the graph at a point $(x_0, f(x_0))$ is found by evaluating the derived function $f'(x) = 2ax + b$ at $x = x_0$.

Checkpoint

1. Explain the difference between the zeros of a polynomial function and the zero polynomial.

2. Why doesn't the constant function $f(x) = 0$ strictly conform to the definition of a polynomial?

3. Write a definition of the y *intercept* of a polynomial function.

4. What are the zeros of a function? How are they found?

Exercises

A ▬ Identify the degree and leading coefficient of each polynomial.

1. $3x^4 - 2x + 1$
2. $\frac{7x^2 - 2x}{5}$
3. $x(4x + 2)$

4. $x^2 - 3x^4 + 2x$
5. $-x^9 - 2x^3 + x$
6. $1 - 3x$

▬ For each linear and quadratic function determine the y intercept, the real zeros (if any), and the slope at $x = 3$. For the quadratic functions determine also the axis of symmetry, the coordinates of the turning point, and whether the graph opens upward or downward.

7. $f(x) = -2x - 3$
8. $f(x) = \frac{1}{2}x + 5$
9. $f(x) = 2x$
10. $f(x) = x^2$
11. $f(x) = x^2 - 4$
12. $f(x) = x^2 + 2x + 1$
13. $f(x) = -x^2$
14. $f(x) = 3x^2 + x + 1$
15. $f(x) = -2x^2 + 4x$
16. $f(x) = x^2 - 5x - 50$

B   17. What is the slope of the line tangent to $f(x) = ax^2 + bx + c$ at $x = -\frac{b}{2a}$?

18. Find the equation of the line tangent to $f(x) = 3x^2$ at
    a. $x = 0$.
    b. $x = 2$.
    c. $x = -3$.
    d. $x = x_0$.

19. Find the y intercept of the line tangent to $f(x) = 3x^2$ at
    a. $x = 2$.
    b. $x = x_0$.

20. In Exercise 19, is there any relationship between the y intercepts found in a and b and $f(2)$ and $f(x_0)$? Explain.

C   21. Show that the sum of two polynomials over a set A is also a polynomial over A. Is this true also for the product of two polynomials?

7–2   Synthetic Substitution

Suppose that you were asked to graph the polynomial function

$$f(x) = a_n x^n + a_{n-1}x^{n-1} + \cdots + a_1 x + a_0.$$

One of the first things you would have to do is to calculate values of the function corresponding to particular values of x. This can always be done by substitution. For $x = c$,

$$f(c) = a_n c^n + a_{n-1}c^{n-1} + \cdots + a_1 c + a_0.$$

EXAMPLE 1.   Find the value of $f(x) = 4x^4 - 2x^3 - 3x^2 - x$ evaluated at $x = 3$.

$$\begin{aligned}
f(3) &= 4(3)^4 - 2(3)^3 - 3(3)^2 - 3 \\
&= 4(81) - 2(27) - 3(9) - 3 \\
&= 324 - 54 - 27 - 3 \\
&= 240
\end{aligned}$$

Certainly for polynomial functions of large degree or for large values of x, substitution leads to many tedious calculations. There is a simpler method to calculate values called **synthetic substitution.**

EXAMPLE 2.   Find the value of $f(x) = 2x^3 - 3x^2 - 5x + 4$ at $x = 3$.
Write $2x^3 - 3x^2 - 5x + 4$ in the alternate form

$$[(2x - 3)x - 5]x + 4.$$

When $x = 3$, this becomes

$$[(2(3) - 3)3 - 5]3 + 4.$$

The evaluation in stages is as follows.

① Multiply 2 (the coefficient of x^3) by 3 and add the product to -3 (the coefficient of x^2): $6 - 3 = 3$.

② Multiply the result of ①, 3, by 3 and add the product to -5 (the coefficient of x): $9 - 5 = 4$.

③ Multiply the result of ②, 4, by 3 and add the product to 4 (the constant term): $12 + 4 = 16$.

Consequently $f(3) = 16$ when $f(x) = 2x^3 - 3x^2 - 5x + 4$. The evaluation of $f(x)$ at $x = c$ in Example 2 follows a definite pattern. Essentially,

Multiply the leading coefficient by c, add the result to the next coefficient, multiply the sum by c, add, multiply, etc. in the same manner.

EXAMPLE 3. Evaluate

$$f(x) = \tfrac{1}{2}x^3 + 2x^2 + 5x - 5 \text{ at } x = 2.$$

Write the coefficients of successive terms (arranged in descending order of powers of x), and write 2 at the far right as shown.

$$\tfrac{1}{2} \quad 2 \quad 5 \quad -5 \quad \underline{|2}$$

To begin the process, bring down the leading coefficient, $\tfrac{1}{2}$. Multiply $\tfrac{1}{2}$ by 2 and add the product to the next coefficient, 2.

$\tfrac{1}{2}$	2	5	-5	$\underline{|2}$
	$(\tfrac{1}{2} \times 2) = 1$	$(3 \times 2) = 6$	$(11 \times 2) = 22$	
$\tfrac{1}{2}$	3	11		$17 = f(2)$

The sum is 3. The process is repeated as shown above. By synthetic substitution, $f(2) = 17$. You can verify this by direct substitution. Each number in the second row is twice the number in the preceding column of the third row. Each number in the third row is the sum of the numbers above it.

Synthetic substitution works for a polynomial function of any degree and for any replacement for x. This is not proved here, but the general case for a third degree polynomial function is worked out in the next example.

EXAMPLE 4. The polynomial function of degree 3 may be written as follows:

$$f(x) = a_3x^3 + a_2x^2 + a_1x + a_0, \quad a_3 \neq 0$$

or

$$f(x) = [(a_3x + a_2)x + a_1]x + a_0$$

Verify that the result of synthetic substitution of c is $f(c)$.
By direct replacement,

$$f(c) = a_3c^3 + a_2c^2 + a_1c + a_0.$$

Synthetic substitution gives the following result:

a_3	a_2	a_1	a_0	$\underline{|c}$
	a_3c	$(a_3c + a_2)c$	$[(a_3c + a_2)c + a_1]c$	
a_3	$(a_3c + a_2)$	$[(a_3c + a_2)c + a_1]$	$[(a_3c + a_2)c + a_1]c + a_0$	

The last entry in the third row is $f(c)$ and is the same as the result obtained by direct substitution.

EXAMPLE 5. Given $f(x) = x^4 - 3x^2 - 2x - 5$, determine $f(2)$.

Notice that there is no term in x^3 in the polynomial $x^4 - 3x^2 - 2x - 5$; that is, the coefficient of x^3 is zero. Thus $f(x) = x^4 + 0x^3 - 3x^2 - 2x - 5$. The complete set of coefficients must be used in the synthetic substitution as shown.

$$
\begin{array}{rrrrr|r}
1 & 0 & -3 & -2 & -5 & \underline{2} \\
  & 2 & 4 & 2 & 0 & \\
\hline
1 & 2 & 1 & 0 & -5
\end{array}
$$

Thus $f(2) = -5$. Check this by direct substitution.

Exercises

A ▬ Use synthetic substitution to evaluate each function at the designated values of x.

   1. $f(x) = x^4 - 2x^3 + 3x^2 - x + 5$ $x = -2, 1, 3$

   2. $g(x) = x^4 + x - 3$ $x = -2, 1, 3$

   3. $f(x) = -3x^3 + x^2 + x - 2$ $x = -1, -3, 0, 2, 4$

   4. $h(x) = 2x^3 - 3x^2 + 1$ $x = \frac{1}{2}, \frac{1}{3}, 1$

   5. $g(x) = x^4 - x^3 + 2x + 3$ $x = \frac{2}{3}, \frac{1}{4}, -2$

   6. $s(x) = 3x^2 + x - x^4 + 2$ $x = -\frac{1}{2}, \frac{1}{3}, -2, 2$

B   **7.** If $r(x) = 2x^3 + 3x^2 - 3x + k$, find k so that $r(2) = 8$.

       8. If $s(x) = x^3 - 7x + 3k$, find k so that $s(-1) = 6$.

       9. If $f(x) = 3x^3 - kx^2 + 2x$, find k so that $f(1) = -5$.

     10. If $f(x) = 2x^3 - kx^2 + 3x - 2k$, find k so that $f(2) = 4$.

C   **11.** If $f(x) = 2x^4 - 3x^2 + cx + k$, find c and k so that $f(-2) = 20$ and $f(2) = 24$.

     12. If $f(x) = x^4 + 2x^3 - x^2 + cx + k$, find c and k so that $f(1) = 0$ and $f(-1) = 0$.

     13. Let $f(x) = x^3 + 3x^2 + 6x - 20$. By synthetic substitution evaluate $f(x)$ for $x \in \{\pm 4, \pm 3.5, \pm 3, \pm 2.5, \pm 2, \pm 1.5, \pm 1, \pm 0.5, 0\}$. Plot three points on a coordinate plane and connect them with a smooth curve to obtain an approximate graph of $f(x)$.

     ▬ Repeat Exercise 13 for the following functions:

     14. $f(x) = x^3 - 3x^2 + 6x$

     15. $f(x) = x^3 - 3x + 6$

     16. $f(x) = x^3 + 3x - 6$

     17. $f(x) = x^3 + 3x$

7–3   The Remainder and Factor Theorems

The first theorem in this chapter is motivated by examining the evaluation of

$$f(x) = x^3 - 4x^2 + x + 6$$

at $x = 4$ using synthetic substitution.

$$
\begin{array}{rrrr|r}
1 & -4 & 1 & 6 & \underline{4} \\
  & 4 & 0 & 4 & \\
\hline
1 & 0 & 1 & \multicolumn{1}{|r}{10}
\end{array}
$$

Now rewrite the first row in the pattern so that it appears as the original polynomial. Then attach the same power of x to each number in a given column.

$$
\begin{array}{rrrr|r}
1x^3 & -4x^2 & +1x & +6 & \underline{4} \\
 & +4x^2 & +0x & +4 & \\
\hline
1x^3 & 0x^2 & +1x & \multicolumn{1}{|r}{+10}
\end{array}
$$

The polynomial in the third row is the sum of the polynomials in the first two rows.
Since

$$f(x) = x^3 - 4x^2 + x + 6 \qquad \text{and} \qquad f(4) = 10,$$

the addition can be rewritten as follows.

$$f(x) + (4x^2 + 0x + 4) = x^3 + 0x^2 + x + f(4).$$

Factoring gives

$$f(x) + 4(x^2 + 0x + 1) = x(x^2 + 0x + 1) + f(4).$$

Notice that $x^2 + 0x + 1$ appears on both sides of this equation. Now solve the equation for $f(x)$ by combining terms and factoring.

$$
\begin{aligned}
f(x) &= x(x^2 + 0x + 1) - 4(x^2 + 0x + 1) + f(4) \\
f(x) &= (x - 4)(x^2 + 0x + 1) + f(4)
\end{aligned}
$$

This last expression has the same form as the well-known relationship,

$$\text{Dividend} = (\text{Divisor})(\text{Quotient}) + \text{Remainder}.$$

Thus, if $f(x) = x^3 - 4x^2 + x + 6$ is divided by $x - 4$, the quotient will be $x^2 + 1$, the remainder will be $f(4) = 10$, and both the quotient and remainder can be found by synthetically substituting $x = 4$ in $f(x)$. The generalization of this result is called the **Remainder Theorem.**

Theorem 7-1 (Remainder Theorem) If $f(x)$ is a polynomial function of degree n, $n > 0$, and if c is a number, then the remainder in the division of $f(x)$ by $x - c$ is $f(c)$. In symbols,

$$f(x) = (x - c)Q(x) + f(c)$$

where the quotient $Q(x)$ is a polynomial of degree $n - 1$.

Proof: Dividing $f(x)$ by $x - c$, you obtain a quotient $Q(x)$ and a remainder r (a real number). Then

$$f(x) = (x - c)Q(x) + r$$

for all values of x. If the degree of $f(x)$ is n, the degree of $Q(x)$ is $n - 1$. Since the equation is true for all x, it must be true for $x = c$. Then,

$$f(c) = (c - c)Q(c) + r, \quad \text{or } f(c) = r.$$

It is important to note that the theorem is stated in terms of $x - c$, the *difference* between x and the number c.

EXAMPLE 1. Divide $f(x) = 2x^3 + x - 2$ by $x - 1$. Find the quotient $Q(x)$ and the remainder.

Use synthetic substitution.

$$
\begin{array}{rrrr|r}
2 & 0 & 1 & -2 & \underline{1} \\
  & 2 & 2 & 3 & \\
\hline
2 & 2 & 3 & 1 &
\end{array}
$$

The numbers in the third row, other than the last one at the right which is the remainder, are the coefficients of the quotient $Q(x)$.
Thus

$$Q(x) = 2x^2 + 2x + 3 \quad \text{and} \quad f(1) = 1.$$

Consequently

$$f(x) = (x - 1)(2x^2 + 2x + 3) + 1.$$

Since the synthetic substitution of $x = c$ in $f(x)$ can also be used to divide $f(x)$ by $x - c$, the process is alternately called **synthetic division** of $f(x)$ by $x - c$. The polynomial $Q(x)$ is called the **depressed polynomial.**

EXAMPLE 2. Use synthetic division to divide $f(x) = x^3 - 4x^2 + x + 6$ by $x + 1$. Identify the quotient and remainder.

To divide by $x - c$, c is substituted synthetically. Since $x + 1 = x - (-1)$, -1 is substituted synthetically in $f(x)$.

$$\begin{array}{r|rrrr} & 1 & -4 & 1 & 6 \underline{|-1} \\ & & -1 & 5 & -6 \\ \hline & 1 & -5 & 6 & 0 \end{array}$$

The remainder is 0, and the depressed polynomial is $Q(x) = x^2 - 5x + 6$, hence:

$$f(x) = (x + 1)(x^2 - 5x + 6) + 0.$$

In Example 2, the remainder $f(-1)$ is 0 and therefore -1 is a zero of $f(x)$. Consequently $x + 1$ and $Q(x)$ are factors of $f(x)$. Stated formally, this result is the **Factor Theorem.**

Theorem 7–2 (Factor Theorem) A number c is a zero of a polynomial function f of degree n, $n > 0$, if and only if $x - c$ is a factor of $f(x)$.

Proof Part 1 (only if):
 The Remainder Theorem implies that there exists a polynomial $Q(x)$ of degree $n - 1$ such that

$$f(x) = (x - c)Q(x) + f(c).$$

If c is a zero, then $f(c) = 0$ and

$$f(x) = (x - c)Q(x).$$

Consequently $x - c$ is a factor of $f(x)$.

Part 2 (if):
 If $x - c$ is a factor of $f(x)$ then there is a polynomial $Q(x)$ such that you have the following.

$$f(x) = (x - c)Q(x)$$

When x is replaced by c,

$$\begin{aligned} f(c) &= (c - c)Q(c) \\ &= 0. \end{aligned}$$

Consequently c is a zero of f.

There are two reasons for the importance of the Factor Theorem. First, it provides a test as to whether or not a number is a zero of a polynomial function. This test is simplified by using synthetic substitution. The second reason is that linear factors of $f(x)$ may be found by identification of the zeros of f. Synthetic substitution simplifies this task also.

To test whether or not a linear polynomial $mx + b$, $m \neq 0$, is a factor of $f(x)$, you write

$$mx + b = m\left(x + \frac{b}{m}\right)$$

$$= m\left[x - \left(-\frac{b}{m}\right)\right]$$

and see whether $f\left(-\frac{b}{m}\right) = 0$. (By the Factor Theorem, $mx + b$ is a factor of $f(x)$ if and only if $f\left(-\frac{b}{m}\right) = 0$.)

Exercises

A ▬ Find $Q(x)$ and $f(c)$ so that $f(x) = (x - c)Q(x) + f(c)$.

1. $f(x) = 3x^3 + 4x^2 - 10x - 15$ $c = 2$

2. $f(x) = x^3 + 3x^2 + 2x + 12$ $c = -3$

3. $f(x) = -2x^4 + 3x^3 + 6x - 10$ $c = 1$

4. $f(x) = 2x^4 + 3x^3 - x^2 + 1$ $c = -\frac{1}{2}$

5. $f(x) = 9x^3 - x + 1$ $c = \frac{2}{3}$

▬ Find the quotient and remainder when $f(x)$ is divided by the linear factor at the right.

6. $f(x) = 2x^3 - 3x^2 + 2x - 4$ $x - 2$

7. $f(x) = 2x^3 - 3x^2 + 2x - 8$ $x - 2$

8. $f(x) = x^4 - x^3 + x - 5$ $x + 1$

9. $f(x) = 3x^3 + x^2 - 6x + 3$ $x + \frac{1}{3}$

10. $f(x) = x^7 - 31x^2$ $x - 2$

B **11.** If $f(x)$ of degree n, $n > 0$, is divided by $g(x)$ of degree m, $m > 0$, so that a quotient $Q(x)$ and a remainder $r(x)$ are obtained, what is the degree of $Q(x)$? of $(r)x$?

12. Find the value of $f(x) = x^3 - x^2 - 4x + 4$ at $x = -3, -2, -1$, 0, 1, 2, 3. What are the factors of $f(x)$?

13. Find the value of $f(x) = 6x^3 + 35x^2 - 7x - 6$ at $x = -6, -2$, $-\frac{1}{3}, \frac{1}{2}, 3$. Name three linear factors of $f(x)$.

14. Find the value of k so that $f(x) = x^4 + kx^3 - 2kx^2 + 3x - 5$ has a factor $x - 1$.

15. Find the values of k so that $f(x) = x^3 - x^2 + kx - 12$ has a factor $x - 3$.

16. Determine k so that $x - k$ will divide $f(x) = x^2 + 4x + 2$ with a remainder of -1.

C **17.** If $f(x) = x^2 + px + q$ is exactly divisible by $x - a$ and $x - b$, show that $p = -a - b$ and $q = ab$.

18. Show that $x - a$ is a factor of $x^n - a^n$ when n is even.

19. Show that $x + a$ is a factor of $x^n + a^n$ when n is odd. What is $Q(x)$?

20. Show that $3x - 6$ is a factor of $3x^3 - 15x + 6$.

21. Prove Theorem 7–1 for the case

$$f(x) = a_3x^3 + a_2x^2 + a_1x + a_0.$$

(*Hint:* Follow the pattern used in the text for $f(x) = x^3 - 4x^2 + x + 6$.)

━━━ Use the quadratic formula to find the zeros of each quadratic function in Exercises 22–25. Express the quadratic function as the product of two linear functions with complex coefficients (real or imaginary).

22. $f(x) = 2x^2 + 7x - 15$

23. $f(x) = x^2 - x - 1$

24. $f(x) = 2x^2 - 3x + 2$

25. $f(x) = x^2 + 4$

7–4 Locating Real Zeros

The Factor Theorem enables you to answer the question: Given a polynomial function f and a real number c, is c a zero of f? This theorem does not, however, tell you *how* to find c.

For polynomial functions of degree one and two, linear and quadratic functions, you already know how to find the zeros. There are also methods that can be used to determine the zeros of third and fourth degree polynomial functions. Surprising as it may seem, the best way to determine the zeros of a polynomial function of degree greater than two is to *guess*. The following theorem is an aid to making intelligent guesses.

Theorem 7–3 (Locater Theorem) If f is a polynomial function and a and b are real numbers such that $f(a)$ and $f(b)$ have opposite signs, then there is at least one zero of f between a and b.

Geometrically the Locater Theorem says that if the point $(a, f(a))$ is below the x axis and the point $(b, f(b))$ is above the x axis, then there must be *at least one* point between $x = a$ and $x = b$ on the x axis where the graph intersects the axis.

Although this Theorem is not proved here, the basic reason for its validity lies in the fact that every polynomial function is continuous on each interval $[a, b]$. Consequently there are no "gaps" in the graph, and it must intersect the x axis at least once.

The figure at the right illustrates the Locater Theorem. Since $f(a) < 0$ and $f(b) > 0$, $f(a)$ and $f(b)$ have opposite signs. Thus, the graph of f must intersect the x axis at least once

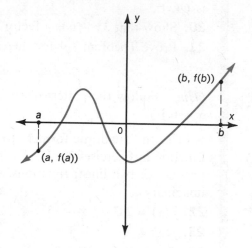

between $x = a$ and $x = b$. In fact, in the figure, f intersects the x axis three times and thus at least once.

EXAMPLE 1. Locate between successive tenths a real zero of the following function.

$$f(x) = x^4 - 2x^3 + 4x - 4$$

Use synthetic substitution to find two integers a and b, for which $f(a)$ and $f(b)$ have opposite signs. The work is tabulated below, using selected values for c.

Coefficients

		1	-2	0	4	-4
zero⟶	-2	1	-4	8	-12	20
	-1	1	-3	3	1	-5
	0	1	-2	0	4	-4
zero⟶	1	1	-1	-1	3	-1
	2	1	0	0	4	4
	3	1	1	3	13	35
	c					$f(c)$

Hence there is at least one zero between -2 and -1 and at least one zero between 1 and 2.

Choose one of the pairs of numbers, say 1 and 2, and "close in" on the zero by finding $f(c)$ for $1 < c < 2$. Since $-1\,(f(1))$ is closer to 0 than is $4\;(f(2))$, it seems reasonable to pick a number that is closer to 1, such as 1.3.

$$
\begin{array}{rrrrr|r}
1 & -2 & 0 & 4 & -4 & \underline{\;1.3} \\
 & 1.3 & -0.91 & -1.183 & 3.6621 & \\
\hline
1 & -0.7 & -0.91 & 2.817 & -0.3379 &
\end{array}
$$

Because $f(1.3) = -0.3379$ and $f(2) = 4$ there is a zero of the polynomial function between 1.3 and 2.

$$
\begin{array}{rrrrr|r}
1 & -2 & 0 & 4 & -4 & \underline{\;1.4} \\
 & 1.4 & -0.84 & -1.176 & 3.9536 & \\
\hline
1 & -0.6 & -0.84 & 2.824 & -0.0464 &
\end{array}
$$

Hence $f(1.4) = -0.0464$, and there is a zero between 1.4 and 2.

$$
\begin{array}{rrrrr|r}
1 & -2 & 0 & 4 & -4 & \underline{\;1.5} \\
 & 1.5 & -0.75 & -1.125 & 4.3125 & \\
\hline
1 & -0.5 & -0.75 & 2.875 & 0.3125 &
\end{array}
$$

Since $f(1.4)$ and $f(1.5)$ have opposite signs, there is at least one zero between 1.4 and 1.5.

In Example 1 at least two real zeros of a polynomial function f were located, but no mention was made of the possibility of there being other real zeros. In fact, the table in Example 1 allows you to conclude that all of the real zeros of f are between $x = -2$ and $x = 3$.

Theorem 7–4 Let f be a polynomial function. Let c be a positive real number substituted synthetically in $f(x)$. If
(1) all the coefficients of the depressed polynomial $Q(x)$ are positive, and
(2) $f(c)$ is positive, then all the real zeros of f are less than c, and thus c is an upper bound for the zeros of f.

Proof: By the Remainder Theorem, $f(x) = (x - c)Q(x) + f(c)$. For $x = c, f(x) = f(c) > 0$. Thus, $x = c$ is not a zero.
    For $x > c, (x - c) > 0, Q(x) > 0$ and $f(c) > 0$. Thus,

$$(x - c)Q(x) + f(c) > 0.$$

Consequently, any x equal to or greater than c is not a zero of f, and all real zeros must be less than c.

You may ask how a real number that is less than all the real zeros of a polynomial function can be determined. If such a number exists, it is called a **lower bound** for the zeros of a function f. One way to determine a lower bound for the zeros of f is to examine $f(-x)$ and apply Theorem 7–4.

Suppose c is a zero of $f(x)$, $c < 0$.
Then

$$f(x) = (x - c)Q(x)$$

and

$$\begin{aligned} f(-x) &= (-x - c)Q(-x) \\ &= -(x + c)Q(-x) \\ &= -(x - [-c])Q(-x). \end{aligned}$$

Thus, $-c > 0$ is a zero of $f(-x)$. That is, the negative zeros of $f(x)$ are positive zeros of $f(-x)$. Consequently, an upper bound for the positive zeros of $f(-x)$ is a lower bound for the negative zeros of $f(x)$.

EXAMPLE 2. Find an upper bound and a lower bound for the roots of the polynomial function of Example 1.

$$f(x) = x^4 - 2x^3 + 4x - 4$$

Find $f(3)$ by synthetic substitution and observe the signs of the coefficients of the depressed polynomial.

1	-2	0	4	-4	$\lfloor 3$
	3	3	9	39	
1	1	3	13	35	

The coefficients 1, 1, 3, and 13 are positive, and hence by Theorem 7–4 the number 3 is an *upper bound* for the zeros of f. A lower bound for the zeros of f may be found by finding an upper bound for the zeros of $f(-x)$.

$$f(-x) = x^4 + 2x^3 - 4x - 4$$

1	2	0	-4	-4	$\lfloor 2$
	2	8	16	24	
1	4	8	12	20	

Hence -2 is a lower bound for the zeros of f.

There is a simpler test for a lower bound of the zeros of f that is frequently substituted for the one described above. Substitute synthetically a negative number c in a polynomial. If the coefficients of the depressed polynomial of $f(x)$ and the number $f(c)$ alternate in sign, then c is a lower bound for the zeros of f.

EXAMPLE 3. Use the test just stated to find a lower bound for the zeros of the function

$$f(x) = x^4 - 2x^3 + 4x - 4.$$

By synthetic substitution,

1	-2	0	4	-4	$\lfloor -2$
	-2	8	-16	24	
1	-4	8	-12	20	

Since the signs of the terms in the last row alternate, -2 is a lower bound for the zeros of f. Notice that the same result was obtained in Example 2.

Checkpoint

How would you try to find an upper bound for the zeros of a polynomial function f? a lower bound for the zeros of the function?

Exercises

A ▬▬ Find the intervals between consecutive integers that contain real zeros of f.

1. $f(x) = x^3 - 3x^2 + 3$

2. $f(x) = 2x^4 - 2x - 3$

3. $f(x) = x^4 - 3x^2 - 6x - 2$

4. $f(x) = x^3 - 6x^2 + 11x - 5$

5. $f(x) = x^4 + 3x - 13$

6. $f(x) = x^3 - 12x + 3$

7. $f(x) = 3x^3 - 3x + 1$ (*Hint:* Try $f(\tfrac{1}{2})$.)

8. Determine the upper and lower bounds for the zeros of the functions in Exercises 1–7.

B ▬▬ Locate between successive tenths one real zero of each polynomial function.

9. $f(x) = x^3 + 3x - 2$ **10.** $f(x) = x^4 + x - 1$

11. $f(x) = x^3 - x + 7$ **12.** $f(x) = -x^3 + 2x - 1$

13. Determine the range of values of k for which $f(x) = x^3 - 2x^2 + 4x - k$ has at least one real zero between

    a. 0 and 1.   **b.** 1 and 2.

7–5 Rational Zeros

In this section you will be concerned only with polynomials over the integers, that is, polynomials with integral coefficients. The following theorem is of major importance. It is extremely useful in helping you to find possible rational zeros for polynomial functions over the integers.

> **Theorem 7–5** Let f be a polynomial function over the integers.
>
> $$f(x) = a_n x^n + a_{n-1} x^{n-1} + \cdots + a_1 x + a_0, \quad a_i \in I$$
>
> If f has a rational zero $\frac{r}{s}$, $\frac{r}{s} \neq 0$, $s > 0$, and $\frac{r}{s}$ is expressed in lowest terms, then r is a divisor of a_0 and s is a divisor of a_n.

Proof:

By assumption, $\frac{r}{s}$ is a zero of f. Thus $f\left(\frac{r}{s}\right) = 0$ and

$$a_n \frac{r^n}{s^n} + a_{n-1} \frac{r^{n-1}}{s^{n-1}} + a_{n-2} \frac{r^{n-2}}{s^{n-2}} + \cdots + a_1 \frac{r}{s} + a_0 = 0. \qquad 1$$

Multiplying **1** by s^n ($s \neq 0$) gives

$$a_n r^n + a_{n-1} r^{n-1} s + a_{n-2} r^{n-2} s^2 + \cdots + a_1 r s^{n-1} + a_0 s^n = 0. \qquad 2$$

Equation **2** can be written in two convenient forms. The first is obtained by solving **2** for $a_0 s^n$ and dividing by r; the second by solving **2** for $a_n r^n$ and dividing by s.

$$\frac{a_0 s^n}{r} = -[a_n r^{n-1} + a_{n-1} r^{n-2} s + a_{n-2} r^{n-3} s^2 + \cdots + a_1 s^{n-1}] \qquad 3$$

$$\frac{a_n r^n}{s} = -[a_{n-1} r^{n-1} + a_{n-2} r^{n-2} s + \cdots + a_1 r s^{n-2} + a_0 s^{n-1}] \qquad 4$$

The coefficients $a_0, a_1, \cdots, a_n$ and n and s are integers and so the expressions on the right side of equations **3** and **4** are also integers. Thus the left side must also be integers. Since $\frac{r}{s}$ is in lowest terms, s does not divide r, and r does not divide s. Thus r does not divide s^n (Why?), and s does not divide r^n. Consequently, $\frac{a_0 s^n}{r}$ being an integer and r not dividing s^n implies r divides a_0. In a similar manner it follows from **4** that s divides a_n. Thus the theorem is proved.

Theorem 7–6 is a special case of Theorem 7–5.

Theorem 7–6   If

$$f(x) = x^n + a_{n-1}x^{n-1} + a_{n-2}x^{n-2} + \cdots + a_1x + a_0$$

is a polynomial with integral coefficients, $a_0 \neq 0$, and the co-efficient of the highest power of x is one, then the only rational numbers that may be zeros of f are the integral divisors of a_0.

EXAMPLE 1.   Find the only rational numbers that may be zeros of

$$f(x) = 3x^3 - 8x^2 + 3x + 2.$$

For $f(x) = 3x^3 - 8x^2 + 3x + 2$, $a_n = 3$ and $a_0 = 2$.   Thus by Theorem 7–5, the possible rational zeros of f are to be found among the rational numbers whose numerators are the positive and negative divisors of $a_0 = 2$ and whose denominators are the positive divisors of $a_n = 3$.   The integral divisors, r, of 2 are: ± 1, ± 2.   The whole number divisors, s, of 3 are: 1, 3.   Thus the possible rational zeros are $\frac{r}{s}$: $\pm\frac{1}{1}$, $\pm\frac{1}{3}$, $\pm\frac{2}{1}$, $\pm\frac{2}{3}$.

EXAMPLE 2.   Find the only rational numbers that may be zeros of

$$f(x) = x^4 - 2x^3 + 3x^2 - 2x + 2.$$

The possible rational zeros are ± 1 and ± 2 by Theorem 7–6.   To find the *actual* rational zeros, the *possible* zeros must be tested.

EXAMPLE 3.   Find the rational zeros of the following function.

$$f(x) = 3x^4 - 5x^3 - 5x^2 - 19x - 6$$

The divisors of -6 are: ± 1, ± 2, ± 3, ± 6.   The positive divisors of 3 are: 1, 3.   Hence the possible rational zeros of f are: ± 1, ± 2, ± 3, ± 6, $\pm\frac{1}{3}$, $\pm\frac{2}{3}$.   Substituting synthetically you find that 3 is a zero of f.

3	-5	-5	-19	-6	$\underline{\lfloor 3}$
	9	12	21	6	
3	4	7	2	0	

Thus $f(x) = (x - 3)(3x^3 + 4x^2 + 7x + 2)$.   If $f(x)$ has any other rational zeros, they must be zeros of the depressed polynomial $3x^3 + 4x^2 + 7x + 2$.   This is true because if $x - c$, $c \neq 3$, is to divide $f(x)$, it must divide $3x^3 + 4x^2 + 7x + 2$.   Hence $3x^3 + 4x^2 + 7x + 2$ can be used to determine the remaining zeros (if any).

For the depressed polynomial, the only rational numbers that may be the zeros are: ± 1, ± 2, $\pm\frac{1}{3}$, $\pm\frac{2}{3}$. Notice that the number of possible zeros has been decreased by using the depressed polynomial. Synthetic substitution shows that $-\frac{1}{3}$ is a zero.

$$
\begin{array}{rrrr|l}
3 & 4 & 7 & 2 & \underline{\;-\frac{1}{3}} \\
  & -1 & -1 & -2 & \\
\hline
3 & 3 & 6 & 0 &
\end{array}
$$

This $f(x) = (x - 3)(x + \frac{1}{3})(3x^2 + 3x + 6)$. Again, $3x^2 + 3x + 6$ is a depressed polynomial that can be written $Q(x) = 3(x^2 + x + 2)$. The only possible rational zeros of $Q(x)$ are integers, namely, ± 1 and ± 2. Synthetic substitution shows that none of these is a zero. Thus the rational zeros of $f(x)$ are 3, $-\frac{1}{3}$, and $f(x) = 3(x - 3)(x + \frac{1}{3})(x^2 + x + 2)$.

Exercises

A ▬ Find all rational zeros and, if possible, all other real zeros of $f(x)$.

1. $f(x) = x^3 - x^2 - 14x + 24$
2. $f(x) = x^3 - 8x^2 + 5x + 14$
3. $f(x) = x^3 - 2x^2 - 7x - 4$
4. $f(x) = x^3 + 2x^2 - x - 2$
5. $f(x) = 8x^3 - 26x^2 + 23x - 6$
6. $f(x) = 6x^3 + 5x^2 - 8x - 7$
7. $f(x) = 3x^3 - x^2 - 6x + 2$ (*Hint:* Use the quadratic formula to find the real zeros that are not rational.)
8. $f(x) = 2x^3 - 5x^2 + 1$
9. $f(x) = x^3 - x^2 - 14x + 24$
10. $f(x) = 2x^3 - x^2 + 2x - 1$
11. $f(x) = x^3 + 5x^2 + 8x + 6$
12. $f(x) = 8x^5 - 27x^2$ (Three rational and two complex zeros.)
13. $f(x) = x^4 - 4x^3 - 14x^2 + 36x + 45$
14. $f(x) = 4x^4 - 8x^3 - 5x^2 + 2x + 1$
15. $f(x) = 12x^3 + x^2 - 15$

B 16. Show that if all the coefficients of $f(x)$ have the same sign, then $f(x)$ has no positive real zeros.

17. Find a cubic polynomial function whose zeros are -1, 2, and -3.

18. Find a cubic polynomial function whose zeros are $\frac{1}{2}$, $-\frac{2}{3}$, and 6.

C ▬▬ You may know that if $f(x) = ax^2 + bx + c$ has zeros r_1 and r_2, then

$$r_1 + r_2 = -\frac{b}{a} \quad \text{and} \quad r_1 \cdot r_2 = \frac{c}{a}.$$

Similar relationships exist between the zeros and the coefficients of polynomials of third degree and higher. The following exercises develop this relationship for third degree polynomials. Use the zeros of the polynomial derived in Exercise 17 in each of the following Exercises.

19. Find the sum of the zeros. Compare the sum with the coefficient of x^2.

20. Find the sum of all possible two-factor products of the zeros, for example, $(-1 \cdot 2) + (-1 \cdot -3) + (2 \cdot -3)$. Compare the result with the coefficient of x.

21. Find the product of the zeros. Compare the result with the constant term.

▬▬ The zeros of a third degree polynomial function are 2, $\frac{1}{2}$, and $-\frac{3}{2}$. Use this information in Exercises 22–25.

22. Find the sum of the zeros.

23. Find the sum of all possible two-factor products of the zeros.

24. Find the product of the zeros.

25. Write the equation of a polynomial function having the given zeros. Check your result by using the Factor Theorem.

26. Use the Factor Theorem to write the equation of a third-degree polynomial function with zeros r_1, r_2, and r_3.

27. Use the result of Exercise 26 and the fact that $f(x) = a_3x^3 + a_2x^2 + a_1x + a_0$ can be written

$$f(x) = a_3\left(x^3 + \frac{a_2}{a_3}x^2 + \frac{a_1}{a_3}x + \frac{a_0}{a_3}\right)$$

to find expressions for the coefficients $\frac{a_2}{a_3}$, $\frac{a_1}{a_3}$, and $\frac{a_0}{a_3}$ in terms of r_1, r_2 and r_3.

28. Find the polynomial function f of degree three that has rational zeros 2, -1, and 3, and that satisfies the condition $f(0) = 18$.

29. Follow the procedure of Exercises 26 and 27 to find expressions for the coefficients $\frac{a_3}{a_4}$, $\frac{a_2}{a_4}$, $\frac{a_1}{a_4}$, and $\frac{a_0}{a_4}$ of the function

$$f(x) = a_4\left(x^4 + \frac{a_3x^3}{a_4} + \frac{a_2x^2}{a_4} + \frac{a_1x}{a_4} + \frac{a_0}{a_4}\right)$$

in terms of the zeros r_1, r_2, r_3 and r_4 of f.

7–6   Number of Zeros of a Polynomial Function

Two important questions about the zeros of a polynomial function have not been answered. Does every polynomial function have a zero? How many zeros does such a polynomial function have? The first question is answered by the following theorem called the **Fundamental Theorem of Algebra.**

Theorem 7–7   Every polynomial function of degree greater than zero has at least one real or imaginary zero.

The proof of the theorem is not given, since it is beyond the scope of this book.

Notice that the Fundamental Theorem does not tell you how to find a zero, but it does assure you that a zero exists.

Before the second question can be answered, the notion of a *multiple zero* and the *multiplicity* of a zero must be discussed. The function

$$f(x) = x^2 + 8x + 16 = (x + 4)(x + 4)$$

has exactly one zero, namely $x = -4$. Since it appears in more than one factor, -4 is called a *multiple zero*. Since -4 appears in exactly two factors, it has *multiplicity* 2. More formally:

Definitions   Given a polynomial function f and a zero r of f.
a. r is a multiple zero of f if and only if $(x - r)^k$, $k > 1$, divides $f(x)$. If $k = 1$, the zero is called a simple zero.
b. The multiplicity of a zero r is the greatest exponent k such that $(x - r)^k$ divides $f(x)$.

EXAMPLE 1. It is easy to verify that 0 and 1 are zeros of $f(x) = x^5 - 3x^4 + 3x^3 - x^2$. Find the multiplicity of each zero.

Since $x^5 - 3x^4 + 3x^3 - x^2 = x^2(x^3 - 3x^2 + 3x - 1)$, $x^2 = (x - 0)^2$ divides $f(x)$. Thus $x = 0$ is a zero of multiplicity 2. Since $(x - 1)^3 = x^3 - 3x^2 + 3x - 1$, $x = 1$ is a zero of multiplicity 3. In factored form, $f(x) = x^2(x - 1)^3$. The number of zeros can now be determined for a polynomial of degree n.

Theorem 7–8 Let f be a polynomial of degree n, $n > 0$. Then f has at least one and at most n complex zeros (including real zeros), and the sum of the multiplicities of the zeros is n.

The proof is based on Theorem 7–7 and is left for you to do.

EXAMPLE 2. Find all the complex zeros of

$$f(x) = 2x^5 - 4x^3 + 4x^2 - 6x + 4$$

and write $f(x)$ as the product of linear terms and a constant.

First note that $f(x) = 2(x^5 - 2x^3 + 2x^2 - 3x + 2)$. Using synthetic substitution you can show easily that 1 is a zero of multiplicity 2 and -2 is a simple zero. Thus

$$f(x) = 2(x - 1)(x - 1)(x + 2)(x^2 + 1).$$

Now $x^2 + 1$ has no real zero, but i and $-i$ are zeros. So $x^2 + 1 = (x - i)(x + i)$. Consequently, the complex zeros of f are 1, 1, -2, i, $-i$ and $f(x) = 2(x - 1)(x - 1)(x + 2)(x - i)(x + i)$.

Example 2 illustrates two ideas. First, some of the complex zeros may be real. (Recall that the real numbers are complex numbers of the form $a + 0i$.) Secondly, when there is a nonreal complex zero of a polynomial with *real* coefficients, there is another such zero. In fact, if $a + bi$ is a complex zero of f, then its conjugate $a - bi$ is also a zero. Since nonreal complex zeros occur in pairs, every polynomial of odd degree with real coefficients has at least one real zero.

Theorem 7–9 If f is a polynomial function with real coefficients and $f(a + bi) = 0$, $b \neq 0$, then $f(a - bi) = 0$.

Theorem 7–10 If f is a polynomial function of odd degree with real coefficients, then f has at least one *real* zero.

The proofs of these two theorems are left for you.

Checkpoint

1. What is the meaning of the Fundamental Theorem of Algebra?

2. What is the largest number of zeros that a polynomial of degree n ($n > 0$) may have?

Exercises

A For Exercises 1–12 find the zeros of each function. Show that the sum of the multiplicities in each exercise equals the degree of the polynomial.

1. $f(x) = x^3 - 3x - 2$

2. $f(x) = x^3 - 3x + 2$

3. $f(x) = x^4 + 5x^3 + 9x^2 + 7x + 2$

4. $f(x) = x^5 + 4x^4 + x^3 - 10x^2 - 4x + 8$

5. $f(x) = x^3 - 1$

6. $f(x) = x^3 + 1$

7. $f(x) = x^4 + 5x^2 + 4$

8. $f(x) = x^4 - 2x^3 + 10x^2 - 18x + 9$

9. $f(x) = x^6 - 2x^3 + 1$

10. $f(x) = x^6 + 2x^3 + 1$

11. $f(x) = x^6 + 2x^5 + 3x^4 + 4x^3 + 3x^2 + 2x + 1$

12. $f(x) = x^6 - 2x^5 + 3x^4 - 4x^3 + 3x^2 - 2x + 1$

B Let f be a polynomial function with the given zeros. Write a polynomial with the smallest degree and integral coefficients that could define f.

13. $1, -1, 2$

14. $\frac{1}{2}, \frac{3}{2}, -1$

15. $1 + \sqrt{3}, 2$

16. $1, \dfrac{1 + \sqrt{3}i}{2}$

17. $2, 0, 1 + i$

18. $5, 2, -3i$

19. A double zero $1 + 2i$.

20. A double zero $2; 1 + 2i$.

21. A triple zero of i.

22. Given the polynomial function

$$f(x) = x^3 - 3x^2 + 9x + 13,$$

find the other zeros if one zero is $2 + 3i$.

23. Given the polynomial function

$$f(x) = 2x^4 - 9x^3 + 13x^2 - 81x - 45,$$

find the other zeros is one zero is $3i$.

24. A triple zero of

$$f(x) = 8x^5 - 12x^4 + 38x^3 - 49x^2 + 24x - 4$$

is $\frac{1}{2}$. Find the other zeros.

C **25.** Prove Theorem 7–8. (*Hint:* By Theorem 7–7, f has at least one zero, r. Thus, by the factor Theorem

$$f(x) = (x - r)Q(x),$$

where $Q(x)$ has degree $n - 1$. If $n - 1 = 0$, you are finished. If $n - 1 \neq 0$, repeat the process on $Q(x)$.)

26. Prove Theorem 7–9.

7–7   Maxima and Minima

In Section 6–6 the derived function f' evaluated at $x = c$ was given a geometric interpretation: $f'(c)$ is the slope of the line tangent to the graph of f at the point $(c, f(c))$. If $f'(c) = 0$, then the tangent at $(c, f(c))$ is a line parallel to the x axis. Two of the forms that the graph of the function may take in a small neighborhood of $(c, f(c))$ are shown below.

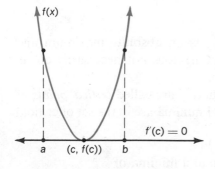

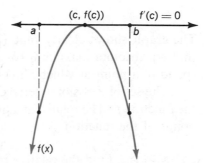

Figure 1   Figure 2

In Figure 1, the graph of f is above the tangent for all values of x in a small closed interval $[a, b]$ and in this case $(c, f(c))$ is called a **relative minimum** for f. It is indeed a *minimum* since $f(c) < f(x)$ for all $x \in [a, b]$. It is a *relative* minimum because there may be values of $f(x)$ that are less than $f(c)$ if x is not in $[a, b]$. If $f(c)$ is less than all other $f(x)$ for x in the domain of f, then $(c, f(c))$ is an **absolute minimum** for f.

In Figure 2, each point of the graph of f for x in a small neighborhood $[a, b]$ of c is below the tangent and $(c, f(c))$ is a **relative maximum** of the function. If $f(c)$ is greater than $f(x)$ for all x in the domain of f, then $(c, f(c))$ is an **absolute maximum** for f.

A function f is graphed in Figure 3 on the interval $[a, b]$. The points for which $f'(x) = 0$ are as follows:

a. Relative minimum — $(c_1, f(c_1))$.

b. Absolute (as well as relative) minimum — $(c_2, f(c_2))$.

c. Relative maximum — $(c_3, f(c_3))$.

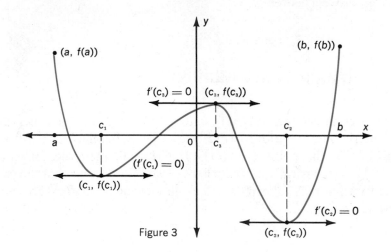

Figure 3

The graph shows clearly that $(b, f(b))$ is an absolute maximum and that an absolute maximum (or minimum) does not necessarily correspond to a point at which $f'(x)$ is zero.

The set of zeros of a derived function f' are called *critical points* of the function f. The relative maxima and minima are in the set of critical points of the function.

EXAMPLE. Find the relative maxima and minima of
$$f(x) = 2x^3 - 3x^2 - 12x - 7.$$

First find the derived function.
$$f'(x) = 6x^2 - 6x - 12$$
$$= 6(x - 2)(x + 1)$$

Find the values of x when $f'(x) = 0$.
$$f'(x) = 0 = 6(x - 2)(x + 1)$$
$$x - 2 = 0 \quad \text{or} \quad x + 1 = 0$$

You must now determine the character of f near $x = 2$ and $x = -1$.
$$f(x) = 2x^3 - 3x^2 - 12x - 7$$
$$= (2x - 7)(x + 1)(x + 1)$$

① $$f(-1) = (-9)(0)(0) = 0$$
$$f(-\tfrac{1}{2}) = (-8)(\tfrac{1}{2})(\tfrac{1}{2}) = -2$$
$$f(-\tfrac{3}{2}) = (-10)(-\tfrac{1}{2})(-\tfrac{1}{2}) = -2.5$$

By further testing you see that $(-1, 0)$ is a relative maximum.

② $$f(2) = (-3)(3)(3) = -27$$
$$f(\tfrac{3}{2}) = (-4)(2.5)(2.5) = -25$$
$$f(\tfrac{5}{2}) = (-2)(3.5)(3.5) = -24.50$$

By further testing you see that $(2, -27)$ is a relative minimum.

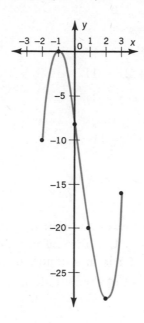

The graph of f for $x \in [-2, 3]$ is shown above. (Note that the scales on the x and y axes are in a 2 : 1 ratio.) Notice that the relative maximum and relative minimum that have been identified are also absolute for $x \in [-2, 3]$. The absolute maximum and minimum will change if the domain of f is changed. For instance, if the domain is $[-3, 4]$, then $f(-3) = -52$, $f(4) = 25$, and $(-3, -52)$ is the absolute minimum while $(4, 25)$ is the absolute maximum. For $x \in R$ there is no absolute maximum or minimum. However, the relative maximum and minimum found in the example remain unchanged. Notice also that $f'(-3) = 60$ and $f'(4) = 60$. Thus, a point may be an absolute maximum or minimum and not be associated with a tangent line with zero slope. For this reason the discussion in this section is restricted to finding relative maxima and minima that are associated with values of x for which $f'(x) = 0$.

Exercises

A ▬ Identify the critical points of each polynomial function f. Determine whether each critical point is a relative maximum or minimum.

1. $f(x) = 2x^3 - 3x^2 - 12x$

2. $f(x) = x^3 + 3x^2$

3. $f(x) = x^3 - 3x^2$

4. $f(x) = x^2 - 7x + 6$

5. $f(x) = -x^2 + 7x - 6$

6. $f(x) = 3 - 2x - x^2$

7. $f(x) = x^3 + 12x$

8. $f(x) = \frac{x^3}{3} + \frac{3x^2}{2} + 2x - 11$

9. $f(x) = x^3 - 2x^2 + 5$

10. $f(x) = x^4 - 16x^2 - 12$

11. $f(x) = -2x^3 - 3x^2 + 11$

12. $f(x) = x^7 - 31$

13. $f(x) = ax^2 + 6x + c, a \neq 0$

14. $f(x) = ax^3 - 2x + c, a > 0$

B ▬ A ball is thrown upward so that its height t seconds later is s feet above the earth. Use this information and $s = 96t - 16t^2$, where s is in feet and t is in seconds, in the following exercises.

15. What is the height of the ball after

    a. 1 second?

    b. 4 seconds?

    c. 6 seconds?

16. What is the time when the ball reaches its maximum height?

17. What is the maximum height of the ball?

▬ The formula $s = 160t - 16t^2$ describes the motion (vertically upward) of a toy rocket, where s is in feet and t is in seconds. Use this information in Exercises 18–20.

18. How high is the rocket when $t = 3$? when $t = 7$?

19. Explain why the height of the rocket is the same when $t = 3$ and when $t = 7$.

20. Use the derived function to determine at what time t the rocket reached a maximum height. (*Hint:* At what time t does the derived function equal zero?)

C 21. Find the dimensions of a rectangle with perimeter 72 feet that will enclose the maximum area.

22. Find the dimensions of a rectangular field with maximum area to be enclosed with 200 yards of fencing if one side of the field is along a straight river and needs no fence.

7–8 Points of Inflection

In a small neighborhood of $(c, f(c))$, a point at which $f'(c) = 0$, the graph of the polynomial function f may also appear as in Figures 1 and 2 below.

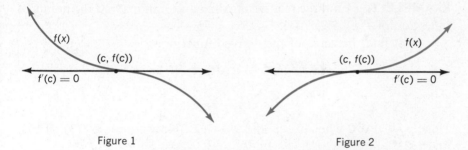

Figure 1   Figure 2

In Figure 1 the graph of f is above the tangent at $(c, f(c))$ for $x < c$ and below the tangent for $x > c$. The situation is reversed in Figure 2. The point $(c, f(c))$ is called a **point of inflection** of f.

You have undoubtedly noticed that the horizontal line through $(c, f(c))$ in Figures 1 and 2 is not what you have been accustomed to call a tangent since it crosses the graph of f. Rather than relying on intuitive notions of the tangent (from geometry), you must now think of the tangent to the graph of a function at a point $(a, f(a))$ as the line whose slope is the limit of

$$\frac{f(a + h) - f(a)}{h}$$

as h tends to 0 (see Section 6–6). That is, the **tangent** is the limiting position of a secant through $(a, f(a))$ and $(a + h, f(a + h))$. (There are inflection points at which the slope of the tangent is not 0, but they will not be discussed until a later section.)

Since $f' = 0$ at $(c, f(c))$, a point of inflection is also a critical point. To identify such a point, you must investigate the values of $f(x)$ for $x > c$ and for $x < c$.

The results of this and the previous section can now be summarized.

Given a polynomial function f and its derived function f', where $f'(c) = 0$:
  i. If $f(x) > f(c)$ for all x close to c, then $(c, f(c))$ is a relative minimum of f.
 ii. If $f(x) < f(c)$ for all x close to c, then $(c, f(c))$ is a relative maximum of f.
iii. If $f(x) < f(c)$ for $x < c$ and $f(x) > f(c)$ for $x > c$; or if $f(x) > f(c)$ for $x < c$ and $f(x) < f(c)$ for $x > c$, then $(c, f(c))$ is a point of inflection.

EXAMPLE 1.   Find the relative maxima and minima and the points of inflection of $f(x) = 2x^3 - 3x^2 - 36x + 75$.

First find the zeros of the derived function.

$$f'(x) = 6x^2 - 6x - 36$$
$$= 6(x^2 - x - 6)$$
$$= 6(x - 3)(x + 2)$$

Hence, $f'(x) = 0$ when $x = 3$ and $x = -2$. Now compute $f(3)$, $f(3.1)$, and $f(2.9)$.

2	-3	-36	$+75$	$\underline{3}$
	6	9	-81	
2	3	-27	$-6 = f(3)$	

2	-3	-36	75	$\underline{3.1}$
	6.2	9.92	-80.848	
2	3.2	-26.08	$-5.848 = f(3.1)$	

2	-3	-36	75	$\underline{2.9}$
	5.8	8.12	-80.852	
2	2.8	-27.88	$-5.852 = f(2.9)$	

You can see that $(3, -6)$ is a relative minimum.

Similarly $$f(-2) = 119$$

and
$$f(-2.1) = 118.848$$
$$f(-1.9) = 118.852.$$

You can see that $(-2, 119)$ is a relative maximum of f. No points of inflection have been found.

EXAMPLE 2. Find the relative maxima and minima, and the points of inflection of

$$f(x) = x^3.$$
$$f'(x) = 3x^2$$
$$f'(x) = 0 \quad \text{when } x = 0$$

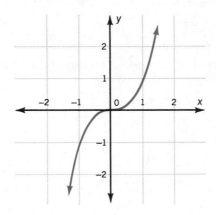

By substitution you can verify the following:

$$f(0) = 0$$
$$f(0.1) = 0.001$$
$$f(-0.1) = -0.001$$

You can see that $(0, 0)$ is a point of inflection of f. There are no relative maxima or minima.

Exercises

A — Identify and determine the character of the critical points of each function f.

1. $f(x) = 2x^3 + 3x^2 - 12x + 1$

2. $f(x) = x^3 - 12x$

3. $f(x) = x^4 - 2x^3 + 5$

4. $f(x) = (x - 2)(x + 3)^2$

5. $f(x) = \dfrac{x^4 - 6x^2 + 6}{8}$

6. $f(x) = x^2(2x + 5)$

7. $f(x) = 8x^2 - x^4$

8. $f(x) = -x^3 + 3x - 1$

9. $f(x) = x^4$

10. $f(x) = x^3 - 2x^2 + 5$

11. $f(x) = x^7 - 31$

12. $f(x) = 3x^4 - 8x^3 + 6x^2 + 1$

13. $f(x) - 12x^5 - 30x^4 \mid 20x^3 - 1$

14. $f(x) = x^m, m \geq 1, m \in N$

15. $f(x) = (x - a)^3$

16. $f(x) = (x - a)^4$

B ━━ The point $A(1, 1)$ is on the graph of each function below. For which function is A a relative minimum, a relative maximum, a point of inflection, or none of these?

17. $f(x) = 2x^3 - 6x^2 + 6x - 1$

18. $g(x) = 2x^3 - 9x^2 + 12x - 4$

19. $h(x) = 2x^3 - 3x^2 - 12x + 14$

20. $r(x) = 2x^3 - 6x + 5$

C **21.** Find two numbers whose sum is 10 such that

    a. their product is a maximum.

    b. the sum of their squares is a minimum.

22. Find two numbers whose sum is 12 such that the sum of one number and the square of the second is a minimum.

23. Find two numbers whose sum is 50 such that the product of the first and twice the second is a maximum.

7–9 Sketching Polynomials

You are now in a position to sketch an accurate graph of a polynomial function quite easily. The information that is available from the equation defining a polynomial function and that is also valuable in graphing the function follows.

    Given: $f(x) = a_n x^n + a_{n-1} x^{n-1} + \cdots + a_1 x + a_0$

①   The y intercept is $(0, a_0)$.

②   The value of f at $x = c$ is found by direct or synthetic substitution.

③   The real zeros of f are found (when possible) by application of the ideas in Sections 7–3 to 7–5.

④   The relative maxima and minima and inflection points are found by determining the zeros of $f'(x)$.

EXAMPLE 1. Sketch the graph of the following.

$$f(x) = x^3 + 3x^2 - 4.$$

① The y intercept is $(0, -4)$ because $f(0) = -4$.

② Using synthetic substitution,

$$f(x) = x^3 + 3x^2 - 4$$
$$= (x + 2)^2(x - 1).$$

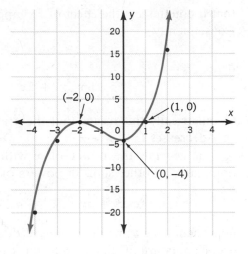

Thus the zeros of f are $x = -2$ and $x = 1$; $x = -2$ is a zero of multiplicity two.

③ Compile a table of values of f for an interval that includes the zeros of f, in this case $[-4, 3]$.

x	-4	-3	-2	-1	0	1	2	3
$f(x)$	-20	-4	0	-2	-4	0	16	50

④ $f'(x) = 3x^2 + 6x$
$\qquad = x(3x + 6)$

The zeros of f' are $x = 0$ and $x = -2$. Since $f(x) < f(-2)$ for x close to -2, $(-2, 0)$ is a *relative maximum*. Since $f(x) > f(0)$ for x close to 0, $(0, -4)$ is a *relative minimum*.

Two questions which have not been answered in the analysis of Example 1 are: What happens to the graph of f as $x \longrightarrow +\infty$? What happens to the graph of f as $x \longrightarrow -\infty$? You can answer these questions by considering the following limits.

a. $\lim_{x \to +\infty} x^3 + 3x^2 - 4$ 　　　　 b. $\lim_{x \to -\infty} x^3 + 3x^2 - 4$

It is clear that $x^3 + 3x^2 - 4 \longrightarrow +\infty$ as $x \longrightarrow +\infty$. That is, as x increases without bound so does $x^3 + 3x^2 - 4$. The fact is denoted as follows.

$$\lim_{x \to +\infty} x^3 + 3x^2 - 4 = +\infty$$

Geometrically this means that the graph continues to rise to the right as x increases.

The situation for **b** is not quite as clear, for as $x \longrightarrow -\infty$, $x^3 \longrightarrow -\infty$ and $3x^2 \longrightarrow +\infty$. Thus it appears that the limit of $x^3 + 3x^2$ could be zero. However this is not the case, for x^3 *dominates* x^2. That is, as $x \longrightarrow -\infty$, $\dfrac{x^3}{3x^2} = \dfrac{x}{3} \longrightarrow -\infty$. Thus x^3 approaches $-\infty$ so fast that it counteracts the effect of $3x^2$ approaching $+\infty$.
Consequently

$$x^3 + 3x^2 - 4 \longrightarrow -\infty \quad \text{as} \quad x \longrightarrow -\infty,$$

or

$$\lim_{x \to -\infty} x^3 + 3x^2 - 4 = -\infty.$$

Geometrically this means that the graph continues to drop to the left as x decreases ($x \longrightarrow -\infty$).

In general, the power of x with the greatest positive exponent dominates all other sums of powers of x, and the limit of

$$a_n x^n + a_{n-1} x^{n-1} + a_{n-2} x^{n-2} + \cdots + a_0$$

approaches the same limit as $a_n x^n$ does as x approaches $+\infty$ or $-\infty$.

The nature of $\lim\limits_{x \to +\infty} f$ and $\lim\limits_{x \to -\infty} f$ is a fifth characteristic of f which should be determined when graphing f. This is illustrated in the next example.

EXAMPLE 2. Sketch the graph of

$$f(x) = x^3 - 3x.$$

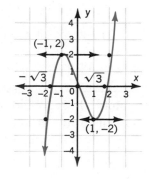

① Since $f(0) = 0$, the y intercept is $(0, 0)$.

② The zeros of $f(x) = x(x^2 - 3)$ are 0, $\sqrt{3}, -\sqrt{3}$.

③ Compile a table of values of f for

$$x \in [-3, 3].$$

x	-3	-2	-1	0	1	2	3
$f(x)$	-18	-2	2	0	-2	2	18

④ $f'(x) = 3x^2 - 3$. The zeros of f' are $x = 1$ and $x = -1$. Consequently, $(1, -2)$ and $(-1, 2)$ are critical points. Since $f(x) > -2$ for x near 1, $(1, -2)$ is a relative minimum. Since $f(x) < 2$ for x near -1, $(-1, 2)$ is a relative maximum.

⑤ $\lim\limits_{x \to +\infty} x^3 - 3x = +\infty$, $\lim\limits_{x \to -\infty} x^3 - 3x = -\infty$.

Exercises

A ▬▬ Find the y intercept, functional values for $-4 < x < 4$, zeros, relative maxima and minima and inflection points, and $\lim\limits_{x\to+\infty} f$ and $\lim\limits_{x\to-\infty} f$ for each function. Graph the function.

1. $f(x) = 3x^2 - 12x + 12$
2. $f(x) = \dfrac{4x^3 + 15x^2 - 72x + 6}{6}$
3. $f(x) = x^3 - 3x^2 + 4$
4. $f(x) = 2x^3 - 9x^2 + 12x + 1$
5. $f(x) = 2x^3 + 3x^2 - 12x - 2$
6. $f(x) = x^4 - 6x^2 + 8x$
7. $f(x) = x^4 - 4x^3 + 6x^2$
8. $f(x) = 2x^3 + 3x^2 - 12x - 7$
9. $f(x) = x^4 + 5x^3 + 9x^2 + 7x + 2$
10. $f(x) = -2x^3 + 3x^2 + 12x + 7$
11. $f(x) = x^4$
12. $f(x) = x^5$
13. $f(x) = (x - 4)^3$
14. $f(x) = (x - 4)^4$
15. $f(x) = 12x^5 - 30x^4 + 20x^3 - 1$
16. $f(x) = 3x^4 - 8x^3 + 6x + 1$
17. $f(x) = -3x^4 + 8x^3 - 6x - 1$
18. $f(x) = 2x^3 - 3x^2 - 12x + 14$
19. $f(x) = x^3 + x^2 - x + 5$
20. $f(x) = x^2(x - 6)^3$

B 21. $f(x) = x^6 + 2x^5 + 3x^4 + 4x^3 + 3x^2 + 2x + 1$
22. $f(x) = x^6 - 2x^5 + 3x^4 - 4x^3 + 3x^2 - 2x + 1$
23. $f(x) = (x - 1)^3(x^2 + 1)$
24. $f(x) = (x - 1)^3(x + 1)(x^2 + 1)$
25. $f(x) = (x - 7)^2$
26. $f(x) = 5x^4 + 2x^3 - 3x^2 - 4x - 5$
27. $f(x) = (2x^2 - 3x - 2)^2$
28. $f(x) = x(x + 2)^2(x - 2)^3$
29. $f(x) = x^5 - 5x^4$
30. $f(x) = 3x^5 - 20x^3$
31. $f(x) = (2 + x)^2(1 - x)^3$
32. $f(x) = -2x^3 - 3x^2 + 12x + 10$

7–10   Concavity and other Inflection Points

Before considering inflection points at which f' is not 0, several other concepts must be introduced.

> A function f is increasing on an interval $[a, b]$ if and only if for all $x_1, x_2 \in [a, b]$ and $x_2 > x_1, f(x_2) > f(x_1)$.
>
> A function f is decreasing on $[a, b]$ if and only if for all $x_1, x_2 \in [a, b]$ and $x_2 > x_1, f(x_2) < f(x_1)$.

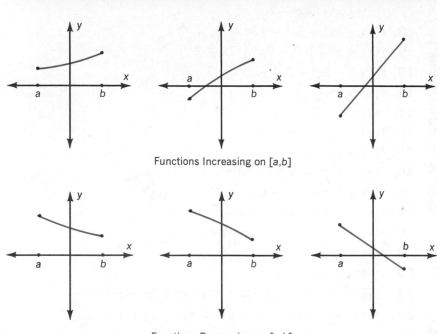

Functions Increasing on [a,b]

Functions Decreasing on [a,b]

Choose any point on a graph of one of the increasing functions depicted above. At that point place a straightedge tangent to the curve and notice that the slope of the tangent is positive. Repeat the procedure for the decreasing functions. What do you notice about the slope? In general it is true that if a function f is increasing on $[a, b]$, then $f'(x) > 0$ for all $x \in \langle a, b \rangle$. (If f is decreasing on $[a, b]$ then $f'(x) < 0$ for all $x \in \langle a, b \rangle$.) The converse statement is also true, that is, if $f'(x) > 0$ $(f'(x) < 0)$ for all $x \in \langle a, b \rangle$ then f is an increasing (decreasing) function on $[a, b]$.

A polynomial function may be increasing on one subset of an interval, yet decreasing on another subset of the same interval. In Figure 1 $f(x)$ is increasing on $[a, c]$ and decreasing on $[c, b]$. Notice that f changes from an increasing to a decreasing function at $(c, f(c))$ and that $f'(c) = 0$. Thus c is a critical point for f, and c separates the graph into an increasing part and a decreasing part. In general, the set of critical points of a polynomial function determines the end points of the intervals for which the function is increasing or decreasing.

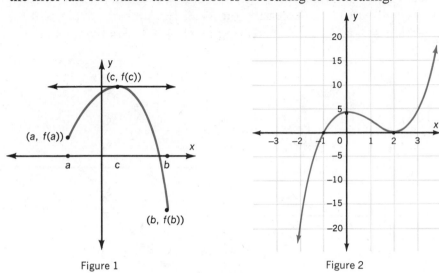

Figure 1   Figure 2

EXAMPLE 1.   Given the polynomial function

$$f(x) = x^3 - 3x^2 + 4,$$

find the critical points and the intervals on which $f(x)$ is increasing and decreasing. See Figure 2.

$$f'(x) = 3x^2 - 6x = 3x(x - 2)$$
$$f'(x) = 0, \text{ when } x = 0 \quad \text{and} \quad \text{when } x = 2$$

Consider now the intervals

$$\langle -\infty, 0], \qquad [0, 2], \qquad \text{and} \qquad [2, +\infty).$$

① For $x \in \langle -\infty, 0\rangle$, $3x < 0$ and $x - 2 < 0$.   Consequently $3x(x - 2) > 0$ and $f(x)$ is increasing on $\langle -\infty, 0]$.

② For $x \in \langle 0, 2\rangle$, $3x > 0$ and $x - 2 < 0$. Thus $3x(x - 2) < 0$ and $f(x)$ is decreasing on $[0, 2]$.

③ For $x \in \langle 2, +\infty\rangle$, $3x > 0$ and $x - 2 > 0$. Hence, $3x(x - 2) > 0$ and $f(x)$ is increasing on $[2, +\infty)$.

The function $f(x) = x^3 - 3x^2 + 4$ of Example 1 has a derived function $f'(x) = 3x^2 - 6x$. See Figure 3. Notice that $f'(x)$ is itself a polynomial and thus it has a derived function. The derived function of the derived function is called the **second derived function** of f and is denoted $f''(x)$ (read "f double prime of x"). In this case $f''(x) = 6x - 6$.

The derived function, $f'(x) = 3x^2 - 6x$, can be analyzed with the aid of its derived function, $f''(x) = 6x - 6$. The critical point of $f'(x)$ occurs where $x = 1$ because $f''(x) = 0$ at $x = 1$. Since $f''(x) < 0$ when $x \in (-\infty, 1)$, $f'(x)$ is decreasing on $(-\infty, 1]$. Similarly $f''(x) > 0$ for $x \in (1, +\infty)$, and $f'(x)$ is increasing on $[1, +\infty)$. See Figure 4.

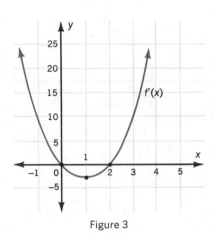

Figure 3   Figure 4

The question to be answered now is: What does the fact that $f'(x)$ is increasing or decreasing tell you about the shape of the graph of $f(x)$?

Consider two lines l_1 and l_2 with slopes m_1 and m_2, $m_2 < m_1$, and $l_1 \cap l_2 = \{T\}$, as in the figure at the right. It is clear that if $m_2 < m_1$, then l_1 must be rotated clockwise about T to make it coincide with l_2. That is, *decreasing* the slope of a line corresponds to turning it *clockwise*. A similar argument shows that *increasing* the slope of a line corresponds to turning it *counterclockwise*.

Now $f''(x) > 0$ implies $f'(x)$ is increasing for increasing x, and thus the tangents to f are turning counterclockwise. When the tangents to a curve turn counterclockwise as x increases, the curve is said to be **concave upward.** See Figure 5.

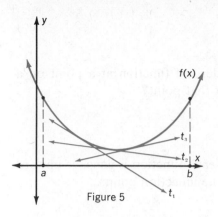

Figure 5

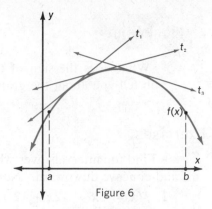

Figure 6

Similarly $f''(x) < 0$ implies $f'(x)$ is decreasing. Thus the tangents to f are turning clockwise. When the tangents to a curve turn clockwise as x increases, the curve is said to be **concave downward**. See Figure 6.

The graph of a function f is concave downward on an interval $[a, b]$ if and only if $f''(x) < 0$ for all $x \in \langle a, b \rangle$.

The graph of a function f is concave upward on an interval $[a, b]$ if and only if $f''(x) > 0$ for all $x \in \langle a, b \rangle$.

Points at which the graph changes concavity are points of inflection. Since the second derived function must change sign when the curve changes concavity, $f''(x)$ is zero at a point of inflection. However, the converse is not true; that is, $f''(c) = 0$ *does not* imply a point of inflection at $x = c$. Thus the points of inflection will be a subset of the zeros of $f''(x)$.

EXAMPLE 2. Determine the points of inflection and the intervals on which $f(x)$ is concave upward and concave downward if

$$f(x) = x^3 - 3x^2 + 4.$$
$$f'(x) = 3x^2 - 6x$$
$$f''(x) = 6x - 6$$

The set of zeros of $f''(x)$ is $\{1\}$. Thus, if there is an inflection point it must be $x = 1$. Since $f''(x) < 0$ for all $x \in I_1 = \langle -\infty, 1 \rangle$, $f(x)$ is concave downward on I_1. Since $f''(x) > 0$ for all $x \in I_2 = \langle 1, +\infty \rangle$, $f(x)$ is concave upward on I_2. Since $f(x)$ changes from concave downward to concave upward at the point where $x = 1$, $(1, 2)$ is a point of inflection. See Figure 2 on page 337.

Checkpoint

What does the sign of the derived function at a point on a graph tell you about the graph at that point?

Exercises

A ▬ Find the intervals over which each function is concave upward and concave downward. Name the inflection points.

1. $f(x) = 3x^2 - 12x + 12$

2. $f(x) = 2x^3 - 9x^2 + 12x + 1$

3. $f(x) = 2x^3 + 3x^2 - 12x - 2$

4. $f(x) = x^4 - 4x^3 + 6x^2$

5. $f(x) = 2x^3 + 3x^2 - 12x - 7$

6. $f(x) = x^4 + 5x^3 + 9x^2 + 7x + 2$

▬ Find the y-intercept, zeros, maxima and minima, points of inflection, intervals where the graph is concave upward or downward, and limits as $x \longrightarrow +\infty$ and $x \longrightarrow -\infty$. Sketch the graph of each function.

7. $f(x) = 2x^2 - x^3$

8. $f(x) = x^3$

9. $f(x) = x^4$

10. $f(x) = x^3 + 2x^2 + x - 2$

11. $f(x) = x^3 - 6x^2 + 9x + 1$

12. $f(x) = x^4 - 9x^2$

B **13.** $f(x) = 4x^3 - 9x^2 + 5$

14. $f(x) = \frac{x^3}{3} + 4x - 4$

15. $f(x) = (x - 1)^2(x + 1)^2$

16. $f(x) = x^3 + x^2 + x + 1$

17. $f(x) = 2x^3 - 3x^2 - 36x + 25$

18. $f(x) = 24x^2 - x^4$

19. $f(x) = x(x^2 - 4)^2$

20. Given: $f'(x) = 0$ at $x = c$

a. Suppose $f''(c) > 0$. What can you conclude about the point $(c, f(c))$?

b. Suppose $f''(c) < 0$. What can you conclude about the point $(c, f(c))$?

340   CHAPTER 7

C **21.** The following theorem is proved in more advanced mathematics.

> **Mean Value Theorem** If f is continuous on $[a, b]$ and has a derived function on $\langle a, b\rangle$, then there is a point $x_0 \in \langle a, b\rangle$ such that
> $$f'(x_0) = \frac{f(b) - f(a)}{b - a}$$

a. Geometrically, what is $\frac{f(b) - f(a)}{b - a}$?

b. Interpret $f'(x_0)$ geometrically.

c. Depict the equality of $f'(x_0)$ and $\frac{f(b) - f(a)}{b - a}$.

7–11   Rational Functions

Polynomial functions in x are obtained by a finite number of additions, subtractions, and multiplications of constants and x's. When division of these expressions is also permitted, the class of functions called **rational functions** results.

Recall from Section 6–4 that a rational function $R(x)$ is the quotient of two polynomials.

$$R(x) = \frac{P(x)}{Q(x)}$$

For $R(x)$ to be zero, clearly $P(x)$ must be zero. However, if $P(x)$ is zero, it may be that $R(x)$ is not defined. For example, if $R(x) = \frac{(x - 1)(x - 2)}{x - 1}$, then $P(2) = 0$ and $P(1) = 0$, but $R(x)$ is zero at $x = 2$. At $x = 1$, $R(x)$ is undefined. Thus every zero of a rational function $R(x)$ is also a zero of the polynomial $P(x)$.

Whenever the denominator $Q(x)$ of $R(x)$ is zero, the rational function is undefined. Thus the domain of $R(x)$ must be restricted to those real numbers for which $Q(x) \neq 0$.

The set of numbers excluded from the domain and the set of zeros of a rational function are valuable aids in sketching a graph. Additional valuable aids are the limits discussed in Section 6–4 and the idea of an asymptote. The next example illustrates how these ideas can be used to sketch a graph of a rational function.

EXAMPLE 1. Sketch a graph of the rational function

$$R(x) = \frac{(x-1)(x-4)}{(x-3)(x+1)}.$$

① Notice that $R(x)$ is not defined for $x \in \{-1, 3\}$. Sketch the graphs of $x = -1$ and $x = 3$. These lines are to remind you that $R(x)$ is not defined for $x \in \{-1, 3\}$. Furthermore, there may be either a "hole" in the graph or an asymptote at these points. See Figure 1.

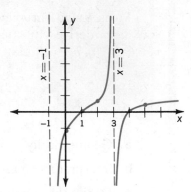

Figure 1

② Determine the zeros of $R(x)$. They are $x = 1$ and $x = 4$. Plot these points on the graph. Calculate a few additional values of $R(x)$. Plot them.

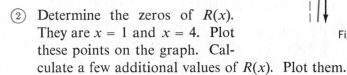

x	0	1	2	4	5
$R(x)$	$-\frac{4}{3}$	0	$\frac{2}{3}$	0	$\frac{1}{3}$

③ Examine the nature of the graph near the lines where $R(x)$ is undefined (near $x = -1$ and $x = 3$). A systematic approach is best. Determine first what the graph is on either side of $x = -1$ and of $x = 3$. This is done by evaluating four limits.

a. $\lim\limits_{x \to -1^-} \dfrac{(x-1)(x-4)}{(x-3)(x+1)}$ **b.** $\lim\limits_{x \to -1^+} \dfrac{(x-1)(x-4)}{(x-3)(x+1)}$

c. $\lim\limits_{x \to 3^-} \dfrac{(x-1)(x-4)}{(x-3)(x+1)}$ **d.** $\lim\limits_{x \to 3^+} \dfrac{(x-1)(x-4)}{(x-3)(x+1)}$

(Recall that $x \longrightarrow -1^-$ means x near -1 but always less than -1.) As in Section 6–4, these limits are as follows:

a. $\lim\limits_{x \to -1^-} R(x) = +\infty$

b. $\lim\limits_{x \to -1^+} R(x) = -\infty$

c. $\lim\limits_{x \to 3^-} R(x) = +\infty$

d. $\lim\limits_{x \to 3^+} R(x) = -\infty$

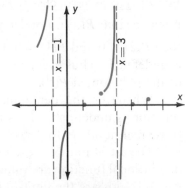

Figure 2

Thus, $x = -1$ and $x = 3$ are vertical asymptotes to the graph of $R(x)$. You can sketch part of the graph as in Figure 2.

④ The final step is to see what the graph is like for large and for small values of x. This is done by evaluating these two limits.

  a. $\lim\limits_{x \to -\infty} R(x)$ **b.** $\lim\limits_{x \to +\infty} R(x)$

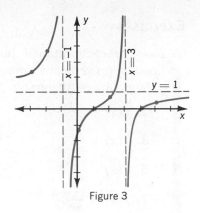

Figure 3

These each have 1 as a limit. Thus, $y = 1$ is a horizontal asymptote. Notice that for $x \longrightarrow -\infty$, $R(x)$ is always larger than 1. Thus, the graph nears $y = 1$ from above. The opposite happens for $x \longrightarrow +\infty$. The complete graph may now be sketched as in Figure 3.

EXAMPLE 2. Sketch a graph of $R(x) = \dfrac{1}{x}$.

① Zeros: None (why?).

② Undefined points: $x = 0$ (Why?)

③ Calculate a few points:

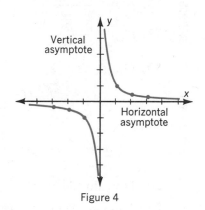

Vertical asymptote

Horizontal asymptote

Figure 4

x	-3	-2	-1	1	2	3
$R(x)$	$-\frac{1}{3}$	$-\frac{1}{2}$	-1	1	$\frac{1}{2}$	$\frac{1}{3}$

Plot them.

④ Vertical asymptotes:

  Evaluate: $\lim\limits_{x \to 0^-} \dfrac{1}{x} = -\infty$

  and

$$\lim\limits_{x \to 0^+} \dfrac{1}{x} = +\infty$$

The line $x = 0$ is a vertical asymptote.

⑤ Horizontal asymptotes:

  Evaluate: $\lim\limits_{x \to -\infty} \dfrac{1}{x} = 0$ (Through values less than zero or greater than zero?)

  and

$$\lim\limits_{x \to +\infty} \dfrac{1}{x} = 0$$

Thus, $y = 0$ is a horizontal asymptote.

⑥ Sketch the graph using steps ①–⑤, as in Figure 4.

Exercises

A ▬ For each rational function identify (a) zeros, (b) excluded points, (c) vertical asymptotes, (d) horizontal asymptotes, and (e) a few points on the graph. Sketch the graph.

1. $f(x) = \dfrac{1}{x - 1}$

2. $f(x) = \dfrac{1}{x + 1}$

3. $f(x) = \dfrac{-2}{x - 3}$

4. $f(x) = \dfrac{-6}{2x - 5}$

5. $f(x) = \dfrac{2x}{x + 5}$

6. $f(x) = \dfrac{-x}{2 - x}$

7. $f(x) = \dfrac{2x - 3}{x + 4}$

8. $f(x) = \dfrac{3x + 4}{2x - 5}$

9. $f(x) = \dfrac{-3x}{x^2 + 3x + 2}$

10. $f(x) = \dfrac{4x}{(x - 2)(2x + 3)}$

11. $f(x) = \dfrac{x - 5}{(x + 1)(x - 5)}$

12. $f(x) = \dfrac{3x - 4}{(2x - 3)(3x - 2)}$

13. $f(x) = \dfrac{x(x - 5)}{(x + 2)(4x - 1)}$

14. $f(x) = \dfrac{x}{x^2 + 1}$

15. $f(x) = \dfrac{x^2 - 5x + 6}{x^2 + 5x + 6}$

16. $f(x) = \dfrac{x(x - 1)(x + 4)}{(x + 1)(x + 2)(x + 3)}$

17. $f(x) = \dfrac{2x}{x^2 + x + 1}$

18. $f(x) = \dfrac{-x(2 - x)}{x^2 - 16}$

B **19.** Graph

$$f(x) = \frac{1}{x - 1}$$

and

$$g(x) = \frac{x + 2}{(x + 2)(x - 1)}.$$

20. How do the graphs of $f(x)$ and $g(x)$ in Exercise 19 differ?

21. Suppose $P(x) = t(x)s(x)$ and $Q(x) = t(x)g(x)$. Let $R_1(x) = \dfrac{P(x)}{Q(x)}$ and $R_2(x) = \dfrac{s(x)}{g(x)}$. How do the graphs of $R_1(x)$ and $R_2(x)$ differ?

▬ Sketch the graph of each rational function.

22. $f(x) = \dfrac{x^2(x - 2)}{x(x - 2)}$

23. $f(x) = \dfrac{x^2(x - 2)}{x(x - 2)^2}$

24. $f(x) = \dfrac{(x - 1)(x - 2)}{(x^2 - 1)(x)}$

25. $f(x) = \dfrac{(x - 1)x}{(x - 1)^2}$

C **26.** In Exercise 25 the graph of

$$f(x) = \frac{x(x - 1)}{(x - 1)^2}$$

did not have a "hole" in it like those in Exercises 22–24. Explain.

7–12 Real Algebraic Functions

Polynomial functions and rational functions can be obtained by a finite number of additions, subtractions, multiplications, and divisions of expressions in a variable x. If the additional operation of extraction of roots is allowed, a larger class of functions results, namely, the **algebraic functions.**

Recall that the domain of a rational function

$$R(x) = \frac{P(x)}{Q(x)}$$

must be restricted to those real numbers for which $Q(x) \neq 0$. In a similar manner, the domain of a real algebraic function $A(x)$ is restricted to those real numbers r for which $A(r)$ is a real number. Only real algebraic functions are discussed.

EXAMPLE 1. Restrict the real replacements for x so that the range of $A(x) = \sqrt{16 - x^2}$ is a subset of the real numbers.

The range of $A(x)$ is real when the expression under the radical is positive or zero. You must find the set of real numbers such that

$$16 - x^2 \geq 0.$$

This is equivalent to

$$(4 - x)(4 + x) \geq 0.$$

This last inequality is true when

    1. both factors are positive or zero, or
    2. both factors are negative or zero.

Condition **1** implies

$$4 - x \geq 0 \quad and \quad 4 + x \geq 0$$

or
$$4 \geq x \quad and \quad 4 \geq -x$$

which is equivalent to

$$-4 \leq x \leq 4.$$

Condition **2** implies

$$4 - x \leq 0 \quad and \quad 4 + x \leq 0$$

or
$$4 \leq x \quad and \quad 4 \leq -x$$

and there are no values of x that satisfy these inequalities simultaneously. Thus if the domain is $\{x : -4 \leq x \leq 4\}$, then the range of $A(x)$ will be a subset of **R**.

EXAMPLE 2. Is the range of $A(x) = \sqrt[3]{x}$ a subset of the real numbers or must the domain be restricted?

Every real number has exactly one real cube root. The following illustrates the situation for positive and negative numbers and for 0.

$$\sqrt[3]{-8} = -2$$
$$\sqrt[3]{0} = 0$$
$$\sqrt[3]{27} = 3$$

Because $\sqrt[3]{x}$ is defined and is a real number for all $x \in R$, there is no need to restrict the domain.

EXAMPLE 3. Specify the domain of

$$A(x) = 4 - \frac{1}{\sqrt{x}}$$

so that its range will be a subset of the real numbers. Then graph $A(x)$.

Since $\sqrt{x}$ is real only for $x \geq 0$, the largest possible domain is $[0, +\infty)$. However, since $\sqrt{x}$ appears in a denominator, $x = 0$ must be excluded from the domain. Consequently the domain is

$$\langle 0, +\infty \rangle \quad \text{or} \quad x > 0, \quad \textit{and} \quad x \text{ real}.$$

Once the domain of an algebraic function has been defined, the procedures used in graphing the function follow those used in graphing rational functions.

① The zeros are found by solving $A(x) = 0$.

$$4 - \frac{1}{\sqrt{x}} = 0$$
$$4\sqrt{x} = 1$$
$$\sqrt{x} = \tfrac{1}{4}$$
$$x = \tfrac{1}{16}$$

② The line $x = 0$ is a vertical asymptote. For $x = 0$, the numerator of $A(x)$ is nonzero, but the denominator is zero.

$$\lim_{x \to 0^+}\left(4 - \frac{1}{\sqrt{x}}\right) = -\infty$$

$A(x)$ decreases without bound as x tends to zero from the right.

③ The line $y = 4$ is a horizontal asymptote because

$$\lim_{x \to \infty}\left(4 - \frac{1}{\sqrt{x}}\right) = 4.$$

(4) Selected values of x and $A(x)$ and a portion of the graph are shown below. See Figure 1.

x	$\frac{1}{16}$	1	2	3	4
$A(x)$	0	3	3.293	3.423	3.500

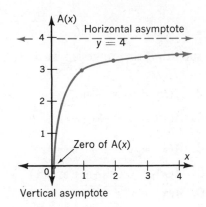

Figure 1

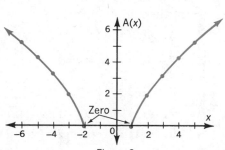

Figure 2

EXAMPLE 4. Sketch the graph of $A(x) = \sqrt{(x-1)(x+2)}$ on the appropriate domain.

The domain of A is found by solving

$$(x - 1)(x + 2) \geq 0.$$

This inequality is satisfied if and only if

$$(x - 1) \geq 0 \quad and \quad (x + 2) \geq 0$$
$$or \qquad\qquad (x - 1) \leq 0 \quad and \quad (x + 2) \leq 0$$

that is, if and only if

$$x \geq 1 \quad and \quad x \geq -2 \qquad 1$$
$$or \qquad\qquad x \leq 1 \quad and \quad x \leq -2. \qquad 2$$

Inequality **1** is satisfied when $x \geq 1$ and inequality **2** is satisfied when $x \leq -2$.
So $(x - 1)(x + 2) \geq 0$ when

$$x \geq 1 \quad or \quad x \leq -2.$$

Thus, the domain of $A(x)$ is $\langle-\infty, -2] \cup [1, +\infty)$. The zeros of $A(x)$ are -2 and 1.

There are no vertical or horizontal asymptotes.
Selected values of x and $A(x)$ are as follows. See Figure 2.

x	1	2	3	4	5	-2	-3	-4	-5	-6
$A(x)$	0	2	3.16	4.24	5.29	0	2	3.16	4.24	5.29

Checkpoint

What classes of functions does the set of algebraic functions include as subsets?

Exercises

A ━━ Find the largest domain of $A(x)$ such that the range is a subset of the real numbers.

1. $A(x) = \sqrt{x^2 - 4}$ **2.** $A(x) = \sqrt[3]{x^2 - 4}$

3. $A(x) = \sqrt[4]{x^2 - 4}$ **4.** $A(x) = 1 - \dfrac{1}{\sqrt{x - 1}}$

5. $A(x) = 1 - \dfrac{1}{\sqrt{1 - x}}$ **6.** $A(x) = x - 2 + \dfrac{1}{\sqrt{x - 2}}$

7. $A(x) = \sqrt{(x - 1)(x - 2)}$ **8.** $A(x) = \sqrt{(x^2 + 1)(x + 1)}$

9. $A(x) = \sqrt{(x + 2)x(x - 2)}$ **10.** $A(x) = \sqrt[3]{x - 1} + \sqrt[3]{x - 1}$

11. $A(x) = x^{\frac{2}{3}}$ **12.** $A(x) = \dfrac{1}{(1 - x)^{\frac{2}{3}}}$

B ━━ Graph each function on the appropriate domain.

13. $A(x) = \sqrt[3]{x^2 - 4}$ **14.** $A(x) = 1 - \dfrac{1}{\sqrt{1 - x}}$

15. $A(x) = \sqrt{(x + 2)(x - 3)}$ **16.** $A(x) = \sqrt{(x + 2)(3 - x)}$

17. $A(x) = \dfrac{-\sqrt{x + 1}}{\sqrt{x}}$ **18.** $A(x) = \dfrac{1}{\sqrt{(x + 2)(3 - x)}}$

19. $A(x) = \sqrt[3]{x^2}$ **20.** $A(x) = \sqrt{x^3}$

C **21.** Often algebraic functions are written in an implicit form like

$$y^2 - 2y - x^2 = 0,$$

where

$$y = A(x).$$

In a case like this, you can find an explicit representation by solving the equation for $y = A(x)$.

$$y = 1 + \sqrt{1 + x^2} \quad or \quad y = 1 - \sqrt{1 + x^2}$$

Thus, two explicit algebraic functions result from the one implicit representation. Graph each of these on the same coordinate system.

22. Find the two explicit algebraic functions that result from solving

$$y^2 - 2y + x^2 = 0$$

for y. Graph each on the same coordinate system.

In general, if A is a continuous function and if $y = A(x)$ and x and y satisfy an algebraic equation

$$P_0(x)y^n + P_1(x)y^{n-1} + P_2(x)y^{n-2} + \cdots + P_n(x) = 0, \qquad \textbf{1}$$

where $P_0, P_1, P_2, \cdots, P_n$ are polynomials in x, then A is an **algebraic function.** For example, in the algebraic equation

$$y^2 - 2y - x^2 = 0, P_0(x) = 1, P_1(x) = -2 \quad and \quad P_2(x) = -x^2.$$

Show that $y = A(x)$ satisfies an equation of the form **1** when $A(x)$ equals each of the following.

23. $y = 1 - \sqrt{1 - x^2}$ **24.** $y = 1 + \sqrt[3]{x}$

25. $y = \sqrt{x + \sqrt{x}}$ **26.** $y = \sqrt[3]{x^2}$

27. $y = \sqrt[3]{\dfrac{x}{x^2 + 1}}$ **28.** $y = \sqrt{x} + \dfrac{1}{\sqrt{x}}$

7–13 Polynomial Curve Fitting

Suppose that a chemist has a solution that is at $-12°$ Celsius at the beginning of an experiment. He subjects the solution to a constant heat and notes that one minute later the temperature is $-6°$ Celsius. After two and three minutes the temperature is found to be 6°C and 36°C, respectively. The chemist wants to approximate

① the time when the solution will have a temperature of 0°C, and

② the temperature after 2.7 minutes.

Eliminating the physical ideas, the problem can be stated: Given $(0, -12)$, $(1, -6)$, $(2, 6)$, and $(3, 36)$, is there a continuous function f that contains these ordered pairs and that closely approximates the temperature of the solution at any time t for $0 \le t \le 3$? Such a function is a mathematical model of the physical situation.

To solve his problem the chemist uses the following theorem.

Theorem 7–11 If (x_1, y_1), (x_2, y_2), $\cdots$, (x_n, y_n) are n distinct points and if all the x_i are distinct, then there exists a polynomial function of degree less than or equal to $n - 1$ that contains the n points.

EXAMPLE.   Find a polynomial function of degree less than or equal to 3 that contains $(0, -12)$, $(1, -6)$, $(2, 6)$, and $(3, 36)$.

According to Theorem 7–11, $f(x) = a_3x^3 + a_2x^2 + a_1x + a_0$ will contain the four given points. This is called *fitting the polynomial to the points*. Proceed now to determine the coefficients a_0, a_1, a_2, and a_3. Substitution of the ordered pairs yields four equations.

$$-12 = a_3(0) + a_2(0) + a_1(0) + a_0 = a_0$$
$$-6 = a_3(1) + a_2(1) + a_1(1) + a_0$$
$$6 = a_3(8) + a_2(4) + a_1(2) + a_0$$
$$36 = a_3(27) + a_2(9) + a_1(3) + a_0$$

This is a system of four linear equations in the four variables a_0, a_1, a_2, and a_3 and hence has a unique solution. A method ordinarily employed for simultaneous equations will be used to solve this system.

From the first equation it is clear that $a_0 = -12$. Substitute this value of a_0 in the remaining equations.

$$a_3 + a_2 + a_1 = 6$$
$$8a_3 + 4a_2 + 2a_1 = 18$$
$$27a_3 + 9a_2 + 3a_1 = 48$$

Eliminate a_1.

$$6a_3 + 2a_2 = 6$$
$$24a_3 + 6a_2 = 30$$

Then eliminate a_2.

$$6a_3 = 12$$
$$a_3 = 2$$

It follows that $a_2 = -3$ and $a_1 = 7$. Consequently,

$$f(x) = 2x^3 - 3x^2 + 7x - 12.$$

The chemist's problem requires that you find x when $f(x) = 0$ and $f(x)$ when $x = 2.7$. Verify by synthetic substitution that $f(1.62) = -.0301$. Consequently, $f(x) = 0$ when x is approximately 1.62. Verify by synthetic substitution that $f(2.7) = 24.396$.

For the chemist to accept this model, function values $f(x)$ other than the four used in finding the coefficients must be good approximations of his laboratory data. If the "fit" is acceptable, that is, if the temperatures computed from f are close to observed values, then $f(x) = 2x^3 - 3x^2 + 7x - 12$ will be a useful model for the variation of temperature of the solution in the time interval $0 \leq x \leq 3$. If f does not produce results consistent with observations, the scientist will construct a more accurate model by taking more laboratory data and finding another polynomial function of higher degree.

Exercises

A ▬▬ Find a polynomial of smallest degree which contains the members of the set of ordered pairs.

1. $(0, 1)$, $(1, 2)$, $(3, 21)$, $(-1, 0)$
2. $(-1, 0)$, $(1, 8)$, $(2, 57)$, $(-2, -7)$
3. $(-1, -25)$, $(0, 0)$, $(1, 1)$, $(2, -16)$
4. $(-2, -15)$, $(-1, -8)$, $(1, -6)$, $(2, 1)$
5. $(1, 0)$, $(2, 0)$, $(3, 0)$, $(4, 6)$
6. $(-2, -15)$, $(-1, 0)$, $(0, 9)$, $(1, 0)$, $(2, 15)$
7. $(0, 3)$, $(1, -3)$, $(2, 3)$, $(4, 9)$

B ▬▬ The following ordered pairs represent hour of the day and temperature at that hour. Use this information in Exercises 8–10.

$$(1, 32), (2, 35), (3, 30), (4, 25)$$

8. Find a polynomial function f which could be a model for the temperature for time t if $1 \leq t \leq 4$.
9. Find $f(2.5)$. Interpret the result.
10. Is there a relative maximum of f for $1 \leq t \leq 4$? If so, what is the value of t and the corresponding value of f?
11. A mile off shore on Lake Michigan a fisherman searches for Coho Salmon. With an electronic thermometer he finds the following depth-temperature readings.

$$(5, 71°), (20, 65°), (30, 60°), (45, 50°)$$

His thermometer then failed after the reading $(45, 50°)$. If Coho Salmon stay in water near $55°F$, approximately at what depth should the fisherman fish?

7–14 Maxima and Minima: Applications

Problems in the physical world often require for their solution the maximum or minimum value that a variable can assume under certain conditions. You will see in the following examples how information in such problems can be used to construct a polynomial function which may then be maximized or minimized by finding the zeros of the derived function.

EXAMPLE 1. What is the area of the largest rectangular garden that a farmer can enclose with 400 feet of fencing if one side of the garden has already been fenced?

The quantity you wish to maximize in this problem is the area A of the rectangular garden. You must express A as a function of a single variable and then find the derived function, A'. A sketch will be helpful. The garden is to be rectangular, so you can let two sides have the same measure, say x, and the third side have some other measure, say y.

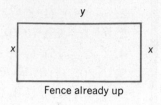

Fence already up

The area of a rectangular region is the product of its length and its width, so the formula

$$A = xy \qquad 1$$

expresses the relationship between the area and the linear dimensions.

In **1**, the area A is expressed as a function of *two* variables. Since you do not know how to find the derived function of such an expression, you must find a way to express A as a function of *one* variable. You can do this by using the condition that only 400 feet of fencing are available. Hence

$$400 = 2x + y$$

or

$$400 - 2x = y.$$

Substitute the last expression for y in **1** to obtain

$$A = x(400 - 2x)$$
$$= 400x - 2x^2.$$

Now that the area A is expressed as a polynomial in x, the task of finding the zeros of the derived function A' is easy.

$$A' = 400 - 4x$$

The zeros of A' are found by solving

$$0 = 400 - 4x.$$
$$x = 100,$$

and

$$y = 400 - 2x$$
$$= 400 - 200$$
$$= 200.$$

It is easy to check that this is indeed a relative maximum of A. The maximum area the farmer can enclose with 400 feet of fencing is

$$A = 100 \cdot 200 = 20{,}000 \text{ square feet.}$$

Summarizing, the main steps in the solution of the problem are as follows:

① Find the quantity (A) that is to be maximized or minimized.
② Express that quantity as a function of the other variables ($A = xy$).
③ Express either x or y in terms of the other ($y = 400 - 2x$).
④ Calculate the derived function of the polynomial function. (If $A = 400x - 2x^2$, then $A' = 400 - 4x$.)
⑤ Find the zeros of the derived function ($x = 100$).
⑥ Determine whether or not the zero corresponds to a maximum (or minimum).
⑦ Calculate the maximum area.

EXAMPLE 2. A manufacturer has 100 tons of a product that he can sell now with a profit of $5 per ton. For each week that he delays shipment, he can produce an additional 10 tons. However, for each week's delay the profit decreases 25¢ per ton. If he can sell all of the product that he has on hand at any time, when should he ship so that his profit will be a maximum?

The manufacturer's profit P is to be a maximum. Now P is the product of the number of tons shipped and the profit per ton. Recall that the number of tons available for shipment depends on the number of weeks they are delayed. Similarly the profit per ton depends on the number of weeks they are delayed. Thus, the tons shipped after x weeks' delay is

$$100 + 10x,$$

and the profit per ton after x weeks' delay is

$$5.00 - 0.25x.$$

Since P equals tons shipped times profit per ton,

$$P = (100 + 10x)(5.00 - 0.25x)$$

expresses the profit after x weeks' delay. Since P is to be a maximum, you need to find the critical points of P', the derived function. Thus if

$$P = 500 + 25x - 2.5x^2,$$

then

$$P' = 25 - 5x,$$

and $P' = 0$ when $x = 5$. Consequently, P is a maximum when $x = 5$. The manufacturer should wait 5 weeks to ship. His profit will be $562.50.

EXAMPLE 3. Given a 20-inch square of sheet metal, find the dimensions of the open box of greatest volume that can be made from the metal by cutting congruent squares from the corners

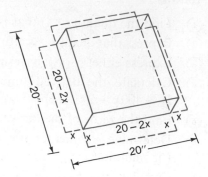

If the squares to be cut from the corners measure x inches by x inches, then the dimensions of the completed box will be x inches, $20 - 2x$ inches, and $20 - 2x$ inches. The volume V is to be a maximum. V is the product of three linear measures. Hence

$$V = x(20 - 2x)^2$$
$$= 400x - 80x^2 + 4x^3.$$

The maximum will be found at a zero of V'.

$$V' = 400 - 160x + 12x^2$$
$$= 4(100 - 40x + 3x^2)$$
$$= 4(10 - 3x)(10 - x)$$

Thus the zeros of V' are $x = 10$ and $x = \frac{10}{3}$. When $x = 10$, the volume of the box is certainly a minimum — there is no box! It is easy to show that $x = \frac{10}{3}$ gives the maximum volume, namely,

$$\frac{10}{3}\left(20 - \frac{20}{3}\right)^2 = \frac{16,000}{27} \text{ cubic inches.}$$

Exercises

A **1.** A rectangular garden is to be enclosed on three sides by fencing; the fourth side is the side of a barn. What is the largest garden that can be enclosed by 50 feet of fencing? What are the dimensions of the garden?

2. Find a number such that the sum of the number and its square will be as small as possible.

3. Show that the largest rectangle with a perimeter of 20 inches is a square.

4. A trough with a rectangular cross section is to be made from a long sheet of metal 24 inches wide by turning up strips along each side. Find the amount that must be turned up to give the greatest cross section.

5. A rectangle has two of its vertices as the x axis. The other two vertices are on the parabola whose equation is $y = 18 - x^2$. What are the dimensions of the rectangle if its area is to be a maximum?

6. A body moves such that its distance, s, in feet from a given point, A, is expressed by the formula $s = 5t^2 - 3t + 6$. For what value of t is the body closest to point A? At that time, how far will it be from A?

B   **7.** Find three numbers such that the first is the sum of the second and third, the second is the square of the third, and the sum of the three numbers is a minimum.

8. There are 900 yards of fencing available to enclose a rectangular plot of ground with a fence down the middle and parallel to two ends. What is the maximum area which can be enclosed?

9. A bus line carries 2000 passengers per day at a rate of 20¢ per passenger. In contemplating a rate change, the management estimates that they would lose 200 passengers for every 5¢ they increased the rates. What rate should they charge to maximize their revenue?

10. A wire 14 feet in length is cut into two pieces. One part is used to make a square. The other part is bent into a rectangle such that $l = 3w$. How should the wire be cut if the sum of the areas is to be a minimum?

11. Find the dimensions of the right circular cylinder of greatest volume that can be inscribed in a right circular cone with a height of 9 units and a base with a radius of 6 units.

C   **12.** The sum of two positive numbers is 5. Find the numbers such that:

     a. Their product is a maximum.

     b. The sum of their squares is a minimum.

     c. The product of one number and the square of the other will be a maximum.

13. Find the dimensions of the right circular cylinder of greatest volume that can be inscribed in a right circular cone with radius of base r and height P.

14. Find the least amount of material needed to make a square-based open box that has a volume of 4000 cubic inches.

15. Find the least amount of material needed to make a square-based box with a top that has a volume of N cubic inches. What are the dimensions when $N = 81$?

CHAPTER OBJECTIVES AND REVIEW

Objective: *To know the meaning of the important mathematical terms of this chapter.*

1. Here are many of the mathematical terms used in this chapter. Be sure that you know them thoroughly and can use them correctly.

rational expression (*300*)
algebraic expression (*300*)
constant function (*302*)
y intercept (*302*)
zero polynomial (*302*)
linear function (*302*)
quadratic function (*303*)
zero of a function (*303*)
axis of symmetry (*304*)
turning point (*304*)
quadratic formula (*304*)
discriminant (*304*)
synthetic substitution (*306*)
Remainder Theorem (*309*)
synthetic division (*310*)

depressed polynomial (*310*)
Factor Theorem (*311*)
Fundamental Theorem of
    Algebra (*322*)
relative minimum or maximum
    (*325*)
absolute minimum or maximum
    (*325*)
point of inflection (*329*)
tangent (*329*)
second derived function (*338*)
concave upward or downward
    (*338–9*)
rational function (*341*)
algebraic function (*345*)

Objective: *To use synthetic substitution* (1) *to determine whether* $(x - a)$ *is a factor of* $P(x)$ *and* (2) *to determine the value of* $P(x)$ *at* $x = a$.

■■■Evaluate each polynomial $P(x)$ for each value of x. Use synthetic substitution.

2. $P(x) = x^4 - 2x^3 + 2x^2 - 5$ $\qquad x \in \{-2, \frac{1}{2}, 3, 0\}$
3. $P(x) = -5x^3 - 2x + 7$ $\qquad x \in \{-1, 0, 1, 2\}$
4. $P(x) = x^4 - 16$ $\qquad x \in \{-3, -2, -1, 0, 1, 2, 3\}$

■■■Which, if any, of the following linear expressions are factors of $P(x)$?

5. $P(x) = x^4 - 2x^3 + 2x^2 - 5$ $\qquad (x - 1); \ (x + 1); \ (x - 2)$
6. $P(x) = -5x^3 - 2x + 7$ $\qquad (x - 1); \ (x + 1); \ (x + 2)$
7. $P(x) = x^4 - 16$ $\qquad (x - 1); \ (x + 1); \ (x + 2); \ (x - 2)$

Objective: *To use synthetic substitution to locate real zeros of a polynomial and to identify upper and lower bounds on the real zeros.*

8. Locate one real zero of $P(x) = x^4 - 2x^3 + x - 5$ between successive tenths. What other real zeros are there?

■ Identify upper and lower bounds for the real zeros of each polynomial in Exercises 9–11.

9. $P(x) = x^4 - 2x^3 + 2x^2 - 5$

10. $P(x) = -5x^3 - 2x + 7$

11. $P(x) = 2x^4 + 15x^3 + 28x^2 + 15x$

Objective: *To identify the possible rational zeros of a polynomial over the integers and express a polynomial as a product of linear factors with complex coefficients.*

Find the set of possible rational zeros for each $P(x)$. Determine which, if any, of these are zeros of $P(x)$.

12. $P(x) = 2x^4 + 15x^3 + 28x^2 + 15x$

13. $P(x) = -5x^3 - 2x + 7$

14. $P(x) = 9x^3 + 6x^2 - 5x - 2$

15. Write each polynomial in Exercises 12–14 as a product of linear factors with complex coefficients.

16. a. What are the zeros of $P(x) = x^6 - 4x^5 + 8x^4 - 16x^3 + 16x^2$

b. Identify any multiple zeros and their multiplicity.

Objective: *To find the relative maxima and minima and points of inflection of a polynomial.*

■ Identify the relative maxima, the relative minima and the points of inflection for each polynomial.

17. $P(x) = x^3$

18. $P(x) = x^3 - 9x$

19. $P(x) = x^5 - 1$

20. $P(x) = 3x^4 - 20x^3 + 36x^2 + 60$

21. In each Exercise 17–20 identify the intervals for which $P(x)$ is concave upward and concave downward using the second derived function.

Objective: *To sketch the graphs of polynomials using y intercepts, zeros, relative maxima and minima, inflection points, and limits.*

■ Sketch the graph of each polynomial using y intercepts, zeros, relative maxima and minima, inflection points, and limits.

22. $P(x) = x^4 - 4x^3 + 8x^2 - 16x + 16$

23. $P(x) = x^3 - 1$

24. $P(x) = x^3 - 3x^2 - 6x + 8$

25. $P(x) = 9x^3 + 81x^2 - 45x - 36$

Objective: *To identify restricted domain values and asymptotes of rational and real algebraic functions and sketch graphs of such functions.*

▬ Sketch each function. Identify restricted values and asymptotes where appropriate.

26. $f(x) = \dfrac{(x)(x-4)}{(x+2)(x-2)}$

27. $f(x) = \sqrt{x^2 - 25}$

28. $f(x) = \dfrac{3x(x+3)}{(x-1)(x-5)}$

29. $f(x) = x + \sqrt{x}$

Objective: *To fit a polynomial to a set of noncollinear points.*

▬ Find a polynomial function which contains the given points.

30. $(3, 2), (2, 3), (-3, -2)$

31. $(1, 0), (0, 1), (-1, 0), (-4, 0)$

Objective: *Apply the concepts of maximum and minimum of polynomial functions to verbal problems.*

32. Find two numbers whose sum is 10 and the sum of their squares is a minimum.

33. A right triangular lot has sides 240 feet and 300 feet. Find the dimensions of the largest rectangular building that can be constructed on the lot with the sides parallel to the sides of the triangle.

34. What rectangle of fixed perimeter p has the maximum area?

CHAPTER TEST ▬▬▬▬▬▬▬▬▬▬▬

▬ Given $P(x)$, find $P(a)$ for each value of a by synthetic substitution.

1. $P(x) = -3x^4 + 2x^2 + 5$ $\qquad\qquad a = -2, \frac{5}{3}, 1, 0$

2. $P(x) = 3x^4 - 2x^3 - 27x^2 + 18x$ $\qquad a = 3, 1, 0, -1, -3$

3. Determine all rational zeros for $P(x)$ in Exercise 1. Determine all zeros, irrational and complex, in Exercise 1.

4. Repeat Exercise 3 for: $P(x) = 3x^4 - 2x^3 - 27x^2 + 18x$.

5. Express in your own words the meaning of the Factor Theorem and the Remainder Theorem.

6. What is the maximum number of complex zeros of a degree 7 polynomial with real coefficients? Explain your answer.

7. Locate one real zero of $P(x) = 2x^3 + x - 1$ between successive tenths.

Identify the critical points of each polynomial function. Determine whether each critical point is a relative maximum or minimum or a point of inflection.

8. $P(x) = x^4 - 4x^2$

9. $P(x) = (x - 1)^3$

10. $P(x) = 3x^4 + 24x^3 + 30x^2 - 168x - 1$

Identify the y intercepts, the real zeros, the critical points of each polynomial. Sketch the graph using this information.

11. $P(x) = x^4 - 4x^2$

12. $P(x) = x^3 - 3x^2$

13. $P(x) = x^3 - 6x^2 + 12x - 8$

14. For each polynomial in Exercises 11–13 find the intervals for which the graph is concave upward or concave downward.

Sketch the graph of each function. Restrict the domain where necessary.

15. $f(x) = 1 + \sqrt{25 - x^2}$

16. $f(x) = \dfrac{x^4 - 4x^2}{x^2 - 4}$

17. $f(x) = \dfrac{1}{(x + 1)(x - 3)}$

18. Find a polynomial of degree 3 which contains the four points $A(1, 2)$, $B(2, 3)$, $C(0, 0)$ and $D(-1, 1)$.

19. The sum of two positive numbers is 12. Find the numbers so that the product of one and the square of the other is a maximum.

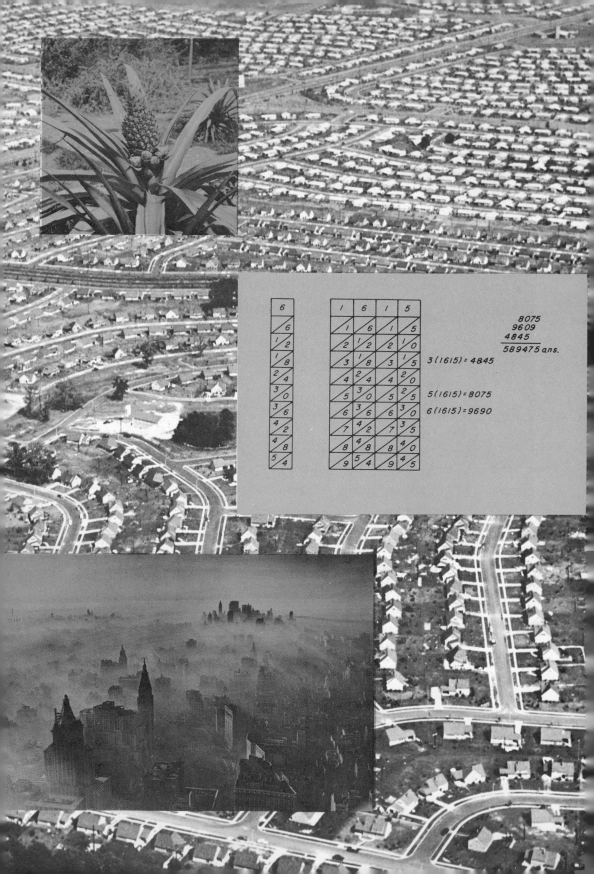

		1	6	1	5
6		1/6	6/6	1/6	5/6
1/2		2/2	2/1	2/2	1/0
1/8		3/1	8/1	3/1	5/1
2/4		4/2	4/4	4/2	4/0
3/0		5/3	0/3	5/0	5/2
3/6		6/3	6/6	6/3	0/3
4/2		7/4	2/4	7/4	3/5
4/8		8/4	8/4	8/4	0/4
5/4		9/5	4/5	9/5	4/5

$$3(1615) = 4845$$

$$5(1615) = 8075$$

$$6(1615) = 9690$$

$$
\begin{array}{r}
8075 \\
9609 \\
4845 \\
\hline
589475 \text{ ans.}
\end{array}
$$

CHAPTER 8

EXPONENTIAL AND LOGARITHMIC FUNCTIONS

The line drawing on the opposite page shows some sticks known as Napier's Bones, a mechanical device for multiplication. In the problem shown, 1615 is being multiplied by 365. The Bones were invented by John Napier, a Scottish baron who lived from 1550 until 1617. In his search for easier ways of multiplying, Napier discovered *logarithms*, which allow you to multiply by adding. He in fact, invented the name logarithm. Napier then spent the last twenty-five years of his life computing his logarithmic tables.

While there is no easy way of computing logarithmic tables from scratch, logarithms are frequently found in nature. Logarithmic spirals can be seen on snail shells, heads of chrysanthemums, and pineapples.

Logarithms are inverse *exponential functions*. Population growth can be represented by an explicit exponential function. The spread of housing and other development across the country testifies to the expanding nature of this kind of exponential function.

The photograph at the lower left is of lower Manhattan. It was taken from the top of the Empire State Building during a temperature inversion. A temperature inversion is a natural occurrence in which the order of temperatures is reversed. During such an occurrence the dust and smoke particles are trapped in a stagnant mass of air close to the earth. In mathematics there are *functional inverses* which reverse the operations of functions.

8-1   Rational Exponents

In your earlier study of mathematics, integral exponents were defined by the following equations.

1 $\qquad\qquad\qquad a^0 = 1$ if $a \neq 0 \qquad\qquad$ (0^0 is not defined.)

2 $\qquad\qquad\qquad a^1 = a$

3 $\qquad\qquad\qquad a^n = a \cdot a \cdot \;\cdots\; \cdot a \qquad$ to n factors when n is an integer greater than 1.

4 $\qquad\qquad\qquad a^{-n} = \dfrac{1}{a^n}$, $\qquad\qquad$ when n is a positive integer.

You are familiar with the properties of integral exponents from these theorems.

5 $\qquad\qquad\qquad a^n \cdot a^m = a^{n+m}$

6 $\qquad\qquad\qquad \dfrac{a^n}{a^m} = a^{n-m}$ or $\dfrac{1}{a^{m-n}}$, $a \neq 0$

7 $\qquad\qquad\qquad (a^m)^n = a^{m \cdot n}$

The next step is to assign meaning to a symbol such as $3^{\frac{2}{3}}$. This step is not hard to take because there is a natural relationship between $\sqrt[p]{a}$ and $a^{\frac{1}{p}}$ when p is a positive integer. First,

$$y = \sqrt[p]{a} \qquad \text{iff} \qquad y^p = a.$$

In words, y is the pth root of a if and only if the pth power of y is a. Now you want to define $a^{\frac{1}{p}}$ in such a way that properties **5, 6,** and **7** hold. In particular, you want property **7** to be valid for rational exponents. Thus, you want

$$y = a^{\frac{1}{p}}$$

to imply

$$y^p = (a^{\frac{1}{p}})^p$$

and **7** to imply

$$(a^{\frac{1}{p}})^p = a^{\frac{p}{p}} = a.$$

Thus, since

$$y = \sqrt[p]{a} \qquad \text{iff} \qquad y^p = a$$

and you want $y = a^{\frac{1}{p}}$ to imply $y^p = a$ by property **7,** you make the following definition.

8 $$a^{\frac{1}{p}} = \sqrt[p]{a} \qquad p \in \mathbf{N}$$

To extend **8** to the case where the numerator of the exponent is not 1, you make the following definition.

9 $$a^{\frac{q}{p}} = (a^{\frac{1}{p}})^q \qquad a \neq 0, q \text{ an integer}, p \text{ a natural}$$
number, and $\frac{q}{p}$ in lowest terms.

From **8** and **9**, properties **5**, **6**, and **7** are easily shown to be valid for rational exponents.

So that there is no ambiguity about the meaning of $\sqrt[p]{a}$ and $a^{\frac{1}{p}}$, both symbols are taken to indicate the *principal root*. The **principal root**, $\sqrt[p]{a}$ or $a^{\frac{1}{p}}$, is the positive root when there is more than one real root and the real root when there is only one real root. Thus, $\sqrt[3]{8} = 2$ and $\sqrt{9} = 3$, not -3.

The symbol $\sqrt[p]{a}$ names a real number except when $a < 0$ and p is even. In this case, $\sqrt[p]{a}$ is imaginary. For example, $\sqrt[2]{-4} = 2i$.

Another irregularity occurs when a is a negative real number. There are cases for which a^{r_1} raised to the exponent r_2 is not equal to a^{r_2} raised to the exponent r_1. That is $[a^{r_1}]^{r_2}$ may not equal $[a^{r_2}]^{r_1}$ for $a < 0$. The following example illustrates what occurs if a is not restricted to nonnegative real numbers when p is an even number in Definition **9**.

EXAMPLE. Evaluate $[(-4)^2]^{\frac{1}{2}}$ and $[(-4^{\frac{1}{2}})]^2$ by performing the operations in order left to right. This will show that $[(-4)^2]^{\frac{1}{2}} \neq [(-4)^{\frac{1}{2}}]^2$.

$$[(-4)^2]^{\frac{1}{2}} = [16]^{\frac{1}{2}}$$
$$= 4$$
$$[(-4)^{\frac{1}{2}}]^2 = [2i]^2$$
$$= -4$$

Since $4 \neq -4$, the result is *not* independent of the order of operations when the base is a *negative* real number and the root is even. The solution to this dilemma is to restrict the base to only nonnegative real numbers for even roots. When this is done, the order of exponentiation does not affect the result.

A property of a number raised to a rational exponent is given in the next theorem. Notice that it is an obvious extension of a similar result for integral exponents.

> **Theorem 8–1** If r and s are rational numbers and $r < s$ and $a > 1$, then $a^r < a^s$.

Proof: Notice that if

    a. $a > 1$, then $a^n > 1$ $\forall n \in W$.
    b. $a = 1$, then $a^n = 1$ $\forall n \in W$.
    c. $0 < a < 1$, then $a^n < 1$ $\forall n \in W$.

You can now prove that for $a > 1$,

$$a^{\frac{m}{n}} > 1 \text{ for } m, n \in W.$$

The proof is indirect.

① Suppose $a^{\frac{m}{n}} = 1$.
    Then $a^m = 1^n = 1$. (Why?)

But this contradicts **a** above.

② Suppose $a^{\frac{m}{n}} < 1$.
    Then $a^m < 1^n = 1$. (Why?)

But this contradicts **a** above.

③ Since $a^{\frac{m}{n}}$ is not equal to 1 nor less than 1, it must be greater than 1 by the Trichotomy Principle. Now the rest of the proof is easy. Let r and s be any rational numbers such that $r < s$. Then $s - r$ is some positive rational number, say $\frac{m}{n}$. Since

$$a^{s-r} = a^{\frac{m}{n}} > 1$$

it follows that $a^r(a^{s-r}) > a^r$ (because $a^r > 0$) or

$$a^s > a^r.$$

Now try these

━━ Evaluate each of the following.

  1. $(8^{-\frac{2}{3}})^3$ **2.** $(-45)^{\frac{1}{2}}$ **3.** $(.0016)^{\frac{1}{4}} \cdot (27)^{\frac{2}{3}}$

━━ Perform the indicated operations.

  4. $(x^{\frac{2}{3}} \cdot x^{-\frac{3}{4}})^{-1}$ **5.** $2y^{-2} \cdot 3y^{-3}$ **6.** $[(2x^2)(y^{-3})]^{\frac{1}{2}}$

Answers: **1.** $\frac{1}{64}$ **2.** $3i\sqrt{5}$ **3.** 1.8   **4.** $x^{\frac{1}{12}}$ **5.** $6y^{-5}$ **6.** $|x|\sqrt{\frac{2}{y^3}}$

Checkpoint

1. What is the formal definition of $a^{\frac{p}{q}}$? In your own words, state the definition.

2. What restriction must be placed on a in $a^{\frac{p}{q}}$ when q is even? Explain.

Exercises

A ━━ Evaluate each of the following.

1. $4^{-2} \cdot 4^{\frac{1}{2}}$

2. $5^{-1} \cdot 8^{\frac{1}{3}}$

3. $7^6 \cdot 7^{-3}$

4. $5^{-2} \cdot 5^2$

5. $(4^{\frac{3}{2}})^{-1}$

6. $(\sqrt[3]{-8})^2$

━━ Simplify each of the following. The replacement set for each variable is the set of positive real numbers.

Example.

$$[(x^{-2})(x^3 y^{-4})(5y^{-3})]^{-\frac{1}{2}} = (5xy^{-7})^{-\frac{1}{2}}$$
$$= \left(\frac{5x}{y^7}\right)^{-\frac{1}{2}} = \sqrt{\frac{y^7}{5x}} = y^3 \sqrt{\frac{y}{5x}}$$

7. $(x^3)(2y^{-1})(x^2 \cdot y^{-2})^{-1}$

8. $[(x^2)(2^{-2} \cdot y^4]^{-\frac{1}{2}}$

9. $[(a^4)(a^{-\frac{2}{3}})]^{\frac{3}{2}}$

10. $(x^{\frac{3}{4}})(x^{-\frac{2}{3}})(x^{\frac{1}{5}})$

11. $\left(\frac{x^{-2}}{x^{-3}}\right)^2 \left(\frac{x^{-2}}{x^{-1}}\right)^2$

12. $(a^{\frac{1}{2}} - b^{\frac{1}{2}})(a^{\frac{1}{2}} + b^{\frac{1}{2}})$

━━ Evaluate each of the following.

13. $800(8^{-\frac{2}{3}})$

14. $[(-8)^3]^{\frac{1}{3}}$

15. $64(\frac{16}{9})^{-\frac{3}{2}}$

16. $[(-8)^{\frac{1}{3}}]^3$

17. What do the results to Exercises 14 and 16 illustrate with regard to $(a^q)^{\frac{1}{p}}$ and $(a^{\frac{1}{p}})^q$?

18. Arrange the following numbers in increasing order of magnitude.

$$2, (4^{\frac{7}{2}})(16^{-1}), (\tfrac{1}{2})^{-\frac{4}{3}}, 2^{-3}, (2^{-\frac{2}{5}})^5$$

B ━━ Find the value of p in each of the following.

19. $8^p = (2^3)^3$

20. $8^p = 2^{(3^3)}$

21. $(3^2)^3 = 9^p$

22. $3^{(2^3)} = 9^p$

23. $16^p = 2^{(4^5)}$

24. $16^p = (2^4)^5$

■ Solve for x.

25. $x^{\frac{2}{3}} = 16$ **26.** $2x^{\frac{3}{2}} = 8$

27. $2x^{\frac{1}{2}} = 4$ **28.** $x^{-\frac{3}{2}} = 8$

29. Prove: If $a > 0$ and r_1 and r_2 are rational numbers, then the following are true.

    a. $a^{r_1} \cdot a^{r_2} = a^{r_1+r_2}$ **b.** $\dfrac{a^{r_1}}{a^{r_2}} = a^{r_1-r_2}$

    c. $(a^{\frac{1}{p}})^{\frac{1}{q}} = a^{\frac{1}{pq}}$ $(p, q \in W)$

30. Prove: If r and s are rational numbers, $r < s$, and $0 < a < 1$, then $a^r > a^s$.

8–2   Real Exponents

At the moment the symbol a^x $(a > 0)$ has been defined for all rational replacements of x. If you were to graph the function

$$f(x) = a^x \quad (a > 0),$$

the domain of f would have to be restricted to rational x, because a^x has not been defined for irrational numbers.

For example, choose $a = 2$ and consider 2^x where x is a real number. You know how 2^x is defined for rational numbers, but no meaning has been attached to, say, $2^{\sqrt{3}}$ or to 2^{π} since $\sqrt{3}$ and π are irrational numbers. The method of defining 2^x for irrational x is illustrated in the following example.

EXAMPLE 1.   Define $2^{\sqrt{3}}$.

By Theorem 8–1, $2^r < 2^s$ when r and s are rational and $r < s$. It seems reasonable to require that this same property hold when r and s are irrational numbers. Thus, for $x = \sqrt{3}$ and for all rational numbers r and s such that

$$r < \sqrt{3} < s \qquad\qquad\qquad\qquad\qquad 1$$

you would like to have

$$2^r < 2^{\sqrt{3}} < 2^s. \qquad\qquad\qquad\qquad\qquad 2$$

Clearly, **1** and **2** place severe restriction on the choice of the value of $2^{\sqrt{3}}$. In fact, **1** and **2** uniquely determine the value of $2^{\sqrt{3}}$. To see why this is true consider two sets of rational approximations to $\sqrt{3}$ given in the table.

r	$<$	$\sqrt{3}$	$<$	s
1.7	$<$	$\sqrt{3}$	$<$	1.8
1.73	$<$	$\sqrt{3}$	$<$	1.74
1.732	$<$	$\sqrt{3}$	$<$	1.733
1.7320	$<$	$\sqrt{3}$	$<$	1.7321

By **1** and **2** you have the following table.

2^r	$<$	$2^{\sqrt{3}}$	$<$	2^s
$2^{1.7}$	$<$	$2^{\sqrt{3}}$	$<$	$2^{1.8}$
$2^{1.73}$	$<$	$2^{\sqrt{3}}$	$<$	$2^{1.74}$
$2^{1.732}$	$<$	$2^{\sqrt{3}}$	$<$	$2^{1.733}$
$2^{1.7320}$	$<$	$2^{\sqrt{3}}$	$<$	$2^{1.7321}$

Converting the left and right hand columns to approximations to their real number equivalents, you have the following. (The method for conversion will be considered later.)

2^r	$<$	$2^{\sqrt{3}}$	$<$	2^s
3.25	$<$	$2^{\sqrt{3}}$	$<$	3.48
3.317	$<$	$2^{\sqrt{3}}$	$<$	3.341
3.3219	$<$	$2^{\sqrt{3}}$	$<$	3.3246
3.32192	$<$	$2^{\sqrt{3}}$	$<$	3.32260

Thus, if **2** is to hold, you have a three decimal place approximation to $2^{\sqrt{3}}$.

$$2^{\sqrt{3}} \approx 3.322$$

The procedure is one of "pinching down" on the value of $2^{\sqrt{3}}$ by using rational approximations of $\sqrt{3}$ and $2^{\sqrt{3}}$.

The pinching down process is illustrated graphically as follows.

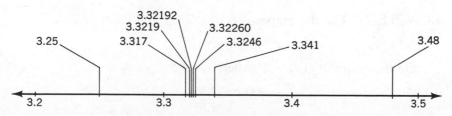

It is proved in advanced mathematics texts that there is one unique number y in each of the intervals of the following sequence of intervals.

$$[2^{1.7},\ 2^{1.8}][2^{1.73},\ 2^{1.74}][2^{1.732},\ 2^{1.733}],\ \cdots$$

That number y is defined to be $2^{\sqrt{3}}$.

The process illustrated for $2^{\sqrt{3}}$ can be applied to any real number x and positive real number a to define a^x, $a > 0$, $x \in R$. Explicitly, this is done as follows:

① Let $r_1, r_2, r_3, \ldots, r_n, \ldots$ be an increasing sequence of rational numbers all less than x and such that $\lim\limits_{n \to \infty} r_n = x$. Let $s_1, s_2, s_3, \ldots,$ $s_n, \ldots$ be a decreasing sequence of rational numbers all greater than x and such that $\lim\limits_{n \to \infty} s_n = x$.

② Let $a > 1$, and consider the sequences $\{a^{r_n}\}$ and $\{a^{s_n}\}$. For each $n \in N$,

$$a^{r_n} \leq y \leq a^{s_n}.$$

③ There is a number y in each of the intervals in the following sequence of intervals.

$$[a^{r_1}, a^{s_1}], [a^{r_2}, a^{s_2}], [a^{r_3}, a^{s_3}], \cdots, [a^{r_n}, a^{s_n}], \cdots$$

The number y in each interval $[a^{r_n}, a^{s_n}]$ is defined to be a^x. A similar procedure is used to define a^x when x is real and $0 < a < 1$.

It is no longer necessary to restrict the domain of the function

$$f : x \longrightarrow a^x, a > 0$$

to the rational numbers only. The function f is now defined for all $x \in R$. In fact, $f(x) = a^x$, $a > 0$ is a *continuous* function, for the definition of a^x for x irrational "fills in" all the holes in the graph of $f(r) = a^r$, $a > 0$ and $r \in Q$. Functions of this type in which the exponent is a variable are called **exponential functions.** (Functions such as $f(x) = x^2$ in which the *base* is a variable are called **power functions.**)

An accurate graph of $f(x) = 2^x$ (for $-2 \leq x \leq 2.75$) is shown at the right. It can be used to obtain a good approximation to 2^x for $-2 \leq x \leq 2.75$, as the next example illustrates.

EXAMPLE 2. Use the graph of $f(x) = 2^x$ to approximate $2^{1.5}$.

METHOD I

On the graph of $f(x) = 2^x$ when $x = 1.5$

$$f(x) \approx 2.85$$

Thus
$$2^{1.5} \approx 2.85$$

METHOD II

Notice that
$$2^{1.5} = 2^1 \cdot 2^{0.5}$$
$$= 2 \cdot 2^{0.5} \quad \text{(Why?)}$$

Hence you can read $2^{0.5}$ on the graph and multiply the result by 2.

From the graph $\qquad 2^{0.5} \approx 1.42$

Thus $\qquad 2^{1.5} \approx 2(1.42) = 2.84.$

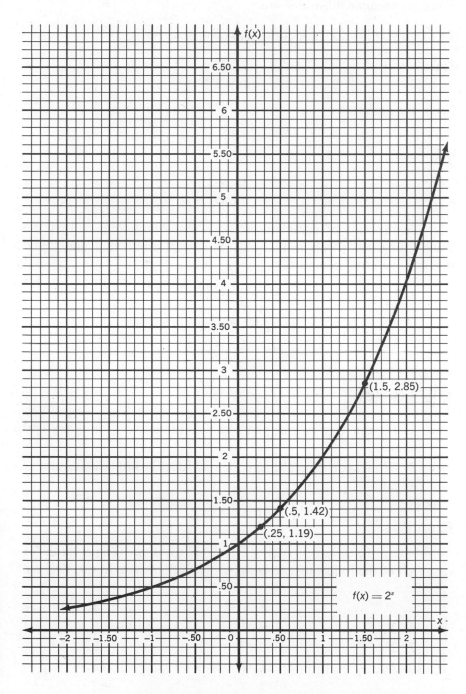

Method II illustrates a procedure whereby 2^x can be approximated using only the graph of $f(x) = 2^x$ for $0 \leq x \leq 1$. The idea is to write x as the sum of an integer and a rational number between 0 and 1. The next example illustrates this.

EXAMPLE 3. Find an approximate value for $2^{4 \cdot 25}$.

Since
$$2^{4 \cdot 25} = 2^4 \cdot 2^{0 \cdot 25},$$
$$2^{4 \cdot 25} = 16 \cdot 2^{0 \cdot 25}$$

From the graph,
$$2^{0 \cdot 25} \approx 1.19$$

Thus
$$2^{4 \cdot 25} \approx 16 \times 1.19$$
$$\approx 19.04.$$

For the sake of completeness, it is important to note that the usual properties of exponents hold for all real numbers x and y and $a > 0$. The proof is omitted.

$$a^x \cdot a^y = a^{x+y}$$
$$\frac{a^x}{a^y} = a^{x-y}$$
$$(a^x)^y = a^{x \cdot y}$$

Checkpoint

1. In your own words, give the definition of a^x, for x any real number.

2. Would you expect all exponential functions to be continuous? Explain.

Exercises

A Use the graph of $f(x) = 2^x$ to find an approximate value for each of the following expressions. Round answers to one decimal place.

1. $2^{0 \cdot 25}$	**2.** $2^{0 \cdot 50}$	**3.** $2^{0 \cdot 75}$
4. $2^{-0 \cdot 25}$	**5.** $2^{-0 \cdot 50}$	**6.** $2^{-0 \cdot 75}$
7. $2^{2 \cdot 6}$	**8.** 2^{π}	**9.** $2^{-0 \cdot 40}$
10. $2^{-4 \cdot 5}$	**11.** $2^{3 \cdot 5}$	**12.** $4^{0 \cdot 75}$

■ From the graph of $f(x) = 2^x$, $2^{1.59} \approx 3$. This fact may be used to approximate 3^x for $x \in R$.

Example.

$$3^{0.5} \approx (2^{1.59})^{0.5}$$
$$\approx 2^{0.795}$$
$$\approx 2^{0.8}$$

From the graph of $f(x) = 2^x$,

$$2^{0.8} \approx 1.7.$$

Thus

$$3^{0.5} \approx 1.7.$$

■ Use the procedure in the above example to approximate each power of 3.

13. $3^{0.25}$	**14.** $3^{1.2}$	**15.** $3^{-0.5}$
16. $3^{0.75}$	**17.** $3^{2.4}$	**18.** $3^{-1.5}$

■ Use the graph of $f(x) = 2^x$ to estimate the value of x in Exercises 19–24.

19. $2^x = 5$	**20.** $2^x = 0.4$	**21.** $2^x = 1.62$
22. $2^x = 3$	**23.** $2^x = 0.27$	**24.** $2^x = 6$

B ■ Given a positive real number x, you can express x as an integral power of 2 multiplied by a number r such that $1 \le r \le 2$.

Example. Let $x = 5$.
    The greatest power of 2 in 5 is 4.
By division you find

$$5 = 2^2(1.25).$$

Thus 5 can be expressed as a power of 2 by expressing 1.25 as a power of 2.
    From the graph of $f(x) = 2^x$,

$$1.25 \approx 2^{0.31}.$$

Thus

$$5 \approx 2^2(2^{0.31}) = 2^{2.31}.$$

■ Use the procedure in the above example to express each of the following numbers as a power of 2.

25. 10	**26.** 3.5	**27.** 18	**28.** 0.25
29. 24	**30.** 6	**31.** 0.75	**32.** 0.10

33. Construct an accurate graph of the function $f : x \longrightarrow (\frac{1}{2})^x$ for $-3 \le x \le 2$.

34. Construct an accurate graph of the function $f : x \longrightarrow 3^x$ for $0 \le x \le 1$.

35. Construct an accurate graph of the function $f : x \longrightarrow 5^x$ for $0 \le x \le 1$.

(*Hint:* Is the fact that $5 \approx 2^{2.31}$ helpful?)

36. How is the graph of $f(x) = a^x$, $a > 0$, related to the graph of $f(x) = (\frac{1}{a})^x$, $a > 0$?

8–3 The Number e

There are two quite famous irrational numbers in mathematics. The first, π, is familiar to you through your work in geometry. To twenty decimal places,

$$\pi \approx 3.14159265358979323846.$$

Using electronic computers, π has been computed to more than 100,000 places.

The second famous number

$$e \approx 2.7182818,$$

is probably less familiar to you.

The numbers π and e are defined as sums of infinite series.

$$\pi = 4\left(\sum_{n=0}^{\infty} (-1)^n \frac{1}{2n+1}\right)$$

That is, $\quad \pi = 4(1 - \frac{1}{3} + \frac{1}{5} - \frac{1}{7} + \frac{1}{9} - \frac{1}{11} + \cdots)$

$$e = \sum_{n=0}^{\infty} \frac{1}{n!} \qquad (n! = 1 \cdot 2 \cdot 3 \cdot \ \cdots \ \cdot n \text{ and } 0! = 1)$$

That is, $\quad e = 1 + \frac{1}{1!} + \frac{1}{2!} + \frac{1}{3!} + \frac{1}{4!} + \frac{1}{5!} + \cdots$

From the definition of e as an infinite series, it is clear that $2 < e$. If you let S_n be the partial sum corresponding to the whole number n then you have the following.

$$S_1 = 1 + \frac{1}{1!} = 2$$

Also, if $n > 1$, then S_n is greater than 2 because the addends are all positive. Thus, $2 < e$.

It is also true that $e < 3$. This follows because

$$a_n = \frac{1}{n!} = \frac{1}{1 \cdot 2 \cdot 3 \cdot \; \cdots \; \cdot n} < \frac{1}{2} \cdot \frac{1}{2} \; \cdots \; \cdot \frac{1}{2} = \frac{1}{2^{n-1}}$$

and thus

$$S_n < 1 + 1 + \frac{1}{2} + \frac{1}{2^2} + \frac{1}{2^3} + \cdots + \frac{1}{2^{n-1}} = 1 + 2 - \frac{1}{2^{n-1}} < 3.$$

It follows that $2 < e < 3$.

The sequence $\{S_n\}$ of partial sums is an increasing sequence because $S_{n+1} = S_n + \dfrac{1}{(n+1)!}$. Since $\{S_n\}$ is increasing and each term is less than 3, it follows that $\{S_n\}$ has a limit. (See Theorem 5-2 of Section 5–7.) This limit is by definition the irrational number e.

$$e = \lim_{n \to \infty} S_n$$

where $\qquad S_n = 1 + \dfrac{1}{1!} + \dfrac{1}{2!} + \cdots + \dfrac{1}{n!} \quad (n \in \{0, 1, 2, \cdots\})$

The series $\displaystyle\sum_{n=0}^{\infty} \dfrac{1}{n!}$ can be used to calculate decimal approximations for e. You are asked to do this in the exercises.

There are other equivalent ways of expressing e as a limit. One of the most common is

$$e = \lim_{n \to \infty} \left(1 + \frac{1}{n}\right)^n \qquad\qquad \mathbf{1}$$

If e is raised to the real power x then

$$e^x = \lim_{n \to \infty} \left(1 + \frac{x}{n}\right)^n \quad \forall x \in R \qquad\qquad \mathbf{2}$$

If $x = -1$, then from **2** it follows that

$$e^{-1} = \frac{1}{e} = \lim_{n \to \infty} \left(1 - \frac{1}{n}\right)^n \qquad\qquad \mathbf{3}$$

Since $n \longrightarrow \infty$ is equivalent to $h \longrightarrow 0$ when $h = \dfrac{1}{n}$, the following limits may also be used to obtain e or e^x.

$$e = \lim_{h \to 0} (1 + h)^{\frac{1}{h}} \qquad\qquad \mathbf{4}$$

and

$$e^x = \lim_{h \to 0} (1 + xh)^{\frac{1}{h}} \qquad\qquad \mathbf{5}$$

The following expression

$$\lim_{n \to \infty} \left(1 + \frac{1}{n}\right)^n$$

is equivalent to

$$e = \sum_{n=0}^{\infty} \frac{1}{n!}$$

as can be seen by expanding $\left(1 + \frac{1}{n}\right)^n$, using the binomial theorem, and simplifying.

$$\left(1 + \frac{1}{n}\right)^n = 1 + n \cdot \frac{1}{n} + \frac{(n)(n-1)}{2!} \cdot \frac{1^2}{n^2} + \frac{n(n-1)(n-2)}{3!} \cdot \frac{1^3}{n^3} + \cdots + \frac{1^n}{n^n}$$

or

$$\left(1 + \frac{1}{n}\right)^n = 1 + \frac{1}{1!} + \frac{1^2}{2!}\left(1 - \frac{1}{n}\right) + \frac{1^3}{3!} \cdot \left(1 - \frac{1}{n}\right)\left(1 - \frac{2}{n}\right) + \cdots$$

$$+ \frac{1^n}{n!}\left(1 - \frac{1}{n}\right)\left(1 - \frac{2}{n}\right) \cdots \left(1 - \frac{n-2}{n}\right)\left(1 - \frac{n-1}{n}\right)$$

Passage to the limit as $n \longrightarrow \infty$ can be accomplished by replacing $\frac{1}{n}$ by 0 in each term as follows.

$$e = 1 + \frac{1}{1!} + \frac{1}{2!} + \frac{1}{3!} + \cdots + \frac{1}{n!} + \cdots$$

If e^x is desired, the same procedure applied to $\left(1 + \frac{x}{n}\right)^n$ yields

$$e^x = 1 + \frac{x}{1!} + \frac{x^2}{2!} + \frac{x^3}{3!} + \cdots + \frac{x^n}{n!} + \cdots. \qquad\qquad 6$$

Checkpoint

The irrational number e can be found to any degree of accuracy. Explain how this may be done.

Exercises

A   1. Use

$$e = 1 + \frac{1}{1!} + \frac{1}{2!} + \cdots + \frac{1}{n!} + \cdots$$

to approximate e correct to 3 decimal places. How many terms of the series are needed to obtain the desired degree of accuracy?

2. Repeat Exercise 1 for 6 decimal places.

3. Use
$$e^x = 1 + \frac{x}{1!} + \frac{x^2}{2!} + \frac{x^3}{3!} + \cdots + \frac{x^n}{n!} + \cdots$$

to approximate $e^{0.01}$ correct to four decimal places. How many terms of the series are needed to obtain the desired degree of accuracy?

4. Repeat Exercise 3 for 8 decimal places.

5. Use
$$e^x = 1 + \frac{x}{1!} + \frac{x^2}{2!} + \cdots + \frac{x^n}{n!} + \cdots$$

to write an expression for e^{-1}.

6. Approximate e^{-1} correct to 3 decimal places.

B   **7.** Use the graph of $f(x) = 2^x$ to estimate x in the equation

$$2^x = e.$$

8. In Exercise 7 you found that $2^{1.44} \approx e$. Use this result to construct a graph of
$$f(x) = e^x \quad \text{for} \quad -1 \leq x \leq 2.$$

C   **9.** Prove that the sum of the first 13 terms of the infinite series for e provides an estimate for e which is accurate to 8 decimal places.

(*Hint:*
$$e = 1 + \frac{1}{1!} + \cdots + \frac{1}{12!} + \frac{1}{13!} + \cdots$$

Thus to show that the "error" of estimation is less than 0.000000005 you must show that

$$\frac{1}{13!} + \frac{1}{14!} + \cdots < 0.000000005.$$

To do this use the fact that

$$\frac{1}{13!} + \frac{1}{14!} + \frac{1}{15!} + \cdots < \frac{1}{13!}\left(1 + \frac{1}{13} + \frac{1}{13^2} + \cdots\right).)$$

10. Use the procedure of Exercise 9 to show that your answer to Exercise 1 is correct.

11. Use the procedure of Exercise 9 to show that your answer to Exercise 2 is correct.

12. Use $e^x = 1 + \frac{x}{1!} + \frac{x^2}{2!} + \frac{x^3}{3!} + \cdots + \frac{x^n}{n!}$ to approximate $x^2 e^x$ where x is the following.

   a. $x = 2$
   b. $x = -2$

8-4 The Function $f : x \rightarrow e^x$

As stated in Section 8–2, $f(x) = a^x$, $a > 0$, is a continuous function. In particular, for $x \in R$,

$$f(x) = e^x$$

is a continuous function with domain equal to R.

Values of e^x and e^{-x}

x	e^x	e^{-x}
0.00	1.0000	1.00000
0.01	1.0101	0.99005
0.02	1.0202	0.98020
0.03	1.0305	0.97045
0.04	1.0408	0.96079
0.05	1.0513	0.95123
0.10	1.1052	0.90484
0.15	1.1618	0.86071
0.20	1.2214	0.81873
0.25	1.2840	0.77880
0.30	1.3499	0.74082
0.35	1.4191	0.70469
0.40	1.4918	0.67032
0.45	1.5683	0.63763
0.50	1.6487	0.60653
0.55	1.7333	0.57695
0.60	1.8221	0.54881
0.65	1.9155	0.52205
0.70	2.0138	0.49659
0.75	2.1170	0.47237
0.80	2.2255	0.44933
0.85	2.3396	0.42741
0.90	2.4596	0.40657
0.95	2.5857	0.38674
1.00	2.7183	0.36788
1.50	4.4817	0.22313
2.00	7.3891	0.13534
3.00	20.086	0.04979
4.00	54.598	0.01832
5.00	148.41	0.00674

The graph of $f(x) = e^x$ is shown below.

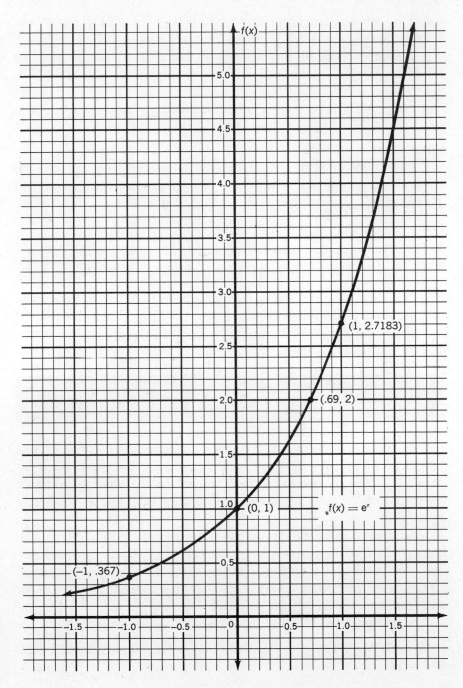

EXAMPLE. Use the graph of $f(x) = e^x$ to estimate x when $e^x = 2$.
Reading from the graph,

$$x \approx 0.69 \text{ corresponds to } f(x) = 2.$$

Checking this estimate in the table, you find $e^{0.70} \approx 2.0138$ and $e^{0.65} \approx$ 1.9155. Thus the estimate of $x = 0.69$ seems fairly good.

A second check on the accuracy of the estimate can be made as follows:

$$e^{0.69} = e^{0.65} \times e^{0.04}$$
$$\approx 1.9155 \times 1.0408$$
$$\approx 1.9936$$

Thus, when $x = 0.69$, $e^x \approx 2$.

The graph of $f(x) = e^x$ has a strange property—a property no other elementary function possesses. If you place a ruler tangent to $f(x) = e^x$ at:

1. $(0, 1)$, you find the slope of the line is 1.
2. $(1, 2.7183)$, you find the slope of the line is 2.7183.
3. $(-1.0, 0.36788)$, you find the slope of the line is 0.36788.

In general, if you place a ruler tangent to $f(x) = e^x$ at (x, e^x) you find the slope of the line is e^x.

Since the slope of a tangent line at a point $(x, f(x))$ is given by the derived function f' evaluated at x, you have the following theorem.

Theorem 8–2 If $f(x) = e^x$, then $f'(x) = e^x$.

The proof of Theorem 8–2 is given in Section 8–11. However, you should convince yourself of its validity by using the graph given on page 377. Copy the curve and draw tangents to the curve at randomly chosen points (x_1, e^{x_1}) and see if the slope of each line is not nearly equal to e^{x_1}.

Applying Theorem 8–2, you can prove that the graph of $f(x) = e^x$ is everywhere concave upward.

First note that $e^x > 0$ for all $x \in R$. Thus, if $f(x) = e^x$ then $f'(x) = e^x$. Since $f'(x) = f(x) = e^x$, $f''(x) = e^x$. Thus $f''(x) > 0$ for all $x \in R$ and $f(x)$ is concave upward.

Note that $\lim_{x \to -\infty} e^x = 0$. Thus the x axis is an asymptote for $f(x) = e^x$. Also, $\lim_{x \to +\infty} e^x = +\infty$ and $f(x) = e^x$ increases without bound as $x \longrightarrow +\infty$.

Now try these

▬ Use the table on page 376 to find an approximation of the value of x.

1. $e^x = 90.02$ **2.** $e^x = 0.0111$ **3.** $x = 1.5^{2.3}$

▬ Determine e^x for each of these values of x.

4. $x = 5$ **5.** $x = 1.6$ **6.** $x = 0.222$

Answers: **1.** 4.5   **2.** −4.5   **3.** 2.5353
       4. 148.41   **5.** 4.9530   **6.** 1.2494

Exercises

A ▬ Use the table on page 376 to estimate the value of the variable.

1. $e^x = 2.65$ **2.** $e^{1.10} = y$ **3.** $e^x = 3$

4. $e^{-1.10} = y$ **5.** $e^x = 0.50$ **6.** $e^{2.5} = y$

▬ Use the table on page 376 to estimate the slope of the tangent to $f(x) = e^x$ at the given point.

7. $(-1, e^{-1})$ **8.** $(0.3, e^{0.3})$

9. $(1.5, e^{1.5})$ **10.** $(-1.5, e^{-1.5})$

11. Use the graph of $f(x) = e^x$ to estimate the slope of the tangent at the points given in Exercises 7–10. Compare your results.

12. Write an equation of the tangent to the graph of f at each point given in Exercises 7–10.

B **13. a.** Through the point (4, 5), draw a line t_1 with slope $m = \frac{2}{3}$.

    b. Draw a line t_2 which is the mirror image of t_1 with respect to the y axis.

    c. To which point on t_2 does (4, 5) correspond?

    d. What is the slope of t_2?

    e. Let (r, s) be on the line t_1 with slope m. Let t_2 be the mirror image of t_1 with respect to the y axis. What point on t_2 corresponds to (r, s)? What is the slope of t_2?

14. a. Plot the point (x, e^x) for which x has the following values.

$$-1.5, -1, -0.5, 0, 0.5, 1.0, 1.5$$

    b. What is the slope of each tangent to $f(x) = e^x$ for the points in **a**? Draw these tangents.

15. Locate the points that are mirror images of the points in Exercise **14a** with respect to the y axis.

16. Draw the lines which are mirror images of the lines in Exercise 14**b** with respect to the y axis.

17. Show that each point of Exercise 15 is on the graph of

$$g(x) = e^{-x}.$$

8–5 Applications – Compound Interest

Several applications of exponential functions will now be considered. The first, *compound interest* is particularly interesting because the number e occurs naturally in the analysis of the problem.

Suppose a sum of money P dollars is invested at an interest rate of r per cent, or $\frac{r}{100}$ per year. Thus at the end of one year you will have

$$P + P\left(\frac{r}{100}\right)$$

or

$$P\left(1 + \frac{r}{100}\right).$$

If no money is withdrawn and the rate remains $\frac{r}{100}$ per year, at the end of a second year you will have

$$P\left(1 + \frac{r}{100}\right) + P\left(1 + \frac{r}{100}\right)\frac{r}{100}$$

or

$$P\left(1 + \frac{r}{100}\right)^2.$$

The process of adding the interest to the principal P is called **compounding.**

In general, if you invest P dollars at an interest rate of $\frac{r}{100}$ per year and compound the interest annually, the total amount A_t you have at the end of t years is given by the following formula.

$$A_t = P\left(1 + \frac{r}{100}\right)^t$$

For some investments the interest is compounded semiannually, quarterly, or, in general, n times per year. In a situation in which the interest is compounded n times a year, the interest rate is $\frac{r}{100n}$ per period, and the number of periods in t years is nt. It follows that the amount A_{nt} after nt periods is

$$A_{nt} = P\left(1 + \frac{r}{100n}\right)^{nt}.$$

EXAMPLE 1. At the end of two years how much money do you have if you invest $100 at an annual interest rate of 4% and the interest is compounded semiannually (every 6 months)?

$$P = 100 \qquad n = 2 \qquad \frac{r}{100} = \frac{4}{100} \qquad t = 2$$

Thus

$$A_4 = 100 \left(1 + \frac{4}{2 \cdot 100}\right)^{2 \cdot 2}$$
$$= 100(1.02)^4$$
$$\approx 100(1.0824)$$
$$\approx 108.24$$

Hence, you have $108.24 at the end of two years.

The more often you compound the interest the more complex the calculation of A_{nt} becomes. In Example 1, if $n = 10$, you would have to calculate $100(1.004)^{20}$, which is clearly not simple. Thus, you need a way of approximating A_{nt}. This is obtained by letting the number of periods, n, increase without bound. Theoretically, this is equivalent to letting the interest be compounded *continuously*.

Compounding interest continuously is equivalent to evaluating the following limit.

$$\lim_{n \to \infty} P \left(1 + \frac{r}{100n}\right)^{nt} \qquad\qquad \textbf{1}$$

The limit **1** can be simplified as follows.

$$\lim_{n \to \infty} P \left(1 + \frac{r}{100n}\right)^{nt} = P \lim_{n \to \infty} \left(1 + \frac{r}{100n}\right)^{nt}$$

$$\text{(since } P \text{ is constant)}$$

$$= P \lim_{n \to \infty} \left[\left(1 + \frac{\frac{r}{100}}{n}\right)^n\right]^t \qquad\qquad \textbf{2}$$

The limit **2** is equal to $Pe^{\frac{rt}{100}}$ because

$$\lim_{n \to \infty} \left(1 + \frac{x}{n}\right)^n = e^x \qquad\qquad \text{(See Section 8-3.)}$$

Thus if interest is **compounded continuously**

$$A_t = Pe^{\frac{rt}{100}} \qquad (t \text{ in years}).$$

The surprising thing here is the occurrence of e.

That $A_t = Pe^{\frac{rt}{100}}$ is a fair approximation to A_{nt} is illustrated in the next example.

EXAMPLE 2. If $P = 100$, $\frac{r}{100} = \frac{4}{100}$ and $t = 2$, what is the amount of money when interest is compounded continuously for two years?

$$A_t = Pe^{\frac{4 \cdot 2}{100}} \quad \text{or} \quad A_t = 100(e^{0.08})$$

The table in Section 8–4 can be used to show the following.

$$
\begin{aligned}
e^{0.08} &= e^{0.05} \cdot e^{0.03} \\
&= (1.0513)(1.0305) \\
&\approx 1.0834
\end{aligned}
$$

Thus
$$
\begin{aligned}
A_t &= 100(1.0834) \\
&= 108.34
\end{aligned}
$$

Comparing this result with Example 1, you find earnings of 10 cents more by continuous compounding.

Now try these

1. Find the compound interest on $100 at 3% semiannually for 2 years.

2. Find the compound amount on $200 at 4% semiannually, for 10 years.

Answers: **1.** $6.14   **2.** $297.19

Exercises

A   **1.** Find the amount of money A_t if $1000 is compounded continuously for 15 years at a rate of 2 per cent.

   In Exercises 2 and 3 find the amount of money A_t if $1000 is invested as stated.

   2. Compounded continuously for 3 years at 2 per cent.

   3. Compounded quarterly for 3 years at 2 per cent.

   4. Compare the results of Exercises 2 and 3.

   Calculate the number of years it would take to double P dollars under the given conditions. Use the approximation $2 \approx e^{0.693}$.

   5. 4 per cent compounded continuously.

   6. 8 per cent compounded continuously.

   7. n per cent compounded continuously.

   In Exercises 8–10, find the annual interest rate compounded continuously in order to double P dollars for the given time period.

   8. 1 year   **9.** 3 years   **10.** 23 years

8–6   Applications – Population Growth

Consider the phenomenon of population growth. It is natural to expect the number of births (and deaths) in equal time intervals for a population to be proportional to the number of members in the population at the beginning of each interval. That is if N_0, N_1 and N_2 represent the number of members in a population at the beginning of equal time intervals, then

$$N_1 = kN_0$$
$$N_2 = kN_1$$

and

$$N_2 = k(kN_0) = k^2N_0$$

where k is the constant of proportionality. Thus, the population N_t at the beginning of the $(t + 1)$th equal time interval is given by the following formula

$$N_t = k^tN_0 \qquad\qquad 1$$

Equation 1 defines an *exponential function*. If you agree that the variable t need not be restricted to integers, then 1 defines a *continuous exponential function* of the constant k.

Consider a population of bacteria. Suppose at time 0 ($t = 0$), there are $N_0 = 1000$ bacteria. Suppose further that the bacteria double in number every day. Thus, the number of bacteria N equals

$$N_0 \quad \text{when } t = 0$$
$$2N_0 \quad \text{when } t = 1 \text{ (day)}$$
$$2(2N_0) = 2^2N_0 \quad \text{when } t = 2 \text{ (days)}$$

and

$$2^nN_0 \quad \text{when } t = n \text{ (days)}$$

In general, then the number N of bacteria present after t days is given by

$$N = 2^tN_0 \qquad\qquad 2$$

or when $N_0 = 1000$

$$N = 2^t(1000) \quad (t \text{ in days})$$

Surely the bacteria do not double themselves exactly at the end of each day. Rather, they reproduce continuously throughout the 24 hours in each interval. Thus it is reasonable to assume that 2 represents the number of bacteria in the colony for all real numbers t greater than or equal to 0.

EXAMPLE. Let $N = 2^t N_0$ represent the number of bacteria in a culture at time $t \geq 0$ (days). If $N_0 = 100$, is the number of bacteria initially,

a. how many bacteria are there $2\frac{1}{2}$ days later?

b. when will there be 500 bacteria?

a. Here $t = 2\frac{1}{2}$.

$$
\begin{aligned}
N &= 2^{\frac{5}{2}}(100) \\
&= 4 \cdot 2^{\frac{1}{2}}(100) \\
&= 400 \cdot \sqrt{2} \\
&\approx 400 \cdot (1.414) \\
&\approx 566 \text{ to the nearest whole number.}
\end{aligned}
$$

There are approximately 566 bacteria when $t = \frac{5}{2}$.

b. Here $N = 500$ and t is unknown.

$$
\begin{aligned}
500 &= 2^t \cdot (100) \\
5 &= 2^t
\end{aligned}
$$

Since
$$
\begin{aligned}
5 &= 2^2 \cdot (1.25) \quad \text{and} \quad 1.25 \approx 2^{0.32}, \\
5 &= 2^{2.32} \quad \text{and} \quad t \approx 2.32 \text{ days.}
\end{aligned}
$$

Notice that even though the discussion in the example dealt with bacteria, the equation

$$N = k^t N_0$$

may be used to estimate the number of members in any population when N_0 and k are known.

Exercises

A ▬ Let a bacteria colony double its members in 24 hours.

1. What equation gives the number of members t days after the beginning of the experiment?

2. The number of bacteria present at the end of $n + 7$ days is how many times the number present at $n + 3$ days from the first count?

3. If there are N bacteria present after 50 days, after how many days were there $\dfrac{N}{8}$ present?

▬ Suppose that there were 90,000 bacteria present at the end of 2 days and 202,500 present at the end of 4 days.

4. Find the number present at the beginning of the count.

5. Find the number present at the end of 5 days.

6. Find the number present at the end of $\frac{1}{2}$ day.

7. Find the number of days at the end of which there are 60,000 bacteria.

8. Find the approximate number of days at the end of which there are 80,000 bacteria.

━━ Suppose a city increases its population by $\frac{1}{8}$ every year. Let N_0 be the number of people at $t = 0$. Use this information in Exercises 9 and 10.

9. Write an equation giving the number N of people in the city at the end of t years.

10. Find the approximate number of years required for the population to double $(N(t) = 2N_0)$.

11. Suppose lemmings triple their population every year and that 1 acre of land supports 100 lemmings. If a herd of 100 lemmings have 100 acres of land, how many years can pass before the land will no longer support the herd? (Assume no lemming dies in the period.)

8–7   Applications – Radioactive Decay

While population growth is an instance of exponential growth, radioactive decay is an example of the opposite phenomenon. You may think of radioactive material as containing a very large number of unstable atoms. These atoms can change spontaneously into stable atoms of another substance. As a result, the number of the unchanged atoms decreases with time. The number $N(x)$ of unchanged atoms at time x, is given by

$$N(x) = N_0 a^{-x}, \qquad\qquad 1$$

where N_0 is the number $N(0)$ at $x = 0$ and a is a suitable constant greater than one.

Since $\forall a > 1$, there is a unique number α (alpha) such that $a = 2^{\alpha}$, equation **1** may be expressed as follows.

$$N(x) = N_0 2^{-\alpha x} \qquad\qquad 2$$

Moreover, since $2 \approx e^{0.693}$, equation **2** may be written as follows.

$$N(x) = N_0 e^{-\alpha(0.693)x}$$

If you let $c = -\alpha(0.693)$ this can be written as follows.

$$N(x) = N_0 e^{-cx} \qquad\qquad 3$$

Clearly, the fraction of radioactive atoms which remain after a given time t is fixed, since

$$\frac{N(x+t)}{N(x)} = \frac{N_0 a^{-(x+t)}}{N_0 a^{-x}} = a^{-t}$$

is independent of the starting time x.

As $t \longrightarrow +\infty$, $\dfrac{N(x+t)}{N(x)} \longrightarrow 0$. Thus, for some time T, $N(x+T)$ must be equal to one half of $N(x)$. The time T at which exactly one half of the radioactive atoms remain is called the half-life of the radio-active matter.

To find the half-life T of a radioactive substance it is convenient to use equation 2. You must solve

$$\tfrac{1}{2}N_0 = N_0 2^{-\alpha x},$$

because you want to determine the time when the number of radio-active atoms equals one half the original number N_0.

The solution follows.

$$\tfrac{1}{2}N_0 = N_0 2^{-\alpha T}$$

and
$$2^{-1} = 2^{-\alpha T}.$$

Thus
$$\alpha T = 1$$

$$T = \frac{1}{\alpha} \quad \text{or} \quad \alpha = \frac{1}{T}.$$

Consequently the equation describing radioactive decay can be written

$$N(x) = N_0 2^{-\frac{x}{T}}, \qquad\qquad 4$$

where T is the half-life of the substance.

EXAMPLE. If a substance decomposes in such a way that at the end of 400 years only one half of it remains, what fraction of the substance remains after 80 years?

The fraction which remains after 80 years is

$$\frac{N(80)}{N(0)}.$$

The data imply that the half-life is 400 years. Thus equation 4 gives you

$$N(80) = N_0 2^{-\frac{80}{400}} = N_0 2^{-\frac{1}{5}},$$

from which you have the following.

$$\frac{N(80)}{N(0)} = 2^{-\frac{1}{5}} \approx e^{-\frac{0.693}{5}} \approx e^{-0.14} \approx 0.869$$

Exercises

A **1.** The half-life of radon is 385 days. What fraction of a sample with N_0 atoms remains at the end of 7.7 days? After 23.1 days?

2. Find the half-life of uranium if $\frac{1}{3}$ of the substance decomposes in 0.26 billion years.

3. The half-life of a radioactive substance is 25 minutes. What fraction of the sample remains after

    a. 12.5 minutes?
    b. 75 minutes?
    c. 150 minutes?

4. The half-life of Polonium (212) is 3×10^{-7} seconds. How much of a given sample remains after

    a. 1 minute?
    b. 12.2 minutes?
    c. 1 day?
    d. 3 days?

B **5.** In living matter the proportion of carbon which is radioactive does not vary with time (supposedly), but it decays from the time of death with a half-life of 5600 years. Date a piece of wood in which the radioactive carbon is 0.78 of the radioactive carbon of a similar specimen of living wood.

6. The half-life of a radioactive substance is 1 hour. What fraction of the substance is radioactive at the end of 1 second? at the end of 3 seconds?

8–8 Inverses

In order to proceed with the major topic of this chapter, it is necessary to review and extend the idea of the inverse of a function. Recall that if f is a function and if g (which may or may not be a function) is the *inverse* of f, then

$$f : x \longrightarrow y \quad (x \in f, y \in g)$$
$$g : y \longrightarrow x \quad (x \in f, y \in g).$$

Each $x \in f$ corresponds to a unique $y \in g$ in the above mappings. However, since g need not be a function, each $y \in g$ need not correspond to a unique $x \in f$. The following examples will illustrate the case where g is a function and the case where g is not a function.

EXAMPLE 1. Identify the inverse of the function sin = $\{(x, y) : y = \sin x, x \in R\}$ and tell whether it is a function.

The inverse is

$$g = \text{arc sin} = \{(x, y) : x = \sin y, x \in [-1, 1]\}$$
$$= \{(x, y) : y = \text{arc sin } x, x \in [-1, 1]\}.$$

Arc sin is not a function.

If the inverse of a function is itself a function then it is referred to as the **inverse function** of f and may be denoted by f^{-1}, which is read "f inverse."

EXAMPLE 2. Identify the inverse of the function

$$\text{Sin} = \left\{ (x, y) : y = \sin x, x \in \left[-\frac{\pi}{2}, \frac{\pi}{2} \right] \right\}$$

and tell whether it is a function.

The inverse is

$$f^{-1} = \text{Arc sin} = \{(x, y) : x = \text{Sin } y, x \in [-1, 1]\}$$
$$= \{(x, y) : y = \text{Arc sin } x, x \in [-1, 1]\}$$

Because of the restricted domain of Sin, Arc sin *is* a function.

A good way to picture a function f and its inverse function, f^{-1}, is to think of a diagram such as the following.

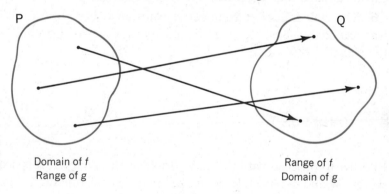

P   Q

Domain of f Range of f
Range of g Domain of g

If f associates each member of P with one and only one member of Q, then the inverse function of f associates each number of Q with one and only one member of P. The function f would be represented by arrows going from P to Q while for f^{-1} the same arrows would point in the opposite direction. Clearly turning the arrows around can be done in only one way. Thus it is intuitively evident that the inverse of a function is unique. By definition it follows that

$$f^{-1}((f(x)) = x \quad \text{and} \quad f(f^{-1}(y)) = y.$$

388   CHAPTER 8

Theorem 8-3 If f has an inverse function, f^{-1}, and $x_1 \neq x_2$ are points in the domain of f, then $f(x_1) \neq f(x_2)$.

Proof: The proof is indirect. Suppose $f(x_1) = f(x_2)$, f has an inverse function and $x_1 \neq x_2$, then

$$f^{-1}(f(x_1)) = f^{-1}(f(x_2))$$

and $\qquad\qquad\qquad x_1 = x_2$

by the definition of inverse function. But

$$x_1 \neq x_2 \qquad\qquad\qquad \text{by assumption.}$$

Thus you have a contradiction, and the theorem is proved.

A function for which $f(x_1) \neq f(x_2)$ whenever $x_1 \neq x_2$ is a **one-to-one function.** Theorem 8–3 may be restated as:

If a function f has an inverse function then it is one-to-one.

The converse of Theorem 8–3 is also true. You shall find it and a related theorem valuable in the next section.

Theorem 8-4 If a function f is one-to-one, then f has an inverse function.

Proof: The hypothesis that f is one-to-one allows you to construct a function g which will turn out to be the inverse function of f.

Let y be an element in the range of f. Then, since f is one-to-one, there is one and only one element x in the domain of f such that $y = f(x)$. Let g be the function that associates each y with the unique x, that is $g(y) = x$ when $y = f(x)$. Clearly the domain of g is the range of f. Also, since $y = f(x)$,

$$g(y) = g(f(x)) = x$$

and since $\qquad\qquad\qquad x = g(y)$

$$f(x) = f(g(y)) = y.$$

Thus g is the inverse of f and $g = f^{-1}$.

Definition A function f is *strictly increasing* if and only if for any two elements x_1 and x_2 in the domain of f, $x_1 < x_2$ implies $f(x_1) < f(x_2)$.

Intuitively, a strictly increasing function has a graph which is everywhere rising to the right.

Theorem 8–5 If f is a strictly increasing function, then f has an inverse function.

Proof: Let x_1 and x_2 be any two distinct members of the domain of f. There are two possible relations between x_1 and x_2. They are the following.

$$x_1 < x_2 \quad \text{or} \quad x_2 < x_1$$

If $x_1 < x_2$, then by hypothesis $f(x_1) < f(x_2)$.
If $x_2 < x_1$, then $f(x_2) < f(x_1)$.
In either case, $f(x_1) \neq f(x_2)$, and f is one-to-one. Hence, f has an inverse function by Theorem 8–4.

The simple relation between the graph of a function f and its inverse function f^{-1} is familiar to you. If t and u are real numbers so that $t = f(u)$, then $P(u, t)$ is a point of the graph of f. But if $t = f(u)$, then $u = f^{-1}(t)$ and $Q(t, u)$ is a point of the graph of f^{-1}. Thus the graph f^{-1} can be obtained from the graph of f by plotting the points obtained by interchanging the coordinates of the points of f. This relation is illustrated in the figure below.

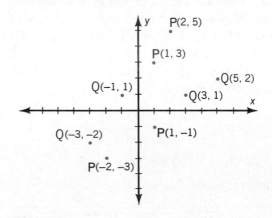

It can be shown that each point $Q(t, u)$ of the graph of f^{-1} is the mirror image of the point $P(u, t)$ of f with respect to the line $y = x$. This is done by showing that $y = x$ is the perpendicular bisector of the segment PQ. It is left for you to do in the exercises.

Now try these

1. If $f(x) = 5x - 3$ find the inverse function if it exists.

2. If g is the inverse of f in Exercise 1, write 3 ordered pairs in f, interchange the elements and check the new ordered pairs in g.

3. Suppose that f is defined by $f : x \longrightarrow 2x + 5$. Find an expression for f^{-1}.

4. The function f is described by $f(x) = \frac{x}{3} - 1$.

    a. Show that f is a one-to-one function.

    b. Describe f^{-1}.

Answers: **1.** $f^{-1} = \dfrac{f + 3}{5}$ **2.** $f(x) : \{(0, -3), (1, 2), (-1, -8), \ldots\}$

    3. $f^{-1} : x \longrightarrow \dfrac{x - 5}{2}$ **4a.** $\dfrac{x_1}{3} - 1 = \dfrac{x_2}{3} - 1$ implies $x_1 = x_2$.

                                                b. $f^{-1} : x \longrightarrow 3(x + 1)$

Exercises

A In Exercises 1–4, find the inverse of each function.

    1. $f : x \longrightarrow 3x - 2$ **2.** $f : x \longrightarrow -\frac{1}{2}x + 1$

    3. $f : x \longrightarrow \frac{2}{x} + 1$ **4.** $f : x \longrightarrow x^3 - 2$

In Exercises 5–8, solve each equation for x in terms of y. Compare your results with those you obtained in Exercises 1–4.

    5. $y = 3x - 2$ **6.** $y = -\frac{1}{2}x + 1$

    7. $y = \frac{2}{x} + 1$ **8.** $y = x^3 - 2$

9. Sketch the graph of $f(x) = x^2$, $x \in R$.

    a. Show that f does not have an inverse function.

    b. Sketch the graphs of $f_1(x) = x^2$, $x \geq 0$ and $f_2(x) = x^2$, $x < 0$, and identify the inverse functions.

    c. What relationship exists among the domains of f, f_1 and f_2? (f_1 is said to be the **restriction** of f to the domain $\{x : x \geq 0\}$ and f_2 is the restriction of f to the domain $\{x : x < 0\}$.)

10. Sketch the graph of $f(x) = \sqrt{9 - x^2}$. Does f have an inverse function? If not, how could the domain be restricted so that the resulting functions have inverses?

B **11.** Define a strictly decreasing function.

12. Prove: Every strictly decreasing function has an inverse function.

13. Prove: The line $y = x$ is the perpendicular bisector of the segment $\overline{PQ}$, where the coordinates of P are (t, u) and for Q are (u, t), thus showing that the graphs of a function and its inverse are mirror images.

14. Sketch the graph of f and its inverse. (Use Exercise 13.)

   a. $f(x) = 3x - 2$ **b.** $f(x) = x^3 - 2$

C **15.** For $f(x) = \frac{2}{3}x - 4$ sketch the graphs and find the slopes of f and f^{-1}.

16. Repeat Exercise 15 for $g(x) = \frac{1}{2}x + 1$ and $h(x) = mx + b$, $m \neq 0$.

17. State a relation between the slope of a linear function and the slope of its inverse.

—— Use the function $f(x) = x^2$, $x \geq 0$ in Exercises 18–20.

18. What is the slope of the tangent to f at $x = 4$?

19. Find f^{-1} and the slope of the tangent to f^{-1} at $x = 16$.

20. State a relation suggested by Exercises 18 and 19.

8–9 Logarithmic Functions

Does an exponential function have an inverse function? Clearly the answer is yes, for when $a > 1$, $a^{x_1} < a^{x_2}$ whenever $x_1 < x_2$. Thus applying Theorem 8–5 (or Exercise 12, Section 8–8 when $0 < a < 1$) the exponential function $f : x \longrightarrow a^x$, $a > 0$ has an inverse function. For the remainder of this section let a be restricted to real numbers greater than 1.

If $f(x) = a^x$, then the graph of $f^{-1}(x)$ is the mirror image of the graph of f with respect to the line $y = x$ since (u, t) is in f^{-1} if and only if (t, u) is in f. Since the domain of f is R and the range is the set of positive real numbers, the domain of f^{-1} is the set of positive real numbers, and the range is R. The graphs of f and f^{-1} are shown.

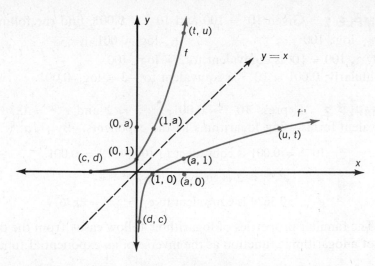

The function f^{-1} is called the **logarithm to the base** a and is denoted by the symbol $\log_a$. Thus

$$f^{-1} : x \longrightarrow \log_a x.$$

Now
$$f : x \longrightarrow a^x$$
and
$$f^{-1} : x \longrightarrow \log_a x$$

are inverse functions. Thus

$$f(f^{-1}(x)) = x$$

and

$$f^{-1}(f(x)) = x.$$

From this it follows that

$$f(\log_a x) = x \qquad\qquad\qquad 1$$

and

$$f^{-1}(a^x) = x \qquad\qquad\qquad 2$$

or using exponential and logarithmic notation exclusively

$$a^{\log_a x} = x \qquad\qquad\qquad 1'$$

and

$$\log_a a^x = x. \qquad\qquad\qquad 2'$$

From **1'** you can see that "$\log_a x$" is the exponent to which a must be raised to yield x. Thus

$$y = \log_a x \quad \text{and} \quad x = a^y \qquad\qquad 3$$

are equivalent equations. This relationship accounts for the fact that logarithms are frequently defined as exponents.

EXAMPLE 1. Given $10^2 = 100$ and $10^{-3} = 0.001$, find the following.

   a. $\log_{10} 100$ b. $\log_{10} 0.001$

a. By **3**, $100 = 10^2$ is equivalent to $2 = \log_{10} 100$.

b. Similarly, $0.001 = 10^{-3}$ is equivalent to $-3 = \log_{10} 0.001$.

EXAMPLE 2. Express $10^{-3} = 0.001$, $e^{0.693} \approx 2$ and $e^{-1} \approx 0.3679$ in equivalent forms using logarithms as the exponents. By **1′**, $a^{\log_a x} = x$.

Thus $10^{-3} = 0.001$ is equivalent to $10^{\log_{10} 0.001} \approx 0.001$.

$$e^{0.693} \approx 2 \text{ is equivalent to } e^{\log_e 2} \approx 2.$$

and $e^{-1} \approx 0.3679$ is equivalent to $e^{\log_e 0.3679} \approx 0.3679$.

The familiar properties of logarithms follow easily from the definition of a logarithmic function as the inverse of an exponential function.

Theorem 8-6 $\log_a 1 = 0$.

Proof: If $f : x \longrightarrow a^x$, then $f(x) = a^x$ and $f(0) = a^0 = 1$. Thus $f^{-1}(1) = 0$ or $\log_a 1 = 0$.

Theorem 8-7 $\log_a y_1 \cdot y_2 = \log_a y_1 + \log_a y_2$.

Proof: If $f : x \longrightarrow a^x$, then $f(x) = a^x$ and

$$f(x_1 + x_2) = a^{x_1 + x_2} = a^{x_1} \cdot a^{x_2} = f(x_1) \cdot f(x_2).$$

Thus $f^{-1}(f(x_1 + x_2)) = f^{-1}(f(x_1) \cdot f(x_2))$.   **4**

By definition: $f^{-1}(f(x_1 + x_2)) = x_1 + x_2$.

Let $y_1 = f(x_1)$ and $y_2 = f(x_2)$. Thus $f^{-1}(y_1) = x_1$ and $f^{-1}(y_2) = x_2$. Substitution in **4** gives

$$x_1 + x_2 = f^{-1}(y_1 \cdot y_2).$$

But $x_1 + x_2 = f^{-1}(y_1) + f^{-1}(y_2)$.

Thus $f^{-1}(y_1 \cdot y_2) = f^{-1}(y_1) + f^{-1}(y_2)$.

Changing to logarithmic notation you have

$$\log_a y_1 \cdot y_2 = \log_a y_1 + \log_a y_2$$

for all positive real numbers y_1 and y_2.

Proof: If
$$f : x \longrightarrow a^x,$$
then
$$f(x) = a^x.$$

Therefore
$$f(xp) = a^{xp}$$
$$= [a^x]^p$$
$$= [f(x)]^p.$$

Using the inverse relation
$$f^{-1}([f(x)]^p) = f^{-1}[f(xp)]$$
$$= xp. \qquad\qquad 5$$

Let $y = f(x)$ and $x = f^{-1}(y)$.

Substitute in 5.
$$f^{-1}(y^p) = [f^{-1}(y)]p$$

Changing to logarithmic notation you have the following.
$$\log_a y^p = p \log_a y$$

The following theorems are easy consequences of Theorems 8-7 and 8-8. They are left for you to prove in the exercises.

The table of values for e^x in Section 8-4 can be used to find the logarithms to the base e of certain numbers. Since
$$e^{0.65} \approx 1.9155,$$
$$\log_e 1.9155 \approx 0.65.$$

But what is $\log_e 2$? That is, if $e^x = 2$, what is x? A method of finding $\log_e 2$ is illustrated in Example 3.

EXAMPLE 3. Find $\log_e 2$.

The procedure is to express 2 as a product of factors which are in the table of Section 8–4. In this way, using Theorem 8–7 you can find $\log_e 2$.

The largest number not greater than 2 in column 2 of the table is 1.9155.

$$2 \div 1.9155 \approx 1.0441$$

and so $\qquad\qquad 2 \approx 1.9155 \cdot 1.0441$

1.0441 is not in the second column of the table, so choose the greatest entry not greater than 1.0441 and divide.

$$1.0441 \div 1.0408 \approx 1.003$$

Thus $\qquad\qquad 1.0441 \approx 1.0408 \cdot 1.003$

and $\qquad\qquad 2 \approx 1.9155 \cdot 1.0408 \cdot 1.003$

Hence, $\qquad \log_e 2 \approx \log_e 1.9155 + \log_e 1.0408 + \log_e 1.003$

$$\approx .65 + .04 + .003 = .693$$

Finally,

$$\log_e 2 \approx .693 \quad \text{or} \quad e^{0.693} \approx 2.$$

In a manner similar to that illustrated in Example 3 you can show that $\log_e 3 \approx 1.099$.

EXAMPLE 4. Find

    a. $\log_e 6$.   **b.** $\log_e 4$.

    By Theorem 8–7

$$\log_e 6 = \log_e 2 + \log_e 3$$

From Example 3,

$$\log_e 2 \approx 0.693$$

From the comment above,

$$\log_e 3 \approx 1.099$$

Thus $\qquad\qquad \log_e 6 \approx 0.693 + 1.099$

$$= 1.792$$

Since $4 = 2^2$, by Theorem 8–8

$$\begin{aligned} \log_e 4 &= \log_e 2^2 \\ &= 2 \log_e 2 \\ &\approx 2(0.693) \\ &= 1.386 \end{aligned}$$

An accurate graph of $f : x \longrightarrow \log_e x$ follows. You will be asked to use it in the exercises.

396   CHAPTER 8

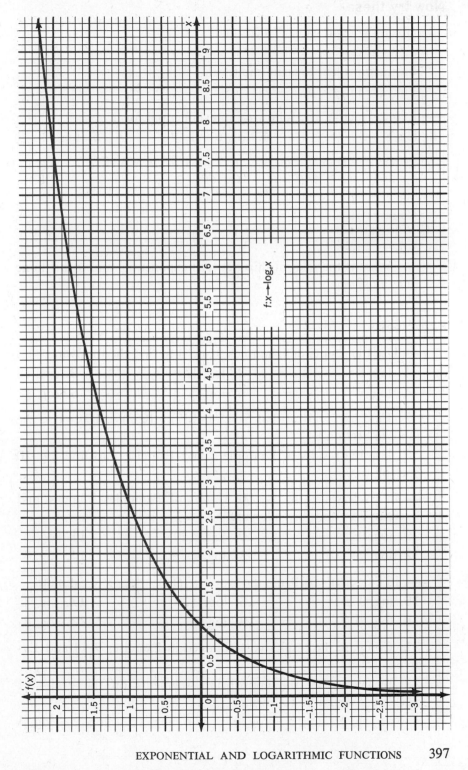

f:x → log_e x

Now try these

1. Given the expression $y = 2^x$, find
   a. its inverse.
   b. an equivalent logarithmic form.
2. Find the inverse of $y = e^x$.

— Express each of the following in exponential form.

3. $\log_2 8 = 3$ 4. $\log_6 6 = 1$ 5. $\log_{16} 2 = \frac{1}{4}$

Answers: **1a.** $x = 2^y$ or $y = \log_2 x$.   **b.** $x = \log_2 y$ **2.** $x = e^y$ or $y = \log_e x$.
      3. $2^3 = 8$.   **4.** $6^1 = 6$.   **5.** $(16)^{\frac{1}{4}} = 2$.

Checkpoint

What is the relationship between exponential and logarithmic functions?

Exercises

A — Use the results of Examples 3 and 4 to find the following.

1. $\log_e 8$ 2. $\log_e 12$ 3. $\log_e 18$
4. $\log_e 9$ 5. $\log_e \frac{3}{2}$ 6. $\log_e \frac{9}{4}$

7. Find $\log_e 5$ given that $5 \approx (4.4817)(1.1052)(1.009)$. Use the table in Section 8–4.

8. Use the results of Example 3 and Exercise 7 to find $\log_e 10$ and $\log_e 100$.

— In Exercises 9–14, use the results of Examples 3 and 4 and Exercise 7 to find the following.

9. $\log_e 0.25$ 10. $\log_e 0.20$ 11. $\log_e \frac{5}{3}$
12. $\log_e \frac{3}{5}$ 13. $\log_e \frac{2}{3}$ 14. $\log_e \frac{2}{5}$

— In Exercises 15–20, use the graph of $f(x) = \log_e x$ to estimate

15. $\log_e 0.25$ 16. $\log_e 0.20$ 17. $\log_e \frac{5}{3}$
18. $\log_e \frac{3}{5}$ 19. $\log_e \frac{2}{3}$ 20. $\log_e \frac{2}{5}$

21. Compare the results you obtained in Exercises 9–14 and Exercises 15–20.

22. By measuring the appropriate segments on the graph of $f(x) = e^x$, verify the following.
   a. $\log_e 2 + \log_e 3 = \log_e 6$ b. $\log_e 1.5 + \log_e 2 = \log_e 3$

B ■ In Exercises 23–28, express each in the exponential form.

23. $\log_{10} x = 5$ **24.** $\log_{10} 19 = y$

25. $\log_3 25 = y$ **26.** $\log_n m = p$

27. $2 \log_3 5 = y$ **28.** $\log_e 5 + \log_e 7 = x$

29. Prove Theorem 8–9.

30. Prove Theorem 8–10.

31. Prove: $\log_a a = 1$.

■ In Exercises 32–37, write each statement in logarithmic form.

32. $81 = 3^4$ **33.** $\sqrt[3]{125} = 5$

34. $10^{-2} = 0.01$ **35.** $\frac{1}{6} = (36)^{-\frac{1}{2}}$

36. $0.04^{\frac{3}{2}} = 0.008$ **37.** $\sqrt{\sqrt{16}} = 2$

■ Given $\log_{10} 5 = 0.6990$, find the following.

38. $\log_{10} 2$ **39.** $\log_{10} \frac{1}{5}$

40. $\log_{10} \frac{25}{4}$ **41.** $\log_{10} \frac{64}{25}$

C   **42.** Find x if

      a. $\log_4 x + \log_4 (x + 6) = 2$

      b. $2 \log_2 x = -2$

■ Given that $a^x = a^y$ if and only if $x = y$, that $a^{\log_a b} = b$, and the laws of exponents prove the following.

43. $\log_a b \cdot c = \log_a b + \log_a c$ (*Hint:* Let $b = a^{\log_a b}$, $c = a^{\log_a c}$ and $bc = a^{\log_a bc}$. Substitute the exponential expressions for b and c in $a^{\log_a bc} = bc$ and simplify.)

44. $\log_a \dfrac{b}{c} = \log_a b - \log_a c$

45. $\log_a b^c = c \log_a b$

8–10   Logarithms with Special Bases

    The two numbers which are most commonly used as the bases of logarithms are ten and e. Logarithms with the base ten are **common logarithms.** Common logarithms are extremely useful in performing long calculations involving repeated multiplication, division, and exponentiation. This application is directly related to the facts that the Hindu-Arabic numeration system uses ten as its base and that every number may be expressed as the product of a number between one and ten and an integral power of ten.

EXAMPLE 1. Given $\log_{10} 2 \approx 0.3010$ find the following.

  a. $\log_{10} 200$ **b.** $\log_{10} 0.0002$

a. Since $200 = 2 \times 10^2$,

$$\begin{aligned} \log_{10} 200 &= \log_{10} 2 + \log_{10} 10^2 \\ &\approx 0.3010 + 2\log_{10} 10 \\ &= 0.3010 + 2 \\ &= 2.3010. \end{aligned}$$

b. Similarly, $0.0002 = 2 \times 10^{-4}$.

  Thus
$$\begin{aligned} \log_{10} 0.0002 &= \log_{10} 2 + \log_{10} 10^{-4} \\ &\approx 0.3010 + -4 \\ &= -4 + .3010, \text{ or } -3.6990 \end{aligned}$$

The number $e \approx 2.7183$ is the second commonly used base of logarithms. Logarithms with base e are called **natural logarithms** and $\log_e x$ is usually denoted "ln x." The name "natural logarithm" is appropriate because when e is the base of a logarithmic function the derived function is especially simple as you will see in Section 8–11.

Since e and ten are usually used as the bases of logarithms, and since extensive tables of these logarithms are available, it is appropriate to consider the question of how a logarithm to another base may be converted to a base e logarithm or base ten logarithm. The general problem of converting the logarithm with any base a to a logarithm with base b is considered first.

By identity **1′** of Section 8–9, page 393,

$$x = b^{\log_b x}. \tag{1}$$

Taking the logarithm to base a of x you find

$$\log_a x = \log_a (b^{\log_b x})$$

or $$\log_a x = \log_b x \cdot \log_a b \tag{2}$$

You can use equation **2** to change from logarithms with base a to those with base b, as Example 2 illustrates.

EXAMPLE 2. Express $\log_4 16$ as a base 2 logarithm.

  By **2**, you have

$$\log_4 16 = \log_2 16 \cdot \log_4 2$$

or $$\log_2 16 = \frac{\log_4 16}{\log_4 2}$$

Since $\log_4 16 = 2$ and $\log_4 2 = \frac{1}{2}$,

$$\log_2 16 = \frac{2}{\frac{1}{2}} = 4.$$

This is as it should be.

Common logarithms can be expressed in terms of natural logarithms in the manner illustrated in Example 2.

$$\ln x = (\log_{10} x)\ln 10$$
$$\log_{10} x = \frac{\ln x}{\ln 10}$$

From Exercise 8, Section 8–9 you know that

$$\ln 10 \approx 2.303.$$

Thus
$$\log_{10} x \approx \frac{\ln x}{2.303} \qquad\qquad\qquad 3$$
$$\log_{10} x \approx 0.434(\ln x) \qquad\qquad 4$$
$$\ln x \approx 2.303(\log_{10} x) \qquad\qquad 5$$

EXAMPLE 3. Find $\log_{10} e$ and $\ln 10$.
Equation 4 for $x = e$ implies

$$\log_{10} e \approx 0.434(\ln e) = 0.434.$$

Equation 5 for $x = 10$ implies

$$\ln 10 = 2.303(\log_{10} 10) = 2.303.$$

The solution of Example 3 has an interesting sidelight. Since $\frac{1}{2.303} \approx 0.434$, it appears that

$$\frac{1}{\ln 10} = \log_{10} e. \qquad\qquad\qquad 6$$

This relation is valid and can be proved by setting $x = 10$, $a = 10$, and $b = e$ in equation 2. More generally:

Theorem 8–11 $\log_a b = \dfrac{1}{\log_b a}$

The proof is left for you to do in the exercises.

Checkpoint

1. Explain how common and natural logarithms differ.
2. Explain how to convert a logarithm in a given base (not e) to a logarithm in base e.
3. Explain how to convert a logarithm in a given base (not e) to a logarithm in base ten.

Exercises

A ━━ Given $\log_{10} 2 = 0.3010$, $\log_{10} 3 = 0.4771$, $\log_{10} 5 = 0.6990$, and $\log_{10} 7 = 0.8451$, find each logarithm.

1. $\log_{10} 12$
2. $\log_{10} 15$
3. $\log_{10} 6$
4. $\log_{10} 1.2$
5. $\log_{10} 0.15$
6. $\log_{10} 0.006$
7. $\log_{10} 48$
8. $\log_{10} 60$
9. $\log_{10} 128$
10. Convert the common logarithms found in Exercises 1–6 to natural logarithms.

━━ Express each logarithm in simplified form.

11. $\log_{0.01} 0.001$
12. $\log_3 \sqrt{81}$
13. $\log_5 \frac{1}{125}$
14. $\log_4 128$
15. $\log_{\frac{1}{2}} 8$
16. $\ln e^3$
17. $\ln \sqrt[3]{e}$
18. $\log_3 \frac{1}{27}$
19. $\log_2 \sqrt[3]{32}$

B ━━ Find the value of x in Exercises 20–31.

20. $3^{\log_3 2} + 5^{\log_5 7} = 6^{\log_6 x}$
21. $\ln (x^2 - 1) - 2 \ln (x - 1) = \ln 5 \quad (x > 0)$
22. $\ln 4 + 2 \ln x - \ln (x^2 + x) = \ln 2 \quad (x > 0)$
23. $11^{\log_x 7} = 7$
24. $7^{\log_7 x} = 3$
25. $\ln x = 0$
26. $\ln x + 1 = 0$
27. $\ln x = 1$
28. $\ln (x - 2) = 3$
29. $\ln x - 2 = -4$
30. $\ln x^2 - 1 = 3$
31. $\ln (2x - 1) + 2 = 0$

C **32.** For what values of x does $(\ln x)^2 = \ln x^2$?

33. For what values of x does $(\log_{10} x)^2 = \log_{10} x^2$?

34. For what values of x does $(\log_b x)^2 = \log_b x^2$?

35. Prove Theorem 8–11.

36. Find x if $\log_{10} x - 2 + \log_x 10 = 0$.

37. Prove: $(\log_a b)(\log_b c)(\log_c d) = \log_a d$

38. Sketch the graph of $f(x) = |\ln x|$.

39. Solve for x. $2^{2x+2} - 8^{x+2} = 0$.

40. Solve for x. $4^{3x} - 8^{4x+1} = 0$.

41. Solve for x. $3^{3x} - 9^{x+1} = 0$.

42. Solve for x. $7^{2x} - 49^{3x+1} = 0$.

8–11 Derived Function of e^x

In Exercises 15–20 of Section 8–8 you found that there was a simple relationship between the derived function of an increasing (or decreasing) function f and the derived function of f^{-1}. The theorem summarizing these results is stated here without proof.

> **Theorem 8–12** If $y = f(x)$ is increasing (or decreasing) and has a derived function at every point of this interval and $f'(x) \neq 0$ in this interval, then the inverse function $x = g(y)$ has a derived function in the corresponding interval and
>
> $$g'(y) = \frac{1}{f'(x)}.$$

EXAMPLE 1. Verify Theorem 8–12 when $f(x) = mx + b$, $m \neq 0$.

Since $f(x) = mx + b$, $f'(x) = m$. By Theorem 8–12, $g'(y)$ should be $\frac{1}{m}$. You can verify that $g'(y) = \frac{1}{m}$ by finding the inverse of $f(x) = y$. Since $y = mx + b$, it follows that

$$x = \frac{y}{m} - \frac{b}{m},$$

or

$$g(y) = \frac{y}{m} - \frac{b}{m}.$$

Then $g'(y) = \frac{1}{m}$ is obtained by finding the derived function of the polynomial function $g(y)$. Hence, the theorem is verified.

EXAMPLE 2. Verify Theorem 8–12 for

$$f(x) = 3x^2 \qquad x > 0.$$

The function $f(x) = 3x^2$ implies

$$f'(x) = 2 \cdot (3x)$$
$$= 6x.$$

Thus by the theorem,

$$g'(y) = \frac{1}{6x} \cdot$$

But since

$$y = 3x^2$$
$$x = \sqrt{\frac{y}{3}}$$

and

$$g'(y) = \frac{1}{6\sqrt{\dfrac{y}{3}}}$$
$$= \frac{1}{2\sqrt{3y}} \cdot$$

Solving $y = 3x^2$ for x yields

$$g(y) = x = \tfrac{1}{3}\sqrt{3y}.$$

By definition, you have the following.

$$g'(y) = \lim_{h \to 0} \left[\frac{1}{3} \, \frac{\sqrt{3(y + h)} - \sqrt{3y}}{h} \right]$$

(You treat y just as you would x.)

$$= \frac{1}{3} \lim_{h \to 0} \left[\frac{3(y + h) - 3y}{h(\sqrt{3(y + h)} + \sqrt{3y})} \right]$$

(Multiply numerator and denominator by $\sqrt{3(y + h)} + \sqrt{3y}$.)

$$= \frac{1}{3} \lim_{h \to 0} \frac{3}{\sqrt{3(y + h)} + \sqrt{3y}}$$

$$= \frac{1}{2\sqrt{3y}}$$

The two results above are the same and therefore Theorem 8–12 is verified.

Theorem 8–12 will be useful to you in proving that if $f(x) = e^x$ then $f'(x) = e^x$. But to use it, you must first find $f'(x)$ when $f(x) = \ln x$. This is done next.

Let $f(x) = \ln x$. Then by definition,

$$f'(x) = \lim_{h \to 0} \left(\frac{\ln (x + h) - \ln x}{h} \right)$$

$$= \lim_{h \to 0} \frac{\ln \left(\dfrac{x + h}{x} \right)}{h}$$

$$= \lim_{h \to 0} \left[\frac{1}{h} \ln \left(1 + \frac{h}{x} \right) \right]$$

$$= \lim_{h \to 0} \ln \left(1 + \frac{h}{x} \right)^{\frac{1}{h}}$$

$$= \ln \left[\lim_{h \to 0} \left(1 + \frac{h}{x} \right)^{\frac{1}{h}} \right]$$

$$= \ln (e^{\frac{1}{x}}) \qquad \text{By equation 5, Section 8–3.}$$

$$= \frac{1}{x} \ln e \qquad \text{Theorem 8–8.}$$

$$= \frac{1}{x}.$$

Thus the derived function of $f(x) = \ln x$ is $f'(x) = \frac{1}{x}$. This is a remarkably simple expression for $f'(x)$. Notice how naturally e arose in the derivation. This is one reason logarithms with base e are called *natural logarithms*.

These results are summarized by the following theorem.

Theorem 8–13   If $f(x) = \ln x$, then $f'(x) = \frac{1}{x}$.

You can now prove Theorem 8–2 (page 378).

$$\text{If } f(y) = e^y, \text{ then } f'(y) = e^y.$$

Proof: Let $y = \ln x$, then $y' = \frac{1}{x}$.

But $f(y) = e^y$ is the inverse of $y = \ln x$.

Thus
$$f'(y) = \frac{1}{y'} \qquad \text{By Theorem 8–12.}$$

$$= \frac{1}{\dfrac{1}{x}} \qquad \text{By Theorem 8–13.}$$

$$= x.$$

But $x = e^y$ since $y = \ln x$. Thus $f'(y) = e^y$, and the theorem is proved.

EXAMPLE 3. Find the derived function $f'(x)$ if $f(x) = \log_a x$.

Since you know that $g(x) = \ln x$ has a derived function $g'(x) = \dfrac{1}{x}$, it is desirable to change $f(x)$ to a natural logarithm. By equation 2 of Section 8–10,

$$f(x) = \log_a x = (\log_a e)(\ln x).$$

Thus, since $\log_a e$ is constant.

$$f'(x) = (\log_a e) \cdot \frac{1}{x}$$

$$= \frac{\log_a e}{x}$$

(See Exercise 16 below.)

Exercises

A ▬▬ Find the derived function for each function f. Evaluate at the given value of the variable.

1. $f(x) = e^x$; $x = \frac{1}{2}$ **2.** $f(x) = \ln x$; $x = 1$

3. $f(x) = \log_2 x$; $x = 4$ **4.** $f(x) = \log_{10} x$; $x = 2$

5. $f(x) = \log_{\frac{1}{2}} x$; $x = 2$ **6.** $f(x) = \log_{\frac{1}{e}} x$; $x = e$

7. $f(x) = \log_b x$; $x = \dfrac{1}{b}$ **8.** $f(x) = \log_{(e^2)} x$; $x = e^3$

9. $f(x) = e^x + \ln x$, $x > 0$; $x = 1$

10. $f(x) = \ln x + \ln x$; $x = 2$

B   **11.** In Exercises 1–5, write the equation of the line tangent to the curve at the point with the given x coordinate.

12. Prove: $\log_{\frac{1}{b}} a = (-1)(\log_b a)$

13. Use Exercise 12 to prove:

$$\text{If } f(x) = \log_{\frac{1}{b}} x, \text{ then } f'(x) = \frac{-\log_b e}{x}.$$

14. Show that if $f(x) = \log_{\frac{1}{e}} x$, then $f'(x) = -\dfrac{1}{x}$.

C   **15.** Use the definition of the derived function to prove:

$$\text{If } f(x) = \ln (ax), \text{ then } f'(x) = \frac{1}{x}.$$

16. Use the definition of the derived function to prove:

$$\text{If } f(x) = a \ln x, \text{ then } f'(x) = \frac{a}{x}.$$

17. Use the inverse relation between $f(x) = \log_a x$ and $g(y) = a^y$ and Theorem 8–12 to prove:

$$\text{If } g(y) = a^y, \text{ then } g'(y) = (\ln a)a^y.$$

━━ Use the results of Exercise 17 to find $f'(x)$.

18. $f(x) = 2^x$

19. $f(x) = 10^x$

20. $f(x) = \left(\frac{1}{e}\right)^x$

21. $f(x) = (e^2)^x$

━━ Use Exercise 17 to find the derived function.

22. $f(x) = (e^n)^x$

23. $f(x) = e^{nx}$

24. $f(x) = (e^{-1})^x$

25. $f(x) = e^{-x}$

26. What is $f'(x)$ if $f(x) = e^{ax}$, $a \in$ R? Explain.

CHAPTER OBJECTIVES AND REVIEW ━━━━━

Objective: *To know the meaning of the important mathematical terms of this chapter.*

1. Here are many of the mathematical terms used in this chapter. Be sure that you know them thoroughly and can use them correctly.

principal *n*th root of a number (*363*)

exponential function (*368*)

inverse function (*388*)

one-to-one function (*389*)

strictly increasing functions (*390*)

logarithmic function (*392*)

logarithms to the base *a* (*393*)

common logarithms (*399*)

natural logarithms (*400*)

Objective: *To evaluate expressions involving rational exponents easily and accurately.*

━━ Simplify each expression. The set of positive real numbers is the replacement set for all variables.

2. $x^{\frac{3}{4}} \cdot x^{-\frac{2}{3}}$

3. $[a^{\frac{4}{5}} \cdot b^{\frac{2}{3}}]^{-\frac{1}{2}}$

4. $\left(\frac{y^{-2}}{x^3}\right)^{\frac{1}{6}} \cdot \left(\frac{x^3}{y^{-2}}\right)^{\frac{1}{3}}$

5. $200 \cdot (16^{-\frac{3}{4}})$

6. $[(-32)^{\frac{1}{5}}]^5$

7. $\left(\frac{9}{16}\right)^{-\frac{5}{2}}$

━━ Find x in each equation.

8. $4^x = 2^{\frac{6}{5}}$

9. $x^{\frac{2}{3}} = 4$

10. $16^x = 32^{\frac{2}{3}}$

11. $x^{\frac{3}{5}} = 8$

Objective: *To explain how the definition of a^x for $x \in Q$ is extended to a definition of a^x for all real numbers x.*

12. In your own words outline the major ideas used to define a^x for $a > 0$ and $x \in$ R.

Objective: *To use graphs of $f : x \longrightarrow a^x$ for selected values of a to find values of a^x and x.*

▬ The graph of 2^x is on page 369, and of e^x on page 377. Use these graphs to find an approximate value of x for each of the following.

13. $2^{0.30} = x$ **14.** $2^{2.30} = x$ **15.** $e^{0.30} = x$

16. $e^{2.30} = x$ **17.** $2^x = 0.5$ **18.** $e^x = 0.5$

19. $e^{-1} = x$ **20.** $2^{-1} = x$ **21.** $e^x = 2$

Objective: *To describe the graphs of the exponential function and the logarithmic function.*

22. Describe the characteristics of the graph of $f : x \longrightarrow e^x$. Include domain, range, zeros, y intercepts, concavity, and asymptotes. Make a sketch.

23. Describe the characteristics of the graph of $f : x \longrightarrow \ln x$. Include domain, range, zeros, y intercepts, concavity and asymptotes.

Objective: *To use exponential functions to solve problems of compound interest, population growth and radioactive decay.*

24. Find the amount of money A_t if \$2000 is compounded continuously for 10 years, at an annual rate of 5 per cent.

25. The city of Adrian doubled its population in the ten years from 1960 to 1970. In 1960 there were 1,500 residents.

a. How many people will reside in Adrian in 1985 if the population continues to grow at the same rate?

b. In what year will the population be 4500?

26. The half life of a substance is 80 days. What fraction of a sample with N_0 atoms remains at the end of 20 days?

Objective: *To use the relation between logarithms and exponents.*

▬ Write each statement in logarithmic form.

27. $27 = 3^3$ **28.** $125^{-\frac{1}{3}} = \frac{1}{5}$

29. $0.008^{\frac{2}{3}} = 0.04$ **30.** $5^0 = 1$

▬ Complete each statement.

31. $\log_a x \cdot y = \log_a x +$ _____

32. $\log_a x = \log_a b \cdot$ _____

33. $\log_a x^5 =$ _____ $\log_a x$

34. $a^{\log_a x} =$ _____

■ Use the derived functions of ln x and e^x to find an equation of a line tangent to the graph of $y = \ln x$ or $y = e^x$.

■ Find the equation of the tangent to the graph at the specified point.

35. $y = e^x$ at $x = 1$
36. $y = \ln x$ at $x = 1$

CHAPTER TEST

1. Calculate $(4^{\frac{5}{2}})^{-1}$

2. Simplify $(x^{\frac{4}{3}}) \cdot (x^{-\frac{2}{5}}) \cdot (x^{\frac{2}{3}})^{-2}$

3. Find x : $(\frac{2}{3})^{\frac{x}{3}} = \frac{4}{9}$

4. Approximate $2^{0.45}$ using the graph on page 369.

5. Approximate x if $2^x = 2.35$. Use the graph on page 369.

6. What is the base of the natural logarithms?

7. Write $8^{\frac{2}{3}} = 4$ in logarithmic form.

8. Write $\log_2 \frac{1}{4} = -2$ in exponential form.

9. Express $\log_5 10$ as a logarithm with base ten.

10. Express $\log_{10} 5$ as a natural logarithm.

11. Find the amount of money A_t if \$100 is compounded continuously at a rate of 3 per cent for 20 years.

12. How are sequences and limits used to define a^r for real exponents?

13. Explain why the logarithmic function is the inverse of the exponential function with the same base. Sketch the graphs of each on the same set of coordinate axes.

14. If $f(x) = \ln x$ and $g(x) = e^x$ what are
   a. $f'(x)$ and
   b. $g'(x)$?

15. What happens to the slope of a line tangent to $y = \ln x$ as $x \longrightarrow +\infty$? as $x \longrightarrow 0$?

CHAPTER 9

VECTORS, LINES,
AND PLANES

Directed line segments or *vectors* are useful for representing various natural phenomena.

A creative gardener in England constructed the maze at Hampton Court pictured on the opposite page. Can you find a way out? If you were to discover a method of escape from the maze you could then leave behind a "trail of vectors" (actually, arrow diagrams) to help the next weary traveler find his way.

Instead of being caught in a maze, you could be trapped in the classic chess situation pictured on the opposite page. This problem was first stated by Alfred de Musset, a French poet, dramatist, and novelist who lived from 1810 to 1857. Can you figure out how to get White to mate in three moves? Could you then represent your solution in terms of vectors?

As well as being used to locate positions or points on the plane, vectors can be used to represent forces.

The parachutist pictured on the opposite page has many different forces acting on him and on his parachute. You could represent the force of the air on the parachute as a vertical line segment directed upwards and the weight of the man's body as a line segment directed towards the center of the earth.

The house called Fallingwater designed by Frank Lloyd Wright, uses cantilevers. These are horizontal beams extending beyond the house. The weight of the house balances the weight of the extended portion of the beam. The forces of gravity acting on these cantilevers can be represented by vectors.

9–1 Vectors

Analytic geometry is a wedding of algebra and geometry. In analytic geometry the geometric concepts such as lines, planes, circles, angles, etc., are examined from an algebraic point of view. For example, the equation

$$y - 2x + 4 = 0, \quad x \in R$$

is an algebraic model of a line, since each point $A(x, y)$ whose coordinates satisfy $y - 2x + 4 = 0$ is on a line, and each point on that line has coordinates which satisfy $y - 2x + 4 = 0$.

Central to the study of analytic geometry is the derivation of algebraic expressions which describe geometric ideas. In this regard, **vectors** play an important role.

Definition A *vector* is a directed line segment.

A vector is usually denoted by a letter with an arrow over it such as $\vec{A}$ or $\vec{r}$. Since a vector is a segment, it has a *length* or *magnitude*. The length of a vector v is symbolized as $|\vec{v}|$. The length of a vector is often called the *absolute value* of the vector. Thus, $|\vec{v}|$ is the *absolute value*, the *length*, or the *magnitude* of $\vec{v}$.

A vector has two endpoints. The direction of the vector is specified by naming the endpoints in *order*. The first named point is the *initial point* or *foot* of the vector; the second named point is the *terminal point* or *tip* of the vector. Thus a vector from A to B can be represented as $\overrightarrow{AB}$; A is the foot, B is the tip.

Vectors are generally represented geometrically by *arrows*. The end with the arrow head is the tip of the vector. Three vectors are illustrated below.

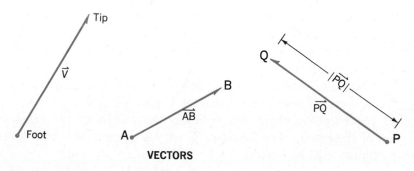

VECTORS

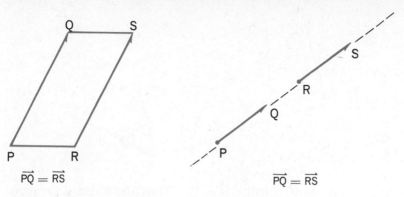

$\overrightarrow{PQ} = \overrightarrow{RS}$ $\overrightarrow{PQ} = \overrightarrow{RS}$

In the definition of equal vectors it is important to notice that the order of the vertices of the parallelogram is important. It is the parallelogram formed by joining in order foot to tip, to tip, to foot, to foot of the given vectors. If a parallelogram is not obtained in this way, the vectors are *not equal.*

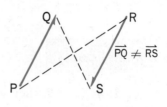

$\overrightarrow{PQ} \neq \overrightarrow{RS}$

Using the definition of equal vectors, you can move a vector to any position in space you may wish. The following example illustrates how this may be done.

EXAMPLE.   Find the vector equal to $\vec{v}$ that has its foot at C. See the figure at the right.

Let D be the tip of the vectors with foot C and equal to $\vec{v}$. Then D is the fourth vertex of parallelogram $ABDC$. The required vector is $\overrightarrow{CD}$ as shown in the figure at the right in red. If C were on the line containing $\overrightarrow{AB}$, how would you proceed to find the vector equal to $\vec{v}$ with foot at C?

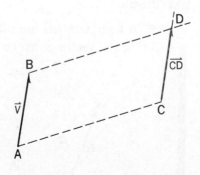

The vectors described in this section are *free vectors* because they do not all have the same foot. But by the definition of equality, any vector may be relocated so that its foot is a specific point. Because of this fact, the notion of the *angle* determined by two vectors is easily understood, even when the two vectors have no point in common.

Suppose you are given $\vec{A}$ and $\vec{B}$ as below.

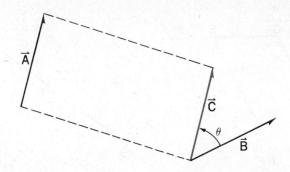

By the definition of equality $\vec{A} = \vec{C}$. Thus the angle determined by $\vec{A}$ and $\vec{B}$ is the angle determined by $\vec{C}$ and $\vec{B}$. Its measure is θ, where $0° \leq \theta \leq 180°$.

Checkpoint

1. If $A \neq B$, then $\overrightarrow{AB}$ is different from $\overrightarrow{BA}$. Explain why this is true.

2. Describe in your own words what is meant by free vectors. by the angle determined by two free vectors.

3. Explain what it means to say $\vec{v} = \vec{r}$.

Exercises

A ━━━ In Exercises 1–2 use the procedure illustrated in the discussion to find the vector equal to $\vec{A}$ with foot at C.

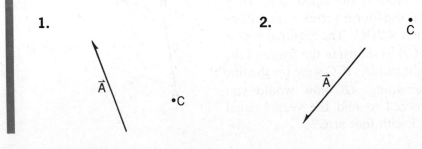

1.

$\vec{A}$ •C

2.   ˙C

$\vec{A}$

■ In Exercises 3–4 use the procedure illustrated in the discussion to find the vector equal to $\vec{A}$ with foot at C.

3.

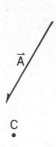

4.

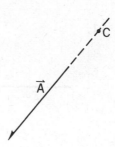

■ In Exercises 5–8 use the procedure illustrated in the previous discussion to find the vector equal to $\vec{B}$ which has its tip at D.

5.

• D

6.

7.

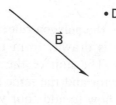

• D

8.

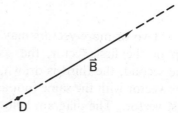

■ In Exercises 9–10 find the measure of the angle between the vectors $\vec{A}$ and $\vec{B}$ by first moving each to C and then measuring with a protractor.

9.

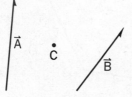

10.

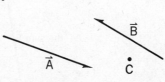

In Exercises 11–14 find the measure of the angle between the vectors $\vec{A}$ and $\vec{B}$ by first moving each to C and then measuring with a protractor.

11. **12.**

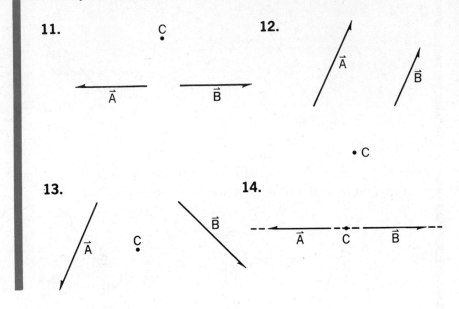

13. **14.**

9–2 Vector Operations

Two or more vectors may be added by the **polygon rule:** from the tip of the first vector, the second vector is drawn; from the tip of the second, the third is drawn, and so on. The sum of the vectors is the vector with the same foot as the first vector and the same tip as the last vector. The diagram below illustrates how to add four vectors by the polygon rule.

$$\vec{v} = \vec{v}_1 + \vec{v}_2 + \vec{v}_3 + \vec{v}_4$$

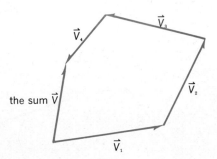

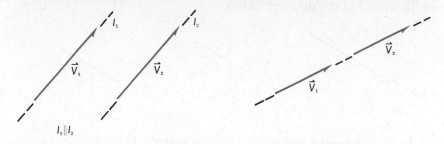

If two nonparallel vectors $\vec{v}_1$ and $\vec{v}_2$ are added, the sum $\vec{v}$ is the third side of a triangle:

$$\vec{v} = \vec{v}_1 + \vec{v}_2.$$

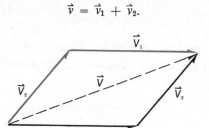

From plane geometry you know that if the opposite sides of a quadrilateral are equal then the figure is a parallelogram. Thus the figure above is a parallelogram. By the definition of equality and addition, $\vec{v}_2 + \vec{v}_1 = \vec{v}$. Thus

$$\vec{v}_1 + \vec{v}_2 = \vec{v}_2 + \vec{v}_1,$$

and addition of vectors is commutative.

If a vector is added to itself, the result is a vector in the same direction and twice as long:

$$\vec{v} + \vec{v} = 2\vec{v}.$$

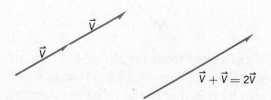

In general if k is any real number, $k \cdot \vec{v}$ is a vector $|\ k\ |$ times as long as $\vec{v}$. If $k > 0$, then $k \cdot \vec{v}$ and $\vec{v}$ have the same direction. If $k < 0$, then $k \cdot \vec{v}$ and $\vec{v}$ have opposite directions. If $k = 0$, then $k \cdot \vec{v}$ is the **zero vector,** denoted $\vec{0}$. No direction is given to the zero vector. These ideas are illustrated in the diagram below.

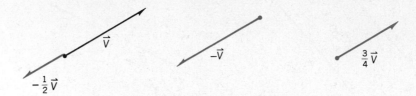

In $k \cdot \vec{v}$ the real number k is called a **scalar.** Thus, $k \cdot \vec{v}$ is a *scalar multiple* of $\vec{v}$. If one vector is a scalar multiple of another, the two vectors are parallel. Conversely if $\vec{v}_1 \parallel \vec{v}_2$, then

$$m \cdot \vec{v}_1 = n \cdot \vec{v}_2,$$

for some m, $n \neq 0$ as pictured below. That is, two vectors are parallel if and only if one is equal to a nonzero scalar multiple of the other.

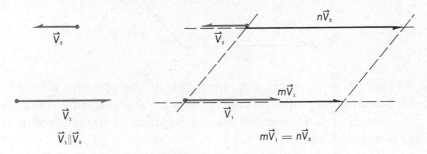

Subtraction of vectors is defined in terms of addition. $\vec{v}_1 - \vec{v}_2$ is the vector which when added to $\vec{v}_2$ gives $\vec{v}_1$.

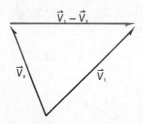

$\vec{v}_1 - \vec{v}_2$, then, is the vector from the tip of $\vec{v}_2$ to the tip of $\vec{v}_1$. $\vec{v}_1 - \vec{v}_2$ can also be obtained by adding $-\vec{v}_2$ to $\vec{v}_1$. That is, $\vec{v}_1 - \vec{v}_2 = \vec{v}_1 + (-\vec{v}_2)$. This is easily seen by referring to the following diagram.

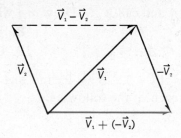

$$\vec{V}_1 + (-\vec{V}_2)$$

Since $\vec{v}_2$ and $-\vec{v}_2$ are scalar multiples of one another, $\vec{v}_2 \parallel -\vec{v}_2$. Also $|\vec{v}_2| = |-\vec{v}_2|$. Since, from plane geometry, you know a quadrilateral is a parallelogram if two sides are parallel and equal, the figure is a parallelogram and

$$\vec{v}_1 - \vec{v}_2 = \vec{v}_1 + (-\vec{v}_2).$$

Checkpoint

1. Convince yourself that the addition of vectors is associative as well as commutative.

2. In your own words define scalar multiplication.

3. In your own words define subtraction for vectors.

Exercises

A — In Exercises 1–5, copy the diagram and find the following.

$$\vec{V} = \vec{A} + \vec{B} \quad \text{and} \quad \vec{T} = \vec{A} - \vec{B}$$

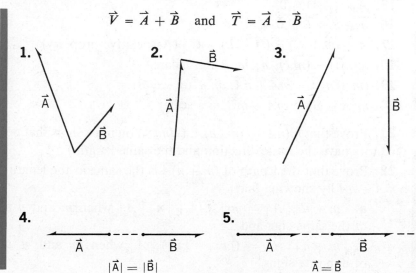

1.

2.

3.

4.

$|\vec{A}| = |\vec{B}|$

5.

$\vec{A} = \vec{B}$

■ Draw a vector and call it $\vec{A}$. Draw $m\vec{A}$ when m is as follows.

6. 3 **7.** $\frac{5}{3}$ **8.** $\frac{1}{3}$ **9.** -2

10. $-\frac{2}{3}$ **11.** $-\frac{7}{2}$ **12.** 0 **13.** $\frac{1}{4}$

14. Let $\vec{A} \parallel \vec{B}$, $|\vec{A}| = 3$, $|\vec{B}| = 2$, and $m\vec{A} = n\vec{B}$. Find m or n as indicated for each of the following.

a. m if $n = 3$.

b. n if $m = \frac{2}{3}$.

c. n if $m = -\frac{2}{3}$ and $\vec{A}$ and $\vec{B}$ have the same direction.

d. n if $m = -\frac{2}{3}$ and $\vec{A}$ and $\vec{B}$ are opposite in direction.

e. m if $n = \frac{3}{4}$ and $\vec{A}$ and $\vec{B}$ are opposite in direction.

f. n if $m = \frac{7}{2}$ and $\vec{A}$ and $\vec{B}$ are in the same direction.

g. n if $m = -\frac{7}{2}$ and $\vec{A}$ and $\vec{B}$ are in the same direction.

h. n if $m = -\frac{7}{2}$ and $\vec{A}$ and $\vec{B}$ are opposite in direction.

i. m if $n = \frac{8}{3}$ and $\vec{A}$ and $\vec{B}$ are opposite in direction.

j. m if $n = -\frac{8}{3}$ and $\vec{A}$ and $\vec{B}$ are in the same direction.

k. m if $n = 1$ and $\vec{A}$ and $\vec{B}$ are in the same direction.

l. m if $n = 1$ and $\vec{A}$ and $\vec{B}$ are opposite in direction.

m. n if $m = -1$ and $\vec{A}$ and $\vec{B}$ are in the same direction.

n. n if $m = -1$ and $\vec{A}$ and $\vec{B}$ are opposite in direction.

o. m if $n = k$ and $\vec{A}$ and $\vec{B}$ are in the same direction.

p. m if $n = k$ and $\vec{A}$ and $\vec{B}$ are opposite in direction.

■ Draw a diagram showing each of the following.

15. $\vec{A} + (-\vec{A}) = \vec{0}$.

16. $\vec{0} + \vec{B} = \vec{B} + \vec{0} = \vec{B}$.

17. $\vec{A} + (\vec{B} + \vec{C}) = (\vec{A} + \vec{B}) + \vec{C}$ (Associative property).

18. $m(n\vec{A}) = (m \cdot n)\vec{A}$; m, n are scalars.

19. $(m + n)\vec{A} = m\vec{A} + n\vec{A}$, m, n are scalars.

20. $m(\vec{A} + \vec{B}) = m\vec{A} + m\vec{B}$, m a scalar.

B **21.** Prove that $m(n\vec{A}) = (m \cdot n)\vec{A}$. (*Hint:* You must show that both vectors have the same direction and the same length.)

22. Prove that the length of $(m + n)\vec{A}$ is the same as the length of $mA + n\vec{A}$ by showing that

a. $|m + n||\vec{A}| = |m||\vec{A}| + |n||\vec{A}|$ when m and n are of the same sign and

b. $|m + n||\vec{A}| = |(|m| - |n|)||\vec{A}|$ when m and n are of opposite signs.

23. Prove $m(\vec{A} + \vec{B}) = m\vec{A} + m\vec{B}$, $m > 0$ by showing that

    a. $m\vec{A} + m\vec{B}$ is in the same direction as $\vec{A} + \vec{B}$ and therefore of $m(\vec{A} + \vec{B})$, and

    b. $|m\vec{A} + m\vec{B}|$ is m times as long as $|\vec{A} + \vec{B}|$.

    (*Hint:* Draw a figure and show that the triangles formed by $\vec{A}$, $\vec{B}$ and $\vec{A} + \vec{B}$ and by $m\vec{A}$, $m\vec{B}$ and $m\vec{A} + m\vec{B}$ are similar.)

24. Given two nonparallel vectors $\vec{A}$ and $\vec{B}$ and that θ is the measure of the angle determined by $\vec{A}$ and $\vec{B}$,

    a. Express $|\vec{A} - \vec{B}|$ in terms of $|\vec{A}|$, $|\vec{B}|$, and θ. (*Hint:* Use the Law of Cosines.)

    b. Express $|\vec{A} + \vec{B}|$ in terms of $|\vec{A}|$, $|\vec{B}|$, and θ. (*Hint:* Use the Law of Cosines.)

9–3 Basis Vectors

The properties of vectors studied so far are valid whether the vectors all lie in space or are restricted to a single plane in space. Now it is advantageous to discuss vectors lying in a single plane separately from those lying in space.

Consider two nonparallel vectors $\vec{A}$ and $\vec{B}$ lying in the same plane. The vector sum $2\vec{A} + 5\vec{B}$ is a vector in the same plane as shown in Figure 2. In fact for any scalars m and n, $m\vec{A} + n\vec{B}$ is a vector in the same plane.

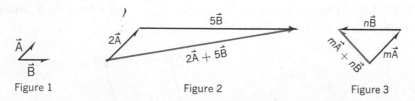

Figure 1   Figure 2   Figure 3

Suppose you have two nonparallel vectors, say $\vec{A}$, $\vec{B}$, in a plane and a vector, call it $\vec{C}$, in the same plane. Are there scalars m and n such that $\vec{C} = m\vec{A} + n\vec{B}$? This leads to the next theorem.

Definition Given scalars m and n and vectors $\vec{A}$ and $\vec{B}$, the vector $\vec{C} = m\vec{A} + n\vec{B}$ is a *linear combination* of $\vec{A}$ and $\vec{B}$.

Proof: Let $\vec{A}$, $\vec{B}$, and $\vec{C}$ have the same foot O. Let P be the tip of $\vec{C}$. Construct the line through P parallel to $\vec{B}$. It intersects the line of $\vec{A}$ in Q. Let $\overrightarrow{OQ} = m\vec{A}$. Since $\overrightarrow{QP}$ is parallel to $\vec{B}$, $\overrightarrow{QP}$ is a scalar multiple of $\vec{B}$. That is $\overrightarrow{QP} = n\vec{B}$. By the construction and the definition of vector addition

$$\vec{C} = m\vec{A} + n\vec{B}.$$

To show uniqueness, suppose

$$\vec{C} = m_1\vec{A} + n_1\vec{B} = m_2\vec{A} + n_2\vec{B}.$$

Then $(m_1 - m_2)\vec{A} = (n_2 - n_1)\vec{B}$. In this case either ① $\vec{A}$ is parallel to $\vec{B}$ because one is a nonzero scalar multiple of the other ② $\vec{A} = \vec{B} = \vec{0}$ or ③ $m_1 - m_2 = n_2 - n_1 = 0$. In either ① or ② a contradiction is reached because $\vec{A}$ and $\vec{B}$ were two nonparallel nonzero vectors. Thus $m_1 = m_2$ and $n_2 = n_1$ and it follows that $m_1\vec{A} + n_1\vec{B} = m_2\vec{A} + n_2\vec{B} = m\vec{A} + n\vec{B}$.

EXAMPLE. Find m and n such that $\vec{C} = m\vec{A} + n\vec{B}$ where $\vec{A}$, $\vec{B}$, and $\vec{C}$ are given as in the figure below.

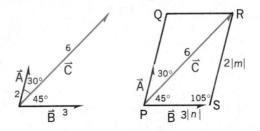

Complete the parallelogram with $\vec{C}$ as diagonal.

$$\overrightarrow{SR} = m\vec{A}, \quad \overrightarrow{PS} = n\vec{B}$$
$$|\overrightarrow{SR}| = |m|\,|\vec{A}| = |m|\,2$$
$$|\overrightarrow{PS}| = |n|\,|\vec{B}| = |n|\,3$$

By the Law of Sines you can find the values of m and n.

$$\text{i.} \quad \frac{6}{\sin 105°} = \frac{2|m|}{\sin 45°}$$

$$\text{ii.} \quad \frac{6}{\sin 105°} = \frac{3|n|}{\sin 30°}$$

From the table $\sin 105° = \sin 75° = 0.9659$; $\sin 45° = \frac{\sqrt{2}}{2}$; $\sin 30° = \frac{1}{2}$.
Thus:

i. $\dfrac{6}{0.9659} = \dfrac{2|m|}{\frac{\sqrt{2}}{2}}$ or $2|m| = \dfrac{3\sqrt{2}}{0.9659}$ and $|m| = \dfrac{3\sqrt{2}}{1.9318}$

ii. $\dfrac{6}{0.9659} = \dfrac{3|n|}{\frac{1}{2}}$ or $3|n| = \dfrac{3}{0.9659}$ and $|n| = \dfrac{1}{0.9659}$

From the figure it is clear that $m > 0$, $n > 0$,

so
$$\vec{C} = \frac{3\sqrt{2}}{1.9318} \vec{A} + \frac{1}{0.9659} \vec{B}.$$

For vectors in space there is a theorem similar to Theorem 9–1.

Theorem 9–2 In three dimensional space let $\vec{A}$, $\vec{B}$, and $\vec{C}$ be any three nonzero vectors not all three parallel to the same plane, with no two of them parallel to each other. Then any given vector $\vec{D}$ is a unique linear combination of $\vec{A}$, $\vec{B}$, and $\vec{C}$. Thus $\vec{D} = l\vec{A} + m\vec{B} + n\vec{C}$, where l, m, and n are unique scalars.

The proof is similar to that of Theorem 9–1. Only the essential ideas are suggested here. See the figure at the right.
The three vectors have the same foot O. Let the line through P, the tip of $\vec{D}$, parallel to $\vec{C}$ intersect the plane of $\vec{A}$ and $\vec{B}$ in Q. Then $\overrightarrow{OQ} = l\vec{A} + m\vec{B}$. (Why?), $\overrightarrow{QP} = n\vec{C}$ and $\vec{D} = \overrightarrow{OQ} + \overrightarrow{QP} = l\vec{A} + m\vec{B} + n\vec{C}$.

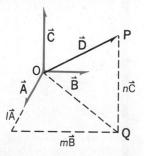

The vectors $\vec{A}$, $\vec{B}$ of Theorem 9–1 and $\vec{A}$, $\vec{B}$ and $\vec{C}$ of Theorem 9–2 form a **base** or **basis** for all the vectors in the plane or space. From the theorems it is clear that there are two base vectors for a plane (2-dimensional space), and three for space (3-dimensional space). The scalars l, m, and n are the **components** of the vector $\vec{D} = l\vec{A} + m\vec{B} + n\vec{C}$. A similar statement is true for $\vec{C} = m\vec{A} + n\vec{B}$ in a plane.

1. Give a geometric interpretation of the concept of basis vectors in a plane.

2. Give a geometric interpretation of the concept of basis vectors in space.

3. State in your own words what is meant by a linear combination of vectors.

4. What are the components of a vector?

Exercises

A ▬ Use a ruler to approximate the values of the scalars m and n when

$$\vec{C} = m\vec{A} + n\vec{B}.$$

1.

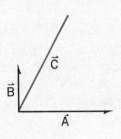

2.

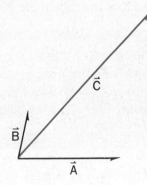

3.

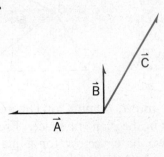

4.

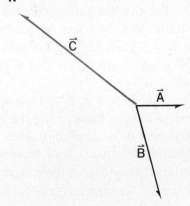

In Exercises 5–12 use the base vectors $\vec{A}$, $\vec{B}$, and $\vec{C}$ as given in Figure 1 to draw each vector $\vec{D}$. The three vectors are perpendicular to each other. Trace the base vectors on your paper first. The following example will illustrate the idea.

Example: $\vec{D} = \vec{A} - \vec{B} + 2\vec{C}$

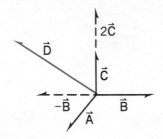

5. $\vec{D} = \vec{A} + \vec{B} + \vec{C}$
6. $\vec{D} = 2\vec{A} + \vec{B} + \frac{1}{2}\vec{C}$
7. $\vec{D} = \vec{A} + 2\vec{B} - 2\vec{C}$
8. $\vec{D} = -2\vec{A} - \frac{1}{2}\vec{B} + 3\vec{C}$
9. $\vec{D}$ has components $(-\frac{1}{2}, 3, -1)$
10. $\vec{D}$ has components $(-1, -1, -1)$
11. $\vec{D}$ has components $(0, 1, 0)$
12. $\vec{D}$ has components $(2, 0, -3)$

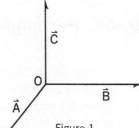

Figure 1

B **13.** Find $\vec{C}$ as a linear combination of $\vec{A}$ and $\vec{B}$ when

$$|\vec{A}| = 2, \quad |\vec{B}| = 2, \quad |\vec{C}| = 1$$

and the angles are as indicated in Figure 2. ($\vec{A}$, $\vec{B}$, and $\vec{C}$ are in the same plane.)

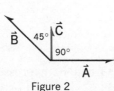

Figure 2

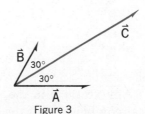

Figure 3

14. Repeat Exercise 13 when

$$|\vec{A}| = 3, \quad |\vec{B}| = 2, \quad |\vec{C}| = 6$$

and angles are as shown in Figure 3.

VECTORS, LINES, AND PLANES   425

15. Repeat Exercise 13 when

$$|\vec{A}| = 2, \quad |\vec{B}| = 3, \quad |\vec{C}| = 4,$$

and angles are as shown in the figure below.

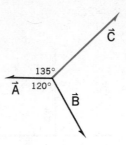

16. Complete the proof of Theorem 9–2.

9–4 Perpendicular Basis

In **two-space** (a plane) it is advantageous to choose the basis for the vectors as perpendicular vectors each of unit length. These vectors are denoted **i** and **j** and their common foot by O. The line determined by **i** is the x axis; the line determined by **j** is the y axis.

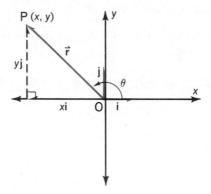

Any vector $\vec{r}$ in the plane with foot at O can be expressed as a linear combination of the basis vectors **i** and **j**

$$\vec{r} = x\mathbf{i} + y\mathbf{j}$$

The components of $\vec{r} = x\mathbf{i} + y\mathbf{j}$ are the coordinates of the tip P of $\vec{r}$.

$$P = (x, y)$$

The vector $\vec{r} = \overrightarrow{OP}$ is a **position vector** because its foot is at the origin and its components are the coordinates of its tip P. A position vector $\vec{r}$ may be designated by the rectangular coordinates of its tip. That is, the coordinates (x, y) of a point P may be thought of as the position vector $\overrightarrow{OP}$:

$$\overrightarrow{OP} = (x, y)$$

Notice that you now have two systems of notation for position vectors.

1. Unit basis vector notation: $x\mathbf{i} + y\mathbf{j}$
2. Ordered pair notation: (x, y)

The first (unit basis) notation will be used more often here than the second (ordered pair) notation. The latter is frequently encountered in more advanced studies of vectors.

The angle from $\mathbf{i}$ to $\vec{r}$ has measure θ. θ ranges in value from $0°$ to $360°$ (2π radians).

$$\theta = \arctan \frac{y}{x} \qquad 0 \le \arctan \frac{y}{x} \le 360° \ (2\pi)$$

Moreover, using your knowledge of polar coordinates (see page 55) and letting $|\vec{r}| = r$, you can see that the following is true.

$$x = r \cos \theta$$
$$y = r \sin \theta$$
$$|\vec{r}| = r = \sqrt{x^2 + y^2}$$

EXAMPLE 1. Let the position vector $\vec{r} = -2\mathbf{i} + 2\mathbf{j}$.
   a. Find $|\vec{r}| = r$.
$$\vec{r} = -2\mathbf{i} + 2\mathbf{j}.$$

Thus
$$r = \sqrt{(-2)^2 + (2)^2}$$
$$= \sqrt{8}$$
$$= 2\sqrt{2}$$

   b. Find θ.
   Since the x component of $\vec{r}$ is negative and the y component is positive,
$$\theta = \arctan \frac{2}{-2}$$

is the measure of an angle in the second quadrant.
   $\theta = 135°$ since $\tan 135° = \frac{2}{-2}$ and $(-2, 2)$ is in Quadrant II.

Consider now three-dimensional space. Choosing a set of mutually perpendicular vectors of unit length one for the basis is advantageous here also. The basis vectors are denoted as **i, j,** and **k.** Their common foot is O.

The position vector

$$\vec{r} = x\mathbf{i} + y\mathbf{j} + z\mathbf{k}$$

has for its components the rectangular coordinates of the point at its tip:

$$P = (x, y, z).$$

(See Figure 1.)

As in the two dimensional case, the ordered triple of coordinates of the tip of the position vector $\vec{r} = \overrightarrow{OP}$ is identified with the following vector.

$$\overrightarrow{OP} = (x, y, z)$$

The length of a position vector $\vec{r}$ is given by

$$|\vec{r}| = r = \sqrt{x^2 + y^2 + z^2}.$$

This should be evident from Figure 2.

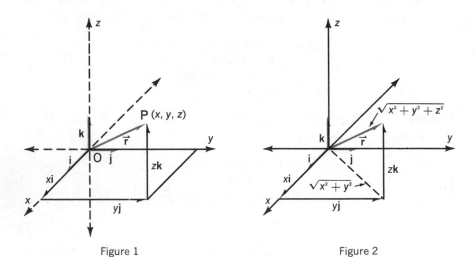

Figure 1   Figure 2

EXAMPLE 2. Show that any vector $\overrightarrow{PQ}$ in space can be expressed as a linear combination of **i, j,** and **k.** That is, any vector $\overrightarrow{PQ}$ can be expressed as follows.

$$\overrightarrow{PQ} = l\mathbf{i} + m\mathbf{j} + n\mathbf{k}$$

Choose a point O for origin and let $P = (x_1, y_1, z_1)$ and $Q = (x_2, y_2, z_2)$. Then $\overrightarrow{OP}$ and $\overrightarrow{OQ}$ are position vectors.

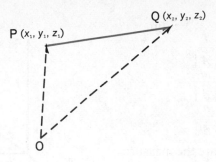

Furthermore,

$$\overrightarrow{PQ} = \overrightarrow{OQ} - \overrightarrow{OP}$$
$$= (x_2\mathbf{i} + y_2\mathbf{j} + z_2\mathbf{k}) - (x_1\mathbf{i} + y_1\mathbf{j} + z_1\mathbf{k})$$
$$= (x_2 - x_1)\mathbf{i} + (y_2 - y_1)\mathbf{j} + (z_2 - z_1)\mathbf{k}$$

Let

$$(x_2 - x_1) = l, \quad (y_2 - y_1) = m, \quad \text{and} \quad (z_2 - z_1) = n.$$

Thus

$$\overrightarrow{PQ} = l\mathbf{i} + m\mathbf{j} + n\mathbf{k}.$$

The same result is valid in two-space. (See Exercise 14.)
The result of Example 2 can be carried further. The length of $\overrightarrow{PQ}$
is

$$|\overrightarrow{PQ}| = \sqrt{l^2 + m^2 + n^2}.$$

But

$$l = (x_2 - x_1), \quad m = (y_2 - y_1), \quad \text{and} \quad n = (z_2 - z_1).$$

Thus

$$|\overrightarrow{PQ}| = \sqrt{(x_2 - x_1)^2 + (y_2 - y_1)^2 + (z_2 - z_1)^2}$$

where

$$P = (x_1, y_1, z_1) \quad \text{and} \quad Q = (x_2, y_2, z_2).$$

This can be stated as follows.

> **The length of a vector is the square root of the sum of the squares of the differences of the coordinates of the tip and foot of a vector.**

Any vector, by Example 2, may be expressed as $\overrightarrow{A} = l\mathbf{i} + m\mathbf{j} + n\mathbf{k}$. The components l, m, and n are called **direction numbers** of $\overrightarrow{A}$. When each is divided by $|\overrightarrow{A}| = \sqrt{l^2 + m^2 + n^2}$ the ratios are **direction cosines** of $\overrightarrow{A}$.

In particular

$$\cos \alpha = \frac{l}{|\vec{A}|}$$

$$\cos \beta = \frac{m}{|\vec{A}|}$$

$$\cos \gamma = \frac{n}{|\vec{A}|}$$

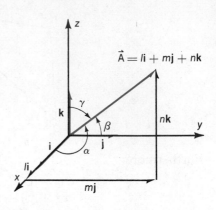

$$\vec{A} = l\mathbf{i} + m\mathbf{j} + n\mathbf{k}$$

where α, β, and γ are the measures of the angles $\vec{A}$ makes with $\mathbf{i}$, $\mathbf{j}$, and $\mathbf{k}$ respectively. (See the figure at the right.) α, β, and γ are called **direction angles.**

Theorem 9–3 If α, β, and γ are direction angles then

$$\cos^2 \alpha + \cos^2 \beta + \cos^2 \gamma = 1.$$

Proof: By definition

$$\cos \alpha = \frac{l}{|\vec{A}|}, \quad \cos \beta = \frac{m}{|\vec{A}|}, \quad \text{and} \quad \cos \gamma = \frac{n}{|\vec{A}|}.$$

Therefore,

$$\cos^2 \alpha + \cos^2 \beta + \cos^2 \gamma = \frac{l^2 + m^2 + n^2}{|\vec{A}|^2}$$

$$= \frac{l^2 + m^2 + n^2}{l^2 + m^2 + n^2}$$

$$= 1.$$

EXAMPLE 3. Suppose $\vec{A}$ has directions angles of $\alpha = 45°$ and $\beta = 45°$. What is γ? Draw the vector.

By Theorem 9–3, $\cos^2 \alpha + \cos^2 \beta + \cos^2 \gamma = 1$. Consequently, since $\cos \alpha = \cos 45 = \frac{\sqrt{2}}{2} = \cos \beta$,

$$\left(\frac{\sqrt{2}}{2}\right)^2 + \left(\frac{\sqrt{2}}{2}\right)^2 + \cos^2 \gamma = 1$$

$$\cos^2 \gamma = 0$$

Thus $\gamma = 90°$. The diagram is at the right. $\vec{A}$ is in the xy plane.

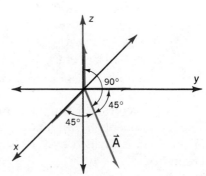

Since its length was unspecified it may have any nonzero length. When only the direction of a vector is required, the vector is called a **direction vector.**

Now try these

1. A vector has $\cos \alpha = \cos \beta = \dfrac{-1}{\sqrt{2}}$. Find γ.

2. What are the direction cosines of

   a. the x axis?
   b. the y axis?
   c. the z axis?

3. Suppose that the direction numbers of a line are l, m, and n. What are the direction cosines?

Answers: **1.** $\gamma = \dfrac{\pi}{2}$ **2a.** $(1, 0, 0)$ **b.** $(0, 1, 0)$ **c.** $(0, 0, 1)$ **3.** $\cos \alpha = \dfrac{l}{k}$,

$\cos \beta = \dfrac{m}{k}$, $\cos \gamma = \dfrac{n}{k}$, where $k^2 = l^2 + m^2 + n^2$

Checkpoint

Explain the geometric difference between direction numbers, direction cosines and direction angles.

Exercises

A — Given the position vector $\vec{r}$, find its length and the measure θ of the angle it makes with **i**. (Express θ to nearest $10'$.)

   1. $\vec{r} = 2\mathbf{i} + 3\mathbf{j}$
   2. $\vec{r} = -2\mathbf{i} + 3\mathbf{j}$
   3. $\vec{r} = -2\mathbf{i} - 3\mathbf{j}$
   4. $\vec{r} = 2\mathbf{i} - 3\mathbf{j}$
   5. $\vec{r} = 2\mathbf{i} - \sqrt{3}\mathbf{j}$
   6. $\vec{r} = -1\mathbf{i} - 1\mathbf{j}$
   7. $\overrightarrow{OP} = (-\sqrt{3}, 1)$
   8. $\vec{r} = (0, 1)$
   9. $\vec{r} = (-1, 0)$
   10. $\overrightarrow{OP} = (1, -1)$
   11. $\overrightarrow{OP} = (0, -5)$
   12. $\vec{r} = (3, 4)$

13. Sketch each vector in Exercises 1–6.

14. Let $P = (x_1, y_1)$, $Q = (x_2, y_2)$. Prove: If $\overrightarrow{PQ}$ is any vector in two-space then

$$\overrightarrow{PQ} = m\mathbf{i} + n\mathbf{j}.$$

15. Prove: If $P = (x_1, y_1)$ and $Q = (x_2, y_2)$ then

$$|\overrightarrow{PQ}| = \sqrt{(x_2 - x_1)^2 + (y_2 - y_1)^2} \qquad \text{(See Exercise 14).}$$

— In Exercises 16–23 find $|\overrightarrow{PQ}|$.

16. $P = (1, 5)$, $Q = (-3, 2)$

17. $P = (-1, 1)$, $Q = (4, 13)$

18. $P = (a, b)$, $Q = (a - 1, b - 3)$

19. $P = (x, y)$, $Q = (x + 2, y + 2)$

20. $P = (1, 1, 1)$, $Q = (2, -1, 3)$

21. $P = (0, 1, 2)$, $Q = (-\sqrt{10}, -4, 1)$

22. $P = (x, y, z)$, $Q = (x + 1, y - 1, z + \sqrt{2})$

23. $P = (a, 2a, -a)$, $Q = (4a, 6a, 4a)$

24. What are the direction cosines of the vector from $(2, -1, 4)$ to $(-1, 3, -8)$?

B **25.** A vector has direction angles $\alpha = 30°$, $\beta = 60°$. Find the third angle γ. Make a sketch of the vector.

26. Repeat Exercise 25 when $\alpha = 45°$ and $\beta = 120°$. How many answers are there?

27. A *unit vector* is a vector with length 1. What is the unit vector in the same direction as

$$\vec{A} = 12\mathbf{i} - 4\mathbf{j} + 3\mathbf{k}?$$

28. What is the unit vector in the same direction as $\vec{A}$, if

$$\vec{A} = l\mathbf{i} + m\mathbf{j} + n\mathbf{k}?$$

29. Show that the direction cosines for the vector from $P = (x_1, y_1, z_1)$ to $Q = (x_2, y_2, z_2)$ are

$$\cos \alpha = \frac{x_2 - x_1}{|\overrightarrow{PQ}|}, \quad \cos \beta = \frac{y_2 - y_1}{|\overrightarrow{PQ}|}, \quad \cos \gamma = \frac{z_2 - z_1}{|\overrightarrow{PQ}|}$$

30. What are the direction cosines of the vector QP where P and Q are as in Exercise 29?

31. Write a definition of the direction numbers of a vector in two-space. What are the direction cosines?

9–5 Dividing a Segment

Consider a segment $\overrightarrow{PQ}$ in space. Let $P = (1, 2, -2)$ and $Q = (-3, 6, 4)$. What are the coordinates of the midpoint of $\overrightarrow{PQ}$?

Vector methods may be used to answer this question. Let O be the origin and consider $\overrightarrow{OP}$, $\overrightarrow{OQ}$, and $\overrightarrow{PQ}$.

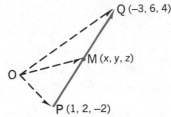

By the definition of subtraction,

$$\overrightarrow{PQ} = \overrightarrow{OQ} - \overrightarrow{OP} \qquad 1$$

Let $M(x, y, z)$ be the midpoint of $\overrightarrow{PQ}$. $\overrightarrow{PM}$ has the same direction as $\overrightarrow{PQ}$, $2\overrightarrow{PM} = \overrightarrow{PQ}$, and $\overrightarrow{PM} = \overrightarrow{OM} - \overrightarrow{OP}$.

Thus

$$\begin{aligned}
\overrightarrow{PQ} &= \overrightarrow{OQ} - \overrightarrow{OP} \\
&= 2\overrightarrow{PM} \\
&= 2(\overrightarrow{OM} - \overrightarrow{OP}).
\end{aligned}$$

But

$$\begin{aligned}
\overrightarrow{PQ} &= (-3 - 1)\mathbf{i} + (6 - 2)\mathbf{j} + (4 - (-2))\mathbf{k} \\
&= -4\mathbf{i} + 4\mathbf{j} + 6\mathbf{k}
\end{aligned}$$

and

$$\begin{aligned}
2(\overrightarrow{PM}) &= 2[(x - 1)\mathbf{i} + (y - 2)\mathbf{j} + (z - (-2))\mathbf{k}] \\
&= 2(x - 1)\mathbf{i} + 2(y - 2)\mathbf{j} + 2(z + 2)\mathbf{k}.
\end{aligned}$$

Thus

$$\begin{aligned}
\overrightarrow{PQ} &= -4\mathbf{i} + 4\mathbf{j} + 6\mathbf{k} \\
&= 2(x - 1)\mathbf{i} + 2(y - 2)\mathbf{j} + 2(z + 2)\mathbf{k} \\
&= 2\overrightarrow{PM}.
\end{aligned}$$

By Theorem 9–2, a nonzero vector is a unique linear combination of basis vectors, and thus

$$-4 = 2(x - 1), \quad 4 = 2(y - 2), \quad \text{and} \quad 6 = 2(z + 2).$$

Solving each equation you find

$$x = \frac{-4 + 2}{2} = -1, \quad y = \frac{4 + 4}{2} = 4, \quad \text{and} \quad z = \frac{6 - 4}{2} = 1.$$

Thus $M = (-1, 4, 1)$.

The procedure used above can be applied in the general case to get a formula for the coordinates of the midpoint.

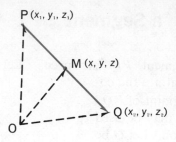

Let $P = (x_1, y_1, z_1)$ and $Q = (x_2, y_2, z_2)$. Let $M = (x, y, z)$ be the midpoint of $\overrightarrow{PQ}$. See the figure above.

$$\overrightarrow{PQ} = (x_2 - x_1)\mathbf{i} + (y_2 - y_1)\mathbf{j} + (z_2 - z_1)\mathbf{k}$$
$$\overrightarrow{PM} = (x - x_1)\mathbf{i} + (y - y_1)\mathbf{j} + (z - z_1)\mathbf{k}$$

and

$$\overrightarrow{PQ} = 2PM.$$

It follows that

$$(x_2 - x_1)\mathbf{i} + (y_2 - y_1)\mathbf{j} + (z_2 - z_1)\mathbf{k}$$
$$= 2(x - x_1)\mathbf{i} + 2(y - y_1)\mathbf{j} + 2(z - z_1)\mathbf{k}.$$

By Theorem 9–2,

$$x_2 - x_1 = 2(x - x_1), \quad y_2 - y_1 = 2(y - y_1), \quad (z_2 - z_1) = 2(z - z_1).$$

Solving for x, y, and z you find the following.

$$x = \frac{x_2 + x_1}{2}, \quad y = \frac{y_2 + y_1}{2}, \quad z = \frac{z_2 + z_1}{2}$$

The midpoint M of $\overrightarrow{PQ}$ is

$$\left(\frac{\text{sum of } x\text{'s}}{2}, \frac{\text{sum of } y\text{'s}}{2}, \frac{\text{sum of } z\text{'s}}{2} \right).$$

The following theorem summarizes the above discussion and gives a general formula for finding the midpoint.

Theorem 9–4 If $P = (x_1, y_1, z_1)$ and $Q = (x_2, y_2, z_2)$ then the midpoint of $\overrightarrow{PQ}$ is

$$M = \left(\frac{x_1 + x_2}{2}, \frac{y_1 + y_2}{2}, \frac{z_1 + z_2}{2} \right)$$

See if you can modify this theorem so it is valid for a segment in the xy plane.

434   CHAPTER 9

Similar methods can be used to find the point of a segment which divides it into any fractional part. Suppose you have points $P(x_1, y_1, z_1)$ and $Q(x_2, y_2, z_2)$ and you want the point M which is $\frac{4}{5}$ the way from P to Q. Stating this in terms of vectors, you want the vector $\overrightarrow{PM}$ which is $\frac{4}{5}\overrightarrow{PQ}$, or $4\overrightarrow{PQ} = 5\overrightarrow{PM}$.

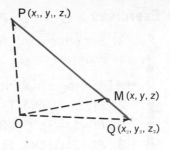

Writing $\overrightarrow{PQ}$ and $\overrightarrow{PM}$ in terms of the basis vector $\mathbf{i}$, $\mathbf{j}$, and $\mathbf{k}$, you find

$$4(x_2 - x_1)\mathbf{i} + 4(y_2 - y_1)\mathbf{j} + 4(z_2 - z_1)\mathbf{k}$$
$$= 5(x - x_1)\mathbf{i} + 5(y - y_1)\mathbf{j} + 5(z - z_1)\mathbf{k}$$

and since the components are equal,

$$4(x_2 - x_1) = 5(x - x_1),\ 4(y_2 - y_1) = 5(y - y_1),\ 4(z_2 - z_1) = 5(z - z_1).$$

Solving for x, y, and z, you find

$$x = \frac{4x_2 + x_1}{5}, \quad y = \frac{4y_2 + y_1}{5}, \quad z = \frac{4z_2 + z_1}{5}.$$

The point $M = \left(\frac{4x_2 + x_1}{5}, \frac{4y_2 + y_1}{5}, \frac{4z_2 + z_1}{5}\right)$ is the point $\frac{4}{5}$ of the way from P to Q. It is also the point which divides $\overrightarrow{PQ}$ in the ratio 4 to 1.

$$\frac{|\overrightarrow{PM}|}{|\overrightarrow{MQ}|} = \frac{4}{1}$$

Now try these

1. What is the z component of any vector in the xy plane?

2. What are the coordinates of the midpoint of a vector in the xy plane if its endpoints are (x_1, y_1) and (x_2, y_2)?

— Find the midpoint of $\overrightarrow{PQ}$ with endpoints as follows.

3. $P(2, -1, 1)$, $Q(-4, 0, 3)$ **4.** $P(3, 1)$, $Q(-5, 5)$

5. $P(1, 2, 3)$, $Q(-6, -5, -4)$ **6.** $P(x_1, y_1, z_1)$, $Q(x_2, y_2, z_2)$

7. $P(a, b)$, $Q(c, 0)$ **8.** $P(3, 2, -4)$, $Q(9, 0, 6)$

Answers: **1.** $(0, 0, z)$ **2.** $\left(\frac{x_1 + x_2}{2}, \frac{y_1 + y_2}{2}\right)$ **3.** $(-1, -\frac{1}{2}, 2)$ **4.** $(-1, 3)$

5. $(-\frac{5}{2}, -\frac{3}{2}, -\frac{1}{2})$ **6.** $\left(\frac{x_1 + x_2}{2}, \frac{y_1 + y_2}{2}, \frac{z_1 + z_2}{2}\right)$ **7.** $\left(\frac{a + c}{2}, \frac{b}{2}\right)$

8. $(6, 1, 1)$

Exercises

A   **1.** State the result for Exercise 2 of *Now try these* as a theorem and prove it.

— Find the midpoint of $\overrightarrow{PQ}$ with endpoints as follows.

2. $P(2, -3)$, $Q(4, 1)$ **3.** $P(1, 2, 3)$, $Q(3, 2, 1)$
4. $P(-5, -3)$, $Q(-2, -1)$ **5.** $P(1, 0, -5)$, $Q(2, 1, 5)$
6. $P(-2, 1)$, $Q(4, 5)$ **7.** $P(-2, -4, -3)$, $Q(1, -3, 2)$
8. $P(4, 2)$, $Q(-1, -3)$ **9.** $P(a, b, c)$, $Q(a + 1, b + 2, c + 3)$
10. $P(a, b)$, $Q(3 - a, 5 - b)$ **11.** $P(a, b, c)$, $Q(-a, -b, -c)$

12. If M is the midpoint of $\overrightarrow{PQ}$, show that $|\overrightarrow{PM}| = |\overrightarrow{QM}|$ for
   a. $\overrightarrow{PQ}$ in the xy plane
   b. $\overrightarrow{PQ}$ in space

13. In the derivation of the coordinates of the midpoint M of $\overrightarrow{PQ}$ in Theorem 9–4, does it make any difference if you consider $\overrightarrow{QP}$ rather than $\overrightarrow{PQ}$? Explain.

B — In Exercises 14–20, M is a point between P and Q where $P(4, 5, 8)$ and $Q(2, -3, 4)$. Find M for each exercise.

14. M is $\frac{2}{3}$ the way from P to Q.
15. M is $\frac{2}{3}$ the way from Q to P.
16. M is $\frac{3}{4}$ the way from P to Q.

17. $\dfrac{|\overrightarrow{PM}|}{|\overrightarrow{MQ}|} = \dfrac{5}{1}$ **18.** $\dfrac{|\overrightarrow{QM}|}{|\overrightarrow{MP}|} = \dfrac{3}{2}$

19. $\dfrac{|\overrightarrow{PM}|}{|\overrightarrow{PQ}|} = \dfrac{1}{6}$ **20.** $\dfrac{|\overrightarrow{QM}|}{|\overrightarrow{QP}|} = \dfrac{2}{5}$

C — A point M is said to *divide* $\overrightarrow{PQ}$ *externally* in the ratio $\dfrac{a}{b}$ if M is not between P and Q and $\dfrac{|\overrightarrow{PM}|}{|\overrightarrow{QM}|} = \dfrac{a}{b}$.

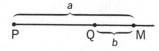

— If $P = (4, 5, 8)$ and $Q = (2, -3, 4)$, find M such that M divides $\overrightarrow{PQ}$ externally in the ratio as indicated in Exercises 21–24.

21. $\frac{4}{3}$ **22.** $\frac{7}{4}$ **23.** $\frac{1}{3}$ **24.** $\frac{2}{5}$

25. Given $P(x_1, y_1, z_1)$ and $Q(x_2, y_2, z_2)$. Let M be the point between P and Q which is $\frac{p}{q}$ $(0 < \frac{p}{q} < 1)$ of the way from P to Q. Find the coordinates of the point M.

9–6 Lines

Two points P and Q in space determine a unique line. Those same two points taken in a prescribed order also determine a unique vector: $\overrightarrow{PQ}$. If R is any other point on the line through P and Q, $\overrightarrow{QR}$ is a scalar multiple of $\overrightarrow{PQ}$.

$$\overrightarrow{QR} = t \cdot \overrightarrow{PQ}$$

This is true because the vectors $\overrightarrow{QR}$ and $\overrightarrow{PQ}$ are collinear. These facts are used to derive several different equations of a line.

Suppose, as in the figure at the right, P and Q are two fixed points on the line. By Example 2 Section 9–4, $\overrightarrow{PQ}$ is a unique linear combination of $\mathbf{i}$, $\mathbf{j}$, and $\mathbf{k}$:

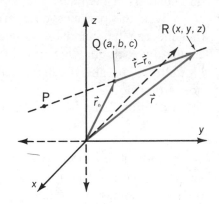

$$\overrightarrow{PQ} = l\mathbf{i} + m\mathbf{j} + n\mathbf{k} \qquad \mathbf{1}$$

Let $R(x, y, z)$ be any point on the line. (You may think of R as a variable point if you wish.) Then $\overrightarrow{QR} = \vec{r} - \vec{r}_0$ is a scalar multiple of $\overrightarrow{PQ}$:

Thus

$$\overrightarrow{QR} = \vec{r} - \vec{r}_0 = t \cdot \overrightarrow{PQ}, \ t \text{ a scalar} \qquad \mathbf{2}$$

But

$$\vec{r} - \vec{r}_0 = (x - a)\mathbf{i} + (y - b)\mathbf{j} + (z - c)\mathbf{k} \qquad \mathbf{3}$$

Substituting $\mathbf{1}$ and $\mathbf{3}$ in $\mathbf{2}$ you find

$$\vec{r} - \vec{r}_0 = (x - a)\mathbf{i} + (y - b)\mathbf{j} + (z - c)\mathbf{k} = t(l\mathbf{i} + m\mathbf{j} + n\mathbf{k}) \qquad \mathbf{4}$$

By the uniqueness of the linear combination of $\mathbf{i}$, $\mathbf{j}$, and $\mathbf{k}$, you find

$$x - a = t \cdot l, \ y - b = t \cdot m, \text{ and } z - c = t \cdot n. \qquad \mathbf{5}$$

Thus

$$\frac{x - a}{l} = t, \ \frac{y - b}{m} = t, \text{ and } \frac{z - c}{n} = t, \ l, m, n \neq 0$$

and

$$\frac{x - a}{l} = \frac{y - b}{m} = \frac{z - c}{n} \ \ l, m, n \neq 0. \qquad \mathbf{6}$$

The equations in $\mathbf{6}$ are the **standard equations** of a line.

Solving for x, y, and z in **5**, gives the **parametric equations** of a line:

$$x = a + t \cdot l$$
$$y = b + t \cdot m \qquad \qquad 7$$
$$z = c + t \cdot n$$

Notice that in the parametric equations of line the first column contains the coordinates of the variable point on the line; the second column, the coordinates (a, b, c) of a fixed point; and the third column, the products of the scalar t (a parameter) and the direction numbers of the fixed vector. These direction numbers are also called **the direction numbers of the line.**

Given the parametric equations of a line, a point $R(x, y, z)$ on the line can be found by assigning a specific real number to t and evaluating each equation. (a, b, c, l, m, n are assumed to be known.) Not all of l, m, and n can be zero because $\overrightarrow{PQ}$ was assumed to be a nonzero vector.

Equation **2** can be written in the shorthand form

$$\vec{r} = \vec{r}_0 + t\overrightarrow{PQ} \qquad \qquad 8$$

where $\vec{r}$ is the position vector of the variable point, $\vec{r}_0$ is the position vector of the fixed point, and $\overrightarrow{PQ}$ is the fixed vector. Equation **8** is the vector equation of a line.

EXAMPLE 1. A line has parametric equations

$$x = 2 + t \cdot 5, \quad y = -1 + t \cdot (-1), \quad z = 0 + t \cdot 3.$$

a. Find the point on the line corresponding to $t = -2$.

Substituting $t = -2$ in the parametric equations, you find

$$x = -8, \quad y = 1, \quad z = -6.$$

The point is $(-8, 1, -6)$.

b. What are the direction numbers of this line?

The direction numbers of the line and the fixed vector are identical: l, m, and n. In this case they are 5, -1, and 3.

c. Write the standard equations of the line.

Solve each equation for t:

$$t = \frac{x - 2}{5}, \quad t = \frac{y + 1}{-1}, \quad t = \frac{z}{3}.$$

The standard equations are thus

$$\frac{x - 2}{5} = \frac{y + 1}{-1} = \frac{z}{3}.$$

EXAMPLE 2. Find the parametric equations of the line through $P(1, 2, 3)$ and $Q(-2, 3, -4)$.

Let the fixed vector be $\overrightarrow{PQ}$.

$$\begin{aligned}\overrightarrow{PQ} &= (-2 - 1)\mathbf{i} + (3 - 2)\mathbf{j} + (-4 - 3)\mathbf{k} \\ &= -3\mathbf{i} + 1\mathbf{j} - 7\mathbf{k}\end{aligned}$$

Let the fixed point be $P(1, 2, 3)$, and let the variable point be $R(x, y, z)$. The position vector to R is

$$\vec{r} = x\mathbf{i} + y\mathbf{j} + z\mathbf{k}$$

while the position vector to P is

$$\vec{r}_0 = 1\mathbf{i} + 2\mathbf{j} + 3\mathbf{k}.$$

By equation **8**

$$\begin{aligned}x\mathbf{i} + y\mathbf{j} + z\mathbf{k} &= 1\mathbf{i} + 2\mathbf{j} + 3\mathbf{k} + t(-3\mathbf{i} + 1\mathbf{j} - 7\mathbf{k}) \\ &= (1 - 3t)\mathbf{i} + (2 + 1t)\mathbf{j} + (3 - 7t)\mathbf{k}.\end{aligned}$$

Thus by uniqueness, the parametric equations are

$$\begin{aligned}x &= 1 - 3t \\ y &= 2 + t \\ z &= 3 - 7t.\end{aligned}$$

Find the parametric equations if $Q(-2, 3, -4)$ is chosen to be the fixed point.

Since $\vec{r}_2 = -2\mathbf{i} + 3\mathbf{j} - 4\mathbf{k}$, the parametric equations are

$$\begin{aligned}x &= -2 - 3t \\ y &= 3 + 1t \\ z &= -4 - 7t\end{aligned}$$

The equations **6**, **7**, and **8**, can be modified to include lines in the xy plane (that is in two-space). Notice that the direction number is n equals 0. This is true because the angle from any line in the xy plane to the z axis is $90°$ ($\cos 90° = 0$). Furthermore the fixed point has coordinates $(a, b, 0)$ because every point in the xy plane has a z coordinate equal to 0.

Thus the standard equations of a line in the xy plane are

$$\frac{x - a}{l} = \frac{y - b}{m}, \quad z = 0, \quad l, m \neq 0. \tag{9}$$

The parametric equations of the same line are

$$\begin{aligned}x &= a + t \cdot l \\ y &= b + t \cdot m \\ z &= 0.\end{aligned} \tag{10}$$

VECTORS, LINES, AND PLANES   439

The vector equation is identical to equation 8 when it is understood that $\vec{r}$, $\vec{r}_0$, and $\overrightarrow{PQ}$ are vectors in one plane. (See the figure.)

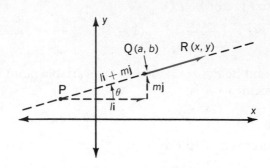

EXAMPLE 3. Find parametric, standard, and vector equations of the line containing $P(1, 4)$ and $Q(2, 7)$.

The fixed vector is $\overrightarrow{PQ} = 1\mathbf{i} + 3\mathbf{j}$. Let $Q(2, 7)$ be the fixed point and $R(x, y)$ be the variable point.

$$\vec{r} = x\mathbf{i} + y\mathbf{j}, \quad \vec{r}_0 = 2\mathbf{i} + 7\mathbf{j}$$

The vector equation is

$$\vec{r} = \vec{r}_0 + t\overrightarrow{PQ}$$

or

$$x\mathbf{i} + y\mathbf{j} = 2\mathbf{i} + 7\mathbf{j} + t(+1\mathbf{i} + 3\mathbf{j})$$
$$= (2 + t)\mathbf{i} + (7 + 3t)\mathbf{j}.$$

By uniqueness of the linear combination of $\mathbf{i}$ and $\mathbf{j}$

$$x = 2 + t$$
$$y = 7 + 3t$$
$$z = 0$$

are the parametric equations. The standard equations are

$$\frac{x - 2}{1} = \frac{y - 7}{3}, \quad z = 0.$$

Now try these

▬ Find the parametric equation of $\overrightarrow{AB}$ if A and B are as follows.

1. $A(1, 2, -3)$, $B(-1, -4, 7)$ **2.** $A(x_1, y_1, z_1)$, $B(x_2, y_2, z_2)$

3. Is it possible to find the parametric equations of a line given a point on the line and its direction cosines? Explain.

Answers: **1.** $x = 1 - 2t$, $y = 2 - 6t$, $z = -3 + 10t$
       2. $x = x_1 + (x_2 - x_1)t$, $y = y_1 + (y_2 - y_1)t$, $z = z_1 + (z_2 - z_1)t$
       3. Yes. The direction cosines are direction numbers for $|\vec{A}| = 1$.

Checkpoint

Explain the difference between the standard equations of a line and the parametric equations of a line.

Exercises

A ━━━ Find the parametric and standard equations (when possible) of each line containing the points A and B.

1. $A(-2, 1, 3)$ $B(1, 0, -3)$ **2.** $A(1, 2, 3)$ $B(5, 5, 5)$

3. $A(-1, -2, -3)$ $B(0, 0, 0)$ **4.** $A(1, 5, -3)$ $B(2, -1, -2)$

5. $A(1, 2, 5)$ $B(2, 1, 5)$ **6.** $A(1, 3, 5)$ $B(2, 3, 5)$

7. $A(1, 2, 0)$ $B(3, 3, 0)$ **8.** $A(1, 2)$ $B(3, 3)$

9. $A(2, -3)$ $B(-4, 5)$ **10.** $A(-2, 1)$ $B(2, 1)$

11. $A(5, -3)$ $B(5, -2)$ **12.** $A(-2, -5)$ $B(5, -2)$

━━━ Use the figure at the right for Exercises 13–15. Let $\overrightarrow{OB} = l\mathbf{i} + m\mathbf{j} + n\mathbf{k}$.

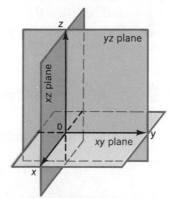

13. If $\overrightarrow{OB}$ is in the xy plane, then $n = \underline{\ ?\ }$

14. If $\overrightarrow{OB}$ is in the yz plane, then $l = \underline{\ ?\ }$

15. If $\overrightarrow{OB}$ is in the xz plane, then $m = \underline{\ ?\ }$

16. What are the standard equations of a line in the xz plane?

17. What are the parametric equations of a line in the yz plane?

18. What are the parametric equations of a line in the
    a. plane parallel to the xy plane and 5 units above it?
    b. plane parallel to xz plane and 3 units to the left?
    c. plane parallel to yz plane and $\frac{1}{2}$ unit in front of it?

B **19.** Find the parametric equations of the line with standard equations $2x - 1 = 4y + 8 = 3z - 5$.

20. What are the direction numbers of the line in Exercise 19?

21. Let $A = (1, -2, 3)$ and $B = (2, 1, 5)$. Find the parametric equations of the line through A and B.
    a. when $\overrightarrow{AB}$ is the fixed vector and B is the fixed point.
    b. when $\overrightarrow{AB}$ is the fixed vector and A is the fixed point.
    c. when $\overrightarrow{BA}$ is the fixed vector and A is the fixed point.

22. Below are given two sets of parametric equations of lines.

$$x = 2 + t$$
$$y = 3 + t \qquad \text{and}$$
$$z = 1 - 2t$$

$$x = 1 - s$$
$$y = 2 - s \qquad t \text{ and } s \text{ parameters.}$$
$$z = 3 + 2s$$

a. What are the direction numbers of the lines?
b. What is the fixed vector for each line?
c. How are the direction vectors related?
d. Are the equations equations of the same line? Explain.

23. How many sets of parametric equations of a line are there? Explain.

C **24.** Find the equation of the line containing the midpoint of $\overline{AB}$ and C when $A = (2, 5)$, $B = (3, 1)$, and $C = (-2, 3)$.

25. Find the parametric equations of the medians of the triangle with vertices $(a, 0)$, $(0, b)$, $(0, c)$.

26. Find the points on each median in Exercise 25 which is $\frac{2}{3}$ the distance from the vertex to the midpoint of the opposite side. What do you notice about these points?

9–7 Lines in two-space

The standard equations of a line in the xy plane are

$$\frac{x - a}{l} = \frac{y - b}{m}, \quad z = 0, \quad l, m \neq 0.$$

It is customary to omit the second equation; $z = 0$.
A direction vector of this line is

$$\vec{A} = l\mathbf{i} + m\mathbf{j}.$$

The slope of the vector $\vec{A}$ is defined to be

$$slope \; \vec{A} = \frac{m}{l} \quad l \neq 0. \qquad 1$$

In words, the slope of a vector $\vec{A} = l\mathbf{i} + m\mathbf{j}$ is the length of the vertical vector $| m\mathbf{j} |$ divided by the length of the horizontal vector $| l\mathbf{i} |$ (recall $| \mathbf{i} | = | \mathbf{j} | = 1$) or the $\mathbf{j}$-component divided by the $\mathbf{i}$-component of the vector.

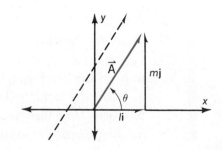

The **slope of a line in two-space** is defined to be the slope of any of its direction vectors. The slope of a line is a unique number because any two direction vectors are parallel and thus have proportional components. That is, if $\vec{A}$ and $\vec{B}$ are direction vectors for the same line,

$$\vec{A} = t\vec{B} \text{ where } t \text{ is a scalar.}$$

Then if slope $\vec{B} = \dfrac{m}{l}$,

$$\text{slope } \vec{A} = \frac{tm}{tl} = \frac{m}{l} = \text{slope } \vec{B}.$$

If a direction vector $\vec{A}$ of a line makes an angle of measure θ with the positive x axis,

$$\frac{m}{l} = \tan \theta, \quad l \neq 0.$$

Thus

$$\text{slope } \vec{A} = \tan \theta = \frac{m}{l} = \lambda. \quad (\lambda \text{ is the Greek letter } lambda.) \qquad 2$$

If $\vec{A} = l\mathbf{i} + m\mathbf{j}$ is a direction vector for a line, then $\vec{A} = l(\mathbf{i} + \lambda\mathbf{j})$ and $\mathbf{i} + \lambda\mathbf{j}$ is a direction vector for the same line. The standard equations of the line containing (x, y) and fixed point (a, b) are

$$\frac{x - a}{1} = \frac{y - b}{\lambda}$$

or

$$y - b = \lambda(x - a). \qquad 3$$

Clearly every point on the line through (a, b) and of slope λ satisfies equation 3. Conversely, any point (x, y) different from (a, b), that satisfies equation 3 must lie on the line; for

$$y - b = \lambda\,(x - a) \quad \text{implies} \quad \frac{y - b}{x - a} = \lambda.$$

Thus the vector from (a, b) to (x, y),

$$(x - a)\mathbf{i} + (y - b)\mathbf{j} = (x - a)\left[\mathbf{i} + \frac{y - b}{x - a}\mathbf{j}\right] = (x - a)[\mathbf{i} + \lambda\mathbf{j}],$$

is a nonzero scalar multiple of the direction vector $\mathbf{i} + \lambda\mathbf{j}$. Therefore, (x, y) is on the line.

Finally (a, b) satisfies equation 3, and any point satisfying 3 lies on the line. Equation 3 is the **point-slope** equation of a line.

EXAMPLE 1. Let a line have a direction vector $3\mathbf{i} + 2\mathbf{j}$ and contain the point $(5, 2)$. Find the equation of the line.

Since $3\mathbf{i} + 2\mathbf{j}$ is a direction vector, then the slope of the line is $\frac{2}{3}$ and, by the point slope equation, the line has equation $(y - 2) = \frac{2}{3}(x - 5)$.

The parametric equations of a line in two-space through (a, b) are

$$x = a + tl$$
$$y = b + tm$$

If $l = 0$, then a direction vector of the line is $\vec{A} = 0\mathbf{i} + m\mathbf{j} = m\mathbf{j}$. Thus the line is parallel to the y axis. It has parametric equations

$$x = a$$
$$y = b + tm$$

Since y takes on all real values and x is always a, only the first equation is used to denote the line. In other words

$$x = a, \qquad\qquad\qquad 4$$

is the equation of a line parallel to the y axis. Similarly, when $m = 0$,

$$y = b \qquad\qquad\qquad 5$$

is the equation of a line parallel to the x axis.

The equations **3**, **4**, and **5** are first degree equations. The derivations of these equations prove the following theorem.

> **Theorem 9–5** Any line in the xy plane is described by an equation of the first degree.

The converse of Theorem 9–5 which follows is also true.

> **Theorem 9–6** Any equation of the first degree in x and y describes a line in the xy plane.

Proof: Let such an equation be $Ax + By + C = 0$, where A, B, and C are constants with A and B not both zero. The strategy is to find a line which has this equation.

Case 1

Let $B \neq 0$. Consider the line containing $\left(0, \frac{-C}{B}\right)$ with slope $\frac{-A}{B}$.
By the *point slope* equation, this line is described by

$$y - \left(\frac{-C}{B}\right) = -\frac{A}{B}\,(x - 0)$$

or

$$Ax + By + C = 0.$$

Since there is a unique line with y intercept $\left(0, \frac{-C}{B}\right)$ and slope $\frac{-A}{B}$,
the original equation describes that line.

Case 2

Let $B = 0$. Consider the line containing $\left(\frac{-C}{A}, 0\right)$ and parallel to
the y axis. The equation of this line is

$$x = \frac{-C}{A}$$

or

$$Ax + 0y + C = 0$$

Case 3

Let $A = 0$. Consider the line through $\left(0, \frac{-C}{B}\right)$ and parallel to the
x axis. Its equation is

$$y = \frac{-C}{B}$$

which reduces to

$$0x + By + C = 0.$$

Thus the linear equation $Ax + By + C = 0$ is always the equation of
a line in the xy plane.

EXAMPLE 2.   The equation of a line in two-space is $2x + 3y - 4 = 0$.
a. Find the slope, λ, of the line.
     The equation $2x + 3y - 4 = 0$ is equivalent to $\frac{2}{3}x + y - \frac{4}{3} = 0$.
Writing the last equation in the point slope form

$$y = -\tfrac{2}{3}x + \tfrac{4}{3} = -\tfrac{2}{3}(x - 2)$$

You see that the slope is $-\frac{2}{3}$.
b. Find a direction vector for the line.
     Since the slope of the line is $-\frac{2}{3}$ a direction vector is the following.

$$\vec{A} = \mathbf{i} - \tfrac{2}{3}\mathbf{j}$$

Find the x and y intercepts.

The x and y intercepts are found by alternately setting y and x equal to zero and solving for x and y.

When $y = 0$,

$$2x + 3 \cdot 0 - 4 = 0 \text{ implies } x = 2.$$

When $x = 0$,

$$2 \cdot 0 + 3y - 4 = 0 \text{ implies } y = \tfrac{4}{3}.$$

Sketch the graph of the line.

From the steps above, we see that $(0, \tfrac{4}{3})$ and $(2, 0)$ are on the line. These two points, or any others, uniquely determine the line. Plot the two points and the line determined by them. (See the figure below.)

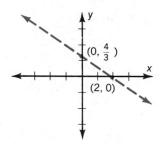

Now try these

▬ Find the equation of the line satisfying the given conditions.

1. The line through $(4, 2)$ with slope $\tfrac{3}{2}$.

2. The line through $(-3, 2)$ with slope $\tfrac{3}{4}$.

3. The line having direction vector $5\mathbf{i} + 4\mathbf{j}$ and containing the point $(7, 4)$.

▬ Given the following equation of a line in two-space,

$$4x + 3y - 8 = 0$$

find each of the following:

4. the slope λ of the line.

5. the x and y intercepts.

6. a direction vector for the line.

Answers: **1.** $3x - 2y - 8 = 0$ **2.** $3x - 4y + 17 = 0$

3. $-4x + 5y + 8 = 0$ **4.** $\lambda = -\tfrac{4}{3}$

5. x intercept is 2; y intercept is $\tfrac{8}{3}$.   **6.** $\vec{A} = \mathbf{i} + \dfrac{-4}{3}\mathbf{j}$

Exercises

A ▬ Find the equation of the line satisfying the given conditions.

1. Slope is $\frac{1}{5}$, contains $(2, -3)$.
2. Slope is $-\frac{5}{3}$, contains $(0, 3)$.
3. Parallel to y axis, contains $(-2, 3)$.
4. Parallel to x axis, contains $(1, 5)$.
5. Slope is 0, contains $(2, -3)$.
6. Slope is undefined, contains $(1, -17)$.
7. A direction vector is $\vec{A} = 3\mathbf{i} - 2\mathbf{j}$, contains $(1, 1)$.
8. A direction vector is $\vec{A} = -5\mathbf{i} + 2\mathbf{j}$, contains $(-3, -1)$.
9. Slope is $\frac{5}{8}$, contains $(7, 1)$.
10. Slope is -8, contains $(0, 0)$.
11. A direction vector is $\vec{A} = \mathbf{i} - 3\mathbf{j}$, contains $(-5, 1)$.
12. A direction vector is $\vec{A} = -\mathbf{i} + 3\mathbf{j}$, contains $(-5, 1)$.
13. A direction vector is $\vec{A} = \mathbf{i} + \frac{2}{7}\mathbf{j}$, contains $(0, 0)$.
14. A direction vector is $\vec{A} = \mathbf{i} + a\mathbf{j}$, contains (b, c).

▬ Find a direction vector for each line whose equation is given.

15. $y - 2 = 3(x - 1)$
16. $y + 5 = -2(x + 3)$
17. $y + \frac{2}{3} = x - 1$
18. $3x + 2y + 4 = 0$
19. $y + 2x - 3 = 0$
20. $x + 2y - 3 = 0$
21. $4x - 3y - 7 = 0$
22. $\frac{1}{2}x - \frac{2}{3}y - \frac{4}{5} = 0$
23. $x = 3 + t5,\ y = 4 + t3$
24. $x = -1 - 4t,\ y = 2 - 3t$
25. Graph each line given in Exercises 15–22.

B 26. Show that two vectors $\overrightarrow{P_1P_2}$, $\overrightarrow{P_3P_4}$, where $P_1(x_1, y_1)$, $P_2(x_2, y_2)$, $P_3(x_3, y_3)$, $P_4(x_4, y_4)$ are equal if and only if $x_2 - x_1 = x_4 - x_3$, and $y_2 - y_1 = y_4 - y_3$.

27. Using the vectors given in Exercise 26, show that two vectors are parallel if and only if $x_2 - x_1 = t(x_4 - x_3)$ and $y_2 - y_1 = t(y_4 - y_2)$, where t is a real nonzero number.

28. Show that if $P_1(x_1, y_1)$ and $P_2(x_2, y_2)$ are two points on a line, then $\lambda = \frac{y_2 - y_1}{x_2 - x_1}$.

29. Make a geometric argument demonstrating that the slope of a line may be determined by dividing the difference of the y coordinate by the difference (nonzero) of the x coordinates of any two points on the line. (*Hint:* Choose two different pairs of points and consider similar triangles.)

Use the result of Exercises 28 and 29 to write the equation of the line that contains each of the following.

30. (2, 1) and (5, 4)

31. (17, 84) and (19, 82)

32. (−5, 2) and (2, −4)

33. (3, −2) and (−1, −3)

34. (x_1, y_1) and (x_2, y_2), $x_1 \neq x_2$ (Note: Your result is the two point equation of a line.)

C 35. a. Show that $Ax + By + C = 0$ may be written in the following form

$$\frac{x}{a} + \frac{y}{b} = 1$$

when $A, B, C \neq 0$.

b. Interpret a and b in terms of the graph of the equation $Ax + By + C = 0$.

36. a. Show that $Ax + By + C = 0$, $B \neq 0$, can be written in the form

$$y = mx + b.$$

b. What interpretation can be given to m and to b?

37. You are given $Ax + By + 5 = 0$, $B \neq 0$.

a. Express the slope of this line in terms of the constants A, B, and 5.

b. What is a direction vector for this line?

c. What is a direction vector for a vector parallel to the vector in Exercise **b**?

d. Using your vector in Exercise **c**, write a linear equation of the line with that direction vector which contains (2, 3).

e. How are the given line and the line you found in Exercise **d** related?

f. How are the equations related?

g. What generalization does the results found in Exercises **a**, **b**, **c**, **d**, **e**, and **f** suggest?

9-8   The Angle Between Two Vectors

Two nonzero vectors, $\vec{A}$ and $\vec{B}$, in space may or may not intersect. However, the angle between the vectors may be determined uniquely because each vector is equal to some unique position vector. (See Example 2, Section 9–4.)

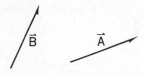

$$\text{Let } \vec{V}_1 = a_1\mathbf{i} + a_2\mathbf{j} + a_3\mathbf{k} \quad \text{and} \quad \vec{V}_2 = b_1\mathbf{i} + b_2\mathbf{j} + b_3\mathbf{k}$$

be the two position vectors that correspond to $\vec{A}$ and $\vec{B}$. The measure of the angle between the vector $\vec{V}_1$ and $\vec{V}_2$ is θ. Clearly $0° \le \theta \le 180°$. $\theta = 0$ when $\vec{V}_2 = t\vec{V}_1$, $t > 0$ and $\theta = 180°$ when $\vec{V}_2 = t\vec{V}_1$, $t < 0$.

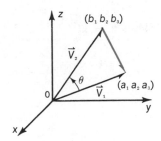

Notice that the vector $\vec{V}_1 - \vec{V}_2$ is the third side of the triangle formed by $\vec{V}_1$ and $\vec{V}_2$. The Law of Cosines can be used to find the cosine of θ.

$$| \vec{V}_1 - \vec{V}_2 |^2 = | \vec{V}_1 |^2 + | \vec{V}_2 |^2 - 2| \vec{V}_1 || \vec{V}_2 | \cos \theta$$

or

$$\cos \theta = \frac{-| \vec{V}_1 - \vec{V}_2 |^2 + | \vec{V}_1 |^2 + | \vec{V}_2 |^2}{+2| \vec{V}_1 | \cdot | \vec{V}_2 |}. \qquad \mathbf{1}$$

But

$$\begin{aligned}
-| \vec{V}_1 - \vec{V}_2 |^2 &= -[(a_1 - b_1)^2 + (a_2 - b_2)^2 + (a_3 - b_3)^2] \\
&= -[a_1^2 - 2a_1b_1 + b_1^2 + a_2^2 - 2a_2b_2 + b_2^2 + a_3 \\
&\qquad\qquad - 2a_3b_3 + b_3^2]
\end{aligned}$$

$$| \vec{V}_1 |^2 = a_1^2 + a_2^2 + a_3^2$$

and

$$| \vec{V}_2 |^2 = b_1^2 + b_2^2 + b_3^2.$$

Substituting the expressions in **1**, you find

$$\cos \theta = \frac{2(a_1b_1 + a_2b_2 + a_3b_3)}{2| \vec{V}_1 | \cdot | \vec{V}_2 |}$$

or

$$\cos \theta = \frac{a_1b_1 + a_2b_2 + a_3b_3}{\sqrt{a_1^2 + a_2^2 + a_3^2} \cdot \sqrt{b_1^2 + b_2^2 + b_3^2}} \qquad \mathbf{2}$$

EXAMPLE 1. Find the measure of the angle between the vectors $\vec{A} = \mathbf{i} + \mathbf{j} + \mathbf{k}$ and $\vec{B} = 2\mathbf{i} + 3\mathbf{j} + 5\mathbf{k}$. Express your answer to the nearest degree. By equation 2

$$\cos \theta = \frac{a_1b_1 + a_2b_2 + a_3b_3}{|\vec{A}| \cdot |\vec{B}|}.$$

so

$$\cos \theta = \frac{1 \cdot 2 + 1 \cdot 3 + 1 \cdot 5}{\sqrt{3} \cdot \sqrt{38}}$$

$$= \frac{10}{\sqrt{114}}$$

$$\approx \frac{10}{10.68} \approx .94$$

Thus $\theta \approx 20°$.

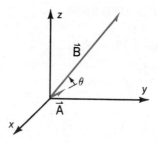

Equation 2 for the cosine of the angle between two vectors in space needs little modification for vectors in the xy plane. The z component for such vectors is 0.

Thus

$$\cos \theta = \frac{a_1b_1 + a_2b_2}{\sqrt{a_1^2 + a_2^2} \cdot \sqrt{b_1^2 + b_2^2}}. \qquad 3$$

Therefore,

$$\vec{V}_1 = a_1\mathbf{i} + a_2\mathbf{j} \quad \text{and} \quad \vec{V}_2 = b_1\mathbf{i} + b_2\mathbf{j}.$$

Notice that the numerator of equation 2 is the sum of the products of the corresponding components of $\vec{V}_1$ and $\vec{V}_2$. This sum is called the **inner product** or **dot product.**

Definition The *inner product* (*dot product*) of two vectors $\vec{V}_1 = a_1\mathbf{i} + a_2\mathbf{j} + a_3\mathbf{k}$ and $\vec{V}_2 = b_1\mathbf{i} + b_2\mathbf{j} + b_3\mathbf{k}$ is:

$$\vec{V}_1 \cdot \vec{V}_2 = a_1b_1 + a_2b_2 + a_3b_3 \qquad 4$$

If $\vec{V}_1$ and $\vec{V}_2$ are in the xy plane, then

$$\vec{V}_1 \cdot \vec{V}_2 = a_1 b_1 + a_2 b_2. \qquad\qquad 5$$

This leads to Theorem 9–7 which you will be asked to prove in the exercises.

Theorem 9–7 **a.** $\vec{V}_1 \cdot \vec{V}_2 = \vec{V}_2 \cdot \vec{V}_1$ (Commutative Property)
 b. $\vec{V}_1 \cdot (\vec{V}_2 + \vec{V}_3) = \vec{V}_1 \cdot \vec{V}_2 + \vec{V}_1 \cdot \vec{V}_3$
(Distributive Property)

In terms of inner products,

$$\cos \theta = \frac{\vec{V}_1 \cdot \vec{V}_2}{|\vec{V}_1| \cdot |\vec{V}_2|}$$

for all nonzero vectors $\vec{V}_1$ and $\vec{V}_2$. Notice that the multiplication shown in the denominator is an ordinary product of two numbers, not a dot product.

EXAMPLE 2. Find the angle between the vectors

$$\vec{A} = 2\mathbf{i} + 4\mathbf{j} + 2\mathbf{k} \quad \text{and} \quad \vec{B} = 3\mathbf{i} - 5\mathbf{j} + 7\mathbf{k}.$$

Interpret the results.

$$\cos \theta = \frac{2 \cdot 3 + 4(-5) + 2 \cdot 7}{\sqrt{24} \cdot \sqrt{83}}$$

$$= \frac{6 - 20 + 14}{\sqrt{24} \cdot \sqrt{83}}$$

$$= 0$$

Since $\cos \theta = 0$, $\theta = 90°$. Thus the vectors $\vec{A}$ and $\vec{B}$ are perpendicular.
    Example 2 suggests the next theorem.

Theorem 9–8 Two vectors $\vec{A}$ and $\vec{B}$ are perpendicular if and only if $\vec{A} \cdot \vec{B} = 0$.

The proof follows from the fact that $\vec{A}$ and $\vec{B}$ are perpendicular if and only if $\theta = 90° \pm 180k$. ($k = 0, 1, 2, 3, \cdots$) and that will happen if and only if $\cos \theta$ is zero. But $\cos \theta = 0$ if and only if $\vec{A} \cdot \vec{B} = 0$. The zero vector is considered to be perpendicular to all vectors.

EXAMPLE 3. Find a nonzero vector $\vec{B}$ which is perpendicular to $\vec{A} = 2\mathbf{i} - 3\mathbf{j}$.

Let $\vec{B} = b_1\mathbf{i} + b_2\mathbf{j}$, then if $\vec{A} \perp \vec{B}$, $\vec{A} \cdot \vec{B} = 0$ or $2b_1 - 3b_2 = 0$. Thus $\frac{b_2}{b_1} = \frac{2}{3}$. You can choose b_2 (or b_1) to be any nonzero real number and b_1 (or b_2) is uniquely determined. Suppose $b_2 = 8$. Then $b_1 = 12$. Thus $\vec{B} = 12\mathbf{i} + 8\mathbf{j}$ will do, and it is only one of an infinite number of satisfactory parallel vectors.

If you wished $\vec{B}$ to have length one, then it is easiest to choose $b_2 = \frac{2}{\sqrt{13}}$ and $b_1 = \frac{3}{\sqrt{13}}$. In this case

$$\vec{B} = \frac{3}{\sqrt{13}}\mathbf{i} + \frac{2}{\sqrt{13}}\mathbf{j}.$$

The vectors found in Example 3 have special names. A vector which is perpendicular to a given vector is said to be a **normal vector** or a **normal** to the given vector. If the normal has length one, it is called a **unit normal**.

The idea of the angle between two vectors is used to define the **angle between two lines.**

Definition The *angle between two lines* l_1 and l_2 is the non-obtuse angle between any two of the direction vectors for the lines.

A **normal to a line** is a vector perpendicular to a direction vector of the line.

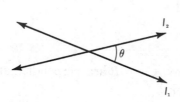

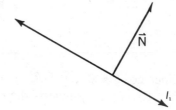

Angle between two lines. $\vec{N}$ is a normal to l_1.

EXAMPLE 4. Let line l_1 have equations $\frac{x-1}{1} = \frac{y-3}{1} = \frac{z-7}{1}$ and line l_2 have equations $\frac{x-5}{2} = \frac{y+1}{3} = \frac{z}{5}$.

a. Find the angle between l_1 and l_2.

A direction vector for l_1 is $\vec{r}_1 = 1\mathbf{i} + 1\mathbf{j} + 1\mathbf{k}$ and a direction vector for l_2 is $\vec{r}_2 = 2\mathbf{i} + 3\mathbf{j} + 5\mathbf{k}$. (Why?)

Thus $$\cos \theta = \frac{1 \cdot 2 + 1 \cdot 3 + 1 \cdot 5}{\sqrt{3} \cdot \sqrt{38}} = \frac{10}{\sqrt{114}}$$

By Example 1, $\theta \approx 20°$.

b. Find a normal to l_1, and a normal to l_2.

Let $\vec{N_1} = n_1\mathbf{i} + n_2\mathbf{j} + n_3\mathbf{k}$ be a normal to l_1. Then $\vec{N_1} \cdot \vec{r_1} = n_1 \cdot 1 + n_2 \cdot 1 + n_3 \cdot 1 = n_1 + n_2 + n_3 = 0$ because of perpendicularity. Any 3 real numbers which are not all zero and whose sum is zero will do. Choose, for example, $n_1 = 1$, $n_2 = -1$ and $n_3 = 0$. Thus $\vec{N_1} = \mathbf{i} - \mathbf{j}$ is normal to l_1. A normal $\vec{N_2}$ to l_2 is found in a similar manner. Verify that $\vec{N_2} = \mathbf{i} + \mathbf{j} - \mathbf{k}$ will do.

Checkpoint

1. Is finding the inner product of two vectors a closed operation on vectors? Explain.

2. Is finding the inner product of two vectors a commutative operation on vectors? an associative operation on vectors? Explain.

Exercises

A ━━ Find the cosine of the angle between each pair of vectors.

1. $\vec{A} = \mathbf{i} + \mathbf{j}$
$\vec{B} = \mathbf{i}$

2. $\vec{A} = \mathbf{i} + \mathbf{j}$
$\vec{B} = \mathbf{j}$

3. $\vec{A} = \mathbf{i} + \mathbf{j} + \mathbf{k}$
$\vec{B} = \mathbf{i} + \mathbf{j}$

4. $\vec{A} = \mathbf{i} + \mathbf{j} + \mathbf{k}$
$\vec{B} = \mathbf{j}$

5. $\vec{A} = \mathbf{i}$
$\vec{B} = \mathbf{j}$

6. $\vec{A} = \mathbf{k}$
$\vec{B} = 5\mathbf{k}$

7. $\vec{A} = 2\mathbf{i} + 3\mathbf{j} + 7\mathbf{k}$
$\vec{B} = -3\mathbf{i} + 5\mathbf{k}$

8. $\vec{A} = 2\mathbf{j} - 3\mathbf{k}$
$\vec{B} = \mathbf{i} + 4\mathbf{j} + 2\mathbf{k}$

9. $\vec{A} = 7\mathbf{i} + 1\mathbf{j}$
$\vec{B} = -3\mathbf{i} + 2\mathbf{j}$

10. $\vec{A} = \mathbf{i} - 2\mathbf{k}, \vec{B} = 3\mathbf{j}$

11. $\vec{A} = 3\mathbf{j} - 2\mathbf{k}, \vec{B} = 2\mathbf{i} - \mathbf{j} - \mathbf{k}$

12. $\vec{P}$ is the vector from $(-4, 2)$ to $(2, 1)$.
$\vec{Q}$ is the vector from $(5, 8)$ to $(6, 2)$.

13. $\vec{r}$ is the vector from $(-2, 1, -3)$ to $(0, 1, 3)$.
$\vec{v}$ is the vector from $(1, 0, 3)$ to $(5, -2, 1)$.

14. $\vec{A}$ is the vector from $(1, 8, 5)$ to $(8, 5, 11)$.
$\vec{B}$ is the vector from $(-2, -3, -4)$ to $(1, 0, -6)$.

15. Find a normal to each vector in Exercises 7–9.

16. Find a unit normal to each vector in Exercises 11 and 13.

B ▬ Find the measure θ of the acute angle between each pair of lines. Find θ to the nearest degree.

17. $\dfrac{x-3}{2} = \dfrac{y-3}{5}, z = 0$

$\dfrac{x+1}{3} = \dfrac{y+2}{1}, z = 0$

18. $\dfrac{x+1}{2} = \dfrac{y-2}{2} = \dfrac{z-1}{2}$

$\dfrac{x-1}{3} = \dfrac{y-2}{5} = \dfrac{z+3}{1}$

19. $y = -3(x - 1)$

$y = \tfrac{1}{2}(x + 2)$

20. $\dfrac{x+1}{1} = \dfrac{y-2}{3}, z = 0$

$\dfrac{x-3}{1} = \dfrac{y+5}{2}, z = 0$

21. $x = 2 - 4t, x = 1 + 5t$

$y = 1 - 2t, y = -2 - t$

$z = 1 + 2t, z = 1 - 2t$

22. $x = 5, y = 2x + 4$

23. Find a unit normal to each line in Exercises 17–22.

24. **a.** Let $\vec{A} = a\mathbf{i} + b\mathbf{j} + c\mathbf{k}$. Find the cosine of the angles formed by $\vec{A}$ and $\mathbf{i}, \mathbf{j}, \mathbf{k}$.

b. What do your answers in part **a** represent?

C **25.** **a.** The standard equations of a line in the xy plane can be written $\dfrac{x-a}{1} = \dfrac{y-b}{\lambda}$, where λ is the slope of the line. If the lines

$$\frac{x-a}{1} = \frac{y-b}{\lambda_1}$$

and

$$\frac{x-c}{1} = \frac{y-d}{\lambda_2}$$

are perpendicular, how must λ_1 and λ_2 be related?

b. Is the converse statement true? Prove or disprove.

26. Prove that the vectors

$$\vec{V}_1 = 7\mathbf{i} - 3\mathbf{j} + 6\mathbf{k}$$
$$\vec{V}_2 = 3\mathbf{i} + 3\mathbf{j} - 2\mathbf{k}$$
$$\vec{V}_3 = 6\mathbf{i} - 16\mathbf{j} - 15\mathbf{k}$$

454   CHAPTER 9

are mutually perpendicular.

27. Find the equation of a line perpendicular to the line with standard equations $\frac{x-1}{2} = \frac{y+3}{1} = \frac{z-1}{5}$.

(*Hint:* What is a direction vector for the desired line?)

28. Prove Theorem 9–7.

9–9 Parallel and Perpendicular Lines: Distance

Suppose you have two lines with equations

$$Ax + By + C_1 = 0 \quad B \neq 0$$

and
$$Ax + By + C_2 = 0 \quad B \neq 0 \qquad \qquad 1$$

Then
$$\mathbf{i} + \frac{-A}{B}\mathbf{j}$$

is a direction vector for each line because $\frac{-A}{B}$ is the slope of each line. Since the lines have the same direction vector, the lines are parallel.

Conversely if two lines are parallel, they have parallel direction vectors. Then one vector is a scalar multiple of the other. If the vectors are $l_1\mathbf{i} + m_1\mathbf{j}$ and $l_2\mathbf{i} + m_2\mathbf{j}$ then

$$l_1\mathbf{i} + m_1\mathbf{j} = tl_2\mathbf{i} + tm_1\mathbf{j}, \quad t \neq 0$$

Thus the slopes are equal for

$$\lambda_1 = \frac{m_1}{l_1} = \frac{tm_2}{tl_2} = \frac{m_2}{l_2} = \lambda_2$$

Letting $\lambda_1 = \lambda_2 = \frac{-A}{B}$, the lines have equations 1 where C_1 and C_2 are constants. The following theorem can now be stated.

Theorem 9–9 Two lines are parallel if and only if they have the same slope.

With regard to Theorem 9–9, two lines $A_1x + B_1y + C_1 = 0$ and $A_2x + B_2y + C_2 = 0$ are parallel if and only if $A_1 = KA_2$ and $B_1 = KB_2$.

The equation of a line perpendicular to $Ax + By + C = 0$ can be determined by vector methods. The theorem is as follows.

Proof: The direction vector of $Ax + By + C = 0$ is $\vec{V}_1 = \mathbf{i} + \frac{-A}{B}\mathbf{j}$. Another line is perpendicular to $Ax + By + C = 0$ if and only if the inner product of its direction vector $\vec{V}_2 = \mathbf{i} + \lambda\mathbf{j}$ and $\mathbf{i} + \frac{-A}{B}\mathbf{j}$ is zero, that is, if and only if

$$V_1 \cdot V_2 = 1 + \lambda\left(\frac{-A}{B}\right) = 0$$

But
$$1 + \lambda\left(\frac{-A}{B}\right) = 0 \quad \text{iff}$$

$$\lambda\left(\frac{-A}{B}\right) = -1 \qquad\qquad\qquad 2$$

From equation 2 it follows that $\lambda = \frac{B}{A}$. Thus the equation of a line perpendicular to

$$Ax + By + C = 0 \qquad\qquad\qquad 3$$
is
$$Bx - Ay + C_1 = 0. \qquad\qquad\qquad 4$$

Notice that in Equation 4 the coefficient of the x and y terms are the reverse of those in 3. Furthermore the sign of one coefficient has been reversed. This fact can help you quickly write the equation of a line perpendicular to a given line. The constant C_1 can be found when a point on the perpendicular line is known.

EXAMPLE 1.   Given line $2x + 3y + 5 = 0$.   Find the parallel line containing $(-2, 1)$.

The equation desired is $2x + 3y + C_1 = 0$.   Since $(-2, 1)$ is on the line $2(-2) + 3(1) + C_1 = 0$.   Solving for C_1, you find $C_1 = 1$.   The equation is $2x + 3y + 1 = 0$.

Find the perpendicular line containing $(-2, 1)$.

The equation is $-3x + 2y + C_2 = 0$. C_2 is found by substituting $(-2, 1)$ in this equation and solving for C_2.

$$-3(-2) + (2)(1) + C_2 = 0$$
$$C_2 = -8$$

The equation is $\qquad -3x + 2y - 8 = 0$.

What equation would you get if you started with $3x - 2y + C_3 = 0$?

The equation of a line perpendicular to a given line, the distance formula, and elementary algebra are useful in deriving a formula for the distance from a point to a line.

> **Theorem 9–11** The distance d from $P(a, b)$ to line $Ax + By + C = 0$ is given by the formula
>
> $$d = \frac{|Aa + Bb + C|}{\sqrt{A^2 + B^2}}.$$

Proof: If $B = 0$, then the line is parallel to the y axis, and d is the absolute value of the difference of a and $x = \frac{-C}{A}$. (Why?) Thus such lines can be excluded from further discussion.

Consider the line $Ax + By + C = 0$ as shown in the figure. The line through $P(a, b)$ parallel to $Ax + By + C = 0$ has equation

$$Ax + By + C_1 = 0 \qquad \textbf{5}$$

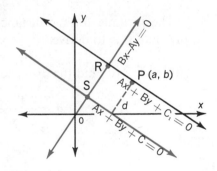

where C_1 can be determined by substituting $x = a$ and $y = b$ in **5**. This substitution will be performed later in the proof since it complicates the manipulations if done now.

The line through the origin which is perpendicular to the parallel lines is defined by the following equation.

$$Bx - Ay + C_2 = 0$$

Since $(0, 0)$ is on this line, $C_2 = 0$ and the equation is

$$Bx - Ay = 0.$$

Let the intersection of $Bx - Ay = 0$ with the parallel lines be R and S. Then $|\overrightarrow{SR}| = d$. (Why?)

The coordinates of R and S can be found by solving

$$\begin{aligned} Bx - Ay &= 0 \\ Ax + By + C_1 &= 0 \end{aligned} \qquad \text{and} \qquad \begin{aligned} Bx - Ay &= 0 \\ Ax + By + C &= 0 \end{aligned}$$

simultaneously. The solutions are

$$R\left(\frac{-C_1 A}{A^2 + B^2}, \frac{-C_1 B}{A^2 + B^2}\right) \qquad \text{and} \qquad S\left(\frac{-CA}{A^2 + B^2}, \frac{-CB}{A^2 + B^2}\right)$$

Now
$$d^2 = |\overrightarrow{RS}|^2 = \left(\frac{-C_1A + CA}{A^2 + B^2}\right)^2 + \left(\frac{-C_1B + CB}{A^2 + B^2}\right)^2$$

$$= \frac{A^2(-C_1 + C)^2 + B^2(-C_1 + C)^2}{(A^2 + B^2)^2}$$

$$= \frac{(A^2 + B^2)(-C_1 + C)^2}{(A^2 + B^2)^2}$$

$$= \frac{(-C_1 + C)}{A^2 + B^2}$$

But
$$C_1 = -Aa - Bb, \quad \text{so}$$

$$d = \sqrt{\frac{(Aa + Bb + C)^2}{A^2 + B^2}}$$

$$= \frac{|Aa + Bb + C|}{\sqrt{A^2 + B^2}}$$

The formula for the distance from a point to a line is easier to apply than it is to derive.

EXAMPLE 2. Find the distance from $(2, -5)$ to $3x + 4y - 3 = 0$.

$$d = \frac{|Aa + Bb + C|}{\sqrt{A^2 + B^2}}$$

Thus

$$d = \frac{|3 \cdot 2 + 4(-5) - 3|}{\sqrt{9 + 16}}$$

$$= \frac{|6 - 20 - 3|}{5}$$

$$= \frac{17}{5} = 3\frac{2}{5}$$

Now try these

▬ State whether the vectors in each pair are parallel or perpendicular.

1. $(1, 2); (-2, 1)$ **2.** $(1, 2); (2, 4)$ **3.** $(1, 2, 3); (2, -1, 0)$

▬ Find the distance from the origin to the lines whose equations are given below. Leave answers in radical form when radicals occur.

4. $x + y + 8 = 0$ **5.** $5x + 12y - 30 = 0$ **6.** $3x + 5y - 8 = 0$

Answers: **1.** Perpendicular **2.** Parallel **3.** Perpendicular **4.** $4\sqrt{2}$ **5.** $\frac{30}{13}$
 6. $\frac{4\sqrt{34}}{17}$

How do you determine whether two lines are parallel? perpendicular?

Exercises

A — Find equations of two lines containing A; one line parallel to the given line and one line perpendicular to the given line.

1. $A(4, 1)$, $2x - 3y + 5 = 0$
2. $A(2, -1)$, $2x - y + 1 = 0$
3. $A(2, -1)$, $2x - y = 0$
4. $A(3, 4)$, $7x + 5y + 4 = 0$
5. $A(0, 0)$, $x - y + 3 = 0$
6. $A(2, -3)$, $8x - y = 0$
7. $A(6, 0)$, $3x + 3y - 1 = 0$
8. $A(2, 5)$, $x = 4$
9. $A(7, 9)$, $y = -3$
10. $A(-2, -5)$, $y = 2x - 1$
11. $A(0, 7)$, $9y + x + 3 = 0$
12. $A(-5, 1)$, $\frac{x}{2} + \frac{y}{3} = 1$

13. Find the distance from the line to the point in Exercises 1–12 above. Leave answers in radical form when radicals occur.

B 14. For the line $Ax + By + C = 0$, find an expression for the distance from the origin to the line.

— Use your results in Exercise 14 to find the distance from the origin to

15. $2x - 3y + 7 = 0$
16. $4x + 5y - 15 = 0$
17. $x = 4$
18. $y = 3$
19. $5x - 12y = 0$
20. $\frac{x}{a} + \frac{y}{b} - 1 = 0$
21. $y = mx + b$

— Let $A(1, 0)$, $B(9, 2)$, $C(3, 6)$ be the vertices of a triangle. Find each of the following.

22. The equations of the lines containing the sides.
23. The equations of the lines containing the medians.
24. The equations of the lines containing the altitudes.
25. The equations of the lines containing the perpendicular bisectors of the sides.
26. The point common to the lines in Exercises 23, 24, and 25.
27. Show that the three points found in Exercise 26 are collinear.
28. Repeat Exercises 22–27, for the vertices $A(0, 0)$, $B(9, 2)$, and $C(2, 7)$.

C **29. a.** Given the line $3x + 2y + 4 = 0$, find a vector $\vec{N}$ normal to this line.

b. How are the components of the normal $\vec{N}$ related to the coefficients of the line?

c. Verify that $P(2, -5)$ is on the line.

d. Let $Q(x, y)$ be a point on the line. Find the components of $\overrightarrow{PQ}$.

e. What is the value of the inner product $\vec{N} \cdot \overrightarrow{PQ}$?

f. Find $\vec{N} \cdot \overrightarrow{PQ}$ and simplify. What is the result?

30. Repeat Exercise 29 for $Ax + By + C = 0$.

31. Generalize your results in Exercises 29 and 30, that is, if $\vec{N}$ is a normal to a line and $\overrightarrow{PQ}$ is a direction vector, the equation of the line is found by what means?

9–10　The Cross Product of Two Vectors

In two-space, if you were asked to find a vector perpendicular to each of two nonparallel, nonzero vectors, you would respond that there was no satisfactory nonzero vector. If one existed, a triangle could have two right angles as shown in Figure 1. Since the zero vector is thought of as perpendicular to any vector, it is the only vector in two-space perpendicular to two nonparallel, nonzero vectors.

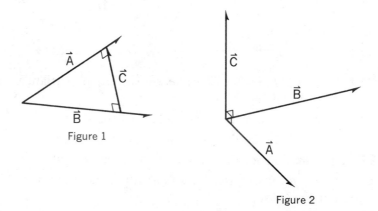

Figure 1

Figure 2

For two (nonzero) nonparallel vectors in three-space, there are many nonzero vectors perpendicular to each. For example, **i** is perpendicular to **j** and to **k**. Another example is shown in Figure 2. It

460　　CHAPTER 9

happens that there is a simple relationship between the components of $\vec{A}$ and $\vec{B}$ and a vector $\vec{C}$ in three-space which is perpendicular to $\vec{A}$ and $\vec{B}$. Let $\vec{A} = a_1\mathbf{i} + a_2\mathbf{j} + a_3\mathbf{k}$, $\vec{B} = b_1\mathbf{i} + b_2\mathbf{j} + b_3\mathbf{k}$, and the required vector be $\vec{C} = l\mathbf{i} + m\mathbf{j} + n\mathbf{k}$. Then $\vec{C} \perp \vec{A}$ and $\vec{C} \perp \vec{B}$ if and only if

$$\vec{C} \cdot \vec{A} = 0 \quad \text{and} \quad \vec{C} \cdot \vec{B} = 0.$$

Or $\qquad\qquad a_1 l + a_2 m + a_3 n = 0 \quad \text{and} \quad b_1 l + b_2 m + b_3 n = 0. \qquad\qquad 1$

Since the components of $\vec{A}$ and $\vec{B}$ are known, equations 1 can be solved simultaneously for l and m in terms of n.

Thus: $\qquad\qquad\qquad\qquad a_1 l + a_2 m = -a_3 n$

$\qquad\qquad$ **i.** $\qquad b_1 l + b_2 m = -b_3 n$

$\qquad\qquad$ **ii.** $a_1 b_2 l + a_2 b_2 m = -a_3 b_2 n$

$\qquad\qquad\qquad a_2 b_1 l + a_2 b_2 m = -a_2 b_3 n$

$\qquad\qquad$ **iii.** $(a_1 b_2 - a_2 b_1)l = (a_2 b_3 - a_3 b_2)n$

$\qquad\qquad$ **iv.** $l = \dfrac{(a_2 b_3 - a_3 b_2)n}{a_1 b_2 - a_2 b_1}, \quad a_1 b_2 - a_2 b_1 \neq 0$

Similarly $m = \dfrac{(a_1 b_3 - a_3 b_1)n}{a_2 b_1 - a_1 b_2} = \dfrac{a_3 b_1 - a_1 b_3}{a_1 b_2 - a_2 b_1} n$ where $a_1 b_2 - a_2 b_1 \neq 0$.

The value of n is arbitrary, so choose it to be

$$n = a_1 b_2 - a_2 b_1.$$

Then $\qquad\qquad\qquad\qquad l = a_2 b_3 - a_3 b_2$

$$m = a_3 b_1 - a_1 b_3.$$

Thus $\qquad \vec{C} = (a_2 b_3 - a_3 b_2)\mathbf{i} + (a_3 b_1 - a_1 b_3)\mathbf{j} + (a_1 b_2 - a_2 b_1)\mathbf{k}. \qquad 2$

The vector $\vec{C}$ in 2 is determined by the components of $\vec{A}$ and $\vec{B}$. To help you remember how the components of $\vec{A}$ and $\vec{B}$ combine to give you the components of $\vec{C}$ define the symbol

$$\begin{vmatrix} a_2 & a_3 \\ b_2 & b_3 \end{vmatrix} = a_2 b_3 - a_3 b_2. \qquad\qquad 3$$

Then using 3, 2 becomes

$$\vec{C} = \begin{vmatrix} a_2 & a_3 \\ b_2 & b_3 \end{vmatrix}\mathbf{i} + \begin{vmatrix} a_3 & a_1 \\ b_3 & b_1 \end{vmatrix}\mathbf{j} + \begin{vmatrix} a_1 & a_2 \\ b_1 & b_2 \end{vmatrix}\mathbf{k}. \qquad\qquad 4$$

Definition Given $\vec{A} = a_1\mathbf{i} + a_2\mathbf{j} + a_3\mathbf{k}$ and $\vec{B} = b_1\mathbf{i} + b_2\mathbf{j} + b_3\mathbf{k}$, the vector $\vec{C}$ is the *cross product* of $\vec{A}$ and $\vec{B}$, $\vec{A} \times \vec{B}$, and defined by equation **4**.

EXAMPLE. Find $\vec{C} \times \vec{D}$ in each of the following.

a. When $\vec{C} = 2\mathbf{i} - 3\mathbf{j} + 4\mathbf{k}$ and $\vec{D} = 5\mathbf{i} + 2\mathbf{j} - 3\mathbf{k}$.

$$\vec{C} \times \vec{D} = \begin{vmatrix} -3 & 4 \\ 2 & -3 \end{vmatrix} \mathbf{i} + \begin{vmatrix} 4 & 2 \\ -3 & 5 \end{vmatrix} \mathbf{j} + \begin{vmatrix} 2 & -3 \\ 5 & 2 \end{vmatrix} \mathbf{k}$$
$$= (9 - 8)\mathbf{i} + (20 + 6)\mathbf{j} + (4 + 15)\mathbf{k}$$
$$= 1\mathbf{i} + 26\mathbf{j} + 19\mathbf{k}$$

b. When $\vec{C} = \mathbf{i}$ and $\vec{D} = \mathbf{j}$.

$$\mathbf{i} \times \mathbf{j} = \begin{vmatrix} 0 & 0 \\ 1 & 0 \end{vmatrix} \mathbf{i} + \begin{vmatrix} 0 & 1 \\ 0 & 0 \end{vmatrix} \mathbf{j} + \begin{vmatrix} 1 & 0 \\ 0 & 1 \end{vmatrix} \mathbf{k}$$
$$= 0\mathbf{i} + 0\mathbf{j} + 1\mathbf{k} = \mathbf{k}$$

c. When $\vec{C} = \mathbf{j}$ and $\vec{D} = \mathbf{i}$.

$$\mathbf{j} \times \mathbf{i} = \begin{vmatrix} 1 & 0 \\ 0 & 0 \end{vmatrix} \mathbf{i} + \begin{vmatrix} 0 & 0 \\ 0 & 1 \end{vmatrix} \mathbf{j} + \begin{vmatrix} 0 & 1 \\ 1 & 0 \end{vmatrix} \mathbf{k}$$
$$= 0\mathbf{i} + 0\mathbf{j} - 1\mathbf{k} = -\mathbf{k}$$

Parts **b** and **c** suggest that $\vec{A} \times \vec{B} \neq \vec{B} \times \vec{A}$, that is, that the operation "cross product" is not commutative. This is, in fact, true. The proofs of the following theorems are left for you.

Theorem 9–12 $\vec{A} \times \vec{B} = -\vec{B} \times \vec{A}$.

Theorem 9–13 (Distributive Property)

$$\vec{A} \times (\vec{B} + \vec{C}) = \vec{A} \times \vec{B} + \vec{A} \times \vec{C}$$

Theorem 9–14 (An Associative Property)

$$m(\vec{A}) \times \vec{B} = m(\vec{A} \times \vec{B}).$$

Remaining unanswered is the question of the length of the vector $\vec{A} \times \vec{B}$. From **2**

$$|\vec{A} \times \vec{B}| = \sqrt{(a_2b_3 - a_3b_2)^2 + (a_3b_1 - a_1b_3)^2 + (a_1b_2 - a_2b_1)^2} \qquad 5$$

There is a more compact form of **5** as indicated in the next theorem.

Theorem 9–15 If $\vec{A} = a_1\mathbf{i} + a_2\mathbf{j} + a_3\mathbf{k}$, $\vec{B} = b_1\mathbf{i} + b_2\mathbf{j} + b_3\mathbf{k}$ and the angle between $\vec{A}$ and $\vec{B}$ has measure θ, $0 \leq \theta \leq 180°$, then

$$|\vec{A} \times \vec{B}| = |\vec{A}| \cdot |\vec{B}| \sin \theta.$$

Proof:

$$|\vec{A} \times \vec{B}| = \sqrt{(a_2b_3 - a_3b_2)^2 + (a_3b_1 - a_1b_3)^2 + (a_1b_2 - a_2b_1)^2}$$

$$= \sqrt{\begin{aligned}&a_2b_3{}^2 - 2a_2a_3b_2b_3 + a_3{}^2b_2{}^2 + a_3{}^2b_1{}^2 - 2a_1a_3b_1b_3 \\ &\quad + a_1{}^2b_3{}^2 + a_1{}^2b_2{}^2 - 2a_1a_2b_1b_2 + a_2{}^2b_1{}^2\end{aligned}}$$

$$= \sqrt{\begin{aligned}&(a_1{}^2 + a_2{}^2 + a_3{}^2)(b_1{}^2 + b_2{}^2 + b_3{}^2) \\ &\quad - [a_1{}^2b_1{}^2 + a_2b_2{}^2 + a_3{}^2b_3{}^2 + 2a_1a_2b_1b_2 + 2a_1a_3b_1b_3 + 2a_2a_3b_2b_3]\end{aligned}}$$

$$= \sqrt{|\vec{A}|^2 \cdot |\vec{B}|^2 - (\vec{A} \cdot \vec{B})^2} \quad \text{(since } \vec{A} \cdot \vec{B} = a_1b_1 + a_2b_2 + a_3b_3\text{).}$$

$$= |\vec{A}| \cdot |\vec{B}| \cdot \sqrt{1 - \left(\frac{\vec{A} \cdot \vec{B}}{|\vec{A}| \cdot |\vec{B}|}\right)^2}$$

Now since $\cos \theta = \dfrac{\vec{A} \cdot \vec{B}}{|\vec{A}||\vec{B}|}$, $\left(\dfrac{\vec{A} \cdot \vec{B}}{|\vec{A}||\vec{B}|}\right)^2 = \cos^2 \theta$,

so

$$|\vec{A} \times \vec{B}| = |\vec{A}| \cdot |\vec{B}| \sqrt{1 - \cos^2 \theta}$$

or since $\sin \theta = \sqrt{1 - \cos^2 \theta}$, $|\vec{A} \times \vec{B}| = |\vec{A}| \cdot |\vec{B}| \sin \theta$.

The geometric interpretation of Theorem 9–15 is interesting. Consider $\vec{A}$ and $\vec{B}$ as shown in the figure.

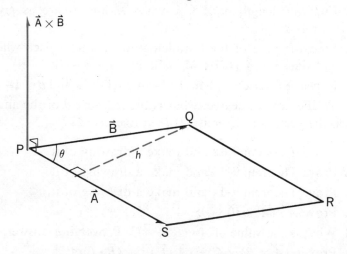

Let h be the length of the perpendicular from the tip of $\vec{B}$ to $\vec{A}$. Then $h = |\vec{B}| \cdot \sin \theta$ (Why?), and h is the altitude of the parallelogram *PQRS*. The length of the base of *PQRS* is $|\vec{A}|$. Thus the area of *PQRS* is

$$|\vec{A}| \cdot |\vec{B}| \sin \theta.$$

Consequently, the *length of the cross product* of $\vec{A}$ and $\vec{B}$ is the *area* of the parallelogram determined by $\vec{A}$ and $\vec{B}$.

Exercises

A ━━ Find each cross product $\vec{A} \times \vec{B}$.
  1. $\vec{A} = 2\mathbf{i} + 3\mathbf{j} - 4\mathbf{k}, \vec{B} = \mathbf{i} - 2\mathbf{j} + \mathbf{k}$
  2. $\vec{A} = \mathbf{i} - 2\mathbf{j} - 2\mathbf{k}, \vec{B} = 3\mathbf{i} - 4\mathbf{j} - 2\mathbf{k}$
  3. $\vec{A} = \mathbf{i} + \mathbf{j} + \mathbf{k}, \vec{B} = \mathbf{i} - \mathbf{j} + \mathbf{k}$
  4. $\vec{A} = 6\mathbf{i} - 3\mathbf{j} - 14\mathbf{k}, \vec{B} = 3\mathbf{i} + 2\mathbf{j} - 3\mathbf{k}$
  5. $\vec{A} = 4\mathbf{i} + 5\mathbf{j} - 6\mathbf{k}, \vec{B} = \mathbf{i} - 2\mathbf{j} + 3\mathbf{k}$
  6. $\vec{A} = 4\mathbf{i} - 2\mathbf{j}, \vec{B} = 3\mathbf{i} + 2\mathbf{k}$
  7. $\vec{A} = \mathbf{i} - 3\mathbf{k}, \vec{B} = \mathbf{j}$
  8. $\vec{A} = 2\mathbf{i} + 3\mathbf{j}, \vec{B} = 4\mathbf{i} - \mathbf{j}$
  9. $\vec{A} = \mathbf{k}, \vec{B} = 3\mathbf{i} + 2\mathbf{j} - 7\mathbf{k}$
  10. $\vec{A} = \frac{1}{3}\mathbf{i} - \frac{2}{3}\mathbf{k}, \vec{B} = \mathbf{j} + 4\mathbf{k}$

━━ Find the cross product of each ordered pair of vectors.

11. (**i**, **i**)	**12.** (**i**, **j**)	**13.** (**i**, **k**)
14. (**j**, **i**)	**15.** (**j**, **j**)	**16.** (**j**, **k**)
17. (**k**, **i**)	**18.** (**k**, **j**)	**19.** (**k**, **k**)

20. Find the length of $\vec{A} \times \vec{B}$ when $\vec{A}$ and $\vec{B}$ are as given in Exercises 1–6.

21. Find the area of the parallelogram in three-space when the adjacent sides are $\vec{A} = 2\mathbf{i} + 4\mathbf{j} - 3\mathbf{k}$ and $\vec{B} = \mathbf{i} - 2\mathbf{k}$.

22. Repeat Exercise 21 when $\vec{A} = -4\mathbf{i} + 2\mathbf{j} - 3\mathbf{k}$ and $\vec{B} = \mathbf{i} + \mathbf{j} + \mathbf{k}$.

23. To the nearest degree, what is the measure θ of the angle between the vectors in Exercise 21? in Exercise 22?

B **24.** Prove Theorem 9–12 and make a drawing of it.
  25. Prove Theorem 9–13 and make a drawing of it.
  26. Prove Theorem 9–14 and make a drawing of it.
  27. Prove $\vec{A} \cdot (\vec{A} \times \vec{B}) = 0$.
  28. What is the value of $\vec{A} \cdot (\vec{B} \times \vec{A})$? Prove your answer.
  29. Prove: $(\vec{A} \times \vec{B}) \times \vec{C} = (\vec{A} \cdot \vec{C})\vec{B} - (\vec{B} \cdot \vec{C})\vec{A}$.
  (This is called the *triple cross product*.)
  30. Find the vector perpendicular to the plane of the points $(3, -1, 2)$, $(4, 5, 3)$ and $(-2, 4, 6)$.
  31. Find the area of the triangle having the vertices given in Exercise 30.
  32. What is the formula for the area of a triangle with vectors $\vec{A}$ and $\vec{B}$ for two sides?

C **33. a.** Show that $\vec{A} \times (\vec{B} \times \vec{C}) \neq (\vec{A} \times \vec{B}) \times \vec{C}$.

  b. Find a formula for $\vec{A} \times (\vec{B} \times \vec{C})$. (See Exercises 24 and 29.)

34. $\begin{vmatrix} a_1 & a_2 \\ b_1 & b_2 \end{vmatrix} = a_1 b_2 - a_2 b_1$ is the *determinant* of the **matrix**

$$\begin{bmatrix} a_1 & a_2 \\ b_1 & b_2 \end{bmatrix}.$$

(A **matrix** is a rectangular array of numbers.)

  a. Show that

$$\begin{vmatrix} ma_1 & ma_2 \\ b_1 & b_2 \end{vmatrix} = m \begin{vmatrix} a_1 & a_2 \\ b_1 & b_2 \end{vmatrix}.$$

  b. Show that

$$\begin{vmatrix} a_1 & a_2 \\ b_1 & b_2 \end{vmatrix} = - \begin{vmatrix} a_2 & a_1 \\ b_2 & b_1 \end{vmatrix}.$$

35. The determinant of a matrix $\begin{bmatrix} a_1 & a_2 & a_3 \\ b_1 & b_2 & b_3 \\ c_1 & c_2 & c_3 \end{bmatrix}$ is

$$a_1 \begin{vmatrix} b_2 & b_3 \\ c_2 & c_3 \end{vmatrix} - a_2 \begin{vmatrix} b_1 & b_3 \\ c_1 & c_3 \end{vmatrix} + a_3 \begin{vmatrix} b_1 & b_2 \\ c_1 & c_2 \end{vmatrix} = \begin{vmatrix} a_1 & a_2 & a_3 \\ b_1 & b_2 & b_3 \\ c_1 & c_2 & c_3 \end{vmatrix}.$$

Show that $\vec{A} \times \vec{B} = \begin{vmatrix} \mathbf{i} & \mathbf{j} & \mathbf{k} \\ a_1 & a_2 & a_3 \\ b_1 & b_2 & b_3 \end{vmatrix}$.

9–11 The Equation of a Plane

A plane is to three-space as a line is to two-space. In each case the dimension of the subset is one less than the dimension of the space: 2 to 3 and 1 to 2. The analogy goes further: In two-space the equation of a line is

$$Ax + By + C = 0. \tag{1}$$

In three-space, as you shall see, the equation of a plane is also a linear equation,

$$Ax + By + Cz + D = 0. \tag{2}$$

The major task of this section is to show that equation 2 is the equation of a plane.

Let Ω (Greek letter *omega*) be a plane, $P(a, b, c)$ a fixed point in Ω, $Q(x, y, z)$ any other point in Ω, and $\vec{N} = A\mathbf{i} + B\mathbf{j} + C\mathbf{k}$ the normal to Ω.

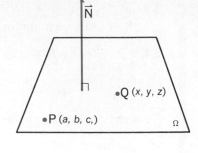

$\vec{N}$, being perpendicular to Ω is perpendicular to every vector in Ω. In particular $\vec{N} \perp \vec{PQ}$.

Consequently,

$$\vec{N} \cdot \vec{PQ} = 0$$

or $(A\mathbf{i} + B\mathbf{j} + C\mathbf{k}) \cdot ((x - a)\mathbf{i} + (y - b)\mathbf{j} + (z - c)\mathbf{k}) = 0$

and $A(x - a) + B(y - b) + C(z - c) = 0$

or $Ax + By + Cz + (-Aa - Bb - Cc) = 0.$

Let $D = -Aa - Bb - Cc$, substitute, and you find

$$Ax + By + Cz + D = 0$$

is the equation of the plane Ω.

Conversely, any equation like **2** is the equation of a plane. Let $P(a, b, c)$ be a point satisfying **2** Then

$$Aa + Bb + Cc + D = 0 \qquad\qquad 3$$

Subtracting **3** from **2** you find the following.

$$A(x - a) + B(y - b) + C(z - c) = 0. \qquad\qquad 4$$

Equation **4** is the inner product of

$$\vec{N} = A\mathbf{i} + B\mathbf{j} + C\mathbf{k}$$

and $\vec{PQ} = (x - a)\mathbf{i} + (y - b)\mathbf{j} + (z - c)\mathbf{k},$

where $Q(x, y, z)$ is any point satisfying **2** and $P(a, b, c)$ is a fixed point. The set of all $Q(x, y, z)$ such that $\vec{PQ}$ is perpendicular to $\vec{N}$ is a plane. This leads to the following theorem.

Theorem 9–16 A figure Ω in three-space is a plane if and only if each point (x, y, z) in Ω satisfies $Ax + By + Cz + D = 0$ (A, B, and C not all zero).

The coefficients of x, y, and z are the components of the normal to the plane. (Compare with Exercises 29 and 30, Section 9–9.)

EXAMPLE 1. Find the equation of the plane containing $(1, 3, 4)$ whose normal is $\vec{N} = 2\mathbf{i} - 3\mathbf{j} - 4\mathbf{k}$.

Since the normal is $\vec{N} = 2\mathbf{i} - 3\mathbf{j} - 4\mathbf{k}$, the equation of the plane is

$$2x - 3y - 4z + D = 0.$$

But $(1, 3, 4)$ is on the plane.

Consequently,

$$2 \cdot 1 - 3 \cdot 3 - 4 \cdot 4 + D = 0$$

and

$$D = 23.$$

The equation is

$$2x - 3y - 4z + 23 = 0.$$

EXAMPLE 2. Find the equation of the plane determined by $A(1, 1, 1)$, $B(2, -3, 4)$, and $C(-1, 3, 2)$.

Since A, B, and C are in the plane, $\overrightarrow{AB}$ and $\overrightarrow{AC}$ are also. The cross product $\overrightarrow{AB} \times \overrightarrow{AC}$ is a vector perpendicular to $\overrightarrow{AB}$ and $\overrightarrow{AC}$ and is a normal to the plane. Consequently

$$\overrightarrow{AB} \times \overrightarrow{AC} = (\mathbf{i} - 4\mathbf{j} + 3\mathbf{k}) \times (-2\mathbf{i} + 2\mathbf{j} + \mathbf{k})$$

$$= \begin{vmatrix} -4 & 3 \\ 2 & 1 \end{vmatrix} \mathbf{i} + \begin{vmatrix} 3 & 1 \\ 1 & -2 \end{vmatrix} \mathbf{j} + \begin{vmatrix} 1 & -4 \\ -2 & 2 \end{vmatrix} \mathbf{k}$$

$$= -10\mathbf{i} - 7\mathbf{j} - 6\mathbf{k} = \vec{N}$$

The plane has equation

$$-10x - 7y - 6z + D = 0.$$

But $D = +23$, so the equation of the plane is

$$-10x - 7y - 6z + 23 = 0.$$

You may find it difficult to sketch planes in space. The **traces** of the plane are helpful in making such a sketch.

> **Definition** The *xy-trace* is the intersection of the given plane with the *xy* plane.
> The *yz-trace* is the intersection of the given plane with the *yz* plane.
> The *xz-trace* is the intersection of the given plane with the *xz* plane.

Each trace is a line. They are found by respectively setting z, x, and y equal to zero in $Ax + By + Cz + D = 0$ and graphing the resulting lines. This is shown in the figure below.

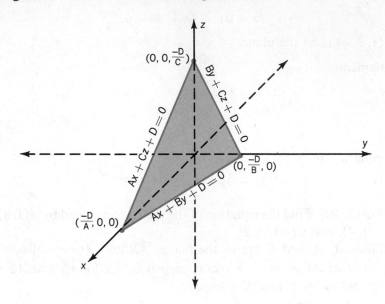

For the plane $Ax + By + Cz + D = 0$. $Ax + By + D = 0$ is the xy-trace. $By + Cz + D = 0$ is the yz-trace. $Ax + Cz + D = 0$ is the xz-trace. Shading helps you to visualize the plane. Only the portion in one octant is usually shown.

EXAMPLE 3. Given

$$2x - 3y - 6z + 12 = 0.$$

Find the three traces and sketch the graph.

The traces are

$$2x - 3y + 12 = 0$$
$$-3y - 6z + 12 = 0$$
$$2x - 6z + 12 = 0.$$

The points common to the axis and the plane are

$(-6, 0, 0)$, $(0, 4, 0)$, $(0, 0, 2)$.

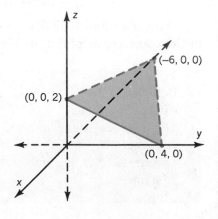

The graph is shown at the right. Notice that the portion shown is behind the yz plane. The dotted traces indicate this fact.

1. Explain the geometric difference between $Ax + By + C = 0$ and $Ax + By + Cz + D = 0$.

2. Explain how traces are used in sketching planes in space.

Exercises

A ▬ Find the equation of the plane satisfying the conditions. $\vec{N}$ is the normal to the plane.

1. $\vec{N} = 3\mathbf{i} + 2\mathbf{j} - 5\mathbf{k}$, contains $(1, 1, 2)$

2. $\vec{N} = 3\mathbf{i} - 2\mathbf{j} - 5\mathbf{k}$, contains $(2, -1, -1)$

3. $\vec{N} = 4\mathbf{i} - \mathbf{j} - \mathbf{k}$, contains $(0, 2, 3)$

4. $\vec{N} = 7\mathbf{i} - 3\mathbf{j} - 2\mathbf{k}$, contains $(1, 1, 2)$

5. $\vec{N} = \frac{1}{2}\mathbf{i} - \frac{2}{3}\mathbf{j} + \frac{3}{4}\mathbf{k}$, contains $(-2, -3, -4)$

6. Parallel to the plane $5x - 2y + 7z + 1 = 0$, contains $(2, 1, 0)$

7. Parallel to the plane $-2x + 3y - 4z - 5 = 0$, contains $(1, -3, -2)$

8. Parallel to the plane $7x - 3y - 2z + 1 = 0$, contains $(1, 0, 2)$

9. Contains $(1, 4, 3)$, $(2, 1, 5)$, $(3, 2, 1)$

10. Contains $(-2, -5, 1)$, $(4, 8, -2)$, $(7, 1, 5)$

11. Contains $(0, 1, 2)$, $(2, 0, 4)$, $(4, 3, 0)$

12. Contains $(2, -2, -1)$, $(-3, 4, 1)$, $(4, 2, 3)$

B **13.** Perpendicular to $5x - 2y + 7z + 1 = 0$, contains $(0, 1, 2)$

14. Perpendicular to $3x - 2y + z - 5 = 0$, contains $(2, 2, 3)$

15. Perpendicular to $x - y - z + 10 = 0$, contains $(0, 0, 0)$

16. Perpendicular to the segment with endpoints $(2, 0, 4)$ and $(0, -8, 4)$ and contains its midpoint.

17. Repeat Exercise 16 where the points are $(1, 1, 2)$ and $(-5, 7, 2)$.

18. Graph each plane in Exercises 1–17. Identify the traces.

19. What is the equation of the xy plane? xz plane? yz plane?

C **20.** Present a convincing argument demonstrating that the measure of the angle between two planes is the same as that of the angles between their normals.

21. What is the measure, to the nearest degree, of the angle between the planes

$$2x + 3y + z = 0 \quad \text{and} \quad -x + 2y + 5z - 8 = 0?$$

9–12   Intersecting Planes and Distance

As you know, the intersection of two planes is either the empty set or a line. Two planes Ω_1 and Ω_2 are parallel if and only if their normals $\vec{N}_1$ and $\vec{N}_2$ are parallel. Since vectors are parallel if and only if

$$\vec{N}_1 = t \cdot \vec{N}_2,\ t \text{ a scalar, } t \neq 0,$$

and the components of the normals are the coefficients of x, y, and z, two planes

$$Ax + By + Cz + D = 0 \quad \text{and} \quad A_1x + B_1y + C_1z + D_1 = 0$$

are parallel if and only if

$$A_1x + B_1y + C_1z = tAx + tBy + tCz. \qquad \textbf{1}$$

Further, if $D_1 = tD$, then the planes are identical; otherwise they are distinct.

Two nonparallel planes intersect in a line. If the two planes Ω_1 and Ω_2 have normals $\vec{N}_1$ and $\vec{N}_2$, then $\vec{N}_1$ and $\vec{N}_2$ are each perpendicular to the line of intersection. Since the cross product (a vector) $\vec{N}_1 \times \vec{N}_2$ is perpendicular to both $\vec{N}_1$ and $\vec{N}_2$, the direction of the line is given by $\vec{N}_1 \times \vec{N}_2 = \vec{L}_1$.

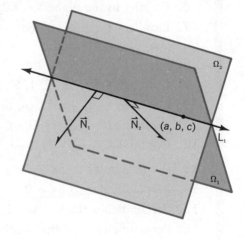

Let $P(a, b, c)$ be a fixed point on the line. Then if $Q(x, y, z)$ is any other point on the line,

$$\overrightarrow{PQ} = (x - a)\mathbf{i} + (y - b)\mathbf{j} + (z - c)\mathbf{k} = t(\vec{N}_1 \times \vec{N}_2). \qquad \textbf{2}$$

Equation 2 is the vector equation of the line. Simplifying, you get the parametric equations of the line:

$$x - a = t \begin{vmatrix} B_1 & C_1 \\ B_2 & C_2 \end{vmatrix} \qquad \vec{N}_1 = A_1\mathbf{i} + B_1\mathbf{j} + C_1\mathbf{k}$$

$$y - b = t \begin{vmatrix} C_1 & A_1 \\ C_2 & A_2 \end{vmatrix} \qquad \vec{N}_2 = A_2\mathbf{i} + B_2\mathbf{j} + C_2\mathbf{k}$$

$$z - c = t \begin{vmatrix} A_1 & B_1 \\ A_2 & B_2 \end{vmatrix}$$

EXAMPLE 1. Find the parametric equations of the line which is the intersection of

$$x + 2y + 3z - 8 = 0$$

and

$$3x - 3y + z + 3 = 0$$

First find the direction vector for the line.

$$\vec{L} = \vec{N_1} \times \vec{N_2} = \begin{vmatrix} 2 & 3 \\ -3 & 1 \end{vmatrix} \mathbf{i} + \begin{vmatrix} 3 & 1 \\ 1 & 3 \end{vmatrix} \mathbf{j} + \begin{vmatrix} 1 & 2 \\ 3 & -3 \end{vmatrix} \mathbf{k}$$

$$= 11\mathbf{i} + 8\mathbf{j} - 9\mathbf{k}$$

Now you must find a point on the line. Since the line must intersect at least one of the xy, the xz, or the yz planes, you can find one point by setting x, y, or z equal to zero and solving the resulting equations for the other two variables.

Here let $z = 0$, then

$$x + 2y = 8$$
$$3x - 3y = -3$$

so

$$-3x - 6y = -24$$
$$3x - 3y = -3$$

or

$$-9y = -27$$
$$y = 3$$

so

$$x = 2.$$

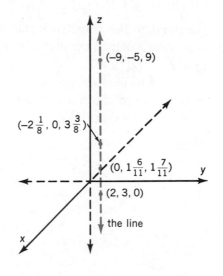

Thus the point $(2, 3, 0)$ is on the line. The parametric equations are the following.

$$x - 2 = 11t$$
$$y - 3 = 8t$$
$$z = -9t$$

Plot two points on the line such as $(2, 3, 0)$ and $(-9, -5, 9)$ (when $t = -1$) and draw the line in question. See the figure. The point $(-2\frac{1}{8}, 0, 3\frac{3}{8})$ is the intersection of the line and the xz plane. The point $(0, 1\frac{6}{11}, 1\frac{7}{11})$ is the intersection of the line and the yz plane.

Vector techniques let you derive an equation for the distance from a point to a plane. It is similar to the equation for the distance from a point to a line.

Theorem 9-17 Let $Ax + By + Cz + D = 0$ be a plane and $P(a, b, c)$ a point. The distance d from the point to the plane is given by

$$d = \frac{|Aa + Bb + Cc + D|}{\sqrt{A^2 + B^2 + C^2}} \qquad \textbf{3}$$

Proof: If $A \neq 0$, then the point $R\left(\frac{-D}{A}, 0, 0\right)$ is on the plane. $\Big($If $A = 0$, choose the point $\left(0, \frac{-D}{B}, 0\right)$ or $\left(0, 0, \frac{-D}{C}\right)$ instead.$\Big)$ Let Q be the point in the plane such that $\overrightarrow{QP}$ is perpendicular to the plane. Notice that $d = |\overrightarrow{QP}|$.

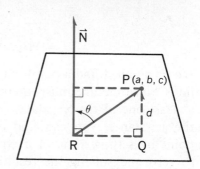

Let θ be the measure of the acute angle between the normal $\vec{N}$ to the plane and the vector $\overrightarrow{RP}$.

Then

$$d = |\overrightarrow{QP}| = |\overrightarrow{RP}| \cos \theta \quad \text{(Why?)}$$

But

$$\cos \theta = \frac{\vec{N} \cdot \overrightarrow{RP}}{|\vec{N}| \cdot |\overrightarrow{RP}|} \quad \text{(inner product)}$$

or

$$|\overrightarrow{RP}| \cos \theta = \frac{\vec{N} \cdot \overrightarrow{RP}}{|\vec{N}|}. \qquad \textbf{4}$$

Now

$$\vec{N} = A\mathbf{i} + B\mathbf{j} + C\mathbf{k}$$

and

$$\overrightarrow{RP} = \left(a + \frac{D}{A}\right)\mathbf{i} + b\mathbf{j} + c\mathbf{k}.$$

Substituting these in equation **4**, you find

$$d = |\overrightarrow{RP}| \cos \theta = \frac{(A\mathbf{i} + B\mathbf{j} + C\mathbf{k}) \cdot \left[\left(a + \frac{D}{A}\right)\mathbf{i} + b\mathbf{j} + c\mathbf{k}\right]}{\sqrt{A^2 + B^2 + C^2}}$$

$$= \frac{A\left(a + \frac{D}{A}\right) + Bb + Cc}{\sqrt{A^2 + B^2 + C^2}}$$

$$= \frac{Aa + Bb + Cc + D}{\sqrt{A^2 + B^2 + C^2}}$$

Since $Aa + Bb + Cc + D$ could be negative, the absolute value is used to ensure that d is positive.

Thus
$$d = \frac{|Aa + Bb + Cc + D|}{\sqrt{A^2 + B^2 + C^2}}$$

EXAMPLE 2. Find the distance from $(1, 3, -2)$ to the plane $x - 2y + 3z + 7 = 0$.

$$d = \frac{|Aa + Bb + Cc + D|}{\sqrt{A^2 + B^2 + C^2}}$$

Thus
$$d = \frac{|1 \cdot 1 - 2 \cdot 3 + 3(-2) + 7|}{\sqrt{1 + 4 + 9}}$$

$$= \frac{|-4|}{\sqrt{14}} = \frac{4}{\sqrt{14}}$$

Exercises

A ━━Find the parametric equations of the line that is the intersection of the given planes (if such a line exists). Graph each line.

1. $2x - 3y + 4z + 1 = 0$
$x + y - z - 2 = 0$

2. $-3x + 2y + 4z - 5 = 0$
$5x - y + 3z + 6 = 0$

3. $5x + 7y - 2z - 3 = 0$
$x - y - z = 0$

4. $3x + y + 4z + 2 = 0$
$x + 3y - z + 3 = 0$

5. $4x + 2y - z - 4 = 0$
$x - y + 2z - 1 = 0$

6. $x - 2y - 3z - 4 = 0$
$3x + y + z + 1 = 0$

7. $4x - 2y + z - 3 = 0$
$-8x + 4y - 2z + 6 = 0$

8. $-x - 3y + z - 4 = 0$
$2x + 6y - 2y - 4 = 0$

9. $4x - 3y + z + 2 = 0$
$4x - 3y + 2z + 1 = 0$

10. $x + y + z - 7 = 0$
$x + 2y + z - 9 = 0$

━━Find the distance from the given point to the given plane.

11. $2x - y + 2z + 3 = 0$, $(1, 1, 3)$

12. $6x + 2y - 3z + 5 = 0$, $(4, -2, 1)$

13. $4x - 2y + 2z - 3 = 0$, $(-1, 2, 1)$

14. $4x - 5y - 3z - 1 = 0$, $(3, 2, -1)$

15. $3x - y - z + 6 = 0$, $(1, 3, -4)$

16. $4x - 2y + 7z - 16 = 0$, $(0, 0, 0)$

17. What formula gives the distance from the origin to the plane $Ax + By + Cz + D = 0$?

B   18. Find the distance between the parallel planes $4x - 2y + 3z - 4 = 0$ and $4x - 2y + 3z + 16 = 0$. How do you know the planes are parallel?

C   19. a. Let $\vec{K}$ be the direction vector of a line l. Let $P(a, b, c)$ be a point in space not on l. Let d be the distance from P to l. If R is a point on l, show that $d = |\overrightarrow{RP}| \sin \theta$.

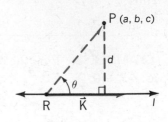

b. What is $|\overrightarrow{RP} \times \vec{K}|$ in terms of $|\overrightarrow{RP}|$, $|\vec{K}|$, and $\sin \theta$?

c. Use your results of **a** and **b** to find a vector formula for d.

20. Use the results of Exercise 19 to find the distance from $P(1, 3, 2)$ and the line of

   a. Exercise 1.   **b.** Exercise 2.   **c.** Exercise 3.   **d.** Exercise 4.

CHAPTER OBJECTIVES AND REVIEW

Objective: *To know the meaning of the important mathematical terms of this chapter.*

1. Here are many of the mathematical terms used in this chapter. Be sure that you know them thoroughly and can use them correctly.

vectors (*412*)	standard equations (*437*)
polygon rule (*416*)	parametric equations (*438*)
zero vector (*418*)	direction numbers of the line (*438*)
scalar (*418*)	slope of a line in two-space (*443*)
base (basis) (*423*)	point-slope equation (*443*)
components (*423*)	inner (dot) product (*450*)
two-space (*426*)	normal vector (*452*)
position vector (*427*)	unit normal (*452*)
direction numbers (*429*)	angle between two lines (*452*)
direction cosines (*429*)	normal to a line (*452*)
direction angles (*430*)	cross product (*461*)
direction vector (*431*)	traces (*467*)

Objective: *To explain and illustrate the concept of vector and the relation equality of vectors.*

2. What are the essential characteristics of a vector? Illustrate these characteristics geometrically.

3. How do you determine whether or not two vectors $\vec{A}$ and $\vec{B}$ are equal? Illustrate geometrically.

4. In each diagram below which vectors appear equal? Explain.

a.

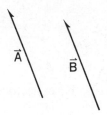

b.

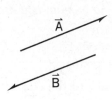

c.

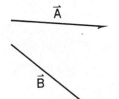

d.

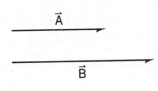

5. Explain how you can use equality of vectors to discuss the angle between vectors $\vec{A}$ and $\vec{B}$ in the diagram below.

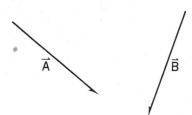

Objective: *To define and illustrate scalar multiplication of a vector, addition of vectors, subtraction of vectors, and linear combination of vectors.*

6. In your own words define scalar multiplication of a vector and vector addition and subtraction.

7. Copy $\vec{A}$ and $\vec{B}$ on your paper.
Make a diagram showing

 a. $3\vec{A}$ **b.** $-2\vec{B}$
 c. $\vec{A} + \vec{B}$ **d.** $2\vec{B} + \vec{A}$
 e. $\vec{B} - \vec{A}$ **f.** $\vec{A} - \vec{B}$
 g. $2\vec{A} - \vec{B}$ **h.** $\frac{2}{3}\vec{A} + \frac{4}{3}\vec{B}$

8. a. What is a linear combination of vectors?
 b. Which of the diagrams in Exercise 7 illustrate linear combinations of vectors?

9. Given $\vec{C} = m\vec{A} + n\vec{B}$.
$$|\vec{A}| = 1, |\vec{B}| = 1, |\vec{C}| = 2$$

Find m and n.

Objective: *To explain and use the ideas of*
a. *basis vectors*
b. *position vectors*
c. *direction numbers.*

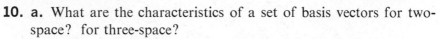

10. a. What are the characteristics of a set of basis vectors for two-space? for three-space?
 b. What are the characteristics of the basis vectors **i, j**, and **k**?
11. a. What is a position vector?
 b. What are direction numbers?
 c. What are direction numbers for a position vector?

Objective: *Given the pairs of points P and Q which determine the vector $\overrightarrow{PQ}$, to find the position vector equal to $\overrightarrow{PQ}$.*

12. $P(2, 3) \quad Q(0, 0)$
13. $P(-2, 1) \quad Q(3, -1)$
14. $P(-1, -7) \quad Q(-3, 2)$
15. $P(1, 2, 3) \quad Q(2, 1, 3)$
16. $P(2, 5, -4) \quad Q(-3, 1, -4)$
17. $P(0, 1, 0) \quad Q(2, -3, 2)$

18. Find the length of each vector $\overrightarrow{PQ}$ in Exercises 12–17. Leave answers in radical form.

Objective: *Given a set of conditions, to find the equations of a line in two- and three-space.*

▬ Write the standard equations and parametric equations for each line.

19. Direction vector
$$\overrightarrow{PQ} = 2\mathbf{i} - 3\mathbf{j} + \mathbf{k},$$

$T(2, -3, 1)$ is on the line.
20. $P(1, 2, -1)$ and $Q(-3, 2, 4)$ are on the line.
21. $P(2, -3)$ and $Q(5, 4)$ are on the line.
22. Direction vector
$$\overrightarrow{PQ} = -3\mathbf{i} + \mathbf{j},$$

$T(0, 5)$ is on the line.
23. Slope $\lambda = -\frac{2}{3}$; $T(5, -7)$ is on the line.

Objective: *To define the inner product of two vectors $(\vec{A} \cdot \vec{B})$ and use it to find the angle between two lines.*

24. a. If

$$\vec{A} = a_1\mathbf{i} + b_1\mathbf{j} + c_1\mathbf{k} \quad \text{and} \quad \vec{B} = a_2\mathbf{i} + b_2\mathbf{j} + c_2\mathbf{k},$$

what is $\vec{A} \cdot \vec{B}$?

b. If θ is the angle between $\vec{A}$ and $\vec{B}$, what is $\cos \theta$?

25. Find θ to the nearest degree if θ is the measure of the angle between

$$\vec{A} = -3\mathbf{i} + 2\mathbf{j} - \mathbf{k} \quad \text{and} \quad \vec{B} = \mathbf{i} - \mathbf{k}.$$

26. Find the measure of the angle between the lines in Exercises 19 and 20; in 21 and 22.

27. a. How is the inner product used to test for perpendicularity of vectors or lines?

b. Find a vector normal to

$$\vec{A} = \mathbf{i} - \mathbf{j} + 3\mathbf{k}.$$

28. Find a vector normal to the line in

a. Exercise 19.

b. Exercise 21.

Objective: *To find equations of lines parallel or perpendicular to a given line.*

━━━ In each exercise find an equation of a line parallel to the given line and an equation of a line perpendicular to the given line.

29. $2x - 3y + 5 = 0$ through the point $(2, 1)$

30. $\dfrac{x - 4}{2} = \dfrac{y + 3}{1}$ through the point $(5, -2)$

31. $x = 3 - 3t, \; y = 2 + t$ through the point $(3, 2)$

Objective: *Given two vectors, to find their cross product.*

━━━ Determine the vector which is the cross product of the given position vectors.

32. $\vec{A} = 3\mathbf{i} + 2\mathbf{j} - \mathbf{k}$ $\vec{B} = -\mathbf{i} + \mathbf{j} + \mathbf{k}$

33. $\vec{A} = \mathbf{i} + \mathbf{j} + \mathbf{k}$ $\vec{B} = 2\mathbf{j} - \mathbf{k}$

34. $\vec{A} = -2\mathbf{i} - 3\mathbf{j} + \mathbf{k}$ $\vec{B} = \mathbf{i} + \mathbf{j} - 4\mathbf{k}$

35. Find the length of the vector perpendicular to the vectors $\vec{A}$ and $\vec{B}$ in Exercise 32. What is $\sin \theta$ where θ is the angle between $\vec{A}$ and $\vec{B}$?

Objective: *Given a set of conditions, find the equation of a plane in three-space.*

▬ Write the equation of the plane satisfying the given conditions.

36. $\vec{N} = 2\mathbf{i} - 3\mathbf{j} - 2\mathbf{k}$ is a normal to the plane which contains the point $(0, 2, 3)$.

37. It is parallel to $7x - 2y + 3z + 4 = 0$ and contains $(1, 1, 1)$.

38. It contains $(1, 1, 1)$, $(2, -3, 1)$ and $(-4, 3, 0)$.

39. If $\vec{N}$ is normal to the plane $Ax + By + Cz + D = 0$, what are the components of $\vec{N}$?

40. Sketch the graph of the plane in Exercise 36 using its traces.

CHAPTER TEST ▬▬▬▬▬▬▬▬

▬ Use the vectors $\vec{A}$, $\vec{B}$, $\vec{C}$, $\vec{D}$, and $\vec{E}$ for Exercises 1–7. Copy these vectors on your paper.

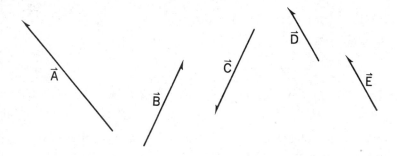

1. Which pair(s) of vectors are equal? What test would you use to prove their equality?

2. Which pair(s) of vectors have the same magnitude?

3. Which pair(s) of vectors are parallel?

4. Find $\vec{A} + \vec{B}$ and $\vec{B} - \vec{E}$.

5. With a protractor measure the angle between $\vec{D}$ and $\vec{C}$.

6. Draw the vector $3\vec{D}$.

7. Estimate the values of m and n such that $\vec{A} = m\vec{C} + n\vec{D}$.

8. Sketch the usual basis vectors for a two-space and those for three-space. Describe each set.

9. Find the position vector equal to $\overrightarrow{PQ}$ where
   a. $P(2, -5)$, $Q(-1, 3)$.
   b. $P(1, 5, -2)$, $Q(0, -3, 1)$.

10. Calculate the length of the vector

$$\vec{A} = 2\mathbf{i} - 2\mathbf{j} - \mathbf{k}.$$

11. Find the standard equations and the parametric equations of the line containing
    a. $A(2, 1)$, $B(-3, 7)$.
    b. $A(1, -3, 5)$, $B(2, 5, -3)$.

12. Given

$$\vec{A} = 2\mathbf{i} - 6\mathbf{j} + 1\mathbf{k} \quad \text{and} \quad \vec{B} = -3\mathbf{i} - \mathbf{j} + 5\mathbf{k},$$

calculate $\vec{A} \cdot \vec{B}$.

13. What is the angle between $\vec{A}$ and $\vec{B}$ in Exercise 12?

14. a. Find a vector $\vec{N}$ which is normal to

$$\vec{A} = 2\mathbf{i} - 6\mathbf{j} + 1\mathbf{k} \quad \text{and} \quad \vec{B} = -3\mathbf{i} - \mathbf{j} + 5\mathbf{k}.$$

    b. What is another name for $\vec{N}$?

15. Let $\vec{N} = 5\mathbf{i} + 7\mathbf{j} - \mathbf{k}$ be a normal to a plane which contains $P(2, -3, 1)$. What is the equation of the plane?

16. Find the equation of the plane which contains $P(1, 2, -3)$ and is parallel to $\vec{A} = 2\mathbf{i} - \mathbf{k}$.

CHAPTER 10

MATRICES, VECTORS, AND LINEAR TRANSFORMATIONS

In Chapter 9 you studied vectors as directed line segments both in a plane and in three dimensional space. In order to add or subtract two vectors it was necessary to draw position vectors which were equivalent to the original ones. Many times it is more efficient simply to "move" the vectors to a more convenient location. The mathematical way of moving vectors is by performing *linear transformations*.

One type of linear transformation is called a *reflection*. A reflection about a line is just the mirror image of that vector about the given line. There are many reflections that occur naturally, such as the reflection of an object in a puddle of water. The reflection of the buildings illustrated on the opposite page is interesting because the parts of the buildings reflected in the water are not the parts of the buildings seen in the picture. Could you reconstruct the buildings by combining their reflected and their actual images?

A second type of linear transformation is called a *rotation*. In this case the foot of the vector remains stationary but the tip is rotated through a given angle. An illustration of a rotation can be seen in Ernest Trona's "Falling Man."

An example of nonlinear transformation is the *translation;* it involves moving the reference axes of the coordinate plane. The transformed vectors under a translation remain parallel to their initial positions. The idea is similar to the use of a submarine periscope grid to locate a plane in the sky. The center of the grid is moved until it is at the correct point. This new position of the center of the grid is then used as the "zero point."

10–1 Matrices

Each of the four arrays of numbers shown below is a **matrix.** Notice that each is a set of numbers arranged in rows and columns and enclosed by a pair of brackets.

$$\begin{bmatrix} 1 & \sqrt{2} \\ 5 & 1 \end{bmatrix} \quad \begin{bmatrix} 3 \\ 0.4 \end{bmatrix} \quad \begin{bmatrix} 1 & 2i & 3 \end{bmatrix} \quad \begin{bmatrix} -2 & \mp 1 & -4 & \sqrt[3]{5} \\ \pi & 3i & 2 & 4-2i \\ 0 & \sqrt{2} & e & 0 \end{bmatrix}$$

> **Definition** A matrix is a rectangular array of numbers arranged into rows and columns. A matrix is written as follows:
>
> $$\begin{bmatrix} a_{11} & a_{12} & \cdots & a_{1n} \\ a_{21} & a_{22} & \cdots & a_{2n} \\ \vdots & \vdots & \vdots & \vdots \\ a_{m1} & a_{m2} & \cdots & a_{mn} \end{bmatrix}$$

This matrix has *m rows* and *n columns.* The numbers *m* and *n* are the *dimensions* of the matrix; it is an *m by n* or $m \times n$ matrix. The numbers a_{ij} $(i = 1, \cdots, m; j = 1, \cdots, n)$ are *entries* of the matrix. The entry a_{ij} is in the *i*th row and *j*th column of the matrix.

It is customary to name matrices with capital letters. Thus if $A = \begin{bmatrix} 1 & -5 \\ 0 & 2 \end{bmatrix}$, you may speak of "matrix A."

EXAMPLE 1.

$$\text{Let } C = \begin{bmatrix} 17 & -2 & 3 \\ 0 & -1 & \sqrt{5} \\ 6 & 1 & -7i \\ 5 & -4 & 2 \end{bmatrix}$$

a. Find the dimensions of C.   **b.** Identify the entries c_{32}, c_{21} and c_{43}.

C has 4 rows and 3 columns, thus C is a 4×3 matrix. $c_{32} = 1$, $c_{21} = 0$ and $c_{43} = 2$ because the subscripts name the row and column of the entry.

Two matrices A and B are equal ($A = B$) if and only if they have the same dimensions and corresponding entries are equal. For example, $A = B$ when

$$A = \begin{bmatrix} 1 & -3 \\ -2 & 5 \end{bmatrix} \quad \text{and} \quad B = \begin{bmatrix} \frac{2}{2} & (5-8) \\ 4 & (1+4) \\ -2 & \end{bmatrix}$$

because A is a 2×2 matrix and B is a 2×2 matrix and $1 = \frac{2}{2}$, $-3 = (5 - 8)$, $-2 = \frac{4}{-2}$ and $5 = (1 + 4)$.

Clearly two matrices A and B are not equal $(A \neq B)$ whenever

a. the dimensions are not identical or

b. for some value of i and j, $a_{ij} \neq b_{ij}$.

Matrices with the same dimensions may be added in a manner similar to the way vectors are added when the components are given.

> **Definition** The sum C of a matrix A with dimensions $m \times n$ and a matrix B with the same dimensions is an $m \times n$ matrix whose entries are given by the following.
>
> $$c_{ij} = a_{ij} + b_{ij} \qquad i \in \{1, 2, \cdots, m\} \quad j \in \{1, 2, \cdots, n\}$$

EXAMPLE 2. Let $A = \begin{bmatrix} 1 & 2 & 4 \\ -2 & -5 & 0 \end{bmatrix}$ and $B = \begin{bmatrix} -2 & 1 & -3 \\ 1 & 4 & -5 \end{bmatrix}$

Find $A + B$.

$$
\begin{aligned}
A + B &= \begin{bmatrix} 1 & 2 & 4 \\ -2 & -5 & 0 \end{bmatrix} + \begin{bmatrix} -2 & 1 & -3 \\ 1 & 4 & -5 \end{bmatrix} \\
&= \begin{bmatrix} (1 + (-2)) & (2 + 1) & (4 + (-3)) \\ (-2 + 1) & (-5 + 4) & (0 + (-5)) \end{bmatrix} \\
&= \begin{bmatrix} -1 & 3 & 1 \\ -1 & -1 & -5 \end{bmatrix}
\end{aligned}
$$

EXAMPLE 3. Let $A = \begin{bmatrix} 1 & 2 \\ 3 & 4 \end{bmatrix}$. Find $(A + A) + A$.

$$
A + A = \begin{bmatrix} 1 + 1 & 2 + 2 \\ 3 + 3 & 4 + 4 \end{bmatrix} = \begin{bmatrix} 2 & 4 \\ 6 & 8 \end{bmatrix}
$$

$$
(A + A) + A = \begin{bmatrix} 2 & 4 \\ 6 & 8 \end{bmatrix} + \begin{bmatrix} 1 & 2 \\ 3 & 4 \end{bmatrix} = \begin{bmatrix} 2 + 1 & 4 + 2 \\ 6 + 3 & 8 + 4 \end{bmatrix} = \begin{bmatrix} 3 & 6 \\ 9 & 12 \end{bmatrix}
$$

Notice each entry in the sum $(A + A) + A$ is three times the corresponding entry in A. This fact suggests a definition for the product of a real number and a matrix A.

> **Definition** If A is an $m \times n$ matrix and k is a real number, the scalar product of k and A (kA) is the $m \times n$ matrix with entries ka_{ij} for all i and j.

EXAMPLE 4. Let $A = \begin{bmatrix} 1 & 2 \\ 3 & 4 \end{bmatrix}$. Find $3A$, $-\frac{1}{2}A$ and kA.

$$3A = \begin{bmatrix} 3 \cdot 1 & 3 \cdot 2 \\ 3 \cdot 3 & 3 \cdot 4 \end{bmatrix} = \begin{bmatrix} 3 & 6 \\ 9 & 12 \end{bmatrix}$$

$$-\frac{1}{2}A = \begin{bmatrix} -\frac{1}{2} \cdot 1 & -\frac{1}{2} \cdot 2 \\ -\frac{1}{2} \cdot 3 & -\frac{1}{2} \cdot 4 \end{bmatrix} = \begin{bmatrix} -\frac{1}{2} & -1 \\ -\frac{3}{2} & -2 \end{bmatrix}$$

$$kA = \begin{bmatrix} k \cdot 1 & k \cdot 2 \\ k \cdot 3 & k \cdot 4 \end{bmatrix} = \begin{bmatrix} k & 2k \\ 3k & 4k \end{bmatrix}$$

Notice that if each entry of a matrix has the same factor, the matrix may be written as a product of a number and a matrix. For example,

$$A = \begin{bmatrix} 8 & -2 \\ -14 & 12 \end{bmatrix}$$
$$= \begin{bmatrix} 2 \cdot 4 & 2 \cdot (-1) \\ 2 \cdot (-7) & 2(6) \end{bmatrix}$$
$$= 2 \begin{bmatrix} 4 & -1 \\ -7 & 6 \end{bmatrix}.$$

Checkpoint

1. How are the dimensions of a matrix determined?

2. Explain the meaning of the i and j in the symbol a_{ij}.

3. When are two matrices equal?

4. Explain how the addition of matrices is similar to the addition of vectors.

5. Explain how multiplying a matrix by a real number is similar to multiplying a vector by a real number.

Exercises

A ━━ Given the following matrices.

$$A = \begin{bmatrix} 2 & -5 & 1 \\ 3 & 1 & -7 \end{bmatrix} \quad B = \begin{bmatrix} -12 & 4 & 6 \\ 8 & -2 & -4 \end{bmatrix} \quad C = \begin{bmatrix} 6 & -2 & -3 \\ -4 & 1 & 2 \end{bmatrix}$$

Find each of the following.

1. $A + B$

2. $A + C$

3. $B + C$

4. $(A + B) + C$

5. $A + -2B$

6. $A + \frac{1}{2}B$

7. $B + 2C$

8. $(2A + -3B) + -6C$

9. $B + A$

10. $2(3A)$

11. $(2 \cdot 3)A$

12. $A + (B + C)$

13. a. Compare your results in Exercises 1 and 9. What appears to be true concerning addition of 2×3 matrices?

  b. Prove or disprove the result for any 2×3 matrices.

  c. State your results formally.

14. a. Compare your results in Exercises 4 and 12. What property seems to hold?

  b. Prove or disprove the result for any 2×3 matrices.

  c. State your results formally.

B **15.** Solve the matrix equation

$$\begin{bmatrix} 2 & 1 & 5 \\ 3 & 4 & 1 \end{bmatrix} = C + \begin{bmatrix} 1 & 2 & -3 \\ 2 & 1 & 4 \end{bmatrix}$$

for the 2×3 matrix C.

16. How would you define subtraction of matrices? (See Exercise 15).

17. Given

$$\vec{A} = 2\mathbf{i} + 3\mathbf{j} - 2\mathbf{k},$$

how might you represent $\vec{A}$ as a matrix? (There are two ways.)

10–2   Square Matrices of Order Two; Addition

A square matrix is one in which the number of rows is the same as the number of columns. This number is the **order** of the square matrix. In particular a square matrix of order 2 has 2 rows and 2 columns and is therefore a two-by-two matrix. From this point on, the entries in the matrices discussed will be real numbers.

Let M_2 be the set of all two-by-two matrices. Then

$$A = \begin{bmatrix} 1 & 3 \\ 2 & 1 \end{bmatrix}, \quad B = \begin{bmatrix} 0 & 1 \\ 0 & 1 \end{bmatrix} \quad \text{and} \quad C = \begin{bmatrix} 5 & 0 \\ 1 & 5 \end{bmatrix}$$

are members of M_2.

You already know how to add two matrices in M_2, how to multiply a matrix by a real number, and how to identify equal matrices. The next theorem states obvious properties of adding matrices in M_2.

Theorem 10–1   (Addition is Commutative and Associative)
If A, B, C are in M_2, then

> **i.** $A + B = B + A$
>
> **ii.** $A + (B + C) = (A + B) + C.$

This theorem may be proved by applications of the definitions of addition and equality. The proof of part **i** is given below. The proof of part **ii** is left for you.

Proof: $A = \begin{bmatrix} a_{11} & a_{12} \\ a_{21} & a_{22} \end{bmatrix} \qquad B = \begin{bmatrix} b_{11} & b_{12} \\ b_{21} & b_{22} \end{bmatrix}$

$A + B = \begin{bmatrix} a_{11} + b_{11} & a_{12} + b_{12} \\ a_{21} + b_{21} & a_{22} + b_{22} \end{bmatrix}$ Definition of addition.

$= \begin{bmatrix} b_{11} + a_{11} & b_{12} + a_{12} \\ b_{21} + a_{21} & b_{22} + a_{22} \end{bmatrix}$ Commutativity of addition in R.

$= \begin{bmatrix} b_{11} & b_{12} \\ b_{21} & b_{22} \end{bmatrix} + \begin{bmatrix} a_{11} & a_{12} \\ a_{21} & a_{22} \end{bmatrix}$ Definition of addition.

$= B + A.$

You can see that $O = \begin{bmatrix} 0 & 0 \\ 0 & 0 \end{bmatrix}$ has the property that for all matrices A in M_2, $A + O = O + A = A$. O is the only member of M_2 with this property. It is the *additive identity* in the set M_2. Theorem 10–2 follows.

Theorem 10–2   There is a unique member O of M_2, called the zero matrix, with the property that for all A in M_2,

> $O + A = A + O = A.$

If you add $A = \begin{bmatrix} -2 & 1 \\ -5 & -3 \end{bmatrix}$ to $B = \begin{bmatrix} 2 & -1 \\ 5 & 3 \end{bmatrix}$, the sum is the zero matrix. Thus B is an *additive inverse* (or **opposite**) of A.

Definition   The matrix $-A$ is the opposite of A. That is, $-A$ has the property that $A + (-A) = (-A) + A = O$.

In a system in which the associative property holds, if there is an opposite for an element, then that opposite is unique. It is also easy to show that $(-1)A$ is an opposite of A.

> **Theorem 10–3** For each A in M_2 there is a unique member $-A$ of M_2 with the property that $A + (-A) = (-A) + A = O$. Furthermore, $-A = (-1)A$. Thus $(-1)A$ is the unique opposite of A.

You can now define subtraction of matrices in M_2. A similar definition can be stated for other sets of matrices on which addition is defined.

> **Definition** For A and B in M_2, the difference $A - B$ is defined by $A - B = A + (-B)$.

Clearly
$$A - B = \begin{bmatrix} a_{11} - b_{11} & a_{12} - b_{12} \\ a_{21} - b_{21} & a_{22} - b_{22} \end{bmatrix}$$

The next theorem is an easy consequence of the definitions given in Section 10–1 and the properties of real numbers.

> **Theorem 10–4** For any A, B in M_2 and p, q in R,
>
> **i.** $1A = A$ **ii.** $p(qA) = pq(A)$
> **iii.** $(p + q)A = pA + qA$ **iv.** $p(A + B) = pA + pB$

The proofs are left for you to do in the exercises.

Now try these

━━━ Assume that A, B, C are $m \times n$ matrices and that a_{ij}, b_{ij}, c_{ij} are respectively the elements in row i and column j, for each i and each j. Answer the following:

1. What element is in the ith row and jth column of $A + B$?

2. What element is in the ith row and jth column of $B + A$?

3. What element is in the ith row and jth column of the sum $(A + B) + C$?

Answers: **1.** $a_{ij} + b_{ij}$ **2.** $b_{ij} + a_{ij}$ **3.** $(a_{ij} + b_{ij}) + c_{ij}$

Checkpoint

1. Define the following terms.
   a. square matrix   **b.** order of a matrix
2. What is the zero matrix in M_2?
3. If $A = \begin{bmatrix} a_{11} & a_{12} \\ a_{21} & a_{22} \end{bmatrix}$ what is $-A$?

Exercises

A ▬ Let $A = \begin{bmatrix} a_{11} & a_{12} \\ a_{21} & a_{22} \end{bmatrix}$, $B = \begin{bmatrix} b_{11} & b_{12} \\ b_{21} & b_{22} \end{bmatrix}$ and $C = \begin{bmatrix} c_{11} & c_{12} \\ c_{21} & c_{22} \end{bmatrix}$

Prove:

1. Theorem 10–1, part **ii.**   2. Theorem 10–3.
3. Theorem 10–4, part **i.**   4. Theorem 10–4, part **ii.**
5. Theorem 10–4, part **iii.**   6. Theorem 10–4, part **iv.**

▬ Let $A = \begin{bmatrix} 1 & -3 \\ -2 & 1 \end{bmatrix}$ $B = \begin{bmatrix} 0 & 1 \\ -4 & 2 \end{bmatrix}$ $C = \begin{bmatrix} -3 & 2 \\ 2 & 1 \end{bmatrix}$. Find each of the following:

7. $-A$ 8. $-B + 2C$
9. $(4 + 3)A$ 10. $-3(2B)$
11. $5(B + C)$ 12. $(4 + 2)(A - B)$
13. $-4(A + B - C)$ 14. $2(3A - 4C)$
15. X if $A + 2X = C$ 16. Y if $B - 3Y = A + 2C$

> **Definition** A <u>mathematical</u> <u>system</u>, denoted $\langle S; \circ \rangle$, is a set S and one or more operations $\circ$, defined on the set S. For example if W is the set of whole numbers, then $\langle W; + \rangle$ is a mathematical system.

Tell for which of the following systems **a.** the associative property holds, **b.** the commutative property holds, **c.** there is an identity element, **d.** there is an inverse element for each element a.

17. $\langle R; + \rangle$ 18. $\langle Q; + \rangle$
19. $\langle N; + \rangle$ 20. $\langle W; + \rangle$
21. $\langle M_2; + \rangle$ 22. $\langle D; \times \rangle$ $D = \{i, -i, 1, -1\}$

C **23.** Prove that if h is an identity element of S under the operation $\circ$ in a mathematical system $\langle S; \circ \rangle$, then h is unique. (*Hint:* Suppose h_1 and h_2 were identity elements. Show that $h_1 = h_2$.)

24. Use the results of Exercise 23 to show that $O = \begin{bmatrix} 0 & 0 \\ 0 & 0 \end{bmatrix}$ is unique in $\langle M_2; + \rangle$.

10–3 Multiplication of Two Matrices

There are many ways to define the product of two matrices in M_2. Experience has shown that the way which is most useful is what is often called *row-by-column* multiplication.

> **Definition** (Multiplication of Matrices) Let $A = \begin{bmatrix} a_{11} & a_{12} \\ a_{21} & a_{22} \end{bmatrix}$ and $B = \begin{bmatrix} b_{11} & b_{12} \\ b_{21} & b_{22} \end{bmatrix}$ be two matrices in M_2. The product C of A and B is the matrix defined by
>
> $$C = AB = \begin{bmatrix} a_{11} & a_{12} \\ a_{21} & a_{22} \end{bmatrix}\begin{bmatrix} b_{11} & b_{12} \\ b_{21} & b_{22} \end{bmatrix} = \begin{bmatrix} (a_{11}b_{11} + a_{12}b_{21}) & (a_{11}b_{12} + a_{12}b_{22}) \\ (a_{21}b_{11} + a_{22}b_{21}) & (a_{21}b_{12} + a_{22}b_{22}) \end{bmatrix}.$$

Notice that if the *rows* of A are thought of as components of vectors and the *columns* of B are also thought of as components of vectors, then the entries in the product matrix can be thought of as *inner products* of vectors.

EXAMPLE 1. Find the product of $A = \begin{bmatrix} 1 & -2 \\ -3 & 1 \end{bmatrix}$ and $B = \begin{bmatrix} 2 & -3 \\ 1 & 4 \end{bmatrix}$.

$$AB = \begin{bmatrix} 1 & -2 \\ -3 & 1 \end{bmatrix}\begin{bmatrix} 2 & -3 \\ 1 & 4 \end{bmatrix}$$

row 1 × column 1 = $(1)(2) + (-2)(1) = 2 + -2 = 0 = c_{11}$
row 1 × column 2 = $(1)(-3) + (-2)(4) = -3 - 8 = -11 = c_{12}$
row 2 × column 1 = $(-3)(2) + (1)(1) = -6 + 1 = -5 = c_{21}$
row 2 × column 2 = $(-3)(-3) + (1)(4) = 9 + 4 = 13 = c_{22}$

Thus

$$AB = \begin{bmatrix} 0 & -11 \\ -5 & 13 \end{bmatrix}.$$

Example 1 illustrates the fact that the entry in the *i*th row and *j*th column of the product matrix is the *inner product* of the *i*th row and *j*th column of the factor matrices. The product of two matrices in M_2 is thus always a matrix in M_2.

EXAMPLE 2. Find AB and BA when $A = \begin{bmatrix} 2 & 1 \\ 4 & 3 \end{bmatrix}$ and $B = \begin{bmatrix} 5 & 1 \\ -3 & 2 \end{bmatrix}$

$$AB = \begin{bmatrix} 2 & 1 \\ 4 & 3 \end{bmatrix}\begin{bmatrix} 5 & 1 \\ -3 & 2 \end{bmatrix} = \begin{bmatrix} 7 & 4 \\ 11 & 10 \end{bmatrix}$$

$$BA = \begin{bmatrix} 5 & 1 \\ -3 & 2 \end{bmatrix}\begin{bmatrix} 2 & 1 \\ 4 & 3 \end{bmatrix} = \begin{bmatrix} 14 & 8 \\ 2 & 3 \end{bmatrix}$$

Notice that

$$A \cdot B \neq B \cdot A.$$

Thus multiplication of matrices in M_2 is *not commutative.*

Even though multiplication of matrices in M_2 is not commutative several other properties which hold for matrices under addition hold for multiplication of matrices.

The next theorem is a direct consequence of the definition of multiplication. The proof is straightforward but somewhat intricate. It is left for you to do in the exercises.

Theorem 10–5 (Associativity of Multiplication) If A, B and C are matrices in M_2, then

$$A(BC) = (AB)C.$$

An important matrix is the **unit matrix** I defined as follows.

$$I = \begin{bmatrix} 1 & 0 \\ 0 & 1 \end{bmatrix}$$

If

$$A = \begin{bmatrix} a_{11} & a_{12} \\ a_{21} & a_{22} \end{bmatrix}$$

then,

$$AI = \begin{bmatrix} a_{11} & a_{12} \\ a_{21} & a_{22} \end{bmatrix}\begin{bmatrix} 1 & 0 \\ 0 & 1 \end{bmatrix} = \begin{bmatrix} a_{11} & a_{12} \\ a_{21} & a_{22} \end{bmatrix} = A \quad \text{and}$$

$$IA = \begin{bmatrix} 1 & 0 \\ 0 & 1 \end{bmatrix}\begin{bmatrix} a_{11} & a_{12} \\ a_{21} & a_{22} \end{bmatrix} = \begin{bmatrix} a_{11} & a_{12} \\ a_{21} & a_{22} \end{bmatrix} = A.$$

Thus I is a unit matrix or a *multiplicative identity* for the set of matrices M_2. From Exercise 23 Section 10–2, it follows that I is unique. Thus you have proved the following theorem.

Theorem 10–6 There is a unique element $I = \begin{bmatrix} 1 & 0 \\ 0 & 1 \end{bmatrix}$ of M_2 with the property that for any A in M_2

$$IA = AI = A.$$

Using the definition of the product of a real number and a matrix, you can easily prove the next theorem. The proof will be left for you to do.

Theorem 10–7 If k is in R and A and B are in M_2, then

$$A(kB) = (kA)B = k(AB).$$

EXAMPLE 3. Compute $\begin{bmatrix} 2 & 8 \\ 4 & 2 \end{bmatrix} \left(\frac{1}{2} \begin{bmatrix} 3 & 1 \\ -2 & 1 \end{bmatrix} \right)$.

Theorem 10–7 allows you to compute as follows.

$$\frac{1}{2} \left(\begin{bmatrix} 2 & 8 \\ 4 & 2 \end{bmatrix} \begin{bmatrix} 3 & 1 \\ -2 & 1 \end{bmatrix} \right) = \frac{1}{2} \begin{bmatrix} -10 & 10 \\ 8 & 6 \end{bmatrix}$$

$$= \begin{bmatrix} -5 & 5 \\ 4 & 3 \end{bmatrix}$$

Now try these

━━ Multiply.

1. $\begin{bmatrix} 2 & 1 \\ -3 & 4 \end{bmatrix} \begin{bmatrix} 0 & 5 \\ 2 & 4 \end{bmatrix}$

2. $\begin{bmatrix} 0 & 1 \\ 1 & 0 \end{bmatrix} \begin{bmatrix} 5 & 2 \\ -9 & 7 \end{bmatrix}$

Answers: **1.** $\begin{bmatrix} 2 & 14 \\ 8 & 1 \end{bmatrix}$

2. $\begin{bmatrix} -9 & 7 \\ 5 & 2 \end{bmatrix}$

Checkpoint

1. What is meant by row-by-column multiplication?

2. Which of the following properties are found in the multiplication of two matrices from M_2?

    a. closure   **b.** associativity

    c. commutativity   **d.** multiplicative identity

3. Define: "multiplicative identity of a square matrix"

Exercises

A In each exercise find AB, BA, $A(2B)$, and $(2A)(3B)$.

1. $A = \begin{bmatrix} 1 & -1 \\ 0 & 1 \end{bmatrix}$ $\qquad B = \begin{bmatrix} 2 & 1 \\ 1 & 2 \end{bmatrix}$

2. $A = \begin{bmatrix} 0 & -1 \\ 1 & 0 \end{bmatrix}$ $\qquad B = \begin{bmatrix} 1 & 1 \\ -1 & -1 \end{bmatrix}$

3. $A = \begin{bmatrix} 0 & 1 \\ 1 & 1 \end{bmatrix}$ $\qquad B = \begin{bmatrix} -1 & -1 \\ 1 & 1 \end{bmatrix}$

4. $A = \begin{bmatrix} 4 & 1 \\ 3 & 2 \end{bmatrix}$ $\qquad B = \begin{bmatrix} 2 & -1 \\ -3 & 4 \end{bmatrix}$

5. $A = \begin{bmatrix} x & y \\ 0 & 0 \end{bmatrix}$ $\qquad B = \begin{bmatrix} y & y \\ -x & -x \end{bmatrix}$

6. $A = \begin{bmatrix} 1 & 2 \\ 3 & 4 \end{bmatrix}$ $\qquad B = \begin{bmatrix} 1 & 0 \\ 0 & 1 \end{bmatrix}$

7. $A = \begin{bmatrix} 4 & 7 \\ -2 & 3 \end{bmatrix}$ $\qquad B = \begin{bmatrix} 0 & 0 \\ 0 & 1 \end{bmatrix}$

8. $A = \begin{bmatrix} 5 & 4 \\ 1 & 1 \end{bmatrix}$ $\qquad B = \begin{bmatrix} 1 & -4 \\ -1 & 5 \end{bmatrix}$

9. Let A^2 denote AA, A^3 denote AAA, etc.

    a. Compute A^2 if $A = \begin{bmatrix} 2 & 1 \\ 1 & 3 \end{bmatrix}$

    b. Compute A^3 if $A = \begin{bmatrix} 1 & 2 \\ 0 & 1 \end{bmatrix}$

B **10.** For $A = \begin{bmatrix} 7 & 1 \\ 5 & -2 \end{bmatrix}$, prove or disprove that $A^2A = AA^2$.

11. For $A = \begin{bmatrix} 1 & 0 \\ 0 & -1 \end{bmatrix}$ compute A^2, A^3, A^4, and A^5. Do you see any pattern?

12. For $A = \begin{bmatrix} 0 & -1 \\ 1 & 0 \end{bmatrix}$ Compute A^2, A^3, A^4, A^5, and A^6. Do you see any pattern?

13. Let A, B be in M_2.

    a. Find $(A - B)(A + B)$

    b. Does $(A - B)(A + B)$ equal $A^2 - B^2$? Explain.

14. Let A, B be in M_2.

    a. Find $(A + B)^2$.

    b. Find $A^2 + 2AB + B^2$.

    c. Compare the results of **a** and **b**.

15. For $A = \begin{bmatrix} 1 & 2 \\ 3 & 1 \end{bmatrix}$, verify that $A^2 - 2A - 5I = O$

$$\left(I = \begin{bmatrix} 1 & 0 \\ 0 & 1 \end{bmatrix},\ O = \begin{bmatrix} 0 & 0 \\ 0 & 0 \end{bmatrix} \right)$$

16. For $A = \begin{bmatrix} 2 & 3 \\ 1 & 2 \end{bmatrix}$, verify that $A^2 - 4A = -I$.

C **17.** Prove Theorem 10–5.

18. Prove Theorem 10–7.

19. Let $L_1 = l_1 I$ and $L_2 = l_2 I$, $l_1 l_2 \in R$. Prove or disprove:

    a. $L_1 + L_2 = (l_1 + l_2)I$.

    b. $L_1 L_2 = (l_1 l_2)I$.

20. Prove or disprove: If l_1 and l_2 are real numbers and $A \in M_2$, then $A^2 - (l_1 + l_2)A + l_1 l_2 I = (A - l_1 I)(A - l_2 I)$.

10–4 Vectors and Matrices

Recall that any vector in two-space is equal to a position vector with its tip at a point (a, b) in the plane. Thus a vector v can be identified by noting the ordered pair of real numbers naming its tip.

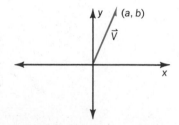

Theorem 10–8 There is a one-to-one correspondence between the vectors in the plane and the ordered pairs of real numbers.

Proof: Each vector v corresponds to a point (a, b) because each vector is equal to a position vector. If two vectors have the same position vector, they are equal by the definition of equal vectors. (They have the same direction and length.) Thus each vector corresponds to exactly one ordered pair (a, b).

Conversely the point (a, b) determines a unique position vector with its tip at (a, b). Thus there is a one-to-one correspondence between vectors in the plane and points in the plane.

Since ordered pairs uniquely determine vectors, you may think of an ordered pair of real numbers as a vector. When you read "the vector (4, 2)," you should think of the position vector whose tip has coordinates (4, 2).

Identifying vectors with ordered pairs of real numbers lets you use matrix notation to denote vectors.

Definition The vector (a, b) is denoted by the 2×1 matrix $\begin{bmatrix} a \\ b \end{bmatrix}$, where a is the first or **i** component of the vector and b is the second or **j** component. $\begin{bmatrix} a \\ b \end{bmatrix}$ is a <u>column vector</u>.

EXAMPLE 1. Name the vector $\overrightarrow{PQ}$, where $P = (2, 5)$ and $Q = (1, 7)$, as a column vector. Sketch the vector.

$$\overrightarrow{PQ} = (1 - 2)\mathbf{i} + (7 - 5)\mathbf{j} = -\mathbf{i} + 2\mathbf{j}$$

Thus

$$\overrightarrow{PQ} = \begin{bmatrix} -1 \\ 2 \end{bmatrix}.$$

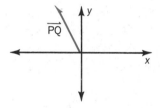

Column vectors and matrices in M_2 can be multiplied. *The product is another column vector.* The procedure used is like that used to multiply two matrices in M_2, except that there is only one column in a column vector, and thus only two inner products are found.

Definition The product of a matrix, $A = \begin{bmatrix} a_{11} & a_{12} \\ a_{21} & a_{22} \end{bmatrix}$ and a vector, $\vec{v} = \begin{bmatrix} x \\ y \end{bmatrix}$, is the column vector, $A\vec{v}$, defined by the following system.

$$\begin{bmatrix} a_{11} & a_{12} \\ a_{21} & a_{22} \end{bmatrix} \begin{bmatrix} x \\ y \end{bmatrix} = \begin{bmatrix} a_{11}x + a_{12}y \\ a_{21}x + a_{22}y \end{bmatrix}$$

EXAMPLE 2. Compute $\begin{bmatrix} 1 & -3 \\ 2 & -1 \end{bmatrix}\begin{bmatrix} 1 \\ 3 \end{bmatrix}$. Sketch the original vector and

the product vector.

1st row by column

$$(1)(1) + (-3)(3) = -8$$

2nd row by column

$$(2)(1) + (-1)(3) = -1$$

Thus $\begin{bmatrix} 1 & -3 \\ 2 & -1 \end{bmatrix}\begin{bmatrix} 1 \\ 3 \end{bmatrix} = \begin{bmatrix} -8 \\ -1 \end{bmatrix}$

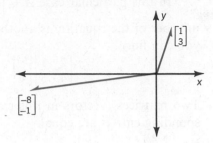

Both vectors are shown at the right.

A theorem like Theorem 10–7 is true for products of matrices and column vectors. It is stated below as Theorem 10–9 and can be easily proved. It is left for you to do in the exercises.

> **Theorem 10–9** For any vector $\vec{v}$ in two-space, for any matrix A in M_2, and for any real number k,
>
> $$A(k\vec{v}) = (kA)\vec{v} = k(A\vec{v}).$$

EXAMPLE 3. Compute $\begin{bmatrix} 4 & 6 \\ -2 & 12 \end{bmatrix}\left(\frac{1}{10}\begin{bmatrix} 7 \\ 2 \end{bmatrix}\right)$

By Theorem 10–9,

$$\begin{bmatrix} 4 & 6 \\ -2 & 12 \end{bmatrix}\left(\frac{1}{10}\begin{bmatrix} 7 \\ 2 \end{bmatrix}\right) = \frac{1}{10}\left(\begin{bmatrix} 4 & 6 \\ -2 & 12 \end{bmatrix}\begin{bmatrix} 7 \\ 2 \end{bmatrix}\right)$$

The latter expression is easier to compute.

$$\frac{1}{10}\left(\begin{bmatrix} 4 & 6 \\ -2 & 12 \end{bmatrix}\begin{bmatrix} 7 \\ 2 \end{bmatrix}\right) = \frac{1}{10}\begin{bmatrix} (4)(7) + (6)(2) \\ (-2)(7) + (12)(2) \end{bmatrix} = \frac{1}{10}\begin{bmatrix} 40 \\ 10 \end{bmatrix} = \begin{bmatrix} 4 \\ 1 \end{bmatrix}$$

Notice that multiplying a matrix A and vector $\vec{v}$ gives a vector $\vec{r}$ that is,

$$A\vec{v} = \vec{r}. \qquad\qquad 1$$

The equation is reminiscent of a linear equation

$$ax = b \qquad\qquad 2$$

where a and b are real numbers and x is a variable. You know that equation 2 can be solved when $a \neq 0$. Equation 1 can often be solved also as the next example illustrates.

EXAMPLE 4. Find $\vec{v} = \begin{bmatrix} x \\ y \end{bmatrix}$ when $\begin{bmatrix} 2 & 1 \\ 4 & 3 \end{bmatrix}\begin{bmatrix} x \\ y \end{bmatrix} = \begin{bmatrix} 1 \\ 0 \end{bmatrix}$.

In this particular case $A = \begin{bmatrix} 2 & 1 \\ 4 & 3 \end{bmatrix}$, $\vec{v} = \begin{bmatrix} x \\ y \end{bmatrix}$, and $\vec{r} = \begin{bmatrix} 1 \\ 0 \end{bmatrix}$. The left member of the equation is another name for the vector, so multiplying you can find

$$\begin{bmatrix} 2 & 1 \\ 4 & 3 \end{bmatrix}\begin{bmatrix} x \\ y \end{bmatrix} = \begin{bmatrix} 2x + y \\ 4x + 3y \end{bmatrix} = \begin{bmatrix} 1 \\ 0 \end{bmatrix}$$

Two matrices (vectors in this case) are equal if and only if the corresponding entries are equal.

Thus
$$2x + y = 1$$
$$4x + 3y = 0$$

Solving these two equations simultaneously you find

$$-4x - 2y = -2$$
$$\underline{4x + 3y = 0}$$
$$y = -2 \quad \text{and} \quad x = \tfrac{3}{2}$$

Thus $\vec{v} = \begin{bmatrix} \frac{3}{2} \\ -2 \end{bmatrix}$. Check this result by computing $A\vec{v}$.

Notice that the *solution vector* is found by finding the coordinates of the point common to the two lines $2x + y = 1$ and $4x + 3y = 0$. If these lines are parallel there is no solution. If they are the same line, there are many solutions. How can you identify parallel lines? The same line? In the next section you will learn an easier method of solving a matrix and vector equation like $A\vec{v} = \vec{r}$.

For completeness, it must be mentioned that the definitions of multiplication given in this section and in Section 10–3 are special instances of a general definition of matrix multiplication. Any two matrices A and B with dimensions $m \times n$ and $n \times p$ may be multiplied by the row-column procedure. The *ij*th entry in $C = A \cdot B$ is the inner product of the *i*th row of A and the *j*th column of B. The dimensions of C are $m \times p$.

EXAMPLE 5. Compute $\begin{bmatrix} 2 & 1 & 4 \\ 3 & 1 & 7 \end{bmatrix}\begin{bmatrix} 1 & 4 & 1 & 5 \\ 2 & 6 & 3 & 2 \\ 3 & 1 & 5 & 7 \end{bmatrix} = AB$

$$AB = \begin{bmatrix} 2 & 1 & 4 \\ 3 & 1 & 7 \end{bmatrix}\begin{bmatrix} 1 & 4 & 1 & 5 \\ 2 & 6 & 3 & 2 \\ 3 & 1 & 5 & 7 \end{bmatrix} = \begin{bmatrix} 16 & 18 & 25 & 40 \\ 26 & 25 & 41 & 66 \end{bmatrix} = C$$

Dimensions of Matrix: 2×3 3×4 ⟶ 2×4

Each entry in the product is found by computing an inner product of a row in A and a column in B. For example

$$C_{23} = 41 = [3 \quad 1 \quad 7] \begin{bmatrix} 1 \\ 3 \\ 5 \end{bmatrix} = [3 + 3 + 35] = [41].$$

Notice that product $A \cdot B$ exists only because the number of columns in A is the same as the number of rows in B.

Checkpoint

1. In what way does the multiplication of column vectors with matrices in M_2 differ from the multiplication of two matrices in M_2?

2. What can you say about BA in Example 5?

Exercises

A ━━ Find the column vector, $\vec{v} = \begin{bmatrix} x \\ y \end{bmatrix}$, for $\overrightarrow{PQ}$ in each of the following.

1. $P(2, 1)$ and $Q = (3, 4)$
2. $P(3, 4)$ and $Q = (2, 1)$
3. $P(-3, 1)$ and $Q = (2, -5)$
4. $P = (\frac{1}{2}, -3)$ and $Q = (4, 2)$
5. $P = (-4, 2)$ and $Q = (2, -1)$
6. $P = (-1, -3)$ and $Q = (1, 2)$
7. $P = (103, 47)$ and $Q = (100, 49)$
8. $P = (1, 3)$ and $Q = (-\frac{2}{3}, -\frac{4}{5})$

━━ Let $A = \begin{bmatrix} 1 & 2 \\ 4 & 1 \end{bmatrix}$, $B = \begin{bmatrix} -2 & 1 \\ 3 & -1 \end{bmatrix}$, $C = \begin{bmatrix} 0 & 1 \\ 2 & 1 \end{bmatrix}$, $\vec{r} = \begin{bmatrix} 2 \\ -2 \end{bmatrix}$, $\vec{t} = \begin{bmatrix} -1 \\ 4 \end{bmatrix}$.

Find the column vector. Make a sketch of each vector.

9. $A\vec{r}$
10. $B\vec{r}$
11. $C\vec{r}$
12. At
13. $B\vec{t}$
14. $C\vec{t}$
15. $A(2\vec{r})$
16. $B(\frac{1}{2}\vec{r})$
17. $C(\vec{r} + \vec{t})$
18. $C\vec{r} + C\vec{t}$
19. $(AB)\vec{r}$
20. $A(B\vec{r})$
21. $(AC)\vec{t}$
22. $A(C\vec{t})$
23. $(A + B)\vec{r}$
24. $A\vec{r} + B\vec{r}$

25. Compare the results of Exercises

a. 17 and 18.
b. 19 and 20.
c. 23 and 24.

B Solve for the vector $\begin{bmatrix} x \\ y \end{bmatrix}$ when possible.

26. $\begin{bmatrix} 4 & 1 \\ 3 & 1 \end{bmatrix} \begin{bmatrix} x \\ y \end{bmatrix} = \begin{bmatrix} 2 \\ 1 \end{bmatrix}$

27. $\begin{bmatrix} -3 & 4 \\ -6 & 1 \end{bmatrix} \begin{bmatrix} x \\ y \end{bmatrix} = \begin{bmatrix} -2 \\ 3 \end{bmatrix}$

28. $\begin{bmatrix} 2 & -3 \\ -4 & 6 \end{bmatrix} \begin{bmatrix} x \\ y \end{bmatrix} = \begin{bmatrix} 1 \\ 0 \end{bmatrix}$

29. $\begin{bmatrix} 1 & 0 \\ 0 & 1 \end{bmatrix} \begin{bmatrix} x \\ y \end{bmatrix} = \begin{bmatrix} 4 \\ 5 \end{bmatrix}$

30. $\begin{bmatrix} 0 & 5 \\ 1 & 0 \end{bmatrix} \begin{bmatrix} x \\ y \end{bmatrix} = \begin{bmatrix} 2 \\ -1 \end{bmatrix}$

31. $\begin{bmatrix} 1 & -2 \\ -2 & 4 \end{bmatrix} \begin{bmatrix} x \\ y \end{bmatrix} = \begin{bmatrix} 2 \\ -4 \end{bmatrix}$

32. $\begin{bmatrix} 1 & 5 \\ 0 & 1 \end{bmatrix} \begin{bmatrix} x \\ y \end{bmatrix} = \begin{bmatrix} 7 \\ 2 \end{bmatrix}$

33. $\begin{bmatrix} 4 & 1 \\ 1 & 0 \end{bmatrix} \begin{bmatrix} x \\ y \end{bmatrix} = \begin{bmatrix} 2 \\ 8 \end{bmatrix}$

C ━━ Complete the products.

34. $\begin{bmatrix} 1 \\ 4 \end{bmatrix} \begin{bmatrix} 2 & 3 \end{bmatrix}$

35. $\begin{bmatrix} 1 & 1 & 1 \\ 4 & 3 & 2 \end{bmatrix} \begin{bmatrix} 1 & 2 \\ 0 & 1 \\ 1 & 4 \end{bmatrix}$

36. $\begin{bmatrix} 1 & 2 & 4 & 1 \\ 5 & 1 & 0 & 3 \end{bmatrix} \begin{bmatrix} 1 & 4 & 3 \\ -2 & 1 & 2 \\ 1 & -5 & 0 \\ 0 & 1 & 0 \end{bmatrix}$

37. $\begin{bmatrix} 1 & 1 & 3 \\ 1 & 3 & 1 \\ 3 & 1 & 1 \end{bmatrix} \begin{bmatrix} 2 & 1 & 1 \\ 1 & 2 & 1 \\ 1 & 1 & 2 \end{bmatrix}$

━━ Let $A = \begin{bmatrix} a_{11} & a_{12} \\ a_{21} & a_{22} \end{bmatrix}$ $B = \begin{bmatrix} b_{11} & b_{12} \\ b_{21} & b_{22} \end{bmatrix}$ $\vec{r} = \begin{bmatrix} x \\ y \end{bmatrix}$ $\vec{t} = \begin{bmatrix} u \\ v \end{bmatrix}$ and k a real

number. Prove each of the following.

38. $A(\vec{r} + \vec{t}) = A\vec{r} + A\vec{t}$

39. $A(B\vec{r}) = (AB)\vec{r}$

40. $(A + B)\vec{r} = A\vec{r} + B\vec{r}$

41. $A(k\vec{r}) = (kA)\vec{r} = k(A\vec{r})$ (Theorem 10–9).

10–5   Inverses and Determinants

In Section 10–4 you learned how to solve a matrix vector equation

$$A\vec{v} = \vec{r}$$

by solving a pair of linear equations. The major objective of this section is to develop matrix methods which can be employed in finding the solution.

The means sought are motivated by the solution procedures used in determining x in the real number equation

$$ax = b.$$

Here, when $a \neq 0$, multiplication of left and right members by $\frac{1}{a}$, the multiplicative inverse of a, provides the solution easily.

If

$$ax = b,$$

then

$$\frac{1}{a}(ax) = \frac{1}{a} \cdot b$$

or

$$x = \frac{b}{a}$$

Similarly, if there is a matrix A^{-1} (read "A inverse") such that $A^{-1}A = I = AA^{-1}$, then $\vec{v}$ will equal $A^{-1}\vec{r}$ because $I\vec{v} = \vec{v}$ and $A^{-1}\vec{r}$ is a column matrix. The procedure would be as follows.

$$A\vec{v} = \vec{r},$$

so

$$A^{-1}(A\vec{v}) = A^{-1}\vec{r}$$

Thus

$$I\vec{v} = A^{-1}\vec{r}$$

or

$$\vec{v} = A^{-1}\vec{r}.$$

There are three questions to be answered: **1.** Are there any matrices that have inverses? **2.** If there are, which ones are they? **3.** What is the inverse of a matrix A?

The first question is easy to answer: Some matrices have inverses. For example, let $A = \begin{bmatrix} 0 & -1 \\ 1 & 0 \end{bmatrix}$. Then if $B = \begin{bmatrix} 0 & 1 \\ -1 & 0 \end{bmatrix}$, B is the inverse of A, because

$$AB = \begin{bmatrix} 0 & -1 \\ 1 & 0 \end{bmatrix}\begin{bmatrix} 0 & 1 \\ -1 & 0 \end{bmatrix} = \begin{bmatrix} 1 & 0 \\ 0 & 1 \end{bmatrix} = I.$$

$$BA = \begin{bmatrix} 0 & 1 \\ -1 & 0 \end{bmatrix}\begin{bmatrix} 0 & -1 \\ 1 & 0 \end{bmatrix} = \begin{bmatrix} 1 & 0 \\ 0 & 1 \end{bmatrix} = I.$$

Thus $AB = BA = I$ and $B = A^{-1}$ (or $A = B^{-1}$).

Theorem 10–10 If A is a matrix in M_2 and if A^{-1} is a matrix with the property that

$$AA^{-1} = A^{-1}A = I,$$

then A^{-1} is unique.

This theorem is a consequence of Exercise 23, Section 10–2 and Theorem 10–5.

It is also true that not all matrices have inverses. For example $O = \begin{bmatrix} 0 & 0 \\ 0 & 0 \end{bmatrix}$ has no inverse for $\begin{bmatrix} 0 & 0 \\ 0 & 0 \end{bmatrix} \begin{bmatrix} a_{11} & a_{12} \\ a_{21} & a_{22} \end{bmatrix} = \begin{bmatrix} 0 & 0 \\ 0 & 0 \end{bmatrix}$ for all matrices A. Thus OA is never equal to $I = \begin{bmatrix} 1 & 0 \\ 0 & 1 \end{bmatrix}$. There are many other square matrices that do not have inverses, also. For example: $\begin{bmatrix} 1 & 0 \\ 0 & 0 \end{bmatrix}$.

The next two examples illustrate the method used to find the inverse of a matrix. The first is a particular case, the second is the general case which constitutes a proof of necessary and sufficient conditions for a matrix A to have an inverse A^{-1}.

EXAMPLE 1. Let $A = \begin{bmatrix} 0 & 2 \\ -1 & 3 \end{bmatrix}$. Find the matrix B, if it exists, such that $AB = BA = I$.

Let $B = \begin{bmatrix} a & b \\ c & d \end{bmatrix}$. If B satisfies the conditions then

$$AB = \begin{bmatrix} 0 & 2 \\ -1 & 3 \end{bmatrix} \cdot \begin{bmatrix} a & b \\ c & d \end{bmatrix} = \begin{bmatrix} 1 & 0 \\ 0 & 1 \end{bmatrix}.$$

Performing the multiplication you find

$$AB = \begin{bmatrix} 2c & 2d \\ -a + 3c & -b + 3d \end{bmatrix} = \begin{bmatrix} 1 & 0 \\ 0 & 1 \end{bmatrix}.$$

By the definition of equality, each entry in the left matrix equals the corresponding entry in the right matrix. Thus you have four equations

$$2c = 1 \qquad\qquad 2d = 0$$
$$-a + 3c = 0 \qquad -b + 3d = 1$$

Solving these equations you find $c = \frac{1}{2}$, $d = 0$, $a = \frac{3}{2}$, and $b = -1$.

Thus
$$B = \begin{bmatrix} \frac{3}{2} & -1 \\ \frac{1}{2} & 0 \end{bmatrix}.$$

Computation of BA shows that $BA = I$. Thus $B = \begin{bmatrix} \frac{3}{2} & -1 \\ \frac{1}{2} & 0 \end{bmatrix}$ satisfies the conditions $AB = BA = I$, and $B = A^{-1}$.

EXAMPLE 2. Let $A = \begin{bmatrix} p & q \\ r & s \end{bmatrix}$. Find the matrix $B = \begin{bmatrix} a & b \\ c & d \end{bmatrix}$ such that $AB = BA = I$ and the conditions on A such that B exists.

For B to satisfy the conditions,

$$AB = \begin{bmatrix} p & q \\ r & s \end{bmatrix}\begin{bmatrix} a & b \\ c & d \end{bmatrix} = \begin{bmatrix} 1 & 0 \\ 0 & 1 \end{bmatrix} = I.$$

Then by multiplication

$$\begin{bmatrix} pa + qc & pb + qd \\ ra + sc & rb + sd \end{bmatrix} = \begin{bmatrix} 1 & 0 \\ 0 & 1 \end{bmatrix}.$$

This matrix equation is equivalent to the four equations:

i. $pa + qc = 1$ iii. $pb + qd = 0$
ii. $ra + sc = 0$ iv. $rb + sd = 1$

Now you must solve these equations for the real numbers $a, b, c,$ and d in terms of the real numbers $p, q, r,$ and s. Solving i and ii for a, (multiply i by s and ii by $-q$ and add the resulting equations) you find

$$psa - qra = s \text{ or } (ps - qr)a = s. \qquad\qquad 1$$

Similarly you find $\qquad (ps - qr)c = -r \qquad\qquad\qquad 2$

$$(ps - qr)b = -q \qquad\qquad\qquad 3$$

$$(ps - qr)d = p. \qquad\qquad\qquad 4$$

Equations 1, 2, 3, and 4 have a unique solution if and only if the number $ps - qr$ is *not* 0. Thus a matrix $A = \begin{bmatrix} p & q \\ r & s \end{bmatrix}$ has no inverse when $ps - qr = 0$.

If, on the other hand, $ps - qr \neq 0$, then $A = \begin{bmatrix} p & q \\ r & s \end{bmatrix}$ has an inverse $\begin{bmatrix} a & b \\ c & d \end{bmatrix}$ whose entries are the following.

$$a = \frac{s}{ps - qr}$$

$$b = \frac{-q}{ps - qr}$$

$$c = \frac{-r}{ps - qr}$$

$$d = \frac{p}{ps - qr}$$

Thus

$$B = \begin{bmatrix} \dfrac{s}{ps - qr} & \dfrac{-q}{ps - qr} \\ \dfrac{-r}{ps - qr} & \dfrac{p}{ps - qr} \end{bmatrix} = \frac{1}{ps - qr}\begin{bmatrix} s & -q \\ -r & p \end{bmatrix}. \qquad 5$$

Direct multiplication verifies that B satisfies $BA = I$. Thus $B = A^{-1}$.

In Example 2 the number $ps - qr$ plays a key role in determining whether a matrix $\begin{bmatrix} p & q \\ r & s \end{bmatrix}$ has an inverse. This number is the **determinant** of the matrix A. It is denoted *det A*.

Following is a formal definition of the determinant of a matrix A in M_2.

Definition For a matrix $A = \begin{bmatrix} a_{11} & a_{12} \\ a_{21} & a_{22} \end{bmatrix}$ the determinant of A, written "det A", is the number defined by,

$$\det A = a_{11}a_{22} - a_{12}a_{21}.$$

Now the necessary and sufficient conditions for the existence of an inverse of a matrix A in M_2 can be stated.

Theorem 10–11 If A is a matrix in M_2, then A has an inverse A^{-1} if and only if $\det A \neq 0$. If $\det A \neq 0$ and $A = \begin{bmatrix} a_{11} & a_{12} \\ a_{21} & a_{22} \end{bmatrix}$, then

$$A^{-1} = \begin{bmatrix} \dfrac{a_{22}}{\det A} & \dfrac{-a_{12}}{\det A} \\ \dfrac{-a_{21}}{\det A} & \dfrac{a_{11}}{\det A} \end{bmatrix} = \frac{1}{\det A}\begin{bmatrix} a_{22} & -a_{12} \\ -a_{21} & a_{11} \end{bmatrix}$$

Definition A matrix A which has an inverse A^{-1} is an _invertible matrix._

EXAMPLE 3. Find the inverse, if it exists, of $A = \begin{bmatrix} 2 & 1 \\ 1 & 2 \end{bmatrix}$

$$\det A = 2 \cdot 2 - 1 \cdot 1 = 4 \cdot 1 = 3$$

Since $\det A \neq 0$ A has an inverse.

$$A^{-1} = \tfrac{1}{3}\begin{bmatrix} 2 & -1 \\ -1 & 2 \end{bmatrix} = \begin{bmatrix} \frac{2}{3} & -\frac{1}{3} \\ -\frac{1}{3} & \frac{2}{3} \end{bmatrix}$$

EXAMPLE 4. Find the inverse, if it exists, of $B = \begin{bmatrix} 4 & 3 \\ -8 & -6 \end{bmatrix}$

$$\det B = 4(-6) - 3(-8) = -24 - (-24) = 0$$

There is no inverse for B.

EXAMPLE 5. Find the inverse, if it exists, of $C = \begin{bmatrix} -1 & 0 \\ 0 & 1 \end{bmatrix}$.

$$\det C = (-1)1 - (0)(0) = -1$$

$$C^{-1} = \frac{1}{-1}\begin{bmatrix} 1 & 0 \\ 0 & -1 \end{bmatrix} = \begin{bmatrix} -1 & 0 \\ 0 & 1 \end{bmatrix}.$$

Thus C is its own inverse. Can you name another matrix which is its own inverse?

EXAMPLE 6. Solve the matrix vector equation

$$\begin{bmatrix} 2 & 2 \\ 1 & 2 \end{bmatrix}\begin{bmatrix} x \\ y \end{bmatrix} = \begin{bmatrix} 4 \\ 5 \end{bmatrix}.$$

If $\begin{bmatrix} 2 & 2 \\ 1 & 2 \end{bmatrix}$ has an inverse, the system can be solved by multiplying both sides of the equation above by that inverse. Since

$$\det A = 2 \times 2 - 2 \times 1 = 4 - 2 = 2$$

the inverse of $\begin{bmatrix} 2 & 2 \\ 1 & 2 \end{bmatrix}$ is $\frac{1}{2}\begin{bmatrix} 2 & -2 \\ -1 & 2 \end{bmatrix} = \begin{bmatrix} 1 & -1 \\ -\frac{1}{2} & 1 \end{bmatrix}$

Thus $\begin{bmatrix} 1 & -1 \\ -\frac{1}{2} & 1 \end{bmatrix}\begin{bmatrix} 2 & 2 \\ 1 & 2 \end{bmatrix}\begin{bmatrix} x \\ y \end{bmatrix} = \begin{bmatrix} 1 & -1 \\ -\frac{1}{2} & 1 \end{bmatrix} \cdot \begin{bmatrix} 4 \\ 5 \end{bmatrix}$

and $I\begin{bmatrix} x \\ y \end{bmatrix} = \begin{bmatrix} -1 \\ 3 \end{bmatrix}$

or $\begin{bmatrix} x \\ y \end{bmatrix} = \begin{bmatrix} -1 \\ 3 \end{bmatrix}$

Now try these

━━ Find the determinant of each matrix and its inverse, if it exists.

1. $\begin{bmatrix} 3 & 2 \\ 6 & 4 \end{bmatrix}$ 　　　　　　　　**2.** $\begin{bmatrix} 3 & 2 \\ -6 & 4 \end{bmatrix}$

Answers: **1.** Det $\begin{bmatrix} 3 & 2 \\ 6 & 4 \end{bmatrix} = 0$. No inverse.

2. Det $\begin{bmatrix} 3 & 2 \\ -6 & 4 \end{bmatrix} = 24$. Inverse $= \frac{1}{24}\begin{bmatrix} 4 & -2 \\ 6 & 3 \end{bmatrix}$.

Checkpoint

1. What is the necessary and sufficient condition for a matrix from M_2 to have an inverse?

2. What is meant by det A?

Exercises

— Find the determinant of each matrix.

1. $\begin{bmatrix} -4 & -1 \\ 6 & 2 \end{bmatrix}$
2. $\begin{bmatrix} 0 & -1 \\ 1 & 0 \end{bmatrix}$
3. $\begin{bmatrix} -1 & 0 \\ 0 & -1 \end{bmatrix}$

4. $\begin{bmatrix} 1 & 0 \\ 0 & -1 \end{bmatrix}$
5. $\begin{bmatrix} 1 & 7 \\ 1 & 5 \end{bmatrix}$
6. $\begin{bmatrix} 10 & 4 \\ 5 & 2 \end{bmatrix}$

7. $\begin{bmatrix} 0 & 1 \\ 0 & 5 \end{bmatrix}$
8. $\begin{bmatrix} 3 & 8 \\ 2 & 5 \end{bmatrix}$
9. $\begin{bmatrix} a & b \\ 0 & 0 \end{bmatrix}$

10. $\begin{bmatrix} 17 & 3 \\ 5 & 1 \end{bmatrix}$
11. $\begin{bmatrix} 84 & 55 \\ 3 & 2 \end{bmatrix}$
12. $\begin{bmatrix} p & q \\ 2 & 3 \end{bmatrix}$

13. For each matrix in Exercises 1–11 find the inverse, if it exists.

14. For the inverse of the matrix in Exercise 12 to exist, what conditions must be placed on p and q?

— Solve each matrix vector equation for the vector $\begin{bmatrix} x \\ y \end{bmatrix}$ when possible. Use the method of Example 6.

15. $\begin{bmatrix} 4 & 1 \\ 3 & 1 \end{bmatrix}\begin{bmatrix} x \\ y \end{bmatrix} = \begin{bmatrix} 2 \\ 1 \end{bmatrix}$
16. $\begin{bmatrix} -3 & 4 \\ -6 & 1 \end{bmatrix}\begin{bmatrix} x \\ y \end{bmatrix} = \begin{bmatrix} -2 \\ 3 \end{bmatrix}$

17. $\begin{bmatrix} 2 & -3 \\ -4 & 6 \end{bmatrix}\begin{bmatrix} x \\ y \end{bmatrix} = \begin{bmatrix} 1 \\ 0 \end{bmatrix}$
18. $\begin{bmatrix} 1 & 0 \\ 0 & 1 \end{bmatrix}\begin{bmatrix} x \\ y \end{bmatrix} = \begin{bmatrix} 4 \\ 5 \end{bmatrix}$

19. $\begin{bmatrix} 0 & 1 \\ 1 & 0 \end{bmatrix}\begin{bmatrix} x \\ y \end{bmatrix} = \begin{bmatrix} 2 \\ -1 \end{bmatrix}$
20. $\begin{bmatrix} 1 & -2 \\ -2 & 4 \end{bmatrix}\begin{bmatrix} x \\ y \end{bmatrix} = \begin{bmatrix} 2 \\ -4 \end{bmatrix}$

21. $\begin{bmatrix} 1 & 5 \\ 0 & 1 \end{bmatrix}\begin{bmatrix} x \\ y \end{bmatrix} = \begin{bmatrix} 7 \\ 2 \end{bmatrix}$
22. $\begin{bmatrix} 4 & 1 \\ 1 & 0 \end{bmatrix}\begin{bmatrix} x \\ y \end{bmatrix} = \begin{bmatrix} 2 \\ 8 \end{bmatrix}$

23. For $a, b \in R$ and $a \neq 0 \neq b$, find the inverse of $A = \begin{bmatrix} a & 0 \\ 0 & b \end{bmatrix}$.

24. For $a \in R$, $a \neq 0$, find the inverse of $A = \begin{bmatrix} a & 0 \\ 0 & a \end{bmatrix}$.

25. Find the inverse of $\begin{bmatrix} 1 & k \\ 0 & 1 \end{bmatrix}$ for $k \in R$.

26. Find the inverse of $\begin{bmatrix} k & 1 \\ 1 & 0 \end{bmatrix}$ for $k \in R$.

27. Find the inverse of $\begin{bmatrix} 1 & a \\ a & 1 \end{bmatrix}$ for $a \in R$, $a \neq \pm 1$.

28. A pair of linear equations

$$\begin{matrix} \textbf{i.} & ax + by = r \\ \textbf{ii.} & cx + dy = s \end{matrix} \qquad r \text{ and } s \text{ not both zero}$$

has a unique solution if and only if the lines are not parallel or identical. State this condition in terms of the slopes of **i** and **ii.**

29. Matrices may be used to denote a pair of equations

1 $\quad$ i. $ax + by = r$ $\qquad$ by writing $\qquad$ $\begin{bmatrix} a & b \\ c & d \end{bmatrix}\begin{bmatrix} x \\ y \end{bmatrix} = \begin{bmatrix} r \\ s \end{bmatrix}$ $\quad$ **2**
$\quad$ ii. $cx + dy = s$

Explain why **1** and **2** are equivalent expressions.

10–6 Linear Transformations of Vectors

A **transformation** is a rule by which one object is paired with another. If the objects happen to be vectors, then a transformation of a vector pairs the vector with another vector.

Transformations of vectors can be described in various ways: by words, by equations, and by matrices (to name just three). Below are four examples of transformations of vectors. In each case the transformation is applied to the vector $\vec{v} = \begin{bmatrix} 1 \\ 2 \end{bmatrix}$, and the graphical representation of $\vec{v}$ and the transformed vector are shown.

EXAMPLE 1. Let T be the transformation defined by the rule: T pairs each vector $\vec{v}$ with itself. The graph in Figure 1 shows $\vec{v} = \begin{bmatrix} 1 \\ 2 \end{bmatrix}$ and "T of $\vec{v}$" which is written $T(\vec{v})$. Here $T(\vec{v}) = \vec{v}$. T is the **identity transformation.**

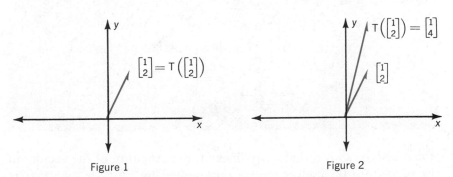

Figure 1 $\qquad\qquad\qquad\qquad$ Figure 2

EXAMPLE 2. Let T be the transformation defined by the rule: T pairs each vector $\vec{v} = \begin{bmatrix} x \\ y \end{bmatrix}$ with the vector $T(\vec{v}) = \begin{bmatrix} x \\ y^2 \end{bmatrix}$ when $\vec{v} = \begin{bmatrix} 1 \\ 2 \end{bmatrix}$, $T(\vec{v}) = \begin{bmatrix} 1 \\ 4 \end{bmatrix}$. (See Figure 2 above.) The original vector, $\vec{v}$, is the **pre-image** and the transformed vector $T(\vec{v})$ is the **image** of $\vec{v}$ under the transformation T.

EXAMPLE 3. Let a transformation T be defined by the following statement.

For all $\vec{v}$, $T(\vec{v}) = \vec{v} + \begin{bmatrix} 2 \\ 3 \end{bmatrix}$. For the vector $\begin{bmatrix} 1 \\ 2 \end{bmatrix}$, $T(\vec{v}) = \begin{bmatrix} 1 \\ 2 \end{bmatrix} + \begin{bmatrix} 2 \\ 3 \end{bmatrix} = \begin{bmatrix} 3 \\ 5 \end{bmatrix}$.

The vector $\vec{v}$ and its image are shown in Figure 3 below.

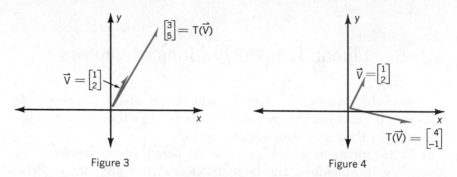

Figure 3   Figure 4

EXAMPLE 4. Define a transformation as follows: For all $\vec{v}$, $T(\vec{v}) = A\vec{v}$

where $A = \begin{bmatrix} 2 & 1 \\ -5 & 2 \end{bmatrix}$. For $\vec{v} = \begin{bmatrix} 1 \\ 2 \end{bmatrix}$, $T(\vec{v}) = \begin{bmatrix} 2 & 1 \\ -5 & 2 \end{bmatrix}\begin{bmatrix} 1 \\ 2 \end{bmatrix} = \begin{bmatrix} 4 \\ -1 \end{bmatrix}$.

This transformation (see Figure 4 above) is an example of a special kind of transformation called a **linear transformation.** It is defined by two properties.

> **Definition** A linear transformation on the set of vectors in two-space is a rule which pairs each vector $\vec{v} = \begin{bmatrix} x \\ y \end{bmatrix}$ with a vector $T(\vec{v})$ of two-space such that for all vectors, $\vec{v}_1$ and $\vec{v}_2$ in two-space and any real number k
>
> i. $T(\vec{v}_1 + \vec{v}_2) = T(\vec{v}_1) + T(\vec{v}_2)$
> ii. $T(k\vec{v}_1) = k \cdot T(\vec{v}_1)$.

It can also be shown that every linear transformation of the vectors in the plane into themselves can be represented by a two-by-two matrix and conversely. (The proof is omitted.) Thus the set M_2 of two-by-two matrices with real number entries can be thought of as the set of linear transformations of the vectors of the plane into themselves. The transformation is carried out by multiplying the vector v_1 by the matrix A in M_2. You can partially convince yourself of the validity of the statements made above by referring to Theorem 10–9 and to Exercise 38 in Section 10–4.

EXAMPLE 5. Verify for the transformation defined by matrix $A = \begin{bmatrix} 1 & 2 \\ 0 & 1 \end{bmatrix}$ that

$$\text{i. } A(\vec{v}_1 + \vec{v}_2) = A\vec{v}_1 + A\vec{v}_2$$
$$\text{ii. } A(k\vec{v}_1) = k(A\vec{v}_1)$$

Let $\vec{v}_1 = \begin{bmatrix} x_1 \\ y_1 \end{bmatrix}$, $\vec{v}_2 = \begin{bmatrix} x_2 \\ y_2 \end{bmatrix}$. Then

i. $A(\vec{v}_1 + \vec{v}_2) = \begin{bmatrix} 1 & 2 \\ 0 & 1 \end{bmatrix}\left(\begin{bmatrix} x_1 \\ y_2 \end{bmatrix} + \begin{bmatrix} x_2 \\ y_2 \end{bmatrix}\right) = \begin{bmatrix} 1 & 2 \\ 0 & 1 \end{bmatrix}\begin{bmatrix} x_1 + x_2 \\ y_1 + y_2 \end{bmatrix}$

$\qquad\qquad = \begin{bmatrix} x_1 + x_2 + 2y_1 + 2y_2 \\ y_1 + y_2 \end{bmatrix}$

$A\vec{v}_1 = \begin{bmatrix} 1 & 2 \\ 0 & 1 \end{bmatrix}\begin{bmatrix} x_1 \\ y_1 \end{bmatrix} = \begin{bmatrix} x_1 + 2y_1 \\ y_1 \end{bmatrix}$, $\quad A\vec{v}_2 = \begin{bmatrix} 1 & 2 \\ 0 & 1 \end{bmatrix}\begin{bmatrix} x_2 \\ y_2 \end{bmatrix} = \begin{bmatrix} x_2 + 2y_2 \\ y_2 \end{bmatrix}$

So $A\vec{v}_1 + A\vec{v}_2 = \begin{bmatrix} x_1 + 2y_1 + x_2 + 2y_2 \\ y_1 + y_2 \end{bmatrix} = \begin{bmatrix} x_1 + x_2 + 2y_1 + 2y_2 \\ y_1 + y_2 \end{bmatrix}$

$\qquad\qquad = A(\vec{v}_1 + \vec{v}_2)$

ii. $A(k\vec{v}_1) = \begin{bmatrix} 1 & 2 \\ 0 & 1 \end{bmatrix}\begin{bmatrix} kx_1 \\ ky_2 \end{bmatrix} = \begin{bmatrix} kx_1 + 2ky_1 \\ ky_1 \end{bmatrix} = k\begin{bmatrix} x_1 + 2y_1 \\ y_1 \end{bmatrix} = k(A\vec{v}_1)$

Often it is interesting to determine the effects of a linear transformation on a set of vectors. See Example 6 below.

EXAMPLE 6. Consider the set of vectors V such that $\vec{v} \in V$ if and only if $\vec{v} = \begin{bmatrix} x \\ y \end{bmatrix} = \begin{bmatrix} 1 + 2t \\ 2 + 3t \end{bmatrix}$, $t \in R$. Let $T = \begin{bmatrix} 1 & 2 \\ 0 & 1 \end{bmatrix}$ define a transformation of V. Find the image of V.

Notice first that the vectors in V are exactly those vectors whose tips are on the line

$$\begin{cases} x = 1 + 2t \\ y = 2 + 3t. \quad t \in R \end{cases}$$

This is the line containing $(1, 2)$ with slope $\frac{3}{2}$. This line is graphed at right. Now apply the transformation $T = \begin{bmatrix} 1 & 2 \\ 0 & 1 \end{bmatrix}$ to the vectors in V.

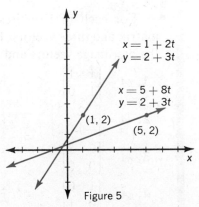

$x = 1 + 2t$
$y = 2 + 3t$

$x = 5 + 8t$
$y = 2 + 3t$

$(1, 2)$
$(5, 2)$

Figure 5

$$T(\vec{v}) = \begin{bmatrix} 1 & 2 \\ 0 & 1 \end{bmatrix}\begin{bmatrix} 1 + 2t \\ 2 + 3t \end{bmatrix} = \begin{bmatrix} 1 & 2 \\ 0 & 1 \end{bmatrix}\left(\begin{bmatrix} 1 \\ 2 \end{bmatrix} + \begin{bmatrix} 2t \\ 3t \end{bmatrix}\right) = \begin{bmatrix} 5 \\ 2 \end{bmatrix} + \begin{bmatrix} 8t \\ 3t \end{bmatrix} = \begin{bmatrix} 5 + 8t \\ 2 + 3t \end{bmatrix}$$

The image of the set of vectors V is the set of vectors $\vec{u} = \begin{bmatrix} 5 + 8t \\ 2 + 3t \end{bmatrix}$, $t \in R$.

This is the set of vectors with their tips on the line

$$\begin{cases} x = 5 + 8t \\ y = 2 + 3t \end{cases}$$

that is, the line containing $(5, 2)$ with slope $\frac{3}{8}$. This line is shown in color in Figure 5. This example demonstrates that the image of the given line is again a line under the transformation $\begin{bmatrix} 1 & 2 \\ 0 & 1 \end{bmatrix}$. Example 6 illustrates why these transformations are called linear transformations; they map lines into lines.

Now try these

— Let $A = \begin{bmatrix} 1 & 2 \\ 4 & 3 \end{bmatrix}$ and $\vec{v} = \begin{bmatrix} 3 \\ 1 \end{bmatrix}$. Find the following.

1. Determine the vector onto which A maps $\vec{v}$.

2. Determine the line onto which A maps the line containing $\vec{v}$. (Recall that $\vec{v}$ is a position vector.)

Answers: **1.** $\begin{bmatrix} 1 & 2 \\ 4 & 3 \end{bmatrix} \begin{bmatrix} 3 \\ 1 \end{bmatrix} = \begin{bmatrix} 5 \\ 15 \end{bmatrix}$ **2.** $y = 3x$

Checkpoint

In your own words define *linear transformation*.

Exercises

A — For each of Exercises 1–10 you are given a transformation matrix and three vectors. Find the image of each vector and sketch the pre-image vectors and the image vectors on a coordinate plane.

1. $A = \begin{bmatrix} 1 & 1 \\ 1 & 0 \end{bmatrix}$ $\vec{v}_1 = \begin{bmatrix} 2 \\ 1 \end{bmatrix}$ $\vec{v}_2 = \begin{bmatrix} -4 \\ 5 \end{bmatrix}$ $\vec{v}_3 = \begin{bmatrix} 3 \\ -7 \end{bmatrix}$

2. $A = \begin{bmatrix} 2 & 3 \\ -1 & 2 \end{bmatrix}$ $\vec{v}_1 = \begin{bmatrix} 1 \\ 1 \end{bmatrix}$ $\vec{v}_2 = \begin{bmatrix} 5 \\ -2 \end{bmatrix}$ $\vec{v}_3 = \begin{bmatrix} -2 \\ -3 \end{bmatrix}$

3. $A = \begin{bmatrix} 2 & 3 \\ 0 & 0 \end{bmatrix}$ $\vec{v}_1 = \begin{bmatrix} 0 \\ 1 \end{bmatrix}$ $\vec{v}_2 = \begin{bmatrix} -2 \\ 4 \end{bmatrix}$ $\vec{v}_3 = \begin{bmatrix} 4 \\ -1 \end{bmatrix}$

4. $A = \begin{bmatrix} 1 & 0 \\ 0 & 1 \end{bmatrix}$ $\vec{v}_1 = \begin{bmatrix} 4 \\ 7 \end{bmatrix}$ $\vec{v}_2 = \begin{bmatrix} -3 \\ -6 \end{bmatrix}$ $\vec{v}_3 = \begin{bmatrix} 1 \\ 0 \end{bmatrix}$

5. $A = \begin{bmatrix} -1 & 0 \\ 0 & 1 \end{bmatrix}$ $\vec{v}_1 = \begin{bmatrix} 1 \\ 2 \end{bmatrix}$ $\vec{v}_2 = \begin{bmatrix} 2 \\ 4 \end{bmatrix}$ $\vec{v}_3 = \begin{bmatrix} -3 \\ -6 \end{bmatrix}$

6. $A = \begin{bmatrix} -1 & 0 \\ 0 & -1 \end{bmatrix}$ $\quad \vec{v}_1 = \begin{bmatrix} 5 \\ 2 \end{bmatrix}$ $\quad \vec{v}_2 = \begin{bmatrix} -3 \\ 1 \end{bmatrix}$ $\quad \vec{v}_3 = \begin{bmatrix} 0 \\ -8 \end{bmatrix}$

7. $A = \begin{bmatrix} 0 & 0 \\ 0 & 0 \end{bmatrix}$ $\quad \vec{v}_1 = \begin{bmatrix} 1 \\ 1 \end{bmatrix}$ $\quad \vec{v}_2 = \begin{bmatrix} 100 \\ 2 \end{bmatrix}$ $\quad \vec{v}_3 = \begin{bmatrix} x \\ y \end{bmatrix}$

8. $A = \begin{bmatrix} 0 & -1 \\ -1 & 0 \end{bmatrix}$ $\quad \vec{v}_1 = \begin{bmatrix} -3 \\ 1 \end{bmatrix}$ $\quad \vec{v}_2 = \begin{bmatrix} 1 \\ -5 \end{bmatrix}$ $\quad \vec{v}_3 = \begin{bmatrix} 3 \\ 4 \end{bmatrix}$

9. $A = \begin{bmatrix} 4 & -2 \\ -2 & 1 \end{bmatrix}$ $\quad \vec{v}_1 = \begin{bmatrix} 4 \\ 7 \end{bmatrix}$ $\quad \vec{v}_2 = \begin{bmatrix} 2 \\ -3 \end{bmatrix}$ $\quad \vec{v}_3 = \begin{bmatrix} -1 \\ -3 \end{bmatrix}$

10. $A = \begin{bmatrix} 0 & 1 \\ 0 & 3 \end{bmatrix}$ $\quad \vec{v}_1 = \begin{bmatrix} 4 \\ 2 \end{bmatrix}$ $\quad \vec{v}_2 = \begin{bmatrix} -1 \\ 5 \end{bmatrix}$ $\quad \vec{v}_3 = \begin{bmatrix} 6 \\ -8 \end{bmatrix}$

11. Prove that under any linear transformation the image of $\begin{bmatrix} 0 \\ 0 \end{bmatrix}$ is itself.

12. Show that under a linear transformation with matrix $\begin{bmatrix} a & b \\ 0 & 0 \end{bmatrix}$, a or $b \neq 0$, every vector in two-space maps onto a vector on the x axis.

13. Show that under a linear transformation with matrix $\begin{bmatrix} 0 & 0 \\ a & b \end{bmatrix}$, a or $b \neq 0$, every vector in two-space maps onto a vector on the y axis.

14. Show that every vector in the plane maps onto a vector on the line through the origin with slope $-\frac{1}{2}$ when the transformation is
$$\begin{bmatrix} 4 & -2 \\ -2 & 1 \end{bmatrix}.$$

B **15.** Find the image of the line $\begin{cases} x = 2 - 3t \\ y = 1 + 2t \end{cases}$

under the transformation $\begin{bmatrix} 2 & 3 \\ 1 & 1 \end{bmatrix}$. Graph the pre-image and image.

16. Repeat Exercise 15 for line $\begin{cases} x = -3 + t \\ y = 0 + 3t \end{cases}$

and transformation $\begin{bmatrix} 0 & -1 \\ 1 & 0 \end{bmatrix}$.

17. Repeat Exercise 15 for line $\begin{cases} x = 7t \\ y = 3t \end{cases}$

and transformation $\begin{bmatrix} 0 & 1 \\ -1 & 0 \end{bmatrix}$.

18. Repeat Exercise 15 for line $\begin{cases} x = 1 - 2t \\ y = 2 + t \end{cases}$

and transformation $\begin{bmatrix} 1 & 0 \\ 0 & -1 \end{bmatrix}$.

19. Find the image of the triangle with vertices $A = \begin{bmatrix} 2 \\ 4 \end{bmatrix}$, $B = \begin{bmatrix} 2 \\ 1 \end{bmatrix}$,

$C = \begin{bmatrix} -1 \\ 1 \end{bmatrix}$ under

    a. $\begin{bmatrix} 1 & 0 \\ 0 & -1 \end{bmatrix}$ **b.** $\begin{bmatrix} -1 & 0 \\ 0 & 1 \end{bmatrix}$

    c. $\begin{bmatrix} 4 & 2 \\ -3 & 1 \end{bmatrix}$ **d.** $\begin{bmatrix} 1 & 5 \\ 0 & 1 \end{bmatrix}$

Graph each pre-image and image.

C   **20.** Prove: If A is an invertible matrix in M_2 and V is the set of all vectors in two-space, then

    i. the image of V is V.

    ii. the transformation A is one-to-one.

21. Prove: If A is an invertible matrix and L is a line:

$$\begin{cases} x = a + lt \\ y = b + mt \end{cases}$$

Then the image of L under the linear transformation represented by A is a line.

22. Prove that the transformation which maps each vector $\begin{bmatrix} x \\ y \end{bmatrix}$ into the vector $\begin{bmatrix} x + 2 \\ y + 3 \end{bmatrix}$ is not a linear transformation. (*Hint:* Show that at least one of the conditions **i** or **ii** of the definition is not satisfied.)

10–7   Special Linear Transformations

There are several linear transformations of a set of vectors which are of particular importance. They also happen to be examples of linear transformations which have easy and useful geometric interpretations.

Consider the linear transformation whose matrix is

$$\begin{bmatrix} 1 & 0 \\ 0 & -1 \end{bmatrix} = A.$$

Notice that det $A = -1$. Thus A is an invertible matrix and maps the set of all vectors in the plane onto themselves in a one-to-one manner. (See Exercise 20, Section 10–6.)

Think now of a vector $\vec{v} = \begin{bmatrix} x \\ y \end{bmatrix}$ and find its image under A; that is, find $A\vec{v}$.

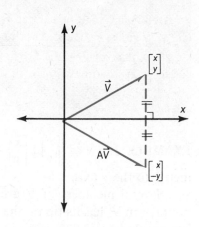

$$A\vec{v} = \begin{bmatrix} 1 & 0 \\ 0 & -1 \end{bmatrix}\begin{bmatrix} x \\ y \end{bmatrix} = \begin{bmatrix} x \\ -y \end{bmatrix}$$

$\vec{v}$ and $A\vec{v}$ are shown at the right. Notice that the line determined by the tips of $\vec{v}$ and $A\vec{v}$ is perpendicular to the x axis. Also each point is the same distance from the x axis. Thus $\vec{v}$ and $A\vec{v}$ are *mirror images* or *reflections* of each other with respect to the x axis. Since $\vec{v}$ is an arbitrary vector each vector has the same property except those of the form $\begin{bmatrix} x \\ 0 \end{bmatrix}$. These latter vectors are their own images. (Why?)

Summarizing this discussion you find the following.

a. Under the linear transformation $\begin{bmatrix} 1 & 0 \\ 0 & -1 \end{bmatrix}$ each image vector $\begin{bmatrix} x \\ -y \end{bmatrix}$, $y \neq 0$ is the reflection with respect to the x axis of its pre-image.

b. Vectors $\vec{v} = \begin{bmatrix} x \\ 0 \end{bmatrix}$ are their own images.

The linear transformation $\begin{bmatrix} 1 & 0 \\ 0 & -1 \end{bmatrix}$ is denoted $r_{x \text{ axis}}$ and is called the *reflection with respect to the x axis.*

By a similar argument you can show that $\begin{bmatrix} x \\ y \end{bmatrix}$, $x \neq 0$ is mapped onto $\begin{bmatrix} -x \\ y \end{bmatrix}$ by $\begin{bmatrix} -1 & 0 \\ 0 & 1 \end{bmatrix}$ and $\begin{bmatrix} 0 \\ y \end{bmatrix}$ is mapped by $\begin{bmatrix} -1 & 0 \\ 0 & 1 \end{bmatrix}$ onto itself for all y. $\begin{bmatrix} -1 & 0 \\ 0 & 1 \end{bmatrix}$ is denoted

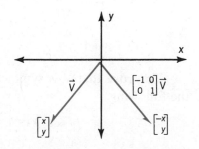

$r_{y \text{ axis}}$ and is called the *reflection with respect to the y axis.* An example is shown at the right.

The linear transformations $r_{x \text{ axis}}$ and $r_{y \text{ axis}}$ provide a natural way to define symmetry with respect to the x axis and the y axis. The formal definition follows.

EXAMPLE 1. $V = \left\{ \begin{bmatrix} x \\ y \end{bmatrix} : \begin{bmatrix} x \\ y \end{bmatrix} = \begin{bmatrix} t \\ t^2 \end{bmatrix}, t \in R \right\}$. Show that V is symmetric to the _y_ axis.

Several members of V are shown in Figure 1. Notice that each vector, $\vec{v}$ in V, has its tip on the graph with equation $x = t, y = t^2$. This is a parabola.

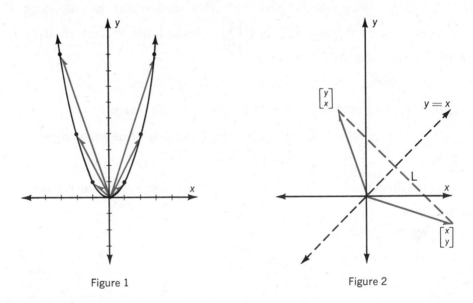

Figure 1   Figure 2

To prove that V is symmetric with respect to the _y_ axis, compute the following.

$$r_{y \text{ axis}} \cdot \vec{v} = \begin{bmatrix} -1 & 0 \\ 0 & 1 \end{bmatrix} \begin{bmatrix} t \\ t^2 \end{bmatrix}$$

$$= \begin{bmatrix} -t \\ t^2 \end{bmatrix}$$

$$= \begin{bmatrix} -t \\ (-t)^2 \end{bmatrix} \quad \text{since } t^2 = (-t)^2$$

Thus the image of each $\vec{v} \in V$ is in V and V is symmetric with respect to the _y_ axis.

The matrix $\begin{bmatrix} 0 & 1 \\ 1 & 0 \end{bmatrix}$ is another important linear transformation. If $\begin{bmatrix} x \\ y \end{bmatrix}$ is any vector, then

$$\begin{bmatrix} 0 & 1 \\ 1 & 0 \end{bmatrix}\begin{bmatrix} x \\ y \end{bmatrix} = \begin{bmatrix} y \\ x \end{bmatrix}.$$

(See Figure 2.) Considering the line L determined by the tips of the vectors $\begin{bmatrix} x \\ y \end{bmatrix}$ and $\begin{bmatrix} y \\ x \end{bmatrix}$ you see that the slope is $\frac{x-y}{y-x} = -1$. Thus L is perpendicular to the line $y = x$. Moreover the midpoint of the vector from $\begin{bmatrix} x \\ y \end{bmatrix}$ to $\begin{bmatrix} y \\ x \end{bmatrix}$ is $\left(\frac{x+y}{2}, \frac{y+x}{2}\right)$. Thus the midpoint of L is on the line $y = x$ and the line $y = x$ is the perpendicular bisector of the segment determined by $\begin{bmatrix} x \\ y \end{bmatrix}$ and its image $\begin{bmatrix} y \\ x \end{bmatrix}$. The vectors are mirror images of each other with respect to the line $y = x$.

The linear transformation $\begin{bmatrix} 0 & 1 \\ 1 & 0 \end{bmatrix}$ is denoted $r_{y=x}$ and is called the *reflection with respect to $y = x$.*

Using a similar argument you can show that the *reflection with respect to $y = -x$* is given by the matrix

$$\begin{bmatrix} 0 & -1 \\ -1 & 0 \end{bmatrix}.$$

This transformation is denoted

$$r_{y=-x}.$$

The image of $\begin{bmatrix} x \\ y \end{bmatrix}$ under $r_{y=-x}$ is $\begin{bmatrix} -y \\ -x \end{bmatrix}$. This is shown in Figure 3 below.

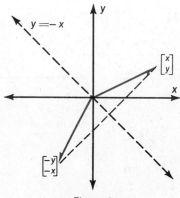

Figure 3

EXAMPLE 2. Show that the set of vectors

$$V = \left\{ \begin{bmatrix} x \\ y \end{bmatrix} : \begin{bmatrix} x \\ y \end{bmatrix} = \begin{bmatrix} t \\ \frac{1}{t} \end{bmatrix}, \; t \in R, \quad t \neq 0 \right\}$$

is symmetric with respect to $y = x$.

Several of the vectors in V are shown in Figure 4. For this set to be symmetric with respect to the line $y = x$, the image vector must be in V. Let

$$\vec{v} = \begin{bmatrix} t \\ \frac{1}{t} \end{bmatrix}.$$

Then,

$$r_{y=x}\vec{v} = \begin{bmatrix} 0 & 1 \\ 1 & 0 \end{bmatrix} \begin{bmatrix} t \\ \frac{1}{t} \end{bmatrix} = \begin{bmatrix} \frac{1}{t} \\ t \end{bmatrix}$$

Since $t \neq 0$, $\frac{1}{t}$ is a real number and $t = \dfrac{1}{\frac{1}{t}}$.

Thus

$$\begin{bmatrix} \frac{1}{t} \\ t \end{bmatrix} = \begin{bmatrix} \frac{1}{t} \\ \frac{1}{\frac{1}{t}} \end{bmatrix}$$

and therefore is in V. Thus V is symmetric with respect to the line $y = x$. Is V symmetric with respect to the line $y = -x$?

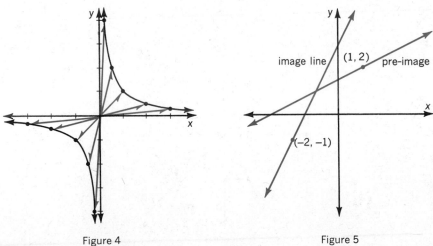

Figure 4   Figure 5

514   CHAPTER 10

EXAMPLE 3. Find the image of the set of vectors

$$V = \left\{ \begin{bmatrix} x \\ y \end{bmatrix} : \begin{bmatrix} x \\ y \end{bmatrix} = \begin{bmatrix} 1 + 2t \\ 2 + t \end{bmatrix}, \ t \in R \right\}$$

under $r_{y=-x}$. Graph the pre-image and image.

V is the set of vectors with tips on the line

$$x = 1 + 2t$$
$$y = 2 + t \quad t \in R.$$

This is the line which contains $(1, 2)$ and has slope $\frac{1}{2}$. (Why?) (See Figure 5.)

The image set is

$$\begin{bmatrix} 0 & -1 \\ -1 & 0 \end{bmatrix} \begin{bmatrix} 1 + 2t \\ 2 + t \end{bmatrix} = \begin{bmatrix} -2 - t \\ -1 - 2t \end{bmatrix}.$$

The image vectors thus have their tips on

$$\begin{cases} x = -2 - t \\ y = -1 - 2t \end{cases}$$

or the line containing $(-2, -1)$ with slope 2. The lines are shown in Figure 5. Show that their intersection is the point $(-1, 1)$.

Checkpoint

Using linear transformations define, in your own words, symmetry with respect to the x and y axes and symmetry with respect to the lines $y = x$ and $y = -x$.

Exercises

A ▬ Match each transformation with the appropriate matrix.

1. $r_{x \text{ axis}}$ **2.** $r_{y=x}$

3. $r_{y \text{ axis}}$ **4.** $r_{y=-x}$

a. $\begin{bmatrix} 1 & 0 \\ 0 & -1 \end{bmatrix}$ **b.** $\begin{bmatrix} 1 & 0 \\ 0 & 1 \end{bmatrix}$

c. $\begin{bmatrix} 0 & -1 \\ -1 & 0 \end{bmatrix}$ **d.** $\begin{bmatrix} -1 & 0 \\ 0 & -1 \end{bmatrix}$

e. $\begin{bmatrix} -1 & 0 \\ 0 & 1 \end{bmatrix}$ **f.** $\begin{bmatrix} 0 & 1 \\ 1 & 0 \end{bmatrix}$

Match each transformation with the appropriate image of $\begin{bmatrix} r \\ s \end{bmatrix}$.

5. $r_{x \text{ axis}}$ **6.** $r_{y \text{ axis}}$

7. $r_{y=x}$ **8.** $r_{y=-x}$

a. $\begin{bmatrix} r \\ -s \end{bmatrix}$ **b.** $\begin{bmatrix} r \\ s \end{bmatrix}$

c. $\begin{bmatrix} -s \\ -r \end{bmatrix}$ **d.** $\begin{bmatrix} -r \\ -s \end{bmatrix}$

e. $\begin{bmatrix} -r \\ s \end{bmatrix}$ **f.** $\begin{bmatrix} s \\ r \end{bmatrix}$

Given the vectors $\begin{bmatrix} 3 \\ 1 \end{bmatrix}$, $\begin{bmatrix} -4 \\ 2 \end{bmatrix}$, $\begin{bmatrix} -1 \\ -3 \end{bmatrix}$, and $\begin{bmatrix} 3 \\ -4 \end{bmatrix}$. Make a graph of these vectors and their images under each of the following.

9. $r_{x \text{ axis}}$ **10.** $r_{y \text{ axis}}$

11. $r_{y=-x}$ **12.** $r_{y=x}$

Given a triangle with vertices at (2, 1), (3, 5), (7, 3). Make a graph of the triangle and its image under each of the following.

13. $r_{x \text{ axis}}$ **14.** $r_{y \text{ axis}}$

15. $r_{y=x}$ **16.** $r_{y=-x}$

17. Find the inverse of $r_{x \text{ axis}}$, $r_{y \text{ axis}}$, $r_{y=x}$, and $r_{y=-x}$. What do you notice?

In Exercises 18–21, determine the line with respect to which the set V is symmetric.

18. $V = \left\{ \begin{bmatrix} 2 \\ 1 \end{bmatrix}, \begin{bmatrix} -3 \\ 2 \end{bmatrix}, \begin{bmatrix} 2 \\ -1 \end{bmatrix}, \begin{bmatrix} 4 \\ 0 \end{bmatrix}, \begin{bmatrix} -3 \\ -2 \end{bmatrix} \right\}$

19. $V = \left\{ \begin{bmatrix} 2 \\ 1 \end{bmatrix}, \begin{bmatrix} 2 \\ 2 \end{bmatrix}, \begin{bmatrix} -3 \\ 2 \end{bmatrix}, \begin{bmatrix} 2 \\ -3 \end{bmatrix}, \begin{bmatrix} 1 \\ 2 \end{bmatrix} \right\}$

20. $V = \left\{ \begin{bmatrix} 2 \\ 1 \end{bmatrix}, \begin{bmatrix} 0 \\ 3 \end{bmatrix}, \begin{bmatrix} -3 \\ -2 \end{bmatrix}, \begin{bmatrix} -2 \\ 1 \end{bmatrix}, \begin{bmatrix} 3 \\ -2 \end{bmatrix} \right\}$

21. $V = \left\{ \begin{bmatrix} 2 \\ 1 \end{bmatrix}, \begin{bmatrix} 3 \\ -3 \end{bmatrix}, \begin{bmatrix} -5 \\ 5 \end{bmatrix}, \begin{bmatrix} -1 \\ -2 \end{bmatrix} \right\}$

B In Exercises 22–34, determine the line(s) with respect to which each set is symmetric.

22. $V = \left\{ \begin{bmatrix} x \\ y \end{bmatrix} : \begin{bmatrix} x \\ y \end{bmatrix} = \begin{bmatrix} t \\ |t| \end{bmatrix}, t \in R \right\}$

23. $V = \left\{ \begin{bmatrix} x \\ y \end{bmatrix} : \begin{bmatrix} x \\ y \end{bmatrix} = \begin{bmatrix} t \\ |t| - 3 \end{bmatrix}, t \in R \right\}$

24. $V = \left\{ \begin{bmatrix} x \\ y \end{bmatrix} : \begin{bmatrix} x \\ y \end{bmatrix} = \begin{bmatrix} t \\ -\frac{1}{t} \end{bmatrix}, t \in R, t \neq 0 \right\}$

25. $V = \left\{ \begin{bmatrix} x \\ y \end{bmatrix} : \begin{bmatrix} x \\ y \end{bmatrix} = \begin{bmatrix} t^2 \\ t \end{bmatrix}, t \in R \right\}$

26. $V = \left\{ \begin{bmatrix} x \\ y \end{bmatrix} : \begin{bmatrix} x \\ y \end{bmatrix} = \begin{bmatrix} t \\ t^2 + t^4 \end{bmatrix}, t \in R \right\}$

27. $V = \left\{ \begin{bmatrix} x \\ y \end{bmatrix} : \begin{bmatrix} x \\ y \end{bmatrix} = \begin{bmatrix} t \\ \pm\sqrt{4 - t^2} \end{bmatrix}, t \in R, -2 \leq t \leq 2 \right\}$

28. $V = \left\{ \begin{bmatrix} x \\ y \end{bmatrix} : \begin{bmatrix} x \\ y \end{bmatrix} = \begin{bmatrix} |t| \\ t \end{bmatrix}, t \in R \right\}$

29. $V = \left\{ \begin{bmatrix} x \\ y \end{bmatrix} : \begin{bmatrix} x \\ y \end{bmatrix} = \begin{bmatrix} t \\ \pm 2\sqrt{1 - t^2} \end{bmatrix}, -1 \leq t \leq 1, t \in R \right\}$

30. $V = \left\{ \begin{bmatrix} x \\ y \end{bmatrix} : \begin{bmatrix} x \\ y \end{bmatrix} = \begin{bmatrix} t \\ t \end{bmatrix}, t \in R \right\}$

31. $V = \left\{ \begin{bmatrix} x \\ y \end{bmatrix} : \begin{bmatrix} x \\ y \end{bmatrix} = \begin{bmatrix} t \\ t^2 + 1 \end{bmatrix}, t \in R \right\}$

32. $V = \left\{ \begin{bmatrix} x \\ y \end{bmatrix} : \begin{bmatrix} x \\ y \end{bmatrix} = \begin{bmatrix} t^2 + 2 \\ t \end{bmatrix}, t \in R \right\}$

33. $V = \left\{ \begin{bmatrix} x \\ y \end{bmatrix} : \begin{bmatrix} x \\ y \end{bmatrix} = \begin{bmatrix} t\sqrt{25 - t^2} \\ t \end{bmatrix}, t \in R \right\}$

34. $V = \left\{ \begin{bmatrix} x \\ y \end{bmatrix} : \begin{bmatrix} x \\ y \end{bmatrix} = \begin{bmatrix} t\sqrt{16 - 2t^2} \\ t \end{bmatrix}, t \in R \right\}$

C **35.** Prove that the four reflections

$$r_{x\,axis}, \qquad r_{y\,axis}, \qquad r_{y=x}, \qquad \text{and} \qquad r_{y=-x}$$

preserve distance between points.

36. Prove that the four reflections

$$r_{x\,axis}, \qquad r_{y\,axis}, \qquad r_{y=x}, \qquad \text{and} \qquad r_{y=-x}$$

preserve the measure of angles between vectors.

37. Under each of the following find the image of the line

$$\begin{cases} x = 1 - 3t \\ y = 2 + t \,. \end{cases}$$

   a. $r_{x=y}$ **b.** $r_{x\,axis}$

   c. $r_{y\,axis}$ **d.** $r_{y=-x}$

Graph each image and pre-image. Find the point of intersection.

38. What line(s) is its own image under

   a. $r_{y\,axis}$ **b.** $r_{x\,axis}$

   c. $r_{y=x}$ **d.** $r_{y=-x}$

10–8   Rotations about the Origin

In Figure 1, vector $\vec{v}$ has been rotated 75° counterclockwise about the origin. The image vector is in color. The purpose of this section is to find a matrix representation of a rotation about the origin.

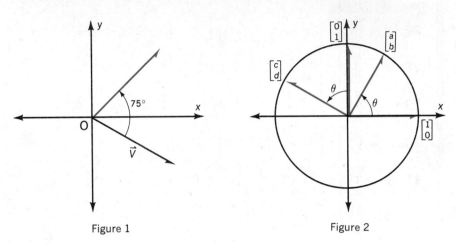

Figure 1   Figure 2

Every vector may be expressed as

$$\vec{v} = a\mathbf{i} + b\mathbf{j},$$

where $\mathbf{i} = \begin{bmatrix} 1 \\ 0 \end{bmatrix}$ and $\mathbf{j} = \begin{bmatrix} 0 \\ 1 \end{bmatrix}$. If a vector is rotated about the origin, then its image is determined by finding the images of $\begin{bmatrix} 1 \\ 0 \end{bmatrix}$ and $\begin{bmatrix} 0 \\ 1 \end{bmatrix}$ under the same rotation. This idea is used to determine the rotation matrix.

Consider the vectors $\begin{bmatrix} 1 \\ 0 \end{bmatrix}$ and $\begin{bmatrix} 0 \\ 1 \end{bmatrix}$. Let each be rotated $\theta°$ counterclockwise to the new positions $\begin{bmatrix} a \\ b \end{bmatrix}$ and $\begin{bmatrix} c \\ d \end{bmatrix}$ as shown in Figure 2. Each of these vectors has its tip on the unit circle with center at the origin. Thus the coordinates of $\begin{bmatrix} a \\ b \end{bmatrix}$ may be expressed in terms of the sine and cosine of θ.

$$a = \cos \theta$$
$$b = \sin \theta \qquad\qquad 1$$

Similarly, the coordinates of $\begin{bmatrix} c \\ d \end{bmatrix}$ are

$$c = \cos (90° + \theta) = -\sin \theta$$
$$d = \sin (90° + \theta) = \cos \theta. \qquad\qquad 2$$

518   CHAPTER 10

The equations **1** and **2** together imply that if $\begin{bmatrix} p & q \\ r & s \end{bmatrix}$ is a matrix for a rotation of θ,

then

$$\begin{bmatrix} p & q \\ r & s \end{bmatrix}\begin{bmatrix} 1 \\ 0 \end{bmatrix} = \begin{bmatrix} \cos \theta \\ \sin \theta \end{bmatrix}$$

and

$$\begin{bmatrix} p & q \\ r & s \end{bmatrix}\begin{bmatrix} 0 \\ 1 \end{bmatrix} = \begin{bmatrix} -\sin \theta \\ \cos \theta \end{bmatrix}$$

or

$$\begin{bmatrix} p \\ r \end{bmatrix} = \begin{bmatrix} \cos \theta \\ \sin \theta \end{bmatrix} \quad \text{and} \quad \begin{bmatrix} q \\ s \end{bmatrix} = \begin{bmatrix} -\sin \theta \\ \cos \theta \end{bmatrix}.$$

From the above it is clear that

$$p = \cos \theta$$
$$q = -\sin \theta$$
$$r = \sin \theta$$
$$s = \cos \theta$$

Thus

$$\begin{bmatrix} p & q \\ r & s \end{bmatrix} = \begin{bmatrix} \cos \theta & -\sin \theta \\ \sin \theta & \cos \theta \end{bmatrix}$$

The matrix $\begin{bmatrix} \cos \theta & -\sin \theta \\ \sin \theta & \cos \theta \end{bmatrix}$ is the linear transformation called the **rotation of θ** about the origin. This transformation is denoted R_θ.

EXAMPLE 1. Find the image of $\begin{bmatrix} 2 \\ 3 \end{bmatrix}$ under R_{135}. Make a sketch showing the two vectors.

$$R_{135} = \begin{bmatrix} \cos 135 & -\sin 135 \\ \sin 135 & \cos 135 \end{bmatrix}$$

$$= \begin{bmatrix} \dfrac{-\sqrt{2}}{2} & \dfrac{-\sqrt{2}}{2} \\ \dfrac{\sqrt{2}}{2} & \dfrac{-\sqrt{2}}{2} \end{bmatrix}$$

$$= \dfrac{\sqrt{2}}{2}\begin{bmatrix} -1 & -1 \\ 1 & -1 \end{bmatrix}.$$

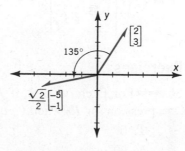

Thus,

$$R_{135} \cdot \begin{bmatrix} 2 \\ 3 \end{bmatrix} = \dfrac{\sqrt{2}}{2}\begin{bmatrix} -1 & -1 \\ 1 & -1 \end{bmatrix}\begin{bmatrix} 2 \\ 3 \end{bmatrix}$$

$$= \dfrac{\sqrt{2}}{2}\begin{bmatrix} -5 \\ -1 \end{bmatrix}$$

EXAMPLE 2. Find the image of the line $\begin{cases} x = 1 + 2t \\ y = 2 + t, \end{cases}$ $t \in R$

under R_{270}. Graph the pre-image and image.

The given line contains $(1, 2)$ and has slope $\frac{1}{2}$. The image is found by multiplying R_{270} by $\begin{bmatrix} 1 + 2t \\ 2 + t \end{bmatrix}$:

$$R_{270} \cdot \begin{bmatrix} 1 + 2t \\ 2 + t \end{bmatrix}$$

$$= \begin{bmatrix} \cos 270 & -\sin 270 \\ \sin 270 & \cos 270 \end{bmatrix}\begin{bmatrix} 1 + 2t \\ 2 + t \end{bmatrix}$$

$$= \begin{bmatrix} 0 & 1 \\ -1 & 0 \end{bmatrix}\begin{bmatrix} 1 + 2t \\ 2 + t \end{bmatrix}$$

$$= \begin{bmatrix} 2 + t \\ -1 - 2t \end{bmatrix}$$

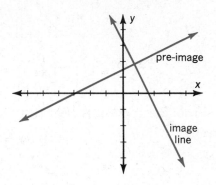

The image line is $\begin{cases} x = 2 + t \\ y = -1 - 2t \end{cases}$.

This line contains $(2, -1)$ and has slope -2. Where do the lines intersect?

Now try these

━ Find the image of $\begin{bmatrix} 3 \\ -2 \end{bmatrix}$ under the following.

1. R_{120} **2.** R_{45}

Answers: **1.** $\begin{bmatrix} \dfrac{-3}{2} + \sqrt{3} \\ \dfrac{3\sqrt{3}}{2} + 1 \end{bmatrix}$ **2.** $\begin{bmatrix} \dfrac{5\sqrt{2}}{2} \\ \dfrac{\sqrt{2}}{2} \end{bmatrix}$

Exercises

A ━ For Exercises 1–8, if $R_\theta = \begin{bmatrix} \cos \theta & -\sin \theta \\ \sin \theta & \cos \theta \end{bmatrix}$ find the explicit expression for R_θ when θ equals

   1. $0°$ **2.** $45°$

   3. $90°$ **4.** $180°$

   5. $270°$ **6.** $30°$

   7. $60°$ **8.** $54°$

   9. Show that $R_{90°} = R_{-270°}$.

   10. Show that $R_\theta = R_{\theta - 360°}$.

In Exercises 11–18, find the image of each vector under **a.** $R_{90°}$, **b.** $R_{180°}$, **c.** $R_{270°}$, **d.** $R_{45°}$. (Use the results of Exercises 2, 3, 4, 5.)

11. $\begin{bmatrix} 2 \\ -3 \end{bmatrix}$ **12.** $\begin{bmatrix} \sqrt{2} \\ -\sqrt{2} \end{bmatrix}$ **13.** $\begin{bmatrix} -3 \\ -4 \end{bmatrix}$ **14.** $\begin{bmatrix} 4 \\ 5 \end{bmatrix}$

15. $\begin{bmatrix} 0 \\ 4 \end{bmatrix}$ **16.** $\begin{bmatrix} -2 \\ 1 \end{bmatrix}$ **17.** $\begin{bmatrix} 4 \\ 1 \end{bmatrix}$ **18.** $\begin{bmatrix} 5 \\ 0 \end{bmatrix}$

Find the image of the triangle with vertices $(2, 7)$, $(4, 1)$, $(6, 3)$ under each rotation. Graph the pre-image and image.

19. $R_{90°}$ **20.** $R_{45°}$

21. $R_{180°}$ **22.** $R_{270°}$ **23.** $R_{30°}$

In Exercises 24–27, find the image of each line under the rotations in Exercises 19–23. Make a graph of each.

24. $\begin{cases} x = -3 + 2t \\ y = 0 - t \end{cases}$ **25.** $\begin{cases} x = 1 - 3t \\ y = 2 + 3t \end{cases}$

26. $\begin{cases} x = 1 + \frac{1}{2}t \\ y = -2 - 2t \end{cases}$ **27.** $\begin{cases} x = -3 - 2t \\ y = -2 + 5t \end{cases}$

B **28.** Show that the length of the vector $\begin{bmatrix} x \\ y \end{bmatrix}$ is identical to that of $R_\theta \begin{bmatrix} x \\ y \end{bmatrix}$. (*Hint:* $\sin^2 \theta + \cos^2 \theta = 1$)

29. Show that the angle between the vectors $\begin{bmatrix} a \\ b \end{bmatrix}$ and $\begin{bmatrix} c \\ d \end{bmatrix}$ is the same as the angle between $R_\theta \cdot \begin{bmatrix} a \\ b \end{bmatrix}$ and $R_\theta \cdot \begin{bmatrix} c \\ d \end{bmatrix}$. (*Hint:* Use the results of Exercise 28 and the hint given there.)

30. Show that every vector on the line $\begin{cases} x = t \\ y = nt \end{cases}$ $t \in R$ has an image on the same line under $R_{180°}$.

C **31.** The rotation R_{180} is a *half turn*. A set of vectors is called symmetric to the origin if and only if the image of every vector under R_{180} is in the original set. For example $\left\{ \begin{bmatrix} 1 \\ 2 \end{bmatrix}, \begin{bmatrix} -1 \\ -2 \end{bmatrix} \right\}$ is symmetric to the origin because $R_{180} \cdot \begin{bmatrix} 1 \\ 2 \end{bmatrix} = \begin{bmatrix} -1 \\ -2 \end{bmatrix}$ and $R_{180} \cdot \begin{bmatrix} -1 \\ -2 \end{bmatrix} = \begin{bmatrix} 1 \\ 2 \end{bmatrix}$. Show that each set below is symmetric to the origin.

a. $V = \left\{ \begin{bmatrix} x \\ y \end{bmatrix} : \begin{bmatrix} x \\ y \end{bmatrix} = \begin{bmatrix} t \\ t^3 \end{bmatrix}, t \in R \right\}$

b. $V = \left\{ \begin{bmatrix} x \\ y \end{bmatrix} : \begin{bmatrix} x \\ y \end{bmatrix} = \begin{bmatrix} t \\ \frac{1}{t} \end{bmatrix}, t \neq 0, t \in R \right\}$

c. $V = \left\{ \begin{bmatrix} x \\ y \end{bmatrix} : \begin{bmatrix} x \\ y \end{bmatrix} = \begin{bmatrix} t \\ \pm\sqrt{4 - t^2} \end{bmatrix}, -2 \leq t \leq 2, t \in R \right\}$

MATRICES, VECTORS, AND LINEAR TRANSFORMATIONS   521

10–9 Compositions of Linear Transformations

In the figure, vector $\begin{bmatrix} 2 \\ -1 \end{bmatrix}$ is shown. The linear transformation $\begin{bmatrix} 1 & 1 \\ 2 & 1 \end{bmatrix}$ is applied to $\begin{bmatrix} 2 \\ -1 \end{bmatrix}$ yielding

$$\begin{bmatrix} 1 & 1 \\ 2 & 1 \end{bmatrix}\begin{bmatrix} 2 \\ -1 \end{bmatrix} = \begin{bmatrix} 1 \\ 3 \end{bmatrix}.$$ Then the linear transformation $\begin{bmatrix} 0 & -1 \\ 1 & 0 \end{bmatrix}$ is applied to $\begin{bmatrix} 1 \\ 3 \end{bmatrix}$ yielding

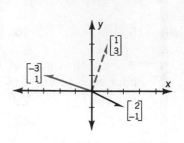

$$\begin{bmatrix} 0 & -1 \\ 1 & 0 \end{bmatrix}\begin{bmatrix} 1 \\ 3 \end{bmatrix} = \begin{bmatrix} -3 \\ 1 \end{bmatrix}.$$

The latter two vectors are shown in color in the figure.

The operation of applying one transformation to the vectors of a set, then applying a second transformation to the vectors in the image set is called **composing transformations.** If A_1 is the matrix of the first transformation and A_2 is the matrix of the second, then the composition of A_1 and A_2 applied to V is

$$A_2(A_1\vec{v}). \qquad\qquad 1$$

Since matrix multiplication is associative, the following is true.

$$A_2(A_1\vec{v}) = (A_2A_1)\vec{v} \qquad\qquad 2$$

(See Exercise 39, Section 10–4.) Thus the composition of two linear transformations may be accomplished by first computing the product A_2A_1 and then applying this transformation to $\vec{v}$.

A_1 and A_2 are two-by-two matrices, thus A_2A_1 is a two-by-two matrix. Therefore, the composite of two linear transformations is again a linear transformation. This argument proves the following theorem.

> **Theorem 10–12** If A_1 and A_2 are linear transformations then the composite of A_1 and A_2 is a linear transformation A and
>
> $$A_2(A_1\vec{v}) = (A_2A_1)\vec{v} = A\vec{v}$$
>
> for all $\vec{v}$.

EXAMPLE 1. Verify Theorem 10–12 for $A_1 = \begin{bmatrix} 1 & 2 \\ -3 & 4 \end{bmatrix}$, $A_2 = \begin{bmatrix} 1 & -2 \\ 1 & 3 \end{bmatrix}$ and $\vec{v} = \begin{bmatrix} -1 \\ 2 \end{bmatrix}$.

$$A_2(A_1\vec{v}) = \begin{bmatrix} 1 & -2 \\ 1 & 3 \end{bmatrix}\left(\begin{bmatrix} 1 & 2 \\ -3 & 4 \end{bmatrix}\begin{bmatrix} -1 \\ 2 \end{bmatrix}\right)$$

$$= \begin{bmatrix} 1 & -2 \\ 1 & 3 \end{bmatrix}\begin{bmatrix} 3 \\ 11 \end{bmatrix} = \begin{bmatrix} -19 \\ 36 \end{bmatrix}$$

$$(A_2A_1)\vec{v} = \left(\begin{bmatrix} 1 & -2 \\ 1 & 3 \end{bmatrix}\begin{bmatrix} 1 & 2 \\ -3 & 4 \end{bmatrix}\right)\begin{bmatrix} -1 \\ 2 \end{bmatrix}$$

$$= \begin{bmatrix} 7 & -6 \\ -8 & 14 \end{bmatrix}\begin{bmatrix} -1 \\ 2 \end{bmatrix} = \begin{bmatrix} -19 \\ 36 \end{bmatrix}$$

Thus $A_2(A_1\vec{v}) = (A_2A_1)\vec{v}$. Since the composite is representable by a 2 by 2 matrix, it is a linear transformation.

Composites of the special linear transformations introduced in Sections 10–7 and 10–8 are particularly interesting because of the patterns which occur. Consider initially the composite of two rotations about the origin, say $R_\phi R_\theta$.

$$R_\phi R_\theta = \begin{bmatrix} \cos\phi & -\sin\phi \\ \sin\phi & \cos\phi \end{bmatrix}\begin{bmatrix} \cos\theta & -\sin\theta \\ \sin\theta & \cos\theta \end{bmatrix}$$

$$= \begin{bmatrix} \cos\phi\cos\theta - \sin\phi\sin\theta & -\cos\phi\sin\theta - \sin\phi\cos\theta \\ \sin\phi\cos\theta + \cos\phi\sin\theta & -\sin\phi\sin\theta + \cos\phi\cos\theta \end{bmatrix} \quad \textbf{3}$$

Recall the identities: $\cos(\phi + \theta) = \cos\phi\cos\theta - \sin\phi\sin\theta$ and
$$\sin(\phi + \theta) = \sin\phi\cos\theta + \cos\phi\sin\theta$$

Substituting these expressions in **3** you find:

$$R_\phi R_\theta = \begin{bmatrix} \cos(\phi + \theta) & -\sin(\phi + \theta) \\ \sin(\phi + \theta) & \cos(\phi + \theta) \end{bmatrix}$$

$$= \begin{bmatrix} \cos\alpha & -\sin\alpha \\ \sin\alpha & \cos\alpha \end{bmatrix}, \quad \text{where } \alpha = \phi + \theta. \quad \textbf{4}$$

The matrix **4** is the matrix of a rotation about the origin with the angle measuring

$$\alpha = \phi + \theta.$$

Theorem 10–13   The composite of two rotations, R_θ and R_ϕ, about the origin is a rotation $R_{\phi+\theta}$ about the origin. The angle of rotation is the sum of the angles of the original rotations. That is

$$R_\phi R_\theta = R_{\phi+\theta}.$$

EXAMPLE 2. Find the matrix for R_{75} without reference to tables.

Since $75 = 30 + 45$, $R_{75} = R_{30}R_{45}$.

Thus,
$$R_{75} = R_{30}R_{45} = \begin{bmatrix} \dfrac{\sqrt{3}}{2} & \dfrac{-1}{2} \\ \dfrac{1}{2} & \dfrac{\sqrt{3}}{2} \end{bmatrix}\begin{bmatrix} \dfrac{\sqrt{2}}{2} & \dfrac{-\sqrt{2}}{2} \\ \dfrac{\sqrt{2}}{2} & \dfrac{\sqrt{2}}{2} \end{bmatrix}$$

$$= \left(\frac{1}{2}\begin{bmatrix} \sqrt{3} & -1 \\ 1 & \sqrt{3} \end{bmatrix}\right)\left(\frac{\sqrt{2}}{2}\begin{bmatrix} 1 & -1 \\ 1 & 1 \end{bmatrix}\right)$$

$$= \frac{\sqrt{2}}{4}\begin{bmatrix} \sqrt{3} & -1 \\ 1 & \sqrt{3} \end{bmatrix}\begin{bmatrix} 1 & -1 \\ 1 & 1 \end{bmatrix}$$

$$= \frac{\sqrt{2}}{4}\begin{bmatrix} \sqrt{3}-1 & -(\sqrt{3}+1) \\ \sqrt{3}+1 & \sqrt{3}-1 \end{bmatrix}$$

Can you find $\sin 75°$? $\cos 75°$?

Composing reflections also yields an interesting pattern. Whereas the composite of two rotations is a rotation, the composite of two reflections is *not* a reflection. To see what it may be, consider the following examples.

1. $r_{y=x}r_{x \text{ axis}} = \begin{bmatrix} 0 & 1 \\ 1 & 0 \end{bmatrix}\begin{bmatrix} 1 & 0 \\ 0 & -1 \end{bmatrix} = \begin{bmatrix} 0 & -1 \\ 1 & 0 \end{bmatrix} = R_{90}$

2. $r_{y \text{ axis}}r_{x \text{ axis}} = \begin{bmatrix} -1 & 0 \\ 0 & 1 \end{bmatrix}\begin{bmatrix} 1 & 0 \\ 0 & -1 \end{bmatrix} = \begin{bmatrix} -1 & 0 \\ 0 & -1 \end{bmatrix} = R_{180}$

3. $r_{y=-x}r_{x \text{ axis}} = \begin{bmatrix} 0 & -1 \\ -1 & 0 \end{bmatrix}\begin{bmatrix} 1 & 0 \\ 0 & -1 \end{bmatrix} = \begin{bmatrix} 0 & 1 \\ -1 & 0 \end{bmatrix} = R_{270}$

In each case above the composite of two reflections is a rotation. The generalization is the following.

The composite of two reflections with respect to intersecting lines is a rotation about the point of intersection.

The converse statement is also true, but neither statement can be proved here since your knowledge of reflections is not extensive enough.

Checkpoint

1. How may two linear transformations represented by matrices be composed?

2. How does the composite of two rotations differ from the composite of two reflections?

Exercises

A ▬▬ Find the single matrix which is the composition of A followed
by B.

1. $A = \begin{bmatrix} 1 & 2 \\ 1 & 4 \end{bmatrix}$ $B = \begin{bmatrix} 2 & 1 \\ -3 & -1 \end{bmatrix}$

2. $A = \begin{bmatrix} 2 & -1 \\ 1 & 5 \end{bmatrix}$ $B = \begin{bmatrix} 1 & 1 \\ 1 & 2 \end{bmatrix}$

3. $A = \begin{bmatrix} -1 & -2 \\ -5 & 1 \end{bmatrix}$ $B = \begin{bmatrix} -3 & 4 \\ 1 & 2 \end{bmatrix}$

4. $A = \begin{bmatrix} 3 & 4 \\ 5 & 7 \end{bmatrix}$ $B = \begin{bmatrix} 7 & -4 \\ -5 & 3 \end{bmatrix}$

5. Find the image of **a.** $\begin{bmatrix} -1 \\ +3 \end{bmatrix}$ **b.** $\begin{bmatrix} 0 \\ 2 \end{bmatrix}$ **c.** $\begin{bmatrix} 4 \\ -1 \end{bmatrix}$ **d.** $\begin{bmatrix} -3 \\ 0 \end{bmatrix}$ and **e.** $\begin{bmatrix} -2 \\ -1 \end{bmatrix}$

under the composite transformation BA using the transformations
given in Exercises 1–4. Draw graphs showing each vector and its
image.

▬▬ Find each rotation matrix without using tables.

6. $R_{105°}$ **7.** $R_{165°}$

8. $R_{15°}$ ($15° = 45° - 30°$)   **9.** $R_{195°}$

10. Find the image of the triangle with vertices at (1, 2), (2, 1) and
(4, 5) under the composite transformation $B \cdot A$ where $A = \begin{bmatrix} 1 & 0 \\ -2 & 1 \end{bmatrix}$
and $B = \begin{bmatrix} 1 & 3 \\ 0 & 1 \end{bmatrix}$. Draw a graph of the triangle and its image.

11. Repeat Exercise 10 for the composite AB. Are the results the
same?

12. Find the image of the line $\begin{cases} x = -3 + t \\ y = 2 + 2t \end{cases}$ under the composite
transformation BA given in Exercise 10. Graph the two lines.

13. Repeat Exercise 12 for the line $\begin{cases} x = 1 + t \\ y = 3t. \end{cases}$

B **14.** Show that composition of rotations about the origin is commutative, that is,
$$R_\phi R_\theta = R_\theta R_\phi.$$

15. Prove that the determinant of a composite transformation
AB is the product of the determinants of A and B, that is,
det (AB) = (det A)(det B).

16. Prove: If A and B are inverse matrices; then det $B = \dfrac{1}{\det A}$.

17. Describe the effect on a vector of the composite transformation of the following.

    a. $A^{-1}A$ **b.** AA^{-1}

18. If A transforms $\vec{v}$ into $\vec{r}$ and A has nonzero determinant, what transformation will transform $\vec{r}$ into $\vec{v}$?

C **19.** Find the area of the triangle with vertices at $(0, 0)$, (a, b) and $(c, 0)$ using the cross product of vectors $a\mathbf{i} + b\mathbf{j} + 0\mathbf{k}$ and $c\mathbf{i} + 0\mathbf{j} + 0\mathbf{k}$. (See Section 9–10.)

20. Let $A = \begin{bmatrix} p & q \\ r & s \end{bmatrix}$ be a linear transformation with nonzero determinant. Let $|\det A| = k$.

    a. Find the image of the triangle given in Exercise 19 under the linear transformation A.

    b. Find the cross product of the images of the vectors $a\mathbf{i} + b\mathbf{j} + 0\mathbf{k}$ and $c\mathbf{i} + 0\mathbf{j} + 0\mathbf{k}$.

    c. Find the length of this cross product.

    d. What is the area of the image triangle?

    e. How are the areas of the pre-image and image triangles related?

    f. State a generalization.

    g. Is the generalization valid for a triangle which has no vertex at the origin? Explain.

21. What does a rotation about the origin do to the area of a triangle? Explain.

22. Answer Exercise 21 for the reflections of Section 10–7.

23. It can be shown that the reflection with respect to $y = mx$ is

$$r_{y=mx} = \begin{bmatrix} \cos 2\theta & \sin 2\theta \\ \sin 2\theta & -\cos 2\theta \end{bmatrix}$$

where θ is the measure of the angle between the positive x axis and the line through the origin $y = mx$. Verify this statement for each of the following.

    a. x axis   **b.** y axis

    c. the line $y = x$ **d.** the line $y = -x$

24. Use Exercise 23 to find the reflection matrix for

    a. $r_{y=\frac{1}{2}x}$ **b.** $r_{y=2x}$

    c. $r_{y=-2x}$ **d.** $r_{y=-\frac{1}{2}x}$

    e. $r_{y=3x}$ **f.** $r_{y=\frac{1}{3}x}$

25. Use Exercise 23 to show that the composite of two reflections over lines through the origin is a rotation through twice the angle between the lines. (*Hint:*

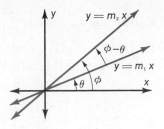

$$r_{y=m_1x} = \begin{bmatrix} \cos 2\theta & \sin 2\theta \\ \sin 2\theta & -\cos 2\theta \end{bmatrix}$$

Find $r_{y=m_2x}r_{y=m_1x}$ and use trigonometric identities.)

10–10   Translations

The transformations considered so far have been ones which left the origin fixed. Thus they were identified with 2×2 matrices. The transformation discussed in this section pairs each point in the plane with a new point. This transformation is called a **translation.**

Let (x, y) be any point in the plane. Then the position vector $\begin{bmatrix} x \\ y \end{bmatrix}$ has its tip at the point (x, y). Suppose you are given a constant vector $\begin{bmatrix} a \\ b \end{bmatrix}$. The vector $\begin{bmatrix} x \\ y \end{bmatrix} + \begin{bmatrix} a \\ b \end{bmatrix} = \begin{bmatrix} x + a \\ y + b \end{bmatrix}$ is a position vector which has its tip at $(x + a, y + b)$. The point (x, y) has been translated to the new position $(x + a, y + b)$. See the figure below.

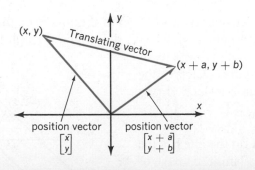

Definition   A translation is a transformation which pairs each point (x, y) with a point $(x + a, y + b)$. The translation is performed by adding the translating vector $\begin{bmatrix} a \\ b \end{bmatrix}$ to the position vector $\begin{bmatrix} x \\ y \end{bmatrix}$.

EXAMPLE 1. Let $\begin{bmatrix} 2 \\ -3 \end{bmatrix}$ be a translating vector. Find the images of

$(1, 1)$, $(-1, -2)$ and $(-4, 3)$.
Graph the points and their images.

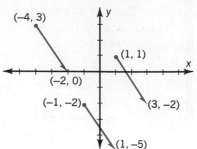

$$\begin{bmatrix} 1 \\ 1 \end{bmatrix} + \begin{bmatrix} 2 \\ -3 \end{bmatrix} = \begin{bmatrix} 3 \\ -2 \end{bmatrix}$$

$$\begin{bmatrix} -1 \\ -2 \end{bmatrix} + \begin{bmatrix} 2 \\ -3 \end{bmatrix} = \begin{bmatrix} 1 \\ -5 \end{bmatrix}$$

$$\begin{bmatrix} -4 \\ 3 \end{bmatrix} + \begin{bmatrix} 2 \\ -3 \end{bmatrix} = \begin{bmatrix} -2 \\ 0 \end{bmatrix}$$

Each point in the figure is

connected to its image by the translating vector $\begin{bmatrix} 2 \\ -3 \end{bmatrix}$.

It is clear from the definition of translation that each point has unique image and each point is the image of a unique point. It is also true, but perhaps not quite so obvious, that under a translation the

a. image of a line is a line.

b. distance between pre-image points and image points is equal.

c. measure of the angles between two vectors and the image vectors is the same.

These results are not difficult to prove and are left for you to do in the exercises.

Knowing that the image of a line is a line allows you to find the equation of the image of a line. This is illustrated in the next example.

EXAMPLE 2. Given $y - x = 3$. Find the image of this line under a translation which pairs $(-1, 2)$ with the origin. Graph both lines.

The graph of $y - x = 3$ is shown in the figure. Clearly the translating vector which maps

$(-1, 2)$ to $(0, 0)$ is $\begin{bmatrix} 1 \\ -2 \end{bmatrix}$.

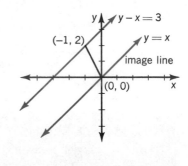

Each point on the line has the form $(t, t + 3)$. Thus the image of $(t, t + 3)$ is:

$$\begin{bmatrix} t \\ t + 3 \end{bmatrix} + \begin{bmatrix} 1 \\ -2 \end{bmatrix} = \begin{bmatrix} t + 1 \\ t + 1 \end{bmatrix}$$

Thus each point on the image line has identical x and y coordinates. The equation of this line is $y = x$. That is, if $x = t + 1$ then $y = t + 1$. So $y = x$ is the equation of the line.

The solution in Example 2 could be shortened considerably by noting that if x and y are coordinates of any point on the pre-image line and x' and y' are the coordinates of the corresponding point on the image line then

$$\begin{bmatrix} x \\ y \end{bmatrix} + \begin{bmatrix} 1 \\ -2 \end{bmatrix} = \begin{bmatrix} x + 1 \\ y - 2 \end{bmatrix} = \begin{bmatrix} x' \\ y' \end{bmatrix}$$

$$x' = x + 1$$
$$y' = y - 2 \qquad\qquad\qquad\qquad 1$$

Equations **1** can be solved for x and y

$$\begin{cases} x = x' - 1 \\ y = y' + 2. \end{cases} \qquad\qquad 2$$

Substituting these values in the equation of the line $y - x = 3$ you find

or
or
$$\begin{cases} (y' + 2) - (x' - 1) = 3 \\ \quad y' - x' + 3 = 3 \\ \quad\quad y' = x' \end{cases}$$

Dropping the primes you find the equation of the image

$$y = x.$$

The generalization is clear. If $\begin{bmatrix} h \\ k \end{bmatrix}$ is the translating vector and $y = mx + b$ is the equation of a line, the image line has equation $(y' - k) = m(x' - h) + b$ since

$$\begin{cases} x = x' - h \\ y = y' - k \end{cases}$$

EXAMPLE 3. Find the equation of the line which is the image of $y = 2x - 3$ under a translation with vector $\begin{bmatrix} -3 \\ 2 \end{bmatrix}$. Graph each line.

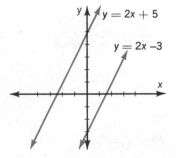

Since

$$\begin{bmatrix} x - 3 \\ y + 2 \end{bmatrix} = \begin{bmatrix} x' \\ y' \end{bmatrix}$$

and

$$\begin{cases} x = x' + 3 \\ y = y' - 2 \end{cases}$$

the equation is

$$(y' - 2) = 2(x' + 3) - 3$$
$$y' = 2x' + 6 - 3 + 2$$
$$y' = 2x' + 5.$$

Dropping primes you find

$$y = 2x + 5$$

The equations

$$\begin{cases} x = x' - h \\ y = y' - k \end{cases} \qquad\qquad 3$$

are called the translation equations. Similar equations define a translation in three-space. These equations are

$$\begin{cases} x = x' - h \\ y = y' - k \\ z = z' - l \end{cases} \qquad\qquad 4$$

where $\begin{bmatrix} h \\ k \\ l \end{bmatrix}$ is the translating vector. The methods you learned in two-space are applicable in three-space also.

Now try these

1. Translate the line $3x + 2y = 6$ so that the y-intercept maps onto the origin. Find the equation of the new line.

2. Given the set of points $\{(1, 2), (3, 4), (6, 8), (3, 5), (1, 7)\}$, list their translations, where $\begin{bmatrix} 3 \\ 0 \end{bmatrix}$ is the translating vector.

Answers: **1.** Translation equations: $x = x' + 0$, $y = y' + 3$. Equation of the line: $3x' + 2y' = 0$.   **2.** $\{(4, 2), (6, 4), (9, 8), (6, 5), (4, 7)\}$.

Checkpoint

How does the use of matrices with translations differ from rotations and reflections?

Exercises

A — Give the coordinates of the new point if the translating vector is $\begin{bmatrix} -3 \\ 5 \end{bmatrix}$.

1. (0, 0)	**2.** (1, 4)	**3.** (3, 5)
4. (−2, −3)	**5.** (−4, 7)	**6.** (0, 5)
7. (8, 0) **8.** (−5, −5)	**9.** (7, −4)	**10.** (−1, 0)

━━ Translate each line so that the *y*-intercept maps onto the origin. Graph each line. Find the equation.

11. $y = 2x - 1$ **12.** $y - 3x + 2 = 0$

13. $2y + 4x = 6$ **14.** $3y - 2x - 5 = 0$

15. $y + 5x = 0$ **16.** $7y - 2x = 14$

17. Translate each line in Exercises 11–16 so that the *x*-intercept maps onto the origin. Graph the lines and find the equation.

B **18.** Prove: The image of a line under a translation is a line.

19. Prove: Distance between points is preserved by a translation.

20. Prove: The measure of an angle is preserved by a translation.

21. Find the image of the triangle with vertices at $(1, 3)$, $(4, 5)$, and $(6, 1)$ under the translation with vector $\begin{bmatrix} -7 \\ 4 \end{bmatrix}$. Graph each.

22. What are the areas of the triangle and its image in Exercise 21.

C ━━ Find the image of the plane under the translation with vector $\begin{bmatrix} -2 \\ 1 \\ 3 \end{bmatrix}$.

23. $x + y + 2 = 0$ **24.** $2x - 3y + 4z = 5$

25. $\frac{1}{2}x - 2y + 3z = 7$ **26.** $x - 7y - 4z = -16$

27. Construct an argument which you could use to convince a classmate that the intersection of two lines maps onto the intersection of the image lines under a translation.

CHAPTER OBJECTIVES AND REVIEW ▬▬▬▬▬

Objective: *To know the meaning of the important mathematical terms of this chapter.*

1. Here are many of the mathematical terms used in this chapter. Be sure that you know them thoroughly and can use them correctly.

matrix (*482*)   pre-image (*505*)
order of a matrix (*485*)   image (*505*)
zero matrix (*486*)   linear transformation (*506*)
opposite (*486*)   rotation through an angle θ
unit matrix (*490*)   (*519*)
determinant (*502*)   composing transformations
transformation (*505*)   (*522*)
identity transformation (*505*)   translation (*527*)

Objective: *To explain and illustrate the concept of matrix and the relation equality of matrices.*

2. In your own words define matrix. Illustrate your definition.

3. What is meant by the dimensions of a matrix? Produce a 5 by 3 matrix.

4. Explain under what conditions matrix A is equal to matrix B.

5. Which pairs of the matrices in **a–d** are equal?

a. $\begin{bmatrix} 2 & -3 \\ 7 & 1 \end{bmatrix}$ b. $\begin{bmatrix} 2 & -3 & 4 \\ 7 & 1 & 0 \end{bmatrix}$ c. $\begin{bmatrix} \frac{4}{2} & (5-8) \\ 7 & -i^2 \end{bmatrix}$ d. $\begin{bmatrix} 2 & 7 \\ -3 & 1 \\ 4 & 0 \end{bmatrix}$

Objective: *To explain under what conditions addition of matrices is defined and to calculate sums.*

6. Suppose that A and B are matrices of dimensions 4×3 and 3×4. Is the sum of A and B defined? Explain.

▬ Use the matrices specified below in Exercises 7–12. In each case that addition is defined, calculate the sum.

$$A = \begin{bmatrix} 2 & -3 \\ 4 & 5 \end{bmatrix} \quad B = \begin{bmatrix} 1 & 1 \\ -1 & 2 \end{bmatrix} \quad C = \begin{bmatrix} 6 & -3 & 1 \\ 2 & 0 & 5 \end{bmatrix} \quad D = \begin{bmatrix} 0 & 1 \\ -1 & 0 \end{bmatrix}$$

7. $A + B$ **8.** $B + C$ **9.** $D + B$

10. $(B + A) + D$ **11.** $C + C$. **12.** $B + (D + C)$

Objective: *To explain under what conditions multiplication of matrices is defined and to calculate products.*

13. Suppose that A and B are matrices of dimensions 4×3 and 3×4. Is the product of A and B defined? Explain.

14. A and B are matrices with dimensions $m \times n$ and $p \times q$. AB is defined.

a. What are the dimensions of AB?

b. What do you know about n and p?

▬ In Exercises 15–20 it is given that

$$A = \begin{bmatrix} 2 & -3 \\ 1 & 2 \end{bmatrix}, \quad B = \begin{bmatrix} 1 \\ -3 \end{bmatrix}, \quad C = \begin{bmatrix} 6 & -3 & 1 \\ 2 & 0 & 5 \end{bmatrix}, \quad D = \begin{bmatrix} 1 & 0 \\ 0 & 1 \end{bmatrix}.$$

Calculate the product indicated if it exists. If it does not exist tell the reason.

15. AB **16.** BA **17.** AC

18. DB **19.** CB **20.** DA

Objective: *To identify properties of the set of 2 × 2 matrices (M_2) under addition and multiplication.*

━━━ Each matrix in Exercise 21–27 is a member of M_2. Identify each statement as either True or False. If a statement is false, produce a counterexample to show that it is false.

21. $A + B$ is in M_2

22. AB is in M_2

23. $A + B = B + A$

24. $AB = BA$

25. There is a matrix C in M_2 such that $C + A = A + C = A$.

26. There is a matrix D in M_2 such that $DA = AD = A$.

27. For each A in M_2 there is a matrix B such that $AB = BA = I$.

Objective: *To illustrate the necessary and sufficient conditions needed for a matrix A in M_2 to be invertible and to be able to calculate the inverse of A when it exists.*

28. Given $A = \begin{bmatrix} a & b \\ c & d \end{bmatrix}$. Explain under what conditions A^{-1} exists.

━━━ In Exercises 29–31 find the inverse of each matrix.

29. $\begin{bmatrix} 2 & -1 \\ 4 & -3 \end{bmatrix}$
30. $\begin{bmatrix} 1 & 5 \\ 0 & 1 \end{bmatrix}$
31. $\begin{bmatrix} 0 & 2 \\ -2 & 0 \end{bmatrix}$

Objective: *To explain the concept of a transformation of a set of vectors and to illustrate linear transformations using matrices.*

32. In your own words describe what a transformation of a set of vectors is.

33. Describe the special properties that define the set of linear transformations.

━━━ In Exercises 34–37 give the matrix representation for each linear transformation. On a coordinate system graph $\vec{v} = \begin{bmatrix} 5 \\ -2 \end{bmatrix}$ and its image under the transformation.

34. $r_{x \text{ axis}}$
35. R_{45}
36. $r_{y \text{ axis}}$
37. $r_{y=-x}$

Objective: *To explain and illustrate the concept of the composite of linear transformations using matrices.*

38. Explain in your own words what it means to find the composite of two linear transformations.

39. How is the composite of two linear transformations represented with matrices?

■ Find the matrix representation of each composite.

40. $r_{x\text{ axis}} \cdot r_{x=y}$

41. $r_{y=x} \cdot r_{y=x}$

42. $R_{45} \cdot R_{135}$

43. $R_{180} \cdot R_{180}$

44. $R_{90} \cdot R_{90}$

45. $R_{30} \cdot R_{15}$

Objective: *To translate points using matrix techniques.*

46. Let $A = \begin{bmatrix} 2 \\ -1 \end{bmatrix}$ be the translating vector. Graph the points $(-2, 1)$ $(4, 3)$ $(-2, -2)$, translate them using A, and graph the images.

47. Find the equation of the image of the line $y = 2x + 1$ after a translation with vector $\begin{bmatrix} -2 \\ -1 \end{bmatrix}$. Graph the line and its image.

CHAPTER TEST

1. $A = \begin{bmatrix} -5 & 3 \\ 0 & 1 \end{bmatrix}$ and $B = \begin{bmatrix} -5 & (2+1) \\ 0 & -1 \end{bmatrix}$. Does $A = B$? Explain.

2. $C = \begin{bmatrix} 2 & -1 & 3 & 1 \\ 4 & 1 & -5 & 7 \\ 0 & -2 & 3 & -6 \end{bmatrix}$

 a. What are the dimensions of C?

 b. Name the entries of C represented by c_{13}, c_{24}, c_{31}.

3. Find the sum of the following matrices if it exists.

$$\begin{bmatrix} 2 & -3 & 1 \\ 4 & -8 & -5 \end{bmatrix} + \begin{bmatrix} 0 & 2 & -1 \\ -3 & 1 & 2 \end{bmatrix}$$

4. Find the sum of the following matrices if it exists.

$$\begin{bmatrix} 2 & 5 \\ 0 & 1 \end{bmatrix} + \begin{bmatrix} -2 & -5 & 1 \\ 0 & -1 & 3 \end{bmatrix}$$

5. Find the product of the following matrices if it exists.

$$\begin{bmatrix} 2 & -3 & 1 \\ 4 & -8 & -5 \end{bmatrix} \begin{bmatrix} 0 & 2 & -1 \\ -3 & 1 & 2 \end{bmatrix}$$

6. Find the product of the following matrices if it exists.

$$\begin{bmatrix} 2 & 5 \\ 0 & 1 \end{bmatrix} \begin{bmatrix} -2 & -5 & 1 \\ 0 & -1 & 3 \end{bmatrix}$$

7. A and B are two matrices for which $A + B$ is defined and AB is defined. What can you conclude about the dimensions of A and B?

8. For matrices in M_2 and k real is it true that

    a. $(A + B) + C = A + (B + C)$?

    b. $(AB)C = A(BC)$?

    c. $(kA)B = k(AB)$?

    d. $AB = BA$?

9. $A = \begin{bmatrix} u & v \\ w & x \end{bmatrix}$. Find det A.

10. If $A = \begin{bmatrix} p & q \\ r & s \end{bmatrix}$ is to have an inverse, what is true about det A?

11. Find the inverse of $\begin{bmatrix} 2 & -3 \\ 1 & -5 \end{bmatrix}$, if it exists.

12. Find the inverse of $\begin{bmatrix} 2 & -3 \\ -4 & 6 \end{bmatrix}$, if it exists.

13. Find the inverse of $\begin{bmatrix} k & -1 \\ -1 & 0 \end{bmatrix}$, if it exists.

14. Let $A = \begin{bmatrix} 2 & 1 \\ 3 & 2 \end{bmatrix}$ represent a transformation.

    a. Find the image of the vectors $\begin{bmatrix} 2 \\ -2 \end{bmatrix}$, $\begin{bmatrix} 1 \\ 0 \end{bmatrix}$, and $\begin{bmatrix} 0 \\ 2 \end{bmatrix}$.

    b. The tips of the vectors in **a** are collinear. Are the tips of the image vectors collinear? Explain.

15. Let $A = \begin{bmatrix} 2 & 1 \\ 3 & 2 \end{bmatrix}$ and $B = \begin{bmatrix} 2 & -1 \\ -3 & 1 \end{bmatrix}$.

    a. What is the composite transformation AB?

    b. What is the composite transformation BA?

16. Find the composite of $r_{y \text{ axis}}$ with itself.

17. Find the composite of $r_{y \text{ axis}}$ with $r_{y=-x}$.

18. Find the image of the line

$$x = 3t + 1$$
$$y = -t - 1$$

under the transformation with matrix $\begin{bmatrix} 2 & -1 \\ 3 & -1 \end{bmatrix}$.

19. Find the image of the line

$$x = t + 1$$
$$y = -t + 1$$

under the translation with vector $\begin{bmatrix} -2 \\ 3 \end{bmatrix}$.

	A	B	C	D	E	F	G	H	
8	18	28	38	48	58	68	78	88	8
7	17	27	37	47	57	67	77	87	7
6	16	26	36	46	56	66	76	86	6
5	15	25	35	45	55	65	75	85	5
4	14	24	34	44	45	46	47	48	4
3	13	23	33	43	53	63	73	83	3
2	12	22	32	42	52	62	72	82	2
1	11	21	31	41	51	61	71	81	1
	A	B	C	D	E	F	G	H	

CHAPTER 11

SYSTEMS OF LINEAR EQUATIONS USING MATRICES

You are very familiar with orderly patterns of horizontal and vertical elements. Some of the most noticeable examples are modern office buildings. The photograph on the opposite page shows a section of the Time-Life Building in Chicago. This was designed by Harry Weese and built in 1970. Horizontal strips of mirror glass alternate with recessions which show as black in the photograph. The vertical supports are placed at wide intervals across the facade. These same orderly patterns are used in mathematics — in *matrices*.

The postal worker on the opposite page is sorting a tray of letters into pigeonholes. These holes are arranged in rows and columns and each is labeled. You can assume that they are labeled in some orderly manner and not just haphazardly. A consistent and logical system of labeling is important to enable the postal employees to work fast and easily.

A consistent labeling system is even more important in international chess games that are played by mail. A player writes his move on a postcard and sends it to his opponent. The opponent then makes his countermove on another postcard. The rows of squares on the chessboard are marked from 1 to 8 and the columns are marked from 1 to 8. Square 25 is therefore located in the second column and the fifth row. Please notice that square 25 is the same square even when the board is upsidedown to you. The numerals 5254 written on a postcard would indicate that the piece on square 52 is being moved to square 54. This international notation is the notation which is used to designate the elements in a matrix.

11–1 Matrices Revisited

In the previous chapter you studied 2×2 matrices, addition and multiplication of these matrices, some properties of 2×2 matrices under addition, multiplication and scalar multiplication, and the interpretation of a 2×2 matrix as a linear transformation. In this chapter you will no longer be restricted to 2×2 matrices. Rather you will use matrices of various dimensions. The major context in which you will use matrices is in the solution of systems of linear equations.

> **Definition** The sum C of a matrix A with dimensions $m \times n$ and a matrix B which is $m \times n$ also is an $m \times n$ matrix whose entries are given by
>
> $$c_{ij} = a_{ij} + b_{ij} \quad i = 1, 2, \cdots, m$$
> $$j = 1, 2, \cdots, n.$$
>
> **Definition** If A is an $m \times n$ matrix and k is a real number, the scalar product, kA, of k and A is the $m \times n$ matrix with entries
>
> $$ka_{ij}, \quad i = 1, 2, \cdots, m$$
> $$j = 1, 2, \cdots, n.$$

Briefly in the previous chapter you met the product of matrices with dimensions greater than 2. The general definition follows.

> **Definition** If A is an $m \times n$ matrix and B is an $n \times p$ matrix, then the product of A and B, $AB = C$, is an $m \times p$ matrix defined by
>
> $$c_{ij} = a_{i1}b_{1j} + a_{i2}b_{2j} + a_{i3}b_{3j} + \cdots + a_{in}b_{nj} \quad i = 1, 2, \cdots, m$$
> $$j = 1, 2, \cdots, p.$$

You can conclude from this definition that a product is defined only when the number of columns of A is the same as the number of rows of B, or, equivalently, only when the number of entries in each row of A is the same as the number of entries in each column of B.

Each entry, c_{ij}, in the product $AB = C$ is the inner product of a row in A and a column in B. This is shown.

$$\begin{bmatrix} \boxed{a_{11}} & a_{12} & \cdots & a_{1n} \\ a_{21} & & & \\ \cdot & & & \\ \cdot & & & \\ \cdot & & & \\ a_{m1} & a_{m2} & \cdots & a_{mn} \end{bmatrix} \cdot \begin{bmatrix} \boxed{b_{11}} & b_{12} & \cdots & b_{1p} \\ b_{21} & & & \\ \cdot & & & \\ \cdot & & & \\ \cdot & & & \\ b_{n1} & b_{n2} & \cdots & b_{np} \end{bmatrix} = \begin{bmatrix} \boxed{c_{11}} & c_{12} & \cdots & c_{1p} \\ c_{21} & & & \\ \cdot & & & \\ \cdot & & & \\ \cdot & & & \\ c_{m1} & c_{m2} & \cdots & c_{mp} \end{bmatrix}$$

The element c_{11} is the inner product of *row 1* of A and column 1 of B. The element c_{ij} is the inner product of row i of A and column j of B:

$$\begin{bmatrix} a_{11} & a_{12} & \cdots & a_{1n} \\ a_{21} & & & \\ \cdot & & & \\ \cdot & & & \\ \boxed{a_{i1} \quad a_{i2} \quad \cdots \quad a_{in}} \\ \cdot & & & \\ \cdot & & & \\ a_{m1} & a_{m2} & \cdots & a_{mn} \end{bmatrix} \cdot \begin{bmatrix} b_{11} & b_{12} & \cdots & b_{1j} & \cdots & b_{1p} \\ b_{21} & & & b_{2j} & & \\ \cdot & & & \cdot & & \\ \cdot & & & \cdot & & \\ \cdot & & & \cdot & & \\ \cdot & & & \cdot & & \\ b_{n1} & b_{n2} & \cdots & b_{nj} & \cdots & b_{np} \end{bmatrix}$$

$$= \begin{bmatrix} c_{11} & c_{12} & \cdots & c_{1j} & \cdots & c_{1p} \\ c_{21} & & & c_{2j} & & \\ \cdot & & & \cdot & & \\ c_{i1} & & & \boxed{c_{ij}} & & \\ \cdot & & & \cdot & & \\ \cdot & & & \cdot & & \\ c_{m1} & c_{m2} & \cdots & c_{mj} & \cdots & c_{mp} \end{bmatrix}$$

EXAMPLE 1. Given $A = \begin{bmatrix} 1 & 2 & -1 \\ 4 & 3 & 1 \end{bmatrix}$, $B = \begin{bmatrix} -2 & 5 \\ -3 & 4 \\ 1 & 2 \end{bmatrix}$, find AB.

Since $AB = C$ then, $\begin{bmatrix} 1 & 2 & -1 \\ 4 & 3 & 1 \end{bmatrix} \cdot \begin{bmatrix} -2 & 5 \\ -3 & 4 \\ 1 & 2 \end{bmatrix}$

$$= \begin{bmatrix} 1(-2) + 2(-3) + (-1)(1) & 1(5) + 2(4) + (-1)(2) \\ 4(-2) + 3(-3) + 1(1) & 4(5) + 3(4) + 1(2) \end{bmatrix}$$

$$= \begin{bmatrix} -2 & -6 & -1 & 5 & +8 & -2 \\ -8 & -9 & +1 & 20 & +12 & +2 \end{bmatrix}$$

$$= \begin{bmatrix} -9 & 11 \\ -16 & 34 \end{bmatrix}$$

The element C_{21} in the product is found by computing the inner product of row 2 of A and column 1 of B:

$$C_{21} = (4 \times -2) + (3 \times -3) + (1 \times 1) = -16$$

EXAMPLE 2. Let A be a 2×3 matrix and B be a 3×5 matrix. AB is a 2×5 matrix, but BA is not defined. Why? If B is a 3×2 matrix, what are the dimensions of AB? of BA?

AB is a 2×2 matrix and BA is a 3×3 matrix.

There are several algebraic properties of matrix operations which are worth noting. Several are identical to theorems stated in Chapter 10. The proofs in general follow directly from the definitions. Most proofs are left for you to do in the exercises.

Theorem 11–1 If A, B, and C are $m \times n$ matrices

a. $A + B = B + A$ **b.** $A + (B + C) = (A + B) + C$

(Commutative Property) (Associative Property)

Theorem 11–2 For any $m \times n$ matrix A

a. there exists a unique $m \times n$ matrix ${}_mO_n$ such that

$$A + {}_mO_n = {}_mO_n + A = A, \text{ and}$$

b. there exists an $m \times n$ matrix B such that $A + B = {}_mO_n$.

Proof of **11–2,** *Part* **a**

Let ${}_mO_n$ be the $m \times n$ matrix such that each entry is 0. Then $A + {}_mO_n = {}_mO_n + A = A$. Thus, there is such a matrix. Suppose now ${}_mT_n$ is another matrix such that for any $m \times n$ matrix A, $A + {}_mT_n = A$. Thus ${}_mO_n + {}_mT_n = {}_mO_n$. (Why?) But ${}_mO_n$ has the same property and ${}_mT_n + {}_mO_n = {}_mT_n$. But ${}_mO_n + {}_mT_n = {}_mT_n + {}_mO_n$ (by Theorem 11–1, part **a**) so ${}_mT_n = {}_mO_n$ and ${}_mO_n$ is unique.

The matrix ${}_mO_n$ is called the $m \times n$ *zero matrix.* Previously "O" denoted the 2×2 zero matrix. Now it would be written ${}_2O_2$.

Theorem 11–3 Let A, B, and C be matrices so that the following operations are defined. Let r and s be real numbers.

a. $(AB)C = A(BC)$ **b.** $r(sA) = (rs)A$ **c.** $A(rB) = r(AB)$

d. $(A + B)C = AC + BC$ **e.** $C(A + B) = CA + CB$

f. $(r + s)A = rA + sA$ **g.** $r(A + B) = rA + rB$

Each of the parts of Theorem 11–3 follow by direct application of definitions and the properties of real numbers.

Now try these

1. Calculate AB, when $A = \begin{bmatrix} 1 & 1 & -1 \\ 2 & 0 & 3 \\ 1 & 2 & -1 \end{bmatrix}$ and $B = \begin{bmatrix} 1 & 2 \\ 3 & 0 \\ -1 & 4 \end{bmatrix}$.

2. Find the products AB and BA, if they exist, for the following two matrices A and B.

$$A = \begin{bmatrix} 2 & 1 \\ 4 & 3 \end{bmatrix} \qquad B = \begin{bmatrix} 2 & -3 & 5 \\ 6 & 2 & 4 \end{bmatrix}$$

3. Verify that $(AB)C = A(BC)$ for $A = \begin{bmatrix} 2 & 0 & -1 \\ -1 & 1 & 3 \end{bmatrix}$, $B = \begin{bmatrix} 1 & 2 \\ 0 & 1 \\ -1 & 2 \end{bmatrix}$, and $C = \begin{bmatrix} 0 & 3 \\ 1 & 2 \end{bmatrix}$.

Answers: **1.** $\begin{bmatrix} 5 & -2 \\ -1 & 16 \\ 8 & -2 \end{bmatrix}$ **2.** $AB = \begin{bmatrix} 10 & -4 & 14 \\ 26 & -6 & 32 \end{bmatrix}$; BA does not exist.

3. $(AB)C$ $=$ $A(BC)$

$$\begin{bmatrix} 3 & 2 \\ -4 & 5 \end{bmatrix}\begin{bmatrix} 0 & 3 \\ 1 & 2 \end{bmatrix} = \begin{bmatrix} 2 & 0 & -1 \\ -1 & 1 & 3 \end{bmatrix}\begin{bmatrix} 2 & 7 \\ 1 & 2 \\ 2 & 1 \end{bmatrix}$$

$$\begin{bmatrix} 2 & 13 \\ 5 & -2 \end{bmatrix} = \begin{bmatrix} 2 & 13 \\ 5 & -2 \end{bmatrix}$$

Exercises

A ━━ Perform the indicated computations when possible.

1. $\begin{bmatrix} 2 & 1 & 3 & 7 \end{bmatrix}\begin{bmatrix} 5 & 1 \\ -2 & 7 \\ -3 & -4 \\ 1 & 0 \end{bmatrix}$ **2.** $\begin{bmatrix} 1 & 3 & 5 \\ 7 & 2 & -3 \\ -1 & 0 & -5 \end{bmatrix}\begin{bmatrix} 5 & 1 \\ -2 & 7 \\ -3 & -4 \end{bmatrix}$

3. $\begin{bmatrix} 5 & 1 \\ -2 & 7 \\ -3 & -4 \end{bmatrix}\begin{bmatrix} 1 & 3 & 5 \\ 7 & 2 & -3 \\ -1 & 0 & -5 \end{bmatrix}$ **4.** $\begin{bmatrix} 1 \\ 2 \\ 3 \\ 4 \end{bmatrix}\begin{bmatrix} 4 & -3 & -2 & 1 \end{bmatrix}$

5. $\begin{bmatrix} 1 & 2 \\ 4 & -1 \\ 2 & 0 \end{bmatrix}\begin{bmatrix} 1 & 3 & -2 \\ 1 & 2 & 1 \end{bmatrix}$ **6.** $\begin{bmatrix} 1 & 3 & -2 \\ 1 & 2 & 4 \end{bmatrix}\begin{bmatrix} 1 & 2 \\ 4 & -1 \\ 2 & 0 \end{bmatrix}$

7. $\begin{bmatrix} 5 & 1 \\ -2 & 7 \\ -3 & -4 \end{bmatrix} + \begin{bmatrix} -5 & 1 \\ -2 & -7 \\ 3 & -4 \end{bmatrix}$ **8.** $\begin{bmatrix} 2 & 1 & 3 \\ 1 & 2 & 3 \\ 3 & 1 & 2 \end{bmatrix} + \begin{bmatrix} 0 & 2 & 1 \\ 1 & 2 & 0 \\ 2 & 1 & 0 \end{bmatrix}$

9. $[1 \quad 2 \quad 3 \quad 4] + \begin{bmatrix} 2 \\ 1 \\ 3 \\ 4 \end{bmatrix}$

10. $\begin{bmatrix} 2 & 1 \\ 3 & 4 \end{bmatrix} \left(\begin{bmatrix} 1 & -2 & 3 \\ 2 & 1 & 4 \end{bmatrix} + \begin{bmatrix} 0 & 2 & -3 \\ -2 & 0 & -4 \end{bmatrix} \right)$

11. Verify Theorem 11–1 part **a**, for $A = \begin{bmatrix} 2 & 1 & 3 \\ 4 & -2 & 1 \end{bmatrix}$ and $B = \begin{bmatrix} -2 & 2 & 3 \\ -4 & 2 & 1 \end{bmatrix}$

12. Verify Theorem 11–1 part **b**, for A and B as given in Exercise 11 and for

$$C = \begin{bmatrix} 1 & 2 & 1 \\ 1 & 1 & 2 \end{bmatrix}$$

13. Given $A = \begin{bmatrix} -1 & 2 & -3 & 4 \\ 5 & -6 & 7 & 8 \\ 9 & 0 & -1 & -2 \end{bmatrix}$, find the matrix B such that $A + B = {}_3O_4$.

14. Let $A = \begin{bmatrix} 1 & 2 & -2 \\ 2 & -3 & 0 \\ -1 & 0 & 1 \end{bmatrix}$, $B = \begin{bmatrix} 5 & -2 & 0 \\ 1 & 0 & -2 \\ -3 & 2 & 1 \end{bmatrix}$ and
$C = \begin{bmatrix} 6 & -2 & -3 \\ 1 & 1 & -1 \\ 2 & 0 & 0 \end{bmatrix}$

Let $r = 3$, $s = 2$. Verify Theorem 11–3.

    a. part a   **b.** part b   **c.** part c   **d.** part d

    e. part e   **f.** part f   **g.** part g

B   **15.** Prove Theorem 11–1, part **a**.

16. Prove Theorem 11–1, part **b**.

17. Prove Theorem 11–3, part **b**.

18. Prove Theorem 11–3, part **d**.

19. Prove Theorem 11–3, part **f**.

20. Prove Theorem 11–3, part **g**.

21. Show that the B of Theorem 11–2, part **b** is $(-1)A$. Is it unique?

Definition   If A is an $m \times n$ matrix, then the transpose of A, A^T, is an $n \times m$ matrix defined by $a_{ij}{}^T = a_{ji}$.

C **22. a.** If $A = \begin{bmatrix} 2 & 1 & 3 \\ -3 & 2 & 0 \end{bmatrix}$ what is A^T?

b. If $B = \begin{bmatrix} 0 & 1 \\ -3 & 5 \end{bmatrix}$ what is B^T?

c. If $C = \begin{bmatrix} 1 & -1 & 2 & -2 \\ -3 & 3 & -1 & 1 \\ 0 & 2 & -3 & 1 \end{bmatrix}$ what is C^T?

d. If $D = \begin{bmatrix} 0 & 2 & -1 \\ -2 & 0 & -3 \\ 1 & 3 & 0 \end{bmatrix}$ what is D^T?

23. Prove: If B is an $m \times n$ matrix, then

$$(B^T)^T = B.$$

24. Prove: If A and B are $m \times n$ matrices, then

$$(A \pm B)^T = A^T \pm B^T.$$

25. Prove: If A is $m \times n$ and B is $n \times p$, then

$$(AB)^T = B^T A^T.$$

(*Hint:* $c_{ij}{}^T = c_{ji} = a_{j1}b_{1i} + a_{j2}b_{2i} + \cdots : + a_{jn}b_{ni}$. Show that $c_{ij}{}^T$ is the i, jth entry in $B^T A^T$.)

Definition If A is an $n \times n$ matrix, then the <u>trace of A</u>, $\mathrm{Tr}(A)$, is defined to be the sum of $a_{11} + a_{22} + a_{33} + \cdots + a_{nn}$.

---

26. a. Prove: $\mathrm{Tr}(cA) = c(\mathrm{Tr}A)$, $c \in R$, A is $n \times n$.
   b. Prove: $\mathrm{Tr}(A + B) = \mathrm{Tr}(A) + \mathrm{Tr}(B)$, A and B are both $n \times n$ matrices.

27. Compute the trace of each matrix if it exists.
   a. $\begin{bmatrix} 1 & 2 \\ 3 & 4 \end{bmatrix}$

   b. $\begin{bmatrix} 2 & -1 & 3 \\ 2 & -5 & 1 \\ 7 & 9 & 2 \end{bmatrix}$

   c. $\begin{bmatrix} 1 & 0 & 0 & 0 \\ 0 & -1 & 0 & 0 \\ 0 & 0 & 0 & -1 \end{bmatrix}$

28. When is the trace of an $n \times n$ matrix zero?

11–2   Systems of Linear Equations

Problems commonly arising in such diverse fields as economics, biology, physics, engineering and mathematics lead to systems of linear equations. The solution of the particular problem, then, depends on solving a system of linear equations such as the one shown below with m equations in n unknowns.

$$\begin{aligned}
a_{11}x_1 + a_{12}x_2 + \cdots + a_{1n}x_n &= b_1 \\
a_{21}x_1 + a_{22}x_2 + \cdots + a_{2n}x_n &= b_2 \\
&\vdots \\
a_{m1}x_1 + a_{m2}x_2 + \cdots + a_{mn}x_n &= b_m
\end{aligned}$$

$\qquad$ 1

A solution to system **1** is an ordered n-tuple, $x_1, x_2, \cdots x_n$, which satisfies each of the m equations. The n-tuple is often written in matrix form;

$$X = \begin{bmatrix} x_1 \\ x_2 \\ \vdots \\ x_n \end{bmatrix}.$$ If the system has no solution, it is said to be *inconsistent*.

A system with one or more solutions is *consistent*.

When the constants $b_1, b_2, b_3, \cdots, b_m$ are each zero, the system is called a **homogeneous system of linear equations.** If at least one b_i, $i = 1, 2, \cdots m$, is not zero, the system is called **nonhomogeneous.** The constants, too, are written in the matrix form: $B = \begin{bmatrix} b_1 \\ b_2 \\ \vdots \\ b_m \end{bmatrix}.$

Clearly $x_1 = x_2 = \cdots = x_n = 0$ is a solution to a homogeneous system. This solution is the **trivial solution.** Any other solution (such that at least one $x_i \neq 0$, $i = 1, 2, \ldots n$) is a **nontrivial** solution.

Suppose you have another system of k linear equations in n unknowns. Suppose further that this system has the same solutions as the system above. Then the two systems are *equivalent*.

EXAMPLE 1.   The system

$$\begin{cases} 3x_1 + 2x_2 = 4 \\ -x_1 + 2x_2 = -4 \end{cases}$$

has a solution $x_1 = 2$, $x_2 = -1$ or $\begin{bmatrix} x_1 \\ x_2 \end{bmatrix} = \begin{bmatrix} 2 \\ -1 \end{bmatrix} = X.$

The system
$$\begin{cases} 2x_1 - 2x_2 = 6 \\ x_1 + 2x_2 = 0 \\ \frac{1}{2}x_1 - x_2 = 2 \end{cases}$$

has the solution $x_1 = 2$ and $x_2 = -1$. Thus you may conclude that the systems are equivalent.

You are familiar with the method of elimination used to solve simple systems of equations. You used it in Section 10–5 for a system of four equations in four unknowns. The elimination procedure amounts to constructing a new system which is equivalent to the original system. Examination of the procedures used to produce an equivalent system leads to the conclusion that there are three manipulations needed. These are as follows.

I. Interchange the ith and the jth equations.

II. Multiply an equation by a nonzero real number, c.

III. Replace the ith equation by the sum of the ith equation and c times the jth equation, $i \neq j$. That is, replace

$$a_{i1}x_1 + a_{i2}x_2 + \cdots + a_{in}x_n = b_i$$

by

$$(a_{i1} + ca_{j1})x_1 + (a_{i2} + ca_{j2})x_2 + \cdots + (a_{in} + ca_{jn})x_n = b_i + cb_j$$

EXAMPLE 2. Solve $\begin{cases} 2x_1 - 2x_2 = 6 \\ x_1 + 2x_2 = 0 \end{cases}$ by using operations I, II, III.

$$\begin{cases} 2x_1 - 2x_2 = 6 \\ x_1 + 2x_2 = 0 \end{cases}$$

is equivalent to

$$\begin{cases} x_1 + 2x_2 = 0 \\ 2x_1 - 2x_2 = 6 \end{cases} \quad \text{by I}$$

which is equivalent to

$$\begin{cases} x_1 + 2x_2 = 0 \\ 0x_1 + -6x_2 = 6 \end{cases} \quad \text{by III} \qquad \text{(What was done?)}$$

which is equivalent to

$$\begin{cases} x_1 + 2x_2 = 0 \\ x_2 = -1 \end{cases} \quad \text{by II}$$

which is equivalent to

$$\begin{cases} x_1 = 2 \\ x_2 = -1 \end{cases} \quad \text{by III}$$

Thus $x_1 = 2$, $x_2 = -1$ is the solution to the original system.

Look back over the solution to Example 2. The essential feature of this solution procedure is that by employing operations I, II and III the original system is replaced by an equivalent system in which the coefficients are either zero or one. The variables $x_1 x_2 \cdots x_n$ play little part in this process. In fact the same manipulations could be carried out on the coefficients and constants of the given system. One way to organize the coefficients conveniently is into a matrix. A matrix of coefficients is the *coefficient* matrix. Here the coefficient matrix is

$$\begin{bmatrix} 2 & -2 \\ 1 & 2 \end{bmatrix}.$$

The elementary manipulations do not leave the constants b_i unchanged. Thus they are included along with the coefficients in the *augmented matrix*.

$$\begin{bmatrix} 2 & -2 & \vdots & 6 \\ 1 & 2 & \vdots & 0 \end{bmatrix}$$

A set of vertical dots is used to separate the coefficients from the constants b_i. For the system 1 the augmented matrix is

$$\begin{bmatrix} a_{11} & a_{12} & \cdots & a_{1n} & \vdots & b_1 \\ a_{21} & a_{22} & \cdots & a_{2n} & \vdots & b_2 \\ \cdot & & & & \vdots & \\ \cdot & & & & \vdots & \\ \cdot & & & & \vdots & \\ a_{n1} & a_{n2} & \cdots & a_{mn} & \vdots & b_m \end{bmatrix} \qquad 2$$

You can now perform manipulations on the rows of the augmented matrix identical to those that you performed on the equations. In this way you can produce an augmented matrix which corresponds to a system equivalent to the original and in which the solution is evident.

EXAMPLE 3. Use the augmented matrix for the system to find the solution.

$$\begin{bmatrix} 2 & -2 & \vdots & 6 \\ 1 & 2 & \vdots & 0 \end{bmatrix}$$

Interchange *row 1* and *row 2*
$$\begin{bmatrix} 1 & 2 & \vdots & 0 \\ 2 & -2 & \vdots & 6 \end{bmatrix}$$

Replace *row 2* by the sum of *row 2* and -2 times *row 1*.
$$\begin{bmatrix} 1 & 2 & \vdots & 0 \\ 0 & -6 & \vdots & 6 \end{bmatrix}$$

Multiply *row 2* by $-\frac{1}{6}$.
$$\begin{bmatrix} 1 & 2 & \vdots & 0 \\ 0 & 1 & \vdots & -1 \end{bmatrix}$$

Replace *row 1* by the sum of *row 1* and -2 times *row 2*.
$$\begin{bmatrix} 1 & 0 & \vdots & 2 \\ 0 & 1 & \vdots & -1 \end{bmatrix}$$

The solution is read from the last augmented matrix. As before it is

$$x_1 = 2, \quad x_2 = -1.$$

Matrices also provide a convenient short hand way of denoting a system of equations. System 1 can be represented

$$AX = B$$

where A is the coefficient matrix for 1, $X = \begin{bmatrix} x_1 \\ x_2 \\ \vdots \\ x_n \end{bmatrix}$, and $B = \begin{bmatrix} b_1 \\ b_2 \\ \vdots \\ b_m \end{bmatrix}$.

EXAMPLE 4. Use the matrix approach to solve

$$\begin{bmatrix} 2 & 1 & -1 \\ -2 & 1 & 2 \\ 1 & 1 & 1 \end{bmatrix} \begin{bmatrix} x_1 \\ x_2 \\ x_3 \end{bmatrix} = \begin{bmatrix} -1 \\ 1 \\ 2 \end{bmatrix}$$

First write the augmented matrix.

$$\begin{bmatrix} 2 & 1 & -1 & : & -1 \\ -2 & 1 & 2 & : & 1 \\ 1 & 1 & 1 & : & 2 \end{bmatrix}$$

Replace *row 2* by the sum of *row 1* and *row 2*.

$$\begin{bmatrix} 2 & 1 & -1 & : & -1 \\ 0 & 2 & 1 & : & 0 \\ 1 & 1 & 1 & : & 2 \end{bmatrix}$$

Replace *row 3* by the sum of *row 3* and $-\frac{1}{2}$ times *row 1*.

$$\begin{bmatrix} 2 & 1 & -1 & : & -1 \\ 0 & 2 & 1 & : & 0 \\ 0 & \frac{1}{2} & \frac{3}{2} & : & \frac{5}{2} \end{bmatrix}$$

Replace *row 1* by the sum of *row 1* and $-\frac{1}{2}$ times *row 2*.

$$\begin{bmatrix} 2 & 0 & -\frac{3}{2} & : & -1 \\ 0 & 2 & 1 & : & 0 \\ 0 & \frac{1}{2} & \frac{3}{2} & : & \frac{5}{2} \end{bmatrix}$$

Replace *row 3* by the sum of *row 3* and $-\frac{1}{4}$ times *row 2*.

$$\begin{bmatrix} 2 & 0 & -\frac{3}{2} & : & -1 \\ 0 & 2 & 1 & : & 0 \\ 0 & 0 & \frac{5}{4} & : & \frac{5}{2} \end{bmatrix}$$

Multiply *row 3* by $\frac{4}{5}$.

$$\begin{bmatrix} 2 & 0 & -\frac{3}{2} & : & -1 \\ 0 & 2 & 1 & : & 0 \\ 0 & 0 & 1 & : & 2 \end{bmatrix}$$

Replace *row 2* by the sum of *row 2* and -1 times *row 3*.

$$\begin{bmatrix} 2 & 0 & -\frac{3}{2} & : & -1 \\ 0 & 2 & 0 & : & -2 \\ 0 & 0 & 1 & : & 2 \end{bmatrix}$$

Replace *row 1* by the sum of *row 1* and $\frac{3}{2}$ times *row 3*.

$$\begin{bmatrix} 2 & 0 & 0 & : & 2 \\ 0 & 2 & 0 & : & -2 \\ 0 & 0 & 1 & : & 2 \end{bmatrix}$$

Multiply *row 2* by $\frac{1}{2}$.

$$\begin{bmatrix} 2 & 0 & 0 & : & 2 \\ 0 & 1 & 0 & : & -1 \\ 0 & 0 & 1 & : & 2 \end{bmatrix}$$

Multiply *row 1* by $\frac{1}{2}$.

$$\begin{bmatrix} 1 & 0 & 0 & : & 1 \\ 0 & 1 & 0 & : & -1 \\ 0 & 0 & 1 & : & 2 \end{bmatrix}$$

Clearly you do not have to obtain the last equivalent system to calculate the values of x_1, x_2, and x_3 easily. Any of the 5 systems preceding the last could be used for this purpose. Of course the last one represents the solution most obviously.

Now try these

━━ Use the augmented matrix and elementary row manipulation method to solve each of the following systems.

1. $\begin{cases} x + 2y - z = 4 \\ 2x - y + 3z = 3 \\ 7x - 2y + 4z = 7 \end{cases}$
    2. $\begin{cases} x + y + z = 4 \\ 2x - 3y - z = 1 \\ x + 2y + 2z = 5 \end{cases}$

Answers: **1.** $(x, y, z) = (1, 2, 1)$ **2.** $(x, y, z) = (3, 2, -1)$

Exercises

A ━━ Use the augmented matrix and elementary row manipulation method to solve each system of equations.

1. $\begin{cases} -3x + 2y = -1 \\ x + y = 2 \end{cases}$
    2. $\begin{cases} 3x - 2y = 1 \\ 6x + 6y = 7 \end{cases}$

3. $\begin{cases} x - 2y = -5 \\ 2x + 3y = 4 \end{cases}$
    4. $\begin{cases} x - 7y = 3 \\ -2x + 7y = 1 \end{cases}$

5. $\begin{cases} x - 3y = 5 \\ -2x + 6y = 5 \end{cases}$
    6. $\begin{cases} 2x + y = 5 \\ -4x - 2y = -10 \end{cases}$

7. $\begin{cases} x + y + z = 6 \\ -2x - 3y + 3x = 1 \\ x - 4y + 2z = -1 \end{cases}$
    8. $\begin{cases} x + y + z = 0 \\ 2x - 2y - z = 9 \\ 3x + 2y + z = 1 \end{cases}$

9. $\begin{cases} x - 2y + z = -2 \\ 2x + 2y - 4z = -1 \\ 4x + y + 2z = 7 \end{cases}$
    10. $\begin{cases} x + y + 2z = 2 \\ 2x - y + 3x = 5 \\ x - y - z = -2 \end{cases}$

11. $\begin{cases} x + 5y - 3z = 0 \\ x + y + z = 0 \\ 2x - 3y + z = 0 \end{cases}$

12. $\begin{cases} w - x + y - z = 0 \\ w + x + y + z = 6 \\ 2w - x + y - z = 1 \\ -4w + x - 2y + 4z = 1 \end{cases}$

B   **13.** $\begin{cases} x_1 + x_2 + x_3 + x_4 + x_5 = 3 \\ x_1 \qquad\qquad\qquad + x_5 = 0 \\ 2x_1 + x_2 + x_3 \qquad\quad = 2 \\ \qquad x_2 + x_3 + x_4 \quad = 3 \\ \qquad\qquad x_3 + x_4 + x_5 = 0 \end{cases}$

14. $\begin{cases} 2x_1 + x_2 + 3x_3 = 1 \\ x_1 \qquad + 2x_3 = 1 \end{cases}$

15. Write the matrix form, $AX = B$, of each of the systems in Exercises 10–14.

11–3   Matrices in Echelon Form

In the last section you were introduced to a matrix method for solving systems of equations. The manipulations of the rows of the augmented matrix of a system were motivated by the standard elimination method. Here you will examine some of the matrix ideas which will clarify Section 11–2 and put it on a firmer mathematical basis.

If you will inspect your solutions to several exercises in Section 11–2, you will find that the solutions were easily read from the augmented matrix when it was similar to this:

$$\begin{bmatrix} 1 & a_{12} & a_{13} & \cdots & a_{1i} & \cdots & a_{1n} & \vdots & b_1 \\ 0 & 1 & a_{23} & \cdots & a_{2i} & \cdots & a_{2n} & \vdots & b_2 \\ & \cdot & \cdot & & \cdot & & \cdot & \vdots & \cdot \\ & \cdot & \cdot & & \cdot & & \cdot & \vdots & \cdot \\ 0 & 0 & 0 & \cdots & 1 & \cdots & a_{kn} & \vdots & b_k \\ & \cdot & \cdot & & \cdot & & \cdot & \vdots & \cdot \\ & \cdot & \cdot & & \cdot & & \cdot & \vdots & \cdot \\ & \cdot & \cdot & & \cdot & & \cdot & \vdots & \cdot \\ 0 & 0 & 0 & \cdots & 0 & \cdots & 0 & \vdots & b_m \end{bmatrix}$$

In this matrix each row of the coefficient matrix which has a non-zero entry is headed by a 1. The entries of the row following the 1 may or may not be zero. The last several rows of the coefficient matrix may all be zeros. Such a matrix is said to be in **row echelon form.**

Definition An $m \times n$ matrix A is in row echelon form if the following is true.

a. There exists an integer k, $1 \leq k \leq m$, such that entries in rows $k + 1$, $k + 2$, ... m are all zero and none of the first k rows consists entirely of zeros.

b. The first (counting from the left) nonzero entry in row i is 1, $i = 1, 2, \ldots, k$.

c. If the 1 in row i occurs in column $c(i)$, then $c(1) < c(2) < \cdots < c(i) < \cdots < c(k)$.
   In words, the initial 1 of any row is to the left of and above the initial 1 of each succeeding row.

d. All entries in column $c(i)$ appearing in rows $i + 1$, $i + 2$, ..., m are zero.

If in addition to these conditions, each entry in the column $c(i)$ other than the 1 in row i is zero, then the $m \times n$ matrix is in **reduced row echelon** form. Notice that if $k = m$, then no rows are zero.

EXAMPLE 1. The matrices

$$A = \begin{bmatrix} 1 & 2 & 3 & 4 \\ 0 & 1 & 1 & 2 \\ 0 & 0 & 0 & 1 \end{bmatrix}, \quad B = \begin{bmatrix} 0 & 0 & 1 & 2 & 3 & 4 & 5 \\ 0 & 0 & 0 & 0 & 1 & -2 & 2 \\ 0 & 0 & 0 & 0 & 0 & 1 & -1 \\ 0 & 0 & 0 & 0 & 0 & 0 & 1 \\ 0 & 0 & 0 & 0 & 0 & 0 & 0 \end{bmatrix},$$

and

$$C = \begin{bmatrix} 1 & 0 & 0 & 0 \\ 0 & 1 & 0 & 0 \\ 0 & 0 & 1 & 0 \\ 0 & 0 & 0 & 1 \end{bmatrix}$$

are in row echelon form. In matrix B, $c(1) = 3$, $c(2) = 5$, $c(3) = 6$, and $c(4) = 7$.

EXAMPLE 2. The matrices

$$D = \begin{bmatrix} 1 & 2 & 0 & 0 \\ 0 & 0 & 1 & 0 \\ 0 & 0 & 0 & 1 \end{bmatrix}, \quad E = \begin{bmatrix} 0 & 0 & 1 & 0 & 0 & 4 & 7 \\ 0 & 0 & 0 & 0 & 1 & 2 & 1 \\ 0 & 0 & 0 & 0 & 0 & 0 & 0 \\ 0 & 0 & 0 & 0 & 0 & 0 & 0 \\ 0 & 0 & 0 & 0 & 0 & 0 & 0 \end{bmatrix},$$

and

$$C = \begin{bmatrix} 1 & 0 & 0 & 0 \\ 0 & 1 & 0 & 0 \\ 0 & 0 & 1 & 0 \\ 0 & 0 & 0 & 1 \end{bmatrix}$$

are in reduced row echelon form. In E, $c(1) = 3$, $c(2) = 5$.

The coefficient matrix of a system of linear equations is put in row echelon form or reduced row echelon form by manipulating rows of the augmented matrix. These manipulations are called **elementary row operations.**

Definition An elementary row operation on a matrix A is any-one of the following operations.
Type I. Interchange rows i and j of A.
Type II. Multiply row i by real number $c \neq 0$.
Type III. Add c times row j to row i, $i \neq j$.

You can easily convince yourself of the following.

a. An $m \times n$ matrix A is row equivalent to A.

b. If A is row equivalent to B, then B is row equivalent to A.

c. If A is row equivalent to B and B is row equivalent to C then A is row equivalent to C.

Thus the operation *is row equivalent to* is an *equivalence relation*. (See Exercises 16–18.)

The stage is now set for three important theorems which are used to justify the matrix solution to systems of linear equations.

Theorem 11–4 Every $m \times n$ matrix A is row equivalent to a matrix in row echelon form.

Proof: Find the first column of A (counting from the left) which is not all zeros. Suppose it is column j. Now find the first entry in column j which is nonzero. Suppose that entry is in row i. Now interchange row 1 and row i (if $i \neq 1$), thus producing a new matrix B which is row equivalent to A and in which $b_{1j} \neq 0$. Multiply row 1 of B by $\frac{1}{b_{1j}}$ producing a matrix C in which $c_{1j} = 1$. Now for each entry c_{hj} in column j of C which is not zero, multiply row 1 of C by $-c_{hj}$ and add it to row h. The procedure replaces each entry of column j (other than c_{1j}) with zero. The matrix is now

$$
\begin{matrix}
 & & & j & & & \\
\end{matrix}
$$

$$
\begin{bmatrix}
0 & 0 & \cdots & 1 & d_{1j+1} & \cdots & d_{1n} \\
0 & & \cdots\cdots & 0 & d_{2j+1} & \cdots & d_{2n} \\
\cdot & & & \cdot & & & \\
\cdot & & & \cdot & & & \\
\cdot & & & \cdot & & & \\
0 & & & 0 & d_{mj+1} & \cdots & d_{mn}
\end{bmatrix}
$$

Repeat the procedure on the matrix outlined in color. Continuing in this manner you produce a matrix row equivalent to A and in row echelon form.

Beginning with an $m \times n$ matrix A which is in row echelon form, you can easily reduce it to a row equivalent matrix in *reduced row echelon form*. This is done by examining each of the rows $i = 2, \cdots m$, to find the column in which the 1 occurs. By multiplying each of these rows by appropriate constants and adding them to each of the preceding rows, zeros are obtained above each 1 (which is the first nonzero entry of a row) as well as below. Thus you have the following theorem.

Theorem 11–5 Every $m \times n$ matrix A is row equivalent to a matrix in reduced row echelon form.

These two theorems allow you to conclude that it is always possible to carry out the matrix method of solving a system of equations. However, you need to know that the elementary matrix operations produce an augmented matrix which represents a system of equations with the same solutions as the original system. That this is so follows from the definition of row equivalence and the fact that the elementary row operations are exactly the same as the manipulations of equations which produce equivalent systems. To summarize Theorem 11–5, let $AX = B$ and $CX = D$ be two systems each of m equations in n unknowns. If the augmented matrices $[A : B]$ and $[C : D]$ are row equivalent, then the systems of equations have the same solutions.

EXAMPLE 3. Solve $\begin{cases} x_1 + 2x_2 + 3x_3 = 6 \\ 2x_1 - 4x_2 + 2x_3 = 16 \\ 3x_1 + x_2 - x_3 = -2 \end{cases}$ by finding a reduced row

echelon matrix row equivalent to the augmented matrix.

$$\left[\begin{array}{ccc:c} 1 & 2 & 3 & 6 \\ 2 & -4 & 2 & 16 \\ 3 & 1 & -1 & -2 \end{array}\right] \begin{array}{l} \text{Multiply} \\ \textit{row 1 by} \\ -2 \text{ and} \\ \text{add it to} \\ \textit{row 2.} \end{array} \left[\begin{array}{ccc:c} 1 & 2 & 3 & 6 \\ 0 & -8 & -4 & 4 \\ 3 & 1 & -1 & -2 \end{array}\right]$$

$$\begin{array}{l} \text{Multiply} \\ \textit{row 1 by} \\ -3 \text{ and} \\ \text{add it to} \\ \textit{row 3.} \end{array} \left[\begin{array}{ccc:c} 1 & 2 & 3 & 6 \\ 0 & -8 & -4 & 4 \\ 0 & -5 & -10 & -20 \end{array}\right] \begin{array}{l} \text{Interchange} \\ \textit{row 2 and} \\ \textit{row 3.} \end{array} \left[\begin{array}{ccc:c} 1 & 2 & 3 & 6 \\ 0 & -5 & -10 & -20 \\ 0 & -8 & -4 & 4 \end{array}\right] \begin{array}{l} \text{Multiply} \\ \textit{row 2} \\ \text{by} -\frac{1}{5}. \end{array}$$

$$\left[\begin{array}{ccc:c} 1 & 2 & 3 & 6 \\ 0 & 1 & 2 & 4 \\ 0 & -8 & -4 & 4 \end{array}\right] \begin{array}{l} \text{Multiply} \\ \textit{row 2 by} \\ 8 \text{ and} \\ \text{add it to} \\ \textit{row 3.} \end{array} \left[\begin{array}{ccc:c} 1 & 2 & 3 & 6 \\ 0 & 1 & 2 & 4 \\ 0 & 0 & 12 & 36 \end{array}\right] \begin{array}{l} \text{Multiply} \\ \textit{row 3 by} \\ \frac{1}{12}. \end{array} \left[\begin{array}{ccc:c} 1 & 2 & 3 & 6 \\ 0 & 1 & 2 & 4 \\ 0 & 0 & 1 & 3 \end{array}\right]$$

At this point, the matrix is in row echelon form. The solution can be easily obtained for

$$x_3 = 3$$
$$x_2 + 2x_3 = 4 \quad \text{or} \quad x_2 = -2$$
$$x_1 + 2x_2 + 3x_3 = 6 \quad \text{or} \quad x_1 = 6 - 9 + 4 = 1$$

To obtain the *reduced row* echelon matrix further elementary row operation must be performed.

$$\begin{bmatrix} 1 & 2 & 3 & \vdots & 6 \\ 0 & 1 & 2 & \vdots & 4 \\ 0 & 0 & 1 & \vdots & 3 \end{bmatrix} \quad \begin{array}{l} \text{Multiply } row\ 2 \\ \text{by } -2 \text{ and} \\ \text{add it to } row\ 1. \end{array} \quad \begin{bmatrix} 1 & 0 & -1 & \vdots & -2 \\ 0 & 1 & 2 & \vdots & 4 \\ 0 & 0 & 1 & \vdots & 3 \end{bmatrix}$$

$$\begin{array}{l} \text{Multiply } row\ 3 \\ \text{by } -2 \text{ and} \\ \text{add it to } row\ 2. \end{array} \begin{bmatrix} 1 & 0 & -1 & \vdots & -2 \\ 0 & 1 & 0 & \vdots & -2 \\ 0 & 0 & 1 & \vdots & 3 \end{bmatrix} \quad \begin{array}{l} \text{Add } row\ 3 \text{ to} \\ row\ 1. \end{array} \begin{bmatrix} 1 & 0 & 0 & \vdots & 1 \\ 0 & 1 & 0 & \vdots & -2 \\ 0 & 0 & 1 & \vdots & 3 \end{bmatrix}$$

The last matrix represents the system

$$x_1 \qquad\qquad = 1$$
$$\qquad x_2 \qquad = -2$$
$$\qquad\qquad x_3 = 3$$

from which the solution is obvious.

The method whereby the solutions to a system of linear equations are found by reducing the augmented matrix to a row equivalent row echelon form, is called *Gaussian elimination*. The method which results in a reduced row echelon form is called *Gauss-Jordan reduction*.

Now try these

Use matrix $A = \begin{bmatrix} 2 & 3 & 1 \\ 1 & 2 & 1 \\ 2 & -3 & 1 \end{bmatrix}$ for Exercises 1 and 2.

1. Find a row equivalent matrix in row echelon form.

2. Find a row equivalent matrix in reduced row echelon form.

Use augmented matrix $A = \begin{bmatrix} 2 & 3 & 1 & \vdots & 14 \\ 1 & 2 & 1 & \vdots & 9 \\ 1 & -1 & 1 & \vdots & 0 \end{bmatrix}$ for Exercises 3 and 4.

3. Solve for x_1, x_2, x_3 using Gaussian elimination.

4. Solve for x_1, x_2, x_3 using Gauss-Jordan reduction.

Answers: **1.** $\begin{bmatrix} 1 & \frac{3}{2} & \frac{1}{2} \\ 0 & 1 & 1 \\ 0 & 0 & 1 \end{bmatrix}$ **2.** $\begin{bmatrix} 1 & 0 & -1 \\ 0 & 1 & 1 \\ 0 & 0 & 0 \end{bmatrix}$ **3.** 2, 3, 1.   **4.** 2, 3, 1.

Exercises

A ■ Let A be given. Find two row equivalent matrices; one of which is in row echelon form and the other in reduced row echelon form.

1. $\begin{bmatrix} 1 & 2 \\ 4 & 3 \end{bmatrix}$

2. $\begin{bmatrix} 1 & 2 \\ 3 & 6 \end{bmatrix}$

3. $\begin{bmatrix} 1 & 2 & 4 \\ 3 & 1 & 2 \end{bmatrix}$

4. $\begin{bmatrix} 0 & 2 & 4 \\ 0 & 1 & 2 \\ 0 & 3 & 1 \end{bmatrix}$

5. $\begin{bmatrix} 1 & 1 & 1 & 1 \\ 1 & 0 & 0 & 1 \\ 1 & 2 & 1 & 0 \end{bmatrix}$

6. $\begin{bmatrix} 0 & 0 & -1 & 2 & 3 \\ 0 & 2 & 3 & 4 & 5 \\ 0 & 3 & 2 & 4 & 1 \end{bmatrix}$

■ In Exercises 7–15 solve each system using **a.** Gaussian elimination and **b.** Gauss-Jordan reduction.

7. $\begin{cases} x_1 + 2x_2 = 1 \\ 4x_1 + 3x_2 = 9 \end{cases}$

8. $\begin{cases} 3x_1 + 2x_2 = 2 \\ 3x_1 - 4x_2 = -1 \end{cases}$

9. $\begin{cases} 2x_1 + 3x_2 = -1 \\ x_1 - x_2 = 2 \\ 4x_1 + 3x_2 = 1 \end{cases}$

10. $\begin{cases} x_1 - x_2 + x_3 = 2 \\ 3x_1 + x_2 + x_3 = 0 \\ -x_1 - x_2 + 2x_3 = 11 \end{cases}$

11. $\begin{cases} 3x_1 + x_3 = 0 \\ 3x_1 - x_2 = 2 \\ x_1 + x_2 - x_3 = 5 \\ 2x_1 - x_2 + x_3 = -2 \end{cases}$

12. $\begin{cases} x_1 + x_2 + 2x_3 = -1 \\ x_1 - 2x_2 + x_3 = -5 \\ 3x_1 + x_2 + x_3 = 3 \end{cases}$

13. $\begin{cases} x_1 + 2x_2 + 3x_3 = 0 \\ x_1 + x_2 + x_3 = 0 \\ x_1 + x_2 + 2x_3 = 0 \end{cases}$

14. $\begin{cases} x_1 + 2x_2 + x_3 = 7 \\ 2x_1 \qquad + x_3 = 4 \\ x_1 \qquad + 2x_3 = 5 \\ x_1 + 2x_2 + 3x_3 = 11 \\ 2x_1 + x_2 + 4x_3 = 12 \end{cases}$

15. $\begin{cases} x_1 + 2x_2 + x_3 = 0 \\ 2x_1 + 3x_2 \qquad = 0 \\ \qquad x_2 + 2x_3 = 0 \\ 2x_1 + x_2 + 4x_3 = 0 \end{cases}$

B **16.** Prove that every matrix is row equivalent to itself.

17. Prove that if A is row equivalent to B, then B is row equivalent to A.

18. Prove that if A is row equivalent to B and B is row equivalent to C, then A is row equivalent to C.

C **19.** Given the system of equations

$$\begin{cases} x_1 + x_2 = 3 \\ x_1 + (a^2 - 8)x_2 = a \end{cases}$$

find all values of "a" such that the system has

    a. no solution.

    b. a unique solution.

    c. infinitely many solutions.

20. A company produces products A, B, and C. Each unit of each product requires work to be done by a technician and by an unskilled laborer.

Product A requires a day's work from each of 5 technicians and 5 laborers for each unit produced.

Product B requires 10 technicians and 10 laborers.

Product C requires 2 technicians and 4 laborers for each unit produced.

    a. How many units of each product A, B, and C should be produced each day to keep all 100 technicians and 150 laborers employed?

    b. Is there a unique answer?

    c. If product B is in greater demand than product A, what is the solution?

    d. What solution is best if product A is in greater demand than product B?

    e. If product C is in greater demand than product A, what is the solution?

11–4   Homogeneous Systems of Equations

Every augmented matrix of a system of linear equations is row equivalent to a reduced row echelon matrix. The corresponding systems have identical solutions and, consequently, are equivalent. In this section you use these facts to examine properties of homogeneous systems.

In matrix form a homogeneous system of m equations in n variables is denoted as follows.

$$AX = {}_mO_1$$

A is the $m \times n$ coefficient matrix, X is the $n \times 1$ matrix of variables, and O is the $m \times 1$ zero matrix.

The solution to the system in Example 1 is an illustration of the form that the solution to a homogeneous system takes. Study the example carefully.

EXAMPLE 1.   Solve the following homogeneous system.

$$\begin{bmatrix} 1 & 3 & 0 & 0 & -2 \\ 0 & 0 & 1 & 0 & 1 \\ 0 & 0 & 0 & 1 & 2 \\ 0 & 0 & 0 & 0 & 0 \end{bmatrix} \begin{bmatrix} x_1 \\ x_2 \\ x_3 \\ x_4 \\ x_5 \end{bmatrix} = \begin{bmatrix} 0 \\ 0 \\ 0 \\ 0 \end{bmatrix}$$

The coefficient matrix is already in reduced row echelon form. It represents the following system.

$$\begin{aligned} x_1 + 3x_2 \quad\quad\quad - 2x_5 &= 0 \\ x_3 \quad\quad + x_5 &= 0 \\ x_4 + 2x_5 &= 0 \end{aligned}$$

The variables x_1, x_3, and x_4, may be expressed in terms of x_2 and x_5. The solution is:

$$\begin{aligned} x_1 &= -3x_2 + 2x_5 \\ x_2 &= x_2 \\ x_3 &= -x_5 \\ x_4 &= -2x_5 \\ x_5 &= x_5 \end{aligned}$$

where x_2 and x_5 may be any real numbers. Thus, the solution to this homogeneous system of linear equations is an infinite set of solutions. In matrix notation this solution can be written either as one matrix or as the sum of matrices.

$$\begin{bmatrix} x_1 \\ x_2 \\ x_3 \\ x_4 \\ x_5 \end{bmatrix} = \begin{bmatrix} -3x_2 + 2x_5 \\ x_2 \\ -\ x_5 \\ -\ 2x_5 \\ x_5 \end{bmatrix}$$

$$= x_2 \begin{bmatrix} -3 \\ 1 \\ 0 \\ 0 \\ 0 \end{bmatrix} + x_5 \begin{bmatrix} 2 \\ 0 \\ -1 \\ -2 \\ 1 \end{bmatrix} \quad \forall x_2, x_5 \in R$$

This is called the *general solution* of the system.

Any row in the augmented matrix which consists entirely of zeros may be ignored since it will place no restrictions on the variables.

Since any augmented matrix for the $m \times n$ $(m < n)$ system $AX = {}_mO_1$ is row equivalent to a reduced row echelon form, let rows $1, 2, \cdots, r$ be the nonzero rows and let the 1 in row i occur in column $c(i)$. Then you are solving a system of $r < n$ equations in n variables. Because the augmented matrix is in reduced row echelon form, each $x_{c(1)}, x_{c(2)}, \cdots,$ $x_{c(r)}$ can be expressed in terms of the remaining $n - r$ variables. The $n - r$ variables may assume any real numbers. Thus there are infinitely many solutions, at least one of which is nontrivial.

A similar argument may be used to prove the following theorem.

Theorem 11–6 If A is an $m \times n$ matrix with $m < n$, then the system of homogeneous linear equations $AX = {}_mO_1$ has a non-trivial solution.

From Theorem 11–6 you can infer that any system of homogeneous linear equations with more variables than equations has infinitely many nontrivial solutions. It also has the trivial solution.

An equivalent form of this theorem is as follows.

Theorem 11–7 If A is an $m \times n$ matrix and $AX = {}_mO_1$ has only the trivial solution, then $m \geq n$.

Theorem 11–7 tells you that any system of homogeneous linear equations which has only the trivial solution must have more equations than variables.

EXAMPLE 2. Find all solutions for the following homogeneous system.

$$\begin{bmatrix} 1 & 2 & 1 & 1 \\ 2 & 4 & -1 & 0 \end{bmatrix} \begin{bmatrix} x_1 \\ x_2 \\ x_3 \\ x_4 \end{bmatrix} = \begin{bmatrix} 0 \\ 0 \end{bmatrix}$$

The augmented matrix is $\begin{bmatrix} 1 & 2 & 1 & 1 & \vdots & 0 \\ 2 & 4 & -1 & 0 & \vdots & 0 \end{bmatrix}$.

This reduces to $\begin{bmatrix} 1 & 2 & 1 & 1 & \vdots & 0 \\ 0 & 0 & -3 & -2 & \vdots & 0 \end{bmatrix} \longrightarrow \begin{bmatrix} 1 & 2 & 1 & 1 & \vdots & 0 \\ 0 & 0 & 1 & \frac{2}{3} & \vdots & 0 \end{bmatrix}$

or to the reduced row echelon form

$$\begin{bmatrix} 1 & 2 & 0 & \frac{1}{3} & \vdots & 0 \\ 0 & 0 & 1 & \frac{2}{3} & \vdots & 0 \end{bmatrix}.$$

The equivalent set of homogeneous equations is

$$x_1 + 2x_2 \qquad + \tfrac{1}{3}x_4 = 0$$
$$x_3 + \tfrac{2}{3}x_4 = 0$$

Solving for x_1 and x_3 in terms of x_2 and x_4, you get

$$x_1 = -2x_2 - \tfrac{1}{3}x_4$$
$$x_3 = 0x_2 - \tfrac{2}{3}x_4$$

Thus the general solution is:

$$\begin{bmatrix} x_1 \\ x_2 \\ x_3 \\ x_4 \end{bmatrix} = \begin{bmatrix} -2x_2 - \tfrac{1}{3}x_4 \\ x_2 + 0x_4 \\ 0x_2 - \tfrac{2}{3}x_4 \\ 0x_2 + x_4 \end{bmatrix} = x_2 \begin{bmatrix} -2 \\ 1 \\ 0 \\ 0 \end{bmatrix} + x_4 \begin{bmatrix} -\tfrac{1}{3} \\ 0 \\ -\tfrac{2}{3} \\ 1 \end{bmatrix}$$

where x_2 and x_4 can be replaced by any real numbers.

EXAMPLE 3. Find all solutions of

$$\begin{bmatrix} 1 & 1 & 1 \\ 1 & 0 & 0 \\ 1 & 2 & 1 \end{bmatrix} \begin{bmatrix} x_1 \\ x_2 \\ x_3 \end{bmatrix} = {}_3O_1.$$

$$\begin{bmatrix} 1 & 1 & 1 & \vdots & 0 \\ 1 & 0 & 0 & \vdots & 0 \\ 1 & 2 & 1 & \vdots & 0 \end{bmatrix} \longrightarrow \begin{bmatrix} 1 & 0 & 0 & \vdots & 0 \\ 1 & 1 & 1 & \vdots & 0 \\ 1 & 2 & 1 & \vdots & 0 \end{bmatrix} \longrightarrow \begin{bmatrix} 1 & 0 & 0 & \vdots & 0 \\ 0 & 1 & 1 & \vdots & 0 \\ 1 & 2 & 1 & \vdots & 0 \end{bmatrix}$$

$$\begin{bmatrix} 1 & 0 & 0 & \vdots & 0 \\ 0 & 1 & 1 & \vdots & 0 \\ 0 & 2 & 1 & \vdots & 0 \end{bmatrix} \longrightarrow \begin{bmatrix} 1 & 0 & 0 & \vdots & 0 \\ 0 & 1 & 1 & \vdots & 0 \\ 0 & 0 & -1 & \vdots & 0 \end{bmatrix} \longrightarrow \begin{bmatrix} 1 & 0 & 0 & \vdots & 0 \\ 0 & 1 & 0 & \vdots & 0 \\ 0 & 0 & -1 & \vdots & 0 \end{bmatrix}$$

$$\longrightarrow \begin{bmatrix} 1 & 0 & 0 & \vdots & 0 \\ 0 & 1 & 0 & \vdots & 0 \\ 0 & 0 & 1 & \vdots & 0 \end{bmatrix}$$

Thus the only solution is the trivial solution: $x_1 = 0$, $x_2 = 0$, $x_3 = 0$.

Notice that in Example 3 each row of the reduced row echelon form is nonzero and that there are exactly as many nonzero rows as variables; namely 3. This illustrates a useful theorem.

Theorem 11–8 A system of homogeneous equations in n variables $x_1, x_2, \ldots x_n$ has a unique solution if the reduced row echelon matrix has exactly n rows with nonzero entries. That solution is the trivial solution.

Now try these

■ Find the general solution for each homogeneous system in Exercises 1 and 2.

1. $\begin{aligned} x_1 + \quad + x_3 &= 0 \\ x_1 + 2x_2 - 3x_3 &= 0 \end{aligned}$

2. $\begin{aligned} x_1 + x_2 \qquad\qquad &= 0 \\ x_1 + \quad + 2x_3 + x_4 &= 0 \\ x_2 + \quad x_3 + x_4 &= 0 \end{aligned}$

Answers: **1.** $\begin{bmatrix} x_1 \\ x_2 \\ x_3 \end{bmatrix} = \begin{bmatrix} -x_3 \\ 2x_3 \\ x_3 \end{bmatrix} = x_3 \begin{bmatrix} -1 \\ 2 \\ 1 \end{bmatrix}$

2. $\begin{bmatrix} x_1 \\ x_2 \\ x_3 \\ x_4 \end{bmatrix} = \begin{bmatrix} +\frac{1}{3}x_4 \\ -\frac{1}{3}x_4 \\ -\frac{2}{3}x_4 \\ x_4 \end{bmatrix} = x_4 \begin{bmatrix} \frac{1}{3} \\ -\frac{1}{3} \\ -\frac{2}{3} \\ 1 \end{bmatrix}$

Exercises

A ■ In Exercises 1–14 find the general solution for each homogeneous system.

1. $\begin{aligned} 3x_1 + 2x_2 - \quad x_3 &= 0 \\ 2x_1 - \quad x_2 + 2x_3 &= 0 \end{aligned}$

2. $\begin{aligned} 2x_1 - \quad x_2 &= 0 \\ x_1 + 4x_2 &= 0 \\ 0x_1 + 0x_2 &= 0 \\ 3x_1 - 3x_2 &= 0 \end{aligned}$

3. $\begin{aligned} x_1 - 3x_2 &= 0 \\ 2x_1 + \quad x_2 &= 0 \end{aligned}$

4. $\begin{bmatrix} 2 & -\frac{1}{2} \\ 4 & -1 \end{bmatrix} \begin{bmatrix} x_1 \\ x_2 \end{bmatrix} = \begin{bmatrix} 0 \\ 0 \end{bmatrix}$

5. $\begin{bmatrix} 3 & -2 & 7 \\ 3 & 2 & -7 \end{bmatrix} \begin{bmatrix} x_1 \\ x_2 \\ x_3 \end{bmatrix} = {}_2O_1$

6. $\begin{bmatrix} 2 & -1 \\ 1 & 2 \\ 3 & -2 \end{bmatrix} \begin{bmatrix} x_1 \\ x_2 \end{bmatrix} = \begin{bmatrix} 0 \\ 0 \\ 0 \end{bmatrix}$

7. $\begin{aligned} 6x_1 - \quad x_2 + 2x_3 &= 0 \\ -x_1 + 3x_2 - \quad x_3 &= 0 \\ 2x_1 + 7x_2 \qquad &= 0 \end{aligned}$

8. $\begin{bmatrix} 10 & 12 & -1 \\ 3 & -7 & 6 \end{bmatrix} \begin{bmatrix} x_1 \\ x_2 \\ x_3 \end{bmatrix} = \begin{bmatrix} 0 \\ 0 \end{bmatrix}$

9.

$$[3 \;\; -2 \;\; 1]\begin{bmatrix} x_1 \\ x_2 \\ x_3 \end{bmatrix} = [0]$$

10.

$$\begin{bmatrix} 1 & 1 & 1 & 1 \\ 1 & -1 & 1 & 1 \\ 1 & -1 & -1 & 1 \\ 1 & -1 & -1 & -1 \end{bmatrix}\begin{bmatrix} x_1 \\ x_2 \\ x_3 \\ x_4 \end{bmatrix} = {}_4O_1$$

B 11.

$$\begin{bmatrix} 2 & 1 & 3 & 0 & 1 & 0 \\ 2 & -2 & 0 & -6 & 0 & 1 \\ 1 & -1 & 0 & -3 & -1 & 0 \\ -2 & 4 & -3 & 6 & 1 & 1 \end{bmatrix}\begin{bmatrix} x_1 \\ x_2 \\ x_3 \\ x_4 \\ x_5 \\ x_6 \end{bmatrix} = {}_4O_1$$

12. $3x_1 + 2x_2 - 7x_3 + 2x_4 + x_5 \qquad\quad = 0$
$\quad\;\; -x_1 + \;\; x_2 \qquad\quad\; - 7x_4 + x_5 + 3x_6 = 0$

C 13. $ix_1 + (1 + i)x_2 + 2x_3 = 0$ $\qquad i = \sqrt{-1}$
$\qquad 2x_1 - (1 - i)x_2 + ix_3 = 0$

14. $(1 + i)x_1 - ix_2 + 2ix_3 = 0$ $\qquad i = \sqrt{-1}$
$\quad\; (1 - 2i)x_1 + \;\; x_2 \qquad\qquad = 0$

15. Show that if for all x

$$c_3x^3 + c_2x^2 + c_1x + c_0 = 0$$

then

$$c_0 = c_1 = c_2 = c_3 = 0.$$

(*Hint:* Make four substitutions for x yielding 4 linear equations in $c_0, c_1, c_2,$ and c_3.)

16. Find all values of k such that the system

$$\begin{bmatrix} 2 & 1 \\ 3 & k \end{bmatrix}\begin{bmatrix} x_1 \\ x_2 \end{bmatrix} = \begin{bmatrix} 0 \\ 0 \end{bmatrix}$$

has only the trivial solution. For what values of k does the system have an infinite number of solutions?

17. Repeat Exercise 16 for the following system.

$$\begin{bmatrix} 1 & 3 \\ 3 & k^2 \end{bmatrix}\begin{bmatrix} x_1 \\ x_2 \end{bmatrix} = \begin{bmatrix} 0 \\ 0 \end{bmatrix}$$

18. Repeat Exercise 16 for the following system.

$$\begin{bmatrix} 1 & 1 & 1 \\ 1 & 2 & -1 \\ 1 & 2 & k^2 - 10 \end{bmatrix}\begin{bmatrix} x_1 \\ x_2 \\ x_3 \end{bmatrix} = {}_3O_1$$

11–5   Nonhomogeneous Systems of Equations

A nonhomogeneous system of m linear equations in n variables

$$AX = B$$

can be reduced to the reduced row echelon form as follows.

$$x_1 + c_{12}x_2 + 0x_3 + c_{14}x_4 + \cdots = d_1$$
$$x_3 + c_{24}x_4 + \cdots = d_2$$
$$\cdot \quad \cdot \quad \cdot \quad \cdot \quad \cdot \quad \cdot \quad \cdot \quad \cdot$$
$$x_{n-1} = d_{k-1}$$
$$x_n = d_k$$
$$0x_1 + 0x_2 + \cdots + 0x_k + \cdots + 0x_n = d_{k+1}$$
$$0x_1 + 0x_2 + \cdots + 0x_k + \cdots + 0x_n = d_m$$

In this system there are k ($k \leq m$) equations with at least one non-zero coefficient. There are $m - k$ equations with all zero coefficients. Denote this system

$$[C : D].$$

Note that if $d_{k+1} = 1$, then $[C : D]$ has no solution because there is at least one equation which can be satisfied by no replacements for x_i, $i = 1, \ldots n$. If $d_{k+1} = 0$, then $d_{k+2} = d_{k+3} = \cdots = d_m = 0$ because the augmented matrix is in reduced row echelon form. In this case there is at least one solution found by setting $x_n = d_k$, $x_{n-1} = d_{k-1}$, and so on, working backwards to find the remaining variables.

If some variables are expressed in terms of others that can take on a real number value, then the system $[C : D]$ has infinitely many solutions. However, if every variable is determined the solution is unique.

EXAMPLE 1.   Let $[C : D] = \begin{bmatrix} 1 & 0 & 0 & 0 & : & 4 \\ 0 & 1 & 0 & 0 & : & 2 \\ 0 & 0 & 1 & 0 & : & 1 \\ 0 & 0 & 0 & 1 & : & 2 \end{bmatrix}$

The solution is unique: $\begin{bmatrix} x_1 \\ x_2 \\ x_3 \\ x_4 \end{bmatrix} = \begin{bmatrix} 4 \\ 2 \\ 1 \\ 2 \end{bmatrix}$

In this case every unknown is determined.

The following example will illustrate the case where there is an infinite set of solutions for the variables.

EXAMPLE 2. Let $[C : D] = \begin{bmatrix} 1 & 0 & 3 & 0 & \vdots & 3 \\ 0 & 1 & 1 & 0 & \vdots & 2 \\ 0 & 0 & 0 & 1 & \vdots & 6 \\ 0 & 0 & 0 & 0 & \vdots & 0 \end{bmatrix}$

This system has an infinite set of solutions for x_1 and x_2 can be expressed in terms of x_3. That is, $x_1 = 3 - 3x_3$

$$x_2 = 2 - x_3$$
$$x_3 = x_3$$
$$x_4 = 6$$

Thus the general solution is

$$\begin{bmatrix} x_1 \\ x_2 \\ x_3 \\ x_4 \end{bmatrix} = \begin{bmatrix} 3 - 3x_3 \\ 2 - x_3 \\ 0 + x_3 \\ 6 + 0x_3 \end{bmatrix} = \begin{bmatrix} 3 \\ 2 \\ 0 \\ 6 \end{bmatrix} + x_3 \begin{bmatrix} -3 \\ -1 \\ 1 \\ 0 \end{bmatrix}, \quad x_3 \in R$$

The general solution to this system illustrates an interesting theorem. Before this theorem is stated consider the next example.

EXAMPLE 3. Find the general solution to the homogeneous system

$$[C : O] = \begin{bmatrix} 1 & 0 & 3 & 0 & \vdots & 0 \\ 0 & 1 & 1 & 0 & \vdots & 0 \\ 0 & 0 & 0 & 1 & \vdots & 0 \\ 0 & 0 & 0 & 0 & \vdots & 0 \end{bmatrix}$$

Clearly the solution is

$$x_1 = -3x_3$$
$$x_2 = - x_3$$
$$x_3 = x_3$$
$$x_4 = 0$$

The general solution then is $\begin{bmatrix} x_1 \\ x_2 \\ x_3 \\ x_4 \end{bmatrix} = x_3 \begin{bmatrix} -3 \\ -1 \\ 1 \\ 0 \end{bmatrix}$

Now compare the results of Examples 2 and 3. You see that the general solution to the homogeneous system $[C : O]$ is part of the general solution to the nonhomogeneous system $[C : D]$. The other part of the general solution of $[C : D]$ is one particular solution. Thus the solution of the nonhomogeneous system is a linear combination of a particular solution to $[C : D]$ and the general solution to the homogeneous system $[C : O]$. This result is stated in the next theorem.

Theorem 11–9 Y is a solution of $AX = B$ iff $Y = Z + c_1Z_1 + c_2Z_2 + \cdots + c_kZ_k$ where Z is a particular solution to $AX = B$ and $c_1Z_1 + c_2Z_2 + \cdots + c_kZ_k$ is the general solution to $AX = O$.

Proof: Suppose $AY = B$. Then by Theorem 11–3, Part **e**,

$$A(Y - Z) = AY - AZ = B - B = 0$$

It follows that $Y - Z$ is a solution to $AX = O$.

Thus

$$Y - Z = c_1Z_1 + c_2Z_2 + \cdots + c_kZ_k$$

or

$$Y = Z + c_1Z_1 + c_2Z_2 + \cdots + c_kZ_k.$$

Conversely if

$$Y = Z + c_1Z_1 + c_2Z_2 + \cdots + c_kZ_k$$

then

$$AY = A(Z + c_1Z_1 + c_2Z_2 + \cdots + c_kZ_k).$$

by Theorem 11–3, Part **c**.

$$= AZ + c_1AZ_1 + c_2AZ_2 + \cdots + c_kAZ_k$$
$$= B + O + O + \cdots + O$$
$$= B$$

Thus Y is a solution to $AX = B$.

Theorem 11–10 If $AX = O$ has only one solution (the trivial solution) then $AX = B$ has no more than one solution.

Proof: Suppose X_1 and X_2 are solutions to $AX = B$ and $X_1 \neq X_2$. Then

$$X_1 - X_2 \neq 0$$

and

$$A(X_1 - X_2) = AX_1 - AX_2$$
$$= B - B$$
$$= O$$

Thus $X_1 - X_2 \neq O$ is a second solution to $AX = O$. This contradicts the assumption that $AX = O$ has only the trivial solution.

EXAMPLE 4. For $A = \begin{bmatrix} 1 & -2 & 3 & 2 \\ -2 & -1 & 4 & 1 \end{bmatrix}$, $X = \begin{bmatrix} 1 \\ 0 \\ 2 \\ -1 \end{bmatrix}$, $B = \begin{bmatrix} 5 \\ 5 \end{bmatrix}$

$AX = B$. Find the general solution and 3 other particular solutions.

Since $X = \begin{bmatrix} 1 \\ 0 \\ 2 \\ -1 \end{bmatrix}$ is a particular solution, you need only find the general solution to $AX = O$.

$\begin{bmatrix} 1 & -2 & 3 & 2 \\ -2 & -1 & 4 & 1 \end{bmatrix}$ is row equivalent to $\begin{bmatrix} 1 & 0 & -1 & 0 \\ 0 & 1 & -2 & -1 \end{bmatrix}$.

The general solution to $AX = O$ is therefore

$$\begin{bmatrix} x_1 \\ x_2 \\ x_3 \\ x_4 \end{bmatrix} = \begin{bmatrix} x_3 \\ 2x_3 + x_4 \\ x_3 \\ 0x_3 + x_4 \end{bmatrix} = x_3 \begin{bmatrix} 1 \\ 2 \\ 1 \\ 0 \end{bmatrix} + x_4 \begin{bmatrix} 0 \\ 1 \\ 0 \\ 1 \end{bmatrix}, \quad x_3, x_4 \in \mathbf{R}$$

The general solution to $AX = B$ is a linear combination of a particular solution to $AX = B$ and the general solution to $AX = O$.

$$\begin{bmatrix} x_1 \\ x_2 \\ x_3 \\ x_4 \end{bmatrix} = \begin{bmatrix} 1 \\ 0 \\ 2 \\ -1 \end{bmatrix} + x_3 \begin{bmatrix} 1 \\ 2 \\ 1 \\ 0 \end{bmatrix} + x_4 \begin{bmatrix} 0 \\ 1 \\ 0 \\ 1 \end{bmatrix}, \quad x_3, x_4 \in \mathbf{R}$$

Three particular solutions are as follows.

$x_3 = 1, x_4 = 0$	$x_3 = 0, x_4 = 1$	$x_3 = 1, x_4 = 10$
$\begin{bmatrix} 2 \\ 2 \\ 3 \\ -1 \end{bmatrix}$	$\begin{bmatrix} 1 \\ 1 \\ 2 \\ 0 \end{bmatrix}$	$\begin{bmatrix} 2 \\ 12 \\ 3 \\ 9 \end{bmatrix}$

Now try these

━━ Write the general and 3 particular solutions if they exist.

1. $x_1 - x_2 = -1$
$x_1 + x_2 = 6$
$x_1 + x_2 = 7$

2. $x_1 - x_2 - x_3 = 3$
$3x_1 + 6x_2 - 7x_3 = -13$

Answers: **1.** No solution. **2.** $\begin{bmatrix} x_1 \\ x_2 \\ x_3 \end{bmatrix} = \begin{bmatrix} 2 \\ -2 \\ 1 \end{bmatrix} + x_3 \begin{bmatrix} \frac{13}{9} \\ \frac{4}{9} \\ 1 \end{bmatrix}, \begin{bmatrix} 15 \\ 2 \\ 10 \end{bmatrix}, \begin{bmatrix} -11 \\ -6 \\ -8 \end{bmatrix}, \begin{bmatrix} 28 \\ 6 \\ 19 \end{bmatrix}$.

Exercises

A ▬ Which of the ordered triples in Exercises 1–6 are solutions to

$$\begin{bmatrix} 1 & 1 & 1 \\ 1 & -1 & 1 \end{bmatrix} \begin{bmatrix} x_1 \\ x_2 \\ x_3 \end{bmatrix} = \begin{bmatrix} 0 \\ 0 \end{bmatrix} ?$$

1. $\begin{bmatrix} -2 \\ 0 \\ 2 \end{bmatrix}$

2. $\begin{bmatrix} 2 \\ 1 \\ -3 \end{bmatrix}$

3. $\begin{bmatrix} -1 \\ 0 \\ 1 \end{bmatrix}$

4. $\begin{bmatrix} 1 \\ 1 \\ -2 \end{bmatrix} + \begin{bmatrix} -1 \\ 0 \\ 1 \end{bmatrix}$

5. $\begin{bmatrix} 0 \\ 0 \\ 0 \end{bmatrix}$

6. $\begin{bmatrix} -c \\ 0 \\ c \end{bmatrix} \ c \in R$

▬ Which of the ordered triples in Exercise 7–12 are solutions to

$$\begin{bmatrix} 1 & 1 & 1 \\ 1 & -1 & 1 \end{bmatrix} \begin{bmatrix} x_1 \\ x_2 \\ x_3 \end{bmatrix} = \begin{bmatrix} 0 \\ -2 \end{bmatrix} ?$$

7. $\begin{bmatrix} -2 \\ 0 \\ 2 \end{bmatrix}$

8. $\begin{bmatrix} 2 \\ 1 \\ -3 \end{bmatrix}$

9. $\begin{bmatrix} -1 \\ 0 \\ 1 \end{bmatrix}$

10. $\begin{bmatrix} -1 \\ 1 \\ 0 \end{bmatrix} + \begin{bmatrix} -1 \\ 0 \\ 1 \end{bmatrix}$

11. $\begin{bmatrix} -6 \\ 1 \\ 5 \end{bmatrix}$

12. $\begin{bmatrix} 1 \\ 1 \\ -2 \end{bmatrix} + \begin{bmatrix} -c \\ 0 \\ c \end{bmatrix} \ c \in R$

▬ Write the general and 3 particular solutions if they exist.

13. $\begin{aligned} x_1 - 3x_2 &= 1 \\ 2x_1 - x_2 &= 4 \end{aligned}$

14. $\begin{aligned} x_1 - 5x_2 &= 2 \\ -3x_1 + 15x_2 &= -6 \end{aligned}$

15. $\begin{aligned} 2x_1 + x_2 + 4x_3 &= 3 \\ x_1 + x_2 + 2x_3 &= 2 \\ 3x_1 + x_2 + 6x_3 &= 6 \end{aligned}$

16. $\begin{aligned} 2x_1 + x_2 + x_3 &= 1 \\ -2x_1 - x_2 + x_3 &= 2 \\ 4x_1 + 2x_2 + 3x_3 &= 1 \end{aligned}$

17.
$$\begin{bmatrix} 2 & 1 & 0 & 1 \\ 3 & 3 & 3 & 5 \\ 3 & 0 & -3 & -2 \end{bmatrix} \begin{bmatrix} x_1 \\ x_2 \\ x_3 \\ x_4 \end{bmatrix} = \begin{bmatrix} 2 \\ 4 \\ 3 \end{bmatrix}$$

18. $\begin{aligned} 2x_1 + x_2 \qquad + x_4 &= 2 \\ 3x_1 \qquad - 3x_3 - 2x_4 &= 3 \\ 3x_1 + 3x_2 + 3x_3 + 5x_4 &= 3 \end{aligned}$

19.
$$\begin{aligned} x_1 \qquad + x_3 + x_4 \qquad - x_6 &= -4 \\ x_1 + x_2 + x_3 \qquad\qquad &= 1 \\ - x_2 + x_3 \qquad + x_5 + x_6 &= 0 \\ x_1 - x_2 + x_3 + x_4 + x_5 + x_6 &= 1 \\ -x_1 \qquad - x_3 \qquad - x_5 + x_6 &= 3 \\ x_4 + x_5 + x_6 &= 4 \end{aligned}$$

B **20.**
$$\begin{bmatrix} 2 & 1 & 2 & 3 & 1 & 1 \\ 0 & 1 & 1 & 2 & 2 & 0 \\ 2 & 1 & 3 & 1 & 0 & 5 \\ 4 & 3 & 6 & 6 & 3 & 10 \\ 0 & 0 & 0 & 3 & 1 & 1 \\ 0 & 1 & 1 & 2 & 4 & 0 \end{bmatrix} \begin{bmatrix} x_1 \\ x_2 \\ x_3 \\ x_4 \\ x_5 \\ x_6 \end{bmatrix} = \begin{bmatrix} 7 \\ -1 \\ 1 \\ -1 \\ 1 \\ 0 \end{bmatrix}$$

21.
$$2x_1 + x_2 + 2x_3 + 3x_4 + x_5 = 1$$
$$x_2 + x_3 + 2x_4 + x_5 = -1$$
$$2x_1 + x_2 + 3x_3 + x_4 = 3$$

In Exercises 22–25 determine all values of k, if possible, for which the resulting system has

a. no solution.

b. a unique solution.

c. infinitely many solutions.

22.
$$x_1 + x_2 - x_3 = 2$$
$$x_1 + 2x_2 + x_3 = 3$$
$$x_1 + x_2 + (k^2 - 5)x_3 = k$$

23.
$$x_1 + x_2 + x_3 = 2$$
$$2x_1 + 3x_2 + 2x_3 = 5$$
$$2x_1 + 3x_2 + (k^2 - 1)x_3 = k + 1$$

24.
$$x_1 + x_2 + x_3 = 2$$
$$x_1 + 2x_2 + x_3 = 3$$
$$x_1 + x_2 + (k^2 - 5)x_3 = k$$

25.
$$x_1 + x_2 + x_3 = 2$$
$$x_1 + 2x_2 - x_3 = -3$$
$$x_1 + 2x_2 + (k^2 - 10)x_3 = k$$

C **26.** A trucking company owns three types of trucks, numbered I, II, III. The trucks are equipped to haul three different types of machines per load according to the following chart

	Trucks		
	I	II	III
Machine X	1	1	1
Machine Y	0	1	2
Machine Z	2	1	1

How many trucks of each type should be sent to haul exactly 15 type X machines, 17 type Y machines, and 20 type Z machines? Assume each truck is fully loaded.

11–6 Invertible Matrices and Elementary Matrices

There is a special method for solving nonhomogeneous systems which have exactly as many equations as variables. In this case the coefficient matrix is $n \times n$. This method is founded on the concepts of invertible matrices and elementary matrices.

Definition An $n \times n$ matrix is invertible iff there is an $n \times n$ matrix B such that

$$AB = BA = \begin{bmatrix} 1 & 0 & 0 & . & . & 0 \\ 0 & 1 & . & . & . & 0 \\ \vdots & & & & & \\ 0 & 0 & . & . & . & 1 \end{bmatrix} = I_n$$

Otherwise A is noninvertible. B is the inverse of A and I_n is the $n \times n$ identity matrix. That is, $AI_n = I_n A = A$.

Some useful theorems on invertible matrices follow.

Theorem 11–11 The inverse of a matrix, if it exists, is unique.

Proof: Let C and D be inverses for A. Then $AC = CA = I_n$ and $AD = DA = I_n$. But $C = CI_n = C(AD) = (CA)D = I_n D = D$. Thus $C = D$ and the inverse is unique. The inverse of A is denoted A^{-1}, read "A inverse".

Theorem 11–12 If A and B are both invertible $n \times n$ matrices, then AB is invertible and $(AB)^{-1} = B^{-1}A^{-1}$.

Proof: $AB(B^{-1}A^{-1}) = A(BB^{-1})A^{-1} = (AI_n)A^{-1} = AA^{-1} = I_n$. Similarly $(B^{-1}A^{-1})AB = B^{-1}(A^{-1}A)B = B^{-1}I_n B = B^{-1}B = I_n$. Thus AB is invertible because $B^{-1}A^{-1}$ is its inverse. Since the inverse is unique,

$$B^{-1}A^{-1} = (AB)^{-1}.$$

The proofs of Theorems 11–13 and 11–14 are left for you to do in the exercises.

Stop a moment and consider the usefulness of A^{-1}, when it exists, in connection with the nonhomogeneous $n \times n$ system $AX = B$. If you know A^{-1}, then multiplying both sides of $AX = B$ by A^{-1} yields the following.

$$A^{-1}(AX) = A^{-1}B$$

or
$$I_n X = A^{-1}B$$

or
$$X = A^{-1}B$$

Thus, no matter what B happens to be, the system is easily solved by multiplying B by A^{-1} on the left. One calculation of A^{-1} is all that is needed to solve infinitely many systems.

The question now is: How can you calculate A^{-1}, when it exists? The answer to this question lies in the notion of elementary matrices.

Definition An $n \times n$ elementary matrix of type I, II or III is a matrix obtained from the identity matrix I_n by performing an elementary row operation of type I, II or III (see Section 11–2).

EXAMPLE 1. Examples of elementary matrices are

$$E_1 = \begin{bmatrix} 0 & 1 & 0 \\ 1 & 0 & 0 \\ 0 & 0 & 1 \end{bmatrix} \quad \text{(interchange of \textit{row 1} and \textit{row 2})}$$

$$E_2 = \begin{bmatrix} 1 & 0 & 0 \\ 0 & 1 & 0 \\ 0 & 0 & -2 \end{bmatrix} \quad \text{(multiplication of \textit{row 3} by } -2\text{)}$$

$$E_3 = \begin{bmatrix} 1 & 0 & 4 \\ 0 & 1 & 0 \\ 0 & 0 & 1 \end{bmatrix} \quad \text{(multiplication of \textit{row 3} by 4 followed by addition to \textit{row 1})}$$

The two recommending features of elementary matrices are
1. each such matrix is invertible and its inverse is an elementary matrix of the same type and
2. a row operation on an $m \times n$ matrix A may be carried out by pre-multiplication of A by an elementary matrix E which is obtained by performing the same row operation on I_m.

These facts are illustrated in Example 2.

EXAMPLE 2. Let E_1, E_2 and E_3 be as in Example 1.

$$E_1^{-1} = \begin{bmatrix} 0 & 1 & 0 \\ 1 & 0 & 0 \\ 0 & 0 & 1 \end{bmatrix} = E_1 \quad \text{(Check this by multiplication.)}$$

$$E_2^{-1} = \begin{bmatrix} 1 & 0 & 0 \\ 0 & 1 & 0 \\ 0 & 0 & -\frac{1}{2} \end{bmatrix} \quad \begin{array}{l} \text{(Check this by computing} \\ E_2^{-1}E_2 \text{ and } E_2 E_2^{-1}.) \end{array}$$

$$E_3^{-1} = \begin{bmatrix} 1 & 0 & -4 \\ 0 & 1 & 0 \\ 0 & 0 & 1 \end{bmatrix} \quad \text{(Check this.)}$$

Thus each inverse is of the same type as the original elementary matrix.

$$\text{Let } A = \begin{bmatrix} 2 & 1 & 3 \\ 3 & 1 & 2 \\ 1 & 2 & 3 \end{bmatrix}. \qquad \text{Then } E_1 A = \begin{bmatrix} 3 & 1 & 2 \\ 2 & 1 & 3 \\ 1 & 2 & 3 \end{bmatrix}.$$

Premultiplication of A by E_1 interchanges rows 1 and 2. (Check this.) Furthermore,

$$E_2 A = \begin{bmatrix} 2 & 1 & 3 \\ 3 & 1 & 2 \\ -2 & -4 & -6 \end{bmatrix} \cdot \quad \begin{array}{l} \text{Premultiplication of } A \text{ by } E_2 \\ \text{multiplies } row\ 3 \text{ by } -2. \\ \text{(Check the multiplication.)} \end{array}$$

$$E_3 A = \begin{bmatrix} 1 & 0 & 4 \\ 0 & 1 & 0 \\ 0 & 0 & 1 \end{bmatrix} \begin{bmatrix} 2 & 1 & 3 \\ 3 & 1 & 2 \\ 1 & 2 & 3 \end{bmatrix} = \begin{bmatrix} 6 & 9 & 15 \\ 3 & 1 & 2 \\ 1 & 2 & 3 \end{bmatrix}$$

$$= \begin{bmatrix} 2 + (4 \times 1) & 1 + (4 \times 2) & 3 + (4 \times 3) \\ 3 & 1 & 2 \\ 1 & 2 & 3 \end{bmatrix}$$

Premultiplication of A by E_3 adds 4 times $row\ 3$ of A to $row\ 1$ of A.

Elementary row operations can be performed by premultiplication by elementary matrices. Thus row equivalent matrices are obtainable from one another by premultiplication by elementary matrices.

Theorem 11–15 If A and B are $m \times n$ matrices, then A is row equivalent to B if and only if $B = E_k E_{k-1} \cdots E_1 A$ where $E_k, E_{k-1}, \cdots, E_1$ are elementary matrices.

The proof is left for you to do in the exercises.

Theorem 11–16 Let A be an $n \times n$ matrix and let $AX = {}_nO_n$ have only the trivial solution $X = {}_nO_1$, then A is row equivalent to I_n.

Proof: Reduce A to the row equivalent matrix B in reduced row echelon form. Then $AX = O$ and $BX = O$ are equivalent, that is both have only the trivial solution. Let k be the number of nonzero rows of B. The homogeneous system consisting of the k nonzero rows of B is equivalent to $BX = O$. Thus it is a $k \times n$ matrix. Since this homogeneous system has only the trivial solution, then by Theorem 11–7, $k \geq n$. Since B is $n \times n$, $k \leq n$. Thus $k = n$. Therefore B has no nonzero rows and $B = I_n$.

A major theorem is now stated.

Theorem 11–17 A is invertible if and only if A is the product of elementary matrices.

Proof: If $A = E_1 E_2 \cdots E_k$ where E_i is an elementary matrix, then A is invertible because each E_i is and so is their product (Theorem 11–13).

Conversely, if A is invertible then $AX = O$ implies that $A^{-1}(AX) = A^{-1}O = O = (A^{-1}A)X$, so that $I_n X = O$ or $X = O$. Thus $AX = O$ has only the trivial solution. Thus by the Theorem 11–16, A is row equivalent to I_n. So there are E_i such that $I_n = E_k E_{k-1} \cdots E_1 A$. Thus $A = E_1^{-1} E_2^{-1} \cdots E_k^{-1}$. (Why?) Since the inverse of each elementary matrix is an elementary matrix, the result is established.

Notice above that $E_k E_{k-1} \cdots E_1 A = I_n$. Thus $A^{-1} = E_k E_{k-1} \cdots E_1$. The inverse of A, if it exists, is the product of the elementary matrices used to reduce A to I_n. A convenient way to organize this into an algorithm is as follows.

Let A be $n \times n$. Write the $n \times 2n$ matrix.

$$[A : I_n]$$

Then

$$(E_k E_{k-1} \cdots E_1)[A : I_n] = [E_k E_{k-1} \cdots E_1 A : E_k E_{k-1} \cdots E_1 I_n]$$
$$= [I_n : A^{-1}]$$

That is, the elementary row operations are performed on the $n \times 2n$ matrix $[A : I_n]$.

An example will illustrate the procedure.

EXAMPLE 3. Find the inverse of $A = \begin{bmatrix} 1 & 2 & 3 \\ 1 & 1 & 2 \\ 0 & 1 & 2 \end{bmatrix}$.

First write $\begin{bmatrix} 1 & 2 & 3 & \vdots & 1 & 0 & 0 \\ 1 & 1 & 2 & \vdots & 0 & 1 & 0 \\ 0 & 1 & 2 & \vdots & 0 & 0 & 1 \end{bmatrix}$.

Then perform the row operations necessary to reduce the left half of the above matrix to I_3.

Add -1 times
row 1 to row 2.
$\begin{bmatrix} 1 & 2 & 3 & \vdots & 1 & 0 & 0 \\ 0 & -1 & -1 & \vdots & -1 & 1 & 0 \\ 0 & 1 & 2 & \vdots & 0 & 0 & 1 \end{bmatrix}$

Add row 2 to row 3.
$\begin{bmatrix} 1 & 2 & 3 & \vdots & 1 & 0 & 0 \\ 0 & -1 & -1 & \vdots & -1 & 1 & 0 \\ 0 & 0 & 1 & \vdots & -1 & 1 & 1 \end{bmatrix}$

Add row 3 to row 2.
$\begin{bmatrix} 1 & 2 & 3 & \vdots & 1 & 0 & 0 \\ 0 & -1 & 0 & \vdots & -2 & 2 & 1 \\ 0 & 0 & 1 & \vdots & -1 & 1 & 1 \end{bmatrix}$

Add 2 times
row 2 to row 1.
$\begin{bmatrix} 1 & 0 & 3 & \vdots & -3 & 4 & 2 \\ 0 & -1 & 0 & \vdots & -2 & 2 & 1 \\ 0 & 0 & 1 & \vdots & -1 & 1 & 1 \end{bmatrix}$

Add -3 times
row 3 to row 1.
$\begin{bmatrix} 1 & 0 & 0 & \vdots & 0 & 1 & -1 \\ 0 & -1 & 0 & \vdots & -2 & 2 & 1 \\ 0 & 0 & 1 & \vdots & -1 & 1 & 1 \end{bmatrix}$

Multiply row 2
by -1.
$\begin{bmatrix} 1 & 0 & 0 & \vdots & 0 & 1 & -1 \\ 0 & 1 & 0 & \vdots & 2 & -2 & -1 \\ 0 & 0 & 1 & \vdots & -1 & 1 & 1 \end{bmatrix}$

Thus, $\begin{bmatrix} 0 & 1 & -1 \\ 2 & -2 & -1 \\ -1 & 1 & 1 \end{bmatrix}$ is the inverse of $\begin{bmatrix} 1 & 2 & 3 \\ 1 & 1 & 2 \\ 0 & 1 & 2 \end{bmatrix}$.

EXAMPLE 4. Solve the following system.

$$\begin{bmatrix} 1 & 2 & 3 \\ 1 & 1 & 2 \\ 0 & 1 & 2 \end{bmatrix} \begin{bmatrix} x_1 \\ x_2 \\ x_3 \end{bmatrix} = \begin{bmatrix} 1 \\ 7 \\ 5 \end{bmatrix}$$

In Example 3 you found

$$\begin{bmatrix} 1 & 2 & 3 \\ 1 & 1 & 2 \\ 0 & 1 & 2 \end{bmatrix}^{-1} = \begin{bmatrix} 0 & 1 & -1 \\ 2 & -2 & -1 \\ -1 & 1 & 1 \end{bmatrix}.$$

Multiply both sides of the equation by this inverse.

$$\begin{bmatrix} 0 & 1 & -1 \\ 2 & -2 & -1 \\ -1 & 1 & 1 \end{bmatrix}\begin{bmatrix} 1 & 2 & 3 \\ 1 & 1 & 2 \\ 0 & 1 & 2 \end{bmatrix} \begin{bmatrix} x_1 \\ x_2 \\ x_3 \end{bmatrix} = \begin{bmatrix} 0 & 1 & -1 \\ 2 & -2 & -1 \\ -1 & 1 & 1 \end{bmatrix}\begin{bmatrix} 1 \\ 7 \\ 5 \end{bmatrix}$$

or

$$\begin{bmatrix} 1 & 0 & 0 \\ 0 & 1 & 0 \\ 0 & 0 & 1 \end{bmatrix} \begin{bmatrix} x_1 \\ x_2 \\ x_3 \end{bmatrix} = \begin{bmatrix} 2 \\ -17 \\ 11 \end{bmatrix}$$

or

$$\begin{bmatrix} x_1 \\ x_2 \\ x_3 \end{bmatrix} = \begin{bmatrix} 2 \\ -17 \\ 11 \end{bmatrix}$$

If in carrying out the algorithm illustrated in Example 3 you should obtain a row of zeros in the left hand half of $[A : I_n]$, then A is not invertible and you may stop the process.

Now try these

▬ For each matrix, find the inverse, if it exists.

1. $\begin{bmatrix} .2 & 0 & 0 & 0 \\ 0 & .2 & 0 & 0 \\ 0 & 0 & .2 & 0 \\ 0 & 0 & 0 & .2 \end{bmatrix}$

2. $\begin{bmatrix} 1 & 2 \\ 3 & 6 \end{bmatrix}$

3. $\begin{bmatrix} a & b \\ c & d \end{bmatrix}$ where $ad - bc \neq 0$

Answers: 1. $\begin{bmatrix} 5 & 0 & 0 & 0 \\ 0 & 5 & 0 & 0 \\ 0 & 0 & 5 & 0 \\ 0 & 0 & 0 & 5 \end{bmatrix}$ 2. Inverse does not exist. 3. $\begin{bmatrix} \dfrac{d}{ad-bc} & \dfrac{-b}{ad-bc} \\ \dfrac{-c}{ad-bc} & \dfrac{a}{ad-bc} \end{bmatrix}$

Exercises

Let $A = \begin{bmatrix} 1 & 1 & 1 & 1 & 1 \\ 1 & -1 & 1 & 1 & 1 \\ 1 & -1 & -1 & 1 & 1 \\ 1 & -1 & -1 & -1 & 1 \end{bmatrix}$

In Exercises 1–7 construct the elementary matrix which will result in each row operation described. Perform the multiplication to substantiate your construction.

1. Interchange *row 2* and *4*.

2. Interchange *row 1* and *4*.

3. Multiply *row 3* by $-\frac{2}{3}$.

4. Multiply *row 1* by 100.

5. Add 3 times *row 2* to *row 3*.

6. Add -1 times *row 1* to *row 2*.

7. Add $\frac{2}{3}$ *row 3* to *row 4*.

8. Find the three elementary matrices needed to replace the first 1 in *rows 2, 3,* and *4* of matrix A by 0.

9. Give a single matrix that will do what the three matrices of Exercise 8 do in combination.

10. What is the matrix row equivalent to A after the three elementary row operations of Exercises 8 or 9?

11. Find the inverse of each elementary matrix found in Exercises 1–7.

Find the inverse, if it exists in Exercises 12–19.

12. $\begin{bmatrix} 1 & 1 & 1 \\ 1 & 2 & 3 \\ 0 & 1 & 1 \end{bmatrix}$

13. $\begin{bmatrix} 1 & 2 & 1 \\ 1 & 3 & 2 \\ 1 & 0 & 1 \end{bmatrix}$

14. $\begin{bmatrix} 1 & 1 & 1 & 1 \\ 1 & -1 & 1 & 1 \\ 1 & -1 & -1 & 1 \\ 1 & -1 & -1 & -1 \end{bmatrix}$

15. $\begin{bmatrix} 1 & 2 & 2 \\ 1 & 3 & 1 \\ 1 & 3 & 2 \end{bmatrix}$

16. $\begin{bmatrix} 1 & 1 & 1 & 1 \\ 1 & 3 & 1 & 2 \\ 1 & 2 & -1 & 1 \\ 5 & 9 & 1 & 6 \end{bmatrix}$

17. $\begin{bmatrix} 1 & 1 & 1 & 1 \\ 1 & 2 & -1 & 2 \\ 1 & -1 & 2 & 1 \\ 1 & 3 & 3 & 2 \end{bmatrix}$

18. $\begin{bmatrix} 1 & 2 & -3 & 1 \\ -1 & 3 & -3 & -2 \\ 2 & 0 & 1 & 5 \\ 3 & 1 & -2 & 5 \end{bmatrix}$

19. $\begin{bmatrix} 1 & 1 & 2 & 1 \\ 0 & -2 & 0 & 0 \\ 1 & 2 & 1 & -2 \\ 0 & 3 & 2 & 1 \end{bmatrix}$

In Exercises 20–25, solve each system using the methods of this section if possible. If these methods are inappropriate, use other methods.

20. $AX = \begin{bmatrix} 2 \\ -2 \\ 1 \end{bmatrix}$ A is the matrix of Exercise 12.

21. $AX = \begin{bmatrix} 5 \\ 0 \\ 1 \end{bmatrix}$ A is the matrix of Exercise 13.

22. $AX = \begin{bmatrix} 0 \\ 0 \\ 1 \end{bmatrix}$ A is the matrix of Exercise 15.

23. $AX = \begin{bmatrix} -1 \\ -1 \\ -1 \\ -1 \end{bmatrix}$ A is the matrix of Exercise 14.

24. $AX = \begin{bmatrix} 1 \\ 0 \\ 0 \\ 1 \end{bmatrix}$ A is the matrix of Exercise 16.

25. $AX = \begin{bmatrix} 0 \\ 1 \\ 2 \\ 3 \end{bmatrix}$ A is the matrix of Exercise 17.

B **26.** Let $A = \begin{bmatrix} 1 & 2 \\ 4 & 6 \end{bmatrix}$.

Find

        a. E_1 which adds -4 times *row 1* to *row 2*.
        b. E_2 which multiplies *row 2* by $-\frac{1}{2}$.
        c. E_3 which multiplies *row 2* by -2 and adds it to *row 1*.
        d. $E_3 E_2 E_1 = B$.
        e. What is BA? What is B?

27. Prove Theorem 11–13.

28. Prove Theorem 11–14.

29. Prove Theorem 11–15.

C **30.** Prove that two $m \times n$ matrices A and B are row equivalent if and only if there exists an invertible matrix P such that $B = PA$. (*Hint:* Use Theorem 11–13 and Theorem 11–15.)

31. Prove: A matrix A is invertible if and only if A is row equivalent to I_n. (*Hint:* Use Theorem 11–13 and 11–14.)

32. Prove: The system of n homogeneous linear equations in n unknowns $AX = O$ has a nontrivial solution if and only if A is noninvertible. (*Hint:* Use Theorem 11–16 and Exercise 31.)

33. Prove: If one row of the $n \times n$ matrix A consists entirely of zeros, then A is noninvertible. (*Hint:* Use an indirect argument. Assume A is invertible; i.e., there exists an $n \times n$ matrix B such that $AB = BA = I_n$. Get a contradiction.)

34. Prove: An $n \times n$ matrix A is noninvertible if A is row equivalent to a matrix B that has a row consisting entirely of zeros. (*Hint:* Let A be row equivalent to B with a row of zeros. Use Exercise 33 and the assumption that A is invertible to get a contradiction.)

CHAPTER OBJECTIVES AND REVIEW

Objective: *To know the meaning of the important mathematical terms of this chapter.*

1. Here are many of the mathematical terms used in this chapter. Be sure that you know them thoroughly and can use them correctly.

scalar product (*538*)
homogeneous system of linear
   equations (*544*)
nonhomogeneous system of
   linear equations (*544*)
trivial solution (*544*)
nontrivial solution (*544*)

row echelon form (*549*)
reduced row echelon form
   (*550*)
elementary row operations
   (*550*)
invertible matrix (*567*)

Objective: *To review the addition and multiplication of matrices for which these operations are defined.*

━━ In Exercises 2–5 find the product, if it exists.

2. $\begin{bmatrix} 2 & 3 & 4 \\ 2 & -1 & 0 \end{bmatrix} \begin{bmatrix} 1 & 2 \\ 3 & -1 \\ 4 & 0 \end{bmatrix}$

3. $\begin{bmatrix} 1 & -2 & -3 & 1 \end{bmatrix} \begin{bmatrix} 1 & 2 & 3 \\ 3 & 2 & 1 \\ 2 & 1 & 3 \\ 3 & 1 & 2 \end{bmatrix}$

4. $\begin{bmatrix} 1 & 2 \\ 3 & -1 \\ 4 & 0 \end{bmatrix} \begin{bmatrix} 1 & 3 & 4 \\ 2 & -1 & 0 \end{bmatrix}$

5. $\begin{bmatrix} 1 \\ -3 \\ 2 \\ 5 \end{bmatrix} \begin{bmatrix} 2 & 3 & 4 & 5 & 1 \end{bmatrix}$

In Exercises 6–9 find the sum, if it exists.

6.
$$\begin{bmatrix} 1 & 3 & 4 \\ 2 & -1 & 0 \end{bmatrix} + \begin{bmatrix} 1 & 2 \\ 3 & -1 \\ 4 & 0 \end{bmatrix}$$

7.
$$\begin{bmatrix} 1 & 2 & 3 \\ 3 & 2 & 1 \\ 4 & 1 & 3 \end{bmatrix} + \begin{bmatrix} -2 & -1 & 3 \\ 0 & 4 & -2 \\ 5 & -1 & -3 \end{bmatrix}$$

8.
$$\begin{bmatrix} 1 & 2 & 3 \end{bmatrix} + \begin{bmatrix} 1 \\ 2 \\ 3 \end{bmatrix}$$

9.
$$\begin{bmatrix} 1 & -2 \\ 2 & -1 \\ 1 & 0 \\ 0 & 1 \end{bmatrix} + \begin{bmatrix} 1 & 2 \\ -2 & 3 \\ -1 & 1 \\ 1 & -1 \end{bmatrix}$$

10. Find the scalar product of the number 3 and each of the following matrices.

$$\begin{bmatrix} 1 & -2 \\ 2 & -1 \\ 1 & 0 \end{bmatrix} \text{ and } \begin{bmatrix} 1 & 2 \\ -2 & 3 \\ -1 & 1 \end{bmatrix}$$

Objective: *To identify homogeneous and nonhomogeneous systems of linear equations and denote them in matrix form.*

11. Tell in your own words what a homogeneous system of linear equations is and what a nonhomogeneous system is. What is the essential difference?

12. Express the system

$$2x_1 + 3x_2 - x_3 = 0$$
$$4x_1 + 0x_2 + 2x_3 = 5$$

in matrix form: $AX = B$. Identify A, X, and B and their dimensions.

Objective: *To define and illustrate the three elementary row operations which when performed on a system of linear equations or its augmented matrix yield an equivalent system.*

13. What are the three manipulations of a system of linear equations that yield an equivalent system?

14. Illustrate each of the manipulations you identified in Exercise 13 with the following system.

$$8x_1 + 3x_2 + 5x_3 = 5$$
$$2x_1 - x_2 + 9x_3 = 3$$

15. What is the augmented matrix for the system in Exercise 14?

16. Illustrate each elementary row operation with the augmented matrix $\begin{bmatrix} 2 & 1 & 3 & \vdots & 2 \\ 1 & 4 & 5 & \vdots & 0 \end{bmatrix}$.

Objective: *To identify matrices in echelon form or in reduced row echelon form and to change matrices to each of these forms.*

17. Which of the matrices below are in row echelon form and which are in reduced row echelon form?

$$A = \begin{bmatrix} 1 & 0 & 0 \\ 0 & 0 & 1 \\ 0 & 0 & 0 \end{bmatrix} \qquad B = \begin{bmatrix} 1 & 1 & 0 \\ 0 & 1 & 1 \\ 0 & 0 & 1 \end{bmatrix}$$

$$C = \begin{bmatrix} 0 & 0 & 1 \\ 0 & 0 & 0 \end{bmatrix} \qquad D = \begin{bmatrix} 2 & 0 & 0 \\ 0 & 1 & 3 \\ 0 & 0 & 1 \end{bmatrix}$$

18. Employ elementary row operations to change each matrix in echelon form in Exercise 17 to its row equivalent matrix in reduced row echelon form.

19. Change $\begin{bmatrix} 1 & 2 & -3 & 4 \\ 2 & 4 & 5 & 6 \end{bmatrix}$ to a row equivalent echelon form.

20. Change the following matrix to a row equivalent reduced row echelon form.

$$\begin{bmatrix} 1 & 2 & -3 \\ 2 & 1 & 3 \\ 4 & 5 & 8 \\ 1 & 3 & 7 \end{bmatrix}$$

Objective: *To use Gaussian elimination and Gauss-Jordan reduction to solve homogeneous and nonhomogeneous systems of linear equations.*

━━ Use Gaussian elimination to solve each system in Exercises 21–24. Write the general solution for each system.

21.
$$\begin{bmatrix} 3 & -1 & 1 \\ 1 & 1 & 1 \end{bmatrix} \begin{bmatrix} x_1 \\ x_2 \\ x_3 \end{bmatrix} = \begin{bmatrix} 0 \\ 2 \end{bmatrix}$$

22. $3x_1 - x_2 + x_3 = 0$
$x_1 + x_2 + x_3 = 0$

23.
$$\begin{bmatrix} 1 & 1 & 1 & 1 \\ 1 & -1 & -1 & -1 \\ 1 & 1 & -1 & -1 \end{bmatrix} \begin{bmatrix} x_1 \\ x_2 \\ x_3 \\ x_4 \end{bmatrix} = \begin{bmatrix} 1 \\ 1 \\ -9 \end{bmatrix}$$

24.
$$\begin{bmatrix} 1 & 1 & 1 & 1 \\ 1 & -1 & -1 & -1 \\ 1 & -1 & -1 & -1 \end{bmatrix} \begin{bmatrix} x_1 \\ x_2 \\ x_3 \\ x_4 \end{bmatrix} = \begin{bmatrix} 0 \\ 0 \\ 0 \end{bmatrix}$$

Use Gauss-Jordan reduction to solve each system in Exercises 25–27. Write the general solution for each system.

25. $\begin{bmatrix} 1 & 1 & 1 \\ 3 & -1 & 1 \\ 4 & 0 & 2 \end{bmatrix} \begin{bmatrix} x_1 \\ x_2 \\ x_3 \end{bmatrix} = \begin{bmatrix} 2 \\ 0 \\ 2 \end{bmatrix}$ **26.** $\begin{bmatrix} 1 & 1 & 1 \\ 3 & -1 & 1 \\ 4 & 0 & 2 \end{bmatrix} \begin{bmatrix} x_1 \\ x_2 \\ x_3 \end{bmatrix} = \begin{bmatrix} 0 \\ 0 \\ 0 \end{bmatrix}$

27.
$$\begin{bmatrix} 1 & -1 & -1 & 1 \\ -1 & 1 & 1 & -1 \\ 1 & 1 & -1 & -1 \end{bmatrix} \begin{bmatrix} x_1 \\ x_2 \\ x_3 \\ x_4 \end{bmatrix} = \begin{bmatrix} 0 \\ 0 \\ 0 \end{bmatrix}$$

Objective: *To obtain the inverse of an $n \times n$ matrix A by performing elementary row operations on $[A : I_n]$.*

In Exercises 28–31 find the inverse of each matrix, if it exists.

28. $\begin{bmatrix} 2 & 5 \\ -3 & 1 \end{bmatrix}$

29. $\begin{bmatrix} 0 & 2 & 4 \\ 1 & 1 & 1 \\ -1 & 1 & 3 \end{bmatrix}$

30. $\begin{bmatrix} 1 & 1 & 1 & -1 \\ 1 & 1 & -1 & 1 \\ 1 & -1 & 1 & 1 \\ -1 & 1 & 1 & 1 \end{bmatrix}$

31. $\begin{bmatrix} 2 & 5 & -1 \\ 3 & 7 & 2 \\ 1 & 5 & 7 \end{bmatrix}$

CHAPTER TEST

1. Find the sum of the following matrices.

$$\begin{bmatrix} 2 & 5 & 3 \\ 1 & 2 & -7 \end{bmatrix} + \begin{bmatrix} -1 & 0 & -3 \\ -4 & 3 & 5 \end{bmatrix}$$

2. When is the sum of two matrices defined?

3. When is the product of two matrices defined?

4. Find the product of the following matrices:

$$\begin{bmatrix} 2 & 5 & 3 \\ 1 & 2 & -7 \end{bmatrix} \begin{bmatrix} 1 & 3 & 5 & 6 \\ -2 & 1 & 3 & 1 \\ 1 & 1 & 1 & 1 \end{bmatrix}$$

5. Find k such that: $k \begin{bmatrix} 2 & 5 \\ -3 & 1 \end{bmatrix} = \begin{bmatrix} -8 & -20 \\ 12 & -4 \end{bmatrix}$

6. Express the following system in matrix form.

$$ax_1 + 4x_2 = 3$$
$$2x_1 + cx_2 = 7$$

7. Translate $\begin{bmatrix} 3 & 2 & -1 \\ 4 & 5 & -7 \end{bmatrix} \begin{bmatrix} x_1 \\ x_2 \\ x_3 \end{bmatrix} = \begin{bmatrix} 0 \\ 0 \end{bmatrix}$ into a system of equations in the variables x_1, x_2 and x_3.

8. Given $AX = {}_mO_1$ where A is an $m \times n$ matrix and X is an $n \times 1$ matrix.

    a. If $AX = {}_mO_1$ has a single solution, what is it?

    b. If $m > n$, how many solutions has $AX = {}_mO_1$?

    c. If $m < n$, how many solutions has $AX = {}_mO_1$?

9. What are the three elementary row operations?

10. Give a 3×3 elementary matrix which does each of the following to a $3 \times n$ matrix.

    a. Interchanges rows *1* and *2*.

    b. Multiplies row *3* by 5.

    c. Adds 3 times row *1* to row *3*.

▬ In Exercises 11–12 reduce each matrix first to echelon form then to reduced row echelon form.

11. $\begin{bmatrix} 2 & -3 & 5 \\ 1 & 7 & 3 \end{bmatrix}$

12. $\begin{bmatrix} 3 & -2 & -5 & 1 \\ 4 & -3 & 2 & 5 \\ 0 & 1 & 3 & 1 \end{bmatrix}$

▬ In Exercises 13–16 use matrix methods to find the general solution to each system.

13. $\begin{bmatrix} 1 & 3 \\ -2 & 5 \end{bmatrix} \begin{bmatrix} x_1 \\ x_2 \end{bmatrix} = \begin{bmatrix} 7 \\ 5 \end{bmatrix}$

14. $\begin{bmatrix} 1 & 3 \\ -2 & -6 \end{bmatrix} \begin{bmatrix} x_1 \\ x_2 \end{bmatrix} = \begin{bmatrix} 1 \\ -2 \end{bmatrix}$

15. $\begin{bmatrix} 1 & 2 & -3 \\ 2 & 1 & -5 \end{bmatrix} \begin{bmatrix} x_1 \\ x_2 \\ x_3 \end{bmatrix} = \begin{bmatrix} 0 \\ 0 \end{bmatrix}$

16. $\begin{bmatrix} 2 & 4 & -2 \\ 2 & 3 & -1 \\ 1 & 1 & 1 \end{bmatrix} \begin{bmatrix} x_1 \\ x_2 \\ x_3 \end{bmatrix} = \begin{bmatrix} 0 \\ 0 \\ 1 \end{bmatrix}$

17. Find the inverse of $\begin{bmatrix} 1 & -2 & -2 \\ 2 & -1 & 1 \\ 1 & -1 & -2 \end{bmatrix}$.

18. The inverse of $\begin{bmatrix} 1 & 2 & 5 \\ 1 & 3 & 7 \\ 1 & 4 & 8 \end{bmatrix}$ is $\begin{bmatrix} 4 & -4 & 1 \\ 1 & -3 & 2 \\ -1 & 2 & -1 \end{bmatrix}$.

Use this fact to solve the following.

$$\begin{bmatrix} 1 & 2 & 5 \\ 1 & 3 & 7 \\ 1 & 4 & 8 \end{bmatrix} \begin{bmatrix} x_1 \\ x_2 \\ x_3 \end{bmatrix} = \begin{bmatrix} 1 \\ 1 \\ 6 \end{bmatrix}$$

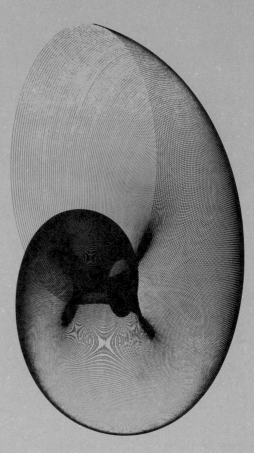

CHAPTER 12

THE CONIC SECTIONS

In this chapter you will study the properties of *ellipses*, *parabolas*, and *hyperbolas*. These curves are interesting not only from a purely mathematical point of view but also for their physical applications.

You are familiar with the fact that the orbit of the Earth around the sun is elliptical. Ellipses can also be used artistically by man. "The Snail", illustrated on the opposite page, was designed by a computer when it was fed a distorted equation of an ellipse.

The shape of a parabola can be used to efficiently focus light onto a small region. Pictured on the opposite page is a sun furnace in France. It is taller than the Arc de Triomphe in Paris. The mathematical properties of parabolic mirrors make them very efficient in the utilization of the sun's rays. This sun furnace is used not only for scientific study but also to study the possibilities of harnessing the sun's rays for industrial purposes.

The shape of parabolas are used in the design of the headlamps of a car. The chrome reflection plates behind the headlamp bulbs are parabolic in shape. Pictured on the opposite page is an electronic headlamp aimer used by automobile manufacturers to test the efficiency of the beams emitted by the car headlamps.

The intersection of two hyperbolas is used in long range navigation in order to determine the exact position of a ship. Signals are sent simultaneously to the ship from two stations on shore. The difference in the times in which the ship receives the signals determines the hyperbola. A repetition of this process from a second set of stations determines the second hyperbola.

12–1   Historical Perspective

The four plane curves circle, parabola, ellipse, and hyperbola are called the **conic sections.** They are called *conic sections* because each curve may be obtained by the intersection of a plane with a right circular conic surface. The figures below show these curves as intersections of planes and conic surfaces.

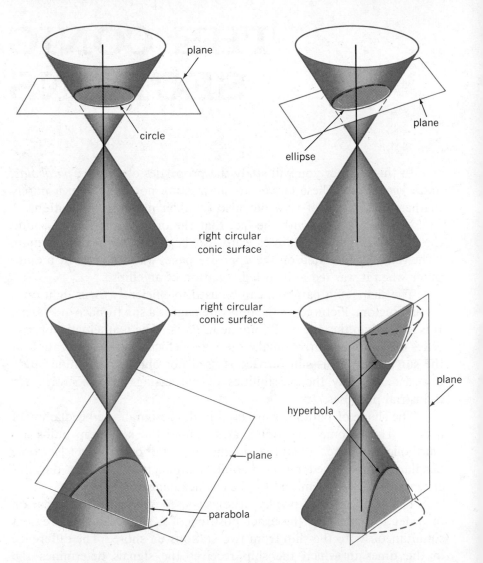

In the early history of Greek mathematics the definitions of the conic sections were stated in terms of planes and conic surfaces. Their properties were studied intensively. Apollonius (ca 220 B.C.) wrote an extensive treatise on these curves. It was called "Conic Sections" and had eight books and about 400 propositions (theorems). Apollonius is also credited with supplying the names *ellipse, parabola*, and *hyperbola*.

Even though each conic section is a subset of a three dimensional figure, each curve lies entirely in one plane. Thus the conic sections are plane curves, and they may be defined in several different ways which make no use of solid geometry. The definitions of the conic sections given in this chapter depend only on the geometry of the plane for their understanding. You should, however, remember that these curves were originally studied as a part of space geometry.

Checkpoint

1. Name the four conic sections.

2. Describe how conic sections are obtained from the conic surfaces in the Figures.

Exercises

A   1. Obtain a book on the history of mathematics from your library or teacher. Look up Apollonius (ca 220 B.C.). Describe some of his mathematical works.

2. Repeat Exercise 1 for Menaechmus (ca 350 B.C.). How is he associated with conic sections?

12–2   The Ellipse

Any plane curve can be described as a set of points which satisfy a given set of conditions. Often such a set of points is called a *locus*. For example, you know that a circle is the set of all points at a given distance from a given point called the center. From these conditions you can derive the equation of the circle by using the distance formula. (See Section 2–1.) Here are two examples.

1. The circle with center $(0, 0)$ and radius r has equation $x^2 + y^2 = r^2$.

2. The circle with center (h, k) and radius r has equation $(x - h)^2 + (y - k)^2 = r^2$.

An **ellipse** is defined in a similar manner by using a locus.

> **Definition** Let F and F' be two points in a plane. The set of all points P in the plane such that the sum of the distances PF and PF' is constant is an ellipse.

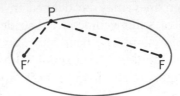

PF′ + PF is a constant

The points F' and F are called the **foci** of the ellipse. The ellipse can be thought of as the curve traced by a pencil restrained by a string of constant length and tied at the ends to F' and F. If $F' = F$, then the curve so traced is a circle. A circle is a special case of an ellipse.

The line determined by the foci F' and F is the **transverse axis** of the ellipse. The perpendicular bisector of $\overline{F'F}$ is the **conjugate axis**. The intersection of the transverse and conjugate axes is the **center** of the ellipse.

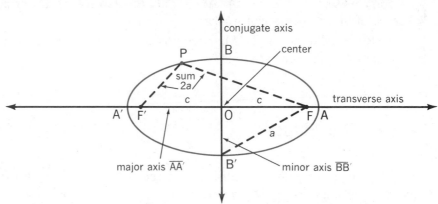

The segment $\overline{A'A}$ is the **major axis** while $\overline{BB'}$ is the **minor axis.**
Letting
$$F'F = 2c \quad \text{and} \quad PF' + PF = 2a,$$
you see that
$$F'O = OF = c.$$
(2a and 2c are used to simplify the algebra that will follow.)

584   CHAPTER 12

Moreover

$$F'A + FA = 2c + 2FA = 2a$$

and

$$F'A' + FA' = 2c + 2F'A' = 2a$$

so

$$FA = F'A'.$$

Thus

$$A'A = A'F' + F'A$$
$$= FA + F'A$$
$$A'A = 2a.$$

That is, the *major axis* is $2a$ units long.

Note also that

$$F'B = FB = a. \qquad \qquad \text{(Why?)}$$

Thus

$$BO = \sqrt{a^2 - c^2}.$$

Similarly

$$F'B' = FB' = a$$

and

$$B'O = \sqrt{a^2 - c^2}.$$

Thus

$$BB' = 2\sqrt{a^2 - c^2}.$$

Let

$$\sqrt{a^2 - c^2} = b,$$

then

$$BB' = 2b.$$

That is, the *minor axis* is $2b$ units long.

Clearly $a > c$, and since $b = \sqrt{a^2 - c^2}$, $a > b$ also. $\overline{OA}$ is the **semimajor axis** while $\overline{OB}$ is the **semiminor axis**. The points A' and A are the vertices of the ellipse.

Having named some of the parts of the ellipse, the next task is to obtain an equation for the curve. For convenience the center is taken to be the origin and the transverse and conjugate axes chosen as the coordinate axes. The foci F' and F have coordinates $(-c, 0)$ and $(c, 0)$ since $FF' = 2c$.

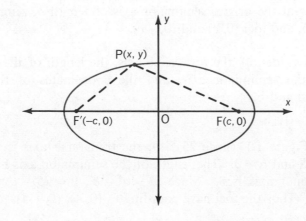

The definition of an ellipse says that $P(x, y)$ must satisfy

$$F'P + FP = 2a \qquad\qquad \textbf{1}$$

Applying the distance formula you find the following.

$$\sqrt{(x + c)^2 + y^2} + \sqrt{(x - c)^2 + y^2} = 2a \qquad\qquad \textbf{2}$$

Thus
$$\sqrt{(x + c)^2 + y^2} = 2a - \sqrt{(x - c)^2 + y^2}$$

$$x^2 + 2cx + c^2 + y^2 = 4a^2 - 4a\sqrt{(x - c)^2 + y^2} + x^2$$
$$- 2cx + c^2 + y^2$$

$$a\sqrt{(x - c)^2 + y^2} = a^2 - cx \qquad\qquad \textbf{3}$$

$$a^2(x^2 - 2cx + c^2 + y^2) = a^4 - 2a^2cx + c^2x^2$$

$$a^2x^2 - 2ca^2x + c^2a^2 + a^2y^2 = a^4 - 2a^2cx + c^2x^2$$

$$(a^2 - c^2)x^2 + a^2y^2 = a^4 - a^2c^2 = a^2(a^2 - c^2)$$

$$b^2x^2 + a^2y^2 = a^2b^2 \qquad (b^2 = a^2 - c^2)$$

or
$$\frac{x^2}{a^2} + \frac{y^2}{b^2} = 1. \qquad\qquad \textbf{4}$$

Before you can say equation **4** is the equation of the ellipse, you must prove that any point $P(x, y)$ which satisfies **4** also satisfies $F'P + FP = 2a$. You are asked to do this in the exercises. Equation **4** is called the *standard form* of the equation of an ellipse with center at the origin, semimajor axis of length a, semiminor axis of length b, and foci $(c, 0)$ and $(-c, 0)$.

If the transverse axis is the y axis rather than the x axis, then the standard equation of an ellipse is

$$\frac{x^2}{b^2} + \frac{y^2}{a^2} = 1, \quad a > b \qquad\qquad \textbf{5}$$

with center at the origin, semimajor axis of length a, semiminor axis of length b, and foci $(0, c)$ and $(0, -c)$.

EXAMPLE. Identify the transverse axis, the length of the semimajor axis and the semiminor axis, and the coordinates of the foci for equations **a** and **b**.

a. $\dfrac{x^2}{9} + \dfrac{y^2}{25} = 1.$

(See Figure 1.) Since $25 > 9$, the transverse axis is the y axis. Thus $a = 5$ and $b = 3$. The length of the semimajor axis is 5, that of the semiminor axis is 3. Since $b^2 = a^2 - c^2$, $9 = 25 - c^2$ or $c^2 = 16$ and $c = 4$. Thus the foci have coordinates $(0, 4)$, $(0, -4)$.

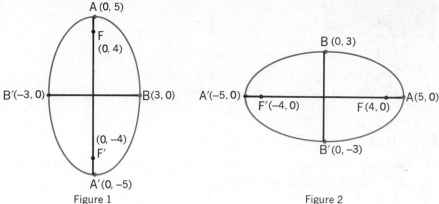

Figure 1   Figure 2

b. $9x^2 + 25y^2 = 225$.

(See Figure 2.) The first step is to write the equation in standard form. This is done by dividing both sides by 225.

$$\frac{9x^2}{225} + \frac{25y^2}{225} = \frac{225}{225}$$

$$\frac{x^2}{25} + \frac{y^2}{9} = 1$$

The transverse axis is the x axis because $25 > 9$ and 25 is the denominator of the term involving x^2.

The procedures used in **a** now produce semimajor axis length = 5, semiminor axis length = 3, coordinates of foci = $(4, 0)$ and $(-4, 0)$.

Now try these

━━ Find the lengths of the semimajor and semiminor axes and the coordinates of the vertices for the following.

1. $\frac{x^2}{36} + \frac{y^2}{25} = 1$

2. $\frac{x^2}{9} + \frac{y^2}{100} = 1$

━━ Put the following equations into standard form.

3. $9x^2 + 8y^2 = 72$

4. $32x^2 + 16y^2 = 64$

5. Find the equation of the ellipse having foci at $(\pm 4, 0)$ and the length of the semimajor axis 5.

Answers: **1.** 6, 5, $(\pm 6, 0)$.   **2.** 10, 3, $(0, \pm 10)$.   **3.** $\frac{x^2}{8} + \frac{y^2}{9} = 1$.

        4. $\frac{x^2}{2} + \frac{y^2}{4} = 1$.   **5.** $\frac{x^2}{25} + \frac{y^2}{9} = 1$ or $9x^2 + 25y^2 = 225$.

Checkpoint

1. Define an ellipse as a locus of points.
2. Define transverse axis and conjugate axis.
3. What is the standard form of the equation of an ellipse?

Exercises

A ━━━ Find the lengths of the axes and the coordinates of the foci, and sketch the curve for Exercises 1–8.

1. $\frac{x^2}{16} + \frac{y^2}{4} = 1$ 　　　　　　　　　 2. $x^2 + 2y^2 = 32$

3. $\frac{x^2}{4} + \frac{y^2}{36} = 1$ 　　　　　　　　　 4. $5x^2 + 2y^2 = 20$

5. $\frac{x^2}{36} + \frac{y^2}{16} = 1$ 　　　　　　　　　 6. $16x^2 + 25y^2 = 400$

7. $\frac{x^2}{8} + \frac{y^2}{16} = 1$ 　　　　　　　　　 8. $16x^2 + 4y^2 = 64$

━━━ Find the equation of each ellipse for Exercises 9–16.

9. Foci at $(\pm 3, 0)$, vertices at $(\pm 5, 0)$.
10. Foci at $(0, \pm 4)$, vertices at $(0, \pm 7)$.
11. Foci at $(\pm 2, 0)$, minor axis of length 3.
12. Foci at $(0, \pm 5)$, major axis of length 26.
13. Foci at $(0, \pm 3)$, vertices at $(0, \pm 6)$.
14. Vertices at $(\pm 4, 0)$, end of minor axis at $(0, 3)$.
15. Foci at $(0, \pm 2)$, one vertex at $(0, -4)$.
16. Vertices at $(\pm 8, 0)$, contains $(4, \sqrt{3})$.

B 17. The transverse axis of an ellipse is the x axis. The lengths of the major and minor axes are in the ratio $3 : 2$. The ellipse contains the point $(2, 1)$. Find its equation.

18. The foci of an ellipse are on the y axis, the major axis is twice as long as the distance FF', the center is $(0, 0)$, and $(\frac{9}{2}, 3)$ is on the ellipse. Find the equation.

19. Let ABC be a triangle with base AB and $A = (2, 0)$, $B = (-2, 0)$. Find the equation such that for all points $C(x, y)$, the product of the slopes of $\overleftrightarrow{AC}$ and $\overleftrightarrow{BC}$ is -4.

20. Show that if $P(x, y)$ satisfies $\frac{x^2}{a^2} + \frac{y^2}{b^2} = 1$, then $PF' + PF = 2a$.

21. Show that $FP = a - \frac{c}{a} x$, $(F(c, 0))$. (*Hint:* See Equation 3.)

C **22.** Suppose the foci of an ellipse are at $(0, 0)$ and $(6, 0)$. Then the center is at $(3, 0)$. Neither standard equation of the ellipse **4** nor **5** is the equation of this ellipse. Use the definition of the ellipse to find the equation of this ellipse when the major axis has length 10.

12–3 Properties of Ellipses

In the derivation of the standard equations of an ellipse in Section 12–2, equation **3** read

$$a\sqrt{(x - c)^2 + y^2} = a^2 - cx$$

or

$$\sqrt{(x - c)^2 + y^2} = a - \frac{c}{a}x \qquad\qquad \textbf{1}$$

The left hand expression in equation **1** is the distance from $F(c, 0)$ to $P(x, y)$; that is $FP = \sqrt{(x - c)^2 + y^2}$.

After slight modification, the right hand side of **1** may also be interpreted geometrically.

$$FP = a - \frac{c}{a}x = \frac{c}{a}\left(\frac{a^2}{c} - x\right) \qquad\qquad \textbf{2}$$

You can see that $\left(\frac{a^2}{c} - x\right)$ is the distance, k, from $P(x, y)$ to the line $x = \frac{a^2}{c}$. (See the figure.) $\frac{c}{a}$ is a constant which is less than 1. Thus

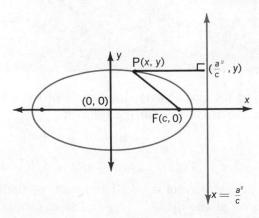

$\frac{c}{a}\left(\frac{a^2}{c} - x\right)$ is a constant times the distance from $P(x, y)$ to $x = \frac{a^2}{c}$.

You can say that the ratio of the distance FP to the distance, k, from P to $x = \frac{a^2}{c}$ is a constant for *all points P on the ellipse.*

$$\frac{FP}{k} = \frac{\frac{c}{a}\left(\frac{a^2}{c} - x\right)}{\left(\frac{a^2}{c} - x\right)} = \frac{c}{a}$$

The constant ratio $0 < \frac{c}{a} = e < 1$ is the **eccentricity** of the ellipse. The line $x = \frac{a^2}{c}$ is a *directrix* of the ellipse. Each ellipse has two *directrix* lines, (directrices), one for each focus. What is the equation of the other directrix line for the ellipse $\frac{x^2}{a^2} + \frac{y^2}{b^2} = 1$ $(a > b)$? $\left(x = -\frac{a^2}{c}\right)$

> **Theorem 12–1** An ellipse is the set of all points whose distance from a fixed point F (the focus) is equal to a constant e $(0 < e < 1)$ times the distance to a fixed line d (the directrix).

Theorem 12–1 is often taken as a definition of an ellipse.

Any segment whose endpoints are on an ellipse is called a **chord** of the ellipse. If the chord contains a focus, it is a **focal chord**. The focal chord which is perpendicular to the transverse axis is called the **latus rectum.**

The lengths of the *latera recta* (latera recta is the plural of latus rectum) of an ellipse are easily found. It is left for you to show that the following theorem is true.

> **Theorem 12–2** The latera recta of an ellipse have length $\frac{2b^2}{a}$.

EXAMPLE. Find the eccentricity, the length of the latera recta, and the equations of the directrices for the following.

a. $\frac{x^2}{9} + \frac{y^2}{25} = 1$

$a = 5, b = 3, c = 4$

The length of the latera recta is $\frac{18}{5}$. The equations of the directrices are $y = \frac{25}{4}$ and $y = -\frac{25}{4}$. The eccentricity is $\frac{4}{5}$.

b. $\frac{x^2}{25} + \frac{y^2}{9} = 1$

$a = 5, b = 3, c = 4$

The length of the latera recta is $\frac{18}{5}$. The equations of the directrices are $x = \frac{25}{4}$ and $x = -\frac{25}{4}$. The eccentricity is $\frac{4}{5}$.

Now try these

1. Find the eccentricity and the length of the latera recta for

$$\frac{x^2}{16} + \frac{y^2}{25} = 1.$$

2. Find the equations of the directrices for $\frac{x^2}{36} + \frac{y^2}{9} = 1$.

Answers: **1.** $e = \frac{3}{5}$, length is $\frac{32}{5}$.　　　**2.** $x = \pm \dfrac{36}{3\sqrt{3}}$ or $x = \pm 4\sqrt{3}$.

Checkpoint

1. Define an ellipse in terms of a directrix and a focus.

2. Describe $\frac{c}{a}$ as a ratio of two distances.

3. What is meant by a latus rectum of an ellipse?

Exercises

A ━━ For the ellipses of Exercises 1–8 find the eccentricity, the length of the latera recta, and the equations of the directrices.

1. $\frac{x^2}{16} + \frac{y^2}{4} = 1$ 　　　　 **2.** $x^2 + 2y^2 = 32$

3. $\frac{x^2}{4} + \frac{y^2}{36} = 1$ 　　　　 **4.** $5x^2 + 2y^2 = 20$

5. $\frac{x^2}{36} + \frac{y^2}{16} = 1$ 　　　 **6.** $16x^2 + 25y^2 = 400$

7. $\frac{x^2}{8} + \frac{y^2}{16} = 1$ 　　　　 **8.** $16x^2 + 4y^2 = 64$

B　**9.** The orbit of the earth around the sun is an ellipse with the sun as a focus. If the shortest and longest distances (center to center) from the sun to earth are 9.3×10^7 miles and 9.6×10^7 miles, what is the eccentricity of the earth's orbit?

10. There are two ellipses with center at the origin, eccentricity $\frac{2}{3}$, and containing the point $(2, 1)$. Find their equations.

11. On the same coordinate axes draw the set of ellipses with vertices A at $(5, 0)$ and A' at $(-5, 0)$ and having eccentricity

　　a. $\frac{9}{10}$. 　　 **b.** $\frac{7}{10}$. 　　 **c.** $\frac{5}{10}$. 　　 **d.** $\frac{3}{10}$. 　　 **e.** $\frac{1}{10}$.

12. a. What pattern is exhibited by the ellipses of Exercise 11?

　　b. When e is close to 1 what is the shape of the ellipse?

　　c. When e is close to 0 what is the shape of the ellipse?

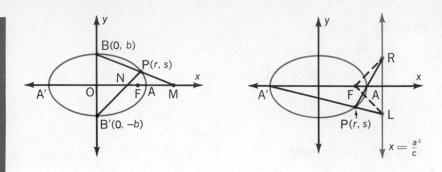

C **13.** Let $P(r, s)$ be any point on the ellipse $\frac{x^2}{a^2} + \frac{y^2}{b^2} = 1$ $(a > b)$. See the figure at the left above. Draw $\overleftrightarrow{BP}$ and $\overleftrightarrow{B'P}$ intersecting the transverse axis in M and N respectively. Prove that $ON \cdot OM = a^2$.

14. Let $P(r, s)$ be any point on the ellipse $\frac{x^2}{a^2} + \frac{y^2}{b^2} = 1$ $(a > b)$. See the figure at the right above. Draw the directrix $x = \frac{a^2}{c}$. Draw $\overleftrightarrow{A'P}$ intersecting $x = \frac{a^2}{c}$ in L, and $\overleftrightarrow{AP}$ intersecting $x = \frac{a^2}{c}$ in R. Prove that $\overrightarrow{FR} \perp \overrightarrow{FL}$. $\left(F \text{ is the focus corresponding to } x = \frac{a^2}{c}.\right)$

15. Let C be a circle with center at the origin and radius r. See the figure at the left below. Let A be any point interior to C. What equation does the set of all points P satisfy if P is equidistant from A and the circle?

16. Given the x axis with points $A'(-a, 0)$ and $A(a, 0)$. See the figure at the right below. Draw the line $x = p$ and let $D(p, r)$ be any point on $x = p$. Draw $\overleftrightarrow{A'D}, \overleftrightarrow{AD}$ and $\overleftrightarrow{A'X}$ where $\overleftrightarrow{A'X} \perp \overleftrightarrow{A'D}$. Let the intersection of $\overleftrightarrow{A'X}$ and $\overleftrightarrow{AD}$ be $T(x, y)$. Find the equation that all points $T(x, y)$ satisfy.

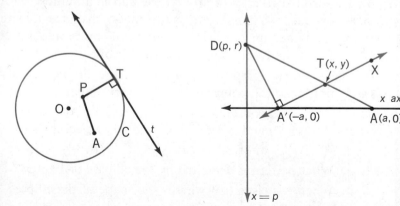

12-4   The Hyperbola

A hyperbola is defined in a manner similar to an ellipse.

Definition A hyperbola is the set of all points such that for any point in the set the difference of its distances from two fixed points is a constant.

The fixed points are the *foci* F' and F which are $2c$ units apart. The constant difference is denoted by $2a$. Letting the coordinates of F' and F be $(-c, 0)$ and $(c, 0)$ respectively, the point $P(x, y)$ is on the hyperbola whenever

$$F'P - FP = 2a \quad \text{or} \quad FP - F'P = 2a$$

Thus $\qquad\qquad F'P - FP = \pm 2a \qquad\qquad \left(\begin{array}{l} + \text{ for right branch} \\ - \text{ for left branch} \end{array}\right)$

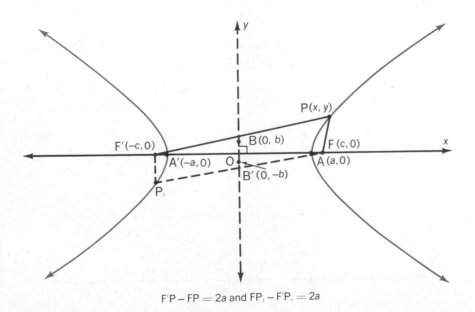

$$F'P - FP = 2a \text{ and } FP_1 - F'P_1 = 2a$$

$\overleftrightarrow{F'F}$ is the transverse axis, A' and A are the vertices, and $\overline{A'A}$ is the major axis. In triangle $F'PF$, when $P(x, y)$ is on the right branch, $a < c$ because $F'P - FP < F'F$. Thus $2a < 2c$ and $a < c$. In a similar manner you can show $a < c$ when $P(x, y)$ is on the left branch.

The conjugate axis is the perpendicular bisector of the transverse axis $\overleftrightarrow{F'F}$. The intersection, O, of the two axes is the **center of the hyperbola**. The points B and B' on the conjugate axis at a distance $b = \sqrt{c^2 - a^2}$ from the center of the hyperbola determine the minor axis $\overline{BB'}$. The length of the semiminor axis, b, may be greater than, equal to, or less than the length of the semimajor axis, a, for a hyperbola. Of course c is greater than either a or b.

The major axis is $2a$ units long, since

$$2a = F'A - FA \qquad \text{by def}$$
$$2a = F'A' + A'A - FA \qquad\qquad 1$$

and also

$$2a = FA' - F'A' \qquad \text{by def}$$
$$2a = FA + A'A - F'A' \qquad\qquad 2$$

Subtracting 2 from 1 you get

$$0 = 2(F'A' - FA)$$

or
$$F'A' = FA. \qquad\qquad 3$$

Then substituting 3 in 1, you see that

$$2a = F'A' + A'A - F'A'$$
$$= A'A.$$

As in the case of the ellipse the quotient $\dfrac{c}{a} = e$ is the *eccentricity*. Since $c > a$, the eccentricity $e > 1$.

The derivation of the equation of the hyperbola with center at $O(0, 0)$ and transverse axis equal to the x axis is similar to that for the ellipse.

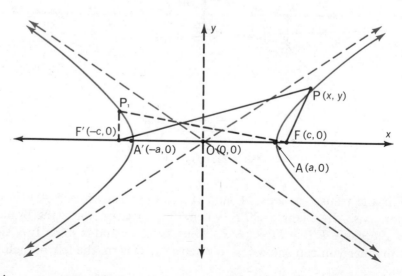

From the definition of a hyperbola, if follows that

$$F'P - FP = \sqrt{(x + c)^2 + y^2} - \sqrt{(x - c)^2 + y^2} = \pm 2a \qquad \textbf{4}$$

Thus

$$\sqrt{(x + c)^2 + y^2} = \pm 2a + \sqrt{(x - c)^2 + y^2} \qquad \left(\begin{array}{l} + \text{ for right branch} \\ - \text{ for left branch} \end{array}\right)$$

$$x^2 + 2cx + c^2 + y^2 = 4a^2 \pm 4a\sqrt{(x - c)^2 + y^2} + x^2 - 2cx + c^2 + y^2$$

$$cx - a^2 = \pm a\sqrt{(x - c)^2 + y^2} \qquad \textbf{5}$$

$$c^2 x^2 - 2ca^2 x + a^4 = a^2(x^2 - 2cx + c^2 + y^2)$$

$$c^2 x^2 + a^4 = a^2 x^2 + c^2 a^2 + a^2 y^2$$

$$(c^2 - a^2)x^2 - a^2 y^2 = a^2(c^2 - a^2) \qquad (c^2 - a^2 = b^2)$$

$$b^2 x^2 - a^2 y^2 = a^2 b^2$$

or

$$\frac{x^2}{a^2} - \frac{y^2}{b^2} = 1 \qquad \textbf{6}$$

Not all of the steps in the derivation are reversible, but it can be shown that **6** is the equation of a hyperbola with the center at the origin, transverse axis on the x axis, and conjugate axis on the y axis.

The standard equation of the hyperbola with the y axis for transverse axis and x axis for conjugate axis is

$$\frac{y^2}{a^2} - \frac{x^2}{b^2} = 1 \qquad \textbf{7}$$

EXAMPLE. A latus rectum of a hyperbola is a focal chord perpendicular to the transverse axis. What is the length of either latus rectum of the hyperbola $\frac{x^2}{a^2} - \frac{y^2}{b^2} = 1$?

Since the transverse axis is the x axis, the line containing the latus rectum is $x = c$ or $x = -c$.

For $x = c$, $\dfrac{c^2}{a^2} - \dfrac{y^2}{b^2} = 1$

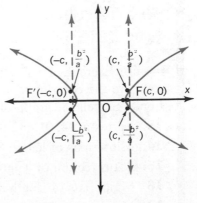

or

$$\frac{c^2}{a^2} - \frac{a^2}{a^2} = \frac{y^2}{b^2}$$

or

$$\frac{c^2 - a^2}{a^2} = \frac{y^2}{b^2}$$

or

$$\frac{b^4}{a^2} = y^2 \quad \text{and} \quad y = \pm \frac{b^2}{a}$$

Thus the length of the latus rectum is $\dfrac{2b^2}{a}$. This is the same formula which gives the length of the latus rectum for an ellipse.

Now try these

■ Find the length of the semimajor and semiminor axes and state whether the x or y axis is the transverse axis for Examples 1–3.

1. $\dfrac{x^2}{25} - \dfrac{y^2}{9} = 1$ **2.** $\dfrac{y^2}{9} - \dfrac{x^2}{36} = 1$ **3.** $\dfrac{x^2}{4} - \dfrac{y^2}{9} = 1$

Answers: **1.** 5, 3, x.   **2.** 3, 6, y.   **3.** 2, 3, x.

Checkpoint

1. Define a hyperbola as a set of points satisfying certain conditions.

2. How does the value of e (eccentricity) differ for the hyperbola and the ellipse?

3. How do the standard equations for the ellipse and hyperbola differ?

Exercises

A ■ For Exercises 1–12 identify each curve and find the vertices, foci, ends of latera recta, and eccentricity. Sketch each curve.

1. $\dfrac{x^2}{16} - \dfrac{y^2}{9} = 1$ **2.** $\dfrac{x^2}{36} - \dfrac{y^2}{64} = 1$

3. $4y^2 - 9x^2 = 36$ **4.** $\dfrac{y^2}{9} - \dfrac{x^2}{25} = 1$

5. $4x^2 - y^2 + 1 = 0$ **6.** $4y^2 - 25x^2 = 100$

7. $y^2 - x^2 = 36$ **8.** $x^2 - 16y^2 - 16 = 0$

9. $\dfrac{x^2}{4} - \dfrac{y^2}{21} = 1$ **10.** $\dfrac{x^2}{9} + \dfrac{y^2}{16} = 1$

11. $\dfrac{y^2}{2} - \dfrac{2x^2}{9} = 2$ **12.** $k^2x^2 - y^2 = k^2,\ k > 0$

■ For Exercises 13–19 write the equation of the hyperbola whose axes are the coordinate axes and which satisfies the given conditions. Sketch the graph of each curve.

13. Vertex at (4, 0), end of minor axis at (0, 3).

14. Minor axis of length 8, foci at (0, ±5).

15. Latus rectum of length 5, focus (3, 0).

16. Major axis of length 8, foci at (±5, 0).

17. Minor axis of length 8, foci at (±5, 0).

18. Passes through (2, 1), (4,′3), x axis is the transverse axis.

19. End of minor axis at (3, 0) and contains (4, $\frac{20}{3}$).

12–5   Asymptotes of the Hyperbola

In Section 6–4 an asymptote to a curve was defined to be a line which the curve approached as the independent variable x neared a fixed number a or as x increased (or decreased) without bound. A hyperbola $\frac{x^2}{a^2} - \frac{y^2}{b^2} = 1$ has two asymptotes given by the equations

$$y = \frac{bx}{a} \quad \text{and} \quad y = \frac{-bx}{a} \qquad\qquad \textbf{1}$$

To show that equations **1** are equations of asymptotes, you must prove that as x increases (decreases) without bound the limit of the distance between the curve and the line is zero. That is, if d is the distance from the curve to the line then $\lim\limits_{x\to\pm\infty} d = 0$.

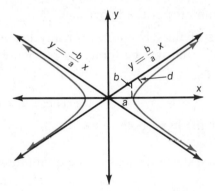

Let $P(r, s)$ be any point on the hyperbola $b^2x^2 - a^2y^2 = a^2b^2$ in the first quadrant. Then the distance d from the curve to the line $bx - ay = 0$ is equal to the following. Remember, the distance, d, from a point $P(x_1, y_1)$ to a line $kx + ly + m = 0$ is equal to

$$d = \frac{|\, kx_1 + ly_1 + m \,|}{\sqrt{k^2 + l^2}} \qquad\qquad \text{(See page 457.)}$$

$$d = \frac{|\, br - as \,|}{\sqrt{b^2 + a^2}} = \frac{|\, br - as \,|}{c} \qquad\qquad \textbf{2}$$

Multiply numerator and denominator of 2 by $br + as$ and noting that $b^2r^2 - a^2s^2 = a^2b^2$ (Why?) you therefore find the following.

$$d = \frac{|\, b^2r^2 - a^2s^2 \,|}{c(br + as)} = \frac{a^2b^2}{c} \cdot \frac{1}{br + as}$$

But $a^2s^2 = b^2r^2 - a^2b^2$ and therefore $as = b\sqrt{r^2 - a^2}$, so

$$d = \frac{a^2b^2}{c} \cdot \frac{1}{br + b\sqrt{r^2 - a^2}}$$

$$= \frac{a^2b}{c} \cdot \frac{1}{r + \sqrt{r^2 - a^2}}$$

Then

$$\lim_{r \to \infty} d = \lim_{r \to \infty} \frac{a^2b}{c} \cdot \frac{1}{r + \sqrt{r^2 - a^2}} = 0$$

because

$$\frac{1}{r + \sqrt{r^2 - a^2}} \longrightarrow 0 \quad \text{as} \quad r \longrightarrow \infty.$$

Thus $y = \frac{b}{a} x$ is an asymptote to the curve $\frac{x^2}{a^2} - \frac{y^2}{b^2} = 1$. Because of the symmetry of the curve and the lines, it is clear that both lines $y = \pm \frac{b}{a} x$ are asymptotes of the hyperbola.

The equations of the asymptotes for any hyperbola whose equation is in standard form may be found by replacing the constant 1 by 0 and factoring. That is, given $\frac{x^2}{a^2} - \frac{y^2}{b^2} = 1$, set $\frac{x^2}{a^2} - \frac{y^2}{b^2} = 0$ and factor. Then you have $\frac{x}{a} - \frac{y}{b} = 0$ or $\frac{x}{a} + \frac{y}{b} = 0$. These last two equations are the asymptotes for the hyperbola.

EXAMPLE 1. Find the equations of the asymptotes of

$$\frac{y^2}{a^2} - \frac{x^2}{b^2} = 1.$$

Let $\frac{y^2}{a^2} - \frac{x^2}{b^2} = 0$. Factor, then you have

$$\frac{y}{a} - \frac{x}{b} = 0 \quad \text{or} \quad \frac{y}{a} + \frac{x}{b} = 0.$$

$by - ax = 0$ and $by + ax = 0$ are the equations of the asymptotes.

Determining the asymptotes of a hyperbola and sketching them will help you to sketch the associated hyperbola.

EXAMPLE 2. Sketch the graph of $\frac{x^2}{9} - \frac{y^2}{16} = 1$. First find the asymptotes. If $\frac{x^2}{9} - \frac{y^2}{16} = 0$, then $\frac{x}{3} \pm \frac{y}{4} = 0$ or $y = \pm\frac{4}{3}x$. Notice that the slope of the asymptote $y = \frac{4}{3}x$ is the ratio: $\frac{\text{semiminor axis}}{\text{semimajor axis}}$. Thus the line $y = \frac{4}{3}x$ is determined by the opposite vertices of the rectangle with base $2a$ and height $2b$. (See the figure.) Similarly for $y = -\frac{4}{3}x$.

The asymptotes are $\overleftrightarrow{PR}$ and $\overleftrightarrow{QS}$. The hyperbola may now be sketched, tangent to $\overline{PS}$ at A and tangent to $\overline{QR}$ at A' and approaching the asymptotes as $x \longrightarrow \pm\infty$.

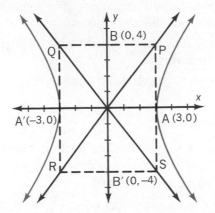

If the asymptotes of a hyperbola are perpendicular, the hyperbola is called a **rectangular hyperbola.** Clearly the asymptotes of a hyperbola are perpendicular whenever their slopes are negative reciprocals, and this occurs only when $a = b$. (This is left for you to prove in the exercises.)

A hyperbola $\frac{x^2}{a^2} - \frac{y^2}{b^2} = 1$ has major axis of length $2a$ along the x axis and minor axis of length $2b$ along the y axis. The hyperbola $\frac{y^2}{b^2} - \frac{x^2}{a^2} = 1$ has major axis of length $2b$ along the y axis and minor axis of length $2a$ along the x axis. Thus the major and minor axes of these two hyperbolas are interchanged. Such hyperbolas are called **conjugate hyperbolas.** Can you show that conjugate hyperbolas have the same asymptotes?

Now try these

■ Find the equations of the asymptotes for the following curves, if they exist.

1. $\frac{x^2}{25} - \frac{y^2}{36} = 1$

2. $\frac{y^2}{9} - \frac{x^2}{4} = 1$

3. $\frac{x^2}{25} + \frac{y^2}{36} = 1$

Answers: **1.** $y = \pm\frac{6}{5}x$. **2.** $y = \pm\frac{3}{2}x$. **3.** No asymptotes. (Ellipses do not have asymptotes.)

Checkpoint

1. Given the standard equation of a hyperbola, how do you find the equations of the asymptotes?

2. What conditions must be satisfied for a hyperbola to be called a rectangular hyperbola?

3. When are two hyperbolas conjugate?

Exercises

A 1–12. For each Exercise 1–12 in Section 12–4 find the equations of the asymptotes if the curve is a hyperbola and sketch the curve using the technique of Example 2.

13. Prove that the asymptotes of $\frac{x^2}{a^2} - \frac{y^2}{b^2} = 1$ are perpendicular if and only if $a = b$.

14. Prove that conjugate hyperbolas have identical asymptotes.

15. Are conjugate hyperbolas congruent when $a = b$?

16. Sketch, on the same axes, the hyperbola $\frac{x^2}{25} - \frac{y^2}{9} = 1$ and its conjugate.

━━ For Exercises 17–20, find the equation of the hyperbola.

17. Vertices at $(\pm 6, 0)$, asymptotes $2x \pm y = 0$.

18. Foci at $(0, \pm 5)$, one asymptote containing $(6, 5)$.

19. Foci at $(\pm 4, 0)$, slope of asymptotes ± 3.

20. Center at the origin, slope of asymptotes $\pm\frac{1}{3}$, and length of latus rectum $\frac{4}{3}$. (two answers)

B 21. Prove that the product of the distances of any point on the hyperbola $x^2 - 4y^2 = 4$ from its asymptotes is constant.

22. Prove the product of the distances of any point on a hyperbola from its asymptotes is constant.

23. Show that the ellipse $9x^2 + 25y^2 = 900$ and the hyperbola $7x^2 - 9y^2 = 252$ have the same foci.

━━ For Exercises 24 and 25, find the equation of the set of points satisfying the given conditions.

24. The distance from $(5, 0)$ is $\frac{5}{4}$ the distance from $x = \frac{16}{5}$.

25. The distance from $y = \frac{25}{3}$ is $\frac{3}{5}$ the distance from $(0, 5)$.

26. Prove that for two conjugate hyperbolas the sum of the squares of the reciprocals of the eccentricities is one.

C **27.** Let $\overleftrightarrow{AP}$ and $\overleftrightarrow{A'P}$ cut d, a directrix, in points M and N respectively where $P(x, y)$ is on the hyperbola. Show that $\angle MFN$ is a right angle (F is the focus on the same side of the center as d.) (See the figure below.)

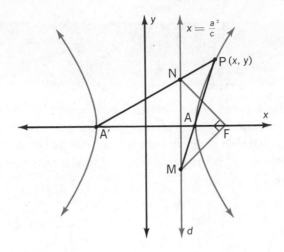

28. Let C be a circle with center at the origin and radius r. Let A be any point exterior to circle C. What equation does the set of all points P satisfy if P is equidistant from point A and the circle C? (*Hint:* See Exercise 15, Section 12–3.) (See the figure at the left below.)

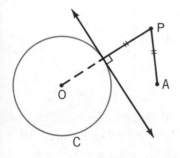

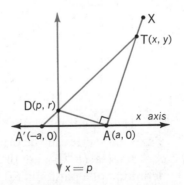

29. Given the x axis with points $A'(-a, 0)$ and $A(a, 0)$. Draw the line $x = p$ $(-a < p < a)$ and let $D(p, r)$ be any point on $x = p$. Draw $\overleftrightarrow{A'D}$, $\overleftrightarrow{AD}$ and $\overleftrightarrow{AX}$ where $\overleftrightarrow{AX} \perp \overleftrightarrow{AD}$. Let $\overleftrightarrow{AX} \cap \overleftrightarrow{A'D} = T(x, y)$. Find the equation which all points $T(x, y)$ satisfy. (*Hint:* Find equations for $\overleftrightarrow{A'D}$ and $\overleftrightarrow{AX}$ and eliminate r from these two equations to get one equation.) (See the figure at the right above).

12–6 The Parabola

The parabola is the final conic section to be discussed in this chapter. Its definition follows.

> **Definition** A parabola is the set of all points P equidistant from a fixed point and a fixed line.

The fixed point is the focus, the fixed line is the directrix. The line perpendicular to the directrix from F is the **axis of symmetry.** The point of intersection of the curve and the axis of symmetry is the **vertex.** The focal chord which is perpendicular to the axis is the latus rectum. (See Figure 1.)

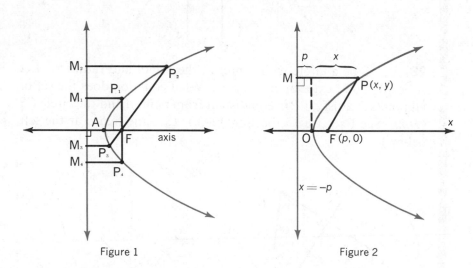

Figure 1   Figure 2

The equation of the parabola with axis of symmetry along the x axis and vertex at the origin is easily obtained. In Figure 2 let F have coordinates $(p, 0)$ and the directrix have equation $x = -p$. By the definition of a parabola $FP = PM$. (See Figure 2.) $FP = \sqrt{(x - p)^2 + y^2}$ by the distance formula, and $PM = p + x$. Thus

$$FP = \sqrt{(x - p)^2 + y^2} = p + x = PM \qquad\qquad 1$$

Squaring this expression you find

$$x^2 - 2px + p^2 + y^2 = p^2 + 2px + x^2$$

or
$$y^2 = 4px \qquad\qquad 2$$

The equation $y^2 = 4px$ is the equation of the parabola with vertex at the origin and focus at the point $F(p, 0)$. If $p > 0$ then the parabola opens to the right; if $p < 0$, the parabola opens to the left.

The parabola with vertex at the origin and focus at $F(0, p)$ has equation

$$x^2 = 4py \qquad\qquad 3$$

It opens up when $p > 0$ and down when $p < 0$. You should verify these statements.

For the parabola

$$y^2 = 4px,$$

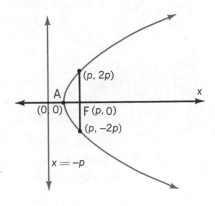

since the latus rectum is the focal chord perpendicular to the axis of symmetry, its equation is $x = p$ and therefore it intersects the curve at $x = p$. Its length may be found by substituting p for x in $y^2 = 4px$. You get $y^2 = 4p^2$ and therefore $y = \pm 2p$. (Similarly for the parabola $x^2 = 4py$.)

Thus the length of the latus rectum is $4p$. More accurately the length is $|4p|$, because if the curve opens to the left or downward, p is less than zero. This result is stated in the following theorem.

Theorem 12–3 The length of the latus rectum of a parabola $y^2 = 4px$ or $x^2 = 4py$ is $|4p|$.

EXAMPLE. Find the coordinates of the focus, the equation of the directrix, and coordinates of the endpoints of the latus rectum of the parabola $y^2 = -12x$ and sketch the curve.

From the equation $y^2 = -12x$, it follows that $4px = -12x$ and $p = -3$. Thus the focus is $F(-3, 0)$ and $x = 3$ is the directrix. The endpoints of the latus rectum are $(-3, 6)$ and $(-3, -6)$. The curve is sketched at the right to go through $(0, 0)$, $(-3, 6)$, and $(-3, -6)$.

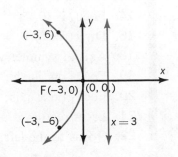

Now try these

▬ Find the value of p, the axis of symmetry and state in which direction the parabola opens for Exercises 1–4. (p is the nonzero coordinate of the focus of a parabola whose vertex is at the origin.)

1. $y^2 = -16x$ **2.** $x^2 = 16y$

3. $x^2 = -36y$ **4.** $y^2 = 12x$

Answers: **1.** $p = -4$, x axis, to the left.
              2. $p = 4$, y axis, upward.
              3. $p = -9$, y axis, downward.
              4. $p = 3$, x axis, to the right.

Checkpoint

1. Define a parabola as a set of points.

2. What is the axis of symmetry of a parabola?

3. How does the equation for a parabola differ from that of an ellipse and a hyperbola?

Exercises

A ▬ Find the coordinates of the focus, equation of the directrix, and coordinates of the latus rectum, and sketch each parabola for Exercises 1–9.

1. $y^2 = 4x$ **2.** $x^2 = y$ **3.** $y^2 = -11x$

4. $x^2 = -24y$ **5.** $y^2 = -6x$ **6.** $x^2 = 8y$

7. $y^2 = 3x$ **8.** $x^2 = \frac{1}{4}y$ **9.** $4x^2 - 9y = 0$

▬ In Exercises 10–22 use the information given to write the equation of each parabola with vertex at the origin. Sketch each curve.

10. Focus is $(3, 0)$ **11.** Focus is $(-\frac{3}{2}, 0)$

12. Directrix: $x = -2$ **13.** Directrix: $x = 4$

14. Focus is $(0, 2)$ **15.** Focus is $(0, -\frac{7}{8})$

16. Directrix: $y = -1$ **17.** Directrix: $y = 3$

18. Axis of symmetry along x axis; $(4, -8)$ on the parabola.

19. Focus on y axis; $(-3, 2)$ on the parabola.

20. Focus on x axis; $(-4, -2)$ on the parabola.

21. Latus rectum is 12; opens downward.

22. Opens to the left; $(-1, -1)$ on the parabola.

B **23.** Show that the angle whose vertex is at the vertex of the parabola $y^2 = 4x$ and whose sides contain the points $(1, 2)$ and $(16, -8)$ is a right angle.

24. Given the line determined by the two points $(1, 2)$ and $(16, -8)$ and the parabola $y^2 = 4x$. Let M be the point of intersection of the line and the axis of symmetry of the parabola. Show that the distance from the point M to the vertex of the parabola is equal to the length of the latus rectum.

25. Suppose $x = -2$ is the directrix of a parabola with focus $F(4, 0)$, then the vertex is $A(1, 0)$. Then the standard forms for the equation of a parabola that were derived are not applicable. Use the definition of a parabola to derive an equation for the parabola described above.

26. Given a parabola with vertex at $A(-3, 0)$ and focus at $F(-1, 0)$. The standard forms for the equation of a parabola that were derived are not applicable. Use the definition of a parabola to derive an equation for this parabola.

27. Given a parabola with directrix $y = 2$ and focus at $F(0, -6)$. The standard forms for the equation of a parabola that were derived are not applicable. Use the definition of a parabola to derive an equation for this parabola.

C **28.** In the figure at the left below let $P(x_1, y_1)$ and $Q(x_2, y_2)$ be the ends of a focal chord for $y^2 = 4px$. Show that

    a. $PQ = x_1 + x_2 + 2p$. (See Equation **1**.)

    b. the distance from the midpoint M of focal chord PQ to the directrix is $\frac{1}{2}PQ$.

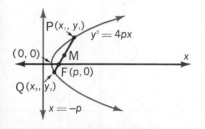 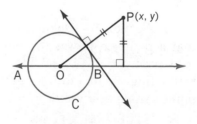

29. Let C be a circle with center at the origin and radius r. In the figure at the right above let $\overleftrightarrow{AB}$ be a line determined by a fixed diameter. Find the equation of the set of all points $P(x, y)$ satisfying the condition that P is equidistant from the line $\overleftrightarrow{AB}$ and the circle C.

Consider the parabola $y^2 = 4px$, $p > 0$. The point $M(4p, 0)$ is at a distance from the vertex equal to the length of the latus rectum. Every line through $M(4p, 0)$ has equation $y = m(x - 4p)$ or $x = 4p$ (if the line is perpendicular to the axis of symmetry.)

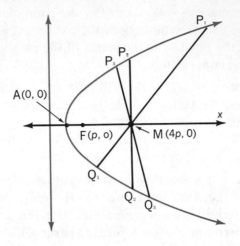

30. Find the points common to $x = 4p$ and $y^2 = 4px$.
31. Show that $\angle P_2AQ_2$ is a right angle.
32. Find the points common to $y = m(x - 4p)$ and $y^2 = 4px$.
33. Show that $\angle P_1AQ_1$ (or P_3AQ_3) is a right angle.
34. Generalize Exercises 30–33.

12–7 Translating Conics

In Section 10–10 you learned that a point (x, y) was translated to a point (x', y') by adding the translating vector to the initial point written as a vector,

$$\begin{bmatrix} x \\ y \end{bmatrix} + \begin{bmatrix} a \\ b \end{bmatrix} = \begin{bmatrix} x' \\ y' \end{bmatrix}$$

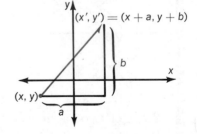

or by adding the coordinates of the translating point to the original point.

$$(x + a, y + b) = (x', y')$$

You also saw in Section 10–10 that a set of points could be translated to a new position by employing the *translation equations*

$$x = x' - h$$
$$y = y' - k$$

where the translation vector is $\begin{bmatrix} h \\ k \end{bmatrix}$. The translation equations can be used to obtain equations of conics that do not have their centers at the origin (or vertex at the origin for a parabola). When a conic is translated to a new position in the plane the properties of the conic section are preserved. That is, the original conic and its translation image are congruent.

Standard Equations for the Parabola

Given

$$y^2 = 4px$$

and the translation equations $x = x' - h$, $y = y' - k$. By substituting, you find

$$(y' - k)^2 = 4p(x' - h) \qquad \textbf{1}$$

Since $(0, 0)$ maps onto (h, k) under the translation, the vertex of the image parabola is at (h, k). See Figure 1 below. Thus, dropping primes, the equation of the parabola with vertex at (h, k) and axis parallel to the x axis is

$$(y - k)^2 = 4p(x - h) \qquad \textbf{2}$$

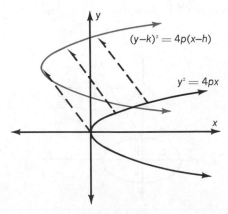

Figure 1

The corresponding equation for the parabola with its axis parallel to the y axis is

$$(x - h)^2 = 4p(y - k) \qquad \textbf{3}$$

EXAMPLE 1. Find the focus, the vertex, and the latus rectum of the parabola $(x - 2)^2 = 8(y + 3)$ and sketch the curve. $(x - 2)^2 = 8(y + 3)$ or $(x - 2)^2 = 4 \cdot 2(y + 3)$.

Clearly the vertex A has coordinates $(2, -3)$. The focus is on the axis of symmetry $x = 2$ and since $p = +2$ you know that the curve opens upward and the focus is 2 units above the vertex. The focus has coordinates $(2, -1)$. The endpoints of the latus rectum are four units to the right and to the left of $F(2, -1)$. The coordinates are $B(-2, -1)$ and $C(6, -1)$.

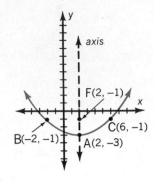

Standard Equations for the Ellipse

Translating the ellipse $\dfrac{x^2}{a^2} + \dfrac{y^2}{b^2} = 1$ by means of the translating equations

$$x = x' - h \qquad y = y' - k$$

and dropping the primes, yields the standard equation.

$$\frac{(x - h)^2}{a^2} + \frac{(y - k)^2}{b^2} = 1, \, a > b \qquad\qquad 4$$

The center of **4** is at (h, k), the vertices have coordinates $(h - a, k)$ and $(h + a, k)$, the ends of the minor axis are at $(h, k + b)$ and $(h, k - b)$, and the latus rectum is $\dfrac{2b^2}{a}$ in length.

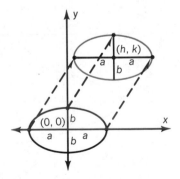

The standard equation for an ellipse with transverse axis parallel to the y axis and with center at (h, k) is

$$\frac{(y - k)^2}{a^2} + \frac{(x - h)^2}{b^2} = 1, \, a > b \qquad\qquad 5$$

EXAMPLE 2. Find the coordinates of the center, the vertices and the foci for the given ellipse.

$$\frac{(x-6)^2}{25} + \frac{(y+10)^2}{9} = 1$$

The center has coordinates $(6, -10)$. $a^2 = 25$, therefore the length of the semimajor axis is 5. The coordinates of the vertices are

$$(6 - 5, -10) \quad \text{and} \quad (6 + 5, -10)$$

or

$$(1, -10) \quad \text{and} \quad (11, -10)$$

$a^2 = 25$ and $b^2 = 9$, therefore $c^2 = \sqrt{a^2 - b^2} = \sqrt{25 - 9} = \sqrt{16} = 4$. The coordinates of the foci are therefore,

$$(6 - 4, -10) \quad \text{and} \quad (6 + 4, -10)$$

or

$$(2, -10) \quad \text{and} \quad (10, -10)$$

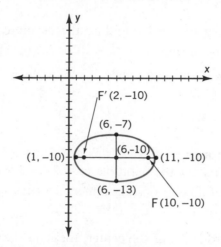

Standard Equations for the Hyperbola

By translating the hyperbolas $\frac{x^2}{a^2} - \frac{y^2}{b^2} = 1$ and $\frac{y^2}{a^2} - \frac{x^2}{b^2} = 1$ using the translating equations $x = x' - h$ and $y = y' - k$ and dropping the primes you can derive the equations

$$\frac{(x-h)^2}{a^2} - \frac{(y-k)^2}{b^2} = 1 \qquad\qquad 6$$

and

$$\frac{(y-k)^2}{a^2} - \frac{(x-h)^2}{b^2} = 1 \qquad\qquad 7$$

Each of these hyperbolas has center (h, k). **6** has a horizontal transverse axis. And **7** has a vertical transverse axis.

EXAMPLE 3. Find the equation of the hyperbola with foci at $F'(-4, 2)$ and $F(2, 2)$ and semiminor axis of length 1 unit. Sketch the curve.

The center of the hyperbola is the midpoint of $\overline{F'F}$, which is the point $(-1, 2)$. Since the transverse axis is parallel to the x axis, the equation has standard form **6**. Since you know $b = 1$, at this point you can write,

$$\frac{(x + 1)^2}{a^2} - \frac{(y - 2)^2}{1} = 1.$$

c is half of $F'F = 6$, so $c = 3$ and $a^2 = c^2 - b^2 = 9 - 1 = 8.$ Thus

$$\frac{(x + 1)^2}{8} - \frac{(y - 2)^2}{1} = 1.$$

The sketch is easily drawn by finding the asymptotes of the curve. These are found by setting $\frac{(x + 1)^2}{8} - \frac{(y - 2)^2}{1} = 0$. They are $\frac{x + 1}{2\sqrt{2}} \pm (y - 2) = 0$ and contain the center of the hyperbola $(-1, 2)$.

Now try these

1. Find the coordinates of the vertex and focus and the equation of the axis of symmetry for the parabola $(y - 2)^2 = 12(x - 3)$.

2. Find the coordinates of the center, vertices, and ends of the minor axis for the ellipse $\frac{(x + 3)^2}{16} + \frac{(y - 2)^2}{9} = 1$.

3. Find the coordinates of the center, foci and the equations of the, asymptotes for the hyperbola $\frac{(x - 2)^2}{9} - \frac{(y - 4)^2}{4} = 1$.

Answers: **1.** $(3, 2)$, $(6, 2)$, $y = 2$.

2. $(-3, 2)$, $(-7, 2)$ and $(1, 2)$, $(-3, 5)$ and $(-3, -1)$.

3. $(2, 4)$, $(2 - \sqrt{13}, 4)$ and $(2 + \sqrt{13}, 4)$, $\frac{y - 4}{2} \pm \frac{(x - 2)}{3} = 0$.

Checkpoint

When a translation of a conic section is made what is true about the properties of that conic?

Exercises

A ■■■ Find the equation of each conic for Exercises 1–16 and sketch each curve.

1. Hyperbola: Center $(1, 3)$, vertex $(4, 3)$, end of minor axis at $(1, 1)$.

2. Hyperbola: Vertex $(-4, 0)$, foci at $(-5, 0)$ and $(1, 0)$.

3. Hyperbola: Ends of minor axis at $(3, -1)$ and $(3, 5)$, focus at $(-1, 2)$.

4. Hyperbola: Vertices at $(-1, 3)$ and $(5, 3)$, length of minor axis is 6.

5. Hyperbola: Vertices at $(0, 0)$ and $(12, 0)$, asymptotes $4x - 3y - 24 = 0$ and $4x + 3y - 24 = 0$.

6. Ellipse: Center at $(5, 1)$, vertex at $(5, 4)$, end of minor axis at $(3, 1)$.

7. Ellipse: Vertex at $(6, 3)$, foci at $(-4, 3)$ and $(4, 3)$.

8. Ellipse: Ends of minor axis at $(-1, 2)$ and $(-1, -4)$, focus at $(1, -1)$.

9. Ellipse: Vertices at $(-1, 3)$ and $(5, 3)$, length of minor axis is 4.

10. Ellipse: One vertex at $(9, 2)$, ends of minor axis at $(4, -1)$ and $(4, 5)$.

11. Parabola: Vertex at $(2, 3)$, focus at $(6, 3)$.

12. Parabola: Vertex at $(-2, 5)$, focus at $(-2, -2)$.

13. Parabola: Vertex at $(3, -2)$, endpoints of latus rectum at $(-3, 1)$ and $(9, 1)$.

14. Parabola: Vertex at $(-1, -2)$, length of latus rectum is 12, opens downward.

15. Parabola: Focus at $(4, -1)$, latus rectum has length 8, opens to left.

B **16.** Prove that the length of the latus rectum of the parabola $(y - k)^2 = 4p(x - h)$ is $4p$.

17. Prove that the length of the latera recta of the hyperbola $\dfrac{(x - h)^2}{a^2} - \dfrac{(y - k)^2}{b^2} = 1$ and the ellipse $\dfrac{(x - h)^2}{a^2} + \dfrac{(y - k)^2}{b^2} = 1$ is $\dfrac{2b^2}{a}$.

18. Find the directrix for $\dfrac{(x - h)^2}{a^2} - \dfrac{(y - k)^2}{b^2} = 1$.

19. Find the directrix for $\dfrac{(x - h)^2}{a^2} + \dfrac{(y - k)^2}{b^2} = 1$.

12–8 Equations of the Second Degree: Translations

If A, B, C, D, E, and F are real numbers (A, B, C not all zero) the equation

$$Ax^2 + Bxy + Cy^2 + Dx + Ey + F = 0 \qquad \mathbf{1}$$

is an equation of the second degree. In general every equation in the form of **1** is a conic or a *degenerate conic*, that is, a point, a straight line, two intersecting or parallel lines, or no graph at all.

In order to identify the conic section represented by **1**, you would like to change the equation so that the curve is more recognizable. This can be accomplished by moving the curve to a new position in the plane.

Translation can be used to change the position in the plane of the curve represented by **1** and also to get a new equation. By choosing the correct translation you get a new equation of the conic that has at most one first degree term and possibly none at all.

For example, when $B = 0$ in equation **1**, by use of a translation you could reduce equation **1** to the form

$$A'x^2 + C'y^2 + F' = 0 \qquad \mathbf{2}$$

If A' and C' have the same sign, then equation **2** describes an ellipse or one of its degenerate forms; a circle, a point, or no graph. (What values must A', C', and F' assume to get each degenerate form?) If A' and C' have opposite signs, the equation describes a hyperbola or a degenerate form; two intersecting straight lines. Equation **1** can also be reduced to the following

$$A'x^2 + E'y + F' = 0 \qquad \mathbf{3}$$

Equation **3** describes a parabola or one of its degenerate forms; two parallel straight lines, distinct, coincident or imaginary. (How?)

The procedure used to obtain these equations from Equation **1** is illustrated below. First, recall that the translation equations are

$$x = x' - h$$
$$y = y' - k$$

If $B = 0$, then equation **1** has the form

$$Ax^2 + Cy^2 + Dx + Ey + F = 0 \qquad \mathbf{1'}$$

Substituting the translation equations in **1'** you have

$$A(x' - h)^2 + C(y' - k)^2 + D(x' - h) + E(y' - k) + F = 0 \qquad \mathbf{2'}$$

Simplifying, you have the following equation.

$$Ax'^2 + Cy'^2 + (-2Ah + D)x' + (-2Ck + E)y'$$
$$+ (Ah^2 + Ck^2 - Dh - Ek + F) = 0 \qquad 3'$$

To eliminate the x' and y' terms, you need

$$-2Ah + D = 0$$

and $\qquad\qquad -2Ck + E = 0 \qquad\qquad\qquad\qquad 4'$

This system has a solution in h and k if and only if $\begin{bmatrix} -2A & 0 \\ 0 & -2C \end{bmatrix}$ has an inverse. (See Section 10–5 Exercise 29.) The matrix has an inverse if and only if the determinant

$$4AC - 0 \neq 0$$

or $\qquad\qquad\qquad 4AC \neq 0. \qquad\qquad\qquad\qquad 5'$

When $4AC = 0$, one of x' and y' cannot be eliminated. Notice that when $4AC = 0$, then either A or C must be zero. (Why?) In this case, the curve is a parabola. (See Equation 3.) When $4AC < 0$, A and C are opposite in sign and the curve is a hyperbola, or a degenerate conic. (See Equation 2.) Similarly when $4AC > 0$, the curve is an ellipse or circle, or a degenerate conic. (See Equation 2.)

In general when $B \neq 0$, substitution of the translation equations in 1 gives the following

$$A(x' - h)^2 + B(x' - h)(y' - k) + C(y' - k)^2$$
$$+ D(x' - h) + E(y' - k) + F = 0. \qquad 4$$

Simplifying you find

$$Ax'^2 + Bx'y' + Cy'^2 + (-2Ah - Bk + D)x' + (-2Ck - Bh + E)y'$$
$$+ (Ah^2 + Bkh + Ck^2 - Dh - Ek + F) = 0 \qquad 5$$

To eliminate the x' and the y' terms, you need

$$-2Ah - Bk + D = 0$$

and $\qquad\qquad -Bh - 2Ck + E = 0. \qquad\qquad\qquad 6$

This system has a solution if and only if the matrix $\begin{bmatrix} -2A & -B \\ -B & -2C \end{bmatrix}$ has an inverse. (See Section 10–5 Exercise 29.) The matrix has an inverse if and only if the determinant

$$4AC - B^2 \neq 0. \qquad\qquad\qquad\qquad 7$$

When $4AC - B^2 = 0$, the curve must be a parabola because one of x' and y' cannot be eliminated. It is also true that when $4AC - B^2 < 0$, the curve is a hyperbola and when $4AC - B^2 > 0$ it is an ellipse.

EXAMPLE 1. Translate the curve represented by

$$4x^2 + 9y^2 + 8x - 36y + 4 = 0$$

so that the curve is in standard position and the equation is a standard form.

First $4 \cdot AC = 4 \cdot 4 \cdot 9 > 0$ and the curve is therefore an ellipse. To find the correct translation, substitute $x = x' - h$, $y = y' - k$ and simplify.

$$4(x'^2 - 2hx' + h^2) + 9(y'^2 - 2ky' + k^2)$$
$$+ 8(x' - h) - 36(y' - k) + 4 = 0$$
$$4x'^2 + 9y'^2 + (-8h + 8)x' + (-18k - 36)y'$$
$$+ (4h^2 + 9k^2 - 8h + 36k + 4) = 0 \qquad \textbf{8}$$

For x' and y' to be eliminated, you need

$$-8h + 8 = 0$$
$$h = 1$$

$$-18k - 36 = 0$$
$$k = -2.$$

Substituting $h = 1$, $k = -2$ in equation **8** you find

$$4x'^2 + 9y'^2 + (4 + 36 - 8 - 72 + 4) = 0$$
or $\qquad 4x'^2 + 9y'^2 = 36.$

The last equation is the equation of an ellipse, and hence as was already known, the original curve is an ellipse.

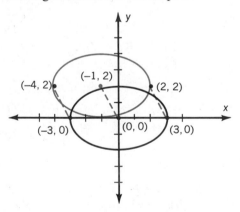

Notice that the translating vector is $\begin{bmatrix} 1 \\ -2 \end{bmatrix}$. To sketch a graph of the original curve all you need do is translate $4x^2 + 9y^2 = 36$ under the vector $\begin{bmatrix} -1 \\ 2 \end{bmatrix}$ which is the opposite of the original vector.

EXAMPLE 2. Translate the curve represented by

$$2x^2 - 4x - y + 5 = 0$$

so that the curve is in standard position and the equation is in a standard form.

First note that $4AC = 4 \cdot 2 \cdot 0 = 0$ and thus the curve is a parabola. Find the correct translation by substituting $x = x' - h$, $y = y' - k$.

$$2(x'^2 - 2x'h + h^2) - 4(x' - h) - (y' - k) + 5 = 0$$
or $\quad 2x'^2 + (-4h - 4)x' - y' + (2h^2 + 4h + k + 5) = 0 \qquad$ **9**

Clearly $-4h - 4 = 0$ when $h = -1$. For the moment leave k unspecified. Substituting $h = -1$ in **9** and dropping primes, you have

$$2x^{2'} - y + (2 - 4 + 5 + k) = 0$$
or $\qquad 2x^2 = y - (3 + k)$

For this to be in standard form $(3 + k)$ must be zero so $k = -3$. Then the image of $2x^2 - 4x - y + 5 = 0$ under the translation with vector $\begin{bmatrix} -1 \\ -3 \end{bmatrix}$ is $2x^2 = y$ or $x^2 = \frac{1}{2}y$.

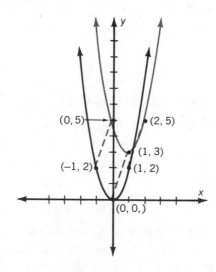

Now try these

■ Find the values of h and k that will eliminate the x and y terms in Exercises 1 and 2. Also use $4AC$ to identify each curve.

1. $x^2 + y^2 - 6x + 12y + 33 = 0$
2. $x^2 - 2y^2 - 3x + 4y + 7 = 0$

Answers: **1.** $h = -3$, $k = 6$, ellipse. $\qquad$ **2.** $h = -\frac{3}{2}$, $k = -1$, hyperbola.

Exercises

A ━━ Translate each curve so that its center (or vertex for the parabola) is at the origin. Sketch the image curve and then the original curve.

1. $x^2 + y^2 - 2x - 4y - 20 = 0$

2. $x^2 - 4y^2 - 2x - 16y - 19 = 0$

3. $x^2 - 4y^2 + 8x + 24y - 20 = 0$

4. $2x^2 - 4x - y + 5 = 0$

5. $y^2 - 6x - 4y + 22 = 0$

6. $3x^2 + 4y^2 + 12x + 8y + 8 = 0$

7. $9x^2 + y^2 + 36x - 8y + 43 = 0$

8. $2x^2 + 2y^2 - 8x + 5 = 0$

9. $16x^2 - 4y^2 - 160x - 24y + 300 = 0$

10. $2y^2 - 6x + 12y + 33 = 0$

11. $x^2 + y^2 - 4x - 2y - 20 = 0$

12. $2y^2 - 4y - x + 5 = 0$

13. $9x^2 + 4y^2 - 36x + 8y + 4 = 0$

12–9 The General Second Degree Equation: Rotations

In the last section you learned how to remove the linear (first degree) terms from

$$Ax^2 + Bxy + Cy^2 + Dx + Ey + F = 0 \qquad \textbf{1}$$

by translating the curve to a new position. When $B \neq 0$ the term Bxy can be removed from **1** by rotating the curve through an angle θ.

Before discussing how to eliminate Bxy, recall that the equations (see Section 10–8)

$$\begin{bmatrix} \cos \theta & -\sin \theta \\ \sin \theta & \cos \theta \end{bmatrix} \begin{bmatrix} x \\ y \end{bmatrix} = \begin{bmatrix} x' \\ y' \end{bmatrix} \qquad \textbf{2}$$

rotate a point (x, y) through an angle of θ to (x', y'). However, the rotation desired is the inverse of **2** since you want equations for x and y in terms of x' and y'. The equations are easily found by multiplying both sides of **2** by the inverse of the rotation matrix. (See Section 10–5.)

(Note that the inverse exists for all θ. Why?) The result is

$$\begin{bmatrix} x \\ y \end{bmatrix} = \begin{bmatrix} \cos\theta & \sin\theta \\ -\sin\theta & \cos\theta \end{bmatrix}\begin{bmatrix} x' \\ y' \end{bmatrix}$$

or
$$\begin{aligned} x &= x'\cos\theta + y'\sin\theta \\ y &= -x'\sin\theta + y'\cos\theta \end{aligned} \qquad \textbf{3}$$

Equations **3** are the *rotation equations*.

EXAMPLE 1. Rotate the curve represented by $x^2 - y^2 - 9 = 0$ through an angle of 45°. Sketch both curves.

When $\theta = 45°$, the rotation equations are

$$x = \frac{x'}{\sqrt{2}} + \frac{y'}{\sqrt{2}} \qquad y = \frac{-x'}{\sqrt{2}} + \frac{y'}{\sqrt{2}}$$

Substitution in $x^2 - y^2 - 9 = 0$ yields

$$\left(\frac{x' + y'}{\sqrt{2}}\right)^2 - \left(\frac{-x' + y'}{\sqrt{2}}\right)^2 - 9 = 0$$

or
$$x'^2 + 2x'y' + y'^2 - x'^2 + 2x'y' - y'^2 - 18 = 0$$

or
$$2x'y' = 9.$$

Since $2x'y' = 9$ is the image of $x^2 - y^2 = 9$ under a rotation and the properties of conics are preserved under rotations, both are hyperbolas.

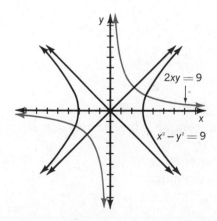

In Example 1 you found that the rotation image of $x^2 - y^2 = 9$ had an equation which involved an xy-term. Conversely, given a second degree equation with an xy-term, rotations can be used to eliminate that term. Clearly the major objective is to find the angle θ through which you should rotate.

Suppose you have a second degree equation, $B \neq 0$.

$$Ax^2 + Bxy + Cy^2 + Dx + Ey + F = 0.$$

Rotate this curve through an angle θ by substituting the rotation equations

$$x = x' \cos \theta + y' \sin \theta \qquad y = -x' \sin \theta + y' \cos \theta$$

The results, in simplified form, are

$$A'x'^2 + B'x'y' + C'y'^2 + D'x' + E'y' + F' = 0$$

where
$$\begin{aligned}
A' &= A \cos^2 \theta - B \sin \theta \cos \theta + C \sin^2 \theta \\
B' &= B(\cos^2 \theta - \sin^2 \theta) + (2A - 2C) \sin \theta \cos \theta \\
C' &= A \sin^2 \theta + B \sin \theta \cos \theta + C \cos^2 \theta \\
D' &= D \cos \theta - E \sin \theta \\
E' &= D \sin \theta + E \cos \theta \\
F' &= F
\end{aligned}$$

To eliminate $x'y'$, B' must be zero.

Let
$$B' = B(\cos^2 \theta - \sin^2 \theta) + (2A - 2C) \sin \theta \cos \theta = 0$$

or
$$B \cos 2\theta + (A - C) \sin 2\theta = 0 \quad \text{(Why?)}$$

Since $B \neq 0$ (if it were there would be nothing to do) and $\sin 2\theta \neq 0$. (Why?)

$$\frac{\cos 2\theta}{\sin 2\theta} = \frac{C - A}{B}$$

or
$$\cot 2\theta = \frac{C - A}{B} \qquad\qquad 4$$

By restricting θ to an acute angle, $\sin \theta$ and $\cos \theta$ can be computed by using the formulas

$$\sin \theta = \sqrt{\frac{1 - \cos 2\theta}{2}}, \quad \cos \theta = \sqrt{\frac{1 + \cos 2\theta}{2}} \qquad\qquad 5$$

Thus to eliminate the xy-term from 1, find $\cot 2\theta$ by using 4, $\sin \theta$ and $\cos \theta$ using 5 and rotate using the rotation equations 3.

EXAMPLE 2. Rotate $2x^2 + \sqrt{3}xy + y^2 - 8 = 0$ in such a manner that the xy term is eliminated.

By 4 $\cot 2\theta = \dfrac{1 - 2}{\sqrt{3}} = \dfrac{-1}{\sqrt{3}}$.

The angle θ is acute and $\cot 2\theta = \dfrac{x}{y}$, and so $x = -1$, $y = \sqrt{3}$. (See the diagram.) Recall that $\cos 2\theta = \dfrac{x}{r}$ where $r = \sqrt{x^2 + y^2}$. Thus

$$\cos 2\theta = -\tfrac{1}{2}.$$

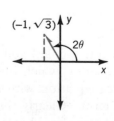

Now substituting in **5,** you see that

$$\sin \theta = \sqrt{\dfrac{1 - \dfrac{-1}{2}}{2}} \qquad \cos \theta = \sqrt{\dfrac{1 + \dfrac{-1}{2}}{2}}$$

$$= \sqrt{\dfrac{2+1}{4}} \qquad\qquad = \sqrt{\dfrac{1}{4}}$$

$$= \dfrac{\sqrt{3}}{2} \qquad\qquad\quad = \dfrac{1}{2}$$

The rotating equations are

$$x = \dfrac{x' + \sqrt{3}y'}{2}$$

$$y = \dfrac{-\sqrt{3}x' + y'}{2}$$

Substituting these in the original equation, you get

$$2\left(\dfrac{x' + y'\sqrt{3}}{2}\right)^2 + \sqrt{3}\left(\dfrac{x' + y'\sqrt{3}}{2}\right)\left(\dfrac{-x'\sqrt{3} + y'}{2}\right)$$

$$+ \left(\dfrac{-x'\sqrt{3} + y'}{2}\right)^2 - 8 = 0$$

Multiplying out and collecting terms you find

$$2x'^2 + 10y'^2 = 32$$

or

$$x'^2 + 5y'^2 = 16.$$

The figure below shows the original ellipse and its image in standard position. What is the measure of the angle through which the ellipse was rotated? (*Hint:* What is sin θ? cos θ?)

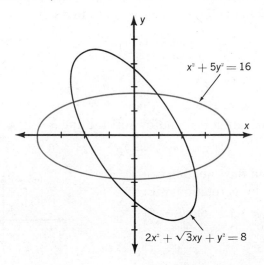

$$x^2 + 5y^2 = 16$$

$$2x^2 + \sqrt{3}xy + y^2 = 8$$

EXAMPLE 3. By a translation and a rotation move the curve $4x^2 - 4xy + 7y^2 + 12x + 6y - 9 = 0$ to the standard position. Find the equation of the curve in standard position.

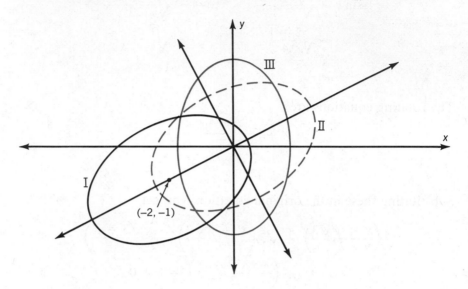

Check $4AC - B^2$. It is greater than zero, so a translation will eliminate the linear terms. Use the equations

$$x = x' - h$$
$$y = y' - k$$

Then

$$4(x'^2 - 2x'h + h^2) - 4(x'y' - x'k - y'h + hk)$$
$$+ 7(y'^2 - 2y'k + k^2) + 12(x' - h) + 6(y' - k) - 9 = 0 \quad \textbf{6}$$

Thus to eliminate the linear terms you need to solve

$$-8h + 4k + 12 = 0$$
$$4h - 14k + 6 = 0$$

or
$$h = 2,$$
$$k = 1.$$

The resulting equation is found by substituting $h = 2$, $k = 1$ in **6.**

$$4x'^2 - 4x'y' + 7y'^2 - 24 = 0 \quad \textbf{7}$$

The $x'y'$ term in this equation can be eliminated by a rotation with $\cot 2\theta = \dfrac{7-4}{-4} = -\dfrac{3}{4}$. $\operatorname{Sin} \theta = \dfrac{2}{\sqrt{5}}$ and $\cos \theta = \dfrac{1}{\sqrt{5}}$.

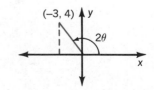

620   CHAPTER 12

The rotating equations are therefore

$$x' = \frac{x' + 2y'}{\sqrt{5}}; \quad y' = \frac{-2x' + y'}{\sqrt{5}}.$$

Substitution in 7 yields

$$8x'^2 + 3y'^2 - 24 = 0.$$

Thus the curve is an ellipse with major axis along the y axis.

In the figure, the original ellipse is I. It was translated to position II, and finally II was rotated to position III.

Now try these

━━ Find the cosine and sine of the angle of rotation that will eliminate the xy term from the following equations.

1. $2x^2 + 12xy + 7y^2 - 4x + 5y - 23 = 0$

2. $-2x^2 + 4xy + y^2 - 10x - 11y - 17 = 0$

Answers: **1.** $\cos\theta = \dfrac{3}{\sqrt{13}}$, $\sin\theta = \dfrac{2}{\sqrt{13}}$.   **2.** $\cos\theta = \dfrac{2}{\sqrt{5}}$, $\sin\theta = \dfrac{1}{\sqrt{5}}$.

Checkpoint

In your own words explain under which circumstances you would use a rotation or a translation to simplify the equation of a conic.

Exercises

A ━━ Translate and rotate each curve until it is in standard position and its equation is in standard form. Sketch each curve.

1. $2x^2 + 4xy + 5y^2 - 8x - 14y + 5 = 0$

2. $x^2 - 2xy + y^2 - 8\sqrt{2}y - 8 = 0$

3. $3x^2 + 12xy + 8y^2 - 24x - 40y + 60 = 0$

4. $73x^2 - 72xy + 52y^2 + 380x - 160y + 400 = 0$

5. $11x^2 + 6xy + 3y^2 - 12x - 12y - 12 = 0$

6. $3x^2 - 10xy + 3y^2 + 22x - 26y + 43 = 0$

7. $6x^2 + 12xy + y^2 - 36x - 6y = 0$

8. $104x^2 + 60xy + 41y^2 - 60x - 82y - 75 = 0$

9. $12x^2 - 7xy - 12y^2 - 17x + 31y - 13 = 0$

10. $25x^2 + 120xy + 144y^2 + 86x - 233y + 270 = 0$ (Rotate this curve before translating it.)

CHAPTER OBJECTIVES AND REVIEW

Objective: *To know the meaning of the important mathematical terms of this chapter.*

1. Here are many of the mathematical terms used in this chapter. Be sure that you know them thoroughly and can use them correctly.

conic sections *(582)*

ellipse *(584)*

foci *(584)*

transverse axis *(584)*

conjugate axis *(584)*

center of an ellipse *(584)*

semimajor axis *(585)*

semiminor axis *(585)*

eccentricity *(590)*

focal chord *(590)*

latus rectum *(590)*

hyperbola *(593)*

center of a hyperbola *(594)*

rectangular hyperbola *(599)*

conjugate hyperbola *(599)*

parabola *(602)*

axis of symmetry of a parabola *(602)*

vertex of a parabola *(602)*

Objective: *To define each conic section and write the equations for the conics in standard form.*

2. Define an ellipse as a set of points.

3. Define a hyperbola as a set of points.

4. Define a parabola as a set of points.

5. Write the equation of the ellipse

   a. with center at the origin and foci on the x axis.

   b. with center at the origin and foci on the y axis.

   c. with center at $(3, 5)$ and foci on $y = 5$.

   d. with center at $(3, 5)$ and foci on $x = 3$.

   e. with center at $(0, 2)$ and foci on $x = 0$.

   f. with center at $(0, 2)$ and foci on $y = 2$.

   g. with center at $(2, 0)$ and foci on $y = 0$.

6. Write the equation of the hyperbola

   a. with center at the origin and foci on the x axis.

   b. with center at the origin and foci on the y axis.

   c. with center at $(3, 5)$ and foci on $x = 3$.

   d. with center at $(3, 5)$ and foci on $y = 5$.

   e. with center at $(0, 2)$ and foci on $x = 0$.

   f. with center at $(0, 2)$ and foci on $y = 2$.

   g. with center at $(6, 6)$ and foci on $x = 6$.

7. Write the equation of the parabola

    a. with vertex at the origin and focus on the x axis.

    b. with vertex at the origin and focus on the y axis.

    c. with vertex at $(3, 5)$ and focus on $y = 5$.

    d. with vertex at $(3, 5)$ and focus on $x = 3$.

Objective: *Given an equation of a conic section to determine each of the following as appropriate: length of major axis, minor axis, and latus rectum, coordinates of vertices, minor axis, center, and foci, eccentricity, and equations of directrices and asymptotes.*

■ For each equation in Exercises 8–13

    a. identify the conic.

    b. determine if appropriate the length of major axis, minor axis, and latus rectum, coordinates of vertices, minor axis, center, and foci, eccentricity and equations of directrices and asymptotes.

    c. sketch the conic.

8. $\dfrac{x^2}{12} + \dfrac{y^2}{16} = 1$

9. $(x - 3)^2 = 12(y + 2)$

10. $\dfrac{x^2}{16} - \dfrac{y^2}{9} = 1$

11. $\dfrac{(x - 1)^2}{25} + \dfrac{(y + 5)^2}{9} = 1$

12. $y^2 = -8x$

13. $\dfrac{(y - 2)^2}{64} - \dfrac{(x + 3)^2}{36} = 1$

Objective: *Given an equation of the second degree to identify the nature of the graph by examination of the coefficients.*

■ For each equation in Exercises 14–21 identify the nature of the graph.

14. $3x^2 + 2xy - y^2 + 2x = 5$ *hy*

15. $3x^2 + 4xy + y^2 + 2x = 5$ *ellips*

16. $3x^2 + 2xy + y^2 + 2x = 5$ *ellipse*

17. $2x^2 + 2xy + y^2 + 2y = 5$ *ellipse*

18. $2x^2 + 2xy - y^2 + 2y = 5$ *hyper.*

19. $-3x^2 - 3y^2 + 2x + 2y = 25$ *circle*

20. $-2x^2 + 2xy - y^2 + 2x = 17$ *ellips*

21. $9x^2 + 3x + 2y - 1 = 0$ *parabole*

Objective: *To translate and rotate a conic so that it may be represented by an equation of a congruent conic in standard position.*

▬ In Exercises 22–29 use translation, rotation or both, to move each curve so that its center (or vertex for parabolas) is at the origin and so that its axis is the x or y axis. In each case identify the translation vector and angle of rotation.

22. $x^2 + y^2 - 4x - 2y - 20 = 0$

23. $-4x^2 + y^2 - 16x - 2y - 19 = 0$

24. $x^2 - 6y - 4x + 22 = 0$

25. $16x^2 - 9y^2 + 32x + 36y + 205 = 0$

26. $x^2 - 4xy + y^2 + 5 = 0$

27. $2x^2 + 8xy - 4y^2 - 7 = 0$

28. $5x^2 - 24xy - 2y^2 + x + 3y + 4 = 0$

29. $9x^2 - 6xy + y^2 + 12x + 6y + 4 = 0$

CHAPTER TEST ▬▬▬▬▬▬▬▬

1. Write the equation of the parabola with axis of symmetry parallel to the x axis and containing $(4, 2)$, $(2, -1)$, $(4, 1)$.

2. Write the equation of the ellipse with axes on, or parallel to, the coordinate axes whose

    a. foci are at $(0, \pm 1)$ and vertices are at $(0, \pm 3)$

    b. semiminor axis is 4 and foci are at $(\pm 3, 0)$

    c. center is at $(2, -3)$, one vertex at $(2, -9)$ and eccentricity is $\frac{2}{3}$.

3. Write the equation of the hyperbola with axes on, or parallel to, the coordinate axes whose

    a. foci are at $(0, \pm 7)$ and vertices are at $(0, \pm 5)$

    b. foci are at $(-2, -2)$ and $(6, -2)$, and the eccentricity is $\frac{4}{3}$

    c. center is at the origin, one focus is at $(-10, 0)$ and minor axis has length 12.

4. What are the equations of the asymptotes of $\frac{y^2}{25} - \frac{x^2}{24} = 1$?

5. Find the length of the latus rectum of $\frac{(x-1)^2}{9} + \frac{(y-3)^2}{4} = 1$.

6. What is the equation of the directrix of $y^2 + 2x - 4y - 14 = 0$?

7. What are the lengths of the semimajor and semiminor axes of $\frac{(y-3)^2}{36} + \frac{(x-2)^2}{20} = 1$?

8. What are the coordinates of the center, vertices, and foci of

$$\frac{(x + 1)^2}{25} - \frac{(y + 2)^2}{144} = 1?$$

9. What conic is represented by

$$4x^2 + 3y^2 - 32y - 48 = 0?$$

10. What conic is represented by

$$5x^2 - 4y^2 + 12x + 16y - 124 = 0?$$

11. What conic is represented by

$$3y^2 - 4x - y + 2 = 0?$$

12. Use translation to eliminate the first degree terms in

$$5x^2 - 4y^2 + 10x + 16y - 124 = 0.$$

13. Remove the xy term in

$$9x^2 - 12xy + 4y^2 - 4 = 0$$

by rotating the conic through an angle θ.

14. Use translation and rotation to remove the x, the y, and the xy terms in

$$46x^2 + 48xy + 32y^2 + 5x + 12y - 7 = 0.$$

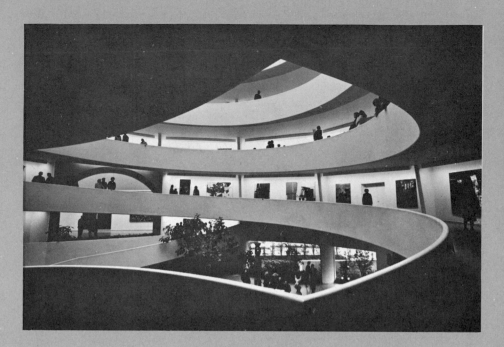

CHAPTER 13

GRAPHS IN THREE SPACE

An interesting aspect of certain shapes in three space is their relationship to basic shapes from two space. Mathematicians, architects, and artisans all find satisfaction in starting with a straight line, circle, or other simple figure and allowing it to move in some regular manner to create a new and pleasing object.

The *surface of revolution* is a good example of the kind of shapes that can be formed. You can see a practical application in the manufacture of pottery. In the picture on the opposite page you can visualize an imaginary stack of circles, infinite in number, all having their centers on the axis of the whirling potter's wheel.

The two twin apartment towers that you see are each examples of the *circular cylinder*, a shape that is especially interesting since it can be generated from simple elements in more than one way. One way is first to allow a point to revolve in a plane about fixed straight line and a constant distance from it. The points of the resulting circle are then permitted to move in paths that are parallel to the fixed line. Another way of generating the circular cylinder is described in this chapter on page 628 and has the advantage that, unlike the method just described, it can be used to generate all cylinders, not just circular ones.

Suppose, as in the previous paragraph, that you allow a point to revolve about a fixed line while remaining at a fixed distance from it. This time, however, allow the point to move not only in its circular path, but also in a direction parallel to the line. In this case you will not generate a surface at all but rather a curve in three space called a *helix*. A simple example of a helix are the threads of a metal screw. Another one is the spiral promenade in the interior of the Guggenheim Museum in New York City.

13–1 Cylinders

In Section 9–11 you learned that the equation

$$Ax + By + Cz + D = 0 \qquad \textbf{1}$$

is the equation of a plane in space whenever A, B, and C are not all zero and x, y, $z \in$ R. A plane is an example of a surface. A set of points in space which is the graph of a relation described by a single equation is a **surface.**

A second example of a surface is a sphere. A **sphere** is the set of all points at a fixed distance r from a fixed point O (a, b, c). By the distance formula it follows that each point on the sphere satisfies the following equation.

$$(x - a)^2 + (y - b)^2 + (z - c)^2 = r^2 \qquad \textbf{2}$$

Figure 1 below illustrates Equation **2.**

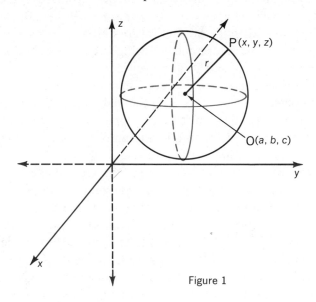

Figure 1

There are many other surfaces in space. One of the simplest classes of surfaces is the **cylinders.**

Let C be a curve in a plane π. Let L be the set of lines which are perpendicular to π and contain a point of the curve C. The set of all points on the lines in L is a cylindrical surface, or a cylinder. See Figure 2.

The curve C is the *directrix* of the cylinder, and each line in L is an *element* of the cylinder. Do you know why the elements of a cylinder are parallel to each other?

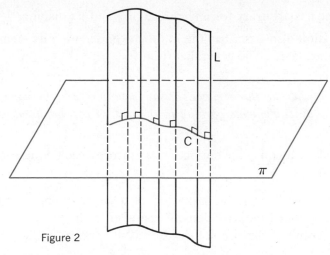

Figure 2

The intersection of a plane perpendicular to an element of a cylinder is a **normal section of the cylinder.** Each normal section of a cylinder is congruent to the directrix. Can you explain why?

A cylinder is often named after the curve which is its directrix. If the directrix is a parabola, the cylinder is a parabolic cylinder. In a similar manner a cylinder could be *hyperbolic, elliptic,* or even a plane.

As you know, you may arbitrarily choose a coordinate system for space. The equations of cylinders are quite simple if you choose the coordinate system so that one of the coordinate planes is perpendicular to the elements of the cylinder.

For example, in the figure at the right suppose that the directrix of a cylinder is an ellipse. Choose the coordinate system so that the ellipse is in standard position in the xy plane. Then that ellipse has equation

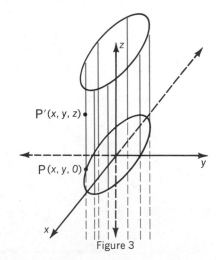

Figure 3

$$\frac{x^2}{a^2} + \frac{y^2}{b^2} = 1$$

in the xy plane. Notice that each element of the cylinder is perpendicular to the xy plane. Thus if $P(x, y, 0)$ is a point on the directrix, then $P'(x, y, z)$, for $z \in R$, is a point on the cylinder. This follows because each point on one element of the cylinder has the same x and y coordinates.

Since z is arbitrary for any choice of x and y satisfying $\frac{x^2}{a^2} + \frac{y^2}{b^2} = 1$, this equation also describes the elliptic cylinder with its elements parallel to the z axis. The generalization is:

The graph in three space of an equation in two variables is a cylinder with its elements parallel to the axis of the unnamed variable.

EXAMPLE. Identify the surfaces described by each equation.

a. $x^2 + z^2 = 4$ **b.** $y^2 = 4(z - 2)$

a. Since $x^2 + z^2 = 4$ is the equation of a circle in the xz plane, it is a circular cylinder with its elements parallel to the y axis.

    The graph of the circular cylinder is illustrated below.

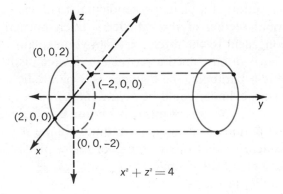

b. $y^2 = 4(z - 2)$ is a parabola in the yz plane with vertex at $(0, 0, 2)$. Thus the surface is a parabolic cylinder with its elements parallel to the x axis.

    The graph of the parabolic cylinder is illustrated below.

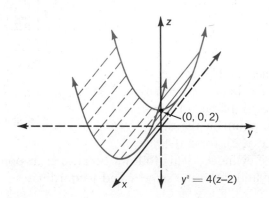

Now try these

━━ Given the following graphs in two space, identify the cylindrical surface and the axis to which its elements are parallel.

1. $\frac{x^2}{16} + \frac{y^2}{8} = 1$ **2.** $3x^2 + 3z^2 = 9$ **3.** $3y^2 - 4z^2 = 12$

Answers: **1.** Elliptic cylinder, z axis   **2.** Circular cylinder, y axis   **3.** Hyperbolic cylinder, x axis

Checkpoint

1. Define a "surface".

2. Describe in your own words what a cylindrical surface is.

3. What determines the name of the cylindrical surface (that is, elliptical, circular, etc.)

Exercises

A ━━ Identify each surface and construct its graph for Exercises 1–14.

1. $(x - 2)^2 + y^2 = 9$ **2.** $(x - 2)^2 + z^2 = 9$

3. $(y - 2)^2 + z^2 = 9$ **4.** $3x + 4y = 12$

5. $x^2 + y^2 + z^2 = 4$ **6.** $x^2 = 8z$

7. $y^2 = 4z$ **8.** $\frac{x^2}{16} - \frac{y^2}{9} = 1$

9. $4x^2 + 9z^2 = 36$ **10.** $x^2 + z^2 - 4x - 6z + 9 = 0$

11. $x^2 + 4y^2 - 4x - 32y = 64$ **12.** $z^2 + y^2 - 4y = 0$

13. $y = \sin x \quad 0 \le x \le \pi$ **14.** $y = e^x$

15. Compare the graphs of **a.** $x^2 + 4y^2 = 16$ and **b.** $x^2 + 4y^2 = 16$, $z = 2$. Sketch each graph.

━━ Sketch a graph of each equation for Exercises 16–21.

16. $x^2 + y^2 + z^2 = 16$ **17.** $x^2 + y^2 + z^2 = 16$, $z = 3$

18. $y^2 = 8(z - 3)$ **19.** $y^2 = 8(z - 3)$, $x = -2$

20. $(x - 2)^2 + 4z^2 = 4$ **21.** $(x - 2)^2 + 4z^2 = 4$, $y = 1$

B **22.** Find the equation of the surface whose points have the property that the square of the distance of each point from the x axis is equal to twice its distance from the xy plane. Construct the graph.

23. Find the equation of the set of points which are equidistant from $(1, 2, 7)$ and $(1, 5, 7)$. Construct the graph.

13–2   Surfaces of Revolution

Given a curve C and a line L in a plane π, the surface generated by revolving C about L is called a **surface of revolution.** The line L is the **axis of rotation.** The curve C is the **generating curve.**

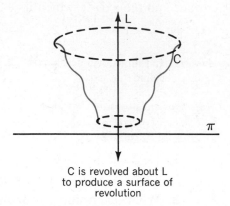

C is revolved about L
to produce a surface of
revolution

The curve formed by the intersection of a plane and a surface is a **plane section** of the surface. When the intersecting plane is perpendicular to the axis of rotation of a surface of revolution the plane section is said to be perpendicular to the axis of rotation. It should be clear to you that each perpendicular plane section of a surface of revolution is either a circle, one point, or the empty set. The converse of the previous statement is also true. The following is a statement of the converse.

> If for a given surface there is a line L such that each plane section perpendicular to L is a circle, one point, or the empty set, then the surface is a surface of revolution.

These comments imply that whenever you are given the equation of a surface you can determine whether it is a surface of revolution by identifying the nature of the plane sections perpendicular to some line L. The catch here is that choosing L is difficult. The problem is substantially simplified by specifying initially that you are only interested in determining whether a surface is a surface of revolution with respect to one of the coordinate axes. Then, because of the simple nature of the equation of a plane perpendicular to an axis, the procedure is straightforward. That procedure is illustrated in the next example.

EXAMPLE 1.   Show that $4x^2 + y^2 + 4z^2 - 6y = 0$ is a surface of revolution with the y axis as the axis of rotation.

To accomplish the task you must show that for each plane perpendicular to the y axis the plane section is a circle, a point, or the empty set.

Recall that the equation of a plane perpendicular to the y axis is $y = k$, where k is some real number. The intersection of the surface $4x^2 + y^2 + 4z^2 - 6y = 0$ and the plane $y = k$ is the set of points with y-coordinate k and therefore satisfying the following equation.

$$4x^2 + 4z^2 + k^2 - 6k = 0$$

or
$$4x^2 + 4z^2 = k(6 - k) \qquad\qquad \textbf{1}$$

Thus, in the plane $y = k$, the plane section is described by **1**. Is the graph of **1** a circle, a point, or the empty set for every $k \in$ R and *never* anything else? Clearly such is the case because

$$x^2 + z^2 = \tfrac{1}{4}k(6 - k)$$

is a circle for $0 < k < 6$; it is a point for $k = 0$ or $k = 6$; and it is the empty set when $k < 0$ or $k > 6$. Another way to say the same thing is to say that it is a circle when $k(6 - k) > 0$; a point when $k(6 - k) = 0$ and the empty set when $k(6 - k) < 0$.

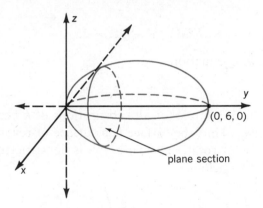

plane section

Recall that to graph a plane in three-space you made use of the traces, that is, the intersections of the plane with the coordinate planes. These were found by setting successively x, y, and z equal to zero and graphing the resulting line in the appropriate coordinate plane. The same idea applies here.

Setting $z = 0$, in $4x^2 + y^2 + 4z^2 - 6y = 0$, you have the ellipse in the xy plane with equation

$$4x^2 + y^2 - 6y = 0.$$

in the xy plane. Similarly the trace of the surface in the yz plane is an ellipse with equation

$$4z^2 + y^2 - 6y = 0.$$

These two ellipses are used to graph the surface shown above.

EXAMPLE 2. Determine the coordinate axis for which the graph of

$$x^2 + y^2 - 9z^2 = 25$$

is a surface of revolution. What are the traces of the surface in the three coordinate planes?

Check the traces first. If any one of the traces is not a circle then the surface is not a surface of revolution with the eliminated variable as axis of rotation.

$x = 0$	$y^2 - 9z^2 = 25$	a hyperbola
$y = 0$	$x^2 - 9z^2 = 25$	a hyperbola
$z = 0$	$x^2 + y^2 = 25$	a circle

Thus the axis of rotation *may* be the z axis. Check further by determining the nature of all perpendicular plane sections. You see that substituting

$$z = k$$

into

$$x^2 + y^2 - 9z^2 = 25$$

yields the following equation.

$$x^2 + y^2 = 25 + 9k^2$$

The graph of this is a circle for all substitutions of k because $25 + 9k^2$ is always positive. Thus the surface is a surface of revolution with the z axis as the axis of rotation. The graph is constructed by using the traces. It is shown below.

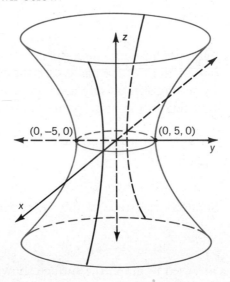

Now try these

▬ Find the traces and identify the axis or axes of rotation.

1. $3x^2 + 3y^2 + 3z^2 = 1$ **2.** $7x^2 - 8y^2 - 8z^2 = -2$

Answers: **1.** $3x^2 + 3y^2 = 1$, $3y^2 + 3z^2 = 1$, $3x^2 + 3z^2 = 1$, x, y, z axes
          2. $7x^2 - 8y^2 = -2$, $7x^2 - 8z^2 = -2$, $4y^2 + 4z^2 = 1$, x axis

Exercises

A ▬ For each equation find the traces and determine if the graph is a surface of revolution. If it is, identify the axis or axes of rotation. Sketch the graph of the surface.

1. $\frac{1}{4}(x^2 + z^2) = y$ **2.** $y^2 = x^2 + z^2$

3. $9z^2 + 16(x^2 + y^2) = 144$ **4.** $x^2 + y^2 + z^2 = 25$

5. $x^2 + 4y^2 + 9z^2 = 36$ **6.** $y^2 + x^2 = 4z$

7. $x^2 + y^2 + z^2 = 6y$ **8.** $9y^2 - 16x^2 - 16z^2 = 144$

9. $x^2 - 16y^2 + z^2 = 0$ **10.** $8x^2 + 8y^2 - z^2 = 0$

B **11.** The graph of the equation

$$Ax^2 + By^2 + Cz^2 + Dx + Ey + Fz + G = 0$$

is, under certain circumstances, a surface of revolution. What are the circumstances?

12. How would you determine the axis of rotation for the surface in Exercise 11 when it was a surface of revolution?

13–3   Quadric Surfaces

The graph of a second degree equation in space is a **quadric surface.** Many of the surfaces you studied earlier in this chapter are quadric surfaces. The study of general quadric surfaces is quite difficult, but, by restricting the second degree equations to those with no xy-, xz-, and yz-terms the properties of the resulting surfaces are relatively easy to study.

There are three tools valuable in describing a quadric surface. These are 1. traces, 2. the plane sections, and 3. symmetry with respect to a plane. You are familiar with the methods used to find the traces and to identify plane sections. Symmetry with respect to a plane is equally as easy.

Two points P and Q are symmetric with respect to a plane π if and only if π is the perpendicular bisector of the line segment PQ. (See Figure 1.)

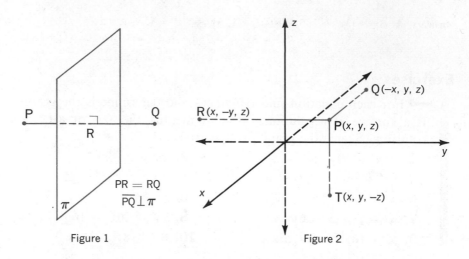

<table>
<tr><td>Figure 1</td><td>Figure 2</td></tr>
</table>

$PR = RQ$
$\overline{PQ} \perp \pi$

The symmetry planes of greatest interest are the coordinate planes. For example, in Figure 2 $P(x, y, z)$ and $Q(-x, y, z)$ are symmetric with respect to the yz plane. Similarly $P(x, y, z)$ and $R(x, -y, z)$ are symmetric to the xz plane and $P(x, y, z)$ and $T(x, y, -z)$ are symmetric with respect to the xy plane.

Now if a surface S is to be symmetric with respect to, say, the yz plane, then for each point P of S there is a point Q of S such that P and Q are symmetrically located with respect to the yz plane. Thus $P(x, y, z)$ being in S implies $Q(-x, y, z)$ is in S. This means that the equation of the surface is satisfied by the coordinates of each point. This can happen only when even powers of x occur in the equation because only then will $(x)^n = (-x)^n$. Therefore, a quadric surface is symmetric to the yz plane if and only if x occurs only to even powers in the equation of the surface. Corresponding statements hold for symmetry with respect to the xz and xy planes. Can you state them?

A simple and familiar quadric surface is the sphere:

$$x^2 + y^2 + z^2 = r^2. \qquad\qquad 1$$

The properties of the sphere are easily summarized: The sphere **1**

1. is symmetric to each coordinate plane,
2. has traces that are circles, and
3. has plane sections that are circles, single points, or the empty set.

The next quadric surface discussed here is the *ellipsoid*. The equation of an **ellipsoid** is the following

$$\frac{x^2}{a^2} + \frac{y^2}{b^2} + \frac{z^2}{c^2} = 1. \qquad\qquad 2$$

The characteristics of an ellipsoid are not hard to derive: First, since x, y, and z occur raised to the exponent 2, the ellipsoid is symmetric with respect to each coordinate plane. The traces are formed by setting x, y, and z equal to zero one at a time. In each case you see that the trace is an ellipse. The equations of the traces are the following.

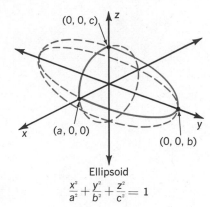

Ellipsoid

$$\frac{x^2}{a^2} + \frac{y^2}{b^2} + \frac{z^2}{c^2} = 1$$

xy plane:

$$\frac{x^2}{a^2} + \frac{y^2}{b^2} = 1, z = 0.$$

xz plane:

$$\frac{x^2}{a^2} + \frac{z^2}{c^2} = 1, y = 0.$$

yz plane:

$$\frac{y^2}{b^2} + \frac{z^2}{c^2} = 1, x = 0.$$

The plane section perpendicular to the z axis is the graph of the system:

$$\frac{x^2}{a^2} + \frac{y^2}{b^2} = 1 - \frac{k^2}{c^2}, \quad z = k.$$

For $1 - \frac{k^2}{c^2} > 0$, the plane section is an ellipse and for $1 - \frac{k^2}{c^2} = 0$, the section is a point. Similar remarks may be made for plane sections perpendicular to the x and y axes. A graph of an ellipsoid is shown above.

Notice that when $a^2 = b^2 = c^2$ the ellipsoid is a sphere. What conditions on the constants a^2, b^2, and c^2 would allow you to conclude that the ellipsoid is a surface of revolution?

There are five other quadric surfaces with which you should be familiar. These are identified on pages 638–9, along with their graphs. The determination of the characteristics of each is left for you.

Elliptic Paraboloid:

$$\frac{x^2}{a^2} + \frac{y^2}{b^2} = cz, c > 0 \qquad 3$$

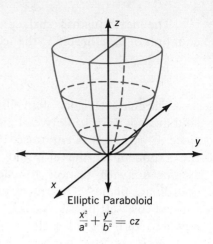

Elliptic Paraboloid
$$\frac{x^2}{a^2} + \frac{y^2}{b^2} = cz$$

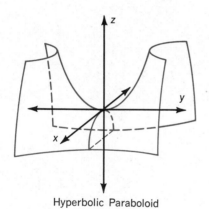

Hyperbolic Paraboloid:

$$\frac{y^2}{a^2} - \frac{x^2}{b^2} = cz, c > 0 \qquad 4$$

Hyperbolic Paraboloid
$$\frac{y^2}{a^2} - \frac{x^2}{b^2} = cz$$

Elliptic Cone:

$$\frac{x^2}{a^2} + \frac{y^2}{b^2} - \frac{z^2}{c^2} = 0 \qquad 5$$

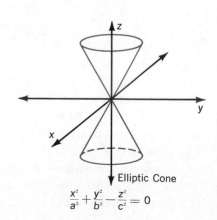

Elliptic Cone
$$\frac{x^2}{a^2} + \frac{y^2}{b^2} - \frac{z^2}{c^2} = 0$$

Hyperboloid of one Sheet:

$$\frac{x^2}{a^2} + \frac{y^2}{b^2} - \frac{z^2}{c^2} = 1$$ 6

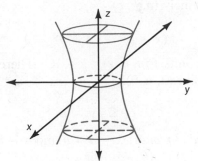

Hyperboloid of one sheet
$$\frac{x^2}{a^2} + \frac{y^2}{b^2} - \frac{z^2}{c^2} = 1$$

Hyperboloid of two Sheets:

$$\frac{y^2}{b^2} - \frac{x^2}{a^2} - \frac{z^2}{c^2} = 1$$ 7

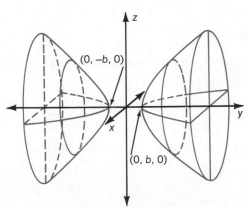

Hyperboloid of two sheets
$$\frac{y^2}{b^2} - \frac{x^2}{a^2} - \frac{z^2}{c^2} = 1$$

Since the hyperboloid and paraboloid have centers of symmetry, they are called **central quadrics.**

It should be noted that similar diagrams will result if the variables x, y, and z are interchanged in any of the quadric surfaces listed above.

In addition to the quadric surfaces described here there are *degenerate* quadric surfaces. For example the graph of the equation

$$(x - a)^2 + (y - b)^2 + (z - c)^2 = 0 \qquad\qquad 8$$

is a single point, namely (a, b, c).

The equation

$$(x - a)^2 + (y - b)^2 = 0 \qquad\qquad 9$$

is satisfied by all points $P(a, b, z)$, $z \in R$. Therefore the graph is a line through the point $(a, b, 0)$.

The equation

$$(x - a)^2 = b^2 \qquad\qquad 10$$

represents *two parallel planes*: $x - a = b$ and $x - a = -b$. The graph of the equation

$$(x - a)^2 = 0 \qquad\qquad 11$$

represents a single plane with equation $x - a = 0$.

Finally the graph of

$$\frac{x^2}{a^2} - \frac{y^2}{b^2} = 0 \qquad\qquad 12$$

represents two intersecting planes with equations $\frac{x}{a} + \frac{y}{b} = 0$ and $\frac{x}{a} - \frac{y}{b} = 0$. Their intersection is the z axis.

Now try these

── For Exercises 1–3, identify symmetries of the quadric surfaces.

1. $2x^2 + y^2 + 3y + z^2 - 2z = 7$

2. $3x^2 + 4y^2 + 2z = 3$

3. $x^2 - 2x + y^2 - 2y + z^2 = 3$

── For Exercises 4–5, identify the quadric surface.

4. $\frac{x^2}{4} - \frac{z^2}{10} = 3y$

5. $\frac{x^2}{3} + \frac{y^2}{3} + \frac{z^2}{3} = 1$

Answers: **1.** *yz* plane.　　**2.** *yz* and *xz* plane.　　**3.** *xy* plane.　　**4.** Hyperbolic Paraboloid.　　**5.** Sphere.

Checkpoint

1. Name three characteristics used to describe a quadric surface.

2. Define symmetry with respect to a plane.

Exercises

A ━━ Determine the characteristics of each quadric surface, that is, identify symmetries, find equations of the traces, and determine the character of the plane sections which are perpendicular to the coordinate axes for Exercises 1–5.

1. Elliptic Paraboloid: $\dfrac{x^2}{a^2} + \dfrac{y^2}{b^2} = cz \quad c > 0$

2. Hyperbolic Paraboloid: $\dfrac{x^2}{a^2} - \dfrac{y^2}{b^2} = cz \quad c > 0$

3. Elliptic Cone: $\dfrac{x^2}{a^2} + \dfrac{y^2}{b^2} - \dfrac{z^2}{c^2} = 0$

4. Hyperboloid of one Sheet: $\dfrac{x^2}{a^2} + \dfrac{y^2}{b^2} - \dfrac{z^2}{c^2} = 1$

5. Hyperboloid of two Sheets: $\dfrac{x^2}{a^2} - \dfrac{y^2}{b^2} - \dfrac{z^2}{c^2} = 1$

━━ For Exercises 6–39, identify the quadric surface and use the traces to sketch the graph of the surface.

6. $\dfrac{x^2}{9} + \dfrac{y^2}{4} + \dfrac{z^2}{16} = 1$

7. $\dfrac{x^2}{4} + \dfrac{y^2}{4} + \dfrac{z^2}{9} = 1$

8. $16x^2 + 9y^2 - z^2 = 144$

9. $\dfrac{x^2}{9} + \dfrac{y^2}{16} - \dfrac{z^2}{4} = 1$

10. $16x^2 - 9y^2 - z^2 = 144$

11. $\dfrac{x^2}{9} - \dfrac{y^2}{16} - \dfrac{z^2}{4} = 1$

12. $16x^2 + 9y^2 - z^2 = 0$

13. $\dfrac{x^2}{9} + \dfrac{y^2}{16} - \dfrac{z^2}{4} = 0$

14. $4x^2 + 9y^2 = 36z$

15. $x^2 + 4z^2 = 12y$

16. $4x^2 - 9y^2 = 36z$

17. $x^2 - 4z^2 = 12y$

18. $x^2 + (y - 4)^2 + z^2 = 0$

19. $x^2 + y^2 + z^2 = 1$

20. $(x + 1)^2 + (y - 2)^2 = 0$

21. $x^2 + (y - 2)^2 = 4$

22. $\dfrac{x^2}{9} - \dfrac{y^2}{16} = 0$

23. $\dfrac{x^2}{9} - \dfrac{y^2}{4} + \dfrac{z^2}{25} = 0$

24. $x^2 + y^2 = 9$

25. $x^2 + y^2 = 9x$

26. $x^2 + y^2 = 9z$

27. $x^2 + y^2 = 0$

28. $\dfrac{x^2}{25} + \dfrac{y^2}{9} - \dfrac{z^2}{64} = 1$

29. $-3x^2 - 3y^2 - 3z^2 = -1$

30. $\dfrac{z^2}{16} - \dfrac{y^2}{4} = 1$

31. $2x^2 + y^2 - 3z^2 = 6$

32. $-\dfrac{x^2}{2} + \dfrac{y^2}{4} - z^2 = 1$

33. $y^2 + z^2 = 3x$

34. $\dfrac{x^2}{7} + \dfrac{z^2}{49} = 0$

35. $2y^2 + z^2 = 4$

36. $\dfrac{y^2}{4} - \dfrac{z^2}{8} = 1$

37. $-\dfrac{x^2}{12} + \dfrac{z^2}{16} = 1$

38. $-\dfrac{x^2}{9} + \dfrac{y^2}{64} - \dfrac{z^2}{25} = 1$

39. $\dfrac{(x-3)^2}{9} + \dfrac{(y-2)^2}{16} - z^2 = 1$

13–4 Cylindrical and Spherical Coordinates

When the directed distance from three mutually perpendicular planes is used to locate a point in space, the coordinates are called *Cartesian coordinates* or *rectangular coordinates*. You are familiar with rectangular coordinates, however there are other coordinate systems which are used to locate points in space.

One such system is called the **cylindrical coordinate system.** In this system each point in space is identified by an ordered triple (r, θ, z). If (x, y, z) and (r, θ, z) name the same point, then the first two coordinates of (r, θ, z) are the polar coordinates of the point $(x, y, 0)$ in the xy plane; that is, r is the length of the vec-

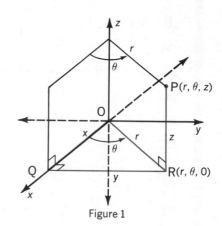

Figure 1

tor from $(0, 0, 0)$ to $(x, y, 0)$ and θ is the measure of the angle from $\overrightarrow{OQ}$ to $\overrightarrow{OR}$. This is shown in the figure.

You should be able to derive the following relations between rectangular and cylindrical coordinates.

$$x = r \cos \theta \qquad\qquad y = r \sin \theta \qquad\qquad r^2 = x^2 + y^2$$

$$\tan \theta = \frac{y}{x} \quad \text{and} \quad z = z$$

EXAMPLE 1. Describe the surface whose equation in cylindrical coordinates is

$$r = 5.$$

There are two solutions. The first is that the set of points satisfying $r = 5$ is the set of all points 5 units from the z axis. Since θ and z are not restricted by the equation they may take on all values. The graph shown in Figure 2 below is clearly a right circular cylinder with its axis being the z axis.

A second solution uses the fact that $r^2 = x^2 + y^2$ and thus $r = 5$, becomes

$$25 = x^2 + y^2.$$

You know that in space, the latter equation has a right circular cylinder for its graph.

A second coordinate system, shown in Figure 3, is the system of **spherical coordinates.** This system uses two angles and a vector to locate each point in space. The coordinates are given by the ordered triple (ρ, θ, ϕ) (rho, theta, phi). If $P(x, y, z)$ and $P(\rho, \theta, \phi)$ name the same point, rho (ρ) is the length of the vector $\overrightarrow{OP}$

$$\rho = |\overrightarrow{OP}|.$$

Theta (θ) is the measure of the same angle as in the cylindrical coordinates for the point (x, y, z). Phi (ϕ) is the measure of the angle between the positive z axis and $\overrightarrow{OP}$.

It is customary to restrict the spherical coordinates (ρ, θ, ϕ) as follows:

$$\rho \geq 0, \qquad 0 \leq \theta \leq 2\pi, \qquad 0 \leq \phi \leq \pi$$

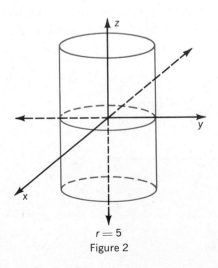

$r = 5$

Figure 2

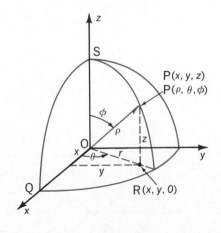

Figure 3

GRAPHS IN THREE SPACE   643

EXAMPLE 2. Identify the surfaces which satisfy the spherical coordinate equations

$$\textbf{a.} \; \rho = 3$$

$$\textbf{b.} \; \phi = \frac{\pi}{4}$$

a. The equation $\rho = 3$ implies that each point on the surface is three
units from the origin. Thus the surface is a sphere of radius 3, center
at the origin. See Figure 4 below.

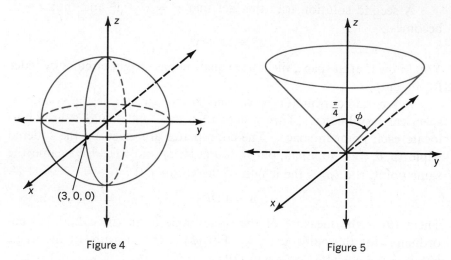

Figure 4   Figure 5

b. In Figure 5, ϕ is the measure of the angle from the z axis to a position vector $\overrightarrow{OP}$. All such points P are on the right circular cone with
its axis along the z axis.

Recall that $\sin(90 - \phi) = \cos\phi$ and $\cos(90 - \phi) = \sin\phi$. These
relations along with Figure 6 below will allow you to derive the following relations between rectangular, cylindrical and spherical coordinates:

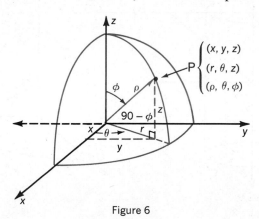

Figure 6

644   CHAPTER 13

$$r = \rho \cos (90 - \phi) = \rho \sin \phi$$
$$z = \rho \sin (90 - \phi) = \rho \cos \phi \qquad \textbf{1}$$
$$\theta = \theta.$$

$$x = r \cos \theta$$
$$y = r \sin \theta \qquad \textbf{2}$$
$$z = z.$$

Therefore:

$$x = \rho \sin \phi \cos \theta$$
$$y = \rho \sin \phi \sin \theta \qquad \textbf{3}$$
$$z = \rho \cos \phi.$$

The equations in **3** are obtained by appropriate substitution of those in **1** into those in **2**.

EXAMPLE 3. Express the equation

$$x^2 + y^2 = 25$$

(a right circular cylinder) in spherical coordinates. Does the equation have a sensible geometric interpretation? $x = \rho \sin \phi \cos \theta$ and $y = \rho \sin \phi \sin \theta$ by **3**. Thus $x^2 + y^2 = 25$ is

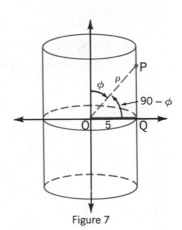

Figure 7

$$\rho^2 \sin^2 \phi \cos^2 \theta + \rho^2 \sin^2 \phi \sin^2 \theta = 25$$

$$\rho^2 \sin^2 \phi (\cos^2 \theta + \sin^2 \theta) = 25$$

or

$$\rho^2 \sin^2 \phi = 25.$$

But since $\rho \geq 0$ and $\sin \phi \geq 0$ for $0 \leq \phi \leq \pi$ you can write

$$\rho \sin \phi = 5$$

This equation may be interpreted geometrically by writing

$$\sin \phi = \frac{5}{\rho}$$

$$\cos (90 - \phi) = \frac{5}{\rho}$$

In the figure the base of the triangle OPQ is always 5, and angle POQ always measures $90 - \phi$ for every point on the cylinder. Thus the relation $\cos (90 - \phi) = \sin \phi = \dfrac{5}{\rho}$ holds for all points on the cylinder.

Now try these

■ For Exercises 1 and 2 change the cylindrical coordinates to rectangular coordinates.

1. $\left(4, \frac{\pi}{3}, 2\right)$ **2.** $(5, 2\pi, -7)$

■ For Exercises 3 and 4 change the spherical coordinates to rectangular coordinates.

3. $\left(2, 2\pi, \frac{\pi}{2}\right)$ **4.** $\left(4, \frac{\pi}{4}, \frac{\pi}{3}\right)$

Answers: **1.** $(2, 2\sqrt{3}, 2)$ **2.** $(5, 0, -7)$ **3.** $(2, 0, 0)$ **4.** $(\sqrt{6}, \sqrt{6}, 2)$

Checkpoint

     1. Compare polar and cylindrical coordinates.
     2. Compare cylindrical and spherical coordinates.

Exercises

A ■ Change cylindrical coordinates to rectangular coordinates for Exercises 1–6.

     1. $(3, 0, 2)$ **2.** $\left(2, \frac{\pi}{4}, -2\right)$

     3. $\left(7, \frac{\pi}{2}, 4\right)$ **4.** $(1, \pi, -2)$

     5. $\left(2, \frac{4\pi}{3}, 3\right)$ **6.** $\left(4, \frac{3\pi}{2}, -5\right)$

■ Change the spherical coordinates to rectangular coordinates for Exercises 7–12.

     7. $\left(7, \frac{\pi}{4}, 0\right)$ **8.** $\left(7, 0, \frac{\pi}{4}\right)$

     9. $\left(7, \pi, \frac{\pi}{2}\right)$ **10.** $\left(12, \frac{2\pi}{3}, \frac{5\pi}{6}\right)$

     11. $\left(8, \frac{\pi}{13}, \pi\right)$ **12.** $\left(2, \frac{11\pi}{6}, \frac{\pi}{3}\right)$

     13. Express ρ in terms of x, y, and z.
     14. Express $\cos \phi$ in terms of x, y, and z.
     15. Express $\tan \theta$ in terms of x, y, and z.
     16. Express $\cos \theta$ in terms of x, y and z.
     17. Express r in terms of x, y and z.
     18. Express $\sin \phi$ in terms of x, y and z.

For Exercises 19–25 change each equation from an equation in the given coordinates into an equation in the two remaining coordinate systems.

19. $x^2 + y^2 + z^2 = 9$

20. $x^2 + y^2 + z^2 - 2z = 0$

21. $z^2 = r^2$ (Change to rectangular coordinates first.)

22. $x^2 + y^2 - x = 0$

23. $\rho = 8 \cos \phi$ (See Exercise 13.)

24. $\frac{x^2}{4} + \frac{y^2}{16} + 2z^2 = 1$

25. $\rho = 4 \sin \theta$

13–5   Curves in Space

A curve in space is the set of points which make up the intersection of two surfaces. For example, you may think of a line as the intersection of two planes. Given the equations of Chapter 9 the planes are the following. (See Section 9–11.)

$$A_1 x + B_1 y + C_1 z + D_1 = 0$$

and

$$A_2 x + B_2 y + C_2 z + D_2 = 0$$

The line of intersection is the set of points satisfying the two equations simultaneously. Thus you may say that the system

$$A_1 x + B_1 y + C_1 z + D_1 = 0$$
$$and$$
$$A_2 x + B_2 y + C_2 z + D_2 = 0$$

is the algebraic representation of a line.

More generally if $F_1(x, y, z) = 0$ and $F_2(x, y, z) = 0$ are equations of surfaces, then the system

$$F_1(x, y, z) = 0 \quad and \quad F_2(x, y, z) = 0 \qquad\qquad 1$$

describes a curve in space. The system **1** is the *two-surface representation* of a curve.

If one of the surfaces in **1** is a plane, then the curve is a **plane curve.** You are familiar with plane sections of quadric surfaces; these are examples of plane curves.

On the other hand, when there is no plane which completely contains the space curve, that curve is then a **twisted curve.**

An example of a twisted curve is the graph of the system

$$x^2 + y^2 + z^2 = 16 \quad and \quad (x - 2)^2 + y^2 = 16$$

This curve, illustrated in Figure 1, is the intersection of a sphere and a right circular cylinder. Its graph in the first octant is shown below in color. (Three mutually perpendicular planes having a common origin divide space into eight equal regions, each of which is called an octant.)

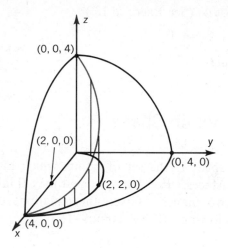

Figure 1

In addition to the two surface representation of a space curve, the curves may be represented by *parametric equations*. Recall that the parametric equations of a line were

$$x = a + t \cdot l$$
$$y = b + t \cdot m$$
$$z = c + t \cdot n$$

where $P(a, b, c)$ was a point on the line, the direction vector was $l\mathbf{i} + m\mathbf{j} + n\mathbf{k}$, and $t \in R$ was the parameter.

In a similar manner a curve can be represented parametrically by three equations

$$x = F_1(t)$$
$$y = F_2(t) \qquad\qquad 2$$
$$z = F_3(t)$$

The three equations are the *parametric representation of a curve* in space. For each replacement of the parameter t, the point with co-ordinates $x = F_1(t)$, $y = F_2(t)$, $z = F_3(t)$ is on the curve.

As an example the curve with parametric equations

$$x = a \cos t, \quad y = a \sin t, \quad z = bt$$

is called a *circular helix*. Notice that (see Figure 2)

$$x^2 + y^2 = a^2 (\cos^2 t + \sin^2 t) = a^2. \qquad\qquad 3$$

Thus each point of the helix is on a right circular cylinder. Also for each t, the point is bt units up (or down) from the xy plane. Thus the helix winds around the cylinder, moving further and further away from the xy plane for increasing values of t. A portion of the graph is shown below.

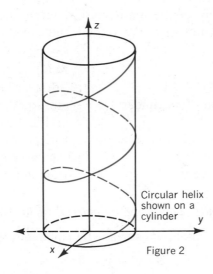

Circular helix shown on a cylinder

Figure 2

In graphing a curve from its parametric equations, it is often useful to eliminate the parameter from a pair of the parametric equations as was done in equation 3 above. Doing this sometimes allows you to identify a simple surface on which the curve lies. Otherwise the procedure used is to plot points, usually in the first octant, and sketch the curve using these points.

Exercises

A ▬ Sketch each curve in the first octant for Exercises 1–11.

1. $x = 6 \sin t, \ y = 6 \cos t, \ z = 5t$

2. $x = 3 \sin 2t, \ y = 3 \cos 2t, \ z = 4t$

3. $x = 3t \cos t, \ y = 3t \sin t, \ z = 4t$

4. $x = t, \ y = 2t, \ z = t^2$

5. $x = t, \ y = t, \ z = \frac{2}{3}t^{\frac{3}{2}}$

6. $x^2 + y^2 = 36$, $y - z = 0$ **7.** $x^2 + y^2 = 25$, $z - x = 0$

8. $y^2 = 4x$, $z = 4x$ **9.** $x^2 + y^2 - 4y = 0$, $y = 2x$

10. $x^2 + y^2 + z^2 = 25$, $x^2 = 9$ **11.** $x = t$, $y = \dfrac{t^2}{\sqrt{2}}$, $z = \frac{1}{3}t^3$

CHAPTER OBJECTIVES AND REVIEW

Objective: *To know the meaning of the important mathematical terms of this chapter.*

1. Here are many of the mathematical terms used in this chapter. Be sure that you know them thoroughly and can use them correctly.

surface *(628)*

sphere *(628)*

cylinders *(628)*

normal section of a cylinder *(629)*

surface of revolution *(632)*

axis of rotation *(632)*

generating curve *(632)*

plane section of a surface *(632)*

quadric surface *(635)*

central quadric *(639)*

cylindrical coordinates *(642)*

spherical coordinates *(643)*

plane curve *(647)*

twisted curve *(647)*

Objective: *To identify and graph cylindrical surfaces.*

▬ Identify each cylindrical surface by name and sketch its graph.

2. $\dfrac{y^2}{16} + \dfrac{z^2}{9} = 1$ **3.** $x^2 - y = 0$ **4.** $x - y = 3$

5. $yz = 4$ **6.** $x^2 + z^2 = 9$ **7.** $x^2 - 4y^2 - 4 = 0$

Objective: *To identify surfaces of revolution and sketch such surfaces.*

▬ Identify each surface which is a surface of revolution. Determine the traces in each coordinate plane, indicate the axis or axes of revolution, and sketch each surface of revolution.

8. $x^2 + z^2 - 4y = 0$ **9.** $9x^2 + 4y^2 + 9z^2 - 36 = 0$

10. $9x^2 - 9y^2 + 4z^2 - 36 = 0$ **11.** $x^2 + 4y^2 + z^2 - 4 = 0$

12. $4x^2 + 4y^2 + 4z^2 = 16$ **13.** $x^2 - 16y^2 + z^2 = 0$

Objective: *To identify and graph quadric surfaces.*

▬ Identify each quadric surface by name and sketch it.

14. $9x^2 + 4y^2 + 6z^2 = 36$ **15.** $\dfrac{x^2}{16} + \dfrac{y^2}{25} = 9z$

16. $4x^2 + 4y^2 - \frac{z^2}{16} = 0$

17. $x^2 + y^2 + z^2 = 25$

18. $9x^2 - 4y^2 = 72z$

19. $\frac{x^2}{16} - \frac{y^2}{25} - \frac{z^2}{36} = 1$

Objective: *To illustrate how a point in three space may be located using rectangular, cylindrical and spherical coordinates and to illustrate and use the relationships between these coordinate systems.*

20. Given a point P which has coordinates

    a. (x, y, z) **b.** (r, θ, z) **c.** (ρ, θ, ϕ)

Make one or more sketches illustrating the meaning of each coordinate.

21. Given $P(r, \theta, z)$. What are the rectangular coordinates of P?

22. Given $P(x, y, z)$. What are the cylindrical coordinates of P?

23. Given $P(\rho, \theta, \phi)$. What are the rectangular coordinates of P?

Objective: *To sketch the graph of a curve in space given a two surface representation or a parametric representation.*

24. Sketch the first octant graph of the curve defined by the curves $y^2 - 4x = 0$ and $z - 4x = 0$.

25. Sketch the first octant graph of the following curve.

$$x = 3 \sin t, \quad y = 3 \cos t, \quad z = \tfrac{1}{2}t.$$

CHAPTER TEST

1. Sketch the graph of the cylindrical surface whose equation is $z^2 - 4y = 0$.

2. Write the equation of the right circular cylinder whose axis is the x axis and whose directrix is a circle with radius 5.

3. Find the equations of the traces of $4x^2 + y^2 - 4z^2 = 4$. Is this a surface of revolution? Explain your answer.

4. Find the traces of $16x^2 - y^2 + 16z^2 = 9$. What is the axis of revolution? Sketch the curve.

5. What quadric surface is represented by the equation $4x^2 + y^2 - 4z^2 = 4$? Sketch it.

6. Let P have spherical coordinates $\left(1, \frac{2\pi}{3}, \frac{3\pi}{4}\right)$. Find the rectangular coordinates for P.

7. Let Q have cylindrical coordinates $\left(2, \frac{\pi}{6}, 5\right)$. Find the rectangular coordinates for Q.

CHAPTER 14

INTRODUCTION TO CALCULUS

The world about you is one of change. Sometimes the change is readily apparent, as in the case of moving objects; other times it must be searched out. The study of change is made easier through the ideas of calculus.

The automobile edging its way onto the highway illustrates two physical concepts, *instantaneous velocity* and *instantaneous acceleration*. These are among the most widely studied and most easily understood examples of the usefulness of calculus. In fact, as you will see in this chapter, phrases such as "instantaneous velocity" would be meaningless without one of the main ideas of calculus, namely, limits.

You can also discern the presence of change in less obvious situations, but ones that also can be analyzed with calculus. For example, when you trace the graph of a function from left to right the slope of the tangent lines is changing continually. (The graph of a straight line is the exception to this statement.) If you were to try to calculate the area bounded by the arch, pictured opposite, its base and two sides you would encounter difficulty not present with simpler shapes. For example, the distance of each point of the arch from the base changes from point to point. You may then wonder how area can be calculated in this case if there is no single number that can be called the height. Calculus provides a way of solving this problem, as you will see.

Another class of problems solved using calculus is that of calculating volumes of solids bounded by curved surfaces. You will study a special case of such solids, namely, those that have an axis of symmetry. The carnival rides pictured opposite help illustrate this kind of solid called a *solid of revolution*.

14–1 The Derivative

In Section 6–5 the derived function $f'(x)$ of a given function $f(x)$ was defined by the following limit

$$f'(x) = \lim_{h \to 0} \frac{f(x + h) - f(x)}{h} \qquad \qquad 1$$

The derived function $f'(x)$ is also called the **derivative** of $f(x)$ and the process of finding the derivative is called **differentiation.** A function f which has a derivative at a point $x = a$ is said to be **differentiable** at $x = a$.

EXAMPLE 1. Use the definition above to find the derivative of $f(x) = x^2 - 2x$.

By definition you must evaluate $\lim_{h \to 0} \frac{f(x + h) - f(x)}{h}$.

$$
\begin{aligned}
f(x + h) &= (x + h)^2 - 2(x + h) = x^2 + 2xh + h^2 - 2x - 2h \\
f(x) &= x^2 - 2x \\
f(x + h) - f(x) &= 2xh - 2h + h^2 \\
\frac{f(x + h) - f(x)}{h} &= 2x - 2 + h
\end{aligned}
$$

Thus

$$\lim_{h \to 0} \frac{f(x + h) - f(x)}{h} = \lim_{h \to 0} (2x - 2 + h) = 2x - 2.$$

So

$$f'(x) = 2x - 2.$$

The geometric interpretation of the derivative was discussed in Section 6–6. There you found that $f'(x)$ evaluated at $x = a$ was the slope of the line tangent to the curve $f(x)$ at the point $(a, f(a))$. The graph of $f(x) = x^2 - 2x$ is shown at the right. Since $f'(x) = 2x - 2$, the tangent lines at $(2, 0)$ and $(-1, 3)$ have slopes of 2 and -4 respectively. They are shown at the right.

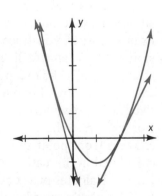

From your previous work you are familiar with the derivatives of several functions. They are summarized here for easy reference.

1. If $f(x) = c$, (c is a constant)   then $f'(x) = 0$
2. If $f(x) = a \cdot x^m$ $m \in W$, a is a constant then $f'(x) = a \cdot m \cdot x^{m-1}$

3. If $f(x) = f_1(x) + f_2(x) + \cdots + f_n(x)$ then $f'(x) =$
$$f_1'(x) + f_2'(x) + \cdots + f_n'(x)$$

4. If $f(x) = \dfrac{1}{x^m}$ $m \in W$ then $f'(x) = \dfrac{-m}{x^{m+1}}$

5. If $f(x) = \ln x$ then $f'(x) = \dfrac{1}{x}$ (See Section 8–11)

6. If $f(x) = e^x$ then $f'(x) = e^x$ (See Section 8–11)

EXAMPLE 2. Find the derivative of $f(x) = 3x^4 - 2x^2 - 3$.

Let $f_1(x) = 3x^4$, $f_2(x) = -2x^2$, $f_3(x) = -3$ then $f_1'(x) = 12x^3$, $f_2'(x) = -4x^1$, $f_3'(x) = 0$. Thus $f'(x) = 12x^3 - 4x$.

Another useful differentiation formula is discussed next. This formula allows you to calculate the derivative of a function f which is the product of two differentiable functions.

Theorem 14–1 If $f(x) = r(x)s(x)$ where r and s are differentiable functions, then $f'(x) = r(x)s'(x) + s(x)r'(x)$.

Proof: By definition

$$f'(x) = \lim_{h \to 0} \frac{r(x + h)s(x + h) - r(x)s(x)}{h}$$

$$= \lim_{h \to 0} \frac{r(x + h)s(x + h) - r(x + h)s(x) + r(x + h)s(x) - r(x)s(x)}{h}$$

$$= \lim_{h \to 0} \frac{r(x + h)[s(x + h) - s(x)] + s(x)[r(x + h) - r(x)]}{h}$$

$$= \lim_{h \to 0} r(x + h) \lim_{h \to 0} \frac{s(x + h) - s(x)}{h} + s(x) \lim_{h \to 0} \frac{r(x + h) - r(x)}{h}$$

$$= r(x)s'(x) + s(x)r'(x)$$

EXAMPLE 3. Find the derivative of $f(x) = (x^2 - 3x)(x^4 + 2x^3)$.

Let $r(x) = x^2 - 3x$ $s(x) = x^4 + 2x^3$.

Then $r'(x) = 2x - 3$ $s'(x) = 4x^3 + 6x^2$

By Theorem 14–1

$$f'(x) = (x^2 - 3x)(4x^3 + 6x^2) + (x^4 + 2x^3)(2x - 3)$$
$$= 6x^5 - 5x^4 - 24x^3$$

If $f(x)$ had been expanded first then

$$f(x) = x^6 - x^5 - 6x^4$$

and thus

$$f'(x) = 6x^5 - 5x^4 - 24x^3$$

Not all products of two functions can be simplified into one function by expansion as was done in the check for Example 3. This fact is the reason for introducing Theorem 14–1. The following example illustrates such a case.

EXAMPLE 4. Find the derivative of $f(x) = xe^x$.

Let $\quad\quad\quad\quad\quad\quad\quad r(x) = x \quad\quad\quad s(x) = e^x.$

Then $\quad\quad\quad\quad\quad\quad r'(x) = 1 \quad\quad\quad s'(x) = e^x.$

Thus by Theorem 14–1

$$f'(x) = xe^x + e^x$$
$$= e^x(x + 1)$$

Now try these

━━ Find the derivatives of the functions in Exercises 1–4.

1. $f(x) = x^3 + 2x^2 - x$ **2.** $f(x) = x^{-5} + 3$
3. $f(x) = x^2 e^x$ **4.** $f(x) = \ln(x^3)$

Answers: **1.** $3x^2 + 4x - 1$ **2.** $-5x^{-6}$ **3.** $x^2 e^x + 2xe^x$ **4.** $\dfrac{3}{x}$

Exercises

A ━━ Find the derivative of the function described by the given equation for Exercises 1–14.

1. $f(x) = -2x^2 + 3x - 1$ **2.** $f(x) = 7x^{100} - 3x^{50}$
3. $f(x) = 7$ **4.** $f(x) = x^{-4}$
5. $f(x) = \dfrac{3}{x^7}$ **6.** $f: x \longrightarrow 5e^x$
7. $f(x) = \ln x + e^x - 4x^3$ **8.** $f: x \longrightarrow 7 \ln x + 3x^{-8}$
9. $f(x) = (x^2 + x)(x - 3)$ **10.** $f: x \longrightarrow (x^2 - x^4)e^x$
11. $f(x) = (e^x + 2)(x^2 - x)$ **12.** $f: x \longrightarrow (\ln x)(x^3 - x^2)$
13. $f(x) = e^x \left(\dfrac{1}{x} - x^2 \right)$ **14.** $f: x \longrightarrow \ln(x^x)$

B **15.** Let $f(x) = e^x$. Then $f'(x) = e^x$. If $f(x) = e^{2x}$ find $f'(x)$ by employing Theorem 14–1. (*Hint:* $e^x \cdot e^x = e^{2x}$)

━━ Use Exercise 15 to aid you in calculating $f'(x)$ for Exercises 16–19.

16. $f(x) = e^{3x}$ **17.** $f(x) = e^{4x}$
18. $f(x) = e^{5x}$ **19.** $f(x) = e^{nx}$

C ━━ $g(x)$, $h(x)$ and $k(x)$ are differentiable functions. Find $f'(x)$ for

20. $f(x) = g(x)h(x)k(x)$.   **21.** $f(x) = \dfrac{h(x)}{g(x)}$, $g(x) \neq 0$.

14-2   Velocity and Acceleration: Rates

Imagine an automobile traveling due west at the rate of 180 miles per hour on the Bonneville Salt Flats. To determine the distance S it traveled from a point O in t minutes at the rate of 180 mph (or 3 miles per minute) you would use the formula $S = 3t$.

On the other hand, if you observed the car at point O at time t_1 and at point P at t_2 and O and P were 1 mile apart, the *average rate* of the car could be determined by dividing the distance traveled by the elapsed time, $t_2 - t_1$. In this case the rate is $\dfrac{1}{t_2 - t_1}$. In general the **average rate** or **average velocity** of an object moving in a straight line is given by the formula

$$\text{Average velocity} = \frac{S_2 - S_1}{t_2 - t_1} \qquad\qquad \textbf{1}$$

where S_2 and S_1 are distances and t_2 and t_1 are measures of time.

EXAMPLE 1.   Find the average velocity of an aircraft flying due west if at 2:00 P.M. it is over O'Hare Field in Chicago and at 3:30 P.M. it is 700 miles west.

Let $\qquad\qquad\qquad S_1 = 0$ at $t_1 = 2{:}00$ P.M.

Then $\qquad\qquad\quad S_2 = 700$ when $t_2 = 3{:}30$ P.M.

Thus $\qquad\quad S_2 - S_1 = 700$ miles

$\qquad\qquad\quad\; t_2 - t_1 = 1.5$ hours

and $\qquad\quad \dfrac{S_2 - S_1}{t_2 - t_1} = \dfrac{700}{\frac{3}{2}} = \dfrac{1400}{3} \approx 467$ m.p.h.

Motion in a straight line is called rectilinear motion. Often a function $S(t)$ is used to describe the distance S of an object from a fixed point at a time t. $S(t)$ is called a **position function.** In such cases no restriction is placed on the moving object other than that it is rectilinear motion. Thus the object need not move at a uniform rate as the car did on the Bonneville Salt Flats; nor does it need to move in only one direction; it may move in opposite directions.

For rectilinear motion described by a position function $S(t)$, the average velocity of the object over an interval of time $[t_1, t_2]$ is defined by

$$\text{average velocity} = \frac{S(t_2) - S(t_1)}{t_2 - t_1}. \qquad\qquad 2$$

For example, a freely falling body will travel $16t^2$ feet in t seconds, thus $S(t) = 16t^2$ for a freely falling body.

The average velocity of the body using equation 2 is

$$\frac{16t_2^{\,2} - 16t_1^{\,2}}{t_2 - t_1} = 16(t_2 + t_1).$$

Thus, for the time interval $[1, 3]$, the average velocity is $16(1 + 3) = 64$ feet per second, while in the interval $[5, 7]$ the average velocity is $16(5 + 7) = 16(12) = 192$ feet per second.

The average velocity of a moving object is a useful concept, but it does not indicate the velocity of an object *at* a given time t. Something more must be done to get the **instantaneous velocity** of an object.

Suppose you wished to know the velocity of a freely falling body 3 seconds from the time it began to fall. The position function is $S(t) = 16t^2$. If you calculate average velocities for small time intervals $[t_1, t_2]$ with $t_1 = 3$, you can get an approximation to the *instantaneous velocity* at $t = 3$. Several of these calculations are shown in the table. Here $t_2 = t_1 + h$, $S(t_1) = 144$, $t_1 = 3$.

t_2	$S(t_2)$	$S(t_2) - S(t_1)$	$t_2 - t_1 = h$	$\dfrac{S(t_2) - S(t_1)}{t_2 - t_1}$
4	256	$256 - 144 = 112$	$4 - 3 = 1$	$\dfrac{112}{1} = 112$
3.5	196	$196 - 144 = 52$	$3.5 - 3 = .5$	$\dfrac{52}{.5} = 104$
3.1	153.76	$153.76 - 144 = 9.76$	$3.1 - 3 = .1$	$\dfrac{9.76}{.1} = 97.6$
3.01	144.9616	$144.9616 - 144 = 0.9616$	$3.01 - 3 = .01$	$\dfrac{.9616}{.01} = 96.16$
$3 + h$	$16(9 + 6h + h^2)$	$16(9 + 6h + h^2) - 16 \cdot 9 = 16(6h + h^2)$	$3 + h - 3 = h$	$\dfrac{16(6h + h^2)}{h} = 16(6 + h)$

Each entry in the last column of the table is an average velocity. Each is also an approximation to the velocity at $t = 3$. These approximations improve as the length of time interval h approaches zero. Thus the velocity of the falling body at $t = t_1$ is defined by this limit, if it exists.

$$\text{instantaneous velocity at time } t_1 = \lim_{h \to 0} \frac{S(t_1 + h) - S(t_1)}{h} \qquad\qquad 3$$

But notice that $\displaystyle\lim_{h \to 0} \frac{S(t_1 + h) - S(t_1)}{h} = S'(t)$ evaluated at $t = t_1$.

Definition Let $S(t)$ be the position function for a rectilinear motion. The <u>velocity</u> of the moving body at $t = t_1$ is the derivative of $S(t)$ evaluated at $t = t_1$. Let $v(t)$ represent the velocity as a function of t. Then

$$v(t) = S'(t) \qquad\qquad 4$$

EXAMPLE 2. Let a particle have a position function

$$S(t) = t^3 - 6t^2 + 9t + 2 \quad \text{for } t \in [0, 4].$$

What is $v(t)$? Find the velocity of the particle at $t = 0, 1, 2, 3$, and 4.

$$v(t) = S'(t).$$

Thus
$$v(t) = 3t^2 - 12t + 9$$
$$= 3(t^2 - 4t + 3)$$

$v(0) =$ 9 — This is the initial velocity.

$v(1) =$ 0 — The particle is not moving.

$v(2) = {}^-3$ — The particle is moving backwards.

$v(3) =$ 0 — The particle has stopped.

$v(4) =$ 9 — The particle is moving forward.

Notice that the velocity of the particle in Example 2 is not constant. In fact at $t = 2$, it is actually negative. The rate of change in the velocity of a particle is the **acceleration** of the particle. The **average acceleration** and **instantaneous acceleration** of a particle are defined by equations **5** and **6** respectively.

$$\text{average acceleration} = \frac{v(t_1 + h) - v(t_1)}{h} \qquad\qquad 5$$

$$\text{instantaneous acceleration} = \lim_{h \to 0} \frac{v(t_1 + h) - v(t_1)}{h} = v'(t_1) \qquad 6$$

Equation **6** tells you that the derivative of the velocity function $v(t)$ evaluated at $t = t_1$, is the **acceleration function** $a(t)$ for the moving particle, that is

$$a(t) = v'(t). \qquad\qquad 7$$

Since
$$v(t) = S'(t)$$

it follows that

$$a(t) = S''(t) \qquad\qquad 8$$

that is, the second derivative of the *position function* is the *acceleration function.*

EXAMPLE 2 Continued

$$S(t) = t^3 - 6t^2 + 9t + 2, \quad t \in [0, 4]$$

What is the acceleration function $a(t)$? Find the acceleration at $t = 0, 1, 2, 3, 4$.
Thus since

$$a(t) = v'(t)$$
$$v(t) = 3t^2 - 12t + 9$$
$$a(t) = 6t - 12$$
$$= 6(t - 2)$$

$a(0) = -12$—The particle is slowing down.

$a(1) = -6$—The particle is slowing down.

$a(2) = 0$—There is no change in the velocity.

$a(3) = 6$—The particle is going faster.

$a(4) = 12$—The particle continues to pick up speed.

Velocity and acceleration are each a rate of change of one variable per unit change in a second variable. In general, for a function $f(x)$, the derivative $f'(x)$ may always be interpreted as the instantaneous rate of change of $f(x)$ per unit change in x.

Now try these

1. If the position function of a moving particle is $S(t) = 2t^2 - 3t$, find the average velocity from $t = 3$ to $t = 4$ and the instantaneous velocity at $t = 3$.

2. If the position function of a moving particle is $S(t) = t^3 + 3$, find the average velocity from $t = 0$ to $t = 2$ and the instantaneous velocity at $t = 2$.

3. Given $S(t) = t^3 + 2t^2 + t$, find $v(t)$ and $a(t)$.

Answers: **1.** 11, 9.   **2.** 4, 12.   **3.** $v(t) = 3t^2 + 4t + 1$, $a(t) = 6t + 4$.

Checkpoint

1. What is the difference between average and instantaneous velocity?

2. What is the difference between average and instantaneous acceleration?

3. What is the relationship among the position function, the velocity function, and the acceleration function?

Exercises

A For Exercises 1–5, let the position function of a moving particle be $S(t) = t^2 - 25$. Find the average velocity from $t = 3$ to

1. $t = 5$.   **2.** $t = 4$.   **3.** $t = 3.1$.   **4.** $t = 3.01$.   **5.** $t = 3 + h$.

For Exercises 6–10, let the position function of a moving particle be $100 - 4t^2$. Find the average velocity from $t = 2$ to

6. $t = 0$.   **7.** $t = 1$.   **8.** $t = 1.9$.   **9.** $t = 1.99$.   **10.** $t = 1.999$.

For Exercises 11–13, let the position function of a moving particle be $S(t) = 3t^2 - 2t + 1$.

11. What is the average velocity of the particle on each interval $[0, 2]$, $[0, 1]$, $[0, 0.1]$, $[0, 0.01]$, $[0, h]$?

12. What is the instantaneous velocity at $t = 0$?

13. What is the instantaneous acceleration of the particle at $t = 0$?

For each position function in Exercises 14–21 find $v(t)$ and $a(t)$. Evaluate each at $t = 0, 1, 2, 3, 4$.

14. $S(t) = 2t^2 + 5t - 12$ **15.** $S(t) = 4t + 3$

16. $S(t) = 4 - 2t - t^2$ **17.** $S(t) = (2t + 3)^2$

18. $S(t) = (4 - t)^2$ **19.** $S(t) = 64t - 16t^2$

20. $S(t) = 2t^3 - 18t^2 + 48t - 6$ **21.** $S(t) = 2t^3 - 9t^2 + 12$

B Use the following information for Exercises 22–26.
If a ball is thrown vertically upward with an initial velocity of 128 feet per second, the ball's height after t seconds is given by $S(t) = 128t - 16t^2$.

22. What is the velocity function?

23. What is the velocity when $t = 2, 4, 6$?

24. At what time is the velocity 48 feet per second?   16 feet per second?   −48 feet per second?

25. When is the velocity zero? What is the height of the ball at that time? Is this the maximum height?

26. When does the ball hit the ground? What is its velocity at that time?

Use the following information for Exercises 27–29.
If a ball is thrown vertically upward with a velocity of 32 feet per second, the ball's height after t seconds is given by $S(t) = 32t - 16t^2$.

27. At what time t does the ball reach its maximum height?

28. What is the maximum height?

29. At what time does the ball hit the ground?

14-3 Area and Approximation

You know how to calculate the area of many plane regions that are enclosed by simple polygons. Likewise, you know that the area of a circular region of radius r is πr^2. But how can you calculate the area of a plane region such as the one shown at the right? The answer to this question is the subject of this section and the sections 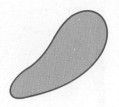 which follow. In this chapter only curves $y = f(x)$ where $f(x)$ is continuous $\forall x$ in $[a, b]$ will be considered. You may assume the above condition is true for all functions discussed in this chapter unless otherwise indicated.

Clearly you must assume that each plane region bounded by plane curves has a unique number associated with it which is its area. Otherwise further discussion would be futile.

Since you do not know the area of a region bounded by curves, it is reasonable to attempt to approximate the area using the areas of regions you can calculate. Consider a simple case first. The triangular region bounded by

$$y = \tfrac{1}{2}x, \quad \text{the } x \text{ axis}, \quad \text{and} \quad x = 8.$$

The region is shown in Figure 1.

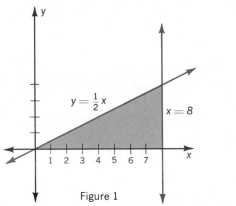

Figure 1

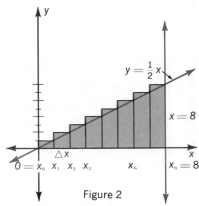

Figure 2

You know that the area, A, of the triangular region is 16, but that is not important here. What is important is the method of approximation used, for it is applicable to regions whose areas you do not know beforehand. The method used is to approximate the area you wish to find with the sum of the areas of rectangles.

First partition the interval [0, 8] into a finite number, n, of intervals of the same length. See Figure 2. Each of these intervals will have length.

$$\frac{8 - 0}{n} = \Delta x$$

Call the endpoints of these intervals

$$0 = x_0, x_1, x_2, \cdots, x_{n-1}, x_n = 8.$$

If $n = 8$ then $\Delta x = 1$ and the intervals are

$$[0, 1], [1, 2], \cdots, [7, 8].$$

Now form the n rectangles of *width Δx* and *length equal to the ordinate of the right hand endpoint of each interval*. The ordinate is $y_i = \frac{1}{2}(0 + i \cdot \Delta x)$. These are shown in Figure 2. Therefore each rectangle has area

$$y_i \, \Delta x, \, i = 1, 2, \cdots, n$$

and the approximation to the area of the triangular region is the sum of the areas of the rectangles.

$$y_1 \, \Delta x + y_2 \, \Delta x + y_3 \, \Delta x + \cdots + y_{n-1} \, \Delta x + y_n \, \Delta x = \sum_{i=1}^{n} y_i \, \Delta x = A_n$$

When $n = 8$, $\Delta x = 1$, the approximation is

$$\sum_{i=1}^{8} y_i \, \Delta x = 1 \cdot (\tfrac{1}{2} + 1 + \tfrac{3}{2} + 2 + \tfrac{5}{2} + 3 + \tfrac{7}{2} + 4)$$

$$= 1(\tfrac{16}{2} + 10)$$

$$= 18$$

Notice that the approximation to the area is larger than the area. You could get an approximation that was smaller than the area by choosing the ordinate of the left-hand endpoint of each interval as the length of each rectangle. In that case the area would be approximated by 14. (You should verify this.)

A better approximation to the true area could be obtained by making a finer partition of the x axis. If, say, sixteen intervals were used rather than 8, the area approximation would be the following. $\left(\text{Remember from Section 1–6, that } \sum_{i=1}^{n} i = \frac{n(n + 1)}{2}.\right)$

$$\sum_{i=1}^{16} y_i \, \Delta x = \tfrac{1}{2}(\tfrac{1}{4} + \tfrac{2}{4} + \tfrac{3}{4} + \tfrac{4}{4} + \tfrac{5}{4} + \cdots + \tfrac{14}{4} + \tfrac{15}{4} + \tfrac{16}{4})$$

$$= \tfrac{1}{8}(1 + 2 + 3 + \cdots + 16)$$

$$= \tfrac{1}{8} \cdot 136 = 17$$

Consider now an example in which you cannot calculate the exact area, but in which the "sum of rectangles" area will give you an approximation to the true area.
Let the region be bounded by the curve $y = \frac{1}{4}x^2$, the x axis, and the line $x = 4$.

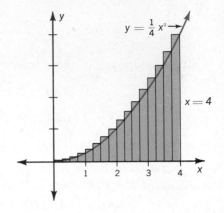

Following the procedure described above, partition $[0, 4]$ into n intervals of length $\Delta x = \dfrac{4 - 0}{n} = \dfrac{4}{n}$. Again choose the right-hand endpoint of each interval and use the ordinate of that point as the length of the rectangle. Thus the area of each rectangle is

$$y_i \, \Delta x, \ i = 1, 2, \cdots, n.$$

The approximation to the area is given by

$$A_n = \sum_{i=1}^{n} y_i \, \Delta x \qquad \qquad \textbf{1}$$

Since the right-hand endpoints of the n intervals are $x_1 = \Delta x$, $x_2 = 2\,\Delta x$, $x_3 = 3\,\Delta x, \ldots, x_i = i \cdot \Delta x$, the ordinates of these points are

$$y_1 = \tfrac{1}{4}(\Delta x)^2, \ y_2 = \tfrac{1}{4}(2\,\Delta x)^2, \ y_3 = \tfrac{1}{4}(3\,\Delta x)^2, \cdots, y_i = \tfrac{1}{4}(i \cdot \Delta x)^2$$

and therefore

$$A_n = \sum_{i=1}^{n} \tfrac{1}{4}(i\,\Delta x)^2 \cdot \Delta x$$

$$= \tfrac{1}{4} \sum_{i=1}^{n} i^2 (\Delta x)^3 \qquad \qquad \textbf{2}$$

Suppose that $n = 16$. Then $\Delta x = \frac{4}{16} = \frac{1}{4}$ and applying **2** you have the following. $\left(\text{Remember from Section 1–6, Exercise 12 that} \right.$

$$\sum_{i=1}^{n} i^2 = \frac{n(n + 1)(2n + 1)}{6} \left. \vphantom{\sum} \right.)$$

$$A_{16} = \tfrac{1}{4} \sum_{i=1}^{16} i^2 (\tfrac{1}{4})^3$$

$$= (\tfrac{1}{4})^4 \sum_{i=1}^{16} i^2$$

$$= \tfrac{1}{256} \cdot (1 + 4 + 9 + \cdots + 256)$$

$$= \tfrac{1}{256} \cdot 1496$$

$$= \tfrac{187}{32} \approx 5.84$$

B ▬ Let a region be bounded by $y = x^3$, the x axis, $x = 0$ and $x = 2$. Approximate the area using the intervals given in Exercises 13 and 14.

13. 4 intervals   **14.** 8 intervals

▬ For Exercises 15–16, use the following information. Let a region be bounded by $y = \frac{1}{4}x^2$, $x = 2$, $x = 4$ and the x axis.

15. If there are 4 intervals, how long is each?

16. What is the approximate area of the region for 4 intervals?

14–4 Trapezoidal Approximation for Area

In the last section you approximated the area of a region bounded by curves with the sum of areas of rectangles. For small numbers of intervals "approximation by rectangles" does not result in a value extremely close to the true area. One method of improving the approximations is to substitute trapezoids for the rectangles.

Suppose you want the area of the region bounded by $y = f(x)$, $f(x) \geq 0 \ \forall x$ in $[a, b]$, $x = a$, $x = b$, $a < b$, and the x axis. $f(x)$ must be continuous in $[a, b]$. Partition the interval $[a, b]$ into n intervals, each of length $\Delta x = \dfrac{b - a}{n}$. The points which do this partitioning are $x_0 = a$, $x_1 = a + \Delta x$, $x_2 = a + 2\Delta x, \ldots, x_{n-1} = a + (n - 1)\Delta x$, $x_n = b$.

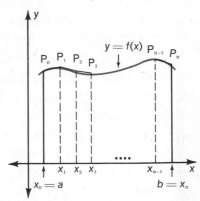

Let $P_0, P_1, \ldots, P_{n-1}, P_n$ be the points on the curve $y = f(x)$ corresponding to $x_0, x_1, \ldots, x_{n-1}, x_n$.

Consider the trapezoid $aP_0P_1x_1$. It has width Δx and the length of its bases are $y_0 = f(x_0)$ and $y_1 = f(x_1)$. Its area is

$$\text{Area } aP_0P_1x_1 = \tfrac{1}{2}(y_0 + y_1)\,\Delta x.$$

Similarly, the areas of the other trapezoids $x_1P_1P_2x_2, x_2P_2P_3x_3, \ldots, x_{n-1}P_{n-1}P_nx_n$ are as follows.

$$\text{Area } x_1P_1P_2x_2 = \tfrac{1}{2}(y_1 + y_2)\,\Delta x$$
$$\text{Area } x_2P_2P_3x_3 = \tfrac{1}{2}(y_2 + y_3)\,\Delta x$$
$$\text{Area } x_{n-1}P_{n-1}P_nx_n = \tfrac{1}{2}(y_{n-1} + y_n)\,\Delta x$$

The true area of this region is 5.$\overline{3}$. The approximate value of 5.84 is too large (as expected) but relatively close to the true value.

Now try these

▬▬ For Exercises 1–3 consider the triangular region bounded by the x axis and the lines $x = 0$, $x = 3$ and $y = x$.

1. Find the true area of the region.

2. Find the approximate area using rectangles whose lengths are determined by the right-hand endpoint of each interval and let the number of intervals be 6.

3. Find the approximate area using rectangles whose lengths are determined by the left-hand endpoint of each interval and let the number of intervals be 6.

Answers: **1.** $\frac{9}{2}$ **2.** $\frac{21}{4}$ **3.** $\frac{15}{4}$

Exercises

A ▬▬ Let a region be bounded by the following curves: $y = \frac{3}{2}x$, $x = 0$, $x = 2$ and the x axis. Find an approximation to the area using n intervals for the given values of n in Exercises 1–3.

1. $n = 2$ **2.** $n = 4$ **3.** $n = 16$

4. What is the true area of the region given above?

5. Repeat Exercises 1–4 when the region is bounded by $y = 2x + 1$, the y axis, the x axis, and $x = 2$.

6. Repeat Exercises 1–3, but use the left-hand endpoints of the intervals to determine the rectangles.

7. Repeat Exercise 5, but use the left-hand endpoints of the intervals to determine the rectangles.

▬▬ Let a region be bounded by $y = x^2$, $x = 0$, $x = 2$ and the x axis. Approximate the area of this region using the intervals given in Exercises 8 and 9.

8. 4 intervals **9.** 8 intervals

▬▬ Let a region be bounded by $y = \sqrt{x}$, $x = 4$ and the x axis. Approximate the area of the region using the intervals given in Exercises 10 and 11.

10. 4 intervals **11.** 16 intervals

12. Repeat Exercises 8–11 but use the left-hand endpoints of intervals to determine the rectangles.

The sum of the areas of the trapezoids is an approximation to the area of the region. If you call that sum T, it follows that

$$T = \tfrac{1}{2}(y_0 + y_1)\,\Delta x + \tfrac{1}{2}(y_1 + y_2)\,\Delta x + \tfrac{1}{2}(y_2 + y_3)\,\Delta x$$
$$+ \cdots + \tfrac{1}{2}(y_{n-1} + y_n)\,\Delta x$$
$$= \tfrac{1}{2}(y_0 + 2y_1 + 2y_2 + 2y_3 + \cdots + 2y_{n-1} + y_n)\,\Delta x$$
$$= (\tfrac{1}{2}y_0 + y_1 + y_2 + y_3 + \cdots + y_{n-1} + \tfrac{1}{2}y_n)\,\Delta x \qquad \mathbf{1}$$

Equation **1** is the formula for the trapezoidal approximation to the area bounded by $y = f(x)$, $x = a$, $x = b$ and the x axis, where $y_i = f(x_i)$ and $\Delta x = \dfrac{b - a}{n}$.

The trapezoidal approximation formula is illustrated in the next examples.

EXAMPLE 1. Approximate the area of the region bounded by $y = \tfrac{1}{4}x^2$, $x = 0$, $x = 4$ and the x axis with the trapezoidal approximation for 16 intervals.

Since $a = 0$ and $b = 4$, $\Delta x = \dfrac{4 - 0}{16} = \tfrac{1}{4}$.

$y_0 = \tfrac{1}{4}(0)^2 = 0$

$y_1 = \tfrac{1}{4}(\tfrac{1}{4})^2 = \tfrac{1}{4}\cdot\tfrac{1}{16}$

$y_2 = \tfrac{1}{4}(\tfrac{2}{4})^2 = \tfrac{1}{4}\cdot\tfrac{4}{16}$

$y_3 = \tfrac{1}{4}(\tfrac{3}{4})^2 = \tfrac{1}{4}\cdot\tfrac{9}{16}$

$y_4 = \tfrac{1}{4}(\tfrac{4}{4})^2 = \tfrac{1}{4}\cdot\tfrac{16}{16}$

$y_5 = \tfrac{1}{4}(\tfrac{5}{4})^2 = \tfrac{1}{4}\cdot\tfrac{25}{16}$

$y_6 = \tfrac{1}{4}(\tfrac{6}{4})^2 = \tfrac{1}{4}\cdot\tfrac{36}{16}$

$y_7 = \tfrac{1}{4}(\tfrac{7}{4})^2 = \tfrac{1}{4}\cdot\tfrac{49}{16}$

$y_8 = \tfrac{1}{4}(\tfrac{8}{4})^2 = \tfrac{1}{4}\cdot\tfrac{64}{16}$

$y_9 = \tfrac{1}{4}(\tfrac{9}{4})^2 = \tfrac{1}{4}\cdot\tfrac{81}{16}$

$y_{10} = \tfrac{1}{4}(\tfrac{10}{4})^2 = \tfrac{1}{4}\cdot\tfrac{100}{16}$

$y_{11} = \tfrac{1}{4}(\tfrac{11}{4})^2 = \tfrac{1}{4}\cdot\tfrac{121}{16}$

$y_{12} = \tfrac{1}{4}(\tfrac{12}{4})^2 = \tfrac{1}{4}\cdot\tfrac{144}{16}$

$y_{13} = \tfrac{1}{4}(\tfrac{13}{4})^2 = \tfrac{1}{4}\cdot\tfrac{169}{16}$

$y_{14} = \tfrac{1}{4}(\tfrac{14}{4})^2 = \tfrac{1}{4}\cdot\tfrac{196}{16}$

$y_{15} = \tfrac{1}{4}(\tfrac{15}{4})^2 = \tfrac{1}{4}\cdot\tfrac{225}{16}$

$y_{16} = \tfrac{1}{4}(\tfrac{16}{4})^2 = \tfrac{1}{4}\cdot\tfrac{256}{16}$

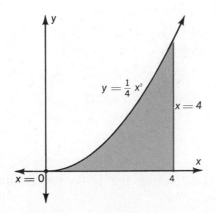

$y = \tfrac{1}{4}x^2$

$x = 4$

$x = 0$

You now add $\tfrac{1}{2}y_0$ and $\tfrac{1}{2}y_{16}$ to the remaining y_i's, $i = 2, 15$. The sum is

$$\tfrac{1}{4}\cdot\tfrac{1}{16}(1 + 4 + 9 + 16 + \cdots + 196 + 225 + 128) \quad \text{or} \quad \tfrac{1}{4}\cdot\tfrac{1}{16}\cdot 1368$$

Thus $\quad T = (\tfrac{1}{4}\cdot\tfrac{1}{16}\cdot 1368)\cdot\Delta x = (\tfrac{1}{4}\cdot\tfrac{1}{16}\cdot 1368)\cdot\tfrac{1}{4} = \tfrac{171}{32} \approx 5.34$

The true area of the region is $5.3\overline{3}$. Thus the trapezoidal approximation for 16 intervals is less than one one-hundredth too large. This is a better approximation than the one obtained using rectangles, (page 664). The approximate value obtained then (5.84) was about one tenth too large.

EXAMPLE 2. Find the trapezoidal approximation for the area of the region bounded by $y = x^2$, $x = 1$, $x = 2$ and the x axis, using $n = 4$.

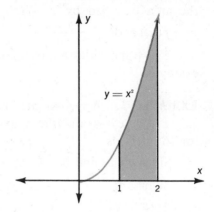

$\Delta x = \dfrac{2-1}{4} = \frac{1}{4}$. Thus

$$
\begin{aligned}
x_0 &= a &&= 1 & y_0 &= 1^2 = \tfrac{16}{16} \\
x_1 &= a + \Delta x &&= 1\tfrac{1}{4} & y_1 &= (\tfrac{5}{4})^2 = \tfrac{25}{16} \\
x_2 &= a + 2\Delta x &&= 1\tfrac{2}{4} & y_2 &= (\tfrac{6}{4})^2 = \tfrac{36}{16} \\
x_3 &= a + 3\Delta x &&= 1\tfrac{3}{4} & y_3 &= (\tfrac{7}{4})^2 = \tfrac{49}{16} \\
x_4 &= b &&= 2 & y_4 &= (\tfrac{8}{4})^2 = \tfrac{64}{16}
\end{aligned}
$$

Then $\frac{1}{2}y_0 = \frac{8}{16}$ and $\frac{1}{2}y_4 = \frac{32}{16}$. Thus

$$
\begin{aligned}
T &= \tfrac{1}{4}(\tfrac{8}{16} + \tfrac{25}{16} + \tfrac{36}{16} + \tfrac{49}{16} + \tfrac{32}{16}) \\
&= \tfrac{1}{4} \cdot \tfrac{75}{8} \\
&= \tfrac{75}{32} \approx 2.34
\end{aligned}
$$

The true area of the region is $2.3\overline{3}$. The next section shows why.

Now try these

━━ Find the trapezoidal approximation for the areas of the regions in Exercises 1–3, using $n = 3$.

1. Region bounded by $y = 2x$, $x = 0$, $x = 1$ and the x axis.

2. Region bounded by $y = \sqrt{x}$, $x = 0$, $x = 9$ and the x axis.

3. Region bounded by $y = 2x + 1$, $x = 0$, $x = 6$, and the x axis.

Answers: **1.** 1   **2.** ≈ 17 **3.** 42

Exercises

A ━━ Find the trapezoidal approximation for the areas of the regions in Exercises 1–12, using the given n. Round answers to two decimal places.

1. $f(x) = x$, $x = 0$, $x = 2$, x axis, $n = 4$

2. $f(x) = x^3$, $x = 0$, $x = 2$, x axis, $n = 4$

3. $f(x) = x^3$, $x = 1$, $x = 2$, x axis, $n = 4$

4. $f(x) = \sqrt{x}$, $x = 0$, $x = 4$, x axis, $n = 4$

5. $f(x) = \sqrt{x}$, $x = 2$, $x = 4$, x axis, $n = 4$

6. $f(x) = \dfrac{1}{x^2}$, $x = 1$, $x = 2$, x axis, $n = 2$

B   **7.** $f(x) = \sqrt{x^3 - 1}$, $x = 2$, $x = 3$, x axis, $n = 6$

8. $f(x) = \sqrt{4 - x^2}$, $x = -1$, $x = 1$, x axis, $n = 5$

9. $f(x) = 3x^2$, $x = 1$, $x = 9$, x axis, $n = 8$

10. $f(x) = x\sqrt{9 + x^2}$, $x = 0$, $x = 4$, x axis, $n = 4$

11. $f(x) = x\sqrt{9 + x^2}$, $x = 0$, $x = 4$, x axis, $n = 8$

12. $f(x) = \dfrac{1}{\sqrt{4 + x^3}}$, $x = 0$, $x = 4$, x axis, $n = 4$

13. Let $y = mx$, $x = a$, $x = b$ ($a, b, m > 0$) and the x axis define a region. What is the trapezoidal approximation to the area of the region for $n = 4$? for $n = 8$? How do you explain the two results found?

14–5   Area as a Limit

You have seen how the area of a region can be approximated by summing areas of rectangles or areas of trapezoids. In either case, as the number of intervals increases the approximate area nears the true area of the region. The definition of the area of a region bounded by curves involves approximations by rectangles and a limit. Note that as the number of intervals increases without bound the width of each rectangle decreases and approaches zero as a limit.

Definition   Suppose that $f(x) \geq 0 \ \forall x$ in $[a, b]$. Then the area of the region, A, bounded by $y = f(x)$, $x = a$, $x = b$, and the x axis is given by

$$A_a^b f(x) = \lim_{n \to \infty} \left(\sum_{i=1}^{n} f(x_i) \, \Delta x \right)$$

where $\Delta x = \dfrac{b - a}{n}$ and x_i is the right-hand endpoint of the ith interval $[x_{i-1}, x_i]$.

In the above definition if $f(x) < 0 \ \forall x$ in $[a, b]$, then the area is defined as $-\lim\limits_{n \to \infty} \left(\sum\limits_{i=1}^{n} f(x_i) \, \Delta x \right)$.

Thus in either case

$$A_a^b f(x) = \left| \lim_{n \to \infty} \left(\sum_{i=1}^{n} f(x_i) \, \Delta x \right) \right|.$$

Figure 1 below depicts a typical rectangle used in calculating the area bounded by $y = f(x)$, $f(x) \geq 0$, $x = a$, $x = b$, and the x axis. The sum of the areas of all such rectangles as the width of the rectangles nears zero is very close to the exact area of the region.

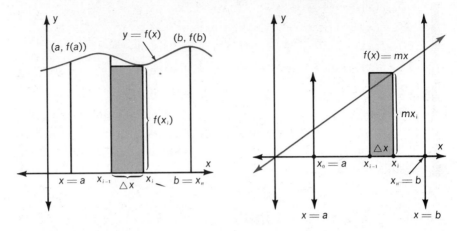

Figure 1   Figure 2

EXAMPLE 1. Find the area of the region bounded by $f(x) = mx$, $x = a$, $x = b$ the x axis. $(a, b, m > 0, a < b)$ See Figure 2.

The first step is to find the expression for the approximate value of the area for n. As usual: $\Delta x = \dfrac{b - a}{n}$ and $x_0 = a$, $x_1 = a + \Delta x$, $x_2 = a + 2\Delta x$, $\cdots$, $x_i = a + i\Delta x$, $\cdots$, $x_n = b$. Thus $f(x_1) = m(a + \Delta x)$, $f(x_2) = m(a + 2\Delta x)$, $\cdots$, $f(x_i) = m(a + i\Delta x)$, $\cdots$, $f(x_n) = mb$. The approximate area A_n for n intervals is the following.

$$
\begin{aligned}
A_n &= \sum_{i=1}^{n} m(a + i \cdot \Delta x)\, \Delta x \\
&= \sum_{i=1}^{n} \left[ma\, \frac{(b - a)}{n} + mi \cdot \left(\frac{b - a}{n} \right)^2 \right] \\
&= ma\, \frac{(b - a)}{n} \cdot n + m \left(\frac{b - a}{n} \right)^2 \sum_{i=1}^{n} i
\end{aligned}
$$

$$
A_n = ma(b - a) + m \left(\frac{b - a}{n} \right)^2 \cdot \sum_{i=1}^{n} i \qquad\qquad \textbf{1}
$$

You know that $\qquad \displaystyle\sum_{i=1}^{n} i = 1 + 2 + 3 + \cdots + n = \frac{n(n + 1)}{2}.$ $\qquad$ **2**

Substituting **2** in equation **1** you get

$$
A_n = ma(b - a) + m \left(\frac{b - a}{n} \right)^2 \cdot \frac{n(n + 1)}{2}. \qquad\qquad \textbf{3}
$$

Equation 3 will yield an approximate value for the area for any given n. For example, if $m = \frac{1}{2}$, $a = 0$, $b = 8$ and $n = 8$, $A_n = 18$. (Compare this with the results obtained in Section 14–3.)

By definition the exact area of the region is

$$A_a^b(mx) = \lim_{n\to\infty} \left(\sum_{i=1}^{n} m(a + i \cdot \Delta x)\, \Delta x \right) = \lim_{n\to\infty} A_n$$

$$= \lim_{n\to\infty} \left[ma(b - a) + m\left(\frac{b - a}{n}\right)^2 \cdot \frac{n(n + 1)}{2} \right]$$

$$= ma(b - a) + m(b - a)^2 \lim_{n\to\infty} \frac{n(n + 1)}{2n^2}$$

$$= ma(b - a) + (m(b - a)^2)\tfrac{1}{2} \qquad\qquad \text{(Why?)}$$

$$= m\left[ab - a^2 + \frac{b^2}{2} - ab + \frac{a^2}{2} \right]$$

$$= m\left(\frac{b^2}{2} - \frac{a^2}{2} \right).$$

Thus $\qquad A_a^b(mx) = \dfrac{m}{2}(b^2 - a^2).$ $\qquad\qquad\qquad\qquad\qquad$ **4**

Equation **4** can be read as follows: The area between $y = mx$ and the x axis from $x = a$ to $x = b$ is $\dfrac{m}{2}(b^2 - a^2)$.

Equation **4** may be used to calculate the area bounded by any line through the origin, $x = a$, $x = b$ $(a < b)$ and the x axis. If $m < 0$ then the area is $-\dfrac{m}{2}(b^2 - a^2)$.

EXAMPLE 2. Find the area bounded by the curves, $f(x) = x^2$, $x = a$, $x = b$, and the x axis. $(a < b)$. $\Delta x = \dfrac{b - a}{n}$, $x_0 = a$, $x_1 = a + \Delta x$, $x_2 = a + 2\,\Delta x$, $\cdots$, $x_i = a + i \cdot \Delta x$, $\cdots$, $x_n = b$.

$f(x_i) = (a + i\Delta x)^2$. Thus for n,

$$A_n = \sum_{i=1}^{n} f(x_i)\, \Delta x = \sum_{i=1}^{n} (a + i\Delta x)^2\, \Delta x$$

$$= \sum_{i=1}^{n} [a^2\, \Delta x + 2ai(\Delta x)^2 + i^2(\Delta x)^3]$$

$$= \sum_{i=1}^{n} \left[a^2 \left(\frac{b - a}{n}\right) + 2ai\left(\frac{b - a}{n}\right)^2 + i^2\left(\frac{b - a}{n}\right)^3 \right]$$

$$= na^2\left(\frac{b - a}{n}\right) + 2a\left(\frac{b - a}{n}\right)^2 \sum_{i=1}^{n} i + \left(\frac{b - a}{n}\right)^3 \sum_{i=1}^{n} i^2$$

Recall that $\sum_{i=1}^{n} i = \dfrac{n(n + 1)}{2}$ and $\sum_{i=1}^{n} i^2 = \dfrac{n(n + 1)(2n + 1)}{6}$. (See Section 1-6 page 23 and page 25 Exercise 12.) Thus

$$A_n = a^2(b - a) + 2a \left(\dfrac{b - a}{n}\right)^2 \dfrac{n(n + 1)}{2}$$

$$+ \left(\dfrac{b - a}{n}\right)^3 \dfrac{n(n + 1)(2n + 1)}{6}. \qquad 5$$

The required area is therefore

$$A_a^b(x^2) = \lim_{n \to \infty} A_n$$

$$= \lim_{n \to \infty} a^2(b - a) + \lim_{n \to \infty} \left[2a \left(\dfrac{b - a}{n}\right)^2 \dfrac{n(n + 1)}{2}\right]$$

$$+ \lim_{n \to \infty} \left[\left(\dfrac{b - a}{n}\right)^3 \dfrac{n(n + 1)(2n + 1)}{6}\right]$$

$$= a^2(b - a) + a(b - a)^2 \lim_{n \to \infty} \dfrac{n(n + 1)}{n^2}$$

$$+ \dfrac{(b - a)^3}{6} \lim_{n \to \infty} \dfrac{n(n + 1)(2n + 1)}{n^3}$$

$$= a^2 b - a^3 + a(b^2 - 2ab + a^2) + \left(\dfrac{b^3 - 3b^2 a + 3ba^2 - a^3}{6}\right) \cdot 2$$

$$= \dfrac{b^3 - a^3}{3}.$$

Thus the area from $x = a$ to $x = b$ of the region between $y = x^2$ and the x axis is

$$A_a^b(x^2) = \dfrac{b^3 - a^3}{3}.$$

The key in calculating exact areas is to change the expression for the sum of the areas of the rectangles to a form whose limit as n increases without bound is easily determined. The following facts will help you to do this.

1. $\sum_{i=1}^{n} p = np$, p a constant

2. $\sum_{i=1}^{n} pi = p \sum_{i=1}^{n} i$

3. $\sum_{i=1}^{n} i = 1 + 2 + 3 + \cdots + n = \dfrac{n(n + 1)}{2}$

4. $\sum_{i=1}^{n} i^2 = 1^2 + 2^2 + \cdots + n^2 = \dfrac{n(n + 1)(2n + 1)}{6}$

5. $\sum_{i=1}^{n} i^3 = 1^3 + 2^3 + \cdots + n^3 = \dfrac{n^2(n + 1)^2}{4}$

Now try these

■ Calculate the exact area of the regions in Exercises 1–3.
1. The region bounded by $y = 2x + 1$, the x axis, $a = 0$ and $b = 2$.
2. The region bounded by $y = x^3$, $a = 0$, $b = 4$ and the x axis.
3. The region bounded by $y = x^2$, $a = 1$, $b = 4$ and the x axis.

Answers: **1.** 6   **2.** 64   **3.** 21

Exercises

A ■ Use the formulas found in Example 1 and Example 2 to calculate the exact areas for Exercises 1–16.

1. $y = 2x$, $a = 2$, $b = 5$
2. $y = 5x$, $a = 2$, $b = 5$
3. $y = 3x$, $a = 2$, $b = 5$
4. $y = \frac{1}{2}x$, $a = 1$, $b = 4$
5. $y = 0.1x$, $a = 5$, $b = 20$
6. $y = \frac{1}{100}x$, $a = 0$, $b = 100$
7. $y = x^2$, $a = 0$, $b = 3$
8. $y = x^2$, $a = 1$, $b = 7$
9. $y = x^2$, $a = 5$, $b = 6$
10. $y = x^2$, $a = 7$, $b = 8$
11. $y = x^2$, $a = -2$, $b = 4$
12. $y = x^2$, $a = -3$, $b = 3$

B 13. $y = -x$, $a = 2$, $b = 4$
14. $y = -2x$, $a = 3$, $b = 7$
15. $y = x$, $a = -2$, $b = 0$ (The answer is negative. Can you explain why?)
16. $y = 4x$, $a = -2$, $b = 0$ and $a = 0$, $b = 4$. What would the area from $a = -2$ to $b = 4$ be?

■ Use the definition of exact area to calculate the true area for Exercises 17–23. Assume $f(x) \geq 0$ for all x in $[a, b]$.
17. $f(x) = px^2$, $x = a$, $x = b$, x axis
18. $f(x) = p$, $x = a$, $x = b$, x axis
19. $f(x) = x^3$, $x = a$, $x = b$, x axis
20. $f(x) = px^3$, $x = a$, $x = b$, x axis

C 21. $f(x) = x^2 + 1$, $x = a$, $y = b$, x axis
22. $f(x) = x^2 + x + 1$, $x = a$, $x = b$, x axis
23. $f(x) = x^3 + 3$, $x = a$, $x = b$, x axis

24. By any means you wish find the area of the region bounded by $f(x) = x^3$ and $g(x) = 2x^2$. (*Hint:* You can use subtraction if you are clever.)

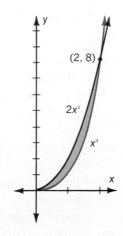

14–6   The Definite Integral

The definition of area as stated in the previous section made use of sums which had two essential characteristics:

1. The number of terms was increasing, and
2. The size of each term was decreasing.

Thus the area of a region became the limit of the sum of an increasing number of addends of decreasing absolute value.

In studying other physical quantities such as work done by a variable force, volumes, fluid pressure, and arc length, the same sort of sums and their limits occur. Mathematicians, transcending physical interpretations, have *defined* the definite integral as the limit of a sum of an increasing number of addends of decreasing absolute value.

Definition   Let $f(x)$ be a function whose domain contains the closed interval $[a, b]$. The <u>definite integral of $f(x)$ from $x = a$ to $x = b$, denoted $\int_a^b f(x)\, dx$,</u> is defined by the equation

$$\int_a^b f(x)\, dx = \lim_{n \to \infty} \left(\sum_{i=1}^n f(x_i)\, \Delta x \right) \qquad \mathbf{1}$$

where $a = x_0, x_1, \cdots, x_{n-1}, x_n = b$ effect the partitioning of $[a, b]$ into n equal intervals of length $\Delta x = \dfrac{b - a}{n}$, and $f(x_i)$ is the ordinate of an arbitrary point x_i in $[x_{j-1}, x_j]$.

The definite integral exists when the limit in **1** is a finite number. In $\int_a^b f(x)\, dx$ a is called the **lower bound of integration,** b is called the **upper bound of integration** and $f(x)$ is called the **integrand.** The terms lower bound and upper bound as used here are not to be confused with the upper and lower bounds of a function as those terms have been used in earlier chapters.

It can be shown that the partitioning points, x_j, $j = 0, 1, \ldots, n$ need not be equally spaced as long as the longest interval nears zero as n increases without bound. The definite integral defined here is called the **Riemann integral.** There are also other types of integrals such as the **Lebesgue** and the **Stieljes integrals.**

From the definition of the definite integral when the addends in the defining sum are interpreted as areas of rectangles you have

674   CHAPTER 14

$$A_a^b(f(x)) = \int_a^b f(x)\, dx, \; f(x) \geq 0, \, x \in [a, b].$$

In a later section another application of the definite integral will be discussed. At this moment the first task is to get some means of evaluating definite integrals so that you need not evaluate the limit of the sum as you did to find the area bounded by curves. The theorems stated below will not be proved here, but reference to the definition should make them seem reasonable.

Since $\displaystyle\lim_{n\to\infty} \sum_{i=1}^{n} pf(x_i)\Delta x = p \lim_{n\to\infty} \sum_{i=1}^{n} f(x_i)\Delta x$, p a constant, the following theorem seems reasonable.

Theorem 14–2 $\displaystyle\int_a^b pf(x)\, dx = p \int_a^b f(x)\, dx$ p a constant

In other words, the integral of a constant times a function is equal to the constant times the integral of the function.

You also know that $\displaystyle\lim_{n\to\infty} \sum_{i=1}^{n} [f_1(x_i) + f_2(x_i)]\Delta x = \lim_{n\to\infty} \sum_{i=1}^{n} f_1(x_i)\Delta x +$

$\displaystyle\lim_{n\to\infty} \sum_{i=1}^{n} f_2(x_i)\Delta x$. The same results are true for any finite number of addends $f_j(x_i)\Delta x$. Thus the next theorem is reasonable.

Theorem 14–3 $\displaystyle\int_a^b [f_1(x) + f_2(x) + \cdots + f_n(x)]\, dx$

$$= \int_a^b f_1(x)\, dx + \cdots + \int_a^b f_n(x)\, dx$$

That is, the integral of the sum of functions is the sum of the integrals of the functions.

In Section 14–5 you found

in Example 1 $A_a^b(mx) = \dfrac{m}{2}(b^2 - a^2)$

in Example 2

$$A_a^b(x^2) = \tfrac{1}{3}(b^3 - a^3),$$

and in Exercise 18

$$A_a^b(p) = \left|\dfrac{p}{1}(b - a)\right|$$

Each of these definite integrals interpreted as an area is a specific instance of the next theorem. Do you see the pattern?

Theorems 14-2, 14-3, and 14-4 are sufficient to find the definite integral of any polynomial function. The next examples illustrate this statement.

EXAMPLE 1. Evaluate $\displaystyle\int_1^3 (2x + 3) \, dx$. Cite a reason for each step.

$$\int_1^3 (2x + 3) \, dx = \int_1^3 2x \, dx + \int_1^3 3 \, dx \qquad \text{Theorem 14-3}$$

$$= 2 \int_1^3 x \, dx + 3 \int_1^3 dx \qquad \text{Theorem 14-2}$$

$$= \tfrac{2}{2}(3^2 - 1^2) + 3(3 - 1) \qquad \text{Theorem 14-4}$$

$$= 8 + 6$$

$$= 14$$

EXAMPLE 2. Evaluate $\displaystyle\int_{-1}^1 (5x^3 + x) \, dx$

$$\int_{-1}^1 (5x^3 + x) \, dx = \int_{-1}^1 5x^3 \, dx + \int_{-1}^1 x \, dx \qquad \text{(Why?)}$$

$$= 5 \int_{-1}^1 x^3 \, dx + \int_{-1}^1 x \, dx \qquad \text{(Why?)}$$

$$= \tfrac{5}{4}((1)^4 - (-1)^4) + \tfrac{1}{2}(1^2 - (-1)^2) \qquad \text{(Why?)}$$

$$= \tfrac{5}{4}(0) + \tfrac{1}{2}(0) = 0$$

(Can you explain geometrically why the answer is 0?)

EXAMPLE 3. Show that $\displaystyle\int_{-2}^1 x^2 \, dx + \int_1^2 x^2 \, dx = \int_{-2}^2 x^2 \, dx$.

$$\int_{-2}^1 x^2 \, dx = \tfrac{1}{3}[1^3 - (-2)^3] = \tfrac{1}{3} \cdot 9 = 3$$

$$\int_1^2 x^2 \, dx = \tfrac{1}{3}[2^3 - 1^3] = \tfrac{1}{3} \cdot 7 = 2\tfrac{1}{3}$$

$$\int_{-2}^2 x^2 \, dx = \tfrac{1}{3}[2^3 - (-2)^3] = \tfrac{1}{3} \cdot 16 = 5\tfrac{1}{3}$$

Since

$$3 + 2\tfrac{1}{3} = 5\tfrac{1}{3},$$

you have shown that

$$\int_{-2}^1 x^2 \, dx + \int_1^2 x^2 \, dx = \int_{-2}^2 x^2 \, dx.$$

Now try these

▬ Evaluate the definite integral for Exercises 1–4.

1. $\int_0^2 x^2\, dx$ **2.** $\int_1^5 (x+3)\, dx$

3. $\int_{-1}^0 x^{101}\, dx$ **4.** $\int_1^3 x^3\, dx$

Answers: **1.** $\frac{8}{3}$ **2.** 24   **3.** $-\frac{1}{102}$ **4.** 20

Checkpoint

1. How are the definite integral and the true area of a region related?

2. If $\int_a^b f(x)\, dx = 0$, $(a < b)$, interpret this geometrically. How could integrals be used to find the true area of the region bounded by $x = a$, $x = b$, the x axis, and $f(x)$? (Ignore the case where $f(x) = 0\ \forall x$.)

Exercises

A ▬ Evaluate the definite integral for Exercises 1–12.

1. $\int_0^3 3x^2\, dx$ **2.** $\int_{-1}^4 2x^3\, dx$

3. $\int_1^2 -\tfrac{1}{2}x^2\, dx$ **4.** $\int_{-2}^2 (x^2 - 1)\, dx$

5. $\int_{-2}^2 (x^2 - 3x + 2)\, dx$ **6.** $\int_0^1 25x^{49}\, dx$

7. $\int_2^4 (x - 2)^2\, dx$ **8.** $\int_{-3}^0 5(x^4 + x^2)\, dx$

9. $\int_4^9 5\, dx$ **10.** $\int_{-1}^1 (x^7 - x^3)\, dx$

11. $\int_0^1 x^6 - x^2\, dx$ **12.** $\int_{-4}^2 (x - 3)\, dx$

B ▬ Compare the values of each pair of definite integrals, for Exercises 13–18.

13. $\int_1^2 x\, dx,\ \int_2^1 x\, dx$ **14.** $\int_0^3 2x^2\, dx,\ \int_3^0 2x^2\, dx$

15. $\int_{-1}^3 x^4\, dx,\ \int_3^{-1} x^4\, dx$ **16.** $\int_{-2}^{-3} 2x\, dx,\ \int_{-3}^{-2} 2x\, dx$

17. $\int_{-2}^0 x^3\, dx,\ \int_0^{-2} x^3\, dx$ **18.** $\int_a^b (x^2 + x)\, dx,\ \int_b^a (x^2 + x)\, dx$

19. What relationship did you find between the pairs of integrals in Exercises 13–18. State your generalization and test it for other examples.

Compare the sum of the first two integrals with the value of the third for Exercises 20–23.

20. $\int_{-2}^{0} x\,dx,\ \int_{0}^{3} x\,dx,\ \int_{-2}^{3} x\,dx$

21. $\int_{1}^{2} 2x^2\,dx,\ \int_{2}^{5} 2x^2\,dx,\ \int_{1}^{5} 2x^2\,dx$

22. $\int_{-3}^{-2} (x^2 - 1)\,dx,\ \int_{-2}^{0} (x^2 - 1)\,dx,\ \int_{-3}^{0} (x^2 - 1)\,dx$

23. $\int_{a}^{c} 3x^2\,dx,\ \int_{c}^{b} 3x^2\,dx,\ \int_{a}^{b} 3x^2\,dx \quad a < c < b$

24. What pattern did you observe in Exercises 20–23? State your generalization and test your generalization on other examples.

C ━━ Let $G(x) = 2x^3 - x + 2$, for Exercises 25–27.

25. Find $G'(x)$.   **26.** Find $\int_{a}^{b} G'(x)\,dx$.

27. Find $G(b) - G(a)$.   **28.** Compare the results of Exercises 26 and 27.

━━ The generalization implied in Exercises 28 is: If $G'(x) = f(x)$, then $\int_{a}^{b} f(x)\,dx = G(b) - G(a)$. Test this generalization for Exercises 29–34. (This generalization is true. It is called the **Fundamental Theorem of Calculus.**)

29. $G(x) = x$ **30.** $G(x) = x^2$

31. $G(x) = x^3$ **32.** $G(x) = 2x^2$

33. $G(x) = x^2 - 1$ **34.** $G(x) = x^m$

14–7   Areas by Integrals

You have already seen that the definition of the definite integral and the definition of the area of the region bounded by $f(x) \geq 0$, $x = a$, $x = b$, $(a < b)$ and x axis are the same.

$$A_a^b f(x) = \int_{a}^{b} f(x)\,dx \qquad f(x) \geq 0 \qquad x \in [a, b]$$

Determining areas of plane regions bounded by curves was one of the initial applications of integration. (Attempts to find areas led to the definition of the integral.) In the physical sciences specification of such areas remains an important application.

The next three examples illustrate the definite integral used to determine areas of regions. Study these examples thoroughly.

EXAMPLE 1. Area between Two Curves. Find the area of the region bounded by the parabola

$$f(x) = 2 - x^2$$

and the line

$$g(x) = -x$$

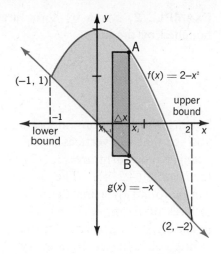

The first step in the solution is to sketch a graph of the region. Notice that the curves intersect at the points $(-1, 1)$ and $(2, -2)$. Thus the lower bound of integration is -1, while the upper bound of integration is 2.

The region under consideration can be approximately covered by rectangular regions like the one shown in the diagram. Each such rectangular region has *width*

$$\Delta x = \frac{2 - (-1)}{n} = \frac{3}{n}. \qquad 1$$

The height of the rectangular region is the length of the segment AB. This length is found by *subtracting the y-coordinate of B from that of A.* (Why?) But the y-coordinate of A for $x = x_i$ is $f(x_i) = 2 - x_i^2$ and the y-coordinate of B is $g(x_i) = -x_i$. Thus the length of AB is

$$f(x_i) - g(x_i) = 2 - x_i^2 - (-x_i). \qquad 2$$

Multiplying **1** and **2** you get the area of the rectangular region

$$[f(x_i) - g(x_i)] \Delta x = [2 - x_i^2 + x_i] \Delta x. \qquad 3$$

The sum of all such terms (for x_i, $i = 1, \ldots, n$)

$$\sum_{i=1}^{n} [f(x_i) - g(x_i)] \Delta x = \sum_{i=1}^{n} [2 - x_i^2 + x_i] \Delta x \qquad 4$$

is the approximate area. The exact area is found by taking the limit of **4** as n increases without bound. But this is the definite integral

$$\int_{-1}^{2} [f(x) - g(x)] \, dx = \int_{-1}^{2} (2 - x^2 + x) \, dx. \qquad 5$$

Evaluating **5** you see that

$$\text{Area} = \int_{-1}^{2} (2 - x^2 + x) \, dx$$

$$= \left[2 \cdot 2 - \frac{(2^3)}{3} + \frac{(2)^2}{2} \right] - \left[2(-1) - \frac{(-1)^3}{3} + \frac{(-1)^2}{2} \right] = 4\tfrac{1}{2}$$

EXAMPLE 2. Area by Two Integrals. Find the area of the region bounded by the lines

$$y = 2x - 8$$
$$y = -\tfrac{2}{7}x + \tfrac{24}{7}$$
$$y = -\tfrac{6}{5}x + \tfrac{8}{5}$$

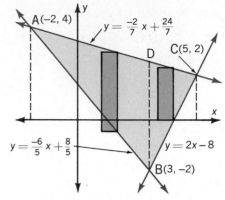

Solving the equations in pairs you see that the vertices of the triangle they form are $(3, -2)$, $(5, 2)$ and $(-2, 4)$. The area can be found by using the procedures of Example 1, but *not in one step*. By considering the figure you can see that every rectangle with sides parallel to the y axis used to approximate the area has one vertex on the line $y = -\tfrac{2}{7}x + \tfrac{24}{7}$. However at the other end, some rectangles have a vertex on $y = -\tfrac{6}{5}x + \tfrac{8}{5}$ and others on $y = 2x - 8$. Thus the area of $\triangle ABC$ cannot be found in one step; it must be calculated using two steps. Since area of $\triangle ABD$ + area of $\triangle BCD$ = area of $\triangle ABC$, you must find 1. the area of $\triangle ABD$, 2. the area of $\triangle BCD$.

By the procedures explained in Example 1, you can see that the area is the following.

$$\text{Area of } \triangle ABD = \int_{-2}^{3}\left[\left(-\frac{2x}{7} + \frac{24}{7}\right) - \left(-\frac{6}{5}x + \frac{8}{5}\right)\right]dx$$

$$= \int_{-2}^{3} \tfrac{1}{35}(32x + 64)\,dx$$

$$= \tfrac{32}{35}\int_{-2}^{3}(x + 2)$$

$$= \tfrac{32}{35}\left(\tfrac{25}{2}\right) = \tfrac{80}{7} = 11\tfrac{3}{7}$$

$$\text{Area of } \triangle BCD = \int_{3}^{5}\left[\left(-\tfrac{2}{7}x + \tfrac{24}{7}\right) - (2x - 8)\right]dx$$

$$= \int_{3}^{5} \tfrac{16}{7}(-x + 5)\,dx$$

$$= \tfrac{16}{7}(2)$$

$$= 4\tfrac{4}{7}$$

$$\text{Area of } \triangle ABC = \text{Area } \triangle ABD + \text{Area } \triangle BCD$$
$$\text{So Area of } \triangle ABC = 11\tfrac{3}{7} + 4\tfrac{4}{7} = 16$$

EXAMPLE 3. Area of Region Below The x Axis. Find the area of the region bounded by the x axis and

$$f(x) = x^2 + x - 6.$$

The zeros of $f(x) = x^2 + x - 6$ are $(-3, 0)$ and $(2, 0)$. Thus the region is the shaded portion in the figure below. A typical rectangular region is shown. Since the x axis has equation $y = 0$, the desired area can be considered as the area of a region between the two following curves.

$$y = 0 \quad \text{and} \quad f(x) = x^2 + x - 6.$$

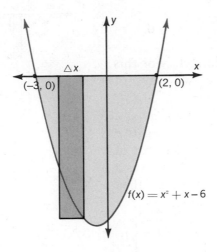

Thus the height of a typical rectangle is

$$0 - (x^2 + x - 6).$$ **6**

The width of a typical rectangle is Δx and therefore the area is equal to the following integral.

$$\int_{-3}^{2} [0 - (x^2 + x - 6)]\, dx$$

or

$$\int_{-3}^{2} (-x^2 - x + 6)\, dx$$

$$= \left(-\frac{(2)^3}{3} - \frac{(2)^2}{2} \right) + 6(2) - \left[\left(-\frac{(-3)^3}{3} - \frac{(-3)^2}{2} \right) + 6(-3) \right]$$

$$= -\tfrac{8}{3} - 2 + 12 - 9 + \tfrac{9}{2} + 18$$

$$= 19 + 4\tfrac{1}{2} - 2\tfrac{2}{3}$$

$$= 20\tfrac{5}{6}$$

EXAMPLE 4. **Area of Region Symmetric to x axis.** Find the area of the region bounded by the x axis, $f(x) = x^3$, $a = -3$ and $b = +3$.

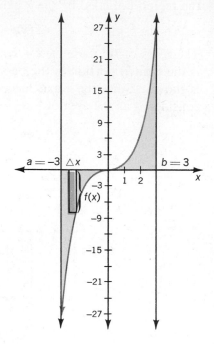

Sketching the curve you can see that part of the region falls below the x axis and part above. A typical rectangular region is shown. The height of a typical rectangle is x^3. The width of a typical rectangle is Δx and therefore

$$A^3_{-3}(x^3) = \int_{-3}^{3} x^3\, dx = 0.$$

This is clearly incorrect. For this problem there are two ways of finding the true area.

Since the part of the region below the x axis gives a negative value for the area and the part of the region above the x axis gives a positive value for the area, then the area is the following.

$$A^3_{-3}(x^3) = \left| \int_{-3}^{0} x^3\, dx \right| + \int_{0}^{3} x^3\, dx$$

$$= \left| -\tfrac{81}{4} \right| + \tfrac{81}{4}$$

$$= \tfrac{81}{2}$$

Another way of approaching the problem is to realize that the region below the x axis is symmetric to the region above the x axis and therefore

$$A^3_{-3}(x^3) = 2 \int_{0}^{3} x^3\, dx \qquad \text{or} \qquad 2 \left| \int_{-3}^{0} x^3\, dx \right|$$

$$= 2(\tfrac{81}{4}) = \tfrac{81}{2}$$

The key idea illustrated in Examples 1–3 is that the area of a region bounded by two or more curves can be found by integration. The integrand is $(g(x) - f(x))$ when $g(x) > f(x)$ for all x in the interval of integration. The bounds of integration are usually found by determining the points of intersection of the curves. In some cases it may be necessary to use more than one integral. The idea illustrated in Example 4 is that if $f(x)$ or $(g(x) - f(x))$ crosses the x axis in $[a, b]$ then more than one integral may be necessary.

Now try these

━━ Using the definite integral, find the area of the given regions in Exercises 1–3.

1. The region bounded by $y = x^2$, $x = 0$, $x = 4$ and the x axis.

2. The region bounded by the curves $y = x^2$, and $y = x$.

3. The region bounded by the curves x^3, $x = 0$ and $x = 4$ and the x axis.

Answers: **1.** $\frac{64}{3}$ **2.** $\frac{1}{6}$ **3.** 64

Exercises

A ━━ Find the area of the region bounded by the given curves. Sketch each region.

    1. x axis and $y = 2x - x^2$

    2. $y = x^2$, $y = 0$, $x = 2$, $x = 4$

    3. $y = x^2 - 9$, $y = 0$, $x = 1$, $x = 4$

    4. $y = 6x - x^2$, $y = 0$

    5. $y = 2x - x^2$, $y = -3$

    6. $y = x^2$, $y = x$

    7. $y = x^4 - 2x^2$, $y = 2x^2$

    8. $y = 9 - x^2$, $y = x + 7$

    9. $y = x^3 - x^2 - 2x$, $y = 0$

    10. $y = x^3 - 6x^2 + 9x$, $y = x$

    11. $y = x^3 - x$, $y = 3x$

    12. $y = x^3 - 3x$, $y = x$

B   **13.** Interpret $\int_0^1 x^n \, dx \ (n \in W)$ as the area of a region.

    14. How is the area of Exercise 13 related to the unit square?

    15. What happens to the number $\int_0^1 x^n \, dx$ as n increases?

    16. Find the area of the region bounded by $y = x^2$, $y = 0$, $x = 0$, and $x = 2$.

    17. Find the area of the region bounded by $y = x^2 + x$, $y = x$, $x = 0$, and $x = 2$.

    18. Are the areas in Exercises 16 and 17 the same?

    19. Are the regions in Exercises 16 and 17 the same?

    20. $\int_1^3 (x^2 - x) \, dx$ can be interpreted as the area of many different regions. Draw two such regions.

21. Is the area of the region in the first quadrant bounded by $y = x^2 + x^3$ and $y = x^3 + 1$ the same as the area of the region in the first quadrant bounded by $y = 1$ and $y = x^2$? Are the regions the same?

14–8   Volumes by Integration

You have seen that the area of a plane region with curves for boundaries can be found by evaluating a definite integral. In the same manner the volume (a number) of a space region with *surfaces* for boundaries can be found by integration.

The space regions (solids) for which it is easiest to calculate volumes are those bounded by *surfaces of revolution*. These regions are the only ones discussed here.

The procedures for calculating the volume of a space region are similar to those used in area; that is, the space region is approximated by regions for which a means of calculating the volume is known. Then these volumes are added, and the limit is taken.

For solids of revolution a convenient space region which may be used to approximate the solid is the *circular cylinder*. Since a plane perpendicular to the axis of rotation intersects a solid of revolution in a *circular disc*, that solid and its volume may be approximated by a "stack of thin circular cylinders."

The procedures used are illustrated in the next examples.

EXAMPLE 1.   Consider the solid of revolution formed by rotating the line $y = \frac{1}{2}x + 1$ about the x axis. Find the volume of the portion of the solid between $x = 0$ and $x = 4$. The solid of revolution is shown in the figure. Now partition the interval $[0, 4]$ into n intervals, each of length

$$\Delta x = \frac{4 - 0}{n},$$

with the points $x_0 = 0$, x_1, x_2, x_3, ..., $x_n = 4$. Imagine planes perpendicular to the x axis at each point x_i, $i = 0, 1, 2, \ldots, n$. They intersect the solid in circular discs. Then think of the stack of cylinders, each having as its base the circular disc at x_i, $i = 1, 2, \ldots, n$ respectively and having height Δx. The solid is approximated by the stack of cylinders, and the volume is approximated by the sum of the volumes of these cylinders.

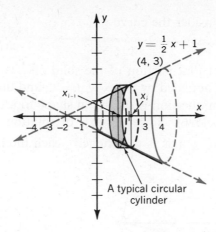

$$y = \tfrac{1}{2}x + 1$$

$(4, 3)$

A typical circular cylinder

The volume of a circular cylinder with height $= h$ and the radius of the base $= r$, is $V = \pi r^2 h$. For each cylinder above, $h = \Delta x$, and the radius of the base is the distance from the x axis at $x = x_i$ to the line $y = \tfrac{1}{2}x + 1$, so

$$r_i = y_i = \tfrac{1}{2}x_i + 1 \text{ for each } i = 1, 2, \ldots, n.$$

Thus the volume of one circular cylinder is

$$V_i = \pi(y_i)^2 \Delta x = \pi(\tfrac{1}{2}x_i + 1)^2 \Delta x.$$

The volume of *all* the circular cylinders is

$$\sum_{i=1}^{n} V_i = \sum_{i=1}^{n} \pi(\tfrac{1}{2}x_i + 1)^2 \Delta x.$$

Therefore the volume of the solid is by definition

$$V = \lim_{n \to \infty} \sum_{i=1}^{n} V_i = \lim_{n \to \infty} \sum_{i=1}^{n} \pi(\tfrac{1}{2}x_i + 1)^2 \Delta x.$$

The last limit is the type that defines a definite integral. Thus the volume V of the solid is given by the equation

$$V = \int_0^4 \pi(\tfrac{1}{2}x + 1)^2 \, dx. \qquad\qquad 1$$

It is a simple task to evaluate **1**. The result is $V = 17\tfrac{1}{3}\pi$ cubic units.

Equation **1** for the volume of a solid of revolution with the x axis as the axis of rotation can be easily generalized to

$$V = \pi \int_a^b y^2 \, dx = \pi \int_a^b [f(x)]^2 \, dx. \qquad\qquad 2$$

The factor "$\pi[f(x)]^2$" is the area of the base and "dx" is the height of the circular cylinder.

The same procedures may be used when a plane curve is rotated about the y axis.

EXAMPLE 2. Consider the curve

$$y = \sqrt{x}.$$

Find the volume of that portion of the solid of revolution formed by rotating the region bounded by $y = \sqrt{x}$, $y = 2$, and the y axis about the y axis. The solid in question is similar in shape to a trumpet. (See the figure at the left below.) Since the axis of rotation is the y axis, the interval $[0, 2]$ on the y axis is partitioned—each interval is $\dfrac{2 - 0}{n} = \Delta y$.

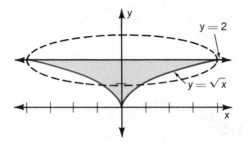
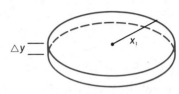

A typical circular cylinder

The radius of a typical cylinder is the distance from the y axis to the curve (see the figure at the right above)—that is, the radius is x_i. Thus, the volume of a circular cylinder is $V_i = \pi x_i^2 \Delta y$. Since $y_i = \sqrt{x_i}$, $y_i^4 = x_i^2$ and thus

$$V_i = \pi y_i^4 \Delta y.$$

Thus the integral

$$\pi \int_0^2 y^4 \, dy = V$$

gives the volume. Evaluating this you find

$$V = \tfrac{32}{5}\pi \text{ cubic units.}$$

EXAMPLE 3. Find the volume of the solid formed by rotating the region in the first quadrant bounded by y axis, $y = 4$ and $y = x^2$ about the x axis.

The solid is shown in the diagram. Since the axis of rotation is the x axis, the interval $[0, 2]$ on the x axis is partitioned into n intervals of length

$$\frac{2 - 0}{n} = \Delta x.$$

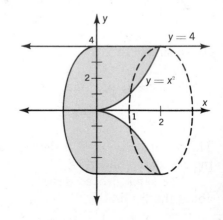

A typical "slice" of the solid is no longer a circular cylinder. It resembles more a metal washer. Such a "washer" is sketched at the right. Its thickness is Δx. The area of its base is $\pi(r_2^2 - r_1^2)$ because it is the difference of the areas of the two circular regions.

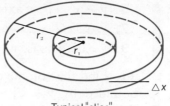

Typical "slice"

For the solid under discussion r_2 is the distance from the x axis to the line $y = 4$. Thus

$$r_2 = 4$$

r_1 is the distance from the x axis to the curve $y = x^2$. Thus

$$r_1 = y_i = x_i^2$$

Thus the volume of a typical slice of the solid is

$$V_i = \pi(r_2^2 - r_1^2)\,\Delta x = \pi(4^2 - (y_i)^2)\,\Delta x$$
$$= \pi(4^2 - x_i^4)\,\Delta x$$

The volume then is the value of the definite integral

$$V = \pi \int_0^2 (4^2 - x^4)\,dx.$$

It is easy to find V. $V = 32 \cdot \frac{4}{5}\pi = \frac{128}{5}\pi$.

Now try these

━━ For Exercises 1–3, find the volume of the solid generated by rotating the given region about the x axis.

1. $y = x$, $x = 0$ and $x = 4$

2. $y = x^3$, $x = 0$ and $x = 2$

3. $y^2 = x - 9$, $y \geq 0$ and $x = 12$

Answers: **1.** $\frac{64}{3}\pi$ **2.** $\frac{128}{7}\pi$ **3.** $\frac{9}{2}\pi$

Exercises

A ━━ For Exercises 1–10 find the volume of the solid generated by rotating the given region about the x axis.

1. $y = 2x + 1$, x axis, y axis, $x = 3$

2. $y = 2x + 1$, $y = 7$, y axis

3. $y = x^2 + 1$, x axis, y axis, $x = 2$

4. $y = x^2 + 1$, y axis, $y = 5$

5. $y = x - x^2$, x axis   **6.** $y = 3x - x^2$, x axis
7. $y = 5x - x^2$, $y = x$ **8.** $y = x^3$, x axis, $x = 2$
9. $y = x^3$, y axis, $y = 8$ **10.** $y = x$, $y = 2$, y axis

B **11.** Find the volume of the solid generated by rotating the region bounded by $y = x^2$, $y = 2$ and y axis about the y axis. (The height is Δy.)

12. Find the volume of the solid generated by rotating the region bounded by $y = x^2$ and $y = x$ about the x axis.

13. Repeat Exercise 12 with the y axis as the axis of rotation.

14. Find the volume of the solid generated by rotating the region bounded by $y = x^2$ and $y = x^3$ about the x axis.

C ▬ Find the volume of the solid generated by rotating the region bounded by the y axis, $y = 4$ and $y = x^2$ about the given axis.

15. the y axis   **16.** the x axis
17. the line $y = 4$ **18.** the line $x = 2$
19. the line $x = 4$ **20.** the line $y = 6$

21. Find the volume of the ellipsoid generated by rotating the region bounded by the x axis and $y = \frac{b}{a}\sqrt{a^2 - x^2}$ about the x axis.

22. Find the volume of the sphere of radius r generated by rotating the region bounded by the x axis and $y = \sqrt{r^2 - x^2}$ about the x axis.

CHAPTER OBJECTIVES AND REVIEW ▬▬▬

Objective: *To know the meaning of the important mathematical terms of this chapter.*

1. Here are many of the mathematical terms used in this chapter. Be sure that you know them thoroughly and can use them correctly.

derivative of $f(x)$ *(654)*
differentiation *(654)*
differentiable *(654)*
average velocity *(657)*
position function *(657)*
instantaneous velocity *(658)*
average acceleration *(659)*
instantaneous acceleration *(659)*

acceleration function $a(t)$ *(659)*
lower bound of integration *(674)*
upper bound of integration *(674)*
integrand *(674)*
Riemann integral *(674)*

Objective: *To calculate derivatives of polynomial, exponential and logarithmic functions and their products.*

2. Given $f(x) = p(x) \cdot q(x)$ where $p(x)$ and $q(x)$ are differentiable functions, find $f'(x)$.

━━ In Exercises 3–9 calculate the derivative for each function.

3. $f(x) = x^3$

4. $f(x) = 5e^x$

5. $f(x) = \ln x^2$

6. $f(x) = 3x^4 - 2x^3 + 3$

7. $f(x) = \dfrac{7}{x^5}$

8. $f(x) = x^2 \cdot e^x$

9. $f(x) = (x^2 + 1)(x^3 - 3x)$

Objective: *To define and calculate average rates and instantaneous rates of change for position functions describing rectilinear motion.*

10. In your own words define the average velocity of a particle from t_1 to t_2 whose motion is given by $R(t)$. Define the instantaneous velocity of the particle at $t = 4$.

11. Let $R(t) = 7t^2 - 5t + 3$ be a position function describing rectilinear motion of a particle.

    a. Find the average velocity of the particle from $t = 1$ to $t = 3$.

    b. Find the instantaneous velocity of the particle at $t = 3$.

12. Let $S(t) = 12t^2 - 6t$ be a position function for a particle.

    a. Find $v(t)$.

    b. Find $a(t)$.

    c. What is the velocity at $t = 3$?

    d. What is the acceleration at $t = 3$?

    e. What is the velocity at $t = 0$?

    f. What is the acceleration at $t = 0$?

13. A bullet is shot straight upward with an initial velocity of 1280 feet per second. The bullet's height after t seconds is given by $S(t) = 1280t - 16t^2$.

    a. What is the velocity function?

    b. What is the velocity when $t = 20, 40, 60$?

    c. What is the acceleration function?

    d. At what time t does the bullet hit the ground?

    e. What is the velocity of the bullet when it hits the ground?

Objective: *To use approximation methods to calculate an approximate value for the area of a region bounded by plane curves.*

14. Given $f(x) > 0$ for all $x \in [a, b]$. Illustrate and describe in your own words how you would find an approximation to the area of the region bounded by $y = f(x)$, $x = a$, $x = b$ and the x axis using

    a. rectangles and 16 intervals.

    b. trapezoids and 8 intervals.

15. Let $y = 4x^2$. Use 16 rectangles to approximate the area of the region bounded by $y = 4x^2$, $x = 0$, $x = 3$, and the x axis.

16. Let $y = 3x^2$. Use 16 trapezoids to calculate an approximation of the area of the region bounded by $y = 3x^2$, $x = 0$, $x = 4$ and the x axis.

Objective: *To define the definite integral, evaluate it, and use it to determine the area of a region bounded by plane curves.*

17. Write a definition of $\int_a^b f(x)\,dx$.

18. Evaluate $\int_a^b x^m\,dx$.

19. Evaluate $\int_1^2 5x^3\,dx$.

20. Evaluate $\int_1^3 (x^4 - x^3)\,dx$.

━━ In Exercises 21–25 use definite integrals to find the area of the region bounded by the given curves.

21. $f(x) = 3x^2$, $x = 3$, $x = 9$, x axis

22. $f(x) = x^4$, $g(x) = x^3$

23. $f(x) = x^4$, $g(x) = x^3$, $x = 2$

24. $y = -\frac{1}{2}x + \frac{1}{2}$, $y = \frac{2}{3}x + \frac{5}{3}$, $y = 3x - 3$

25. $y = x^2$, $y = 2$

Objective: *To use the definite integral to calculate volumes of surfaces of revolution.*

26. Find the volume of the solid generated by rotating about the x axis, the region bounded by $y = 3x + 1$, $x = 1$, $x = 3$, and the x axis.

27. Find the volume of the solid generated by rotating about the y axis, the region bounded by $y = x^2$, $y = 4$, and the y axis.

28. Find the volume of the solid generated by rotating about the x axis, the region bounded by $y = x^3$, $x = 2$, and the x axis.

29. Find the volume of the solid generated by rotating about the y axis, the region bounded by $y = x^3$, $y = 8$, and the y axis.

CHAPTER TEST

1. Find $f'(x)$ if $f(x) = x^2 - 3x + e^x$.
2. Find $f'(x)$ if $f(x) = xe^x$.
3. Find $g'(x)$ if $g(x) = e^x \ln x$.

━━ For Exercises 4–9 let $S(t) = 24t^2 - 6t^3$ be the position function for a rectilinearly moving particle, with $0 \le t \le 4$.

4. Find $v(t)$.
5. Find $a(t)$.
6. For what value of t is the particle not moving?
7. For what values of t is the acceleration positive?
8. How far from its starting point is the particle at $t = 1, 2, 3, 4$?
9. What is the average velocity of the particle from $t = 1$ to $t = 3$?
10. Calculate two approximations to the area of the region bounded by the curves $y = x^3$, $x = 2$ and the x axis for 16 subdivisions of $[0, 2]$. The first approximation should use rectangles; the second trapezoids.
11. Calculate the true area of the region in Exercise 10 by using a definite integral.

━━ Evaluate each integral in Exercises 12–15.

12. $\int_{-1}^{2} x^3 \, dx$

13. $\int_{0}^{5} (3x^2 + 5x^4) \, dx$

14. $\int_{1}^{2} (x + 1)(2x - 3) \, dx$

15. $\int_{0}^{5} (mx + b) \, dx$

16. Find the volume of the surface of revolution obtained by rotating the region bounded by $y = \frac{2}{3}x^2 + 1$, y axis, x axis, and $x = 3$ about the x axis.

Table of Values of the Trigonometric Functions

θ Deg.	θ Rad.	Sin θ	Cos θ	Tan θ	Cot θ	Sec θ	Csc θ		
0° 00'	.0000	.0000	1.0000	.0000		1.000		1.5708	90° 00'
10'	.0029	.0029	1.0000	.0029	343.77	1.000	343.8	1.5679	50'
20'	.0058	.0058	1.0000	.0058	171.89	1.000	171.9	1.5650	40'
30'	.0087	.0087	1.0000	.0087	114.59	1.000	114.6	1.5621	30'
40'	.0116	.0116	.9999	.0116	85.940	1.000	85.95	1.5592	20'
50'	.0145	.0145	.9999	.0145	68.750	1.000	68.76	1.5563	10'
1° 00'	.0175	.0175	.9998	.0175	57.290	1.000	57.30	1.5533	89° 00'
10'	.0204	.0204	.9998	.0204	49.104	1.000	49.11	1.5504	50'
20'	.0233	.0233	.9997	.0233	42.964	1.000	42.98	1.5475	40'
30'	.0262	.0262	.9997	.0262	38.188	1.000	38.20	1.5446	30'
40'	.0291	.0291	.9996	.0291	34.368	1.000	34.38	1.5417	20'
50'	.0320	.0320	.9995	.0320	31.242	1.001	31.26	1.5388	10'
2° 00'	.0349	.0349	.9994	.0349	28.636	1.001	28.65	1.5359	88° 00'
10'	.0378	.0378	.9993	.0378	26.432	1.001	26.45	1.5330	50'
20'	.0407	.0407	.9992	.0407	24.542	1.001	24.56	1.5301	40'
30'	.0436	.0436	.9990	.0437	22.904	1.001	22.93	1.5272	30'
40'	.0465	.0465	.9989	.0466	21.470	1.001	21.49	1.5243	20'
50'	.0495	.0494	.9988	.0495	20.206	1.001	20.23	1.5213	10'
3° 00'	.0524	.0523	.9986	.0524	19.081	1.001	19.11	1.5184	87° 00'
10'	.0553	.0552	.9985	.0553	18.075	1.002	18.10	1.5155	50'
20'	.0582	.0581	.9983	.0582	17.169	1.002	17.20	1.5126	40'
30'	.0611	.0610	.9981	.0612	16.350	1.002	16.38	1.5097	30'
40'	.0640	.0640	.9980	.0641	15.605	1.002	15.64	1.5068	20'
50'	.0669	.0669	.9978	.0670	14.924	1.002	14.96	1.5039	10'
4° 00'	.0698	.0698	.9976	.0699	14.301	1.002	14.34	1.5010	86° 00'
10'	.0727	.0727	.9974	.0729	13.727	1.003	13.76	1.4981	50'
20'	.0756	.0756	.9971	.0758	13.197	1.003	13.23	1.4952	40'
30'	.0785	.0785	.9969	.0787	12.706	1.003	12.75	1.4923	30'
40'	.0814	.0814	.9967	.0816	12.251	1.003	12.29	1.4893	20'
50'	.0844	.0843	.9964	.0846	11.826	1.004	11.87	1.4864	10'
5° 00'	.0873	.0872	.9962	.0875	11.430	1.004	11.47	1.4835	85° 00'
10'	.0902	.0901	.9959	.0904	11.059	1.004	11.10	1.4806	50'
20'	.0931	.0929	.9957	.0934	10.712	1.004	10.76	1.4777	40'
30'	.0960	.0958	.9954	.0963	10.385	1.005	10.43	1.4748	30'
40'	.0989	.0987	.9951	.0992	10.078	1.005	10.13	1.4719	20'
50'	.1018	.1016	.9948	.1022	9.7882	1.005	9.839	1.4690	10'
6° 00'	.1047	.1045	.9945	.1051	9.5144	1.006	9.567	1.4661	84° 00'
10'	.1076	.1074	.9942	.1080	9.2553	1.006	9.309	1.4632	50'
20'	.1105	.1103	.9939	.1110	9.0098	1.006	9.065	1.4603	40'
30'	.1134	.1132	.9936	.1139	8.7769	1.006	8.834	1.4573	30'
40'	.1164	.1161	.9932	.1169	8.5555	1.007	8.614	1.4544	20'
50'	.1193	.1190	.9929	.1198	8.3450	1.007	8.405	1.4515	10'
7° 00'	.1222	.1219	.9925	.1228	8.1443	1.008	8.206	1.4486	83° 00'
10'	.1251	.1248	.9922	.1257	7.9530	1.008	8.016	1.4457	50'
20'	.1280	.1276	.9918	.1287	7.7704	1.008	7.834	1.4428	40'
30'	.1309	.1305	.9914	.1317	7.5958	1.009	7.661	1.4399	30'
40'	.1338	.1334	.9911	.1346	7.4287	1.009	7.496	1.4370	20'
50'	.1367	.1363	.9907	.1376	7.2687	1.009	7.337	1.4341	10'
8° 00'	.1396	.1392	.9903	.1405	7.1154	1.010	7.185	1.4312	82° 00'
10'	.1425	.1421	.9899	.1435	6.9682	1.010	7.040	1.4283	50'
20'	.1454	.1449	.9894	.1465	6.8269	1.011	6.900	1.4254	40'
30'	.1484	.1478	.9890	.1495	6.6912	1.011	6.765	1.4224	30'
40'	.1513	.1507	.9886	.1524	6.5606	1.012	6.636	1.4195	20'
50'	.1542	.1536	.9881	.1554	6.4348	1.012	6.512	1.4166	10'
9° 00'	.1571	.1564	.9877	.1584	6.3138	1.012	6.392	1.4137	81° 00'
		Cos θ	Sin θ	Cot θ	Tan θ	Csc θ	Sec θ	θ Rad.	θ Deg.

Table of Values of the Trigonometric Functions

θ Deg.	θ Rad.	Sin θ	Cos θ	Tan θ	Cot θ	Sec θ	Csc θ		
9° 00'	.1571	.1564	.9877	.1584	6.3138	1.012	6.392	1.4137	81° 00'
10'	.1600	.1593	.9872	.1614	6.1970	1.013	6.277	1.4108	50'
20'	.1629	.1622	.9868	.1644	6.0844	1.013	6.166	1.4079	40'
30'	.1658	.1650	.9863	.1673	5.9758	1.014	6.059	1.4050	30'
40'	.1687	.1679	.9858	.1703	5.8708	1.014	5.955	1.4021	20'
50'	.1716	.1708	.9853	.1733	5.7694	1.015	5.855	1.3992	10'
10° 00'	.1745	.1736	.9848	.1763	5.6713	1.015	5.759	1.3963	80° 00'
10'	.1774	.1765	.9843	.1793	5.5764	1.016	5.665	1.3934	50'
20'	.1804	.1794	.9838	.1823	5.4845	1.016	5.575	1.3904	40'
30'	.1833	.1822	.9833	.1853	5.3955	1.017	5.487	1.3875	30'
40'	.1862	.1851	.9827	.1883	5.3093	1.018	5.403	1.3846	20'
50'	.1891	.1880	.9822	.1914	5.2257	1.018	5.320	1.3817	10'
11° 00'	.1920	.1908	.9816	.1944	5.1446	1.019	5.241	1.3788	79° 00'
10'	.1949	.1937	.9811	.1974	5.0658	1.019	5.164	1.3759	50'
20'	.1978	.1965	.9805	.2004	4.9894	1.020	5.089	1.3730	40'
30'	.2007	.1994	.9799	.2035	4.9152	1.020	5.016	1.3701	30'
40'	.2036	.2022	.9793	.2065	4.8430	1.021	4.945	1.3672	20'
50'	.2065	.2051	.9787	.2095	4.7729	1.022	4.876	1.3643	10'
12° 00'	.2094	.2079	.9781	.2126	4.7046	1.022	4.810	1.3614	78° 00'
10'	.2123	.2108	.9775	.2156	4.6382	1.023	4.745	1.3584	50'
20'	.2153	.2136	.9769	.2186	4.5736	1.024	4.682	1.3555	40'
30'	.2182	.2164	.9763	.2217	4.5107	1.024	4.620	1.3526	30'
40'	.2211	.2193	.9757	.2247	4.4494	1.025	4.560	1.3497	20'
50'	.2240	.2221	.9750	.2278	4.3897	1.026	4.502	1.3468	10'
13° 00'	.2269	.2250	.9744	.2309	4.3315	1.026	4.445	1.3439	77° 00'
10'	.2298	.2278	.9737	.2339	4.2747	1.027	4.390	1.3410	50'
20'	.2327	.2306	.9730	.2370	4.2193	1.028	4.336	1.3381	40'
30'	.2356	.2334	.9724	.2401	4.1653	1.028	4.284	1.3352	30'
40'	.2385	.2363	.9717	.2432	4.1126	1.029	4.232	1.3323	20'
50'	.2414	.2391	.9710	.2462	4.0611	1.030	4.182	1.3294	10'
14° 00'	.2443	.2419	.9703	.2493	4.0108	1.031	4.134	1.3265	76° 00'
10'	.2473	.2447	.9696	.2524	3.9617	1.031	4.086	1.3235	50'
20'	.2502	.2476	.9689	.2555	3.9136	1.032	4.039	1.3206	40'
30'	.2531	.2504	.9681	.2586	3.8667	1.033	3.994	1.3177	30'
40'	.2560	.2532	.9674	.2617	3.8208	1.034	3.950	1.3148	20'
50'	.2589	.2560	.9667	.2648	3.7760	1.034	3.906	1.3119	10'
15° 00'	.2618	.2588	.9659	.2679	3.7321	1.035	3.864	1.3090	75° 00'
10'	.2647	.2616	.9652	.2711	3.6891	1.036	3.822	1.3061	50'
20'	.2676	.2644	.9644	.2742	3.6470	1.037	3.782	1.3032	40'
30'	.2705	.2672	.9636	.2773	3.6059	1.038	3.742	1.3003	30'
40'	.2734	.2700	.9628	.2805	3.5656	1.039	3.703	1.2974	20'
50'	.2763	.2728	.9621	.2836	3.5261	1.039	3.665	1.2945	10'
16° 00'	.2793	.2756	.9613	.2867	3.4874	1.040	3.628	1.2915	74° 00'
10'	.2822	.2784	.9605	.2899	3.4495	1.041	3.592	1.2886	50'
20'	.2851	.2812	.9596	.2931	3.4124	1.042	3.556	1.2857	40'
30'	.2880	.2840	.9588	.2962	3.3759	1.043	3.521	1.2828	30'
40'	.2909	.2868	.9580	.2994	3.3402	1.044	3.487	1.2799	20'
50'	.2938	.2896	.9572	.3026	3.3052	1.045	3.453	1.2770	10'
17° 00'	.2967	.2924	.9563	.3057	3.2709	1.046	3.420	1.2741	73° 00'
10'	.2996	.2952	.9555	.3089	3.2371	1.047	3.388	1.2712	50'
20'	.3025	.2979	.9546	.3121	3.2041	1.048	3.356	1.2683	40'
30'	.3054	.3007	.9537	.3153	3.1716	1.049	3.326	1.2654	30'
40'	.3083	.3035	.9528	.3185	3.1397	1.049	3.295	1.2625	20'
50'	.3113	.3062	.9520	.3217	3.1084	1.050	3.265	1.2595	10'
18° 00'	.3142	.3090	.9511	.3249	3.0777	1.051	3.236	1.2566	72° 00'
		Cos θ	Sin θ	Cot θ	Tan θ	Csc θ	Sec θ	θ Rad.	θ Deg.

693

Table of Values of the Trigonometric Functions

θ Deg.	θ Rad.	Sin θ	Cos θ	Tan θ	Cot θ	Sec θ	Csc θ		
18°00′	.3142	.3090	.9511	.3249	3.0777	1.051	3.236	1.2566	72°00′
10′	.3171	.3118	.9502	.3281	3.0475	1.052	3.207	1.2537	50′
20′	.3200	.3145	.9492	.3314	3.0178	1.053	3.179	1.2508	40′
30′	.3229	.3173	.9483	.3346	2.9887	1.054	3.152	1.2479	30′
40′	.3258	.3201	.9474	.3378	2.9600	1.056	3.124	1.2450	20′
50′	.3287	.3228	.9465	.3411	2.9319	1.057	3.098	1.2421	10′
19°00′	.3316	.3256	.9455	.3443	2.9042	1.058	3.072	1.2392	71°00′
10′	.3345	.3283	.9446	.3476	2.8770	1.059	3.046	1.2363	50′
20′	.3374	.3311	.9436	.3508	2.8502	1.060	3.021	1.2334	40′
30′	.3403	.3338	.9426	.3541	2.8239	1.061	2.996	1.2305	30′
40′	.3432	.3365	.9417	.3574	2.7980	1.062	2.971	1.2275	20′
50′	.3462	.3393	.9407	.3607	2.7725	1.063	2.947	1.2246	10′
20°00′	.3491	.3420	.9397	.3640	2.7475	1.064	2.924	1.2217	70°00′
10′	.3520	.3448	.9387	.3673	2.7228	1.065	2.901	1.2188	50′
20′	.3549	.3475	.9377	.3706	2.6985	1.066	2.878	1.2159	40′
30′	.3578	.3502	.9367	.3739	2.6746	1.068	2.855	1.2130	30′
40′	.3607	.3529	.9356	.3772	2.6511	1.069	2.833	1.2101	20′
50′	.3636	.3557	.9346	.3805	.6279	1.070	2.812	1.2072	10′
21°00′	.3665	.3584	.9336	.3839	.6051	1.071	2.790	1.2043	69°00′
10′	.3694	.3611	.9325	.3872	2.5826	1.072	2.769	1.2014	50′
20′	.3723	.3638	.9315	.3906	2.5605	1.074	2.749	1.1985	40′
30′	.3752	.3665	.9304	.3939	2.5386	1.075	2.729	1.1956	30′
40′	.3782	.3692	.9293	.3973	2.5172	1.076	2.709	1.1926	20′
50′	.3811	.3719	.9283	.4006	2.4960	1.077	2.689	1.1897	10′
22°00′	.3840	.3746	.9272	.4040	2.4751	1.079	2.669	1.1868	68°00′
10′	.3869	.3773	.9261	.4074	2.4545	1.080	2.650	1.1839	50′
20′	.3898	.3800	.9250	.4108	2.4342	1.081	2.632	1.1810	40′
30′	.3927	.3827	.9239	.4142	2.4142	1.082	2.613	1.1781	30′
40′	.3956	.3854	.9228	.4176	2.3945	1.084	2.595	1.1752	20′
50′	.3985	.3881	.9216	.4210	2.3750	1.085	2.577	1.1723	10′
23°00′	.4014	.3907	.9205	.4245	2.3559	1.086	2.559	1.1694	67°00′
10′	.4043	.3934	.9194	.4279	2.3369	1.088	2.542	1.1665	50′
20′	.4072	.3961	.9182	.4314	2.3183	1.089	2.525	1.1636	40′
30′	.4102	.3987	.9171	.4348	2.2998	1.090	2.508	1.1606	30′
40′	.4131	.4014	.9159	.4383	2.2817	1.092	2.491	1.1577	20′
50′	.4160	.4041	.9147	.4417	2.2637	1.093	2.475	1.1548	10′
24°00′	.4189	.4067	.9135	.4452	2.2460	1.095	2.459	1.1519	66°00′
10′	.4218	.4094	.9124	.4487	2.2286	1.096	2.443	1.1490	50′
20′	.4247	.4120	.9112	.4522	2.2113	1.097	2.427	1.1461	40′
30′	.4276	.4147	.9100	.4557	2.1943	1.099	2.411	1.1432	30′
40′	.4305	.4173	.9088	.4592	2.1775	1.100	2.396	1.1403	20′
50′	.4334	.4200	.9075	.4628	2.1609	1.102	2.381	1.1374	10′
25°00′	.4363	.4226	.9063	.4663	2.1445	1.103	2.366	1.1345	65°00′
10′	.4392	.4253	.9051	.4699	2.1283	1.105	2.352	1.1316	50′
20′	.4422	.4279	.9038	.4734	2.1123	1.106	2.337	1.1286	40′
30′	.4451	.4305	.9026	.4770	2.0965	1.108	2.323	1.1257	30′
40′	.4480	.4331	.9013	.4806	2.0809	1.109	2.309	1.1228	20′
50′	.4509	.4358	.9001	.4841	2.0655	1.111	2.295	1.1199	10′
26°00′	.4538	.4384	.8988	.4877	2.0503	1.113	2.281	1.1170	64°00′
10′	.4567	.4410	.8975	.4913	2.0353	1.114	2.268	1.1141	50′
20′	.4596	.4436	.8962	.4950	2.0204	1.116	2.254	1.1112	40′
30′	.4625	.4462	.8949	.4986	2.0057	1.117	2.241	1.1083	30′
40′	.4654	.4488	.8936	.5022	1.9912	1.119	2.228	1.1054	20′
50′	.4683	.4514	.8923	.5059	1.9768	1.121	2.215	1.1025	10′
27°00′	.4712	.4540	.8910	.5095	1.9626	1.122	2.203	1.0996	63°00′
		Cos θ	Sin θ	Cot θ	Tan θ	Csc θ	Sec θ	θ Rad.	θ Deg.

Table of Values of the Trigonometric Functions

θ Deg.	θ Rad.	Sin θ	Cos θ	Tan θ	Cot θ	Sec θ	Csc θ		
27° 00′	.4712	.4540	.8910	.5095	1.9626	1.122	2.203	1.0996	63° 00′
10′	.4741	.4566	.8897	.5132	1.9486	1.124	2.190	1.0966	50′
20′	.4771	.4592	.8884	.5169	1.9347	1.126	2.178	1.0937	40′
30′	.4800	.4617	.8870	.5206	1.9210	1.127	2.166	1.0908	30′
40′	.4829	.4643	.8857	.5243	1.9074	1.129	2.154	1.0879	20′
50′	.4858	.4669	.8843	.5280	1.8940	1.131	2.142	1.0850	10′
28° 00′	.4887	.4695	.8829	.5317	1.8807	1.133	2.130	1.0821	62° 00′
10′	.4916	.4720	.8816	.5354	1.8676	1.134	2.118	1.0792	50′
20′	.4945	.4746	.8802	.5392	1.8546	1.136	2.107	1.0763	40′
30′	.4974	.4772	.8788	.5430	1.8418	1.138	2.096	1.0734	30′
40′	.5003	.4797	.8774	.5467	1.8291	1.140	2.085	1.0705	20′
50′	.5032	.4823	.8760	.5505	1.8165	1.142	2.074	1.0676	10′
29° 00′	.5061	.4848	.8746	.5543	1.8040	1.143	2.063	1.0647	61° 00′
10′	.5091	.4874	.8732	.5581	1.7917	1.145	2.052	1.0617	50′
20′	.5120	.4899	.8718	.5619	1.7796	1.147	2.041	1.0588	40′
30′	.5149	.4924	.8704	.5658	1.7675	1.149	2.031	1.0559	30′
40′	.5178	.4950	.8689	.5696	1.7556	1.151	2.020	1.0530	20′
50′	.5207	.4975	.8675	.5735	1.7437	1.153	2.010	1.0501	10′
30° 00′	.5236	.5000	.8660	.5774	1.7321	1.155	2.000	1.0472	60° 00′
10′	.5265	.5025	.8646	.5812	1.7205	1.157	1.990	1.0443	50′
20′	.5294	.5050	.8631	.5851	1.7090	1.159	1.980	1.0414	40′
30′	.5323	.5075	.8616	.5890	1.6977	1.161	1.970	1.0385	30′
40′	.5352	.5100	.8601	.5930	1.6864	1.163	1.961	1.0356	20′
50′	.5381	.5125	.8587	.5969	1.6753	1.165	1.951	1.0327	10′
31° 00′	.5411	.5150	.8572	.6009	1.6643	1.167	1.942	1.0297	59° 00′
10′	.5440	.5175	.8557	.6048	1.6534	1.169	1.932	1.0268	50′
20′	.5469	.5200	.8542	.6088	1.6426	1.171	1.923	1.0239	40′
30′	.5498	.5225	.8526	.6128	1.6319	1.173	1.914	1.0210	30′
40′	.5527	.5250	.8511	.6168	1.6212	1.175	1.905	1.0181	20′
50′	.5556	.5275	.8496	.6208	1.6107	1.177	1.896	1.0152	10′
32° 00′	.5585	.5299	.8480	.6249	1.6003	1.179	1.887	1.0123	58° 00′
10′	.5614	.5324	.8465	.6289	1.5900	1.181	1.878	1.0094	50′
20′	.5643	.5348	.8450	.6330	1.5798	1.184	1.870	1.0065	40′
30′	.5672	.5373	.8434	.6371	1.5697	1.186	1.861	1.0036	30′
40′	.5701	.5398	.8418	.6412	1.5597	1.188	1.853	1.0007	20′
50′	.5730	.5422	.8403	.6453	1.5497	1.190	1.844	.9977	10′
33° 00′	.5760	.5446	.8387	.6494	1.5399	1.192	1.836	.9948	57° 00′
10′	.5789	.5471	.8371	.6536	1.5301	1.195	1.828	.9919	50′
20′	.5818	.5495	.8355	.6577	1.5204	1.197	1.820	.9890	40′
30′	.5847	.5519	.8339	.6619	1.5108	1.199	1.812	.9861	30′
40′	.5876	.5544	.8323	.6661	1.5013	1.202	1.804	.9832	20′
50′	.5905	.5568	.8307	.6703	1.4919	1.204	1.796	.9803	10′
34° 00′	.5934	.5592	.8290	.6745	1.4826	1.206	1.788	.9774	56° 00′
10′	.5963	.5616	.8274	.6787	1.4733	1.209	1.781	.9745	50′
20′	.5992	.5640	.8258	.6830	1.4641	1.211	1.773	.9716	40′
30′	.6021	.5664	.8241	.6873	1.4550	1.213	1.766	.9687	30′
40′	.6050	.5688	.8225	.6916	1.4460	1.216	1.758	.9657	20′
50′	.6080	.5712	.8208	.6959	1.4370	1.218	1.751	.9628	10′
35° 00′	.6109	.5736	.8192	.7002	1.4281	1.221	1.743	.9599	55° 00′
10′	.6138	.5760	.8175	.7046	1.4193	1.223	1.736	.9570	50′
20′	.6167	.5783	.8158	.7089	1.4106	1.226	1.729	.9541	40′
30′	.6196	.5807	.8141	.7133	1.4019	1.228	1.722	.9512	30′
40′	.6225	.5831	.8124	.7177	1.3934	1.231	1.715	.9483	20′
50′	.6254	.5854	.8107	.7221	1.3848	1.233	1.708	.9454	10′
36° 00′	.6283	.5878	.8090	.7265	1.3764	1.236	1.701	.9425	54° 00′
		Cos θ	Sin θ	Cot θ	Tan θ	Csc θ	Sec θ	θ Rad.	θ Deg.

Table of Values of the Trigonometric Functions

θ Deg.	θ Rad.	Sin θ	Cos θ	Tan θ	Cot θ	Sec θ	Csc θ		
36° 00'	.6283	.5878	.8090	.7265	1.3764	1.236	1.701	.9425	54° 00'
10'	.6312	.5901	.8073	.7310	1.3680	1.239	1.695	.9396	50'
20'	.6341	.5925	.8056	.7355	1.3597	1.241	1.688	.9367	40'
30'	.6370	.5948	.8039	.7400	1.3514	1.244	1.681	.9338	30'
40'	.6400	.5972	.8021	.7445	1.3432	1.247	1.675	.9308	20'
50'	.6429	.5995	.8004	.7490	1.3351	1.249	1.668	.9279	10'
37° 00'	.6458	.6018	.7986	.7536	1.3270	1.252	1.662	.9250	53° 00'
10'	.6487	.6041	.7969	.7581	1.3190	1.255	1.655	.9221	50'
20'	.6516	.6065	.7951	.7627	1.3111	1.258	1.649	.9192	40'
30'	.6545	.6088	.7934	.7673	1.3032	1.260	1.643	.9163	30'
40'	.6574	.6111	.7916	.7720	1.2954	1.263	1.636	.9134	20'
50'	.6603	.6134	.7898	.7766	1.2876	1.266	1.630	.9105	10'
38° 00'	.6632	.6157	.7880	.7813	1.2799	1.269	1.624	.9076	52° 00'
10'	.6661	.6180	.7862	.7860	1.2723	1.272	1.618	.9047	50'
20'	.6690	.6202	.7844	.7907	1.2647	1.275	1.612	.9018	40'
30'	.6720	.6225	.7826	.7954	1.2572	1.278	1.606	.8988	30'
40'	.6749	.6248	.7808	.8002	1.2497	1.281	1.601	.8959	20'
50'	.6778	.6271	.7790	.8050	1.2423	1.284	1.595	.8930	10'
39° 00'	.6807	.6293	.7771	.8098	1.2349	1.287	1.589	.8901	51° 00'
10'	.6836	.6316	.7753	.8146	1.2276	1.290	1.583	.8872	50'
20'	.6865	.6338	.7735	.8195	1.2203	1.293	1.578	.8843	40'
30'	.6894	.6361	.7716	.8243	1.2131	1.296	1.572	.8814	30'
40'	.6923	.6383	.7698	.8292	1.2059	1.299	1.567	.8785	20'
50'	.6952	.6406	.7679	.8342	1.1988	1.302	1.561	.8756	10'
40° 00'	.6981	.6428	.7660	.8391	1.1918	1.305	1.556	.8727	50° 00'
10'	.7010	.6450	.7642	.8441	1.1847	1.309	1.550	.8698	50'
20'	.7039	.6472	.7623	.8491	1.1778	1.312	1.545	.8668	40'
30'	.7069	.6494	.7604	.8541	1.1708	1.315	1.540	.8639	30'
40'	.7098	.6517	.7585	.8591	1.1640	1.318	1.535	.8610	20'
50'	.7127	.6539	.7566	.8642	1.1571	1.322	1.529	.8581	10'
41° 00'	.7156	.6561	.7547	.8693	1.1504	1.325	1.524	.8552	49° 00'
10'	.7185	.6583	.7528	.8744	1.1436	1.328	1.519	.8523	50'
20'	.7214	.6604	.7509	.8796	1.1369	1.332	1.514	.8494	40'
30'	.7243	.6626	.7490	.8847	1.1303	1.335	1.509	.8465	30'
40'	.7272	.6648	.7470	.8899	1.1237	1.339	1.504	.8436	20'
50'	.7301	.6670	.7451	.8952	1.1171	1.342	1.499	.8407	10'
42° 00'	.7330	.6691	.7431	.9004	1.1106	1.346	1.494	.8378	48° 00'
10'	.7359	.6713	.7412	.9057	1.1041	1.349	1.490	.8348	50'
20'	.7389	.6734	.7392	.9110	1.0977	1.353	1.485	.8319	40'
30'	.7418	.6756	.7373	.9163	1.0913	1.356	1.480	.8290	30'
40'	.7447	.6777	.7353	.9217	1.0850	1.360	1.476	.8261	20'
50'	.7476	.6799	.7333	.9271	1.0786	1.364	1.471	.8232	10'
43° 00'	.7505	.6820	.7314	.9325	1.0724	1.367	1.466	.8203	47° 00'
10'	.7534	.6841	.7294	.9380	1.0661	1.371	1.462	.8174	50'
20'	.7563	.6862	.7274	.9435	1.0599	1.375	1.457	.8145	40'
30'	.7592	.6884	.7254	.9490	1.0538	1.379	1.453	.8116	30'
40'	.7621	.6905	.7234	.9545	1.0477	1.382	1.448	.8087	20'
50'	.7650	.6926	.7214	.9601	1.0416	1.386	1.444	.8058	10'
44° 00'	.7679	.6947	.7193	.9657	1.0355	1.390	1.440	.8029	46° 00'
10'	.7709	.6967	.7173	.9713	1.0295	1.394	1.435	.7999	50'
20'	.7738	.6988	.7153	.9770	1.0235	1.398	1.431	.7970	40'
30'	.7767	.7009	.7133	.9827	1.0176	1.402	1.427	.7941	30'
40'	.7796	.7030	.7112	.9884	1.0117	1.406	1.423	.7912	20'
50'	.7825	.7050	.7092	.9942	1.0058	1.410	1.418	.7883	10'
45° 00'	.7854	.7071	.7071	1.0000	1.0000	1.414	1.414	.7854	45° 00'
		Cos θ	Sin θ	Cot θ	Tan θ	Csc θ	Sec θ	θ Rad.	θ Deg.

Table of Common Logarithms

N	0	1	2	3	4	5	6	7	8	9
1.0	0000	0043	0086	0128	0170	0212	0253	0294	0334	0374
1.1	0414	0453	0492	0531	0569	0607	0645	0682	0719	0755
1.2	0792	0828	0864	0899	0934	0969	1004	1038	1072	1106
1.3	1139	1173	1206	1239	1271	1303	1335	1367	1399	1430
1.4	1461	1492	1523	1553	1584	1614	1644	1673	1703	1732
1.5	1761	1790	1818	1847	1875	1903	1931	1959	1987	2014
1.6	2041	2068	2095	2122	2148	2175	2201	2227	2253	2279
1.7	2304	2330	2355	2380	2405	2430	2455	2480	2504	2529
1.8	2553	2577	2601	2625	2648	2672	2695	2718	2742	2765
1.9	2788	2810	2833	2856	2878	2900	2923	2945	2967	2989
2.0	3010	3032	3054	3075	3096	3118	3139	3160	3181	3201
2.1	3222	3243	3263	3284	3304	3324	3345	3365	3385	3404
2.2	3424	3444	3464	3483	3502	3522	3541	3560	3579	3598
2.3	3617	3636	3655	3674	3692	3711	3729	3747	3766	3784
2.4	3802	3820	3838	3856	3874	3892	3909	3927	3945	3962
2.5	3979	3997	4014	4031	4048	4065	4082	4099	4116	4133
2.6	4150	4166	4183	4200	4216	4232	4249	4265	4281	4298
2.7	4314	4330	4346	4362	4378	4393	4409	4425	4440	4456
2.8	4472	4487	4502	4518	4533	4548	4564	4579	4594	4609
2.9	4624	4639	4654	4669	4683	4698	4713	4728	4742	4757
3.0	4771	4786	4800	4814	4829	4843	4857	4871	4886	4900
3.1	4914	4928	4942	4955	4969	4983	4997	5011	5024	5038
3.2	5051	5065	5079	5092	5105	5119	5132	5145	5159	5172
3.3	5185	5198	5211	5224	5237	5250	5263	5276	5289	5302
3.4	5315	5328	5340	5353	5366	5378	5391	5403	5416	5428
3.5	5441	5453	5465	5478	5490	5502	5514	5527	5539	5551
3.6	5563	5575	5587	5599	5611	5623	5635	5647	5658	5670
3.7	5682	5694	5705	5717	5729	5740	5752	5763	5775	5786
3.8	5798	5809	5821	5832	5843	5855	5866	5877	5888	5899
3.9	5911	5922	5933	5944	5955	5966	5977	5988	5999	6010
4.0	6021	6031	6042	6053	6064	6075	6085	6096	6107	6117
4.1	6128	6138	6149	6160	6170	6180	6191	6201	6212	6222
4.2	6232	6243	6253	6263	6274	6284	6294	6304	6314	6325
4.3	6335	6345	6355	6365	6375	6385	6395	6405	6415	6425
4.4	6435	6444	6454	6464	6474	6484	6493	6503	6513	6522
4.5	6532	6542	6551	6561	6571	6580	6590	6599	6609	6618
4.6	6628	6637	6646	6656	6665	6675	6684	6693	6702	6712
4.7	6721	6730	6739	6749	6758	6767	6776	6785	6794	6803
4.8	6812	6821	6830	6839	6848	6857	6866	6875	6884	6893
4.9	6902	6911	6920	6928	6937	6946	6955	6964	6972	6981
5.0	6990	6998	7007	7016	7024	7033	7042	7050	7059	7067
5.1	7076	7084	7093	7101	7110	7118	7126	7135	7143	7152
5.2	7160	7168	7177	7185	7193	7202	7210	7218	7226	7235
5.3	7243	7251	7259	7267	7275	7284	7292	7300	7308	7316
5.4	7324	7332	7340	7348	7356	7364	7372	7380	7388	7396

Table of Common Logarithms

N	0	1	2	3	4	5	6	7	8	9
5.5	7404	7412	7419	7427	7435	7443	7451	7459	7466	7474
5.6	7482	7490	7497	7505	7513	7520	7528	7536	7543	7551
5.7	7559	7566	7574	7582	7589	7597	7604	7612	7619	7627
5.8	7634	7642	7649	7657	7664	7672	7679	7686	7694	7701
5.9	7709	7716	7723	7731	7738	7745	7752	7760	7767	7774
6.0	7782	7789	7796	7803	7810	7818	7825	7832	7839	7846
6.1	7853	7860	7868	7875	7882	7889	7896	7903	7910	7917
6.2	7924	7931	7938	7945	7952	7959	7966	7973	7980	7987
6.3	7993	8000	8007	8014	8021	8028	8035	8041	8048	8055
6.4	8062	8069	8075	8082	8089	8096	8102	8109	8116	8122
6.5	8129	8136	8142	8149	8156	8162	8169	8176	8182	8189
6.6	8195	8202	8209	8215	8222	8228	8235	8241	8248	8254
6.7	8261	8267	8274	8280	8287	8293	8299	8306	8312	8319
6.8	8325	8331	8338	8344	8351	8357	8363	8370	8376	8382
6.9	8388	8395	8401	8407	8414	8420	8426	8432	8439	8445
7.0	8451	8457	8463	8470	8476	8482	8488	8494	8500	8506
7.1	8513	8519	8525	8531	8537	8543	8549	8555	8561	8567
7.2	8573	8579	8585	8591	8597	8603	8609	8615	8621	8627
7.3	8633	8639	8645	8651	8657	8663	8669	8675	8681	8686
7.4	8692	8698	8704	8710	8716	8722	8727	8733	8739	8745
7.5	8751	8756	8762	8768	8774	8779	8785	8791	8797	8802
7.6	8808	8814	8820	8825	8831	8837	8842	8848	8854	8859
7.7	8865	8871	8876	8882	8887	8893	8899	8904	8910	8915
7.8	8921	8927	8932	8938	8943	8949	8954	8960	8965	8971
7.9	8976	8982	8987	8993	8998	9004	9009	9015	9020	9025
8.0	9031	9036	9042	9047	9053	9058	9063	9069	9074	9079
8.1	9085	9090	9096	9101	9106	9112	9117	9122	9128	9133
8.2	9138	9143	9149	9154	9159	9165	9170	9175	9180	9186
8.3	9191	9196	9201	9206	9212	9217	9222	9227	9232	9238
8.4	9243	9248	9253	9258	9263	9269	9274	9279	9284	9289
8.5	9294	9299	9304	9309	9315	9320	9325	9330	9335	9340
8.6	9345	9350	9355	9360	9365	9370	9375	9380	9385	9390
8.7	9395	9400	9405	9410	9415	9420	9425	9430	9435	9440
8.8	9445	9450	9455	9460	9465	9469	9474	9479	9484	9489
8.9	9494	9499	9504	9509	9513	9518	9523	9528	9533	9538
9.0	9542	9547	9552	9557	9562	9566	9571	9576	9581	9586
9.1	9590	9595	9600	9605	9609	9614	9619	9624	9628	9633
9.2	9638	9643	9647	9652	9657	9661	9666	9671	9675	9680
9.3	9685	9689	9694	9699	9703	9708	9713	9717	9722	9727
9.4	9731	9736	9741	9745	9750	9754	9759	9763	9768	9773
9.5	9777	9782	9786	9791	9795	9800	9805	9809	9814	9818
9.6	9823	9827	9832	9836	9841	9845	9850	9854	9859	9863
9.7	9868	9872	9877	9881	9886	9890	9894	9899	9903	9908
9.8	9912	9917	9921	9926	9930	9934	9939	9943	9948	9952
9.9	9956	9961	9965	9969	9974	9978	9983	9987	9991	9996

Table of Natural Logarithms

N	0	1	2	3	4	5	6	7	8	9
1.0	0.0000	0.0100	0.0198	0.0296	0.0392	0.0488	0.0583	0.0677	0.0770	0.0862
1.1	0.0953	0.1044	0.1133	0.1222	0.1310	0.1398	0.1484	0.1570	0.1655	0.1740
1.2	0.1823	0.1906	0.1989	0.2070	0.2151	0.2231	0.2311	0.2390	0.2469	0.2546
1.3	0.2624	0.2700	0.2776	0.2852	0.2927	0.3001	0.3075	0.3148	0.3221	0.3293
1.4	0.3365	0.3436	0.3507	0.3577	0.3646	0.3716	0.3784	0.3853	0.3920	0.3988
1.5	0.4055	0.4121	0.4187	0.4253	0.4318	0.4383	0.4447	0.4511	0.4574	0.4637
1.6	0.4700	0.4762	0.4824	0.4886	0.4947	0.5008	0.5068	0.5128	0.5188	0.5247
1.7	0.5306	0.5365	0.5423	0.5481	0.5539	0.5596	0.5653	0.5710	0.5766	0.5822
1.8	0.5878	0.5933	0.5988	0.6043	0.6098	0.6152	0.6206	0.6259	0.6313	0.6366
1.9	0.6419	0.6471	0.6523	0.6575	0.6627	0.6678	0.6729	0.6780	0.6831	0.6881
2.0	0.6931	0.6981	0.7031	0.7080	0.7129	0.7178	0.7227	0.7275	0.7324	0.7372
2.1	0.7419	0.7467	0.7514	0.7561	0.7608	0.7655	0.7701	0.7747	0.7793	0.7839
2.2	0.7885	0.7930	0.7975	0.8020	0.8065	0.8109	0.8154	0.8198	0.8242	0.8286
2.3	0.8329	0.8372	0.8416	0.8459	0.8502	0.8544	0.8587	0.8629	0.8671	0.8713
2.4	0.8755	0.8796	0.8838	0.8879	0.8920	0.8961	0.9002	0.9042	0.9083	0.9123
2.5	0.9163	0.9203	0.9243	0.9282	0.9322	0.9361	0.9400	0.9439	0.9478	0.9517
2.6	0.9555	0.9594	0.9632	0.9670	0.9708	0.9746	0.9783	0.9821	0.9858	0.9895
2.7	0.9933	0.9969	1.0006	1.0043	1.0080	1.0116	1.0152	1.0188	1.0225	1.0260
2.8	1.0296	1.0332	1.0367	1.0403	1.0438	1.0473	1.0508	1.0543	1.0578	1.0613
2.9	1.0647	1.0682	1.0716	1.0750	1.0784	1.0818	1.0852	1.0886	1.0919	1.0953
3.0	1.0986	1.1019	1.1053	1.1086	1.1119	1.1151	1.1184	1.1217	1.1249	1.1282
3.1	1.1314	1.1346	1.1378	1.1410	1.1442	1.1474	1.1506	1.1537	1.1569	1.1600
3.2	1.1632	1.1663	1.1694	1.1725	1.1756	1.1787	1.1817	1.1848	1.1878	1.1909
3.3	1.1939	1.1969	1.2000	1.2030	1.2060	1.2090	1.2119	1.2149	1.2179	1.2208
3.4	1.2238	1.2267	1.2296	1.2326	1.2355	1.2384	1.2413	1.2442	1.2470	1.2499
3.5	1.2528	1.2556	1.2585	1.2613	1.2641	1.2669	1.2698	1.2726	1.2754	1.2782
3.6	1.2809	1.2837	1.2865	1.2892	1.2920	1.2947	1.2975	1.3002	1.3029	1.3056
3.7	1.3083	1.3110	1.3137	1.3164	1.3191	1.3318	1.3244	1.3271	1.3297	1.3324
3.8	1.3350	1.3376	1.3403	1.3429	1.3455	1.3481	1.3507	1.3533	1.3558	1.3584
3.9	1.3610	1.3635	1.3661	1.3686	1.3712	1.3737	1.3762	1.3788	1.3813	1.3838
4.0	1.3863	1.3888	1.3913	1.3938	1.3962	1.3987	1.4012	1.4036	1.4061	1.4085
4.1	1.4110	1.4134	1.4159	1.4183	1.4207	1.4231	1.4255	1.4279	1.4303	1.4327
4.2	1.4351	1.4375	1.4398	1.4422	1.4446	1.4469	1.4493	1.4516	1.4540	1.4563
4.3	1.4586	1.4609	1.4633	1.4656	1.4679	1.4702	1.4725	1.4748	1.4770	1.4793
4.4	1.4816	1.4839	1.4861	1.4884	1.4907	1.4929	1.4951	1.4974	1.4996	1.5019
4.5	1.5041	1.5063	1.5085	1.5107	1.5129	1.5151	1.5173	1.5195	1.5217	1.5239
4.6	1.5261	1.5282	1.5304	1.5326	1.5347	1.5369	1.5390	1.5412	1.5433	1.5454
4.7	1.5476	1.5497	1.5518	1.5539	1.5560	1.5581	1.5602	1.5623	1.5644	1.5665
4.8	1.5686	1.5707	1.5728	1.5748	1.5769	1.5790	1.5810	1.5831	1.5851	1.5872
4.9	1.5892	1.5913	1.5933	1.5953	1.5974	1.5994	1.6014	1.6034	1.6054	1.6074
5.0	1.6094	1.6114	1.6134	1.6154	1.6174	1.6194	1.6214	1.6233	1.6253	1.6273
5.1	1.6292	1.6312	1.6332	1.6351	1.6371	1.6390	1.6409	1.6429	1.6448	1.6467
5.2	1.6487	1.6506	1.6525	1.6544	1.6563	1.6582	1.6601	1.6620	1.6639	1.6658
5.3	1.6677	1.6696	1.6715	1.6734	1.6752	1.6771	1.6790	1.6808	1.6827	1.6845
5.4	1.6864	1.6882	1.6901	1.6919	1.6938	1.6956	1.6974	1.6993	1.7011	1.7029

Table of Natural Logarithms

N	0	1	2	3	4	5	6	7	8	9
5.5	1.7047	1.7066	1.7084	1.7102	1.7120	1.7138	1.7156	1.7174	1.7192	1.7210
5.6	1.7228	1.7246	1.7263	1.7281	1.7299	1.7317	1.7334	1.7352	1.7370	1.7387
5.7	1.7405	1.7422	1.7440	1.7457	1.7475	1.7492	1.7509	1.7527	1.7544	1.7561
5.8	1.7579	1.7596	1.7613	1.7630	1.7647	1.7664	1.7681	1.7699	1.7716	1.7733
5.9	1.7750	1.7766	1.7783	1.7800	1.7817	1.7843	1.7851	1.7867	1.7884	1.7901
6.0	1.7918	1.7934	1.7951	1.7967	1.7984	1.8001	1.8017	1.8034	1.8050	1.8066
6.1	1.8083	1.8099	1.8116	1.8132	1.8148	1.8165	1.8181	1.8197	1.8213	1.8229
6.2	1.8245	1.8262	1.8278	1.8294	1.8310	1.8326	1.8342	1.8358	1.8374	1.8390
6.3	1.8405	1.8421	1.8437	1.8453	1.8469	1.8485	1.8500	1.8516	1.8532	1.8547
6.4	1.8563	1.8579	1.8594	1.8610	1.8625	1.8641	1.8656	1.8672	1.8687	1.8703
6.5	1.8718	1.8733	1.8749	1.8764	1.8779	1.8795	1.8810	1.8825	1.8840	1.8856
6.6	1.8871	1.8886	1.8901	1.8916	1.8931	1.8946	1.8961	1.8976	1.8991	1.9006
6.7	1.9021	1.9036	1.9051	1.9066	1.9081	1.9095	1.9110	1.9125	1.9140	1.9155
6.8	1.9169	1.9184	1.9199	1.9213	1.9228	1.9242	1.9257	1.9272	1.9286	1.9301
6.9	1.9315	1.9330	1.9344	1.9359	1.9373	1.9387	1.9402	1.9416	1.9430	1.9445
7.0	1.9459	1.9473	1.9488	1.9502	1.9516	1.9530	1.9544	1.9559	1.9573	1.9587
7.1	1.9601	1.9615	1.9629	1.9643	1.9657	1.9671	1.9685	1.9699	1.9713	1.9727
7.2	1.9741	1.9755	1.9769	1.9782	1.9796	1.9810	1.9824	1.9838	1.9851	1.9865
7.3	1.9879	1.9892	1.9906	1.9920	1.9933	1.9947	1.9961	1.9974	1.9988	2.0001
7.4	2.0015	2.0028	2.0042	2.0055	2.0069	2.0082	2.0096	2.0109	2.0122	2.0136
7.5	2.0149	2.0162	2.0176	2.0189	2.0202	2.0215	2.0229	2.0242	2.0255	2.0268
7.6	2.0281	2.0295	2.0308	2.0321	2.0334	2.0347	2.0360	2.0373	2.0386	2.0399
7.7	2.0412	2.0425	2.0438	2.0451	2.0464	2.0477	2.0490	2.0503	2.0516	2.0528
7.8	2.0541	2.0554	2.0567	2.0580	2.0592	2.0605	2.0618	2.0631	2.0643	2.0656
7.9	2.0669	2.0681	2.0694	2.0707	2.0719	2.0732	2.0744	2.0757	2.0769	2.0782
8.0	2.0794	2.0807	2.0819	2.0832	2.0844	2.0857	2.0869	2.0882	2.0894	2.0906
8.1	2.0919	2.0931	2.0943	2.0956	2.0968	2.0980	2.0992	2.1005	2.1017	2.1029
8.2	2.1041	2.1054	2.1066	2.1078	2.1090	2.1102	2.1114	2.1126	2.1138	2.1150
8.3	2.1163	2.1175	2.1187	2.1199	2.1211	2.1223	2.1235	2.1247	2.1258	2.1270
8.4	2.1282	2.1294	2.1306	2.1318	2.1330	2.1342	2.1353	2.1365	2.1377	2.1389
8.5	2.1401	2.1412	2.1424	2.1436	2.1448	2.1459	2.1471	2.1483	2.1494	2.1506
8.6	2.1518	2.1529	2.1541	2.1552	2.1564	2.1576	2.1587	2.1599	2.1610	2.1622
8.7	2.1633	2.1645	2.1656	2.1668	2.1679	2.1691	2.1702	2.1713	2.1725	2.1736
8.8	2.1748	2.1759	2.1770	2.1782	2.1793	2.1804	2.1815	2.1827	2.1838	2.1849
8.9	2.1861	2.1872	2.1883	2.1894	2.1905	2.1917	2.1928	2.1939	2.1950	2.1961
9.0	2.1972	2.1983	2.1994	2.2006	2.2017	2.2028	2.2039	2.2050	2.2061	2.2072
9.1	2.2083	2.2094	2.2105	2.2116	2.2127	2.2138	2.2148	2.2159	2.2170	2.2181
9.2	2.2192	2.2203	2.2214	2.2225	2.2235	2.2246	2.2257	2.2268	2.2279	2.2289
9.3	2.2300	2.2311	2.2322	2.2332	2.2343	2.2354	2.2364	2.2375	2.2386	2.2396
9.4	2.2407	2.2418	2.2428	2.2439	2.2450	2.2460	2.2471	2.2481	2.2492	2.2502
9.5	2.2513	2.2523	2.2534	2.2544	2.2555	2.2565	2.2576	2.2586	2.2597	2.2607
9.6	2.2618	2.2628	2.2638	2.2649	2.2659	2.2670	2.2680	2.2690	2.2701	2.2711
9.7	2.2721	2.2732	2.2742	2.2752	2.2762	2.2773	2.2783	2.2793	2.2803	2.2814
9.8	2.2824	2.2834	2.2844	2.2854	2.2865	2.2875	2.2885	2.2895	2.2905	2.2915
9.9	2.2925	2.2935	2.2946	2.2956	2.2966	2.2976	2.2986	2.2996	2.3006	2.3016
10.0	2.3026	2.3036	2.3046	2.3056	2.3066	2.3076	2.3086	2.3096	2.3106	2.3116

Table of Values of the Logarithms of Trigonometric Functions

θ Deg.	θ Rad.	Log Sin θ	Log Cos θ	Log Tan θ	Log Cot θ		
0° 00'	.0000	—	10.0000	—	—	1.5708	90° 00'
10'	.0029	7.4637	10.0000	7.4637	12.5363	1.5679	50'
20'	.0058	7.7648	10.0000	7.7648	12.2352	1.5650	40'
30'	.0087	7.9408	10.0000	7.9409	12.0591	1.5621	30'
40'	.0116	8.0658	10.0000	8.0658	11.9342	1.5592	20'
50'	.0145	8.1627	10.0000	8.1627	11.8373	1.5563	10'
1° 00'	.0175	8.2419	9.9999	8.2419	11.7581	1.5533	89° 00'
10'	.0204	8.3088	9.9999	8.3089	11.6911	1.5504	50'
20'	.0233	8.3668	9.9999	8.3669	11.6331	1.5475	40'
30'	.0262	8.4179	9.9999	8.4181	11.5819	1.5446	30'
40'	.0291	8.4637	9.9998	8.4638	11.5362	1.5417	20'
50'	.0320	8.5050	9.9998	8.5053	11.4947	1.5388	10'
2° 00'	.0349	8.5428	9.9997	8.5431	11.4569	1.5359	88° 00'
10'	.0378	8.5776	9.9997	8.5779	11.4221	1.5330	50'
20'	.0407	8.6097	9.9996	8.6101	11.3899	1.5301	40'
30'	.0436	8.6397	9.9996	8.6401	11.3599	1.5272	30'
40'	.0465	8.6677	9.9995	8.6682	11.3318	1.5243	20'
50'	.0495	8.6940	9.9995	8.6945	11.3055	1.5213	10'
3° 00'	.0524	8.7188	9.9994	8.7194	11.2806	1.5184	87° 00'
10'	.0553	8.7423	9.9993	8.7429	11.2571	1.5155	50'
20'	.0582	8.7645	9.9993	8.7652	11.2348	1.5126	40'
30'	.0611	8.7857	9.9992	8.7865	11.2135	1.5097	30'
40'	.0640	8.8059	9.9991	8.8067	11.1933	1.5068	20'
50'	.0669	8.8251	9.9990	8.8261	11.1739	1.5039	10'
4° 00'	.0698	8.8436	9.9989	8.8446	11.1554	1.5010	86° 00'
10'	.0727	8.8613	9.9989	8.8624	11.1376	1.4981	50'
20'	.0756	8.8783	9.9988	8.8795	11.1205	1.4952	40'
30'	.0785	8.8946	9.9987	8.8960	11.1040	1.4923	30'
40'	.0814	8.9104	9.9986	8.9118	11.0882	1.4893	20'
50'	.0844	8.9256	9.9985	8.9272	11.0728	1.4864	10'
5° 00'	.0873	8.9403	9.9983	8.9420	11.0580	1.4835	85° 00'
10'	.0902	8.9545	9.9982	8.9563	11.0437	1.4806	50'
20'	.0931	8.9682	9.9981	8.9701	11.0299	1.4777	40'
30'	.0960	8.9816	9.9980	8.9836	11.0164	1.4748	30'
40'	.0989	8.9945	9.9979	8.9966	11.0034	1.4719	20'
50'	.1018	9.0070	9.9977	9.0093	10.9907	1.4690	10'
6° 00'	.1047	9.0192	9.9976	9.0216	10.9784	1.4661	84° 00'
10'	.1076	9.0311	9.9975	9.0336	10.9664	1.4632	50'
20'	.1105	9.0426	9.9973	9.0453	10.9547	1.4603	40'
30'	.1134	9.0539	9.9972	9.0567	10.9433	1.4573	30'
40'	.1164	9.0648	9.9971	9.0678	10.9322	1.4544	20'
50'	.1193	9.0755	9.9969	9.0786	10.9214	1.4515	10'
7° 00'	.1222	9.0859	9.9968	9.0891	10.9109	1.4486	83° 00'
10'	.1251	9.0961	9.9966	9.0995	10.9005	1.4457	50'
20'	.1280	9.1060	9.9964	9.1096	10.8904	1.4428	40'
30'	.1309	9.1157	9.9963	9.1194	10.8806	1.4399	30'
40'	.1338	9.1252	9.9961	9.1291	10.8709	1.4370	20'
50'	.1367	9.1345	9.9959	9.1385	10.8615	1.4341	10'
8° 00'	.1396	9.1436	9.9958	9.1478	10.8522	1.4312	82° 00'
10'	.1425	9.1525	9.9956	9.1569	10.8431	1.4283	50'
20'	.1454	9.1612	9.9954	9.1658	10.8342	1.4254	40'
30'	.1484	9.1697	9.9952	9.1745	10.8255	1.4224	30'
40'	.1513	9.1781	9.9950	9.1831	10.8169	1.4195	20'
50'	.1542	9.1863	9.9948	9.1915	10.8085	1.4166	10'
9° 00'	.1571	9.1943	9.9946	9.1997	10.8003	1.4137	81° 00'
		Log Cos θ	Log Sin θ	Log Cot θ	Log Tan θ	θ Rad.	θ Deg.

The tables give the logarithms increased by 10. In each case, 10 should be subtracted.

701

Table of Values of the Logarithms of Trigonometric Functions

θ Deg.	θ Rad.	Log Sin θ	Log Cos θ	Log Tan θ	Log Cot θ		
9° 00'	.1571	9.1943	9.9946	9.1997	10.8003	1.4137	81° 00'
10'	.1600	9.2022	9.9944	9.2078	10.7922	1.4108	50'
20'	.1629	9.2100	9.9942	9.2158	10.7842	1.4079	40'
30'	.1658	9.2176	9.9940	9.2236	10.7764	1.4050	30'
40'	.1687	9.2251	9.9938	9.2313	10.7687	1.4021	20'
50'	.1716	9.2324	9.9936	9.2389	10.7611	1.3992	10'
10° 00'	.1745	9.2397	9.9934	9.2463	10.7537	1.3963	80° 00'
10'	.1774	9.2468	9.9931	9.2536	10.7464	1.3934	50'
20'	.1804	9.2538	9.9929	9.2609	10.7391	1.3904	40'
30'	.1833	9.2606	9.9927	9.2680	10.7320	1.3875	30'
40'	.1862	9.2674	9.9924	9.2750	10.7250	1.3846	20'
50'	.1891	9.2740	9.9922	9.2819	10.7181	1.3817	10'
11° 00'	.1920	9.2806	9.9919	9.2887	10.7113	1.3788	79° 00'
10'	.1949	9.2870	9.9917	9.2953	10.7047	1.3759	50'
20'	.1978	9.2934	9.9914	9.3020	10.6980	1.3730	40'
30'	.2007	9.2997	9.9912	9.3085	10.6915	1.3701	30'
40'	.2036	9.3058	9.9909	9.3149	10.6851	1.3672	20'
50'	.2065	9.3119	9.9907	9.3212	10.6788	1.3643	10'
12° 00'	.2094	9.3179	9.9904	9.3275	10.6725	1.3614	78° 00'
10'	.2123	9.3238	9.9901	9.3336	10.6664	1.3584	50'
20'	.2153	9.3296	9.9899	9.3397	10.6603	1.3555	40'
30'	.2182	9.3353	9.9896	9.3458	10.6542	1.3526	30'
40'	.2211	9.3410	9.9893	9.3517	10.6483	1.3497	20'
50'	.2240	9.3466	9.9890	9.3576	10.6424	1.3468	10'
13° 00'	.2269	9.3521	9.9887	9.3634	10.6366	1.3439	77° 00'
10'	.2298	9.3575	9.9884	9.3691	10.6309	1.3410	50'
20'	.2327	9.3629	9.9881	9.3748	10.6252	1.3381	40'
30'	.2356	9.3682	9.9878	9.3804	10.6196	1.3352	30'
40'	.2385	9.3734	9.9875	9.3859	10.6141	1.3323	20'
50'	.2414	9.3786	9.9872	9.3914	10.6086	1.3294	10'
14° 00'	.2443	9.3837	9.9869	9.3968	10.6032	1.3265	76° 00'
10'	.2473	9.3887	9.9866	9.4021	10.5979	1.3235	50'
20'	.2502	9.3937	9.9863	9.4074	10.5926	1.3206	40'
30'	.2531	9.3986	9.9859	9.4127	10.5873	1.3177	30'
40'	.2560	9.4035	9.9856	9.4178	10.5822	1.3148	20'
50'	.2589	9.4083	9.9853	9.4230	10.5770	1.3119	10'
15° 00'	.2618	9.4160	9.9849	9.4281	10.5719	1.3090	75° 00'
10'	.2647	9.4177	9.9846	9.4331	10.5669	1.3061	50'
20'	.2676	9.4223	9.9843	9.4381	10.5619	1.3032	40'
30'	.2705	9.4269	9.9839	9.4430	10.5570	1.3003	30'
40'	.2734	9.4314	9.9836	9.4479	10.5521	1.2974	20'
50'	.2763	9.4359	9.9832	9.4527	10.5473	1.2945	10'
16° 00'	.2793	9.4403	9.9828	9.4575	10.5425	1.2915	74° 00'
10'	.2822	9.4447	9.9825	9.4622	10.5378	1.2886	50'
20'	.2851	9.4491	9.9821	9.4669	10.5331	1.2857	40'
30'	.2880	9.4533	9.9817	9.4716	10.5284	1.2828	30'
40'	.2909	9.4576	9.9814	9.4762	10.5238	1.2799	20'
50'	.2938	9.4618	9.9810	9.4808	10.5192	1.2770	10'
17° 00'	.2967	9.4659	9.9806	9.4853	10.5147	1.2741	73° 00'
10'	.2996	9.4700	9.9802	9.4898	10.5102	1.2712	50'
20'	.3025	9.4741	9.9798	9.4943	10.5057	1.2683	40'
30'	.3054	9.4781	9.9794	9.4987	10.5013	1.2654	30'
40'	.3083	9.4821	9.9790	9.5031	10.4969	1.2625	20'
50'	.3113	9.4861	9.9786	9.5075	10.4925	1.2595	10'
18° 00'	.3142	9.4900	9.9782	9.5118	10.4882	1.2566	72° 00'
		Log Cos θ	Log Sin θ	Log Cot θ	Log Tan θ	θ Rad.	θ Deg.

Table of Values of the Logarithms of Trigonometric Functions

θ Deg.	θ Rad.	Log Sin θ	Log Cos θ	Log Tan θ	Log Cot θ		
18° 00′	.3142	9.4900	9.9782	9.5118	10.4882	1.2566	**72° 00′**
10′	.3171	9.4939	9.9778	9.5161	10.4839	1.2537	50′
20′	.3200	9.4977	9.9774	9.5203	10.4797	1.2508	40′
30′	.3229	9.5015	9.9770	9.5245	10.4755	1.2479	30′
40′	.3258	9.5052	9.9765	9.5287	10.4713	1.2450	20′
50′	.3287	9.5090	9.9761	9.5329	10.4671	1.2421	10′
19° 00′	.3316	9.5126	9.9757	9.5370	10.4630	1.2392	**71° 00′**
10′	.3345	9.5163	9.9752	9.5411	10.4589	1.2363	50′
20′	.3374	9.5199	9.9748	9.5451	10.4549	1.2334	40′
30′	.3403	9.5235	9.9743	9.5491	10.4509	1.2305	30′
40′	.3432	9.5270	9.9739	9.5531	10.4469	1.2275	20′
50′	.3462	9.5306	9.9734	9.5571	10.4429	1.2246	10′
20° 00′	.3491	9.5341	9.9730	9.5611	10.4389	1.2217	**70° 00′**
10′	.3520	9.5375	9.9725	9.5650	10.4350	1.2188	50′
20′	.3549	9.5409	9.9721	9.5689	10.4311	1.2159	40′
30′	.3578	9.5443	9.9716	9.5727	10.4273	1.2130	30′
40′	.3607	9.5477	9.9711	9.5766	10.4234	1.2101	20′
50′	.3636	9.5510	9.9706	9.5804	10.4196	1.2072	10′
21° 00′	.3665	9.5543	9.9702	9.5842	10.4158	1.2043	**69° 00′**
10′	.3694	9.5576	9.9697	9.5879	10.4121	1.2014	50′
20′	.3723	9.5609	9.9692	9.5917	10.4083	1.1985	40′
30′	.3752	9.5641	9.9687	9.5954	10.4046	1.1956	30′
40′	.3782	9.5673	9.9682	9.5991	10.4009	1.1926	20′
50′	.3811	9.5704	9.9677	9.6028	10.3972	1.1897	10′
22° 00′	.3840	9.5736	9.9672	9.6064	10.3936	1.1868	**68° 00′**
10′	.3869	9.5767	9.9667	9.6100	10.3900	1.1839	50′
20′	.3898	9.5798	9.9661	9.6136	10.3864	1.1810	40′
30′	.3927	9.5828	9.9656	9.6172	10.3828	1.1781	30′
40′	.3956	9.5859	9.9651	9.6208	10.3792	1.1752	20′
50′	.3985	9.5889	9.9646	9.6243	10.3757	1.1723	10′
23° 00′	.4014	9.5919	9.9640	9.6279	10.3721	1.1694	**67° 00′**
10′	.4043	9.5948	9.9635	9.6314	10.3686	1.1665	50′
20′	.4072	9.5978	9.9629	9.6348	10.3652	1.1636	40′
30′	.4102	9.6007	9.9624	9.6383	10.3617	1.1606	30′
40′	.4131	9.6036	9.9618	9.6417	10.3583	1.1577	20′
50′	.4160	9.6065	9.9613	9.6452	10.3548	1.1548	10′
24° 00′	.4189	9.6093	9.9607	9.6486	10.3514	1.1519	**66° 00′**
10′	.4218	9.6121	9.9602	9.6520	10.3480	1.1490	50′
20′	.4247	9.6149	9.9596	9.6553	10.3447	1.1461	40′
30′	.4276	9.6177	9.9590	9.6587	10.3413	1.1432	30′
40′	.4305	9.6205	9.9584	9.6620	10.3380	1.1403	20′
50′	.4334	9.6232	9.9579	9.6654	10.3346	1.1374	10′
25° 00′	.4363	9.6259	9.9573	9.6687	10.3313	1.1345	**65° 00′**
10′	.4392	9.6286	9.9567	9.6720	10.3280	1.1316	50′
20′	.4422	9.6313	9.9561	9.6752	10.3248	1.1286	40′
30′	.4451	9.6340	9.9555	9.6785	10.3215	1.1257	30′
40′	.4480	9.6366	9.9549	9.6817	10.3183	1.1228	20′
50′	.4509	9.6392	9.9543	9.6850	10.3150	1.1199	10′
26° 00′	.4538	9.6418	9.9537	9.6882	10.3118	1.1170	**64° 00′**
10′	.4567	9.6444	9.9530	9.6914	10.3086	1.1141	50′
20′	.4596	9.6470	9.9524	9.6946	10.3054	1.1112	40′
30′	.4625	9.6495	9.9518	9.6977	10.3023	1.1083	30′
40′	.4654	9.6521	9.9512	9.7009	10.2991	1.1054	20′
50′	.4683	9.6546	9.9505	9.7040	10.2960	1.1025	10′
27° 00′	.4712	9.6570	9.9499	9.7072	10.2928	1.0996	**63° 00′**
		Log Cos θ	Log Sin θ	Log Cot θ	Log Tan θ	θ Rad.	θ Deg.

Table of Values of the Logarithms of Trigonometric Functions

θ Deg.	θ Rad.	Log Sin θ	Log Cos θ	Log Tan θ	Log Cot θ		
27° 00'	.4712	9.6570	9.9499	9.7072	10.2928	1.0996	63° 00'
10'	.4741	9.6595	9.9492	9.7103	10.2897	1.0966	50'
20'	.4771	9.6620	9.9486	9.7134	10.2866	1.0937	40'
30'	.4800	9.6644	9.9479	9.7165	10.2835	1.0908	30'
40'	.4829	9.6668	9.9473	9.7196	10.2804	1.0879	20'
50'	.4858	9.6692	9.9466	9.7226	10.2774	1.0850	10'
28° 00'	.4887	9.6716	9.9459	9.7257	10.2743	1.0821	62° 00'
10'	.4916	9.6740	9.9453	9.7287	10.2713	1.0792	50'
20'	.4945	9.6763	9.9446	9.7317	10.2683	1.0763	40'
30'	.4974	9.6787	9.9439	9.7348	10.2652	1.0734	30'
40'	.5003	9.6810	9.9432	9.7378	10.2622	1.0705	20'
50'	.5032	9.6833	9.9425	9.7408	10.2592	1.0676	10'
29° 00'	.5061	9.6856	9.9418	9.7438	10.2562	1.0647	61° 00'
10'	.5091	9.6878	9.9411	9.7467	10.2533	1.0617	50'
20'	.5120	9.6901	9.9404	9.7497	10.2503	1.0588	40'
30'	.5149	9.6923	9.9397	9.7526	10.2474	1.0559	30'
40'	.5178	9.6946	9.9390	9.7556	10.2444	1.0530	20'
50'	.5207	9.6968	9.9383	9.7585	10.2415	1.0501	10'
30° 00'	.5236	9.6990	9.9375	9.7614	10.2386	1.0472	60° 00'
10'	.5265	9.7012	9.9368	9.7644	10.2356	1.0443	50'
20'	.5294	9.7033	9.9361	9.7673	10.2327	1.0414	40'
30'	.5323	9.7055	9.9353	9.7701	10.2299	1.0385	30'
40'	.5352	9.7076	9.9346	9.7730	10.2270	1.0356	20'
50'	.5381	9.7097	9.9338	9.7759	10.2241	1.0327	10'
31° 00'	.5411	9.7118	9.9331	9.7788	10.2212	1.0297	59° 00'
10'	.5440	9.7139	9.9323	9.7816	10.2184	1.0268	50'
20'	.5469	9.7160	9.9315	9.7845	10.2155	1.0239	40'
30'	.5498	9.7181	9.9308	9.7873	10.2127	1.0210	30'
40'	.5527	9.7201	9.9300	9.7902	10.2098	1.0181	20'
50'	.5556	9.7222	9.9292	9.7930	10.2070	1.0152	10'
32° 00'	.5585	9.7242	9.9284	9.7958	10.2042	1.0123	58° 00'
10'	.5614	9.7262	9.9276	9.7986	10.2014	1.0094	50'
20'	.5643	9.7282	9.9268	9.8014	10.1986	1.0065	40'
30'	.5672	9.7302	9.9260	9.8042	10.1958	1.0036	30'
40'	.5701	9.7322	9.9252	9.8070	10.1930	1.0007	20'
50'	.5730	9.7342	9.9244	9.8097	10.1903	.9977	10'
33° 00'	.5760	9.7361	9.9236	9.8125	10.1875	.9948	57° 00'
10'	.5789	9.7380	9.9228	9.8153	10.1847	.9919	50'
20'	.5818	9.7400	9.9219	9.8180	10.1820	.9890	40'
30'	.5847	9.7419	9.9211	9.8208	10.1792	.9861	30'
40'	.5876	9.7438	9.9203	9.8235	10.1765	.9832	20'
50'	.5905	9.7457	9.9194	9.8263	10.1737	.9803	10'
34° 00'	.5934	9.7476	9.9186	9.8290	10.1710	.9774	56° 00'
10'	.5963	9.7494	9.9177	9.8317	10.1683	.9745	50'
20'	.5992	9.7513	9.9169	9.8344	10.1656	.9716	40'
30'	.6021	9.7531	9.9160	9.8371	10.1629	.9687	30'
40'	.6050	9.7550	9.9151	9.8398	10.1602	.9657	20'
50'	.6080	9.7568	9.9142	9.8425	10.1575	.9628	10'
35° 00'	.6109	9.7586	9.9134	9.8452	10.1548	.9599	55° 00'
10'	.6138	9.7604	9.9125	9.8479	10.1521	.9570	50'
20'	.6167	9.7622	9.9116	9.8506	10.1494	.9541	40'
30'	.6196	9.7640	9.9107	9.8533	10.1467	.9512	30'
40'	.6225	9.7657	9.9098	9.8559	10.1441	.9483	20'
50'	.6254	9.7675	9.9089	9.8586	10.1414	.9454	10'
36° 00'	.6283	9.7692	9.9080	9.8613	10.1387	.9425	54° 00'
		Log Cos θ	Log Sin θ	Log Cot θ	Log Tan θ	θ Rad.	θ Deg.

Table of Values of the Logarithms of Trigonometric Functions

θ Deg.	θ Rad.	Log Sin θ	Log Cos θ	Log Tan θ	Log Cot θ		
36° 00'	.6283	9.7692	9.9080	9.8613	10.1387	.9425	54° 00'
10'	.6312	9.7710	9.9070	9.8639	10.1361	.9396	50'
20'	.6341	9.7727	9.9061	9.8666	10.1334	.9367	40'
30'	.6370	9.7744	9.9052	9.8692	10.1308	.9338	30'
40'	.6400	9.7761	9.9042	9.8718	10.1282	.9308	20'
50'	.6429	9.7778	9.9033	9.8745	10.1255	.9279	10'
37° 00'	.6458	9.7795	9.9023	9.8771	10.1229	.9250	53° 00'
10'	.6487	9.7811	9.9014	9.8797	10.1203	.9221	50'
20'	.6516	9.7828	9.9004	9.8824	10.1176	.9192	40'
30'	.6545	9.7844	9.8995	9.8850	10.1150	.9163	30'
40'	.6574	9.7861	9.8985	9.8876	10.1124	.9134	20'
50'	.6603	9.7877	9.8975	9.8902	10.1098	.9105	10'
38° 00'	.6632	9.7893	9.8965	9.8928	10.1072	.9076	52° 00'
10'	.6661	9.7910	9.8955	9.8954	10.1046	.9047	50'
20'	.6690	9.7926	9.8945	9.8980	10.1020	.9018	40'
30'	.6720	9.7941	9.8935	9.9006	10.0994	.8988	30'
40'	.6749	9.7957	9.8925	9.9032	10.0968	.8959	20'
50'	.6778	9.7973	9.8915	9.9058	10.0942	.8930	10'
39° 00'	.6807	9.7989	9.8905	9.9084	10.0916	.8901	51 °00'
10'	.6836	9.8004	9.8895	9.9110	10.0890	.8872	50'
20'	.6865	9.8020	9.8884	9.9135	10.0865	.8843	40'
30'	.6894	9.8035	9.8874	9.9161	10.0839	.8814	30'
40'	.6923	9.8050	9.8864	9.9187	10.0813	.8785	20'
50'	.6952	9.8066	9.8853	9.9212	10.0788	.8756	10'
40' 00'	.6981	9.8081	9.8843	9.9238	10.0762	.8727	50° 00'
10'	.7010	9.8096	9.8832	9.9264	10.0736	.8698	50'
20'	.7039	9.8111	9.8821	9.9289	10.0711	.8668	40'
30'	.7069	9.8125	9.8810	9.9315	10.0685	.8639	30'
40'	.7098	9.8140	9.8800	9.9341	10.0659	.8610	20'
50'	.7127	9.8155	9.8789	9.9366	10.0634	.8581	10'
41° 00'	.7156	9.8169	9.8778	9.9392	10.0608	.8552	49° 00'
10'	.7185	9.8184	9.8767	9.9417	10.0583	.8523	50'
20'	.7214	9.8198	9.8756	9.9443	10.0557	.8494	40'
30'	.7243	9.8213	9.8745	9.9468	10.0532	.8465	30'
40'	.7272	9.8227	9.8733	9.9494	10.0506	.8436	20'
50'	.7301	9.8241	9.8722	9.9519	10.0481	.8407	10'
42° 00'	.7330	9.8255	9.8711	9.9544	10.0456	.8378	48° 00'
10'	.7359	9.8269	9.8699	9.9570	10.0430	.8348	50'
20'	.7389	9.8283	9.8688	9.9595	10.0405	.8319	40'
30'	.7418	9.8297	9.8676	9.9621	10.0379	.8290	30'
40'	.7447	9.8311	9.8665	9.9646	10.0354	.8261	20'
50'	.7476	9.8324	9.8653	9.9671	10.0329	.8232	10'
43° 00'	.7505	9.8338	9.8641	9.9697	10.0303	.8203	47° 00'
10'	.7534	9.8351	9.8629	9.9722	10.0278	.8174	50'
20'	.7563	9.8365	9.8618	9.9747	10.0253	.8145	40'
30'	.7592	9.8378	9.8606	9.9772	10.0228	.8116	30'
40'	.7621	9.8391	9.8594	9.9798	10.0202	.8087	20'
50'	.7650	9.8405	9.8582	9.9823	10.0177	.8058	10'
44° 00'	.7679	9.8418	9.8569	9.9848	10.0152	.8029	46° 00'
10'	.7709	9.8431	9.8557	9.9874	10.0126	.7999	50'
20'	.7738	9.8444	9.8545	9.9899	10.0101	.7970	40'
30'	.7767	9.8457	9.8532	9.9924	10.0076	.7941	30'
40'	.7796	9.8469	9.8520	9.9949	10.0051	.7912	20'
50'	.7825	9.8482	9.8507	9.9975	10.0025	.7883	10'
45° 00'	.7854	9.8495	9.8495	10.0000	10.0000	.7854	45° 00'
		Log Cos θ	Log Sin θ	Log Cot θ	Log Tan θ	θ Rad.	θ Deg.

Index

Boldfaced numerals indicate the pages that contain formal or informal definitions. Numerals in parentheses refer to exercises.

Harmonic sequence, **242**
Helix, **649**
Hero(n)'s formula for the
    area of a triangle, **168**
Homogeneous system(s) of
    linear equations, **544,**
    556–59
  general solution of, **556–57,**
    58
  nontrivial solution of, **544,**
    557
  trival solution of, **544,**
    557–59
  unique solution of, **559**
Horizontal asymptote, **282**
Hyperboloid
  of one sheet, 639
  of two sheets, 639
Hyperbola, **593–95**
  asymptotes of, **597–99**
  center of, **594–95**
  conic section, 582–83
  conjugate, **599**
  conjugate axis, **594–95**
  eccentricity, **594**
  focal chord, 595
  foci, **593–95**
  latus rectum, **595**
  major axis, **593–94**
  minor axis, **594**
  polar equation of, 204 (28)
  rectangular, **599**
  semimajor axis, **594**
  semiminor axis, **594**
  standard equation of, **595,**
    609–10
  transverse axis, **593–95**
Hyperbolic spiral, polar
    equation of, 204 (25)
Hypotenuse, **128**

Identities, **103**–06, 133–53
  sin, cos, table of, 79
Identity
  additive, for matrices, **486,**
    540
  function, **40** (37), **44**
  matrix, **567**
  multiplicative, for matrices,
    490–91
  property, **6, 7**
  transformation, **505**
Image, **505**–08
Imaginary part (of complex
    number), **48**
Independent variable, **31**
Indeterminate, rational
    function at a point, **284**
    (43–47)
Indirect proof, **9**
Induction hypothesis, **22**
Inequalities
  quadratic, **19**
  solution of, 17–21

triangle, 30 (30, 33), 56 (26)
  trigonometric, 185–87
Infinite sequence, 210–11
Initial side, **112**
Inner product, **450**–51, 490
  commutative property of,
    451
  distributive property of, **451**
  See also Angle between two
    vectors
Instantaneous
  acceleration, **659**–60
  velocity, **658**
Integral
  area by, **678**–82
  of a constant times
    a function, **675**–76
  definite, **674**–76, 678–82
  integrand, **674**
  Lebesque, 674
  lower bound of, **674**
  of a power, **676**
  Riemann, 674
  Sticijes, 674
  of a sum, **675**
  upper bound of, **674**
  volume by, 684–87
Integrand, **674**
  See also Integral
Interpolation, 130
Interval
  closed, **15–16**
  notation, 15–16
  open, **16, 217**
Into, 32, 36
Inverse
  circular functions, 171–80
  of a function, 44, **45**–48,
    387, **388**–91
  of a matrix, 499–**502,** 503,
    567–68, 570–71
  property, **6, 7**
  trigonometric functions,
    171–80
Invertible matrix (matrices),
    502, 567–68, 570
"Is close to", **219**–21

Latus rectum (latera recta)
  of ellipse, **590**
  of hyperbola, **595**
Law
  of cosines, **160**–66
  of sines, 156, **157**–60
Least upper bound, **237**–39
  axiom, **238**
Lemniscate, polar equation of,
    204 (22, 23)
Length
  of a segment, **62**–63
  of vector, 187, **412, 429**
  See also Magnitude
Limaçon, polar equation of,
    204 (18–21)

Limit
  area as a, **669**–72
  of a function, **266**–67, 268,
    280–82
  of a function, at a point,
    269, **270**–72, 274 (14)
  one-sided, **272**
  of a polynomial, 274,
    275–76, 277
  of a sequence, 227, **228**–231,
    239, 248–51, 254–56
  See also Derived function
Line(s)
  angle between two, **452**–53
  direction numbers of, **438**–39
  graph of, 446
  normal to, **452**–53
  parallel, **455**–56
  parametric equations of,
    438–40
  perpendicular, 455, **456**–57
  point slope equation of,
    443, 445
  polar equation and graph
    of, 200
  slope in two space, **443,** 445
  standard equations of,
    437–40, 442
  in two space, 442–46
  vector equation, 440
Linear combination of vectors,
    421–23, 426–29
  unique, **422–23**
Linear equations, system of,
    544–47
  equivalent, **544**
  homogeneous, **544,** 556–59
  nonhomogeneous, **544,**
    561–64
  solutions by Gaussian
    elimination, **553**
  trivial (nontrivial) solution
    of, **544**
Linear function(s), **39 (28)**
    301–03
Linear interpolation, 130
Linear transformation, **506**–07,
    510–15
  composites of, **522**–24
  mirror image, **511**
  reflection, **511**–13
Locater theorem, **313**
Logarithm(s), 392, **393**–97
  to the base a, **393**
  common, **399**–401
  graph of, 393, 397
  natural, **400**–01
  of a power, **395**
  product of, **394**
  quotient of, **395**
Logarithmic function, 392,
    393–97
Lower bound of intergration,
    674

Answers to Odd-Numbered Exercise

PAGE 5   Exercises

1. R, Q   3. R, Q, I, W   5. R, Q, I, W, N   7. R, Q   9. R, Q   11. R, Q   13. False.   15. False.

17. False.   19. True.   21. True.   23. False.   25. $\frac{5}{4}$ 27. $\frac{1043}{10,000}$ 29. $\frac{1}{100}$ 31. $\frac{311,117}{8325}$

33. $\frac{1}{2}$ 35. Let x = .00$\overline{9}$. Then 1.13$\overline{9}$ = 1.13 + x. 10x = .0$\overline{9}$ = .09 + x. Therefore, 9x = .09

and x = .01. Therefore, 1.13$\overline{9}$ = 1.13 + .01 = 1.14.   37. Upon dividing r by s, the resulting

decimal either terminates or does not. If it doesn't terminate, there are at most s different

remainders occurring in the division process after the decimal point, and since all digits of

the numerator are 0 after the decimal point, a given remainder in one place will lead to the

same remainder in the next place time and again, thus we get a repeating decimal.   39. In

those decimals which terminate, the denominators have, aside from the factor 1, only factors

which are expressible as products of only twos and fives. The others involve other primes in

their factorization.

PAGES 10-11   Exercises

1. 4, 5, 10   3. 10   5. 1, 4, 6, 9   7. The result follows immediately from Theorem 1-1 with

a = 0, b = -0, c = 0.

9.   0 - a = 0 + (-a)   by definition of subtraction.

        0 + (-a) = (-a) + 0   by Postulate 2.

        (-a) + 0 = -a   by Postualte 4. Using Post. 14 completes proof.

11. Proceeding as in Exercise 10, it is only necessary to show that (a - b) + [b + (-a)] = 0.

Details are similar to Exercise 10.   13. By Postulate 10, $\exists$ $\frac{1}{a}$ such that a $\cdot$ $(\frac{1}{a})$ = 1. Multiplying

both sides by $\frac{1}{a}$ gives $\frac{1}{a}$ $\cdot$ (a $\cdot$ b) = $\frac{1}{a}$ $\cdot$ (a $\cdot$ c).

        Then, [a $\cdot$ $(\frac{1}{a})$] $\cdot$ b = [a $\cdot$ $(\frac{1}{a})$] $\cdot$ c   (Postulates 7 and 8)

                1 $\cdot$ b = 1 $\cdot$ c   (Postulate 10)

                b $\cdot$ 1 = c $\cdot$ 1   (Postulate 7)

                b = c   (Postulate 9)

15. $a \cdot 0 + 0 = a \cdot 0$ (Postulate 4)

            $a \cdot 0 = a(0 + 0)$ (postulate 4)

        $a \cdot (0 + 0) = a \cdot 0 + a \cdot 0$ (Postulate 11)

        $a \cdot 0 + 0 = a \cdot 0 + a \cdot 0$ (Postulate 14)

              $0 = a \cdot 0$ (Cancellation property for addition)

           $a \cdot 0 = 0$ (Postulate 13)

17.   Part 1:   If $a \div b = c$, then $a = c \cdot b$

       Proof: $a \div b = c$

                 $a \cdot (\frac{1}{b}) = c$ (Definition of division)

Multiply both sides by b, we get

                $[a \cdot (\frac{1}{b})] \cdot b = c \cdot b.$

     Then, $a \cdot (\frac{1}{b} \cdot b) = c \cdot b$ (Postulate 8)

                 $a \cdot 1 = c \cdot b$ (Postulate 10)

                 $a = c \cdot b$ (Postulate 9)

       Part 2:   If $a = c \cdot b$, then $a \div b = c$ $(b \neq 0)$.

        Proof: $a = c \cdot b$, divide both sides by b, i.e. multiply by $\frac{1}{b}$.

    Then, $a \cdot (\frac{1}{b}) = (c \cdot b) \cdot (\frac{1}{b})$

         $a \div b = c \cdot (b \cdot \frac{1}{b})$ (Def. of division and Post. 8)

         $a \div b = c \cdot 1$ (Postulate 10)

         $a \div b = c$ (Postulate 9)

PAGE 14   Exercises

1. True.   3. False.   5. True.   7. False.   9. Theorem 1-6 with $a = 2, b = 5, c = 3$.   11. $x < z$ by Theorem 1-4.   13. Continuing from the text's outline, $(b - a) + (c - b) = (b + (-a)) + (c + (-b))$. (Definition of subtraction.)

     $(b + (-a)) + (c + (-b)) = (-a + b) + (-b + c)$ (Postulate 2)

     $(-a + b) + (-b + c) = ((-a + b) + (-b)) + c$ (Postulate 3)

     $((-a + b) + (-b)) + c = (-a + (b + (-b))) + c$ (Postulate 3)

$(-a + (b + (-b))) + c = (-a + 0) + c$ (Postulate 5)

$(-a + 0) + c = -a + c$ (Postulate 4)

$-a + c = c + (-a)$ (Postulate 2)

$c + (-a) = c - a$ (Def. of subtraction.)

Thus, $(b - a) + (c - b) = c - a$ which is therefore positive.

15. All steps in showing $(b + c) - (a + c) = b - a$ are reversible, therefore the converse of Theorem 1-5 follows easily. 17. If $ac < bc$ with c positive, then $\exists \frac{1}{c}$. Thus, it can be shown that $\frac{1}{c}$ must be positive, and therefore from Theorem 1-6, we have $ac(\frac{1}{c}) < bc(\frac{1}{c})$ or from Postulate 8, $a \cdot (c \cdot (\frac{1}{c})) < b \cdot (c \cdot (\frac{1}{c}))$ which implies $a \cdot 1 < b \cdot 1$ or $a < b$. 19. Part 1: Assume $a < 0$. Then $0 - a$ is positive. But $0 - a = 0 + (-a) = -a + 0 = -a$. Thus $-a$ is positive, hence a is negative. Part 2: The steps in Part 1 are reversible completing the proof. 21. $x \leq y$ implies that eigher $x = y$ or $y - x$ is positive. $y \leq x$ implies that either $x = y$ or $x - y$ is positive. If in either of the above assertions, $x = y$ we are finished, since if $x = y$, neither $x - y$ nor $y - x$ may be positive. However, in the remaining case, if both $x - y$ and $y - x$ are assumed positive, this would imply $(x - y) + (y - x)$ is positive. However, it is easily shown that $(x - y) + (y - x) = 0$ which leads to a contradiction, therefore this case is impossible, and $x = y$.

PAGES 17-18   Exercises

1. All real numbers less than -1 but not including -1. 3. The numbers -2 and 0. 5. All real numbers between 0 and 3, including 3 but not 0. 7. All real numbers between $\frac{2}{3}$ and $\frac{7}{4}$, including $\frac{2}{3}$ but not $\frac{7}{4}$. 9. All real numbers less than 5 and including 5. 11. All real numbers between 1 and 3, including 1 but not 3. 13. All real numbers between -4 and 3, including both -4 and 3. 15. All real numbers between -2 and 3, not including -2 nor 3. 17. The integers 0, 1, 2, 3, 4, 5. 19. All real numbers less than -2, not including -2, also all real numbers between 1 and 3, including 1 but not 3. 21. $y : y > 5$ 23. $t : t < 2$ 25. $n : n > \frac{18}{5}$ 27. $t : t > 5$ 29. $p : p > 0$

31. 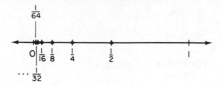 33.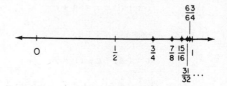

PAGES 19-21   Exercises

1. $\left\{x : 2 < x < \frac{7}{3}\right\}$ 3. $\left\{x : -2 < x < 1\right\}$ 5. $\left\{x : \frac{3}{5} < x < 2\right\}$ 7. Empty set.

9. $\left\{x : 0 < x < \frac{9}{2}\right\}$ 11. $\left\{x : x < -2 \;\;\cup\;\; x : x > \frac{1}{2}\right\}$ 13. $\left\{x : x < 0 \;\;\cup\;\; x : x > 5\right\}$

15. Empty set.   17. $\left\{x : x = 1\right\}$ 19. $\left\{x : -1 < x < 5\right\}$ 21. $\left\{x : x < 2 \;\;\cup\;\; x : x > 5\right\}$

23. $\left\{x : -\frac{1}{4} < x < \frac{1}{4}\right\}$ 25. $\left\{x : x < 2 \;\;\cup\;\; x : x > 5\right\}$ 27. $\left\{x : x = 3\right\}$ 29. $\left\{x : x < 1 \;\;\cup\right.$

$\left. x : 2 < x < 3\right\}$ 31. $\left\{x : x < -2 \;\;\cup\;\; x : -\frac{3}{2} < x < \frac{1}{3}\right\}$ 33. 10   35. Disjoint.

PAGES 25-26   Exercises

1. $2(1) - 1 = 1$; $1^2 = 1$, therefore P_1 is true. Assume P_k true, i.e. $1 + 3 + 5 + \cdots + (2k - 1) = k^2$. Since $k^2 + 2(k + 1) - 1 = k^2 + 2k + 2 - 1 = (k + 1)^2$, it follows that P_{k+1} is true, hence P_n is true for all $n \in N$.

3. $\dfrac{1}{1(1 + 1)} = \dfrac{1}{2}$; $\dfrac{1}{1 + 1} = \dfrac{1}{2}$. $\dfrac{k}{k + 1} + \dfrac{1}{(k + 1)(k + 2)} = \dfrac{k(k + 2) + 1}{(k + 1)(k + 2)} = \dfrac{k + 1}{k + 2}$

5. For $n = 1$ $\dfrac{1 - 2^1}{2^1} = -\dfrac{1}{2}$ For $n + 1$

$$-\frac{1}{2} - \frac{1}{4} - \frac{1}{8} \cdots - \frac{1}{2^n} - \frac{1}{2^{n+1}} = \frac{1 - (2^n)}{2^n} - \frac{1}{2^{n+1}} =$$

$$\frac{2 - 2^{n+1} - 1}{2^{n+1}} = \frac{1 - 2^{n+1}}{2^{n+1}}$$

7. For $n = 1$

$$\frac{5\left(1 - (\frac{1}{3})^1\right)}{1 - \frac{1}{3}} = \frac{5(\frac{2}{3})}{\frac{2}{3}} = 5$$

For $n + 1$

$$5 + 5\left(\frac{1}{3}\right) + 5\left(\frac{1}{3^2}\right) + \cdots + 5\left(\frac{1}{3^{n-1}}\right) + 5\left(\frac{1}{3^n}\right)$$

$$= 5\left(\frac{1}{3^n}\right) = 5 \, \frac{\left(1 - (\frac{1}{3})^n\right)}{1 - \frac{1}{3}} + 5\left(\frac{1}{3^n}\right) = 5\left[\frac{1 - \frac{1}{3^n}}{1 - \frac{1}{3}} + \frac{1}{3^n}\right]$$

$$= 5\left[\frac{3^n - 1 + (1 - \frac{1}{3})}{(1 - \frac{1}{3})3^n}\right] = 5\left[\frac{3^n - \frac{1}{3}}{3^n(1 - \frac{1}{3})}\right] = 5\left[\frac{1 - \frac{1}{3^{n+1}}}{1 - \frac{1}{3}}\right] = 5\left[\frac{1 - (\frac{1}{3})^{n+1}}{1 - \frac{1}{3}}\right]$$

9. $\qquad$ $aq^{1-1} = a.$ $\quad a\left(\dfrac{1-q^1}{1-q}\right) = a$

$$a\left(\dfrac{1-q^k}{1-q}\right) + aq^{(k+1)-1} = a\left(\left(\dfrac{1-q^k}{1-q}\right) + q^k\right)$$

$$= a\left((1 + q + q^2 + \cdots + q^{k-1}) + q^k\right) = a\left(\dfrac{1-q^{k+1}}{1-q}\right)$$

11. $1^3 - 1 = 0$ which is divisible by 6. Assume $k^3 - k$ divisible by 6. Then $(k+1)^3 - (k+1) =$

$k^3 + 3k^2 + 3k + 1 - k - 1 = (k^3 - k) + (3k^2 + 3k) = (k^3 - k) + 3(k^2 + k)$. $k^3 - k$ is divisible by

6 by assumption. $3(k^2 + k)$ is obviously divisible by 3 and by 2 also since $k^2 + k$ is even for

any k. Therefore, $3(k^2 + k)$ and also $(k^3 - k) + 3(k^2 + k)$ is divisible by 6. 13. The "sum" of

one positive integer is clearly positive. Let s_k be the sum of k positive integers. Then s_k is a

positive integer by assumption. Let a be any positive integer. Consider $s_{k+1} = s_k + a$. By

Postulate 17, s_{k+1} is positive. 15. For n = 1. $x_0 < x_1$, given. For n + 1. If $x_0 < x_1 < x_2 <$

$\cdots < x_n < x_{n+1}$, then $x_0 < x_n$ and $x_n < x_{n+1}$. By Theorem 1-4 $x_0 < x_{n+1}$.

17. Inductive step only is given in Exercise 17.

a. $x^{k+1} = x^k \cdot x = \underbrace{(x \cdot x \cdot \cdots \cdot x)}_{\text{k factors of x}} \cdot x = \underbrace{(x \cdot x \cdot \cdots \cdot x)}_{\text{k + 1 factors}}$

b. $(x \cdot y)^{k+1} = (x \cdot y)^k (xy) = \underbrace{(xy \cdot xy \cdot \cdots \cdot xy)(xy)}_{\text{k factors of xy}}$

$= \underbrace{(xy \cdot xy \cdot \cdots \cdot xy)}_{\text{k + 1 factors of xy}} = \underbrace{(x \cdot x \cdot \cdots \cdot x)}_{\substack{\text{k + 1 factors} \\ \text{of x}}} \underbrace{(y \cdot y \cdot \cdots \cdot y)}_{\substack{\text{k + 1 factors} \\ \text{of y}}} = x^{k+1} \cdot y^{k+1}$

c. $x^m \cdot x^1 = x^{m+1}$ by Definition II. Assume $x^m \cdot x^k = x^{m+k}$. Then $x^m \cdot x^{k+1} =$

$x^m \cdot (x^k \cdot x^1) = (x^m \cdot x^k) \cdot x^1 =$

$x^{m+k} \cdot x^1 = \underbrace{(x \cdot x \cdot \cdots \cdot x)}_{\substack{\text{m + k factors} \\ \text{of x}}} \cdot x = \underbrace{(x \cdot x \cdot \cdots \cdot x)}_{\substack{\text{m + k + 1 factors} \\ \text{of x}}} = x^{m+(k+1)}$

d. $(x^m)^1 = x^m$ by Definition I. Continue the induction on n. Then $(x^m)^{k+1} = (x^m)^k \cdot x^m$

by Definition II. Thus $(x^m)^{k+1} = x^{mk} \cdot x^m = x^{mk+m}$ (by part c. of this exercise $=$

$x^{m(k+1)}$.

1. $\left\{x : -2 \leq x \leq 2\right\}$ 3. $\left\{r : -3 < r < 3\right\}$ 5. $\left\{x : x < -1 \ \cup \ x : x > 3\right\}$

7. $\left\{g : g \leq -6 \ \cup \ g : g \geq -2\right\}$ 9. $\left\{r : 3 < r < 7\right\}$ 11. $\left\{g : 10 < g < 12\right\}$

13. $\left\{x : -1 \leq x \leq \frac{1}{5}\right\}$ 15. $\left\{x : \frac{3}{2} \leq x \leq \frac{9}{2}\right\}$ 17. $\left\{x : x \geq 4\right\}$ 19. $\left\{r : r < \frac{3}{4}\right\}$

21. $\left\{y : y < -\frac{8}{21}\right\}$ 23. The empty set.   25. If $x \geq 0$, $y \geq 0$, then $|x| = x$, $|y| = y$, $|xy| = xy$.

If $x < 0$, $y < 0$, then $|x| = -x$, $|y| = -y$, $|xy| = xy$. If $x \geq 0$, $y < 0$, $|x| = x$, $|y| = -y$, $|xy| = -xy$.

If $x < 0$, $y \geq 0$, then $|x| = -x$, $|y| = y$, $|xy| = -xy$. In any of these cases, we therefore have

$|xy| = |x| \cdot |y|$.   27. If $x - y \geq 0$, then $|x - y| = x - y$. However $x - y \geq 0$ implies $y - x < 0$.

Thus $|y - x| = x - y$ also. Now, if $x - y < 0$, we have $|x - y| = y - x$. But $x - y < 0$ implies

$y - x \geq 0$. Thus $|y - x| = y - x$ also. In either case $|x - y| = |y - x|$.   29. If $x \geq 0$, $|x| = x$, and

$|x|^2 = x^2$. If $x < 0$, $|x| = -x$, and $|x| = (-x)^2 = x^2$.   31. By Exercise 30, $|(x + y) + (-y)| \leq$

$|x - y| + |+y|$. But, by Exercise 27, $|-y| = |y|$. Therefore, since $|(x + y) - y| = |x|$, we obtain

$|x| \leq |x + y| + |y|$ which becomes $|x| - |y| \leq |x + y|$.   33. By Exercise 30, $|x_1 + x_2| \leq |x_1| +$

$|x_2|$. Assume $|x_1 + x_2 + \cdots + x_k| \leq |x_1| + |x_2| + \cdots + |x_k|$ for some $k \in N$. Then

$|x_1 + x_2 + \cdots + x_{k+1}| = |(x_1 + x_2 + \cdots + x_k) + x_{k+1}| \leq |x_1| + |x_2| + \cdots + |x_k| +$

$|x_{k+1}|$.

1. $\left\{-5, -7, -9, -3, -1, 1\right\}$ 3. $\left\{4, 1, 0\right\}$ 5. $\left\{3, 2, 1, 0, -1, -2, -3\right\}$ 7. $\left\{0, 1, 4, 16, 64, 144\right\}$

9. $\left\{t : t > -4\right\}$ 11. $\left\{y : y \leq 0\right\}$ 13. $\left\{-2, -1, 0, 1, 2\right\}$ 15. Into.   17. Into.   19. Onto.

21. Into.   23. Onto.

25. a.

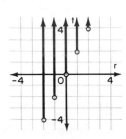

29. a.

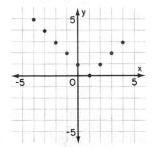

b. Graph done in similar manner.   27. Range = $[0, 3]$.   b.-c. Graphs done in a similar manner.

PAGES 38-40   Exercises

1. $\left\{0, \frac{1}{2}, 1, \frac{3}{2}, 2, \cdots\right\}$ 3. 3   5. x   7. Function.   9. Not a function.   11. Function.

13. Function.   15. Not a function.   17. Function.

19.
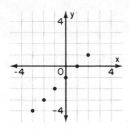

The graphs for Exercises 8, 10, 11, 12

13, 14, 17 and 18 are done in a similar

manner.

21. $\left\{14, 7, 2, -1, -2\right\}$ 23. 1   25. 6   27. n!

29.
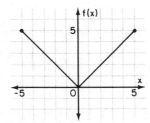

31. Two line segments intersecting at (0, 1). One has slope 1 and one has slope -1.   33. Line

segments parallel to the x axis for $y \in \left\{-5, -4, \cdots, 4, 5\right\}$. Each segment contains all real

numbers between two specific consecutive integers, but including only the left endpoint.

Example: One line segment has domain $-5 \leq x < -4$ and range $y = -5$.   35. Similar to

Exercise 33.   37. A line passing through (0, 0) having a slope of 1.   39. A line passing

through (0, 0) and having a slope of -1.   41. $f : x \to \frac{1}{x}$

43.
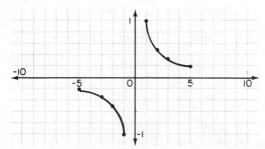

PAGES 43-44   Exercises

1. 1, 2   3. gf = [(1,3), (3,5), (5,7)] domain = [1,3,5], range = [3,5,7].

5. Graph done in a similar manner to Exercise 3. domain: $\{1, 3, 4\}$, range: $\{3, 4, 6\}$,

fh = $\{(1, 3), (3, 4), (4, 6)\}$. 7. 36 (6 from A to B, so that all of B is used in the domain of

g, and 6 from B to C). 9. $(3x - 4)^2 + 3$ 11. $-6x + 9$ 13. $-6x^2 - 9$ 15. -73 17. $(x^2 + 3)^2 + 3$

19. a, c 21. ac, ac. They are equal. The slope of the composition of two linear functions is

independent of the order of composition. 23. -3 25. Identity function: $ff(x) = x$. 27. $x + 3$

29. Equal. 31. x^6, x^6 33. Both are x^5. 35. $(x - 3)(x + 2)$ 37. $x^2 - 3$ 39. $(x^2 - 3)(x^2 + 2)$

41. Yes.

PAGES 47-48   Exercises

1.
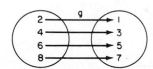

3. Interchanging first and second coordinates in each ordered pair. 5. $f^{-1} = \{(y, x) : y =$

$f(x)\}$ 7. $3x$ 9. $\dfrac{r - 1}{2}$ 11. $\sqrt[3]{x}$ 13. $\pm\sqrt{x + 4}$ Not a function, e.g. $f^{-1} : 0 \nearrow^{2}_{-2}$. 15. $\dfrac{5}{2}(y + 5)$

17. $x - 3$ 19. $\dfrac{1}{x}$ 21 and 23. Same answers as 17 and 19. 25. Solve for x in terms of y, then

replace y by x in the final answer. 27. $y = x^3 + 27$; $y - 27 = x^3$; $x = \sqrt[3]{y - 27}$, $\therefore$ inverse is

$\sqrt[3]{x - 27}$. The 4 given pts. 31. Line passing through $(0, 0)$ with slope 1. 33. f is a line

through $(0, -4)$ with a slope of 3. f^{-1} is a line $(0, \dfrac{4}{3})$ with a slope of $\dfrac{1}{3}$. The graphs of f, f^{-1} are

reflections of each other in $y = x$ $(I : x \rightarrow x)$.

35. a.
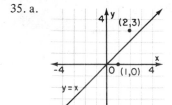

b. It is a line passing through $(1, 0)$

and $(2, 3)$. The line has slope of

3 and a y intercept of -3.

37. Consider $f : x \rightarrow ax + b$, $a \neq 0$. $x \in R$. Then $f^{-1} : x \rightarrow \dfrac{x - b}{a}$ $x \in R$.

1. $-1 + 3i$ 3. $0 - 2i$ 5. $-1 + 8i$ 7. $10 + 24i$ 9. $\frac{1}{5} + \frac{3}{5}i$ 11. $2 - 2i$ 13. $2 + i$ 15. $\frac{1}{5}$

17. $(1 + i)^2 - 2(1 + i) + 2 = 1 + 2i - 1 - 2 - 2i + 2 = 0$. Also $(1 - i)^2 - 2(1 - i) + 2 = 1 - 2i - 1 - 2$

$+ 2i + 2 = 0$.   19. Assume $z_1\, z_2 = 0$ and suppose $z_1 \neq 0$ and $z_2 \neq 0$. Let $z_1 = a + bi$ and $z_2 =$

$c + di$ $a, b, c, d, \in R$. Then either $a \neq 0$ or $b \neq 0$ or both and either $c \neq 0$ or $d \neq 0$ or both.

There are nine possible cases. In the first one $a \neq 0$, $b = 0$, $c \neq 0$, $d = 0$. Then $z_1\, z_2 =$

$(ac - bd) + (bc + ad)\,i$ and $ac - bd \neq 0$ since $ac \neq 0$ and $bd = 0$. Hence $z_1\, z_2 \neq 0$. This

contradicts our assumption. Similiarly the eight other cases result in contradictions. There-

fore the supposition must be false and $z_1 = 0$ or $z_2 = 0$ or both.   21. Let $z_1 = a_1 + b_1 i$, $z_2 =$

$a_2 + b_2 i$, $z_3 = a_3 + b_3 i$, $a_1, a_2, a_3, b_1, b_2, b_3 \in R$. Then $(z_1 + z_2) + z_3 = ((a_1 + b_1 i) +$

$(a_2 + b_2 i)) + (a_3 + b_3 i) = ((a_1 + a_2) + a_3) + ((b_1 + b_2) + b_3)i = (a_1 + b_1 i) + ((a_2 + b_2 i) + (a_3 + b_3 i)) =$

$z_1 + (z_2 + z_3)$.   23. Let $z_1 = a_1 + b_1 i$, $z_2 = a_2 + b_2 i$, $z_3 = a_3 + b_3 i$, $a_1, a_2, a_3, b_1, b_2, b_3 \in R$.

Then $z_1(z_2 + z_3) = (a_1 + b_1 i)((a_2 + a_3) + (b_2 + b_3)i) = a_1(a_2 + a_3) - b_1(b_2 + b_3) + (b_1(a_2 + a_3)$

$+ a_1(b_2 + b_3))\,i = [(a_1 a_2 - b_1 b_2) + (a_2 b_1 + a_1 b_2)\,i] + [(a_1 a_3 - b_1 b_3) + (a_3 b_1 + a_1 b_3)] =$

$z_1 z_2 + z_1 z_3$.

1. $z_1 + z_2 = -2 + 4i$

$z_1 - z_2 = -4 - 2i$

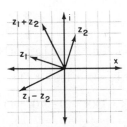

3. $z_1 + z_2 = -8i$, $z_1 - z_2 = 6$ 5. $z_1 + z_2 = 2 + 4i$, $z_1 - z_2 = 2 - 4i$ 7. $z_1 + z_2 = 5i$, $z_1 - z_2 = i$

9. Exercise 1: $1 - 3i$; Exercise 2: $4 + 2i$; Exercise 3: $-3 + 4i$; Exercise 4: $-2 - 3i$; Exercise 5: $-4i$;

Exercise 6: 2; Exercise 7: $-2i$.   11. $\dfrac{-4 + 7i}{5}$ 13. $\dfrac{-11 + 23i}{25}$ 15. Let $z = a + bi$, where $a, b \in R$.

$\bar{z} = z \Leftrightarrow a - bi = a + bi \Leftrightarrow 2bi = 0 \Leftrightarrow b = 0 \Leftrightarrow z$ is real.   17. Let $z = a + bi$, where $a, b \in R$. Then

$|z| = \sqrt{a^2 + b^2} = \sqrt{a^2 + (-b)^2} = |\bar{z}|$.   19. $\overline{z_1 + z_2} = \overline{(a_1 + a_2) + (b_1 + b_2)i} = a_1 + a_2 - (b_1 + b_2)i =$

$(a_1 - b_1 i) + (a_2 - b_2 i) = \bar{z}_1 + \bar{z}_2$ 21. $\overline{z_1 z_2} = \overline{(a_1 + b_1 i)(a_2 + b_2 i)} = \overline{(a_1 a_2 - b_1 b_2) + (a_1 b_2 + a_2 b_1)i} =$

$(a_1 a_2 - b_1 b_2) - (a_1 b_2 + a_2 b_1)i = (a_1 - b_1 i) \cdot (a_2 - b_2 i) = \bar{z}_1 \cdot \bar{z}_2$ 23. $|z_1 \cdot z_2|^2 = z_1 \cdot z_2 \cdot \overline{z_1 z_2} =$

$(z_1 \overline{z_1})(z_2 \overline{z_2}) = |z_1|^2 \cdot |z_2|^2$ Therefore $|z_1 z_2| = |z_1| |z_2|$ 25. Let $z = a + bi$, $a, b \in R$. a. $|z| = \sqrt{a^2 + b^2}$. Since $b^2 \geq 0$, we have $a^2 + b^2 \geq a^2$, $\therefore \sqrt{a^2 + b^2} \geq a$. b. $|z| = \sqrt{a^2 + b^2}$. Since $a^2 \geq 0$, $a^2 + b^2 \geq b^2$. But $|bi| = \sqrt{b^2} = |b|$. $\therefore a^2 + b^2 \geq |bi|^2$ $\therefore \sqrt{a^2 + b^2} \geq |bi|$.   27. Inductive step: $z_1 z_2 \cdots z_k + 1 = z_1 \cdot z_2 \cdot \cdots \cdot z_k \cdot z_k + 1$ by Exercise 21., and this in turn is equal to $(\overline{z_1} \cdot \overline{z_2} \cdot \cdots \cdot \overline{z_k}) \cdot \overline{z_k + 1}$ by the inductive hypothesis. The last expression is then equal to $\overline{z_1} \cdot \overline{z_2} \cdot \cdots \cdot \overline{z_k + 1}$ by the associative property.

PAGES 56-59   Chapter Objectives and Review

3. Real, rational.   5. Complex.   7. Real, rational.   9. .285714   11. $\frac{39}{200}$ 13. Distributive law.   15. Definition of subtraction.   17. Commutativity of +.   19. Multiplication is associative.   21. Closure of complex numbers under addition.   23. $\left\{ x : x \leq -2 \ \cup \ x : x \geq 3 \right\}$ 25. $\left\{ x : x < -10 \ \cup \ x : x > 10 \right\}$ 27. Half-open interval, union of two rays, open interval, union of two half-lines.   29. $\left\{ -2, -1, 0, 1, 2 \right\}$ 31. Function, inverse is also a function.   33. Function, inverse is also a function.   35. Function, inverse not a function.   37. fg : $x \rightarrow 2x - 4$; gf : $x \rightarrow 2x - 9$ 39. fg : $x \rightarrow \dfrac{1}{\frac{x}{2} - 3}$; gf : $x \rightarrow \dfrac{1}{2x} - 3$ 41. $1 + i$ 43. $3 - 7i$ 45. $4 + 2i$ 47. Answers will vary.

PAGE 59   Chapter Test

1. $\frac{2}{9}$ 3. To show: $2 + 4 + \cdots + 2n = n(n + 1)$. If $n = 1$, we have $2(1) = 1(1 + 1) = 2$. Assume true for $n = k$ N. We must show that P_k : $(k + 1)((k + 1) + 1) = k(k + 1) + 2(k + 1)$ is true. This is true, as $(k + 1)((k + 1) + 1) = (k + 1)(k + 2) = k(k + 1) + 2(k + 1)$.   5. a. [a, b]   b. $< a, b >$ 7. $|x| = \begin{matrix} x \text{ if } x > 0 \\ -x \text{ if } x < 0 \end{matrix}$ 9. See page 15.   11. See page 16.   13. $2x - \frac{5}{2}$ 15. $x - \frac{1}{2}$ 17. .101001000100001 $\cdots$

CHAPTER 2   CIRCULAR FUNCTIONS

PAGES 63-64   Exercises

1. 6   3. 8   5. 5   7. 13   9. $\sqrt{10}$ 11. $\sqrt{68}$ 13. 5   15. $\sqrt{5a}$ 17. $9 = (x - 2)^2 + (y + 5)^2$ 19. $49 = (x + 5)^2 + (y + 1)^2$ 21. $\frac{1}{4} = (x - \frac{2}{3})^2 + (y + \frac{1}{3})^2$ 23. $41 = (x - 1)^2 + (y - 2)^2$ 25. 13,-11   27. $\overline{PQ} = \sqrt{26}$; $\overline{QR} = 4$; $\overline{PR} = \sqrt{2}$ 29. $y = -x$ 31. C (3, 2), $r = 4$

1. $2 + 2\pi, 2 + 4\pi, 2 + 6\pi, 2 + 8\pi, 2 + 10\pi$ 3. $-3 - 2\pi, -3 - 4\pi, -3 - 6\pi, -3 - 8\pi$ 5. $\frac{2\pi}{3} + 2\pi n, \forall n \in N$

7. $\frac{2\pi}{3} \pm 2\pi n, \forall n \in W$ 9. IV   11. IV   13. I   15. II   17. III   19. Quadrántal between quadrants

III and IV.   21. a. $(\frac{3}{5}, -\frac{4}{5})$ b. $(-\frac{3}{5}, -\frac{4}{5})$ c. $(\frac{3}{5}, \frac{4}{5})$ d. $(-\frac{3}{5}, \frac{4}{5})$ 23. a. $(\frac{\sqrt{13}}{14}, -\frac{1}{14})$ b. $(-\frac{\sqrt{13}}{14}, -\frac{1}{14})$

c. $(\frac{\sqrt{13}}{14}, \frac{1}{14})$ d. $(-\frac{\sqrt{13}}{14}, \frac{1}{14})$ 25. a. $(-\frac{1}{2}, -\frac{\sqrt{3}}{2})$ b. $(\frac{1}{2}, -\frac{\sqrt{3}}{2})$ c. $(-\frac{1}{2}, \frac{\sqrt{3}}{2})$ d. $(-\frac{1}{2}, \frac{\sqrt{3}}{2})$ 27. $\frac{\pi}{3}, \frac{\pi}{3}$

29. $\overline{BP} = 2|v| = \overline{PQ}$ 31. $(\frac{\sqrt{3}}{2}, \frac{1}{2})$ 33. $(u, v) = (-\frac{\sqrt{3}}{2}, \frac{1}{2})$ 35. a. $(-1, 1)$ b. $(-1, 0)$ c. $(-1, -1)$

d. $(0, -1)$ e. $(1, -1)$ f. $(1, 0)$ g. $(-\frac{1}{2}, 1)$ h. $(-1, 0)$ i. $(1, 0)$ 37. a. tusoon x = 1 while $0 \le$ soon x

≤ 1 b. soon x = 1 while $-1 \le$ tusoon x < 1 c. tusoon x = -1 while $-1 \le$ soon x < 1 d. soon x =

-1 while $-1 <$ tusoon x < 1 e. tusoon x = 1 while $-1 <$ soon x ≤ 0.

1. II, -, +   3. IV, +, -   5. IV, +, -   7. III, -, -   9. II, -, +   11. III, -, -   13. III, -, -   15. I, +, +

17. $-\frac{5}{13}$ 19. $\frac{4}{5}$ 21. $\frac{2}{\sqrt{5}}$ 23. cos x = $\frac{1}{3\sqrt{2}}$ 25. 0   27. -1   29. -1   31. 0   33. a. cos x b. -cos x

35. For each $x \in [0, 2\pi]$, sin $x \in [-1, 1]$, since the range of y on the unit circle is $-1 \le y \le 1$.

Thus, since all other values of sin x are gotten by repeating points on the unit circle, the

result follows.   37. Th. 2-3   39. Equal arcs have equal chords.   41. $\frac{\sqrt{2}}{2}$ 43. $-\frac{\sqrt{2}}{2}, \frac{\sqrt{2}}{2}$

45. $-\frac{\sqrt{2}}{2}, \frac{\sqrt{2}}{2}$ 47. Equal arcs have equal chords.   49. $-\frac{1}{2}, -\frac{\sqrt{3}}{2}$ 51. $-\frac{1}{2}, \frac{\sqrt{3}}{2}$ 53. Same

argument as Exercise 52., except we use here the fact that $|BS| \le |CB| \le |CB|$, and since

$|\cos x_1 - \cos x_2| = |BS|$, the result follows.   55. Let $x_2 = 0$, $x_1 = x_1$ and the result

immediately follows from Exercise 53.

1.

x	cos x	sin x
$\frac{\pi}{3}$	$\frac{1}{2}$	$\frac{\sqrt{3}}{2}$
$\frac{2\pi}{3}$	$-\frac{1}{2}$	$\frac{\sqrt{3}}{2}$
$\frac{4\pi}{3}$	$-\frac{1}{2}$	$-\frac{\sqrt{3}}{2}$
$\frac{5\pi}{3}$	$\frac{1}{2}$	$-\frac{\sqrt{3}}{2}$

3. False.   5. True.   7. False.   9. True.   11. True.   13. $-\sin\frac{\pi}{8}$ 15. $-\sin\frac{\pi}{9}$

17. $\sin\frac{\pi}{8}$ 19. $\sin\frac{\pi}{7}$ 21. $\cos\frac{\pi}{3}$ 23. $\sin\frac{\pi}{2}$ 25. $-\cos x$ 27. $\sin x$ 29. $-\cos x$

31. $(\cos(\frac{\pi}{4} + x) - 0)^2 + (\sin (\frac{\pi}{4} + x) - 1)^2 = (\cos (\frac{\pi}{4} - x) - 1)^2 + (\sin (\frac{\pi}{4} - x)$

$- 0)^2$, from which $\cos^2 (\frac{\pi}{4} + x) + \sin^2 (\frac{\pi}{4} + x) - 2 \sin (\frac{\pi}{4} + x) + 1 = \cos^2$

$(\frac{\pi}{4} - x) - 2 \cos (\frac{\pi}{4} - x) + 1 + \sin^2 (\frac{\pi}{4} - x)$. Thus $1 - 2 \sin (\frac{\pi}{4} - x) + 1 \therefore -2$

$\sin\left(\frac{\pi}{4} + x\right) = -2\cos\left(\frac{\pi}{4} - x\right) \therefore \sin\left(\frac{\pi}{4} + x\right) = \cos\left(\frac{\pi}{4} - x\right)$ since $\cos\left(\frac{\pi}{4} - x\right) = \pm\sqrt{1 - \sin^2\left(\frac{\pi}{4} - x\right)}$ and

$\sin\left(\frac{\pi}{4} + x\right) = \pm\sqrt{1 - \cos^2\left(\frac{\pi}{4} + x\right)}$ after squaring and equating the right sides of these equations,

we get $\sin\left(\frac{\pi}{4} - x\right) = \cos\left(\frac{\pi}{4} + x\right)$.

PAGES 84-85   Exercises

1. Only the graph for Exercise 1 is shown as the graphs for Exercises 3 and 5 are similar.

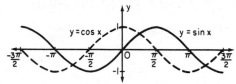

7. The graph should look like the figure at the top of Page 83 with the graph beginning at 0

and ending at 2π. 9. $\frac{\pi}{4}, \frac{5\pi}{4}$, 11. $x \in \left\langle 0, \frac{\pi}{4}\right\rangle \cup \left\langle\frac{5\pi}{4}, 2\pi\right\rangle$ 13. $\frac{3\pi}{4}, \frac{7\pi}{4}$ 15. $0, \frac{3\pi}{2}, 2\pi$ 17. none

19.

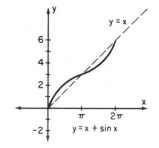

21.

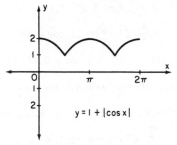

23. By geometrically adding ordinates of the two graphs when superimposed.

25.

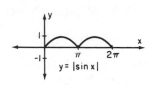

27. The distance remains constant if you look from above. If you look from the edge and let the rod left of the spindle be negative and the rod right of the spindle be positive, you get the sine or cosine curve.

PAGES 89-91   Exercises

1. 3, 2π 3. 2, π 5. $\frac{2}{3}, \frac{3\pi}{2}$ 7. $\frac{1}{18}, 36\pi$ 9. a. $\left(\frac{\pi}{2}, 2\right)$ b. $\left(\frac{3\pi}{2}, -2\right)$ c. $(0, 0), (\pi, 0)$ 11. a. $\left(0, \frac{4}{5}\right)$

b. $\left(\frac{\pi}{2}, -\frac{4}{5}\right)$ c. $\left(\frac{\pi}{4}, 0\right), \left(\frac{3\pi}{4}, 0\right)$ 13. a. $\left(\frac{3\pi}{4}, 5\right)$ b. $\left(\frac{9\pi}{4}, -5\right)$ c. $(0, 0), \left(\frac{3\pi}{2}, 0\right)$ 15. a. $(0, 1)$

b. $\left(\frac{5\pi}{4}, -1\right)$ c. $\left(\frac{5\pi}{8}, 0\right), \left(\frac{15\pi}{8}, 0\right)$ 17. Amplitude is 2, period is 2π. 19. Amplitude is $\frac{4}{5}$, period

is π. 21. Amplitude is 5, period is 3π. 23. Amplitude is 1, period is $\frac{5}{2}\pi$. 25. $y = 3\sin 2x$

27. $y = 12 \sin (\pi x)$ 29. $y = 4 \sin 6x$ 31. $y = 7 \sin (\frac{3}{2}x)$ 33. $y = -2 \sin (\frac{2}{5}x)$

35. Amplitude of A sin x is |A|. Amplitude of -A sin x is |-A|, and |A| = |-A| for all

$A \in R$.   37. 1   39. 60   41. 20   43. $\frac{1}{2\pi}$ 45. $\frac{1}{\pi}$; Period of $\frac{1}{60}$ t for graph between 0 and

$\frac{2}{60}$. Maximum at $\frac{1}{240}$ and $\frac{5}{240}$, minimum at $\frac{3}{240}$ and $\frac{7}{240}$. Curve crosses the t axis at 0,

$\frac{1}{120}, \frac{1}{60}, \frac{3}{120}$ and $\frac{2}{60}$.

PAGES 94-96   Exercises

1. $y = 5 \sin (x - \frac{\pi}{3})$ 3. $y = \frac{2}{3} \sin (8x + \pi)$ 5. $y = 7 \sin (\frac{4x}{3} + \frac{\pi}{3})$ 7. $y = 3 \cos (2x - \frac{4\pi}{3})$

9. $y = 100 \cos (\frac{2x}{3} + \frac{2\pi}{3})$ 11. $y = \frac{7}{3} \cos (\frac{12x}{5} + \frac{12}{5})$

	Amplitude	Period	Phase Shift
13.	3	2π	$\frac{\pi}{4}$
15.	$\frac{2}{3}$	4π	$-\frac{2\pi}{5}$
17.	1	3π	$\frac{3\pi}{2}$
19.	2	π	$\frac{\pi}{4}$
21.	3	1	$-\frac{1}{2}$
23.	2	2	$\frac{1}{2}$
25.	3	$\frac{\pi}{2}$	$-\frac{1}{2}$
27.	5	2π	3

29. Since $\sin (3x - \frac{\pi}{2}) = -\sin (-(3x - \frac{\pi}{2})) = -\sin (-3x + \frac{\pi}{2})$, result follows.   31. i. and iii. have

identical graphs. Likewise with ii. and iv. This follows from the fact that for a $\in$ R, cos (-a) =

cos a.

PAGES 102-103   Exercises

1-4.		Tangent	Secant
	0	0	1
	$\frac{\pi}{6}$	$\frac{1}{\sqrt{3}}$	$\frac{2}{\sqrt{3}}$
	$\frac{\pi}{4}$	1	$\sqrt{2}$

	Tangent	Secant
$\dfrac{\pi}{3}$	$\sqrt{3}$	2
$\dfrac{\pi}{2}$	undefined	undefined
$\dfrac{2\pi}{3}$	$-\sqrt{3}$	-2
$\dfrac{3\pi}{4}$	-1	$-\sqrt{2}$
$\dfrac{5\pi}{6}$	$\dfrac{1}{\sqrt{3}}$	$\dfrac{2}{\sqrt{3}}$
π	0	-1
$\dfrac{7\pi}{6}$	$\dfrac{1}{\sqrt{3}}$	$-\dfrac{2}{\sqrt{3}}$
$\dfrac{5\pi}{4}$	1	$-\sqrt{2}$
$\dfrac{4\pi}{3}$	$\sqrt{3}$	-2
$\dfrac{3\pi}{2}$	undefined	undefined
$\dfrac{5\pi}{3}$	$-\sqrt{3}$	2
$\dfrac{7\pi}{4}$	-1	$\sqrt{2}$
$\dfrac{11\pi}{6}$	$-\dfrac{1}{\sqrt{3}}$	$\dfrac{2}{\sqrt{3}}$
2π	0	1

5. $\tan x = \dfrac{\sin x}{\cos x} = \dfrac{-\sin (x + \pi)}{-\cos (x + \pi)} = \tan (x + \pi)$ 7. $\csc x = \dfrac{1}{\sin x} = \dfrac{1}{\sin (x + 2\pi)}$ 9. I, IV   11. I, III

13. II, III   15. II, IV   17. III, IV   19. $-2\pi, -\pi, 0, \pi, 2\pi$ 21. $-2\pi, -\pi, 0, \pi, 2\pi$ 23.-31. Refer

to the graphs of the tan, cot, sec, and csc on Pages 98-101 of the text. Only the graph for

Exercise 33 is shown as the others are similar. 33. Period $\dfrac{2\pi}{3}$, phase shift $-\dfrac{\pi}{3}$. 35. Even 37.Odd.

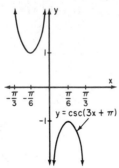

$y = \csc(3x + \pi)$

39. $-\cot x = \dfrac{\cos x}{-\sin x} = \dfrac{\sin (x + \frac{\pi}{2})}{\cos (x + \frac{\pi}{2})} = \tan (x + \frac{\pi}{2})$, therefore the graphs

are the same.   41. $|\cot x| = |\dfrac{\cos x}{\sin x}| = \dfrac{|\cos x|}{|\sin x|}$. For $\sin x \neq 0$, $|\cot x|$

$|\sin x| = |\cos x|$. Then because $|\sin x| \leq 1$, $|\cot x| \geq |\cos x|$.

43. $|\cot x| = |\dfrac{\cos x}{\sin x}| = |\cos x| |\dfrac{1}{\sin x}|$, $|\csc x| = |\dfrac{1}{\sin x}|$. And $|\cos x|$

$|\dfrac{1}{\sin x}| < |\dfrac{1}{\sin x}|$ follows from the fact that $|\cos x| \leq 1$.

PAGES 105-106   Exercises

1. $\tan x = \dfrac{\sin x}{\cos x} = \sin x\,(\dfrac{1}{\cos x}) = \sin x \sec x$ 3. $\operatorname{Tan}^2 x = \dfrac{\sin^2 x}{\cos^2 x} = \dfrac{1 - \cos^2 x}{\cos^2 x}$ 5. $1 + \tan^2 x =$

$\dfrac{\cos^2 x}{\cos^2 x} + \dfrac{\sin^2 x}{\cos^2 x} = \dfrac{\cos^2 x + \sin^2 x}{\cos^2 x} = \dfrac{1}{\cos^2 x} = \sec^2 x$ 7. $\csc^4 x - \cot^4 x = (\csc^2 x + \cot^2 x) \cdot$

$(\csc^2 x - \cot^2 x) = (\csc^2 x + \cot^2 x) \cdot 1$ (See Exercise 4.)   9. $(1 - \tan x)^2 = 1 - 2\tan x +$

$\tan^2 x = (1 + \tan^2 x) - 2\tan x = \sec^2 x - 2\tan x$ 11. $\dfrac{\cos^2 x}{\sin x} + \sin x = \dfrac{\cos^2 x + \sin^2 x}{\sin x} =$

$\dfrac{1}{\sin x} = \csc x$ 13. $\dfrac{\tan x}{1 - \cos^2 x} = \dfrac{\tan x}{\sin^2 x} = \dfrac{\sin x}{\cos x} \cdot \dfrac{1}{\sin^2 x} = \dfrac{1}{\sin x \cos x} = \sec x \csc x$ 15. $2\sin^2 x - 1$

$= 2(1 - \cos^2 x) - 1 = 2 - 2\cos^2 x - 1 = 1 - 2\cos^2 x$ 17. a. $\pm\dfrac{\sin x}{\sqrt{1 - \sin^2 x}}$ b. $\pm\dfrac{\sqrt{1 - \cos^2 x}}{\cos x}$

c. $\pm\sqrt{\sec^2 x - 1}$ 19. a. $\pm\dfrac{\cos x}{\sqrt{1 - \cos^2 x}}$ b. $\dfrac{1}{\tan x}$ 21. $\dfrac{\cos x - \sin x}{\cos x} = \dfrac{\cos x}{\cos x} - \dfrac{\sin x}{\cos x} = 1 - \tan x$

23. $\tan x\,(\tan x + \cot x) = \tan^2 x + 1 = \sec^2 x$ 25. $\dfrac{\cos x + 1}{\sin^3 x} = \dfrac{\cos x + 1}{\sin x\,(1 - \cos^2 x)} =$

$\dfrac{\cos x + 1}{(\cos x + 1)\,(1 - \cos x)\sin x} = \dfrac{1}{1 - \cos x} \cdot \dfrac{1}{\sin x} = \dfrac{\csc x}{1 - \cos x}$ 27. $\dfrac{\tan x}{\sec x} + \dfrac{\cot x}{\csc x} =$

$\dfrac{\frac{\sin x}{\cos x}}{\frac{1}{\cos x}} + \dfrac{\frac{\cos x}{\sin x}}{\frac{1}{\sin x}} = \dfrac{\sin^2 x}{\sin x} + \dfrac{\cos^2 x}{\cos x} = \sin x + \cos x$ 29. $\dfrac{\sin^3 x + \cos^3 x}{1 - 2\cos^2 x} =$

$\dfrac{(\sin x + \cos x)\,(\sin^2 x - \sin x \cos x + \cos^2 x)}{1 - 2\cos^2 x} = \dfrac{(\sin x + \cos x)\,(1 - \sin x \cos x)}{1 - 2\cos^2 x} =$

$\dfrac{\sin x - \sin^2 x \cos x + \cos x - \sin x \cos^2 x}{1 - 2\cos^2 x} = \dfrac{1 - \sin x \cos x}{\sin x - \cos x} = \dfrac{\sec x - \sin x}{\sin x - \cos x}$

31. $\dfrac{\sin x}{1 - \cos x} = \dfrac{\sqrt{1 - \cos^2 x}}{1 - \cos x} = \sqrt{\dfrac{1 - \cos^2 x}{(1 - \cos x)^2}} = \sqrt{\dfrac{(1 + \cos x)\,(1 - \cos x)}{(1 - \cos x)^2}} = \sqrt{\dfrac{1 + \cos x}{1 - \cos x}}$ for x

in QI or II.   33. $\cos\,(x + \dfrac{3\pi}{2}) = \sin\,(\dfrac{\pi}{2} - (x + \dfrac{3\pi}{2})) = \sin\,(-\pi - x) = -\sin\,(\pi + x) = -(-\sin x) = \sin x$

PAGES 107-109   Chapter Objectives and Review

3. $\sqrt{13}$ 5. 15   7. See text Page 66.   9. See Page 71.   11. See Page 97.   13. For $W : x \rightarrow$

$(u, v) \sin x = v$ and $\cos x = u$. But u and v are points on the unit circle. Therefore $u^2 + v^2 =$

1 or $\cos^2 x + \sin^2 x = 1$.   15. See Exercise 14.   17. From Exercise 16, $\sin\,(-x) = -v = -\sin x$.

19. See Page 83.   21. See Page 101.   23. See Page 98.

	Amplitude	Period	Phase Shift
25.	$\dfrac{1}{2}$	2π	0
27.	4	π	0
29.	3	2π	$-\pi$
31.	2	$\dfrac{\pi}{2}$	$\dfrac{\pi}{4}$

33. $\sin^2 x = 1 - \cos^2 x = 1 - \dfrac{1}{\sec^2 x} = \dfrac{\sec^2 x - 1}{\sec^2 x}$ 35. $\sec x + \tan x = \sec x \left(1 + \dfrac{\tan x}{\sec x}\right) = \sec x$

$(1 + \tan x \cdot \cos x) = \sec x \left(1 + \dfrac{\sin x}{\cos x} \cdot \cos x\right) = (1 + \sin x) \sec x$ 37. $\tan(-x) = \dfrac{\sin(-x)}{\cos(-x)} =$

$\dfrac{-\sin x}{\cos x} = -\tan x$

PAGE 109   Chapter Test

1. $AB = \sqrt{74}$; $\overline{BC} = \sqrt{68}$; $\overline{AC} = \sqrt{10}$ 3. $\dfrac{3}{4}$ 5. Answers will vary.   7. a. Magnitude of maxi-

mum height. b. $|A|$; $|A|$ 9. Amplitude 2, period π, phase shift $\dfrac{\pi}{4}$.   11. a. $\{y : y \leq -1 \text{ or } y \geq 1\}$

b. $\{y : y \leq -1 \text{ or } y \geq 1\}$ c. $\{\text{All reals}\}$.

CHAPTER 3   TRIGONOMETRY

PAGES 114-115   Exercises

1. $90°$ 3. $270°$ 5. $-90°$ 7. $-60°$ 9. $150°$ 11. $288°$ 13. $510°$ 15. $-240°$ 17. Answers

will vary. $\theta - 360°$ or $\theta - n360°$, $n \in W$.   19. In Quadrant II $90° + n \cdot 360° < \theta < 180° + n \cdot$

$360°$, $n \in W$. In Quadrant III $180° + n \cdot 360° < \theta < 270° + n \cdot 360°$, $n \in W$. In Quadrant

IV $270° + n \cdot 360° < \theta < (n + 1) 360°$, $n \in W$.   21. I   23. IV   25. II   27. II   29. IV

31. II   33. Points B, C, and D are on the terminal side. Point E is not.   35. For $A \dfrac{x}{r} =$

$\dfrac{-1}{\sqrt{5}}, \dfrac{y}{r} = \dfrac{2}{\sqrt{5}}, \dfrac{y}{x} = -2$. For B, C, and D $\dfrac{x}{r}, \dfrac{y}{r}$, and $\dfrac{y}{x}$ are the same as for A.   37. Point

B is on the terminal side. Points C and D are not. $\overline{AO} = 5$, $\overline{BO} = 10$, $\overline{CO} = 4\sqrt{13}$, and $\overline{DO} =$

$2\sqrt{89}$. For A and B $\dfrac{x}{r} = \dfrac{3}{5}, \dfrac{y}{r} = \dfrac{-4}{5}$, and $\dfrac{y}{x} = \dfrac{-4}{3}$. For C $\dfrac{x}{r} = \dfrac{2}{\sqrt{13}}, \dfrac{y}{r} = \dfrac{-3}{\sqrt{13}}$, and $\dfrac{y}{x} = \dfrac{-3}{2}$. For D $\dfrac{x}{r} =$

$\dfrac{5}{\sqrt{89}}, \dfrac{y}{r} = \dfrac{-8}{\sqrt{89}}$, and $\dfrac{y}{x} = \dfrac{-8}{5}$. For any point on the terminal side of the angle $\dfrac{x}{r} = \dfrac{3}{5}, \dfrac{y}{r} = \dfrac{-4}{5}$, and $\dfrac{y}{x} = \dfrac{-4}{3}$.

PAGES 118-119   Exercises

1. $\dfrac{\pi}{3}$ 3. $-\pi$ 5. $-\dfrac{\pi}{6}$ 7. $\dfrac{3\pi}{4}$ 9. $\dfrac{11\pi}{6}$ 11. $-\dfrac{7\pi}{6}$ 13. $30°$ 15. $90°$ 17. $-240°$ 19. $-144°$

21. $-540°$ 23. $612°$ 25. $-57°17'45''$ 27. $1170°$ 29. $\dfrac{1}{10}$ 31. $\dfrac{\pi}{5}$ 33. a. $\dfrac{1}{4}, 90°, \dfrac{\pi}{2}, 2\pi$ inches

b. $\dfrac{8}{15}, 192°, \dfrac{16\pi}{15}, \dfrac{64\pi}{15}$ inches c. $\dfrac{3}{4}, 270°, \dfrac{3\pi}{2}, 6\pi$ inches d. $\dfrac{5}{6}, 300°, \dfrac{5\pi}{3}, \dfrac{20\pi}{3}$ inches   35. $3°$

37. $\dfrac{\pi}{30}$ inches   39. $\dfrac{44}{\pi}$ revolutions   41. $\dfrac{s}{r}$ 43. A degree is the measure of an angle that

intercepts an arc equal in length to $\dfrac{1}{360}$ the circumference of a circle whose center is the

vertex of the angle.

	sin θ	cos θ	tan θ	csc θ	sec θ	cot θ
1.	$\dfrac{3}{\sqrt{34}}$	$\dfrac{5}{\sqrt{34}}$	$\dfrac{3}{5}$	$\dfrac{\sqrt{34}}{3}$	$\dfrac{\sqrt{34}}{5}$	$\dfrac{5}{3}$
3.	$-\dfrac{3}{\sqrt{34}}$	$-\dfrac{5}{\sqrt{34}}$	$\dfrac{3}{5}$	$-\dfrac{\sqrt{34}}{3}$	$-\dfrac{\sqrt{34}}{5}$	$\dfrac{5}{3}$
5.	$-\dfrac{8}{\sqrt{65}}$	$\dfrac{1}{\sqrt{65}}$	-8	$-\dfrac{\sqrt{65}}{8}$	$\sqrt{65}$	$-\dfrac{1}{8}$
7.	$\dfrac{4}{5}$	$-\dfrac{3}{5}$	$-\dfrac{4}{3}$	$\dfrac{5}{4}$	$-\dfrac{5}{3}$	$-\dfrac{3}{4}$
9.	1	0	undefined	1	undefined	0
11.	0	1	0	undefined	1	undefined
13.	$\dfrac{5}{13}$	$\dfrac{12}{13}$	$\dfrac{5}{12}$	$\dfrac{13}{5}$	$\dfrac{13}{12}$	$\dfrac{12}{5}$
15.	$\dfrac{1}{\sqrt{2}}$	$-\dfrac{1}{\sqrt{2}}$	-1	$\sqrt{2}$	$-\sqrt{2}$	-1
17.	$\dfrac{2}{\sqrt{29}}$	$\dfrac{5}{\sqrt{29}}$	$\dfrac{2}{5}$	$\dfrac{\sqrt{29}}{2}$	$\dfrac{\sqrt{29}}{5}$	$\dfrac{5}{2}$
19.	$-\dfrac{1}{2}$	$\dfrac{\sqrt{3}}{2}$	$-\dfrac{1}{\sqrt{3}}$	-2	$\dfrac{2}{\sqrt{3}}$	$-\sqrt{3}$
21.	$-\dfrac{5}{13}$	$\dfrac{12}{13}$	$-\dfrac{5}{12}$	$-\dfrac{13}{5}$	$\dfrac{13}{12}$	$-\dfrac{12}{5}$
23.	$\dfrac{\sqrt{21}}{5}$	$-\dfrac{2}{5}$	$-\dfrac{\sqrt{21}}{2}$	$\dfrac{5}{\sqrt{21}}$	$-\dfrac{5}{2}$	$-\dfrac{2}{\sqrt{21}}$

25. sin θ $\begin{array}{c|c} + & + \\ \hline - & - \end{array}$ cos θ $\begin{array}{c|c} - & + \\ \hline - & + \end{array}$ tan θ $\begin{array}{c|c} - & + \\ \hline + & - \end{array}$ 27. $\sin \theta = -\dfrac{u}{\sqrt{u^2 + v^2}}$,

$\cos \theta = -\dfrac{v}{\sqrt{u^2 + v^2}}$

PAGES 126-127   Exercises

1. $\cos(-\theta) = \cos \theta$ 3. $\cos(180° + \theta) = -\cos \theta$

5. $\sin(180° - \theta) = \sin \theta$ 7. $\cos(90° + \theta) = -\sin \theta$ 9. $\sin(\theta \pm 360° \cdot n) = \sin \theta$, $n \in W$

11. $\sin(\theta - 45°) = \cos(\theta + 45°)$ 13. $-\tan \theta$ 15. $-\csc \theta$ 17. $\tan \theta$

PAGE 132   Exercises

1. .9205   3. .2493   5. .3173   7. 76° 40′   9. 63° 50′   11. 58°   13. 14° 36′   15. 63° 26′

17. 38° 55′   19. 14.1 inches   21. 88.9 miles   23. 419.2 feet   25. 419.6 feet   27. 10 inches

1. $180° - 78° 50'$ 3. $180° - 38° 30'$ 5. $180° - 18° 20'$ 7. $180° + 3° 20'$ 9. $180° + 44° 50'$

11. $360° - 28° 50'$ 13. $360° - 89° 50'$ 15. $360° - 14° 40'$ 17. $90° + 6° 5'$ 19. $90° - 51° 40'$

21. $90° - 88° 50'$ 23. $\cos \frac{7\pi}{6} = \cos (\pi + \frac{\pi}{6}) = -\cos \frac{\pi}{6} = -\frac{\sqrt{3}}{2}$ 25. $\sin 281° = \sin (360° - 79°) =$

$-\sin 79° = -.9816$ 27. $\tan 265° = \tan (180° + 85°) = \tan 85° = 11.430$ 29. $\cos 335° =$

$\cos (360° - 25°) = .9063$ 31. $\sin (270° - \theta) = \sin [360° - (90° + \theta)] = -\sin (90° + \theta) =$

$-\cos \theta$, $\cos (270° - \theta) = \cos (90° + \theta) = -\sin \theta$, $\tan (270° - \theta) = -\tan (90° + \theta) = \cot \theta$

1. $\frac{\sqrt{2}}{4} (1 - \sqrt{3})$ 3. $-\frac{\sqrt{2}}{4} (1 + \sqrt{3})$ 5. $\frac{\sqrt{2}}{4} (\sqrt{3} + 1)$ 7. $\frac{\sqrt{2}}{4} (1 - \sqrt{3})$ 9. $\cos (\frac{\pi}{2} + \theta) =$

$\cos \frac{\pi}{2} \cos \theta - \sin \frac{\pi}{2} \sin \theta = 0 \cdot \cos \theta - 1 \cdot \sin \theta = -\sin \theta$ 11. $\cos (180° - \theta) = \cos 180° \cos \theta +$

$\sin 180° \sin \theta = -1 \cdot \cos \theta + 0 \cdot \sin \theta = -\cos \theta$ 13. $\cos (\pi + \theta) = \cos\pi \cos\theta - \sin\pi \sin\theta =$

$(-1) \cos\theta - 0 \cdot \sin\theta = -\cos \theta$ 15. 0 17. $\frac{304}{425}$ 19. $-\frac{17}{145}$ 21. (15.) $\frac{24}{25}$ (16.) $\frac{318}{481}$ (17.) $\frac{416}{425}$

(18.) $\frac{56}{65}$ (19.) $\frac{143}{145}$ (20.) $\frac{432}{793}$ 23. $\cos 3x \cos 5x + \sin 3x \sin 5x = \cos (3x - 5x) = \cos (-2x) =$

$\cos 2x$ 25. $\cos (\alpha - \beta) - \cos (\alpha + \beta) = \cos \alpha \cos \beta + \sin \alpha \sin \beta - (\cos \alpha \cos \beta - \sin \alpha \sin \beta) =$

$2 \sin \alpha \sin \beta$ 27. $\cos (\alpha + \beta + \theta) = \cos [(\alpha + \beta) + \theta] = \cos (\alpha + \beta) \cdot \cos \theta - \sin (\alpha + \beta) \sin \theta =$

$(\cos \alpha \cos \beta - \sin \alpha \sin \beta) \cos \theta - \cos [(\frac{\pi}{2} - \alpha) - \beta] \sin \theta = \cos \alpha \cos \beta \cos \theta - \sin \theta \sin \beta \cos \theta -$

$\cos (\frac{\pi}{2} - \alpha) \cos \beta \sin \theta - \sin (\frac{\pi}{2} - \alpha) \sin \beta \sin \theta = \cos \alpha \cos \beta \cos \theta - \sin \alpha \sin \beta \cos \theta - \sin \alpha$

$\cos \beta \sin \theta - \cos \alpha \sin \beta \sin \theta$ 29. No. The proof in Exercise 28 does not generalize to

angles other than positive acute angles.

1. $\frac{\sqrt{6} + \sqrt{2}}{4}$ 3. $\frac{1}{2}$ 5. $\frac{1 + \sqrt{3}}{1 - \sqrt{3}}$ 7. $\frac{1}{\sqrt{3}}$ 9. $\frac{\sqrt{2} - \sqrt{6}}{4}$ 11. $\frac{-\sqrt{6} - \sqrt{2}}{4}$ 13. $\frac{\sqrt{3} - 1}{\sqrt{3} + 1}$

15. $\frac{3 + \sqrt{3}}{3 - \sqrt{3}}$ 17. $\sin (\frac{\pi}{2} + x) = \sin \frac{\pi}{2} \cos x + \sin x \cos \frac{\pi}{2} = 1 \cdot \cos x + \sin x \cdot 0 = \cos x$

19. $\sin (180° + \theta) = \sin 180° \cos \theta + \sin \theta \cos 180° = 0 \cdot \cos \theta + \sin \theta \cdot (-1) = -\sin \theta$

21. $\sin (\pi - \theta) = \sin \pi \cos \theta - \sin \theta \cos \pi = 0 \cdot \cos \theta - \sin \theta \cdot (-1) = \sin \theta$ 23. $\tan (180° + \theta) =$

$\frac{\tan 180° + \tan x}{1 - \tan 180° \tan x} = \frac{0 + \tan x}{1 - 0 \cdot \tan x} = \tan x$ Theorem 3-5 is applicable. 25. $\tan (\frac{3\pi}{2} + \theta) =$

$$\frac{\sin(\frac{3\pi}{2}+\theta)}{\cos(\frac{3\pi}{2}+\theta)} = \frac{\sin\frac{3\pi}{2}\cos\theta + \sin\theta\cos\frac{3\pi}{2}}{\cos\frac{3\pi}{2}\cos\theta - \sin\frac{3\pi}{2}\sin\theta} = -\frac{\cos\theta}{\sin\theta} = -\cot\theta \quad 27.\ \tan(270°-x) = \frac{\sin(270°-x)}{\cos(270°-x)} =$$

$$\frac{\sin 270°\cos x - \sin x\cos 270°}{\cos 270°\cos x + \sin 270°\sin x} = \frac{-1\cdot\cos x - \sin x\cdot 0}{0\cdot\cos x + (-1)\sin x} = \frac{-\cos x}{-\sin x} = \cot x \quad 29.\ \tan\frac{\pi}{3}=\sqrt{3}\ \text{and}$$

$$\sqrt{\frac{1-\cos\frac{2\pi}{3}}{1+\cos\frac{2\pi}{3}}} = \sqrt{\frac{1+\frac{1}{2}}{1-\frac{1}{2}}} = \sqrt{\frac{\frac{3}{2}}{\frac{1}{2}}} = \sqrt{3} \quad 31.\ \tan\frac{3\pi}{4}=-1\ \text{and}\ \frac{\sin\frac{3\pi}{2}}{1+\cos\frac{3\pi}{2}} = \frac{-1}{1+0} = -1 \quad 33.\ \cos\frac{2\pi}{3} = -\frac{1}{2}\ \text{and}$$

$$\cos^2\frac{\pi}{3} - \sin^2\frac{\pi}{3} = (\tfrac{1}{2})^2 - (\tfrac{\sqrt{3}}{2})^2 = \frac{1}{4} - \frac{3}{4} = -\frac{1}{2} \quad 35.\ \sin(\alpha+\beta)+\sin(\alpha-\beta) = \sin\alpha\cos\beta + \sin\beta\cos\alpha$$

$+ \sin\alpha\cos\beta - \sin\beta\cos\alpha = 2\sin\alpha\cos\beta \quad 37.\ \cot(-\alpha) = \frac{\cos(-\alpha)}{\sin(-\alpha)} = \frac{\cos\alpha}{-\sin\alpha} = -\cot\alpha$. Therefore true

for all α.   39. $\sin(\alpha+\beta)\cdot\sin(\alpha-\beta) = (\sin\alpha\cos\beta + \sin\beta\cos\alpha)\cdot(\sin\alpha\cos\beta - \sin\beta\cos\alpha) =$

$\sin^2\alpha\cos^2\beta - \sin^2\beta\cos^2\alpha$ equals $\sin^2\alpha - \sin^2\beta$ when $\cos^2\beta = 1$ and $\sin^2\beta = 0$ or when $\cos^2\alpha =$

1 and $\sin^2\alpha = 0$. This is true when α or $\beta = n\cdot 180°, n\in W$.   41. $\sin(\alpha+\beta)\cdot\sin(\alpha-\beta) =$

$\sin^2\alpha\cos^2\beta - \cos^2\alpha\sin^2\beta$ equals $\cos^2\beta - \cos^2\alpha$ when $\cos^2\beta = 0$ and $\sin^2\beta = 1$ or when $\cos^2\alpha =$

0 and $\sin^2\beta = 1$. Thus the statement is true when $\beta = (2n+1)90°$ or $\alpha = (2n+1)90°, n\in W$.

43. $\sec(\alpha+\beta) = \dfrac{1}{\cos(\alpha+\beta)}$ where $\cos(\alpha+\beta)\neq 0$ and $\alpha+\beta\neq(2n+1)90°, n\in W$. The state-

ment is true for all α and β except $\alpha+\beta = (2n+1)90°, n\in W$.

PAGES 147-148   Exercises

1. $\dfrac{\sqrt{2-\sqrt{3}}}{2}$ 3. $\sqrt{\dfrac{2-\sqrt{3}}{2+\sqrt{3}}}$ 5. $-\dfrac{\sqrt{2-\sqrt{3}}}{2}$ 7. $\dfrac{\sqrt{2+\sqrt{2}}}{2}$ 9. $\sqrt{\dfrac{2+\sqrt{2}}{2-\sqrt{2}}}$ 11. $-\dfrac{\sqrt{2+\sqrt{3}}}{2}$

13. $\dfrac{\sqrt{2-\sqrt{2-\sqrt{3}}}}{2}$ 15. $\dfrac{\sqrt{2-\sqrt{2+\sqrt{2}}}}{\sqrt{2+\sqrt{2+\sqrt{2}}}}$ 17. a. II b. I or II 19. $-\dfrac{12}{13}$ 21. $\dfrac{12}{5}$ 23. $-\dfrac{2}{\sqrt{13}}$

25. $-\dfrac{119}{169}$ 27. $\dfrac{\sqrt{5}}{5}$ 29. $-\dfrac{1}{2}$ 31. $-\dfrac{7}{25}$ 33. $\csc 2\theta = \dfrac{1}{\sin 2\theta} =$

$\dfrac{1}{2\sin\theta\cos\theta} = \dfrac{\csc\theta\sec\theta}{2}$ 35. $\sec 2\theta = \dfrac{1}{\cos 2\theta} = \dfrac{1}{1-2\sin^2\theta} = \dfrac{1}{\frac{\csc^2\theta-2}{\csc^2\theta}} = \dfrac{\csc^2\theta}{\csc^2\theta - 2}$

37. $\cot 2\theta = \dfrac{\cos 2\theta}{\sin 2\theta} = \sqrt{\dfrac{\cos 4\theta+1}{1-\cos 4\theta}} = \sqrt{\dfrac{1+\cos 4\theta}{1-\cos 4\theta}\cdot\dfrac{1+\cos 4\theta}{1+\cos 4\theta}} = \dfrac{1+\cos 4\theta}{\sin 4\theta}$

39. $\csc\dfrac{\theta}{2} = \dfrac{1}{\sin\frac{\theta}{2}} = \pm\sqrt{\dfrac{2}{1-\cos\theta}} = \pm\dfrac{\sqrt{2(1-\cos\theta)}}{1-\cos\theta}$ 41. $\tan\dfrac{\theta}{2} = \sqrt{\dfrac{1-\cos\theta}{1+\cos\theta}\cdot\dfrac{1+\cos\theta}{1+\cos\theta}} =$

$\dfrac{\sin\theta}{1+\cos\theta}$ 43. $\cos 3\alpha = \cos(\alpha+2\alpha) = \cos\alpha\cos 2\alpha - \sin\alpha\sin 2\alpha = \cos\alpha\cdot(2\cos^2\alpha - 1) - \sin\alpha\cdot$

$2\sin\alpha\cos\alpha = 2\cos^3\alpha - \cos\alpha - 2(1-\cos^2\alpha)\cos\alpha = 2\cos^3\alpha - \cos\alpha - 2\cos\alpha + 2\cos^3\alpha =$

$4\cos^3\alpha - 3\cos\alpha$

45. $\cos 4\alpha = \cos [2(2\alpha)] = \cos^2 2\alpha - \sin^2 2\alpha = (\cos^2 \alpha - \sin^2 \alpha)^2 - (2\sin \alpha \cos \alpha)^2 =$

$\cos^4 \alpha - 2\cos^2 \alpha \sin 2\alpha + \sin^4 \alpha - 4\sin^2 \alpha \cos^2 \alpha = \cos^4 \alpha - 2\sin^2 \alpha \cos^2 \alpha + \sin^4 \alpha$

$- 4\sin^2 \alpha \cos^2 \alpha = \cos^4 \alpha - 2(1 - \cos^2 \alpha)\cos^2 \alpha + (1 - \cos^2 \alpha)(1 - \cos^2 \alpha) - 4(1 - \cos^2 \alpha)$

$\cos^2 \alpha = \cos^4 \alpha - 2\cos^2 \alpha + 2\cos^4 \alpha + 1 - 2\cos^2 \alpha + \cos^4 \alpha - 4\cos^2 \alpha + 4\cos^4 \alpha =$

$8\cos^4 \alpha - 8\cos^2 \alpha + 1$

PAGE 150   Exercises

1. $\sin 4x + \sin 2x$ 3. $\cos 7x + \cos 3x$ 5. $-\frac{1}{2}\cos 14x + \frac{1}{2}\cos 6x$ 7. $\frac{1}{2}\sin 12x - \frac{1}{2}\sin 4x$

9. $-2\sin 37° \sin 14°$ 11. $2\cos 87° \sin 44°$ 13. $2\sin \frac{7\pi}{24}\cos \frac{\pi}{24}$ 15. $2\cos \frac{1}{2}\cos \frac{1}{4}$

17. $\frac{\cos 7t + \cos 5t}{\sin 7t - \sin 5t} = \frac{2\cos 6t \cos t}{2\cos 6t \sin t} = \frac{\cos t}{\sin t} = \frac{\csc t}{\sec t}$ 19. $\frac{\sin 4x + \sin 2x}{\cos 4x + \cos 2x} = \frac{2\sin 3x \cos x}{2\cos 3x \cos x} =$

$\tan 3x = \frac{1}{\cot 3x}$ 21. $\frac{\sin 3x - \sin x}{\cos 3x + \cos x} = \frac{2\cos 2x \sin x}{2\cos 2x \cos x} = \tan x$

PAGES 151-152   Chapter Objectives and Review

3.
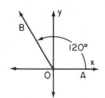

5.

7.
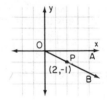

9. See page 113.   11. $180° = \pi$ radians.   13. $-\frac{\pi}{3}$ 15. $\frac{77\pi}{36}$ 17. $-330°$ 19. $630°$ 21. $\cos \theta = \frac{x}{r}$.

23. $\cot \theta = \frac{x}{y}$ 25. $\csc \theta = \frac{r}{y}$ 27. ≈ 1.7 29. ≈ 3.9 31. ≈ 2.2 33. $\cot 17° = \frac{d}{2}$, $d \approx 6.5$ miles

35. See page 141.   37. See page 137.   39. $\cos (\pi + \alpha) + \cos \pi \cos \alpha - \sin \pi \sin \alpha = -1 \cdot \cos \alpha$

$- 0 \cdot \sin \alpha = -\cos \alpha$ 41. $\cos (\alpha + \alpha) = \cos \alpha \cos \alpha - \sin \alpha \sin \alpha = \cos^2 \alpha - \sin^2 \alpha$

PAGE 153   Chapter Test

1. a. clockwise b. IV c. See pages 112-113.   3. a. $\frac{2\pi}{5}$ b. $-\frac{8\pi}{3}$ c. $\frac{\pi}{18}$ 5. a. $\frac{y}{r}$ b. $\frac{x}{r}$ c. $\frac{y}{x}$ d. $\frac{x}{y}$

e. $\frac{r}{x}$ f. $\frac{r}{y}$ 7. $\sin (\pi - \theta) = \sin \pi \cos \theta - \cos \pi \sin \theta = 0 \cdot \cos \theta - (-1)\sin \theta = \sin \theta$ 9. $\frac{\sqrt{2-\sqrt{2}}}{2}$

11. ≈ 2145 feet.   13. a. .6561 b. .2309 c. .9336 d. -1.1504

CHAPTER 4 APPLYING TRIGONOMETRY

PAGES 158-160   Exercises

1. $a = 15.41$, $b = 10.90$, $C = 67°$ 3. $A = 9°$, $b \approx 42$, $c \approx 49$ 5. $A = 90°$, $a = 32.5$, $b = 20.7$

7. $A = 47° 40'$, $C = 32° 20'$, $c = 10.9$ 9. $\dfrac{a}{\sin A} = \dfrac{b}{\sin B} \rightarrow a \sin B = b \sin A$, therefore $\dfrac{a}{b} = \dfrac{\sin A}{\sin B}$.

11. $AC \approx 52$ $BC = \dfrac{(.3502)(40)}{.7009} \approx 20$. 13. $AC \approx 241$, height of the tree ≈ 51. 15. a. ≈ 1090

b. ≈ 1060 feet c. 264 feet 17. $\dfrac{a+b}{a-b} = \dfrac{\sin A + \sin B}{\sin A - \sin B} \rightarrow$

$$\dfrac{2 \sin \frac{1}{2}(A+B) \cos \frac{1}{2}(A-B)}{2 \cos \frac{1}{2}(A+B) \sin \frac{1}{2}(A-B)} \rightarrow \tan \frac{1}{2}(A+B) \cdot \left(\dfrac{1}{\tan \frac{1}{2}(A-B)} \right) \rightarrow \dfrac{\tan \frac{1}{2}(A+B)}{\tan \frac{1}{2}(A-B)}$$

PAGES 164-166   Exercises

1. $c \approx 5.26$ 3. 24.9 5. 17.6 7. 12.29 9. No solution. 11. One solution. 13. No solution.

15. One solution. 17. No solution. 19. $A = 47° 40'$. 21. $114° 38'$, $84° 44'$ 23. $A \approx 139°$,

$B \approx 41°$ 25. $1 = \dfrac{2ab}{2ab}$ and $t = \dfrac{a^2 + b^2 - c^2}{2ab}$, then $1 - t = \dfrac{2ab - (a^2 + b^2 - c^2)}{2ab} =$

$\dfrac{c^2 - a^2 + 2ab - b^2}{2ab} = \dfrac{c^2 - (a-b)^2}{2ab} = \dfrac{(c+a-b)(c-a+b)}{2ab} = \dfrac{(-a+b+c)(a-b+c)}{2ab}$. 27. Since

$\cos C = \dfrac{a^2 + b^2 - c^2}{2ab}$, the result follows from Exercise 25. 29. i. $\sin \left(\dfrac{C}{2}\right) = \sqrt{\dfrac{1 - \cos C}{2}} =$

$\sqrt{\dfrac{(-a+b+c)(a-b+c)}{4ab}}$, then $\dfrac{-a+b+c}{2} = \dfrac{a+b+c}{2} - a = s - a$ and $\dfrac{a-b+c}{2} = \dfrac{a+b+c}{2} - b = s - b$,

therefore $\sin \left(\dfrac{C}{2}\right) = \sqrt{\dfrac{(s-a)(s-b)}{ab}}$. ii. $\cos \left(\dfrac{C}{2}\right) = \sqrt{\dfrac{1 + \cos C}{2}} = \sqrt{\dfrac{(a+b+c)(a+b-c)}{4ab}} =$

$\sqrt{\dfrac{(a+b+c)}{2} \cdot \dfrac{(a+b-c)}{2} \cdot \left(\dfrac{1}{ab}\right)} = \sqrt{\dfrac{s(s-c)}{ab}}$. iii. $\tan \left(\dfrac{C}{2}\right) = \dfrac{\sin \left(\dfrac{C}{2}\right)}{\cos \left(\dfrac{C}{2}\right)} = \sqrt{\dfrac{(s-a)(s-b)}{ab} \cdot \dfrac{ab}{s(s-c)}} =$

$\sqrt{\dfrac{(s-a)(s-b)}{s(s-c)}}$ iv. $\tan \left(\dfrac{C}{2}\right) = \sqrt{\dfrac{(s-a)(s-b)}{s(s-c)}} = \sqrt{\dfrac{(s-a)(s-b)(s-c)}{s}} \cdot \dfrac{1}{s-c} = \dfrac{P}{s-c}$ 31. $\sin C =$

$2 \sin \left(\dfrac{C}{2}\right) \cdot \cos \left(\dfrac{C}{2}\right) = 2 \sqrt{\dfrac{(s-a)(s-b)}{ab}} \sqrt{\dfrac{s(s-c)}{ab}} = \dfrac{2}{ab} \sqrt{s(s-a)(s-b)(s-c)}$.

PAGES 169-170   Exercises

1. 19.485 3. No solution. 5. $K \approx 650$ 7. No Solution. 9. .8660 11. No solution.

13. $b \approx 18.1$ 15. $C = 150°$ 17. $K = 96$ 19. $\dfrac{b^2 \tan \theta}{4}$ 21. $r = \dfrac{K}{s}$ 23. $R = OB = \dfrac{BD}{\sin < BOD} =$

$\dfrac{\frac{a}{2}}{\sin A} = \dfrac{a}{2 \sin A}$ and by the law of sines $R = \dfrac{a}{2 \sin A} = \dfrac{b}{2 \sin B} = \dfrac{c}{2 \sin C}$ 25. Draw triangle

ABC, and drop a perpendicular from C to **AB**, to point D. Consider the case where all the

angles in triangle ABC are acute. Then $AD = b \cos A$, $DB = a \cos B$, so $AB = a \cos B + b \cos$

A. Case 2. is similar.

27. $2Rr = \dfrac{2abc}{4K} \cdot \dfrac{K}{s} = \dfrac{abc}{2} \cdot \dfrac{2}{a+b+c} = \dfrac{abc}{a+b+c}$. 29. $\sin\left(\dfrac{C}{2}\right) = \sqrt{\dfrac{(s-a)(s-b)}{ab}}$ and $\cos\left(\dfrac{C}{2}\right) = \sqrt{\dfrac{s(s-c)}{ab}}$. Multiplying we get $\sin\left(\dfrac{C}{2}\right)\cos\left(\dfrac{C}{2}\right) = \sqrt{\dfrac{s(s-a)(s-b)(s-c)}{ab \cdot ab}} = \dfrac{\sqrt{s(s-a)(s-b)(s-c)}}{ab} = \dfrac{K}{ab}$. Therefore $K = ab \sin\left(\dfrac{C}{2}\right)\cos\left(\dfrac{C}{2}\right)$.

PAGES 173-174   Exercises

1. $\left\{ x : x = \dfrac{3\pi}{4} \pm n\,\pi, n \in W \right\}$ 3. $\left\{ x : x = \pi \pm 2n\pi, n \in W \right\}$ 5. $\left\{ x : x = \pm\dfrac{\pi}{3} \pm 2n\pi, n \in W \right\}$

7. $\left\{ x : x = \dfrac{\pi}{6} \pm n\pi, n \in W \right\}$ 9. $\left\{ x : x = \dfrac{\pi}{3} \pm 2n\pi \text{ or } x = \dfrac{2\pi}{3} \pm 2n\pi, n \in W \right\}$

11. $\left\{ x : x = \dfrac{\pi}{2} \pm 2n\pi, n \in W \right\}$ 13. $\left\{ x : x = 40° \pm n \cdot 360° \text{ or } x = 140° \pm n \cdot 360°, n \in W \right\}$

15. $\left\{ x : x = \dfrac{3\pi}{4} \pm n\pi \text{ or } x = \dfrac{7\pi}{6} \pm 2n\pi \text{ or } x = -\dfrac{\pi}{6} \pm 2n\pi, n \in W \right\}$ 17. $\dfrac{4}{5}$ 19. $\pm\dfrac{25}{24}$ 21. $\pm\dfrac{7}{24}$

23. $\pm\dfrac{\sqrt{17}}{4}$ 25. $\pm\dfrac{u}{\sqrt{1-u^2}}$ 27. $\pm\sqrt{1-u^2}$ 29. $\pm\sqrt{1+u^2}$ 31. $\pm\dfrac{52}{5\sqrt{313}} \pm \dfrac{36}{5\sqrt{313}}$

33. $\pm\dfrac{24}{25}$ 35. $\pm\dfrac{336}{527}$

PAGES 179-180   Exercises

1. $-45°$ 3. $31°$ 5. $60°$ 7. $30°$ 9. $22°$ 11. 4 13. $\dfrac{2}{\sqrt{3}}$ 15. $\dfrac{2}{\sqrt{5}}$ 17. $\dfrac{4}{5}$ 19. $-\dfrac{11}{60}$ 21. $\dfrac{4}{\sqrt{15}}$

23. This curve has two branches. For $x \geq 1, 0 < y \leq \dfrac{\pi}{2}$, and for $x \leq -1, -\dfrac{\pi}{2} \leq y < 0$.   25. Let $a = \text{Arc sin } u$. Then $\cos a = \sqrt{1-u^2}$. Thus $\cos(\text{Arc sin } u) = \sqrt{1-u^2}$.   27. $\dfrac{4}{5}$.   29. $\dfrac{12\sqrt{3}-5}{26}$

31. $\dfrac{136}{305}$ 33. $\dfrac{-240}{289}$ 35. $\dfrac{336}{527}$ 37. $\dfrac{5}{\sqrt{34}}$ 39. $\tan(\text{Arc tan } a + \text{Arc tan } 1) =$

$\dfrac{\tan(\text{Arc tan } a) + \tan(\text{Arc tan } 1)}{1 - \tan(\text{Arc tan } a) \cdot \tan(\text{Arc tan } 1)} = \dfrac{1+a}{1-a}$ 41. $\tan(\text{Arc cos } a + \text{Arc sin } b) =$

$\dfrac{\tan(\text{Arc cos } a) + \tan(\text{Arc sin } b)}{1 - \tan(\text{Arc cos } a) \cdot \tan(\text{Arc sin } b)} = \dfrac{\sqrt{1-a^2} \cdot \sqrt{1-b^2} + ab}{a\sqrt{1-b^2} - b\sqrt{1-a^2}}$

43. $\sin\left(\text{Arc sin}\dfrac{3}{5} + \text{Arc cos}\dfrac{5}{13}\right) = \sin\left(\text{Arc sin}\dfrac{3}{5}\right)\cos\left(\text{Arc cos}\dfrac{5}{13}\right) + \sin\left(\text{Arc cos}\dfrac{5}{13}\right)$

$\cos\left(\text{Arc sin}\dfrac{3}{5}\right) = \dfrac{3}{5} \cdot \dfrac{5}{13} + \dfrac{12}{13} \cdot \dfrac{4}{5} = \dfrac{63}{65}$ 45. $\tan\left(2 \text{ Arc tan}\dfrac{1}{3} + \text{Arc tan}\dfrac{1}{7}\right) =$

$\dfrac{\tan\left(2 \text{ Arc tan}\dfrac{1}{3}\right) + \tan\left(\text{Arc tan}\dfrac{1}{7}\right)}{1 - \tan\left(2 \text{ Arc tan}\dfrac{1}{3}\right)\tan\left(\text{Arc tan}\dfrac{1}{7}\right)}$.   Now, $\tan\left(2 \text{ Arc tan}\dfrac{1}{3}\right) = \dfrac{2\tan\left(\text{Arc tan}\dfrac{1}{3}\right)}{1 - \tan^2\left(\text{Arc tan}\dfrac{1}{3}\right)}$, and

$\tan\left(\text{Arc tan}\dfrac{1}{7}\right) = \dfrac{1}{7}$, therefore the left side of the equation is equal to $\dfrac{\dfrac{2\left(\dfrac{1}{3}\right)}{1 - \dfrac{1}{9}} + \dfrac{1}{7}}{1 - \dfrac{2\left(\dfrac{1}{3}\right)}{1 - \dfrac{1}{9}} \cdot \dfrac{1}{7}} = 1$,

therefore $2 \text{ Arc tan}\dfrac{1}{3} + \text{Arc tan}\dfrac{1}{7} = \dfrac{\pi}{4}$.

47. Similar solution to above Exercises.

PAGES 184-185   Exercises

Note: For Exercise 1 - 35, $n \in W$.   1. $\left\{ x : x = \frac{-\pi}{3} \pm 2n\pi \mathrm{v} x = -\frac{2\pi}{3} \pm 2n\pi \right\}$ 3. $\left\{ x : x = \pm \frac{\pi}{4} \pm 2n\pi \right\}$

5. $\left\{ x : x = 150° \pm n \cdot 360° \mathrm{v}\ 210° \pm n \cdot 360° \right\}$ 7. $\left\{ x : x = \pm 30° \pm n \cdot 360° \mathrm{v} x = \pm 150° \pm \right.$

$\left. n \cdot 360° \right\}$ 9. $\left\{ x : x = \pm 30° \pm 360° \cdot n\ \mathrm{v}\ x = \pm 150° \pm n \cdot 360° \right\}$ 11. $\left\{ x : x = 26° \ 30' \pm \right.$

$180° \cdot n \mathrm{v} x = 116° \ 30' \pm 180° \cdot n \left. \right\}$ 13. $\left\{ x : x = \pm 180° \cdot n \mathrm{v} x = 30° \pm 360° \cdot n \mathrm{v} x = \right.$

$150° \pm 360° \cdot n \left. \right\}$ 15. $\left\{ x : x = 180° \cdot n \right\}$ 17. $\left\{ x : x = \pm 30° \pm 180° \cdot n \right\}$ 19. ϕ

21. $\left\{ x : x = \pm 360° \cdot n \right\}$ 23. $\left\{ x : x = 30° \pm 360° \cdot n \mathrm{v} x = 150° \pm 360° \cdot n \right\}$

25. $\left\{ x : x = -60° \pm 360° \cdot n \mathrm{v} x = -120° \pm 360° \cdot n \right\}$ 27. $\left\{ x : x = \pm 60° \pm 360° \cdot n \right\}$

29. $\left\{ x : x = \pm (2n + 1) \cdot 90° \mathrm{v} x = \pm 120° \pm 360° \cdot n \right\}$ 31. $\left\{ x : x = \pm \frac{n\pi}{2} \right\}$

33. $\left\{ x : x = \pm n \cdot 90° \mathrm{v} x = \pm 120° \pm n \cdot 360° \right\}$ 35. $\left\{ x : x = \pm n \cdot 180° \mathrm{v} x = \pm 20° \pm n \cdot 180° \right\}$

PAGE 187   Exercises

1. $\left\{ x : \frac{4\pi}{3} \le x \le \frac{5\pi}{3} \right\}$ 3. $\left\{ x : 0 \le x \le .46 \mathrm{v} \frac{\pi}{2} < x \le \pi + .46 \mathrm{v} \frac{3\pi}{2} < x \le 2\pi \right\}$

5. $\left\{ x : \frac{\pi}{4} < x < \frac{\pi}{2} \mathrm{v} \frac{5\pi}{4} < x < \frac{3\pi}{2} \right\}$ 7. $\left\{ x : 0 \le x \le \frac{\pi}{6} \mathrm{v} \frac{5\pi}{6} \le x \le \frac{7\pi}{6} \mathrm{v} \frac{11\pi}{6} \le x \le 2\pi \right\}$ 9.

$\left\{ x : \frac{\pi}{4} \le x \le \frac{3\pi}{4} \mathrm{v} \frac{5\pi}{4} \le x \le \frac{7\pi}{4} \right\}$ 11. $\left\{ x : x = 0 \mathrm{v} \pi \le x \le 2\pi \right\}$ 13. $\left\{ x : 0 \le x < \frac{\pi}{4} \mathrm{v} \frac{3\pi}{4} < \right.$

$x < \frac{5\pi}{4} \mathrm{v} \frac{7\pi}{4} < x \le 2\pi \left. \right\}$ 15. $\left\{ x : 0 \le x \le \frac{2\pi}{3} \mathrm{v} \frac{4\pi}{3} \le x \le 2\pi \right\}$ 17. $\left\{ x : 0 < x < 2\pi \wedge x \ne \pi \right\}$

19. $\left\{ x : \frac{\pi}{4} \le x \le \frac{5\pi}{4} \right\}$ 21. ϕ 22. ϕ

PAGES 190-191   Exercises

1. $4\sqrt{2}(\cos 45° + i \sin 45°)$ 3. $1(\cos 300° + i \sin 300°)$ 5. $1(\cos 180° + i \sin 180°)$

7. $1(\cos 270° + i \sin 270°)$ 9. $1(\cos 6° + i \sin 6°)$ 11. $1(\cos 310° + i \sin 310°)$

13. $\frac{1}{4} + \frac{\sqrt{3}}{4}i$ 15. $2\sqrt{3} - 2i$ 17. $0 - i$ 19. $7.7272 + 2.0704i$ 21. $r(\cos 0° + i \sin 0°)$ or

$r(\cos 180° + i \sin 180°)$ 23. If $z_1 = r_1 (\cos \theta_1 + i \sin \theta_1) z_2 = r_2(\cos \theta_2 + i \sin \theta_2) \ne$

$0 + 0i$ then $\dfrac{z_1}{z_2} = \dfrac{r_1(\cos \theta_1 + i \sin \theta_1)}{r_2(\cos \theta_2 + i \sin \theta_2)} = \dfrac{r_1}{r_2} \left(\dfrac{\cos \theta_1 + i \sin \theta_1}{\cos \theta_2 + i \sin \theta_2} \right)$

$= \dfrac{r_1}{r_2} \left(\dfrac{\cos \theta_1 + i \sin \theta_1}{\cos \theta_2 + i \sin \theta_2} \right) \left(\dfrac{\cos \theta_2 - i \sin \theta_2}{\cos \theta_2 - i \sin \theta_2} \right)$

$= \dfrac{r_1}{r_2} \dfrac{(\cos \theta_1 \cos \theta_2 + \sin \theta_1 \sin \theta_2) + i(\sin \theta_1 \cos \theta_2 - \sin \theta_2 \cos \theta_1)}{\cos^2 \theta_2 + \sin^2 \theta_2}$

$= \dfrac{r_1}{r_2}[\cos(\theta_1 - \theta_2) + i \sin(\theta_1 - \theta_2)]$ 25. $z_1 \cdot z_2 = \dfrac{3}{2}(\cos 120° + i \sin 120°) \dfrac{z_1}{z_2} =$

$6(\cos 40° + i \sin 40°)$ 27. $z_1 \cdot z_2 = \dfrac{4}{3}(\cos 285° + i \sin 285°) \dfrac{z_1}{z_2} = 3(\cos(-15°) + i \sin(-15°))$

29. $z_1 \cdot z_2 = -1 - i \dfrac{z_1}{z_2} = 1 + i$

31. Let $z_1 = r_1(\cos \theta_1 + i \sin \theta_1)\, z_2 = r_2(\cos \theta_2 + i \sin \theta_2)$

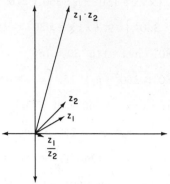

33. $\dfrac{1}{z} = \dfrac{1}{r(\cos \theta + i \sin \theta)} = \dfrac{1}{r} \cdot \dfrac{1}{\cos \theta + i \sin \theta} \cdot \dfrac{\cos \theta - i \sin \theta}{\cos \theta - i \sin \theta} = \dfrac{1}{r} \cdot \dfrac{\cos \theta - i \sin \theta}{\cos^2 \theta + \sin^2 \theta} = \dfrac{1}{r} \cdot$

$(\cos \theta - i \sin \theta)$ but $\overline{z} = r(\cos \theta - i \sin \theta) \therefore \dfrac{1}{z} = \dfrac{1}{r} \cdot \dfrac{\overline{z}}{r} = \dfrac{1}{r^2} \cdot \overline{z}$ 35. $\dfrac{z}{\overline{z}} = \dfrac{r(\cos \theta + i \sin \theta)}{r(\cos \theta - i \sin \theta)} =$

$\dfrac{\cos \theta + i \sin \theta}{\cos \theta - i \sin \theta} \cdot \dfrac{\cos \theta + i \sin \theta}{\cos \theta + i \sin \theta} = \dfrac{(\cos^2 \theta - \sin^2 \theta) + i(2 \sin \theta \cos \theta)}{\cos^2 \theta + \sin^2 \theta} = \cos 2\theta + i \sin 2\theta$

37. Let $z_1 = r_1(\cos \theta_1 + i \sin \theta_1) \neq 0 + 0i\ z_2 = r_2(\cos \theta_2 + i \sin \theta_2) \neq 0 + 0i$ then $\dfrac{z_1}{z_2} = \dfrac{r_1}{r_2}$

$(\cos(\theta_1 - \theta_2) + i \sin(\theta_1 - \theta_2)) = \dfrac{r_1}{r_2}(\cos 0° + i \sin 0°) = \dfrac{r_1}{r_2}(1 + i \cdot 0) = \dfrac{r_1}{r_2}$, which is real.

PAGES 195-196   Exercises

1. $2\sqrt{2}(\cos 225° + i \sin 225°); -2 - 2i$ 3. $\cos 0° + i \sin 0°; 1 + 0i$ 5. $\dfrac{1}{32}(\cos 120° + i \sin 120°);$

$-\dfrac{1}{64} + \dfrac{\sqrt{3}}{64}i$ 7. $\cos 90° + i \sin 90°; 0 + i$ 9. $\cos 0° + i \sin 0°, \cos 90° + i \sin 90°, \cos 180°$

$+ i \sin 180°, \cos 270° + i \sin 270°$ 11. $\cos 60° + i \sin 60°, \cos 180° + i \sin 180°, \cos 300°$

$+ i \sin 300°$ 13. $\sqrt[3]{2}(\cos 40° + i \sin 40°), \sqrt[3]{2}(\cos 160° + i \sin 160°), \sqrt[3]{2}(\cos 280° + i \sin 280°)$

15. $\cos 45° + i \sin 45°, \cos 225° + i \sin 225°$ 17. Let $(\cos \theta + i \sin \theta) = u + vi, u = \cos \theta, v = \sin \theta,$

then $(\cos \theta + i \sin \theta)^4 = \cos 4\theta + i \sin 4\theta$ and $(u + vi)^4 = u^4 + 4u^3(vi) + 6u^2(vi)^2 + 4u(vi)^3 + (vi)^4 =$

$u^4 - 6u^2 v^2 + v^4 + (4u^3 v - 4uv^3)i$. Thus $\cos 4\theta + i \sin 4\theta = \cos^4 \theta - 6 \cos^2 \theta \sin^2 \theta + \sin^4 \theta +$

$(4 \cos^3 \theta \sin \theta - 4 \cos \theta \sin^3 \theta)i \therefore \cos 4\theta = \cos^4 \theta - 6 \cos^2 \theta \sin^2 \theta + \sin^4 \theta \sin 4\theta =$

$4 \cos^3 \theta \sin \theta - 4 \cos \theta \sin^3 \theta$ 19. $\sqrt[3]{2}(\cos 30° + i \sin 30°), \sqrt[3]{2}(\cos 150° + i \sin 150°),$

$\sqrt[3]{2}(\cos 270° + i \sin 270°)$ 21. $1^3 = 1, W^3 = (\cos \dfrac{2\pi}{3} + i \sin \dfrac{2\pi}{3})^3 = \cos 2\pi + i \sin 2\pi = 1,$

$(W^2)^3 = (W^3)^2 = 1^2 = 1$ 23. $r^{-n}[\cos(-n\theta) + i \sin(-n\theta)] = r^{-n}(\cos n\theta - i \sin n\theta)$

25. $\cos 0° + i \sin 0°$, $\cos \frac{2\pi}{3} + i \sin \frac{2\pi}{3}$, $\cos \frac{4\pi}{3} + i \sin \frac{4\pi}{3}$ 27. $\cos 0° + i \sin 0°$; $\cos \frac{\pi}{2} + i \sin \frac{\pi}{2}$,

$\cos \pi + i \sin \pi$ $\cos \frac{3\pi}{2} + i \sin \frac{3\pi}{2}$.   29. $\cos \frac{3\pi}{8} + i \sin \frac{3\pi}{8}$, $\cos \frac{7\pi}{8} + i \sin \frac{7\pi}{8}$, $\cos \frac{11\pi}{8} + i \sin \frac{11\pi}{8}$,

$\cos \frac{15\pi}{8} + i \sin \frac{15\pi}{8}$

PAGE 199 Exercises

1. $(\sqrt{2}, 45°)$, $(\sqrt{2}, 225°)$ 3. $(9, 180°)$, $(-9, 0°)$ 5. $(2, -60°)$, $(-2, 120°)$ 7. $(4\sqrt{5}, 116° \ 30')$,

$(-4\sqrt{5}, 296° \ 30')$ 9. $(0, -2)$ 11. $(\frac{\sqrt{3}}{2}, \frac{1}{2})$ 13. $(-\frac{3}{2} \cdot \frac{3\sqrt{3}}{2})$ 15. $(0, -5)$ 17. $r \cos \theta = 3$

19. $2r \cos \theta - r \sin \theta = 3)$ 21. $r = 4$ 23. $r = -4 \cos \theta$ 25. $r \sin \theta \cdot \tan \theta = 4$ 27. $y = 0$

29. $x^2 + y^2 = 16$ 31. $y = 6$ 33. $y = 5$ 35. $x_1 = r \cos \theta$, $y_1 = r \sin \theta$ while $x_2 = r \cos (-\theta) =$

$r \cos \theta_1 y_2 = r \sin (-\theta) = -r \sin \theta$ $\therefore x_1 = x_2$ $y_1 = -y_2$

PAGES 203-204   Exercises

1. A circle of radius 3 with the center at $(0, 0)$.   3. A straight line through origin with slope =

$\tan 75°$.   5. A circle of radius $\frac{1}{2}$ with the center at $(\frac{1}{2}, 0)$.   7. A circle of radius $\frac{3}{2}$ with the

center at $(-\frac{3}{2}, 0)$.   9. A vertical line   10.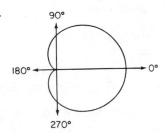

through $(2, 0)$.   11. Using origin as a

center rotate the picture of Exercise

10 through an angle of $90°$.

13. 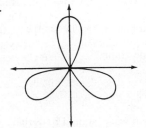   15. 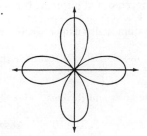   18.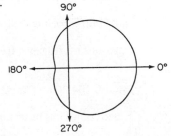

17. Eight-leaved rose with petals symmetric

about the $0°$ line and all the $0° + n \cdot 45°$,

lines n = 1, $\cdots$, 7.

19. Using origin as a center rotate the picture of Exercise 18 90° counterclockwise.

20.

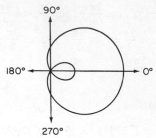

21. Same general shape as Exercise 20 except this curve is symmetric to the 90° line and the major part of it is the third and fourth quadrants.

23. Two leaves, each symmetric about the x axis.

25. Case 1: $\theta > 0$, when $\theta \to 0$, then $r \to \infty$, when $\theta \to \infty$ then $r \to 0$, the graph is as shown, Case 2: $\theta < 0$, the graph is the reflection of the graph as shown with respect to the imaginary axis.

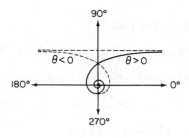

27. Ellipse with center $(\frac{4}{3}, 0)$ and the major axis is the x axis. The equation in Cartesian coordinates is $3x^2 + 4y^2 - 8x - 16 = 0$.   29. Both graphs are the same as the picture of Exercise 11, page 203 but are traced out at different times.   31. The point whose name is (r, θ) in the polar coordinate system is also named $(-r, \theta + \pi)$ and $(r, \theta + 2\pi)$, hence the equations $r = f(\theta)$; $-r = f(\theta + \pi)$ and $r = f(\theta + 2\pi)$ all have the same graph.

PAGES 204-206   Chapter Objectives and Review

1. See definitions in sections.   3. 9.30   5. 31° 10'   7. Answers will vary, should be verbal equivalent of $c^2 = a^2 + b^2 - 2ab \cos c$ 9. 36° 20'   11. 10.14   13. 20.34   15. Arc tan x is single-valued restricted to a particular range, whereas arc tan x is multiple-valued.

17. $\approx \pm 144° \ 43' \pm 360° \cdot n$, $n \in W$ 19. $\pm \frac{n\pi}{2}$ 21. $\frac{\pi}{3}$ 23. $\frac{1}{3}$ 25. $\pm\sqrt{1-u^2}$ 27. $\frac{u}{\sqrt{1-u^2}}$

29. Domain: [-1, 1] See page 176 for the graph of y = Arc cos x.

31. $60° \pm 360° \cdot n$ v $120° \pm 360° \cdot n$, $n \in W$ 33. $15° \pm 180° \cdot n$ v $75° \pm 180° \cdot n$, $n \in W$

35. $\left\{ x : 120° \pm 360° \cdot n < x < 420° \pm 360° \cdot n, \ n \in W \right\}$ 37. $\sqrt{5}(\cos 26° \ 30' + i \sin 26° \ 30')$

39. $2\sqrt{3} \ (\cos 210° + i \sin 210°)$ 41. This exercise whould read "How would you divide the

numbers in Exercise 40?" It reads "in Exercise 39" in the first printing of the book. Divide

the moduli and subtract the angles, i.e., $\frac{r_1}{r_2}(\cos (\theta_1 - \theta_2) + i \sin (\theta_1 - \theta_2))$ provided that

$r_2 \neq 0$ 43. $\sqrt[5]{2}(\cos 30° + i \sin 30°)$, $\sqrt[5]{2}(\cos 102° + i \sin 102°)$, $\sqrt[5]{2}(\cos 174° + i \sin 174°)$,

$\sqrt[5]{2}(\cos 246° + i \sin 246°)$, $\sqrt[5]{2}(\cos 318° + i \sin 318°)$ 45. $(6\sqrt{2}, 135°)$ 47. $(\sqrt{5}, 333° \ 30')$

49. $(-\frac{5}{2}, \frac{5\sqrt{3}}{2})$ 51. The graph of r = 5 is a circle with center at (0, 0) and radius 5.

53. See the solution of Exercise 19 on page 204.

PAGE 207   Chapter Test

1. 42.87   3. 1856.27   5. d = 37,207; 34 sec.   7. $\pm 2\sqrt{6}$ 9. $\frac{\pi}{4}$ 11. $\left\{ x : x = \frac{\pi}{4} \pm \frac{n\pi}{2}, n \in W \right\}$

13. $\sqrt[4]{2}(\cos 30° + i \sin 30°)$, $\sqrt[4]{2}(\cos 120° + i \sin 120°)$, $\sqrt[4]{2}(\cos 210° + i \sin 210°)$,

$\sqrt[4]{2}(\cos 300° + i \sin 300°)$

PAGES 213-215 Exercises

1. 5, 3, 1, -1, -3, -5   3. 3, 6, 12, 24, 48, 96   5. 4, -4, -4, 4, 4, -4

7. 1, 1, 2, 16, $(32)^3$ = 32,768, $(65,536)^4$ 9. 5, 5, $\frac{5}{2}$, $\frac{5}{6}$, $\frac{5}{24}$, $\frac{1}{24}$ 11. 4, 2,

$\frac{4}{3}$, 1, $\frac{4}{5}$ 13. 3, 12, 27, 48, 75   15. 1, 3, 5, 7, 9   17. 1, 1, 3, 5, 7

19. $\frac{3}{5}$, $\frac{4}{7}$, $\frac{5}{9}$, $\frac{6}{11}$, $\frac{7}{13}$ 21. 0, 1, 0, 1, 0   23. a. a_n = n b. a_1 = 1, a_{n+1} =

a_{n+1} 25. a. $a_n = \frac{3}{n!}$ b. a_1 = 3, $a_{n+1} = \frac{a_n}{n+1}$ 27. a. $a_n = (-1)^{n+1}$

b. a_1 = 1, a_{n+1} = $-a_n$ 29. 5, 8, 11, 14   31. -14   33. $a_1 = a_1$, a_{n+1}

= $a_n + d$ 35. $\frac{5}{3}$, $\frac{5}{9}$, $\frac{5}{27}$, $\frac{5}{81}$ 37. $\frac{1}{48}$ 39. $a_1 = b_1 = c_1$ = 1, $a_2 = b_2 = c_2$

= $\frac{1}{2}$, $a_3 = b_3 = c_3 = \frac{1}{3}$, $a_4 = \frac{1}{4}$, $b_4 = \frac{1}{10}$, $c_4 = -\frac{1}{4}$ 41. a. $a_n = \frac{n}{n+1}$ b. a_n =

$\frac{n}{(n+1) + (n-1)(n-2)(n-3)}$ c. $a_n = \frac{n}{(n+1) + \frac{1}{2}(n-1)(n-2)(n-3)}$

PAGES 218-219 Exercises

1. a_1 = -3, a_2 = -1, a_3 = 1, a_4 = 3, a_5 = 5, a_6 = 7, a_7 = 9, for n > 7 $a_n \in$

$\langle 10, \infty \rangle$ 3. a_1 = 1, $a_2 = \frac{1}{3}$, $a_3 = \frac{1}{5}$, $a_4 = \frac{1}{7}$, $a_5 = \frac{1}{9}$, for n > 5 $a_n \in \langle 0, \frac{1}{9} \rangle$

5. $b_1 = b_3 = b_5$ = 1, $b_2 = b_4$ = -1, for n > 5 $b_n \in \langle -1.1, 1.1 \rangle$ 7. $c_1 = \frac{3}{2}$,

$c_2 = \frac{9}{4}$, $c_3 = \frac{27}{8}$, $c_4 = \frac{81}{16}$, $c_5 = \frac{243}{32}$, for n > 5 $c_n \in \langle 8, \infty \rangle$ 9. c_1 = 0, $c_2 = -2\frac{1}{4}$,

$c_3 = -2\frac{2}{3}$, $c_4 = -2\frac{13}{16}$, $c_5 = -2\frac{22}{25}$, for n > 5 $c_n \in \langle -3, -2\frac{22}{25} \rangle$ 11. $\langle 2, 8 \rangle$ =

$\{x : |x - 5| < 3, x \in R\}$ 13. $\langle -\frac{5}{2}, \frac{5}{2} \rangle = \{x : |x| < \frac{5}{2}, x \in R\}$ 15. $\langle -2\frac{1}{4}, \frac{3}{4} \rangle$

= $\{x : |x + \frac{3}{4}| < \frac{3}{2}, x \in R\}$ 17. $\langle \frac{8}{9}, \frac{10}{9} \rangle$ 19. There is no such neighborhood,

since any neighborhood containing all the terms of $\{(-1)^n\}$ for n ≥ 10 also con-

tains the preceding terms.

PAGES 221-222 Exercises

1. a. $a_n > a_{n+1}$ iff $\frac{1}{n} > \frac{1}{n+1}$ iff n + 1 > n (since n and n + 1 > 0) iff 1 > 0.

Thus $a_n > a_{n+1} \forall$ n $\in$ N b. M = 200   3. a. $c_n > c_{n+1}$ iff $\frac{1}{2^n} > \frac{1}{2^{n+1}}$ iff

$1 > \frac{1}{2}$. Thus $c_n > c_{n+1} \forall$ n $\in$ N b. M = 10, M = 20   5. a. $a_n < a_{n+1}$ iff

$\frac{1}{-n} < -\frac{1}{n+1}$ iff -(n + 1) < -n iff n + 1 > n iff 1 > 0. Thus $a_n < a_{n+1} \forall$ n $\in$ N

b. M = 100   7. a. $c_n < c_{n+1}$ iff $\frac{n}{3n+1} < \frac{n+1}{3(n+1)+1}$ iff $\frac{n}{3n+1} < \frac{n+1}{3n+4}$

iff $n(3n + 4) < (3n + 1)(n + 1)$ iff $3n^2 + 4n < 3n^2 + 4n + 1$ iff $0 < 1$. Thus

$c_n < c_{n+1} \forall n \in N$. b. $M = 6$ 9. a. $a_n > a_{n+1}$ iff $\frac{1}{5n} > \frac{1}{5(n+1)}$ iff

$\frac{1}{n} > \frac{1}{n+1}$ iff $n + 1 > n$ iff $1 > 0$. Thus $a_n > a_{n+1} \forall n \in N$ b. $M = \frac{1}{5k}$

PAGE 226 Exercises

1. $\left\{a_n : n \geq 2\right\}$ 3. $\left\{b_n : 5 \leq n \leq 8\right\}$ 5. $\left\{c_n : 1 \leq n \leq 4\right\}$ 7. $\left\{d_1, d_2\right\}$

9. $\left\{e_n : 6 \leq n \leq 14\right\}$ 11. a. Both sides of the inequality are multiplied by 10.

Theorem 1-6. b. Both sides of the inequality are multiplied by 2n. Theorem 1-6.

c. -10 is added to each side of the inequality. Theorem 1-5. d. Both sides of

the inequality are multiplied by $-\frac{1}{2}$. Exercise 20, Section 1-3. e. Both sides of

the inequality are multiplied by $\frac{1}{4}$. Theorem 1-6. The argument proves that n = 1

is the only positive integer for which $\frac{n-1}{2n} < \frac{1}{10}$. 13. a_2, a_1 lies outside the

neighborhood. 15. a_{501}, 500 terms $(a_1, a_2, \cdots, a_{500})$ lie outside the neighbor-

hood. 17. The first term within the neighborhood is $\left\{a_n : \frac{1+R}{2R} < n \leq \frac{1+R}{2R} + 1\right\}$.

All the terms preceding the first term within the neighborhood lie outside the

neighborhood.

PAGE 232 Exercises

1. The general neighborhood $\langle 3 - \epsilon, 3 + \epsilon\rangle$ was used because the limit of the

sequence $\left\{\frac{3n+1}{n}\right\}$ is 3 and therefore the proof must use the general neighborhood

of 3 rather than 0. 3. $\langle -1 - \epsilon, -1 + \epsilon\rangle$ 5. $\langle -\frac{2}{3} - \epsilon, -\frac{2}{3} + \epsilon\rangle$ 7. $\langle 100 - \epsilon,$

$100 + \epsilon\rangle$ 9. $\langle p - \epsilon, p + \epsilon\rangle$ 11. 2 13. $\frac{1}{3}$ 15. 0 17. $\left\{\frac{\frac{1}{2}n+1}{n}\right\} \to \frac{1}{2}$

iff we can find M such that for $n \geq M$, $a_n \in \langle \frac{1}{2} - \epsilon, \frac{1}{2} + \epsilon\rangle$ for an arbitrary $\epsilon > 0$.

$\frac{1}{2} - \epsilon < \frac{\frac{1}{2}n+1}{n} < \frac{1}{2} + \epsilon$ iff $1 - 2\epsilon < \frac{n+2}{n} < 1 + 2\epsilon$ iff $-2\epsilon < \frac{2}{n} < 2\epsilon$ iff $-\epsilon < \frac{1}{n} < \epsilon$.

Thus $M > \frac{1}{\epsilon}$. The proof for Exercise 19 is similar. For Exercise 19 $M > \frac{4}{25\epsilon} + \frac{2}{5}$.

21. Answers will vary. a_n is outside of $\langle 1 - \frac{1}{10}, 1 + \frac{1}{10}\rangle$ for $M > 10$.

PAGE 236 Exercises

The proofs for Exercise 1-11 are similar to the proof in Exercise 17 page 232.

1. M $\dfrac{1}{\sqrt{3\epsilon}}$ 3. $M > \dfrac{\log \epsilon}{\log 3 - \log 4}$ 5. $M > \dfrac{9}{\epsilon^2} - 2$ 7. $-\epsilon < \dfrac{\sqrt{n+2}}{n} < \epsilon$

iff $\dfrac{\sqrt{n+2}}{n} < \epsilon$ (since $\dfrac{\sqrt{n+2}}{n} > -\epsilon$ for all n) iff $\dfrac{n+2}{n^2} < \epsilon^2$ iff $\dfrac{1}{\epsilon^2} < \dfrac{n^2}{n+2}$.

Since $\dfrac{n^2}{n+2} \geq \dfrac{n}{3}$ for all n it is sufficient to solve $\dfrac{1}{\epsilon^2} < \dfrac{n}{3}$ iff $\dfrac{3}{\epsilon^2} < n$. Thus

$M > \dfrac{3}{\epsilon^2}$ 9. $M > \sqrt[3]{\dfrac{2}{\epsilon}} - 5$ 11. $M > \dfrac{\sqrt{1 - \epsilon^2}}{\epsilon}$

PAGES 240-241 Exercises

1. When it is constant, i.e. when $a_1 = a_2 = \cdots = a_n$.   3. Yes; a_1 5. Yes.
7. Yes.   9. No.   11. No.   13. (5.) All terms = 0. Therefore bounded above
and below by 0.   (6.) All terms $\in \{-1, 1\}$. Therefore bounded by -1 and 1.   (7.) Is
bounded by 0 and 1.   (8.) Is bounded below by 1.   (9.) Not bounded.   (10.) Is
bounded by 3 and 4.   (11.) Is bounded by -1 and 1.   (12.) Is bounded below by 1.
15. Answers will vary. $\{a_n\} = \{(-1)^n\}$ or $\{b_n\} = \{1$ if n is a multiple of
3, 2 for all other n$\}$ 17. Let $B = \{-x : x \in A\}$ A, B $\in$ R. A is bounded below,
therefore B is bounded above. By the least upper bound axiom B has a l.u.b. in R,
b = l.u.b.B and then -b = g.l.b.A   19. Answers will vary. $\{n\}$, $\{(n+1)^2\}$,
$\left\{\dfrac{1}{\sin \frac{1}{n}}\right\}$ 21. If a_n is nondecreasing then $a_1 \leq a_2 \leq a_3 \leq \cdots \leq a_n \leq \cdots$. If a_n is not
bounded above there is no real number r such that all $a_n \leq r$. Therefore for any
real number p some a_n must be $\geq$ p, and as $a_1 \leq a_2 \leq a_3 \leq \cdots \leq a_n \leq \cdots$ there is
an $M \in N$ such that $a_n \geq p$ for all $n \geq M$.

PAGES 246-247 Exercises

1. Arithmetic.   3. Arithmetic.   5. For n = 1, $\dfrac{1}{2} = \dfrac{2^1 - 1}{2^1} = \dfrac{2 - 1}{2} = \dfrac{1}{2}$. Assum-

ing $S_k = \dfrac{2^k - 1}{2^k}$, $S_{k+1} = \dfrac{2^k - 1}{2^k} + \dfrac{1}{2^{k+1}} = \dfrac{2^k \cdot 2^{k+1} - 2^{k+1} + 2^k}{2^k \cdot 2^{k+1}} =$

$\dfrac{2^{k+1} - 2^1 + 1}{2^{k+1}} = \dfrac{2^{k+1} - 1}{2^{k+1}}$ 7. For n = 1, $\dfrac{2}{3} = 2\left[1 - (\frac{2}{3})^1\right] = 2\left[\frac{1}{3}\right] = \frac{2}{3}$. Assum-

ing $S_k = 2\left[1 - (\frac{2}{3})^k\right]$, $S_{k+1} = 2\left[1 - (\frac{2}{3})^k\right] + \frac{2}{3}(\frac{2}{3})^{(k+1)-1} = 2 - 2(\frac{2}{3})^k +$

$$\left(\tfrac{2}{3}\right)^{k+1} = 2 - \frac{2^{k+1}}{3^k} + \frac{2^{k+1}}{3^{k+1}} = 2 - \frac{3 \cdot 2^{k+1} - 2^{k+1}}{3^{k+1}} = 2 - 2\left(\tfrac{2}{3}\right)^{k+1} =$$

$$2\left[1 - \left(\tfrac{2}{3}\right)^{k+1}\right] \qquad 9. \text{ For } n = 1, \ a = a\frac{(1 - r^1)}{(1 - r)}. \text{ Assuming } S_k = a\frac{(1 - r^k)}{(1 - r)}, \ S_{k+1}$$

$$= a\frac{(1 - r^k)}{(1 - r)} + ar^{(k+1)-1} = a\left[\frac{(1 - r^k)}{(1 - r)} + r^k\right] = a\left[\frac{1 - r^k + r^k - r^{k+1}}{(1 - r)}\right] =$$

$$a\frac{(1 - r^{k+1})}{(1 - r)} \qquad 11. \ |2 - 1| + |2 - 2| + |2 - 3| + |2 - 4| + |2 - 5|$$

13. $(-1)^1 (1^2 - 1) + (-1)^2 (2^2 - 2) + (-1)^3 (3^2 - 3)$ \qquad 15. $\dfrac{1}{0 + 1} + \dfrac{1}{1 + 1} + \dfrac{1}{2 + 1}$

$+ \dfrac{1}{3 + 1} + \dfrac{1}{4 + 1}$ \qquad 17. $\displaystyle\sum_{i=1}^{4} (5i - 2)$ \qquad 19. $\displaystyle\sum_{i=1}^{4} a_i^2$ \qquad 21. Yes. \qquad 23. No.

25. $S = \dfrac{15}{4}, \ M > \dfrac{\log 4 + \log \epsilon - \log 15}{-\log 3}$ \qquad 27. For $n = 1$, $\displaystyle\sum_{i=1}^{1} ca_i = ca_1 = c\displaystyle\sum_{i=1}^{1} a_i$.

Assume for $n = k$, $\displaystyle\sum_{i=1}^{k} ca_i = c\displaystyle\sum_{i=1}^{k} a_i$. Then for $n = k + 1$, $\displaystyle\sum_{i=1}^{k+1} ca_i =$

$$\sum_{i=1}^{k} ca_i + ca_{k+1} = c\sum_{i=1}^{k} a_i + ca_{k+1} = c\left[\sum_{i=1}^{k} a_i + a_{k+1}\right] = c\sum_{i=1}^{k+1} a_i$$

29. For $n = 1$, $\displaystyle\sum_{i=1}^{1}(a_i + b_i) = a_1 + b_1 = \displaystyle\sum_{i=1}^{1} a_i + \displaystyle\sum_{i=1}^{1} b_i$. Assume for $n = k$,

$$\sum_{i=1}^{k}(a_i + b_i) = \sum_{i=1}^{k} a_i + \sum_{i=1}^{k} b_i. \text{ Then for } n = k + 1, \ \sum_{i=1}^{k+1}(a_i + b_i) =$$

$$\sum_{i=1}^{k}(a_i + b_i) + a_{k+1} + b_{k+1} = \sum_{i=1}^{k} a_i + \sum_{i=1}^{k} b_i + a_{k+1} + b_{k+1} =$$

$$\sum_{i=1}^{k} a_i + a_{k+1} + \sum_{i=1}^{k} b_i + b_{k+1} = \sum_{i=1}^{k+1} a_i + \sum_{i=1}^{k+1} b_i \qquad 31. \ \sum_{i=1}^{n} (a_i + c) =$$

$$\sum_{i=1}^{n} a_i + \sum_{i=1}^{n} c \text{ by Exercise 29} = \sum_{i=1}^{n} a_i + cn \text{ by Exercise 28.}$$

PAGE 252 Exercises

1. $|a_n| < 2$ 3. $|a_n - 2| < .5$ 5. $|a_n - 1| < .01$ 7. $|a_n - 1| < \epsilon$

9. $\langle -.5, .5 \rangle$ 11. $\langle -1.1, -.9 \rangle$ 13. $\langle -\epsilon, \epsilon \rangle$ 15. $\langle .9 - \epsilon, .9 + \epsilon \rangle$

17. $M \geq 5$ 19. $M \geq 1$ 21. $(\frac{10}{9})^n = (1 + \frac{1}{9})^n \geq 1 + \frac{n}{9} > \frac{n}{9}$ Therefore $(\frac{9}{10})^n < \frac{9}{n}$

and $(\frac{9}{10})^n < \frac{1}{10}$ if $\frac{9}{n} < \frac{1}{10}$ iff $n > 90$. Thus $M > 90$.   23. 0, Theorem 5-4   25. -5,

Theorem 5-5   27. 0, Theorem 5-4   29. $\left| \frac{n}{n+1} - 1 \right| = \left| \frac{n - (n+1)}{n+1} \right| = \left| \frac{-1}{n+1} \right| =$

$\frac{1}{n+1} < \epsilon$ iff $1 < \epsilon n + \epsilon$ iff $1 - \epsilon < \epsilon n$ iff $\frac{1 - \epsilon}{\epsilon} < n$. Thus $M > \frac{1 - \epsilon}{\epsilon}$.

PAGE 257 Exercises

1. Converges to $\frac{5}{21}$.   3. Converges to $-\frac{1}{2}$.   5. Converges to $\frac{7}{5}$.   7. Converges

to 10.   9. Converges to 16.   11. Converges to $\frac{1}{2}$.   13. Converges to $\frac{1}{3}$.

15. Converges to 5.   17. a. Never. b. Sometimes, convergent examples $a_n = \frac{1}{n}$

and $b_n = n$, divergent examples $a_n = 1$ and $b_n = n$. c. Sometimes, convergent example

$a_n = 2$ and $b_n = n^2$, divergent examples $a_n = 3$ and $b_n = (-1)^n$.

PAGES 258-260 Chapter Objectives and Review

3. $\frac{5}{3}, \frac{8}{3}, \frac{11}{3}, \frac{14}{3}, \frac{17}{3}$, $a_{15} = \frac{47}{3}$ 5. b, $\frac{b}{10}, \frac{b}{10^2}, \frac{b}{10^3}, \frac{b}{10^4}$, $a_{10} = \frac{b}{10^9}$ 7. -2, 2,

-2, 2, -2, $c_{20} = 2$ 9. $a_1 = -1$, $a_2 = 1$, $a_3 = 3$, $a_4 = 5$, $a_5 = 7$, $\langle 7, \infty \rangle$ 11. c_1

1, $c_2 = .9$, $c_3 = .81$, $c_4 = .729$, $c_5 = .6561$, $\langle 0, .6561 \rangle$ 13. $a_{14}, \cdots, a_{24}$ 15. Al

$c_n, n > 5$.   17. All $c_n, n > \frac{1}{3\epsilon}$ 19. $M > \frac{73}{\epsilon}$ 21. $\langle \frac{3}{8}, \frac{5}{8} \rangle$ 23. a. The sequences

in Exercises 18, 19, and 21 are bounded. b. (18.) lub = 2, glb = 1, (19.) lub =

73, glb = 0, (21.) lub = $\frac{1}{4}$, glb = $\frac{1}{2}$ 25. a. Yes, $-1 < -1 + \frac{1}{n} \leq 0$ for all $n \in N$.

b. Yes, since $a_n > a_{n+1}$ for all $n \in N$ and $\{a_n\}$ is therefore nonincreasing.

c. Yes, $\lim\limits_{n \to \infty} \left\{-1 + \dfrac{1}{n}\right\} = -1$ 27. $\dfrac{1}{43}$ 29. $\dfrac{1}{3}$ 31. 6, 8, 10, 12, 14   33. $\dfrac{7}{2}$,

3, $\dfrac{5}{2}$, 2, $\dfrac{3}{2}$ 35. $S_n = 2 \cdot \dfrac{1 - (\frac{3}{4})^n}{1 - \frac{3}{4}} = 8(1 - (\frac{3}{4})^n)$, $\lim\limits_{n \to \infty} S_n = 8$

PAGES 260-261 Chapter Test

1. $-\dfrac{1}{2}, \dfrac{1}{4}, -\dfrac{1}{6}, \dfrac{1}{8}, -\dfrac{1}{10}, \dfrac{1}{12}, -\dfrac{1}{14}$, $b_{100} = \dfrac{1}{200}$, $b_{101} = -\dfrac{1}{202}$ 3. 3, 5, 9, 17, 33, 65,

129; Exercise 2 is the recursive definition of the sequence defined in Exercise 3

with the general term.   5. There does not appear to be a limit.   7. 2, $M > \dfrac{5}{\epsilon} + 2$

9. Answers will vary. Bounded, $\left\{\dfrac{1}{2^n}\right\}$. Unbounded, $\{n\}$. By Theorems 5-2 and 5-3

a bounded monotone sequence has a limit.   11. $\dfrac{2}{3}$ 13. $-\dfrac{1}{3}, \dfrac{1}{6}, -\dfrac{1}{9}, \dfrac{1}{12}, -\dfrac{1}{15}$

15. $S_n = \dfrac{1 - (\frac{4}{5})^n}{1 - \frac{4}{5}} = 5(1 - (\frac{4}{5})^n)$, $\lim\limits_{n \to \infty} S_n = 5$

CHAPTER 6 FUNCTIONS AND LIMITS

PAGES 268-269 Exercises

1. 1   3. 2   5. 3   7. 1, 0, 2, -1, 3   9. 20   11. 1   13. Answers will

vary.   15. $x_0 = -\dfrac{1}{\epsilon}$ 17. $x_0 > \dfrac{3}{25\epsilon} - \dfrac{1}{5}$ 19. $x_0 > \dfrac{1}{\epsilon}$ 21. Any x_0 will suf-

fice. $x \neq \pm 1$.   23. $|x_0| > \dfrac{4}{5\epsilon}$ 25. $|x_0| > \dfrac{1}{\sqrt{\epsilon}}$

PAGES 273-274 Exercises

1. $\langle 1.9, 2.1 \rangle$ 3. $\left\langle \dfrac{599}{300}, \dfrac{601}{300} \right\rangle$ 5. Impossible.   7. Impossible.   9. $|x^2 - 1|$

$< \dfrac{1}{100}$ iff $|(x - 1)(x + 1)| < \dfrac{1}{100}$ iff $|x - 1| \, |x + 1| < \dfrac{1}{100}$. The neighborhood of

a is $\left\langle \dfrac{299}{300}, \dfrac{301}{300} \right\rangle$ 11. $\lim\limits_{x \to 0} f(x) = 0$, $\lim\limits_{x \to 0^+} f(x) = 0$, $\lim\limits_{x \to 0^-} f(x) = 0$.

13. $\lim\limits_{x \to 2} f(x)$ does not exist, $\lim\limits_{x \to 2} {}_+ f(x) = -2$, $\lim\limits_{x \to 2} {}_- f(x) = 0$ 15. Answers

will vary.

PAGES 278-279 Exercises

1. 4   3. -3   5. $\dfrac{7}{13}$ 7. Doesn't exist.   9. 3   11. 28   13. $\dfrac{3}{7}$

15. Condition iii is not satisfied.   17. Condition iii is not satisfied.

19. $\lim\limits_{x \to 2} 3x = 6$. Let $\epsilon > 0$ be given. Then you must find $\delta > 0$ such that

$|3x - 6| < \epsilon$ whenever $|x - 2| < \delta$ (and $x \neq 2$). Now $|3x - 6| < \epsilon$ iff $3|x - 2|$

$< \epsilon$ iff $|x - 2| < \frac{\epsilon}{3}$. Hence, you can take $\delta = \frac{\epsilon}{3}$.   21. $\lim\limits_{x \to 1} x^2 + 2 = 3$

You must find δ such that $0 < |x - 1| < \delta$ implies $|x^2 + 2 - 3| = |x^2 - 1| =$

$|x - 1| \, |x + 1| < \epsilon$. Require $\delta \leq 1$, thus $|x - 1| < \delta \leq 1$. Thus $|x - 1| < 1$

iff $-1 < x - 1 < 1$ iff $1 < x + 1 < 3$ and $|x + 1| < 3$. Hence $|x^2 + 2 - 3| < \epsilon$ if

$|x + 1| < 3$ and $|x - 1| < \frac{\epsilon}{3}$. Choose $\delta = \frac{\epsilon}{3}$ for $\epsilon \leq 3$ and choose $\delta = 1$ otherwise

23. $|k - k| = 0 < \epsilon$ for any $\epsilon > 0$. Thus δ can be any positive number.

PAGES 282-284 Exercises

1. $\frac{3}{11}$ 3. 1   5. -1, 2   7. 0   9. 1   11. 2   13. None.   15. 2   17. $\frac{5}{3}$

19. 0   21. $-\frac{1}{8}$ 23. $\lim\limits_{x \to 3^+} \frac{x + 3}{(x - 3)^2} = +\infty$ $\lim\limits_{x \to 3^-} \frac{x + 3}{(x - 3)^2} = +\infty$

25. $\lim\limits_{x \to 2^+} \frac{2}{x^2 - 2x} = +\infty$, $\lim\limits_{x \to 2^-} \frac{2}{x^2 - 2x} = -\infty$ 27. $y = 2$ 29. $y = 3$

31. (27.) $x = 0$ (28.) $x = 2$, $x = -2$ (29.) $x = 0$ (30.) $x = -\frac{1}{2}$ 33. Yes,

$x = 0$, $x = 2$ 35. $\frac{1}{3}$ 37. $+\infty$ 39. $-\infty$ 41. 0   43. 1   45. 0

47. -1 For Exercises 49-51, answers will vary.   49. $R(x) = \frac{1000(x - 1)}{(x - 1)}$, $a = 1$

51. $R(x) = \frac{x}{-x^3}$, $a = 0$ 53. 0   55. $+\infty$ 57. $\frac{2}{5}$

PAGES 287-288 Exercises

1. $f'(3) = \lim\limits_{h \to 0} \frac{[2(3 + h) + 5] - (2 \cdot 3 + 5)}{h} = \lim\limits_{h \to 0} \frac{2h}{h} = 2$ 3. 0   5. $\frac{1}{4}$

7. -5   9. 5   11. $6x_0$ 13. $2x_0 - 3$ 15. $3x_0^2$ 17. 2, 1   19. 3, 2

21. $f'(x_0)$ exists. Then $f'(x_0) = \lim\limits_{h \to 0} \frac{f(x_0 + h) - f(x_0)}{h}$. Thus, if you consider

$f(x_0 + h) - f(x_0) = h \cdot \frac{f(x_0 + h) - f(x_0)}{h}$ and take the limit of each side as $h \to 0$,

you obtain $\lim\limits_{h \to 0} (f(x_0 + h) - f(x_0)) = \lim\limits_{h \to 0} f(x_0 + h) - \lim\limits_{h \to 0} f(x_0)$ while $\lim\limits_{h \to 0}$

$h \cdot \dfrac{f(x_0 + h) - f(x_0)}{h} = \lim\limits_{h \to 0} h \cdot f'(x_0) = 0 \cdot f'(x_0) = 0.$ Therefore $\lim\limits_{h \to 0}$

$f(x_0 + h) - \lim\limits_{h \to 0} f(x_0) = 0$ or $\lim\limits_{h \to 0} f(x_0 + h) = \lim\limits_{h \to 0} f(x_0) = f(x_0).$ Let $x_0 + h$

$= x.$ Then as $h \to 0$, $x \to x_0$. Thus $\lim\limits_{x \to x_0} f(x) = f(x_0).$ Therefore $f(x)$ is con-

tinuous at $x = x_0$.

PAGES 290-291 Exercises

1. $\dfrac{2}{3}$ 3. -8 5. 7 7. 3 9. 6 11. 0 13. a. $\dfrac{y_2 - y_1}{x_2 - x_1}$ b. $\dfrac{y_2 - y_1}{h}$

c. $\dfrac{f(x + h) - f(x)}{h}$ d. $\dfrac{f(x + h) - f(x)}{h}$ 15. $f'(-\dfrac{0}{2 \cdot 1}) = 0$ 17. $f'(-\dfrac{1}{2 \cdot 2}) = 0$

19. $f'(-\dfrac{b}{2a}) = 0$ 21. $f'(x) = -\dfrac{1}{x^2}.$ For x close to 0, $f'(x)$ goes to $-\infty$ and the

tangent lines to the graph of $y = f(x)$ to either side of $x = 0$ have negative

slopes of increasing steepness.

PAGE 295 Exercises

1. $7x^6$ 3. 0 5. $\dfrac{-100}{x^{101}}$ 7. $50x^9 + 5x^4 - 4x$ 9. $-36x^{-4}$ 11. $f'(x) = x + 2,$

$m = f'(3) = 5,$ $y_1 = f(3) = \dfrac{21}{2},$ $y - \dfrac{21}{2} = 5(x - 3)$ 13. $y = 2x + 3$ 15. $y - \dfrac{1}{9}$

$= -\dfrac{2}{27}(x - 3)$ 17. $\lim\limits_{h \to 0} \dfrac{f(x + h) - f(x)}{h} = \lim\limits_{h \to 0} \dfrac{k - k}{h} = \lim\limits_{h \to 0} 0 = 0$

19. $\lim\limits_{h \to 0} \dfrac{p(x + h) - p(x)}{h} =$

$\lim\limits_{h \to 0} \left[\dfrac{f(x + h) \cdot g(x + h) - f(x + h) \cdot g(x) + f(x + h) \cdot g(x) - f(x) \cdot g(x)}{h} \right]$

$= \lim\limits_{h \to 0} f(x + h) \left[\dfrac{g(x + h) - g(x)}{h} \right] + \lim\limits_{h \to 0} g(x) \left[\dfrac{f(x + h) - f(x)}{h} \right]$

$= f(x)g'(x) + g(x)f'(x)$ 21. $\dfrac{-2}{x^3}$

PAGES 295-297 Chapter Objectives and Review

For Exercises 3-7 answers will vary.   3. $f(x) = 2 + \dfrac{1}{x}$, $x < 0$ 5. $f(x) = 1 + \dfrac{x}{5}$

7. $f(x) = \dfrac{1}{x + 3}$ 9. c   11. $M \pm N$ 13. $\dfrac{M}{N}$, $N \neq 0$ 15. $\lim\limits_{x \to -3} (x^2 - 2x) =$

$$\lim_{x \to -3} x^2 - \left(\lim_{x \to -3} 2\right) \cdot \left(\lim_{x \to -3} x\right) = (-3)^2 - (2)(-3) = 15 \qquad 17. \quad \lim_{x \to +\infty} \frac{x+1}{x}$$

$$= \lim_{x \to +\infty} 1 + \frac{1}{x} = \lim_{x \to +\infty} 1 + \lim_{x \to +\infty} \frac{1}{x} = 1 + 0 = 1 \qquad 19. \quad \text{When at least one}$$

of the following three conditions is not true: (i) $f(a)$ exists; (ii) $\lim_{x \to a} f(x)$

exists; (iii) $f(a) = \lim_{x \to a} f(x)$ 21. See the diagram on page 271.   23. $f'(a)$

$$= \lim_{h \to 0} \frac{f(a+h) - f(a)}{h} = \lim_{h \to 0} \frac{(a+h)^2 - (a+h) - (a^2 - a)}{h}$$

$$= \lim_{h \to 0} \frac{a^2 + 2ah + h^2 - a - h - a^2 + a}{h} \qquad \lim_{h \to 0} 2a + h - 1 = 2a - 1 \qquad 25. \ 3x^2$$

27. $\dfrac{-12}{x^5}$ 29. $y = x - 2$

PAGE 297   Chapter Test

1. $\lim_{x \to 2} f(x) = 2$ 3. Yes, since $f(2)$ is defined, $\lim_{x \to 2} f(x)$ exists, and $f(2)$

$= \lim_{x \to 2} f(x)$ 5. 0   7. 1   9. $+\infty$

11. $\lim_{h \to 0} \dfrac{3(x+h)^2 - (x+h) + 1 - (3x^2 - x + 1)}{h}$

$= \lim_{h \to 0} \dfrac{3x^2 + 6xh + 3h^2 - x - h + 1 - 3x^2 + x - 1}{h} = \lim_{h \to 0} 6x + 3h - 1 = 6x - 1$

13. $16x^2 + 6x - 2$ 15. 4

CHAPTER 7 ALGEBRAIC FUNCTIONS

PAGE 305   Exercises

1. 4, 3   3. 2, 4   5. 9, -1   7. -3, $\frac{3}{2}$, -2   9. 0, 0, 2   11. -4, $\pm$ 2, 6;

y axis; turning point is $(0, -4)$; upward.   13. 0, 0, -6; axis of symmetry is

$x = 0$; downward.   15. 0, 0 and 2, -8; axis of symmetry is $x = 1$; turning point

is $(1, 2)$; downward.   17. 0   19. a. -12   b. $-3x_0^2$ 21. Let $p(x) =$

$a_m x^m + a_m x^{m-1} + \cdots + a_0$ and $q(x) = b_n x^n + b_{n-1} x^{n-1} + \cdots + b_0$ be polynomial

over A, with a_m and b_n as leading coefficients. We may assume without loss of

generality that $m > n$. Then $p(x) + q(x) = a_m x^m + \cdots + (a_n + b_n)x^n + \cdots +$

$(a_0 + b_0)$ which after setting $c_i = a_i + b_i (i = 0, 1, 2, \cdots, n)$ is certainly a polynomial of degree $m + n$ over A. (The cases where $n < m$ and $m = n$ are done in a similar way.) Also true for product of two polynomials.

PAGE 308 Exercises

1. 51, 6, 56   3. 1, 85, -2, -20, -174   5. $\frac{343}{81}$, $\frac{893}{256}$, 23   7. k = -14

9. k = 10   11. c = 1 and k = 2   13. f(-4) = -60, f(-3.5) = -47.13, f(-3) =

-38, f(-2.5) = -31.88, f(-2) = -28, f(-1.5) = -25.63, f(-1) = -24, f(-.5) = -22.38,

f(0) = -20, f(.5) = -16.125, f(1) = -10, f(1.5) = -.88, f(2) = 12, f(2.5) = 29.37,

f(3) = 52, f(3.5) = 80.62, f(4) = 116   15. f(-4) = -46, f(-3.5) = -26.38, f(-3)

= -12, f(-2.5) = -2.13, f(-2) = 4, f(-1.5) = 7.13, f(-1) = 8, f(-.5) = 7.38,

f(0) = 6, f(.5) = 4.63, f(1) = 4, f(1.5) = 4.88, f(2) = 8, f(2.5) = 14.125, f(3)

= 24, f(3.5) = 38.38, f(4) = 58   17. f(-4) = -76, f(-3.5) = -53.38, f(-3) = -36,

f(-2.5) = -23.13, f(-2) = -14, f(-1.5) = -7.88, f(-1) = -4, f(-.5) = -1.63, f(0)

= 0, f(.5) = 1.62, f(1) = 4, f(1.5) = 7.88, f(2) = 14, f(2.5) = 23.13, f(3) = 36,

f(3.5) = 53.38, f(4) = 76

PAGES 312-313 Exercises

1. $3x^2 + 10x + 10$, f(2) = 5   3. $-2x^3 + x^2 + x + 7$, -3   5. $9x^2 + 6x + 3$, 3

7. $2x^2 + x + 4$, 0   9. $3x^2 - 6$, 5   11. The degree of Q(x) is n - m and the degree of r(x) is less than m and greater than or equal to zero.   13. f(-6) = 0,

f(-2) = 100, $f(-\frac{1}{3}) = 0$, $f(\frac{1}{2}) = 0$, f(3) = 450 so the factors are x + 6, x + $\frac{1}{3}$,

and x $-\frac{1}{2}$.   15. k = -2   17. Use synthetic substitution.

1	p	q	$\underline{a}$		1	p	q	$\underline{b}$
	a	$a^2 + ap$				b	$b^2 + bp$	
1	a + p	$a^2 + ap + q$			1	p + b	$b^2 + bp + q$	

Since in each case the remainder is 0, $a^2 + ap + q = 0$ and $b^2 + bp + q = 0$.

Solving for p and q; $q = -a^2 - ap$, $b^2 + bp + (-a^2 - ap) = 0$, or $p(b - a) = a^2 - b^2$

$= (a + b)(a - b)$. Then $p = \frac{-(b - a)(a + b)}{b - a}$ or $p = -a - b$. Then $q = -b^2 - b(-a - b)$

= ab.   19. $f(-a) = (-a)^n + a^n$. If n is odd, $(-a)^n = -a^n$ and $f(-a) = 0$. There-

fore x + a is a factor of $x^n + a^n$. $Q(x) = x^{n-1} - ax^{n-2} + a^2x^{n-3} - \cdots +$

$\cdots + a^{n-1}$.   21. Let $f(x) = a_3x^3 + a_2x^2 + a_1x + a_0$ and c be a number. To

divide f(x) by x - c use synthetic division. $Q(x) = a_3x^2 + (a_2 + a_3c)x$

$+ a_3c^2 + a_2c + a_1$ and $r = a_3c^3 + a_2c^2 + a_1c + a_0$ which is f(c). 23. $\left(x - \dfrac{(1 - \sqrt{5})}{2}\right)$

$\left(x - \dfrac{(1 + \sqrt{5})}{2}\right)$ 25. $(x - 2i)(x + 2i)$

PAGE 317 Exercises

1. -1 and 0, 1 and 2, 2 and 3   3. -1 and 0, 2 and 3   5. -3 and -2, 1 and 2

7. -2 and -1, 0 and $\dfrac{1}{2}$, $\dfrac{1}{2}$ and 1   9. .5 and .6   11. -2.1 and -2.0

13. a. $0 < k < 3$ b. $3 < k < 8$

PAGES 320-321 Exercises

1. 2, 3, -4   3. -1, 4   5. $\dfrac{1}{2}$, $\dfrac{3}{4}$, 2   7. $\dfrac{1}{3}$, $\pm\sqrt{2}$ 9. 2, 3, -4   11. -3

13. -3, -1, 3, 5   15. No rational zeros. There is one real zero between 1

and 1.1.   17. $x^3 + 2x^2 - 5x - 6$ 19. -2, which is equal to the negative of the

coefficient of x^2.   21. 6, which is equal to the negative of the constant term.

23. $\dfrac{-11}{4}$ 25. $x^3 - x^2 - \dfrac{11}{4}x + \dfrac{3}{2} = 0$ 27. $\dfrac{a_2}{a_3} = -(r_1 + r_2 + r_3)$, $\dfrac{a_1}{a_3} = r_1r_2 +$

$r_1r_3 + r_2r_3$, $\dfrac{a_0}{a_3} = -r_1r_2r_3$ 29. $\dfrac{a_3}{a_4} = -(r_1 + r_2 + r_3 + r_4)$, $\dfrac{a_2}{a_4} = r_1r_2 + r_1r_3$

$+ r_1r_4 + r_2r_3 + r_2r_4 + r_3r_4$, $\dfrac{a_1}{a_4} = -(r_1r_2r_3 + r_1r_2r_4 + r_1r_3r_4 + r_2r_3r_4)$,

$\dfrac{a_0}{a_4} = r_1r_2r_3r_4$

PAGES 324-325 Exercises

1. -1 has multiplicity 2 and 2 is a simple zero.   3. -2 is a simple zero and

-1 has multiplicity 3.   5. 1, $\dfrac{-1 + \sqrt{3}i}{2}$, and $\dfrac{-1 - i\sqrt{3}}{2}$ are all simple zeros.

7. i, -i, 2i, -2i are all simple zeros.   9. 1, $\dfrac{-1 + i\sqrt{3}}{2}$, $\dfrac{-1 - i\sqrt{3}}{2}$ are

roots of multiplicity 2.   11. -1, i, and -i are each roots of multiplicity 2.

13. $x^3 - 2x^2 - x + 2$ 15. $x^3 - 4x^2 + 2x + 4$ 17. $x^4 - 4x^3 + 6x^2 - 4x$

19. $x^4 - 4x^3 + 14x^2 - 20x + 25$ 21. $x^6 + 3x^4 + 3x^2 + 1$ 23. -3i, $-\dfrac{1}{2}$, 5

25. You know by Theorem 7-7 that $f(x)$ has at least one zero, $x = r_1$. This means that by the Factor Theorem $f(x) = (x - r_1)Q_1(x)$, where $Q_1(x)$ has degree $n - 1$. If $n - 1 = 0$ you are done. Otherwise since $Q_1(x)$ is also a polynomial, $Q_1(x)$ has a zero, $x = r_2$. By the Factor Theorem $f(x) = (x - r_1)(x - r_2)Q_2(x)$, where $Q_2(x)$ is of degree $n - 2$. Continue the process and $f(x) = (x - r_1)(x - r_2) \cdots$ $(x - y_n)Q_n(x)$, where $Q_n(x)$ is of degree $n - n = 0$ and therefore $f(x)$ has at most n complex zeros. The reason for "at most" is that some r_i may equal some r_j.

PAGES 328-329 Exercises

1. $(-1, 7)$ is a relative maximum and $(2, -20)$ is a relative minimum. 3. $(0, 0)$ is a relative maximum and $(2, -4)$ is a relative minimum. 5. $(\frac{7}{2}, \frac{25}{4})$ is a relative maximum. 7. None. 9. $(0, 5)$ is a relative maximum and $(\frac{4}{3}, \frac{103}{27})$ is a relative minimum. 11. $(-1, 10)$ is a relative minimum and $(0, 11)$ is a relative maximum. 13. $(-\frac{3}{a}, -\frac{9}{a} + c)$ is a relative minimum if $a > 0$ and a relative maximum if $a < 0$. 15. a. 80 feet. b. 128 feet. c. Zero feet. 17. 144 feet. 19. The heights are the same because the graph of the function representing the height is a parabola which has an axis of symmetry $t = 5$. The points $t = 3$ and $t = 7$ on the parabola are symmetric about the line $t = 5$. 21. $b = 18$ feet and $h = 18$ feet.

PAGES 331-332 Exercises

1. $(-2, 21)$ is a relative maximum and $(1, -6)$ is a relative minimum. 3. $(0, 5)$ is an inflection point and $(\frac{3}{2}, \frac{53}{16})$ is a relative minimum. 5. $(0, \frac{3}{4})$ is a relative maximum and $(-\sqrt{3}, \frac{-3}{8})$ and $(\sqrt{3}, \frac{-3}{8})$ are relative minima. 7. $(\pm 2, 16)$ are relative maxima and $(0, 0)$ is a relative minimum. 9. $(0, 0)$ is a relative minimum. 11. $(0, -31)$ is a point of inflection. 13. $(0, -1)$ and $(1, 1)$ are points of inflection. 15. $(a, 0)$ is a point of inflection. 17. Point of inflection. 19. None of these. 21. a. 5 and 5 b. 5 and 5

PAGE 335 Exercises

1. Functional values: $(-3, 75)$, $(-2, 48)$, $(-1, 27)$, $(0, 12)$, $(1, 3)$, $(2, 0)$,

(3, 3). y intercept = 12. Relative minimum = (2, 0). $\lim\limits_{x \to -\infty} f = \lim\limits_{x \to +\infty} f = +\infty$.

3. Functional values: (-3, -50), (-2, -16), (-1, 0), (0, 4), (1, 2), (2, 0),
(3, 4). -1 is a single zero and 2 is a zero of multiplicity 2. (0, 4) is a relative maximum and (2, 0) is a relative minimum. $\lim\limits_{x \to -\infty} f = -\infty$ and

$\lim\limits_{x \to +\infty} f = +\infty$. 5. Functional values: (-3, 7), (-2, 18), (-1, 11), (0, -2),

(1, -9), (2, 2), (3, 43). The zeros of f are between 0 and -1, 1 and 2, and -3
and -4. (1, -9) is a relative minimum and (-2, 18) is a relative maximum.

$\lim\limits_{x \to -\infty} f = -\infty$ and $\lim\limits_{x \to +\infty} f = +\infty$. 7. Functional values: (-3, 243),

(-2, 72), (-1, 11), (0, 0), (1, 3), (2, 8), (3, 27). The zeros of f are 0 and

$2 \pm \sqrt{2}i$. (0, 0) is a relative minimum. $\lim\limits_{x \to -\infty} f = \lim\limits_{x \to +\infty} f = +\infty$.

9. Functional values: (-3, 8), (-2, 0), (-1, 0), (0, 2), (1, 24), (2, 108),
(3, 320). The zeros of f are -1 and -2. $(-\frac{3}{4}, -\frac{27}{256})$ is a relative minimum.

$\lim\limits_{x \to +\infty} f = \lim\limits_{x \to -\infty} f = +\infty$. (-1, 0) and $(-\frac{3}{2}, -\frac{1}{16})$ are points of inflection.

11. Functional values: (-3, 81), (-2, 16), (-1, 1), (0, 0), (1, 1), (2, 16),
(3, 81). (0, 0) is a relative minimum. No points of inflection. $\lim\limits_{x \to +\infty} f$

$= \lim\limits_{x \to -\infty} f = +\infty$. 13. Functional values: (-3, -343), (-2, -216), (-1, -125),

(0, -64), (1, -27), (2, -8), (3, -1). (4, 0) is a point of inflection.

$\lim\limits_{x \to -\infty} f = -\infty$ and $\lim\limits_{x \to +\infty} f = +\infty$. 15. Functional values: (-3, -5887),

(-2, -1025), (-1, -63), (0, -1), (1, 1), (2, 63), (3, 1025). (0, -1) and (1, 1)

are points of inflection. $\lim\limits_{x \to -\infty} f = -\infty$ and $\lim\limits_{x \to +\infty} f = +\infty$. 17. Functional

values: (-3, -442), (-2, -101), (-1, -6), (0, -1), (1, -2), (2, +3), (3, -46).
There is a relative minimum between 1 and 2 and relative maxima between -1 and -2
and between 1 and 2. 19. Functional values: (-3, -10), (-2, 3), (-1, 6),

(0, 5), (1, 6), (2, 15), (3, 38). $(\frac{1}{3}, \frac{130}{27})$ is a relative minimum and (-1, 6) is

a relative maximum. $(-\frac{1}{3}, \frac{146}{27})$ is a point of inflection. $\lim\limits_{x \to -\infty} f = -\infty$ and

$\lim\limits_{x \to +\infty} f = +\infty$. 21. Functional values: (-3, 400), (-2, 25), (-1, 0), (0, 1),

(1, 16), (2, 225), (3, 1600). (-1, 0) is a relative minimum.

$\lim\limits_{x \to -\infty} f = \lim\limits_{x \to +\infty} f = +\infty$. 23. Functional values: (-3, -640), (-2, -135),

(-1, -16), (0, -1), (1, 0), (2, 5), (3, 80). (1, 0) is a point of inflection.

$\lim\limits_{x \to -\infty} f = -\infty$ and $\lim\limits_{x \to +\infty} f = +\infty$. 25. Functional values: (-3, 100),

(-2, 81), (-1, 64), (0, 49), (1, 36), (2, 25), (3, 16). (7, 0) is a relative

minimum. $\lim\limits_{x \to +\infty} f = \lim\limits_{x \to -\infty} f = +\infty$. 27. Functional values: (-3, 625),

(-2, 144), (-1, 9), (0, 4), (1, 9), (2, 0), (3, 49). (2, 0) is a relative minimum.
$(-\frac{1}{2}, 0)$ is a relative minimum. $(\frac{3}{4}, \frac{625}{64})$ is a relative maximum. $\lim\limits_{x \to -\infty} f =$

$\lim\limits_{x \to +\infty} f = +\infty$. 29. Functional values: (-3, -648), (-2, -112), (-1, -6),

(0, 0), (1, -4), (2, -48), (3, -162). (0, 0) is a relative maximum and (4, -256)

is a relative minimum. (3, -162) is a point of inflection. $\lim\limits_{x \to -\infty} f = -\infty$

and $\lim\limits_{x \to +\infty} f = +\infty$. 31. Functional values: (-3, -64), (-2, 0), (-1, 8),

(0, 4), (1, 0), (2, -16), (3, -200). (-2, 0) is a relative minimum and (-.8, 8.4)

is a relative maximum. (1, 0) is a point of inflection. $\lim\limits_{x \to -\infty} f = +\infty$ and

$\lim\limits_{x \to +\infty} f = -\infty$.

PAGES 340-341 Exercises

1. f(x) is concave upward on the interval $\langle -\infty, +\infty \rangle$. 3. f(x) is concave

upward on $\langle -\frac{1}{2}, +\infty \rangle$. $(-\frac{1}{2}, \frac{9}{2})$ is an inflection point. 5. f(x) is concave

upward on $\langle -\frac{1}{2}, +\infty \rangle$ and concave downward on $\langle -\infty, -\frac{1}{2} \rangle$. $(-\frac{1}{2}, -\frac{1}{2})$ is an inflection point.   7. y intercept = 0, relative maximum = $(\frac{4}{3}, \frac{32}{27})$, relative mini-

mum = (0, 0), point of inflection = $(\frac{2}{3}, \frac{16}{27})$, concave upward for $\left\langle -\infty, \frac{2}{3} \right\rangle$, concave

downward $\left\langle \frac{2}{3}, +\infty \right\rangle$, $\lim\limits_{x \to +\infty} f(x) = -\infty$ and $\lim\limits_{x \to -\infty} f(x) = +\infty$.   9. y intercept

= 0, relative minimum at (0, 0). Concave upward on $\left\langle -\infty, +\infty \right\rangle$. $\lim\limits_{x \to -\infty} f$

= $\lim\limits_{x \to +\infty} f = +\infty$.   11. y intercept = 1, relative maximum = (1, 5), relative

minimum = (3, 1), point of inflection = (2, 3), concave downward on $\left\langle -\infty, 2 \right\rangle$,

concave upward on $\left\langle 2, \infty \right\rangle$, $\lim\limits_{x \to -\infty} f = -\infty$ and $\lim\limits_{x \to +\infty} f = +\infty$.   13. y

intercept = 5, relative maximum = (0, 5), relative minimum = $(\frac{3}{2}, -\frac{7}{4})$, inflection

point = $(\frac{3}{4}, 1\frac{3}{8})$, concave upward on $\left\langle \frac{3}{4}, +\infty \right\rangle$, concave downward on $\left\langle -\infty, \frac{3}{4} \right\rangle$,

$\lim\limits_{x \to -\infty} f = -\infty$ and $\lim\limits_{x \to +\infty} f = +\infty$.   15. y intercept = 1, relative maximum

= (0, 1), relative minima = $(\pm 1, 0)$, inflection points = $(\pm\frac{1}{\sqrt{3}}, \frac{8}{9})$, concave

downward on $\left\langle -\frac{1}{\sqrt{3}}, \frac{1}{\sqrt{3}} \right\rangle$, concave upward everywhere else, $\lim\limits_{x \to -\infty} f = \lim\limits_{x \to +\infty} f$

= $+\infty$.   17. y intercept = 25, relative maximum = (-2, 69), relative minimum

= (3, -56), inflection point = $(\frac{1}{2}, \frac{13}{2})$, concave downward on $\left\langle -\infty, \frac{1}{2} \right\rangle$, concave

upward on $\left\langle \frac{1}{2}, +\infty \right\rangle$, $\lim\limits_{x \to -\infty} f = -\infty$ and $\lim\limits_{x \to +\infty} f = +\infty$.   19. y intercept

= 0, relative maxima = (-2, 0), $(\frac{2}{\sqrt{5}}, \frac{512}{25\sqrt{5}})$, relative minima = (2, 0),

$(-\frac{2}{\sqrt{5}}, -\frac{512}{25\sqrt{5}})$, points of inflection = $(\sqrt{\frac{12}{5}}, \frac{128\sqrt{15}}{125})$, $(-\sqrt{\frac{12}{5}}, -\frac{128\sqrt{15}}{125})$, (0, 0),

$\lim\limits_{x \to -\infty} f = -\infty$ and $\lim\limits_{x \to +\infty} f = +\infty$.   21. a. The slope of the line passing

through (a, f(a)), (b, f(b)). b. The slope of the tangent line to the graph of

y = f(x) at the point $(x_0, f(x_0))$. c. There is a point $(x_0, f(x_0))$, a< x_0< b,

such that the secant line connecting (a, f(a)) and (b, f(b)) is parallel to the

line tangent to f(x) at x_0.

PAGE 344 Exercises

1. Functional values: $(-2, -\frac{1}{3})$, $(-1, -\frac{1}{2})$, (0, -1), (2, 1), (3, $\frac{1}{2}$), (4, $\frac{1}{3}$),

no zeros, x = 1 is an excluded point, x = 1 is a vertical asymptote, y = 0 is a horizontal asymptote.   3. Functional values: $(-1, \frac{1}{2})$, $(0, \frac{2}{3})$, $(4, -2)$, $(5, -1)$, no zeros, x = 3 is an excluded point, x = 3 is a vertical asymptote, y = 0 is a horizontal asymptote. 5. Functional values: $(-6, 12)$, $(-4, -8)$, $(-3, -3)$, zero at x = 0, x = -5 is an excluded value and a vertical asymptote, y = 2 is a horizontal asymptote.   7. Functional values: $(-6, \frac{15}{2})$, $(-2, -\frac{7}{2})$, $(0, -\frac{3}{4})$, $(\frac{3}{2}, 0)$. x = $\frac{3}{2}$ is a zero. x = -4 is an excluded point and a vertical asymptote, y = 2 is a horizontal asymptote.   9. Functional values: $(-3, 4\frac{1}{2})$, $(-\frac{3}{2}, -18)$, $(0, 0)$, $(1, -\frac{1}{2})$, $(2, -\frac{1}{2})$, x = 0 is a zero, x = -1 and x = -2 are excluded points and vertical asymptotes, y = 0 is a horizontal asymptote.   11. Functional values: $(-2, -1)$, $(0, 1)$, $(1, \frac{1}{2})$, $(3, \frac{1}{4})$, $(4, \frac{1}{5})$, $(6, \frac{1}{7})$, no zeros, x = -1 and x = 5 are excluded points, x = -1 is a vertical asymptote, y = 0 is a horizontal asymptote. 13. Functional values: $(-3, \frac{24}{13})$, $(1, -\frac{4}{9})$, $(5, 0)$, x = 0 and x = 5 are zeros, x = -2 and x = $\frac{1}{4}$ are excluded points and vertical asymptotes y = $\frac{1}{4}$ is a horizontal asymptote. 15. Functional values: $(-4, 21)$, $(-1, 6)$, $(0, 1)$, $(1, \frac{1}{6})$, $(2, 0)$, $(3, 0)$, x = 2 and x = 3 are zeros, x = -2 and x = -3 are excluded points and vertical asymptotes, y = 1 is a horizontal asymptote.   17. Functional values: $(-\frac{1}{2}, -\frac{4}{3})$, $(1, \frac{2}{3})$, x = 0 is a zero, no excluded points or vertical asymptotes, y = 0 is a horizontal asymptote.   19. Same graph as Exercise 1.   21. They are identical except for the zeros of t(x), at which $R_1(x)$ is not defined.   23. Functional values: $(-2, \frac{1}{2})$, $(-1, \frac{1}{3})$, $(1, -1)$, $(3, 3)$, $(4, 2)$, there is a hole at $(0, 0)$, x = 2 is an excluded point and a vertical asymptote, y = 1 is a horizontal asymptote. 25. Functional values: $(-3, \frac{3}{4})$, $(-2, \frac{2}{3})$, $(-1, \frac{1}{2})$, $(0, 0)$, $(2, 2)$, $(3, \frac{3}{2})$, $(+\frac{1}{2}, -1)$, $(\frac{3}{4}, -3)$, x = 1 is a vertical asymptote and there are no holes.

PAGES 348-349 Exercises

1. $\langle -\infty, -2] \cup [2, +\infty \rangle$ 3. $\langle -\infty, -2] \cup [2, +\infty \rangle$ 5. $\langle -\infty, 1 \rangle$
7. $\langle -\infty, 1] \cup [2, +\infty \rangle$ 9. $[-2, 0] \cup [2, +\infty \rangle$ 11. The set of real

numbers.   13. Domain = set of all real numbers, real zeros are x = $\pm$ 2, no

vertical or horizontal asymptotes, functional values: (-2, 0), (0, -1.587),

(1, -1.44), (2, 0).   15. Domain = $\left\langle -\infty, -2 \right] \cup \left[3, +\infty \right\rangle$, x = -2 and x = 3

are zeros, functional values: (-4, $\sqrt{14}$), (-2, 0), (4, $\sqrt{6}$), (5, $\sqrt{14}$).

17. Domain = $\left\langle 0, +\infty \right\rangle$, y = -1 is a horizontal asymptote, x = 0 is a vertical

asymptote, functional values: ($\frac{1}{2}$, -$\sqrt{3}$), (1, -$\sqrt{2}$), (2, -$\sqrt{\frac{3}{2}}$).   19. Domain =

all real numbers, range y $\geq$ 0, functional values: (-2, $\sqrt[3]{4}$), (-1, 1), (1, 1),

(2, $\sqrt[3]{4}$), (3, $\sqrt[3]{9}$).   21. y = 1 + $\sqrt{1 + x^2}$ has domain = all real numbers, range

= y $\geq$ 2, functional values: (-3, 4.16), (-1, 2.4), (0, 2), (1, 2.414), (3, 4.16).

y = 1 - $\sqrt{1 + x^2}$ is a mirror image of y = 1 + $\sqrt{1 + x^2}$ about the line y = 1.

23. Let $P_0(x)$ = 1, $P_1(x)$ = -2, and $P_2(x)$ = x^2.   25. $y^4 - 2xy^2 + x^2 - x$ = 0,

so let $P_0(x)$ = 1, $P_2(x)$ = -2x, $P_4(x)$ = x^2 - x.   27. $(x^2 + 1)y^3 + (-x)$ = 0

PAGE 351 Exercises

1. f(x) = $\frac{17}{24}x^3 + \frac{7}{24}x + 1$ 3. f(x) = $x^3 - 12x^2 + 12x$ 5. f(x) = $x^3 - 6x^2$

+ 11x - 6   7. $-\frac{7}{4}x^3 + \frac{45}{4}x^2 - \frac{31}{2}x + 3$ 9. f(2.5) = 33. At 2:30 the temperature

was 33°.   11. 39

PAGES 354-355 Exercises

1. x = $12\frac{1}{2}$; y = 25; A = $312\frac{1}{2}$ square feet.   3. The largest rectangle with a peri

meter of 20 inches is a square with side = 5.   5. $2\sqrt{6}$ by 12   7. First number

= $-\frac{1}{4}$, second number = $\frac{1}{4}$, third number = $-\frac{1}{2}$.   9. 35¢   11. r = 4 and h = 3

13. $\frac{2r}{3}$, $\frac{P}{3}$ 15. $3\sqrt[3]{3}$ by $3\sqrt[3]{3}$ by $3\sqrt[3]{3}$

PAGES 356-358 Chapter Objectives and Review

3. 14, 7, 0, -37   5. x + 1   7. x + 2, x - 2   9. 2 is an upper bound and -1

is a lower bound.   11. 1 is an upper bound and -8 is a lower bound.

13. $\left\{ \pm 1, \pm 7, \pm\frac{1}{5}, \pm\frac{7}{5} \right\}$ of which 1 is a zero.   15. (12.) $2x(x + 1)(x + 5)(x + \frac{3}{2})$

(13.) -5(x - 1) (x + $\frac{5 + i\sqrt{115}}{10}$)(x + $\frac{5 - i\sqrt{115}}{10}$)   (14.) $9(x + 1)(x + \frac{1}{3})(x - \frac{2}{3})$

17. (0, 0) is a point of inflection, no maximum or minimum points.   19. (0, -1)

is a point of inflection. 21. (17.) Concave downward on $\langle -\infty, 0 \rangle$, concave upward on $\langle 0, +\infty \rangle$. (18.) Concave downward on $\langle -\infty, 0 \rangle$, concave upward on $\langle 0, +\infty \rangle$. (19.) Concave downward on $\langle -\infty, 0 \rangle$ and concave upward on $\langle 0, +\infty \rangle$. (20.) Concave downward on $\langle \frac{5 - \sqrt{7}}{3}, \frac{5 + \sqrt{7}}{3} \rangle$, concave upward everywhere else. 23. Functional value: $(-3, -28)$, $(-2, -9)$, $(-1, -2)$, $(0, -1)$, $(1, 0)$, $(2, 7)$, $(3, 26)$. $(0, -1)$ is a point of inflection, no maximum or minimum points. 25. Functional values: $(-3, 585)$, $(-2, 306)$, $(-1, 81)$, $(0, -36)$, $(1, 9)$, $(2, 270)$. Max. $= (-6.27, 1212.07)$, Min. $= (0.27, -42.07)$. 27. Domain $= x \geq +5$ or $x \leq -5$, range $= y \geq 0$. Functional values: $(-5, 0)$, $(-6, \sqrt{11})$, $(-7, \sqrt{24})$, $(5, 0)$, $(6, \sqrt{11})$, $(7, \sqrt{24})$. 29. Domain $= x \geq 0$, range $= y \geq 0$, functional values: $(0, 0)$, $(1, 2)$, $(2, 3.414)$, no maximum or minimum points or points of inflection, concave downward for $x \geq 0$. 31. $-\frac{1}{4}x^3 - x^2 + \frac{1}{4}x + 1$ 33. 120 by 150

PAGES 358-359 Chapter Test

1. -35, $-\frac{340}{27}$, $4, 5$ 3. $\pm\sqrt{\frac{5}{3}}$, $\pm i$ 5. The answers will vary. 7. Between .5 and .6. 9. $(1, 0)$ is an inflection point. 11. Relative maximum at $(0, 0)$, relative minima at $(\pm\sqrt{2}, -4)$, y intercept $= 0$, zeros are $x = 0$ and $x = \pm 2$ 13. No maxima or minima, 2 is a zero, $(2, 0)$ is an inflection point and -8 is the y intercept. 15. Domain $= \left[-5, 5\right]$, maximum $= (0, 6)$, concave downward everywhere. 17. This curve has three branches, the first is asymptotic to $x = -1$ and $y = 0$ and $y > 0$ for all x. The second branch is concave downward, $y < 0$ for all x and it is asymptotic to $x = -1$ and $x = 3$. It has a maximum at $(1, -\frac{1}{4})$. The third branch is asymptotic to $x = 3$ and $y = 0$ and $y > 0$ for all x. 19. $4, 8$

CHAPTER 8 EXPONENTIAL AND LOGARITHMIC FUNCTIONS

PAGES 365-366 Exercises

1. $\frac{1}{8}$ 3. 343 5. $\frac{1}{8}$ 7. $2xy$ 9. a^5 11. 1 13. 200 15. 27 17. They are equal, at least in some instances. 19. 3 21. 3 23. 256 25. 64 27. 4 29. Let $r_1 = \frac{q_1}{p_1}$ and $r_2 = \frac{q_2}{p_2}$ where p_1 and p_2 are natural numbers and

q_1 and q_2 are integers. a. Proof: $a^{r_1 + r_2} = a^{\frac{q_1}{p_1} + \frac{q_2}{p_2}} = a^{\frac{q_1 p_2 + q_2 p_1}{p_1 p_2}}$

$= \left(a^{\frac{1}{p_1 p_2}}\right)^{q_1 p_2 + q_2 p_1}$ (by 9, page 363) $= \left(a^{\frac{1}{p_1 p_2}}\right)^{q_1 p_2} \cdot \left(a^{\frac{1}{p_1 p_2}}\right)^{q_2 p_1}$ (by 5, page 362)

$= a^{\frac{q_1 p_2}{p_1 p_2}} \cdot a^{\frac{q_2 p_1}{p_1 p_2}}$ (by 9, page 363) $= a^{r_1} \cdot a^{r_2}$ b. Proof: $a^{r_1 - r_2} = a^{\frac{q_1}{p_1} - \frac{q_2}{p_2}} = $

$a^{\frac{q_1 p_2 - q_2 p_1}{p_1 p_2}} = \left(a^{\frac{1}{p_1 p_2}}\right)^{q_1 p_2 - q_2 p_1}$ (by 9, page 363) $= \dfrac{\left(a^{\frac{1}{p_1 p_2}}\right)^{q_1 p_2}}{\left(a^{\frac{1}{p_1 p_2}}\right)^{q_2 p_1}}$ (by 6, page 362)

$= \dfrac{a^{\frac{q_1 p_2}{p_1 p_2}}}{a^{\frac{q_2 p_1}{p_1 p_2}}}$ (by 9, page 363) $= \dfrac{a^{r_1}}{a^{r_2}}$ c. Proof: $\left(a^{\frac{1}{p}}\right)^{\frac{1}{q}}$ is the unique positive number y

having $a^{\frac{1}{p}}$ as its qth power; i. e. $\left(a^{\frac{1}{p}}\right)^{\frac{1}{q}} = y$ iff $y^q = a^{\frac{1}{p}}$. Now $y^q = a^{\frac{1}{p}}$ iff $(y^q)^p = $

a or $y^{pq} = a$. Since $y^{pq} = a$ iff $a^{\frac{1}{pq}} = y$, $a^{\frac{1}{pq}} = y$ and therefore $\left(a^{\frac{1}{p}}\right)^{\frac{1}{q}} = a^{\frac{1}{pq}}$.

PAGES 370-372 Exercises

1. 1.2   3. 1.7   5. 0.7   7. 6.1   9. 0.75   11. 11.4   13. 1.3   15. 0.6

17. 14.0   19. 2.3   21. 0.7   23. -1.9   25. $2^{3.31}$ 27. $2^{4.2}$ 29. $2^{4.6}$

31. $2^{-0.4}$ 33.   35.

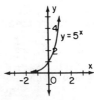

1. 2.718, seven terms. 3. 1.0101, three terms. 5. $\frac{1}{2!} - \frac{1}{3!} + \cdots + \frac{(-1)^n}{n!} + \cdots$

7. 1.44 9. $1 + \frac{1}{13} + \frac{1}{13^2} + \cdots = \frac{1}{1 - \frac{1}{13}} = \frac{13}{12}$. Therefore, $\frac{1}{13!}(1 + \frac{1}{13} + \frac{1}{13^2} + \cdots)$

$= \frac{1}{13!} \cdot \frac{13}{12} = \frac{1}{12}(\frac{1}{12!}) < .000000005$. 11. In Exercise 2, ten terms were needed.

$\frac{1}{10!} + \frac{1}{11!} + \frac{1}{12!} + \cdots < \frac{1}{10!}(\frac{1}{1 - \frac{1}{10}}) = \frac{1}{10!}(\frac{10}{9}) = \frac{1}{9(9!)} < 0.0000005$. Thus the

estimate is accurate to six decimal places.

1. .97 3. 1.1 5. -.69 7. .37 9. 4.48 11. .37, 1.35, 4.48, .22
respectively, the results should be the same as Exercises 7-10.

13. a, b.

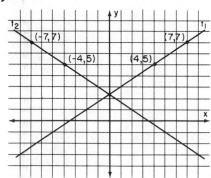

c. (-4, 5)

d. $-\frac{2}{3}$

e. (-r, s), - m

15.

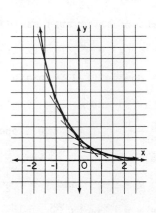

17. The result immediately follows
from the observation in Exercise 13. e.
that (x, y) is on a graph if and only
if (-x, y) is on the mirror image of
the graph with respect to y axis.

1. $13149.90   3. $1061.70   5. 17.325 years.   7. $\frac{69.3}{n}$ years.   9. 23.1%

PAGES 384-385 Exercises

1. $N = 2^t N_0$, where N_0 is the number of bacteria at time t = 0.   3. 47 days.
5. 303,750   7. t = 1   9. $(\frac{9}{8})^t N_0$ 11. 4.2 years.

PAGE 387 Exercises

1. $\frac{N(7.7)}{N(0)} = \frac{N_0 2^{\frac{-7.7}{385}}}{N_0} = 2^{-0.02} = e^{-.0139} \approx 0.986.$ $\frac{N(23.1)}{N(0)} \approx 0.96$ 3. a. 0.70

b. 0.12   c. 0.016   5. $x \approx 2020$ years.

PAGES 391-392 Exercises

1. $f^{-1} : x \to \frac{x+2}{3}$ 3. $f^{-1} : x \to \frac{2}{x-1}$ 5. $x = \frac{y+2}{3}$ 7. $x = \frac{2}{y-1}$

9.

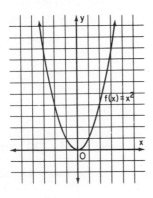

a. Since (-1,1), (1, 1) $\in$ f, two x's correspond
to y = 1, therefore there is no inverse for f.
b. See the picture of this same exercise, when
$x \geq 0$ the graph to the right of the y axis including the (0, 0) point is the graph of
$f_1(x) = x^2 \cdot f_1^{-1}(x) : x \to \sqrt{x}$, when x < 0 the
graph to the left of the y axis excluding (0, 0)
is the graph of $f_2(x) = x^2$, $f_2^{-1}(x) : x \to -\sqrt{x}$.
c. domain (f) = domain $(f_1) \cup$ domain (f_2)

11. f is strictly decreasing iff x_1, $x_2 \in$ domain (f) and $x_1 < x_2$ imply $f(x_1) <$
$f(x_2)$.   13. Proof: Since the slope of $\overline{PQ}$ is $\frac{t-u}{u-t} = -1$ and the slope of y = x
is 1, $\overline{PQ}$ is perpendicular to y = x. Solving the equation of $\overline{PQ}$ is y - u =
-1(x - t) and y = x simultaneously for x and y. $x = \frac{u+t}{2}$ and $y = \frac{u+t}{2}$. Since
the midpoint of $\overline{PQ} = (\frac{t+u}{2}, \frac{t+u}{2})$. The line y = x bisects $\overline{PQ}$.   15. The graph
of f is a straight line through the point (0, -4) with slope $\frac{2}{3}$, the graph of f^{-1}

is a straight line through the point $(-4, 0)$ with slope $\frac{3}{2}$. **17.** The slope of the inverse of a linear function is the reciprocal of the slope of the linear function. **19.** $f^{-1}(x) = \sqrt{x}$, the slope of the tangent to f^{-1} at $x = 16$ is $\frac{1}{8}$.

PAGES 398-399 Exercises

1. 2.079 **3.** 2.890 **5.** 0.406 **7.** 1.609 **9.** -1.386 **11.** 0.511

13. -0.406 **15.** -1.386 **17.** 0.511 **19.** -0.406 **21.** Answers will vary.

23. $10^5 = x$ **25.** $3^y = 25$ **27.** $3^y = 25$ **29.** Proof: $\log_a \frac{y_1}{y_2} = \log_a(y_1 \cdot (y_2^{-1}))$ $= \log_a(y_1) + \log_a(y_2^{-1}) = \log_a y_1 + (-1)\log_a y_2 = \log_a y_1 - \log_a y_2$ **31.** $f : x \to a^x$, then $f(x) = a^x$ and $f(1) = a$ then $f^{-1}(a) = 1$ or $\log_a a = 1$ **33.** $\log_{125} 5 = \frac{1}{3}$

35. $\log_{36} 6 = \frac{1}{2}$ **37.** $\log_{16} 2 = \frac{1}{4}$ **39.** -0.6990 **41.** 0.4080 **43.** Proof: Let $b = a^{\log_a b}$, $c = a^{\log_a c}$, $bc = a^{\log_a bc}$ implies $a^{\log_a bc} = a^{\log_a b} \cdot a^{\log_a c}$ or $a^{\log_a bc} = a^{\log_a b + \log_a c}$ so $\log_a bc = \log_a b + \log_a c$ **45.** Proof: Let $b = a^{\log_a b}$ and $b^c = a^{\log_a b^c}$ implies $a^{\log_a b^c} = \left(a^{\log_a b}\right)^c$; $a^{\log_a b^c} = a^{c \log_a b}$ so $\log_a b^c = c \log_a b$

PAGES 402-403 Exercises

1. 1.0791 **3.** 0.7781 **5.** -0.8239 **7.** 1.6811 **9.** 2.1070 **11.** $\frac{3}{2}$ **13.** -3

15. -3 **17.** $\frac{1}{3}$ **19.** $\frac{5}{3}$ **21.** $\frac{3}{2}$ **23.** 11 **25.** 1 **27.** e **29.** $\frac{1}{e^2}$

31. $\frac{e^2 + 1}{2e^2}$ **33.** 1, 100 **35.** Proof: $\log_a b = x$ is equivalent to $a^x = b$, $\log_b a = y$ is equivalent to $b^y = a$, $a^{xy} = (a^x)^y = b^y = a = a^1$, therefore $xy = 1$ so $x = \frac{1}{y}$ or $\log_a b = \frac{1}{\log_b a}$ **37.** Let $\log_a b = A$ $a^A = b$, $\log_b c = B$ then $b^B = c$, $\log_c d = C$ then $c^C = d$, $d = c^C = (b^B)^C = ((a^A)^B)^C = a^{ABC}$ $\therefore \log_a d = ABC = (\log_a b)(\log_b c)(\log_c d)$ **39.** -4 **41.** 2

PAGES 406-407 Exercises

1. $f'(x) = e^x$, $f'(\frac{1}{2}) = e^{\frac{1}{2}}$ **3.** $f'(x) = \frac{1}{x \ln 2}$, $f'(4) = \frac{1}{4 \ln 2}$ **5.** $f'(x) = -\frac{1}{x \ln 2}$, $f'(2) = -\frac{1}{2 \ln 2}$ **7.** $f'(x) = \frac{1}{x \ln b}$, $f'(\frac{1}{b}) = \frac{b}{\ln b}$ **9.** $f'(x) = e^x + \frac{1}{x}$,

$f'(1) = e + 1$ 11. (1.) $y - \sqrt{e} = \sqrt{e}\left(x - \frac{1}{2}\right)$ (2.) $y = x - 1$ (3.) $y - 2 = \frac{1}{4\ln 2}$

$(x - 4)$ (4.) $y - \log_{10}2 = \frac{1}{2\ln 10}(x - 2)$ (5.) $y + 1 = -\frac{1}{2\ln 2}(x - 2)$ 13. $f'(x)$

$= \frac{1}{x}\log_{\frac{1}{b}}e = \frac{1}{x}(-1)\log_b e = \frac{-\log_b e}{x}$ 15. $f'(x) = \lim\limits_{h \to 0}\left(\frac{\ln(a(x + h)) - \ln ax}{h}\right) =$

$\lim\limits_{h \to 0}\left(\frac{\ln a + \ln(x + h) - \ln a - \ln x}{h}\right) = \lim\limits_{h \to 0}\left(\frac{\ln(x + h) - \ln x}{h}\right) = \frac{1}{x}$ by the proof

on Page 405 of the text.   17. Let $f(x) = \log_a x$ and $g(y) = a^y$ since $f'(x) =$

$\frac{\log_a e}{x}$, $g'(y) = \frac{x}{\log_a e} = \frac{a^y}{\log_a e} = \frac{a^y}{\frac{\ln e}{\ln a}} = (\ln a)a^y$ 19. $f'(x) = (\ln 10)10^x$

21. $f'(x) = 2(e^2)^x$ 23. $f'(x) = ne^{nx}$ 25. $f'(x) = -e^{-x}$

PAGES 407-409   Chapter Objectives and Review

1. See the text.   3. $a^{-\frac{2}{5}} \cdot b^{-\frac{1}{3}}$ 5. 25   7. $\frac{1024}{243}$ 9. 8   11. 32   13. 1.2

15. 1.35   17. -1   19. 0.37   21. 0.7   23. Domain: positive real numbers,

range: all real numbers, $x = 1$ is a zero, y intercepts: none, concave downward

everywhere. The y axis is an asymptote, see Page 397 for graph.   25. a. ≈ 8484

b. ≈ 1976 27. $\log_3 27 = 3$ 29. $\log_{0.008}0.04 = \frac{2}{3}$ 31. $\log_a y$ 33. 5

35. $y - e = e(x - 1)$

PAGE 409   Chapter Test

1. $\frac{1}{32}$ 3. 6   5. 1.22   7. $\log_8 4 = \frac{2}{3}$ 9. $\frac{1}{\log_{10} 5}$ 11. $182.21

13. $f(x) = a^x$ and $g(x) = \log_a x$ are inverses since $a^{(\log_a x)} = \log_a(a^x) = x$, see

Page 393 for sketch.   15. As $x \to +\infty$, the slope goes to 0. As $x \to 0$, the

slope goes to $+\infty$.

CHAPTER 9   VECTORS, LINES, AND PLANES

PAGES 414-416   Exercises

1. First connect the foot of $\vec{A}$ and C, then construct a parallelogram on it. The

side parallel to $\vec{A}$ is the required vector.   3. See Exercise 1.   5. First

connect the tip of vector $\vec{B}$ and point D, then construct a parallelogram on it.
The side parallel to the vector $\vec{B}$ is the required vector.　　7.　See Exercise 5.
9.　Approximately $33°$.　　11.　Approximately $180°$.　　13.　Approximately $70°$.

PAGES 419-421　Exercises

1.　Construct a parallelogram.　The foot of $\vec{A}$ and $\vec{B}$ is the foot of $\vec{A} + \vec{B}$ and the
fourth vertex is the tip of $\vec{A} + \vec{B}$.　The tip of $\vec{B}$ is the foot of $\vec{A} - \vec{B}$, and the tip
of $\vec{A}$ is the tip of $\vec{A} - \vec{B}$.　　3.　Draw a vector equal to $\vec{A}$ that has its foot at the
foot of $\vec{B}$, call it $\vec{A}$ also, then construct a parallelogram, the foot of $\vec{A}$ is the
foot of $\vec{A} + \vec{B}$ and the tip of $\vec{B}$ is the tip of $\vec{A} + \vec{B}$.　The fourth vertex is the
foot of $\vec{A} - \vec{B}$, and the tip of $\vec{A}$ is the tip of $\vec{A} - \vec{B}$.　　5.　$\vec{A} + \vec{B} = 2\vec{A}$, $\vec{A} - \vec{B} = \vec{0}$
7.-13.　Answers will vary.　　15.　The zero vector is the limiting case of the dia-
gonal of the parallelogram whose adjacent sides are $\vec{A}$ and $-\vec{A}$.

17.

19.

21.　The length of $(n\vec{A})$ is $|n||\vec{A}|$ and the length of $m(n\vec{A})$ is $|m|(|n||\vec{A}|) =$
$(|m||n|)(|\vec{A}|) = |(m \cdot n)\vec{A}|$.　Therefore $|m(n\vec{A})| = |(m \cdot n)\vec{A}|$.　The direction of
$m(n\vec{A})$ is the same as $\vec{A}$ when m and n have the same sign and opposite to that of $\vec{A}$
when m and n are opposite in sign.　The same is true for $(m \cdot n)\vec{A}$.　　23.　(See
figure on S-52) a. In the triangles $|\vec{A}|$ and $|\vec{B}|$ are proportional to $|m\vec{A}|$ and $|m\vec{B}|$.
The included angles are congruent because a scalar multiple of a vector is parallel
to the original.　Thus the triangles are similar.　It follows that corresponding
angles are congruent and $m\vec{A} + m\vec{B}$ is the same direction as $\vec{A} + \vec{B}$ and as $m(\vec{A} + \vec{B})$.
b. Since corresponding sides are proportional $|m\vec{A} + m\vec{B}| = m|\vec{A} + \vec{B}|$.

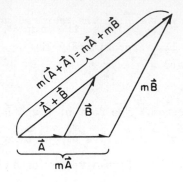

PAGES 424-426 Exercises

1. $m \approx \frac{1}{2}$, $n \approx 2$ 3. $m \approx -\frac{1}{2}$, $n \approx 2$ 5.-11. Drawings omitted.   13. Complete

the parallelogram having $m\vec{A}$, $n\vec{B}$ as two adjacent sides, $\vec{C}$ as the diagonal. $|\vec{C}|$

$= 1$, $|m\vec{A}| = 1$, $|n\vec{B}| = \sqrt{2}$. $|\vec{A}| = 2$, $|\vec{B}| = 2$ $\therefore$ $m = \frac{1}{2}$, $n = \frac{\sqrt{2}}{2}$.   15. Complete

a parallelogram as Exercise 13. $\dfrac{\sin 45^\circ}{\sin 60^\circ} = \dfrac{|n|\,|\vec{B}|}{|\vec{C}|}$ $\therefore$ $|n| = \dfrac{|\vec{C}|}{|\vec{B}|}\dfrac{\sin 45^\circ}{\sin 60^\circ} = \dfrac{4 \cdot \frac{\sqrt{2}}{2}}{3 \cdot \frac{\sqrt{3}}{2}}$

$= \dfrac{4\sqrt{2}}{3\sqrt{3}}$ $\therefore$ $n = -\dfrac{4\sqrt{2}}{3\sqrt{3}}$ because $n\vec{B}$ is opposite direction to $\vec{B}$. $\dfrac{\sin 75^\circ}{\sin 60^\circ}$

$= \dfrac{|m|\,|\vec{A}|}{|\vec{C}|} \Rightarrow |m| = \dfrac{\sin 75^\circ}{\sin 60^\circ} \cdot \dfrac{|\vec{C}|}{|\vec{A}|} = \dfrac{.9659}{\frac{\sqrt{3}}{7}} \cdot \dfrac{4}{2} = \dfrac{3.8636}{\sqrt{3}}$ $\therefore$ $m = -\dfrac{3.8636}{\sqrt{3}}$

PAGES 431-432 Exercises

1. $|\vec{r}| = \sqrt{13}$, $\theta \approx 56^\circ\ 20'$ 3. $|\vec{r}| = \sqrt{13}$, $\theta \approx 236^\circ\ 20'$ 5. $|\vec{r}| = \sqrt{7}$,

$\theta \approx 319^\circ\ 10'$ 7. $r = 2$, $\theta = 150^\circ$ 9. $r = 1$, $\theta = 180^\circ$ 11. $r = 5$, $\theta = 270^\circ$

13. No sketches given.   15. $|\vec{PQ}| = \sqrt{m^2 + n^2} = \sqrt{(x_2 - x_1)^2 + (y_2 - y_1)^2}$

17. 13   19. $2\sqrt{2}$ 21. 6   23. $5\sqrt{2}a$ 25. $\cos^2 \alpha + \cos^2 \beta + \cos^2 \gamma = 1$,

$\frac{3}{4} + \frac{1}{4} + \cos^2 \gamma = 1$, $\cos^2 \gamma = 0$, $\gamma = 90^\circ$ 27. $|\vec{A}| = 13$ $\therefore$ $\frac{1}{13}\vec{A} = \frac{12}{13}i - \frac{4}{13}j + \frac{3}{13}k$

is a unit vector in same direction.   29. $\vec{PQ} = (x_2 - x_1)i + (y_2 - y_1)j +$

$(z_2 - z_1)k$ $\therefore$ $\cos \alpha = \dfrac{(x_2 - x_1)}{|\vec{PQ}|}$, $\cos \beta = \dfrac{(y_2 - y_1)}{|\vec{PQ}|}$, $\cos \gamma = \dfrac{(z_2 - z_1)}{|\vec{PQ}|}$ 31. For $\vec{A}$

$= li + mj$, l and m are direction numbers. $\cos \alpha = \dfrac{l}{|\vec{A}|}$, $\cos \beta = \dfrac{m}{|\vec{A}|}$

1. If $P = (x_1, y_1)$ and $Q = (x_2, y_2)$ then the midpoint of $\overrightarrow{PQ}$ is $M = \left(\dfrac{x_1 + x_2}{2}, \dfrac{y_1 + y_2}{2}\right)$.

Proof: $P = (x_1, y_1, 0)$ and $Q = (x_2, y_2, 0)$. By Theorem 9-4 the midpoint M of $\overrightarrow{PQ}$

$\left(\dfrac{x_1 + x_2}{2}, \dfrac{y_1 + y_2}{2}, \dfrac{0 + 0}{2}\right) = \left(\dfrac{x_1 + x_2}{2}, \dfrac{y_1 + y_2}{2}\right)$ in the xy plane.   3. (2, 2, 2)

5. $(\frac{3}{2}, \frac{1}{2}, 0)$ 7. $(-\frac{1}{2}, -\frac{7}{2}, -\frac{1}{2})$ 9. $(\frac{2a + 1}{2}, b + 1, \frac{2c + 3}{2})$ 11. (0, 0, 0)

13. No. The same point would result.   15. $M = \left(\dfrac{x_2 + 2x_1}{3}, \dfrac{y_2 + 2y_1}{3}, \dfrac{z_2 + 2z_1}{3}\right)$

$= (\frac{10}{3}, \frac{7}{3}, \frac{20}{3})$ 17. $M = \left(\dfrac{5x_2 + x_1}{6}, \dfrac{5y_2 + y_1}{6}, \dfrac{5z_2 + z_1}{6}\right) = (\frac{7}{3}, -\frac{5}{3}, \frac{14}{3})$

19. $M = \left(\dfrac{x_2 + 5x_1}{6}, \dfrac{y_2 + 5y_1}{6}, \dfrac{z_2 + 5z_1}{6}\right) = (\frac{11}{3}, \frac{11}{3}, \frac{22}{3})$ 21. $M = (-4, -27, -8)$

23. $M = (5, 9, 10)$ 25. $x = \dfrac{px_2 + gx_1}{p + g}$, $y = \dfrac{py_2 + gy_1}{p + g}$, $z = \dfrac{pz_2 + gz_1}{p + g}$

1. It is most convenient to use $\vec{r} = \vec{r}_0 + t\overrightarrow{AB}$. $xi + yj + zk = -2i + j + 3k +$

$t(3i - 1j - 6k) \therefore x = -2 + 3t$, $y = 1 - t$, $z = 3 - 6t$ and $\dfrac{x + 2}{3} = \dfrac{y - 1}{-1} = \dfrac{z - 3}{-6}$

3. $xi + yj + zk = 0i + 0j + 0k + t(i = 2j + 3k) \therefore x = 0 + t$, $y = 0 + 2t$,

$z = 0 + 3t$ and $\dfrac{x - 0}{1} = \dfrac{y - 0}{2} = \dfrac{z - 0}{3}$ 5. $xi + yj + zk = i + 2j + 5k +$

$t(i - j + 0_k) \therefore x = 1 + t$, $y = 2 - t$, $z = 5$ and $\dfrac{x - 1}{1} = \dfrac{y - 2}{-1}$, $z = 5$

7. $xi + yj + zk = 1i + 2j + 0k + t(2i + j + 0k) \therefore x = 1 + 2t$, $y = 2 + t$,

$z = 0$ and $\dfrac{x - 1}{2} = \dfrac{y - 2}{1}$, $z = 0$ 9. $xi + yj + 2i - 3j + t(-6i + 8j) \therefore x = 2 - 6t$,

$y = -3 + 8t$ and $\dfrac{x - 2}{-6} = \dfrac{y + 3}{8}$ 11. $xi + yj = 5i - 3j + t(0i + j)$ $x = 5$, $y =$

$-3 + t$ 13. 0   15. 0   17. $x = 0$, $y = b + tm$, $z = c + tn$ 19. $x = \frac{1}{2} + \frac{1}{2}t$,

$y = -2 + \frac{1}{4}t$, $z = \frac{5}{3} + \frac{1}{3}t$ 21. a. $xi + yj + zk = 2i + j + 5k + t(1i + 3j + 2k) \therefore$

$x = 2 + t$, $y = 1 + 3t$, $z = 5 + 2t$ b. $x = 1 + t$, $y = -2 + 3t$, $z = 3 + 2t$ c. x

$= 1 - t$, $y = -2 - 3t$, $z = 3 - 2t$ 23. Infinite number. In fact for each fixed

point there are uncountably many parametric equations.   25. $xi + yj = 0i + cj +$

$t(\frac{a}{2}i + (\frac{b}{2} - c)j) \therefore x = 0 + \frac{a}{2}t$, $y = c + (\frac{b}{2} - c)t$; $xi + yj = ai + 0j +$

$t(-a\mathbf{i} + \frac{b+c}{2}\mathbf{j})$, $x = a - at$, $y = 0 + (\frac{b+c}{2})t$; $x\mathbf{i} + y\mathbf{j} = 0\mathbf{i} + b\mathbf{j} + t(\frac{a}{2}\mathbf{i} + (\frac{c}{2} - b)\mathbf{j})$

$x = 0 + \frac{a}{2}t$, $y = b + (\frac{c}{2} - b)t$

PAGES 447-448 Exercises

1. $y + 3 = \frac{1}{5}(x - 2)$ 3. $x = -2$ 5. $y = -3$ 7. $y - 1 = -\frac{2}{3}(x - 1)$

9. $y - 1 = \frac{5}{8}(x - 7)$ 11. $y - 1 = -3(x + 5)$ 13. $y = \frac{2}{7}x$ 15. $\vec{A} = \mathbf{i} + 3\mathbf{j}$

17. $\vec{A} = \mathbf{i} + \mathbf{j}$ 19. $\vec{A} = \mathbf{i} - 2\mathbf{j}$ 21. $\vec{A} = \mathbf{i} + \frac{4}{3}\mathbf{j}$ 23. $\vec{A} = 5\mathbf{i} + 3\mathbf{j}$ 25. No

sketches given.   27. $\overrightarrow{P_1P_2} \parallel \overrightarrow{P_3P_4}$ iff $\overrightarrow{P_1P_2} = t\overrightarrow{P_3P_4}$ iff $(x_2 - x_1)\mathbf{i} + (y_2 - y_1)\mathbf{j}$

$= t\left[(x_4 - x_3)\mathbf{i} + (y_4 - y_3)\mathbf{j}\right]$ iff $(x_2 - x_1) = t(x_4 - x_3)$ and $(y_2 - y_1) =$

$t(y_4 - y_3)$.   29. The hint is sufficient.   31. $\lambda = \frac{-2}{2}$ ∴ $y - 84 = -1(x - 17)$

33. $\lambda = \frac{-1}{-4}$ ∴ $y + 2 = \frac{1}{4}(x - 3)$ 35. a. $Ax + By + C = 0 \Rightarrow Ax + By =$

$-C \Rightarrow \frac{A}{-C}x + \frac{B}{-C}y = 1 \Rightarrow \frac{x}{\frac{-C}{A}} + \frac{y}{\frac{-C}{B}} = 1$ $A, B \neq 0$ b. a is the x intercept (a, 0), b

is the y intercept (0, b).   37. a. $\lambda = -\frac{A}{B}$ b. $\vec{A} = \mathbf{i} - \frac{A}{B}\mathbf{j}$ c. $\vec{D} = B\mathbf{i} - A\mathbf{j}$ and

multiples (many other answers also). d. $(y - 3) = \frac{-A}{B}(x - 2)$ or $Ax + By - 3B - 2A$

$= 0$ e. Parallel when $-3B - 2A \neq 5$, same line when $-3B - 2A = 5$ f. The coeffi-

cients of x and y are identical. g. Parallel lines in the plane have the same

x and y coefficients.

PAGES 453-455 Exercises

1. $\cos \Theta = \frac{1}{\sqrt{2}}$ 3. $\cos \Theta = \frac{\sqrt{6}}{3}$ 5. $\cos \Theta = 0$ 7. $\cos \Theta = \frac{29}{\sqrt{62} \cdot \sqrt{34}}$

9. $\cos \Theta = \frac{-19}{5\sqrt{2} \cdot \sqrt{13}}$ 11. $\cos \theta = \frac{-1}{\sqrt{6} \cdot \sqrt{13}}$ 13. $\vec{r} = 2\mathbf{i} + 0\mathbf{j} + 6\mathbf{k}$, $\vec{v} =$

$4\mathbf{i} - 2\mathbf{j} - 2\mathbf{k}$, $\cos \theta = -\frac{1}{2\sqrt{15}}$ 15. $\left.\begin{array}{l}\vec{C} = -3\mathbf{i} + 2\mathbf{j}\\ \vec{D} = 5\mathbf{i} + 3\mathbf{k}\end{array}\right\}$ Ex. 7. $\left.\begin{array}{l}\vec{C} = 3\mathbf{j} + 2\mathbf{k}\\ \vec{D} = 2\mathbf{i} - \mathbf{k}\end{array}\right\}$ Ex. 8.

$\left.\begin{array}{l}\vec{C} = -\mathbf{i} + 7\mathbf{j}\\ \vec{D} = 2\mathbf{i} + 3\mathbf{j}\end{array}\right\}$ Ex. 9.   There are many other correct answers.   17. $\Theta \approx 50°$

19. $\Theta \approx 82°$ 21. $\Theta \approx 35°$ 23. (17.) $\frac{-5}{\sqrt{29}}\mathbf{i} + \frac{2}{\sqrt{29}}\mathbf{j}$, $\frac{\mathbf{i}}{\sqrt{10}} - \frac{3}{\sqrt{10}}\mathbf{j}$

(18.) $\frac{\mathbf{i}}{\sqrt{2}} - \frac{\mathbf{k}}{\sqrt{2}}$ and $\frac{\mathbf{i}}{\sqrt{10}} - \frac{3}{\sqrt{10}}\mathbf{k}$ (19.) $\frac{3}{\sqrt{10}}\mathbf{i} + \frac{\mathbf{j}}{\sqrt{10}}$ and $\frac{-\mathbf{i}}{\sqrt{5}} + \frac{2\mathbf{j}}{\sqrt{5}}$

(20.) $\frac{3}{\sqrt{10}}i - \frac{j}{\sqrt{10}}$ and $\frac{2i}{\sqrt{5}} - \frac{j}{\sqrt{5}}$ (21.) $\frac{i}{\sqrt{5}} - \frac{2}{\sqrt{5}}j$ and $\frac{i}{\sqrt{26}} + \frac{5}{\sqrt{26}}j$

(22.) $i - 0j$ and $\frac{2}{\sqrt{5}}i - \frac{j}{\sqrt{5}}$ 25. a. $\dfrac{1 + \lambda_1 \cdot \lambda_2}{\sqrt{1 + \lambda_1^2} \cdot \sqrt{1 + \lambda_2^2}} = 0 \Rightarrow \lambda_1 \cdot \lambda_2 = -1$

or $\lambda_1 = \frac{-1}{\lambda_2}$ b. If $\lambda_1 \cdot \lambda_2 = -1$ then the lines $\frac{x - a}{1} = \frac{y - b}{\lambda_1}$ and $\frac{x - c}{1} = \frac{y - d}{\lambda_2}$

are perpendicular. Proof: The direction vectors are $\vec{A} = i + \lambda_1 j$ and $\vec{B}$

$= i + \lambda_2 j$. The lines are perpendicular iff the direction vectors are. But

$\vec{A} \cdot \vec{B} = \dfrac{1 + \lambda_1 \lambda_2}{\sqrt{1 + \lambda_1} \cdot \sqrt{1 + \lambda_2}} = \dfrac{1 - 1}{|\vec{A}| \cdot |\vec{B}|} = 0$ Thus the lines are perpendicular.

27. The direction vector for the given line is $\vec{A} = 2i + j + 5k$. Thus a normal

vector is $\vec{N} = 2i + j - k$. A line perpendicular to the given line contains

(1, -3, 1) and has direction numbers (2, 1, -1). The standard equations are

$\frac{x - 1}{2} = \frac{y + 3}{1} = \frac{z - 1}{-1}$

PAGES 459-460 Exercises

1. $2x - 3y - 5 = 0$, $3x + 2y - 14 = 0$ 3. $2x - y - 5 = 0$, $x + 2y = 0$ 5. $x - y$

$= 0$, $x + y = 0$ 7. $3x + 3y - 18 = 0$, $3x - 3y - 18 = 0$ 9. $y = 9$, $x = 7$

11. $9y + x - 63 = 0$, $y - 9x - 7 = 0$ 13. (1.) $d = \frac{10}{\sqrt{13}}$; (2.) $d = \frac{6}{\sqrt{5}}$;

(3.) $d = \frac{5}{\sqrt{5}}$; (4.) $d = \frac{45}{\sqrt{74}}$ (5.) $d = \frac{3}{\sqrt{2}}$; (6.) $d = \frac{19}{\sqrt{65}}$; (7.) $d = \frac{17}{3\sqrt{2}}$;

(8.) $d = 2$; (9.) $d = 12$; (10.) $d = 0$; (11.) $d = \frac{66}{\sqrt{82}}$; (12.) $d = \frac{19}{\sqrt{13}}$ 15. $\frac{7}{\sqrt{13}}$

17. 4 19. 0 21. $\frac{|b|}{\sqrt{m^2 + 1}}$ 23. Median from C. $y - 1 = -\frac{5}{2}(x - 5)$. Median

from A. $y - 4 = \frac{4}{5}(x - 6)$. Median from B. $y - 3 = -\frac{1}{7}(x - 2)$. 25. Bisector

of $\overline{AB}$: $(y - 1) = -4(x - 5)$. Bisector of $\overline{AC}$: $(y - 3) = -\frac{1}{3}(x - 2)$. Bisector of

$\overline{BC}$: $(y - 4) = \frac{3}{2}(x - 6)$. 27. Points $(\frac{13}{3}, \frac{8}{3})$, $(\frac{39}{11}, \frac{42}{11})$, and $(\frac{52}{11}, \frac{23}{11})$ are

collinear if a line determined by two of the points contains the third point.

Slope is $\dfrac{\frac{19}{11}}{\frac{-13}{11}} = \frac{-19}{13}$ $(y - \frac{42}{11}) = \frac{-19}{13}(x - \frac{39}{11})$. Try $(\frac{13}{3}, \frac{8}{3})$ in the equation:

$\frac{88}{33} - \frac{126}{33} \stackrel{?}{=} \frac{19}{13}(\frac{143}{33} - \frac{117}{33})$, $-\frac{38}{33} \stackrel{?}{=} -\frac{19}{13}(\frac{26}{33}) = -\frac{38}{33}$. Thus the 3 points are collinear.

The line containing these points is the Euler Line. 29. a. $3i + 2j = \vec{N}$ b. The coefficients are the same as those on x and y. c. $3(2) + (2)(-5) + 4 = 6 - 10 + 4 = 0$. d. $\vec{PQ} = (x - 2)i + (y + 5)j$. e. Zero. f. $\vec{N} \cdot \vec{PQ} = 3(x - 2) + 2(y + 5) = 0$, $3x - 6 + 2y + 10 = 0$, $3x + 2y + 4 = 0$. 31. $\vec{N} \cdot \vec{PQ}$ is the equation of the line with normal $\vec{N}$ and direction vector $\vec{PQ}$.

PAGES 464-465 Exercises

1. $\vec{A} \times \vec{B} = -5i - 6j - 7k$ 3. $\vec{A} \times \vec{B} = 2i + 0j - 2k$ 5. $\vec{A} \times \vec{B} = 3i - 18j - 13k$ 7. $\vec{A} \times \vec{B} = 3i + 0j + k$ 9. $\vec{A} \times \vec{B} = -2i + 3j + 0k$ 11. $i \times i = \vec{0}$ 13. $i \times k = -j$ 15. $j \times j = \vec{0}$ 17. $k \times i = j$ 19. $k \times k = \vec{0}$ 21. $\vec{A} \times \vec{B} = -8i + j - 4k$ ∴ Area parallelogram $= |\vec{A} \times \vec{B}| = 9$ 23. (21.) $\sin\Theta \approx .7475$, $\Theta \approx 48°$ (22.) $\sin\Theta \approx .8442$, $\Theta \approx 58°$ 25. $\vec{A} = a_1 i + a_2 j + a_3 k$, $\vec{B} = b_1 i + b_2 j + b_3 k$, $\vec{C} = c_1 i + c_2 j + c_3 k$ $\vec{B} + \vec{C} = (b_1 + c_1)i + (b_2 + c_2)j + (b_3 + c_3)k$

$$\vec{A} \times (\vec{B} + \vec{C}) = \begin{vmatrix} a_2 & a_3 \\ b_2 + c_2 & b_3 + c_3 \end{vmatrix} i + \begin{vmatrix} a_3 & a_1 \\ b_3 + c_3 & b_1 + c_1 \end{vmatrix} j + \begin{vmatrix} a_1 & a_2 \\ b_1 + c_1 & b_2 + c_2 \end{vmatrix} k$$

$= \left[a_2(b_3 + c_3) - a_3(b_2 + c_2)\right]i + \left[a_3(b_1 + c_1) - a_1(b_3 + c_3)\right]j + \left[a_1(b_2 + c_2) - a_2(b_1 + c_1)\right]k = \left[(a_2 b_3 - a_3 b_2) + (a_2 c_3 - a_3 c_2)\right]i + \left[(a_3 b_1 - a_1 b_3) + (a_3 c_1 - a_1 c_3)\right]j + \left[(a_1 b_2 - a_2 b_1) + (a_1 c_2 - a_2 c_1)\right]k$

$= \left[(a_2 b_3 - a_3 b_2)i + (a_3 b_1 - a_1 b_3)j + (a_1 b_2 - a_2 b_1)k\right] + \left[(a_2 c_3 - a_3 c_2)i + (a_3 c_1 - a_1 c_3)j + (a_1 c_2 - a_2 c_1)k\right]$

$$= \left[\begin{vmatrix} a_2 & a_3 \\ b_2 & b_3 \end{vmatrix} i + \begin{vmatrix} a_3 & a_1 \\ b_3 & b_1 \end{vmatrix} j + \begin{vmatrix} a_1 & a_2 \\ b_1 & b_2 \end{vmatrix} k\right] + \left[\begin{vmatrix} a_2 & a_3 \\ c_2 & c_3 \end{vmatrix} i + \begin{vmatrix} a_3 & a_1 \\ c_3 & c_1 \end{vmatrix} j + \begin{vmatrix} a_1 & a_2 \\ c_1 & c_2 \end{vmatrix} k\right]$$

$= \vec{A} \times \vec{B} + \vec{A} \times \vec{C}$

27. $\vec{A} \times \vec{B}$ is perpendicular to $\vec{A}$ and to $\vec{B}$. Therefore $\vec{A} \cdot (\vec{A} \times \vec{B})$ is the dot product of two perpendicular vectors and $= 0$. 29. Expand $(\vec{A} \times \vec{B}) \times \vec{C}$ and $(\vec{A} \cdot \vec{C})\vec{B} - (\vec{B} \cdot \vec{C})\vec{A}$ and show them to be equal. 31. Area of $\triangle = \frac{1}{2}$ Area of Parallelogram

$\therefore$ Area $\triangle = \frac{1}{2}|\vec{A} \times \vec{B}| = \frac{\sqrt{1667}}{2}$ 33. Do b. first. b. $\vec{A} \times (\vec{B} \times \vec{C}) = -(\vec{B} \times \vec{C}) \times \vec{A}$

(Theorem 9-12) $= -\left[(\vec{B} \cdot \vec{A})\vec{C} - (\vec{C} \cdot \vec{A})\vec{B}\right]$ (By Exercise 29.) $= (\vec{C} \cdot \vec{A})\vec{B} - (\vec{B} \cdot \vec{A})\vec{C}$

a. $(\vec{A} \times \vec{B}) \times \vec{C} = (\vec{A} \cdot \vec{C})\vec{B} - (\vec{B} \cdot \vec{C})\vec{A}$ and $\vec{A} \times (\vec{B} \times \vec{C}) = (\vec{C} \cdot \vec{A})B - (\vec{B} \cdot \vec{A})\vec{C}$. Thus

they are not equal.

PAGE 469 Exercises

1. $3x + 2y - 5z + D = 0$ so $(3 \cdot 1) + (2 \cdot 1) - 5(2) + D = 0$ and $5 - 10 + D = 0$

$\Rightarrow D = 5$ $\therefore$ $3x + 2y - 5z + 5 = 0$ is the equation of the plane. 3. $4x - y - z$

$+ 5 = 0$ 5. $\frac{1}{2}x - \frac{2}{3}y + \frac{3}{4}z + 2 = 0$ 7. $-2x + 3y - 4z + 3 = 0$

9. $\vec{A} \times \vec{B} = (i - 3j + 2k) \times (i + j - 4k) = \begin{vmatrix} -3 & +2 \\ 1 & -4 \end{vmatrix} i + \begin{vmatrix} +2 & 1 \\ -4 & 1 \end{vmatrix} j + \begin{vmatrix} 1 & -3 \\ 1 & 1 \end{vmatrix} k =$

$10i + 6j + 4k$ $\therefore$ $10x + 6y + 4z + D = 0$ But $(1, 4, 3)$ is in plane, so $10 + 24 +$

$12 + D = 0 \Rightarrow D = -46$ $\therefore$ $10x + 6y + 4z - 46 = 0$ 11. $-2x + 12y + 8z - 28 = 0$

13. Being perpendicular to $5x - 2y + 7z + 1 = 0$ means the plane's normal is $\perp$

the normal of the given plane. Thus $\vec{N} = 2i + 5j + 0k$ is the normal to one of

the countless planes satisfying the conditions. Its equation is $2x + 5y - 5 = 0$

15. $2x + y + z = 0$ is one such plane. 17. $\vec{N} = -6i + 6j + 0k$, M(-2, 4, 2), $-6x +$

$6y - 36 = 0$ 19. $z = 0$, $y = 0$, $x = 0$ 21. $\cos \theta = \dfrac{-2 + 6 + 5}{\sqrt{14} \cdot \sqrt{30}} \approx .4392; \theta \approx 64^\circ$

PAGES 473-474 Exercises

1. $\vec{N}_1 \times \vec{N}_2 = -i + 6j + 5k$. For $z = 0$ $\begin{array}{c} 2x - 3y + 1 = 0 \\ 2x + 2y - 4 = 0 \\ -5y + 5 = 0 \end{array}$ so $y = 1$ and $x = 1$ $\therefore$

$x - 1 = -t$, $y - 1 = 6t$, $z - 0 = 5t$. 3. $x - 1 = -9t$, $y - 0 = 3t$, $z - 1 = -12t$

5. $x - 0 = 3t$, $y - 3 = -9t$, $z - 2 = -6t$ 7. $\vec{N}_1 \times \vec{N}_2 = 0i + 0j + 0k$. No line,

same plane. 9. $x - 0 = -3t$, $y - 1 = -4t$, $z - 1 = 0$ 11. $d = \dfrac{|2 - 1 + 6 + 3|}{\sqrt{4 + 1 + 4}}$

$= \dfrac{10}{3}$ 13. $d = \dfrac{9}{2\sqrt{6}}$ 15. $d = \dfrac{10}{\sqrt{11}}$ 17. $d = \dfrac{|D|}{\sqrt{A^2 + B^2 + C^2}}$ 19. a. By def.

of $\sin \Theta$, $\sin \Theta = \dfrac{d}{|\vec{RP}|}$ $\therefore$ $d = |\vec{RP}| \sin \Theta$. b. $|\vec{RP} \times \vec{K}| = |\vec{RP}| \cdot |\vec{K}| \cdot \sin \Theta$

c. $d = |\overrightarrow{RP}| \cdot \sin\theta$ but $\sin\theta = \dfrac{|\overrightarrow{RP} \times \overrightarrow{K}|}{|\overrightarrow{RP}| \cdot |\overrightarrow{K}|}$ $\therefore$ $d = |\overrightarrow{RP}| \cdot \dfrac{|\overrightarrow{RP} \times \overrightarrow{K}|}{|\overrightarrow{RP}| \cdot |\overrightarrow{K}|} = \dfrac{|\overrightarrow{RP} \times \overrightarrow{K}|}{|\overrightarrow{K}|}$

PAGES 474-478 Chapter Objectives and Review

1. See definitions in text. 3. If they form the opposite sides of a parallelogram, they are equal. 5. Move $\hat{A}$ so its foot coincides with the foot of $\hat{B}$. The
angle between $\hat{A}$ and $\hat{B}$ is then obvious. 7. No sketches. 9. $|\overrightarrow{mA}| = 1$
$\Rightarrow m \cdot 1 = 1$ or $m = 1$ $|\overrightarrow{nB}| = \sqrt{3} \Rightarrow n \cdot 1 = \sqrt{3}$ or $n = \sqrt{3}$ 11. a. A vector
with its foot at the origin or other fixed point. b. Numbers proportional to
the cosines of the angle between the basis vectors and the vector. c. The rec-
tangular coordinates of its tip. 13. $\overrightarrow{PQ} = 5i - 2j$ 15. $\overrightarrow{PQ} = i - j + 0k$
17. $\overrightarrow{PQ} = 2i - 4j + 2k$ 19. $xi + yj + zk = 2i - 3j + k + t(2i - 3j + k)$, $x =$
$2 + 2t$, $y = -3 - 3t$, $z = 1 + t$, $\dfrac{x - 2}{2} = \dfrac{y + 3}{-3} = \dfrac{z - 1}{1}$ 21. $\dfrac{x - 2}{3} = \dfrac{y + 3}{7}$;
$x = 2 + 3t$, $y = -3 + 7t$, $z = 0$ 23. $\dfrac{x - 5}{1} = \dfrac{y + 7}{-\frac{2}{3}}$; $x = 5 + t$, $y = -7 - \dfrac{2}{3}t$,
$z = 0$ 25. $\cos\theta = \dfrac{-3 + 1}{\sqrt{14} \cdot \sqrt{2}} \approx -.378, \theta \approx 68°$ 27. a. If
the dot product is 0, the vectors are perpendicular. b. $\hat{A} \cdot \hat{N} = \ln_1 - \ln_2 + 3n_3$
$= 0$, let $n_1 = 1 = n_2$ $\therefore$ $\hat{N} = i + j$. 29. $2x - 3y - 1 = 0$, $3x + 2y - 8 = 0$
31. $x = 3 - 3t$, $y = 2 + t$. $x = 3 + t$, $y = 2 + 3t$. 33. $\hat{A} \times \hat{B} = -3i + j + 2k$
35. $|\hat{A} \times \hat{B}| = \sqrt{9 + 4 + 25} = \sqrt{38}$. $\sin\theta = \dfrac{|\hat{A} \times \hat{B}|}{|\hat{A}| |\hat{B}|} = \dfrac{\sqrt{38}}{\sqrt{14}\sqrt{3}} = \sqrt{\dfrac{19}{21}}$.
37. $7x - 2y + 3z - 8 = 0$ 39. A, B, C; ie $\hat{N} = Ai + Bj + Ck$.

PAGES 478-479 Chapter Test

1. $\hat{D}$ and $\hat{E}$. Do they form opposite sides of a parallelogram? 3. $\hat{D}$ and $\hat{E}$ and
$\hat{B}$ and $\hat{C}$. 5. $125°$ 7. $m \approx \dfrac{1}{3}$, $n \approx 2\dfrac{1}{2}$. 9. a. $\overrightarrow{PQ} = -3i + 8j$
b. $\overrightarrow{PQ} = -i - 8j + 3k$ 11. a. $xi + yj = 2i + j + t(-5i + 6j)$, $x = 2 - 5t$, $y = 1$
$+ 6t$, $\dfrac{x - 2}{-5} = \dfrac{y - 1}{6}$ b. $xi + yj + zk = i - 3j + 5k + t(i + 8j - 8k)$, $x = 1 + t$,
$y = -3 + 8t$, $z = 5 - 8t$, $\dfrac{x - 1}{1} = \dfrac{y + 3}{8} = \dfrac{z - 5}{-8}$ 13. $\cos\theta = \dfrac{5}{\sqrt{41} \cdot \sqrt{35}}$,
$\theta = \text{Arc cos } \dfrac{5}{\sqrt{1435}}$ 15. $5x + 7y - z + 12 = 0$

PAGES 484-485 Exercises

1. $\begin{bmatrix} -10 & -1 & 7 \\ 11 & -1 & -11 \end{bmatrix}$ 3. $\begin{bmatrix} -6 & 2 & 3 \\ 4 & -1 & -2 \end{bmatrix}$ 5. $\begin{bmatrix} 26 & -13 & -11 \\ -13 & 5 & 1 \end{bmatrix}$ 7. $\begin{bmatrix} 0 & 0 & 0 \\ 0 & 0 & 0 \end{bmatrix}$

9. $\begin{bmatrix} -10 & -1 & 7 \\ 11 & -1 & -11 \end{bmatrix}$ 11. $\begin{bmatrix} 12 & -30 & 6 \\ 18 & 6 & -42 \end{bmatrix}$ 13. a. Addition appears to be

commutative. b. Let $A = \begin{bmatrix} a_{11} & a_{12} & a_{13} \\ a_{21} & a_{22} & a_{23} \end{bmatrix}$ and $B = \begin{bmatrix} b_{11} & b_{12} & b_{13} \\ b_{21} & b_{22} & b_{23} \end{bmatrix}$. Then

$A + B = \begin{bmatrix} a_{11}+b_{11} & a_{12}+b_{12} & a_{13}+b_{13} \\ a_{21}+b_{21} & a_{22}+b_{22} & a_{23}+b_{23} \end{bmatrix} = \begin{bmatrix} b_{11}+a_{11} & b_{12}+a_{12} & b_{13}+a_{13} \\ b_{21}+a_{21} & b_{22}+a_{22} & b_{23}+a_{23} \end{bmatrix}$

$= B + A$. c. If A and B are any 2 x 3 matrices, then $A + B = B + A$.

15. $C = \begin{bmatrix} 1 & -1 & 8 \\ 1 & 3 & -3 \end{bmatrix}$ 17. $\vec{A}$ could be represented by the matrix in the one row

$\begin{bmatrix} 2 & 3 & -2 \end{bmatrix}$ or the matrix with one column $\begin{bmatrix} 2 \\ 3 \\ -2 \end{bmatrix}$. The latter method is used later
in this book.

PAGES 488-489 Exercises

1. $(A + B) + C = \begin{bmatrix} (a_{11}+b_{11})+c_{11} & (a_{12}+b_{12})+c_{12} \\ (a_{21}+b_{21})+c_{21} & (a_{22}+b_{22})+c_{22} \end{bmatrix}$ by definition of addition.

$= \begin{bmatrix} a_{11}+(b_{11}+c_{11}) & a_{12}+(b_{12}+c_{12}) \\ a_{21}+(b_{21}+c_{21}) & a_{22}+(b_{22}+c_{22}) \end{bmatrix}$ (by associativity of addition in R)

$= \begin{bmatrix} a_{11} & a_{12} \\ a_{21} & a_{22} \end{bmatrix} + \left(\begin{bmatrix} b_{11} & b_{12} \\ b_{21} & b_{22} \end{bmatrix} + \begin{bmatrix} c_{11} & c_{12} \\ c_{21} & c_{22} \end{bmatrix} \right)$ (by definition of addition) $= A + (B + C)$

3. $1 \cdot A = \begin{bmatrix} 1 \cdot a_{11} & 1 \cdot a_{12} \\ 1 \cdot a_{21} & 1 \cdot a_{22} \end{bmatrix} = \begin{bmatrix} a_{11} & a_{12} \\ a_{21} & a_{22} \end{bmatrix} = A$ 5. $(p + q)A = (p + q)\begin{bmatrix} a_{11} & a_{12} \\ a_{21} & a_{22} \end{bmatrix}$

$= \begin{bmatrix} (p+q)a_{11} & (p+q)a_{12} \\ (p+q)a_{21} & (p+q)a_{22} \end{bmatrix} = \begin{bmatrix} pa_{11}+qa_{11} & pa_{12}+qa_{12} \\ pa_{21}+qa_{21} & pa_{22}+qa_{22} \end{bmatrix} = \begin{bmatrix} pa_{11} & pa_{12} \\ pa_{21} & pa_{22} \end{bmatrix}$

$$+ \begin{bmatrix} qa_{11} & qa_{12} \\ qa_{21} & qa_{22} \end{bmatrix} = p \begin{bmatrix} a_{11} & a_{12} \\ a_{21} & a_{22} \end{bmatrix} + q \begin{bmatrix} a_{11} & a_{12} \\ a_{21} & a_{22} \end{bmatrix} = pA + qA \qquad 7. \begin{bmatrix} -1 & 3 \\ 2 & -1 \end{bmatrix} \qquad 9. \begin{bmatrix} 7 & -21 \\ -14 & 7 \end{bmatrix}$$

11. $\begin{bmatrix} -15 & 15 \\ -10 & 15 \end{bmatrix}$ 13. $\begin{bmatrix} -16 & 16 \\ 32 & -8 \end{bmatrix}$ 15. $\begin{bmatrix} -2 & 2\frac{1}{2} \\ 2 & 0 \end{bmatrix}$ 17. a, b, c, d 19. a, b

21. a, b, c, d 23. Let i, and i_2 be identity elements in $\langle S; o \rangle$. Then for

all $a \in S$ (1.) $i_1 \, {}^o \, a = a \, {}^o \, i_1 = a$ and (2.) $i_2 \, {}^o \, a = a \, {}^o \, i_2 = a$. In particular,

when $a = i_2$, $i_1 \, {}^o \, i_2 = i_2$ by (1.). When $a = i_1$, $i_1 \, {}^o \, i_2 = i_1$ by (2.). By transi-

tivity of equality, $i_1 = i_1 \, {}^o \, i_2 = i_2$ and the identity is unique.

PAGES 492-493 Exercises

1. $AB = \begin{bmatrix} 1 & -1 \\ 1 & 2 \end{bmatrix}$, $BA = \begin{bmatrix} 2 & -1 \\ 1 & 1 \end{bmatrix}$, $A(2B) = \begin{bmatrix} 2 & -2 \\ 2 & 4 \end{bmatrix}$, $(2A)(3B) = \begin{bmatrix} 6 & -6 \\ 6 & 12 \end{bmatrix}$

3. $AB = \begin{bmatrix} 1 & 1 \\ 0 & 0 \end{bmatrix}$, $BA = \begin{bmatrix} -1 & -2 \\ 1 & 2 \end{bmatrix}$, $A(2B) = \begin{bmatrix} 2 & 2 \\ 0 & 0 \end{bmatrix}$, $(2A)(3B) = \begin{bmatrix} 6 & 6 \\ 0 & 0 \end{bmatrix}$

5. $AB = \begin{bmatrix} 0 & 0 \\ 0 & 0 \end{bmatrix}$, $BA = \begin{bmatrix} xy & y^2 \\ -x^2 & -xy \end{bmatrix}$, $A(2B) = \begin{bmatrix} 0 & 0 \\ 0 & 0 \end{bmatrix}$, $(2A)(3B) = \begin{bmatrix} 0 & 0 \\ 0 & 0 \end{bmatrix}$

7. $AB = \begin{bmatrix} 0 & 7 \\ 0 & 3 \end{bmatrix}$, $BA = \begin{bmatrix} 0 & 0 \\ -2 & 3 \end{bmatrix}$, $A(2B) = \begin{bmatrix} 0 & 14 \\ 0 & 6 \end{bmatrix}$, $(2A)(3B) = \begin{bmatrix} 0 & 42 \\ 0 & 18 \end{bmatrix}$

9. a. $\begin{bmatrix} 5 & 5 \\ 5 & 10 \end{bmatrix}$ b. $\begin{bmatrix} 1 & 6 \\ 0 & 1 \end{bmatrix}$ 11. $A^2 = \begin{bmatrix} 1 & 0 \\ 0 & 1 \end{bmatrix}$, $A^3 = \begin{bmatrix} 1 & 0 \\ 0 & -1 \end{bmatrix}$, $A^4 = \begin{bmatrix} 1 & 0 \\ 0 & 1 \end{bmatrix}$,

$A^5 = \begin{bmatrix} 1 & 0 \\ 0 & -1 \end{bmatrix}$. Only 2 elements occur in the set, namely A and I and they alternate.

13. a. $(A - B)(A + B) = A^2 - BA + AB - B^2$ b. $(A - B)(A + B) \neq A^2 - B^2$ because

BA is not necessarily equal to AB. 15. $A^2 = \begin{bmatrix} 7 & 4 \\ 6 & 7 \end{bmatrix}$, $-2A = \begin{bmatrix} -2 & -4 \\ -6 & -2 \end{bmatrix}$, $-5I =$

$\begin{bmatrix} -5 & 0 \\ 0 & -5 \end{bmatrix}$, $A^2 - 2A - 5I = \begin{bmatrix} 0 & 0 \\ 0 & 0 \end{bmatrix} = 0$ 17. The proof is made by multiplying out

A(BC) and (AB)C and comparing results. 19. $L_1 = \begin{bmatrix} 1_1 & 0 \\ 0 & 1_1 \end{bmatrix}$ $L_2 = \begin{bmatrix} 1_2 & 0 \\ 0 & 1_2 \end{bmatrix}$

a. $L_1 + L_2 = \begin{bmatrix} l_1 + l_2 & 0 \\ 0 & l_1 + l_2 \end{bmatrix} = l_1 + l_2 \begin{bmatrix} 1 & 0 \\ 0 & 1 \end{bmatrix} = (l_1 + l_2)I$

b. $L_1 \cdot L_2 = \begin{bmatrix} l_1 l_2 & 0 \\ 0 & l_1 l_2 \end{bmatrix} = l_1 l_2 \begin{bmatrix} 1 & 0 \\ 0 & 1 \end{bmatrix} = (l_1 l_2)I$

PAGES 497-498 Exercises

1. $\begin{bmatrix} 1 \\ 3 \end{bmatrix}$ 3. $\begin{bmatrix} 5 \\ -6 \end{bmatrix}$ 5. $\begin{bmatrix} 6 \\ -3 \end{bmatrix}$ 7. $\begin{bmatrix} -3 \\ 2 \end{bmatrix}$ 9-23. Sketches omitted. 9. $\begin{bmatrix} -2 \\ 6 \end{bmatrix}$

11. $\begin{bmatrix} -2 \\ 2 \end{bmatrix}$ 13. $\begin{bmatrix} 6 \\ -7 \end{bmatrix}$ 15. $\begin{bmatrix} -4 \\ 12 \end{bmatrix}$ 17. $\begin{bmatrix} 2 \\ 4 \end{bmatrix}$ 19. $\begin{bmatrix} 10 \\ -16 \end{bmatrix}$ 21. $\begin{bmatrix} 8 \\ 18 \end{bmatrix}$ 23. $\begin{bmatrix} -8 \\ 14 \end{bmatrix}$

25. a. Same vector. b. Same vector. c. Same vector. 27. $\begin{bmatrix} -\frac{2}{3} \\ -1 \end{bmatrix}$ 29. $\begin{bmatrix} 4 \\ 5 \end{bmatrix}$

31. Any point on the line $x - 2y = 2$ 33. $\begin{bmatrix} 8 \\ -30 \end{bmatrix}$ 35. $\begin{bmatrix} 2 & 7 \\ 6 & 19 \end{bmatrix}$ 37. $\begin{bmatrix} 6 & 6 & 8 \\ 6 & 8 & 6 \\ 8 & 6 & 6 \end{bmatrix}$

39. $A(B\vec{r}) = \begin{bmatrix} a_{11} & a_{12} \\ a_{21} & a_{22} \end{bmatrix} \left(\begin{bmatrix} b_{11} & b_{12} \\ b_{21} & b_{22} \end{bmatrix} \begin{bmatrix} x \\ y \end{bmatrix} \right) = \begin{bmatrix} a_{11} & a_{12} \\ a_{21} & a_{22} \end{bmatrix} \begin{bmatrix} b_{11}x + b_{12}y \\ b_{21}x + b_{22}y \end{bmatrix}$

$= \begin{bmatrix} a_{11}(b_{11}x + b_{12}y) + a_{12}(b_{21}x + b_{22}y) \\ a_{21}(b_{11}x + b_{12}y) + a_{22}(b_{21}x + b_{22}y) \end{bmatrix} = \begin{bmatrix} (a_{11}b_{11} + a_{12}b_{21})x + (a_{11}b_{12} + a_{12}b_{22})y \\ (a_{21}b_{11} + a_{22}b_{21})x + (a_{21}b_{12} + a_{22}b_{22})y \end{bmatrix}$

$= \begin{bmatrix} a_{11}b_{11} + a_{12}b_{21} & a_{11}b_{12} + a_{12}b_{22} \\ a_{21}b_{11} + a_{22}b_{21} & a_{21}b_{12} + a_{22}b_{22} \end{bmatrix} \begin{bmatrix} x \\ y \end{bmatrix} = \left(\begin{bmatrix} a_{11} & a_{12} \\ a_{21} & a_{22} \end{bmatrix} \begin{bmatrix} b_{11} & b_{12} \\ b_{21} & b_{22} \end{bmatrix} \right) \begin{bmatrix} x \\ y \end{bmatrix} = (AB)\vec{r}$

41. Proved in a manner similar to proof in Exercise 39.

PAGES 504-505 Exercises

1. -2 3. 1 5. -2 7. 0 9. 0 11. 3 13. (1.) $\frac{1}{2} \begin{bmatrix} 2 & 1 \\ -6 & -4 \end{bmatrix}$

(2.) $\begin{bmatrix} 0 & 1 \\ -1 & 0 \end{bmatrix}$ (3.) $\begin{bmatrix} -1 & 0 \\ 0 & -1 \end{bmatrix}$ (4.) $(-1)\begin{bmatrix} -1 & 0 \\ 0 & 1 \end{bmatrix}$ (5.) $-\frac{1}{2}\begin{bmatrix} 5 & -7 \\ -1 & 1 \end{bmatrix}$ (6.) No in-

verse. (7.) No inverse. (8.) $(-1)\begin{bmatrix} 5 & -8 \\ -2 & 3 \end{bmatrix}$ (9.) No inverse. (10.) $\frac{1}{2}\begin{bmatrix} 1 & -3 \\ -5 & 17 \end{bmatrix}$

(11.) $\frac{1}{3}\begin{bmatrix} 2 & -55 \\ -3 & 84 \end{bmatrix}$ 15. $\begin{bmatrix} 1 & -1 \\ -3 & 4 \end{bmatrix}\begin{bmatrix} 2 \\ 1 \end{bmatrix} = \begin{bmatrix} 1 \\ -2 \end{bmatrix}$ 17. No solution.   19. $\begin{bmatrix} -1 \\ 2 \end{bmatrix}$

21. $\begin{bmatrix} -3 \\ 2 \end{bmatrix}$ 23. $\frac{1}{ab}\begin{bmatrix} b & 0 \\ 0 & a \end{bmatrix}$ 25. $\begin{bmatrix} 1 & -k \\ 0 & 1 \end{bmatrix}$ 27. $\frac{1}{1-a^2}\begin{bmatrix} 1 & -a \\ -a & 1 \end{bmatrix}$ 29. $\begin{bmatrix} a & b \\ c & d \end{bmatrix}\begin{bmatrix} x \\ y \end{bmatrix}$

$= \begin{bmatrix} r \\ s \end{bmatrix}$ expands to $\begin{bmatrix} ax + by \\ cx + dy \end{bmatrix} = \begin{bmatrix} r \\ s \end{bmatrix}$ or $ax + by = r$, $cx + dy = s$. They are two ways

of writing the same thing.

PAGES 508-510   Exercises

1.-9. No sketches are given.   1. $\begin{bmatrix} 3 \\ 2 \end{bmatrix}$, $\begin{bmatrix} 1 \\ -4 \end{bmatrix}$, $\begin{bmatrix} -4 \\ 3 \end{bmatrix}$ 3. $\begin{bmatrix} 3 \\ 0 \end{bmatrix}$, $\begin{bmatrix} 8 \\ 0 \end{bmatrix}$, $\begin{bmatrix} 5 \\ 0 \end{bmatrix}$

5. $\begin{bmatrix} -1 \\ 2 \end{bmatrix}$, $\begin{bmatrix} -2 \\ 4 \end{bmatrix}$, $\begin{bmatrix} 3 \\ -6 \end{bmatrix}$ 7. $\begin{bmatrix} 0 \\ 0 \end{bmatrix}$, $\begin{bmatrix} 0 \\ 0 \end{bmatrix}$, $\begin{bmatrix} 0 \\ 0 \end{bmatrix}$ 9. $\begin{bmatrix} 2 \\ -1 \end{bmatrix}$, $\begin{bmatrix} 14 \\ -7 \end{bmatrix}$, $\begin{bmatrix} 2 \\ -1 \end{bmatrix}$ 11. Every linear

transformation of the plane corresponds to a matrix in M_2. Thus every linear

transformation can be represented by a matrix $A = \begin{bmatrix} a_{11} & a_{12} \\ a_{21} & a_{22} \end{bmatrix}$, $a_{ij} \in R$. But

$A\begin{bmatrix} 0 \\ 0 \end{bmatrix} = \begin{bmatrix} 0 \\ 0 \end{bmatrix}$ for all A. Thus $\begin{bmatrix} 0 \\ 0 \end{bmatrix}$ is its own image under every linear transformation

of the plane.   13. Let $\begin{bmatrix} x \\ y \end{bmatrix}$ be a vector. Its image is $\begin{bmatrix} 0 & 0 \\ a & b \end{bmatrix}\begin{bmatrix} x \\ y \end{bmatrix} = \begin{bmatrix} 0 \\ ax + by \end{bmatrix}$

which is a vector on the y axis.   15. $\begin{bmatrix} 2 & 3 \\ 1 & 1 \end{bmatrix}\begin{bmatrix} 2 - 3t \\ 1 + 2t \end{bmatrix} = \begin{bmatrix} 4 - 6t + 3 + 6t \\ 2 - 3t + 1 + 2t \end{bmatrix}$

$= \begin{bmatrix} 7 - 0t \\ 3 - t \end{bmatrix}$ The line is x = 7, y = 3 - t.   17. $\begin{array}{l} x = 3t \\ y = -7t \end{array}$ 19. a. $\begin{bmatrix} 2 \\ -4 \end{bmatrix}$,

$\begin{bmatrix} 2 \\ -1 \end{bmatrix}$, $\begin{bmatrix} -1 \\ -1 \end{bmatrix}$ b. $\begin{bmatrix} -2 \\ 4 \end{bmatrix}$, $\begin{bmatrix} -2 \\ 1 \end{bmatrix}$, $\begin{bmatrix} 1 \\ 1 \end{bmatrix}$ c. $\begin{bmatrix} 16 \\ -2 \end{bmatrix}$, $\begin{bmatrix} 10 \\ -5 \end{bmatrix}$, $\begin{bmatrix} -2 \\ 4 \end{bmatrix}$ d. $\begin{bmatrix} 22 \\ 4 \end{bmatrix}$, $\begin{bmatrix} 7 \\ 1 \end{bmatrix}$, $\begin{bmatrix} 4 \\ 1 \end{bmatrix}$

21. Let $A = \begin{bmatrix} a_{11} & a_{12} \\ a_{21} & a_{22} \end{bmatrix}$. Then the image of each point on the line is

$$\begin{bmatrix} a_{11} & a_{12} \\ a_{21} & a_{22} \end{bmatrix} \begin{bmatrix} a + 1t \\ b + mt \end{bmatrix} = \begin{bmatrix} a_{11}(a + 1t) + a_{12}(b + mt) \\ a_{21}(a + 1t) + a_{22}(b + mt) \end{bmatrix} = \begin{bmatrix} a_{11}a + a_{12}b + (a_{11}1 + a_{12}m)t \\ a_{21}a + a_{22}b + (a_{21}1 + a_{22}m)t \end{bmatrix}$$

Thus $x \rightarrow a_{11}a + a_{12}b + pt$ where $p = a_{11}1 + a_{12}m$ and $y \rightarrow a_{21}a + a_{22}b + qt$ where

$q = a_{21}1 + a_{22}m$. This is a parametric equation of a line.

PAGES 515-517 Exercises

1. a   3. e   5. a   7. f   9-15. No graph given.   17. Inverses:

r_x axis, r_x axis; r_y axis, r_y axis; $r_x = y$, $r_x = y$; $r_y = -x$, $r_y = -x$
A transformation which is its own image is an <u>involution</u>.   19. $y = x$

21. $y = -x$ 23. y axis   25. x axis   27. x axis and y axis   29. x axis

and y axis   31. y axis   33. none   35. We do only one proof. Let $\begin{bmatrix} x \\ y \end{bmatrix}$ and

$\begin{bmatrix} u \\ v \end{bmatrix}$ be two points. The distance between these points is $\sqrt{(x - u)^2 + (y - v)^2}$.

The images under r_x axis are $\begin{bmatrix} x \\ -y \end{bmatrix}$ and $\begin{bmatrix} u \\ -v \end{bmatrix}$. The distance between the images is

$\sqrt{(x - u)^2 + (-y + v)^2} = \sqrt{(x - u)^2 + (y - v)^2}$.   37. a. $\begin{cases} x = 2 + t \\ y = 1 - 3t \end{cases}$ $(1\frac{3}{4},\ 1\frac{3}{4})$

b. $\begin{cases} x = 1 - 3t \\ y = -2 - t \end{cases}$ $(7, 0)$ c. $\begin{cases} x = -1 + 3t \\ y = 2 + t \end{cases}$ $(0, 2\frac{1}{3})$ d. $\begin{cases} x = -2 - t \\ y = -1 + 3t \end{cases}$ $(-3\frac{1}{2},\ 3\frac{1}{2})$

PAGES 520-521 Exercises

1. $\begin{bmatrix} 1 & 0 \\ 0 & 1 \end{bmatrix}$ 3. $\begin{bmatrix} 0 & -1 \\ 1 & 0 \end{bmatrix}$ 5. $\begin{bmatrix} 0 & 1 \\ -1 & 0 \end{bmatrix}$ 7. $\frac{1}{2}\begin{bmatrix} 1 & -\sqrt{3} \\ \sqrt{3} & 1 \end{bmatrix}$ 9. Calculate each

matrix.   11. a. $\begin{bmatrix} 3 \\ 2 \end{bmatrix}$ b. $\begin{bmatrix} -2 \\ 3 \end{bmatrix}$ c. $\begin{bmatrix} -3 \\ -2 \end{bmatrix}$ d. $\frac{\sqrt{2}}{2}\begin{bmatrix} 5 \\ -1 \end{bmatrix}$ 13. a. $\begin{bmatrix} 4 \\ -3 \end{bmatrix}$ b. $\begin{bmatrix} 3 \\ 4 \end{bmatrix}$

c. $\begin{bmatrix} -4 \\ 3 \end{bmatrix}$ d. $\frac{\sqrt{2}}{2}\begin{bmatrix} 1 \\ -7 \end{bmatrix}$ 15. a. $\begin{bmatrix} -4 \\ 0 \end{bmatrix}$ b. $\begin{bmatrix} 0 \\ -4 \end{bmatrix}$ c. $\begin{bmatrix} 4 \\ 0 \end{bmatrix}$ d. $\frac{\sqrt{2}}{2}\begin{bmatrix} -4 \\ 4 \end{bmatrix}$ 17. a. $\begin{bmatrix} -1 \\ 4 \end{bmatrix}$

b. $\begin{bmatrix} -4 \\ -1 \end{bmatrix}$ c. $\begin{bmatrix} 1 \\ -4 \end{bmatrix}$ d. $\frac{\sqrt{2}}{2}\begin{bmatrix} 3 \\ 5 \end{bmatrix}$ 19. (-7, 2), (-1, 4), (-3, 6)

No graph given. 21. (-2, -7), (-4, -1), (-6, -3) No graph given.

23. $(\sqrt{3} - \frac{7}{2}, 1 + \frac{7\sqrt{3}}{2})$, $(2\sqrt{3} - \frac{1}{2}, 2 + \frac{\sqrt{3}}{2})$, $(3\sqrt{3} - \frac{3}{2}, 3 + \frac{3\sqrt{3}}{2})$ No graph given.

25. $\begin{cases} x = -2 - 3t \\ y = 1 - 3t, \end{cases}$ $\begin{cases} x = \frac{\sqrt{2}}{2}(-1 - 6t) \\ y = \frac{\sqrt{2}}{2}(3), \end{cases}$ $\begin{cases} x = -1 + 3t & x = 2 + 3t \\ y = -2 - 3t, & y = -1 + 3t, \end{cases}$

$\begin{cases} x = \frac{\sqrt{3}}{2} - 1 - (\frac{3\sqrt{3}}{2} + \frac{3}{2})t \\ y = \frac{1}{2} + \sqrt{3} - (\frac{3}{2} - \frac{3\sqrt{3}}{2})t \end{cases}$ 27. $\begin{cases} x = -2 - 5t \\ y = -3 - 2t, \end{cases}$ $\begin{cases} x = \frac{\sqrt{2}}{2}(-1 - 7t) \\ y = \frac{\sqrt{2}}{2}(-5 + 3t), \end{cases}$ $\begin{cases} x = 3 + 2t \\ y = 2 - 5t, \end{cases}$

$\begin{cases} x = -2 + 5t \\ y = 3 + 2t, \end{cases}$ $\begin{cases} x = -\frac{3\sqrt{3}}{2} + 1 - (\sqrt{3} + \frac{5}{2})t \\ y = -\frac{3}{2} - \sqrt{3} + (\frac{5\sqrt{3}}{2} - 1)t \end{cases}$ 29. $\cos\Theta = \dfrac{ac + bd}{\sqrt{a^2 + b^2}\ \sqrt{c^2 + d^2}}$ where $\mathcal{C}$

is acute angle between $\begin{bmatrix} a \\ b \end{bmatrix}$ and $\begin{bmatrix} c \\ d \end{bmatrix}$.

$\cos\phi = \dfrac{(a\cos\Theta - b\sin\Theta)(c\cos\Theta - d\sin\Theta) + (a\sin\Theta + b\cos\Theta)(c\sin\Theta + d\cos\Theta)}{\sqrt{a^2 + b^2}\ \sqrt{c^2 + d^2}}$

$= \dfrac{ac\cos^2\Theta - bc\sin\Theta\cos\Theta + bd\sin^2\Theta + ac\sin^2\Theta + bc\sin\Theta\cos\Theta + bd\cos^2\Theta}{\sqrt{a^2 + b^2}\ \sqrt{c^2 + d^2}}$

$= \dfrac{ac(\cos^2\Theta + \sin^2\Theta) + bd(\sin^2\Theta + \cos^2\Theta)}{\sqrt{a^2 + b^2}\ \sqrt{c^2 + d^2}} = \dfrac{ac + bd}{\sqrt{a^2 + b^2}\ \sqrt{c^2 + d^2}}$ 31. a. If $\begin{bmatrix} t \\ t^3 \end{bmatrix}$

is in V, then $\begin{bmatrix} -t \\ -t^3 \end{bmatrix} = R_{180°} \circ \begin{bmatrix} t \\ t^3 \end{bmatrix}$ is in V because $\begin{bmatrix} -t \\ -t^3 \end{bmatrix} = \begin{bmatrix} -t \\ (-t)^3 \end{bmatrix}$.

b. $\begin{bmatrix} t \\ 1 \\ t \end{bmatrix} \xrightarrow{R_{180°}} \begin{bmatrix} -t \\ -\frac{1}{t} \end{bmatrix} = \begin{bmatrix} -t \\ \frac{1}{t} \end{bmatrix} \in V.$ c. $\begin{bmatrix} t \\ \pm\sqrt{4 - t^2} \end{bmatrix} \xrightarrow{R_{180°}} \begin{bmatrix} -t \\ \mp\sqrt{4 - t^2} \end{bmatrix} = \begin{bmatrix} -t \\ \pm\sqrt{4 - (-t)^2} \end{bmatrix} \in V.$

PAGES 525-527 Exercises

1. BA = $\begin{bmatrix} 2 & 1 \\ -3 & -1 \end{bmatrix} \begin{bmatrix} 1 & 2 \\ 1 & 4 \end{bmatrix} = \begin{bmatrix} 3 & 8 \\ -4 & -10 \end{bmatrix}$ 3. BA = $\begin{bmatrix} -17 & 10 \\ -11 & 0 \end{bmatrix}$ 5. (1.) a. $\begin{bmatrix} 21 \\ -26 \end{bmatrix}$

b. $\begin{bmatrix} 16 \\ -20 \end{bmatrix}$ c. $\begin{bmatrix} 4 \\ -6 \end{bmatrix}$ d. $\begin{bmatrix} -9 \\ 12 \end{bmatrix}$ e. $\begin{bmatrix} -14 \\ 18 \end{bmatrix}$ (2.) a. $\begin{bmatrix} 9 \\ 23 \end{bmatrix}$ b. $\begin{bmatrix} 8 \\ 18 \end{bmatrix}$ c. $\begin{bmatrix} 8 \\ 7 \end{bmatrix}$ d. $\begin{bmatrix} -9 \\ -12 \end{bmatrix}$

e. $\begin{bmatrix} -10 \\ -17 \end{bmatrix}$ (3.) a. $\begin{bmatrix} 47 \\ 11 \end{bmatrix}$ b. $\begin{bmatrix} 20 \\ 0 \end{bmatrix}$ c. $\begin{bmatrix} -78 \\ -44 \end{bmatrix}$ d. $\begin{bmatrix} 51 \\ 33 \end{bmatrix}$ e. $\begin{bmatrix} 24 \\ 22 \end{bmatrix}$ (4.) a. $\begin{bmatrix} -1 \\ 3 \end{bmatrix}$ b. $\begin{bmatrix} 0 \\ 2 \end{bmatrix}$

c. $\begin{bmatrix} 4 \\ -1 \end{bmatrix}$ d. $\begin{bmatrix} -3 \\ 0 \end{bmatrix}$ e. $\begin{bmatrix} -2 \\ -1 \end{bmatrix}$ 7. $R_{165°} = R_{120°} \cdot R_{45°} = \frac{1}{2}\begin{bmatrix} -1 & -\sqrt{3} \\ \sqrt{3} & -1 \end{bmatrix} \cdot \frac{\sqrt{2}}{2}\begin{bmatrix} 1 & -1 \\ 1 & 1 \end{bmatrix} =$

$\frac{\sqrt{2}}{4}\begin{bmatrix} -1 - \sqrt{3} & 1 - \sqrt{3} \\ \sqrt{3} - 1 & -\sqrt{3} - 1 \end{bmatrix}$ 9. $R_{195°} = R_{135°} R_{60°}$. Details are omitted.

11. $AB = \begin{bmatrix} 1 & 0 \\ -2 & 1 \end{bmatrix}\begin{bmatrix} 1 & 3 \\ 0 & 1 \end{bmatrix} = \begin{bmatrix} 1 & 3 \\ -2 & -5 \end{bmatrix}$. Thus $(1, 2) \rightarrow (7, -12)$; $(2, 1) \rightarrow (5, -9)$;

$(4, 5) \rightarrow (19, -33)$ No. 13. $\begin{cases} x = -5 + 4t \\ y = -2 + t \end{cases}$ 15. Let $A = \begin{bmatrix} a_{11} & a_{12} \\ a_{21} & a_{22} \end{bmatrix}$ and

$B = \begin{bmatrix} b_{11} & b_{12} \\ b_{21} & b_{22} \end{bmatrix}$ det $A = a_{11}a_{22} - a_{12}a_{21}$ det $B = b_{11}b_{22} - b_{12}b_{21}$

$AB = \begin{bmatrix} a_{11}b_{11} + a_{12}b_{21} & a_{11}b_{12} + a_{12}b_{22} \\ a_{21}b_{11} + a_{22}b_{21} & a_{21}b_{12} + a_{22}b_{22} \end{bmatrix}$ det $(AB) =$

$(a_{11}b_{11} + a_{12}b_{21})(a_{21}b_{12} + a_{22}b_{22}) - (a_{11}b_{12} + a_{12}b_{22})(a_{21}b_{11} + a_{22}b_{21}) =$

$a_{11}b_{11}a_{21}b_{12} + a_{11}b_{11}a_{22}b_{22} + a_{12}b_{21}a_{21}b_{12} + a_{12}b_{21}a_{22}b_{22} - a_{11}b_{12}a_{21}b_{11} -$

$a_{11}b_{12}a_{22}b_{21} - a_{12}b_{22}a_{21}b_{11} - a_{12}b_{22}a_{22}b_{21} = a_{11}a_{22}(b_{11}b_{22} - b_{12}b_{21}) +$

$a_{12}a_{21}(b_{21}b_{12} - b_{22}b_{11}) = a_{11}a_{22}(b_{11}b_{22} - b_{12}b_{21}) - a_{12}a_{21}(b_{11}b_{22} - b_{12}b_{21})$

$= (a_{11}a_{22} - a_{12}a_{21})(b_{11}b_{22} - b_{12}b_{21}) = $ det $A \cdot$ det B.   17. a. $A^{-1}A = I$. Thus

the vector is its own image. b. Same as a.   19. $(ai + bj + 0k) \times (ci + 0j + 0k)$

$= \begin{bmatrix} b & 0 \\ 0 & 0 \end{bmatrix}i + \begin{bmatrix} 0 & a \\ 0 & c \end{bmatrix}j + \begin{bmatrix} a & b \\ c & 0 \end{bmatrix}k = 0i + 0j - bck$ ∴ The area of the triangle

$\frac{1}{2}\sqrt{(bc)^2} = \frac{1}{2}|bc|$.   21. Leaves the area unchanged because det $R_\Theta = 1$.

23. a. $\Theta = 0°$ ∴ $r_{y = mx} = \begin{bmatrix} \cos 0° & \sin 0° \\ \sin 0° & -\cos 0° \end{bmatrix} = \begin{bmatrix} 1 & 0 \\ 0 & -1 \end{bmatrix} = r_{x \text{ axis}}$

b. $\Theta = 90°$ ∴ $r_{y = mx} = \begin{bmatrix} \cos 180° & \sin 180° \\ \sin 180° & -\cos 180° \end{bmatrix} = \begin{bmatrix} -1 & 0 \\ 0 & 1 \end{bmatrix} = r_{y \text{ axis}}$

c. $\Theta = 45°$ ∴ $r_{y = mx} = \begin{bmatrix} \cos 90° & \sin 90° \\ \sin 90° & -\cos 90° \end{bmatrix} = \begin{bmatrix} 0 & 1 \\ 1 & 0 \end{bmatrix} = r_{y = x}$

d. $\theta = 135^\circ$ $\therefore$ $r_{y = mx} = \begin{bmatrix} \cos 270^\circ & \sin 270^\circ \\ \sin 270^\circ & -\cos 270^\circ \end{bmatrix} = \begin{bmatrix} 0 & -1 \\ -1 & 0 \end{bmatrix} = r_{y = -x}$

25. $r_{y = m_1x} = \begin{bmatrix} \cos 2\theta & \sin 2\theta \\ \sin 2\theta & -\cos 2\theta \end{bmatrix}$ $r_{y = m_2x} = \begin{bmatrix} \cos 2\phi & \sin 2\phi \\ \sin 2\phi & -\cos 2\phi \end{bmatrix}$

$r_{y = m_2x} \cdot r_{y = m_1x} = \begin{bmatrix} \cos 2\phi & \sin 2\phi \\ \sin 2\phi & -\cos 2\phi \end{bmatrix} \cdot \begin{bmatrix} \cos 2\theta & \sin 2\theta \\ \sin 2\theta & -\cos 2\theta \end{bmatrix} =$

$\begin{bmatrix} \cos 2\phi \cos 2\theta + \sin 2\phi \sin 2\theta & \cos 2\phi \sin 2\theta - \sin 2\phi \cos 2\theta \\ \sin 2\phi \cos 2\theta - \cos 2\phi \sin 2\theta & \sin 2\phi \sin 2\theta + \cos 2\phi \cos 2\theta \end{bmatrix}$

$= \begin{bmatrix} \cos(2\phi - 2\theta) & -\sin(2\phi - 2\theta) \\ \sin(2\phi - 2\theta) & \cos(2\phi - 2\theta) \end{bmatrix} = \begin{bmatrix} \cos 2(\phi - \theta) & -\sin 2(\phi - \theta) \\ \sin 2(\phi - \theta) & \cos 2(\phi - \theta) \end{bmatrix}$ which is

a rotation about the origin through an angle of $2(\phi - \theta)$.

PAGES 530-531 Exercises

1. (-3, 5) 3. (0, 10) 5. (-7, 12) 7. (5, 5) 9. (4, 1) 11. y inter-

cept is (0, -1), translating vector is $\begin{bmatrix} 0 \\ 1 \end{bmatrix}$. x = x' - 0 y = y' - 1 $\therefore$ y' - 1

= 2x' - 1 so y = 2x is the equation. 13. $2y + 4x = 0$ 15. $y + 5x = 0$

17. The equations are identical to those in Exercises 11-16. 19. The distance

d between (x, y) and (u, v) is d = $\sqrt{(x - u)^2 + (y - v)^2}$. Under a translation

with vector $\begin{bmatrix} h \\ k \end{bmatrix}$, (x, y) $\rightarrow$ (x + h, y + k) and (u, v) $\rightarrow$ (u + h, v + k). The

distance d' here is d' = $\sqrt{(x + h - u - h)^2 + (y + k - v - k)^2}$ =

$\sqrt{(x - u)^2 + (y - v)^2}$ = d. 21. (1, 3) $\rightarrow$ (-6, 7), (4, 5) $\rightarrow$ (-3, 9), (6, 1) $\rightarrow$

(-1, 5) 23. x' + 2 + y' - 1 + 2 = 0 or x + y + 3 = 0 25. $\frac{1}{2}x - 2y + 3z = 13$

27. No answer given.

PAGES 531-534 Chapter Objectives and Review

1. See definitions in the text. 3. The dimensions of a matrix are the number

of rows and columns. $\begin{bmatrix} 1 & 1 & 1 \\ 2 & 2 & 1 \\ 3 & 3 & 1 \\ 4 & 4 & 1 \\ 5 & 5 & 1 \end{bmatrix}$ 5. a. and c. 7. $\begin{bmatrix} 3 & -2 \\ 3 & 7 \end{bmatrix}$ 9. $\begin{bmatrix} 1 & 2 \\ -2 & 2 \end{bmatrix}$

11. $\begin{bmatrix} 12 & -6 & 2 \\ 4 & 0 & 10 \end{bmatrix}$ 13. Yes. For multiplication to be defined, the number of

columns of the first matrix must equal the number of rows in the second matrix.

15. $\begin{bmatrix} 11 \\ -5 \end{bmatrix}$ 17. $\begin{bmatrix} 6 & -6 & -13 \\ 10 & -3 & 11 \end{bmatrix}$ 19. Not defined. (2 x 3) and (2 x 1)

21. True. 23. True. 25. True. 27. False. There is no B in M_2 such that

$\begin{bmatrix} 0 & 0 \\ 0 & 0 \end{bmatrix} \cdot B = I.$ 29. $-\frac{1}{2}\begin{bmatrix} -3 & 1 \\ -4 & 2 \end{bmatrix}$ 31. $\frac{1}{4}\begin{bmatrix} 0 & -2 \\ 2 & 0 \end{bmatrix}$ 33. $T(\vec{V}_1 + \vec{V}_2) = T(\vec{V}_1) + T(\vec{V}_2)$

and $T(k\vec{V}_1) = k(T(\vec{V}_1))$ 35. $\frac{\sqrt{2}}{2}\begin{bmatrix} 1 & -1 \\ 1 & 1 \end{bmatrix}$, $\frac{\sqrt{2}}{2}\begin{bmatrix} 7 \\ 3 \end{bmatrix}$ 37. $\begin{bmatrix} 0 & -1 \\ -1 & 0 \end{bmatrix}$, $\begin{bmatrix} 2 \\ -5 \end{bmatrix}$ 39. The

matrices are multiplied. 41. $\begin{bmatrix} 1 & 0 \\ 0 & 1 \end{bmatrix}$ 43. $\begin{bmatrix} 1 & 0 \\ 0 & 1 \end{bmatrix}$ 45. $\frac{\sqrt{2}}{2}\begin{bmatrix} 1 & -1 \\ 1 & 1 \end{bmatrix}$

47. y' + 1 = 2(x' + 2) + 1 or y = 2x + 4.

PAGES 534-535 Chapter Test

1. No. $a_{22} \neq b_{22}$ 3. $\begin{bmatrix} 2 & -1 & 0 \\ 1 & -7 & -3 \end{bmatrix}$ 5. Does not exist. 7. The matrices are

square. 9. det A = ux - vw 11. $-\frac{1}{7}\begin{bmatrix} -5 & 3 \\ -1 & 2 \end{bmatrix}$ 13. $\begin{bmatrix} 0 & -1 \\ -1 & -k \end{bmatrix}$ 15. a. $\begin{bmatrix} 1 & -1 \\ 0 & -1 \end{bmatrix}$

b. $\begin{bmatrix} 1 & 0 \\ -3 & -1 \end{bmatrix}$ 17. $\begin{bmatrix} 0 & 1 \\ -1 & 0 \end{bmatrix}$ 19. $\begin{cases} x = t - 1 \\ y = -t + 4 \end{cases}$ or y = -x + 3

CHAPTER 11 SYSTEMS OF LINEAR EQUATIONS USING MATRICES

PAGES 541-543 Exercises

1. $\begin{bmatrix} 6 & -3 \end{bmatrix}$ 3. Multiplication not defined. 5. $\begin{bmatrix} 3 & 7 & 0 \\ 3 & 10 & -9 \\ 2 & 6 & -4 \end{bmatrix}$ 7. $\begin{bmatrix} 0 & 2 \\ -4 & 0 \\ 0 & -8 \end{bmatrix}$

9. Sum not defined. 11. $A + B = \begin{bmatrix} 2 & 1 & 3 \\ 4 & -2 & 1 \end{bmatrix} + \begin{bmatrix} -2 & 2 & 3 \\ -4 & 2 & 1 \end{bmatrix} = \begin{bmatrix} 0 & 3 & 6 \\ 0 & 0 & 2 \end{bmatrix}$ $B + A =$

$\begin{bmatrix} 0 & 3 & 6 \\ 0 & 0 & 2 \end{bmatrix}$. Thus $A + B = B + A$. 13. $B = \begin{bmatrix} 1 & -2 & 3 & -4 \\ -5 & 6 & -7 & -8 \\ -9 & 0 & 1 & 2 \end{bmatrix} = (-1)A$. 15. Let

$A = \begin{bmatrix} a_{ij} \end{bmatrix}$ represent the matrix with the ijth element a_{ij}. Similarly $B = \begin{bmatrix} b_{ij} \end{bmatrix}$.

Then $A + B = \begin{bmatrix} a_{ij} \end{bmatrix} + \begin{bmatrix} b_{ij} \end{bmatrix} = \begin{bmatrix} a_{ij} + b_{ij} \end{bmatrix}$ (by def. of addition) $= \begin{bmatrix} b_{ij} + a_{ij} \end{bmatrix}$

(commutativity of addition in $\mathbb{R}$) $= \begin{bmatrix} b_{ij} \end{bmatrix} + \begin{bmatrix} a_{ij} \end{bmatrix}$ (by def. of addition) $= B + A$.

17. $r(sA) = r(s\begin{bmatrix} a_{ij} \end{bmatrix}) = r\begin{bmatrix} sa_{ij} \end{bmatrix} = \begin{bmatrix} r(sa_{ij}) \end{bmatrix} = \begin{bmatrix} (rs)a_{ij} \end{bmatrix} = rs\begin{bmatrix} a_{ij} \end{bmatrix} = (rs)A$

19. $(r + s)A = (r + s)\begin{bmatrix} a_{ij} \end{bmatrix} = \begin{bmatrix} (r + s)a_{ij} \end{bmatrix} = \begin{bmatrix} ra_{ij} + sa_{ij} \end{bmatrix} = \begin{bmatrix} ra_{ij} \end{bmatrix} + \begin{bmatrix} sa_{ij} \end{bmatrix}$

$= r\begin{bmatrix} a_{ij} \end{bmatrix} + s\begin{bmatrix} a_{ij} \end{bmatrix} = rA + sA$ 21. $A + (-1)A = \begin{bmatrix} a_{ij} \end{bmatrix} + (-1)\begin{bmatrix} a_{ij} \end{bmatrix} = \begin{bmatrix} a_{ij} \end{bmatrix} +$

$\begin{bmatrix} (-1)a_{ij} \end{bmatrix} = \begin{bmatrix} a_{ij} + (-1)(a_{ij}) \end{bmatrix} = \begin{bmatrix} 0_{ij} \end{bmatrix} = {}_mO_n$ Unique.

23. Let $B = \begin{bmatrix} b_{ij} \end{bmatrix}$ Then $B^T = \begin{bmatrix} b_{ji} \end{bmatrix}$ and $(B^T)^T = \begin{bmatrix} b_{ji} \end{bmatrix}^T = \begin{bmatrix} b_{ij} \end{bmatrix} = B$. 25. The

ijth entry of $AB = a_{i1}b_{1j} + a_{i2}b_{2j} + \cdots + a_{in}b_{nj}$. Thus the jith entry of $(AB)^T$

is $a_{i1}b_{1j} + a_{i2}b_{2j} + \cdots + a_{in}b_{nj}$.

If $B = \begin{bmatrix} b_{11} & b_{12} & b_{13} & \cdots & b_{1j} & \cdots & b_{1p} \\ b_{21} & & & & b_{2j} & & \\ b_{31} & & & & b_{3j} & & \\ \cdot & & & & \cdot & & \\ \cdot & & & & \cdot & & \\ \cdot & & & & \cdot & & \\ b_{n1} & & & & b_{nj} & \cdots & b_{np} \end{bmatrix}$ then $B^T = \begin{bmatrix} b_{11} & b_{21} & b_{31} & \cdots & b_{n1} \\ b_{12} & & & & \\ b_{13} & & & & \\ \cdot & & & & \\ \cdot & & & & \\ \cdot & & & & \\ b_{1j} & b_{2j} & \cdots & & b_{nj} \\ \cdot & & & & \cdot \\ \cdot & & & & \cdot \\ \cdot & & & & \cdot \\ b_{1p} & & & & b_{np} \end{bmatrix}$

Similarly $A^T = \begin{bmatrix} a_{11} & a_{21} & \cdots & a_{i1} & \cdots & a_{m1} \\ a_{12} & & & a_{i2} & & \\ \cdot & & & \cdot & & \end{bmatrix}$

(continued next Page)

Thus the jith element of $B^T A^T$ is

$b_{1j}a_{i1} + b_{2j}a_{i2} + b_{3j}a_{i3} + \cdots +$

$b_{nj}a_{in}$ = the jith entry of $(AB)^T$.

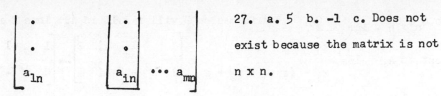

27. a. 5 b. -1 c. Does not exist because the matrix is not $n \times n$.

PAGE 548   Exercises

1. $\begin{bmatrix} -3 & 2 & \vdots & -1 \\ 1 & 1 & \vdots & 2 \end{bmatrix} \rightarrow \begin{bmatrix} 1 & 1 & \vdots & 2 \\ -3 & 2 & \vdots & -1 \end{bmatrix} \rightarrow \begin{bmatrix} 1 & 1 & \vdots & 2 \\ 0 & 5 & \vdots & 5 \end{bmatrix} \rightarrow \begin{bmatrix} 1 & 1 & \vdots & 2 \\ 0 & 1 & \vdots & 1 \end{bmatrix} \rightarrow \begin{bmatrix} 1 & 0 & \vdots & 1 \\ 0 & 1 & \vdots & 1 \end{bmatrix}$

$(x, y) = (1, 1)$ 3. $(-1, 2)$ 5. $\begin{bmatrix} 1 & -3 & \vdots & 5 \\ -2 & 6 & \vdots & 5 \end{bmatrix} \rightarrow \begin{bmatrix} 1 & -3 & \vdots & 5 \\ 0 & 0 & \vdots & 15 \end{bmatrix}$ Since the

last row is all zeros except for the last entry there is no solution to the system.

7. $(1, 2, 3)$ 9. $(\frac{1}{2}, 2, \frac{3}{2})$ 11. $(0, 0, 0)$ 13. $(1, 2, -2, 3, -1)$

15. (10.) $\begin{bmatrix} 1 & 1 & 2 \\ 2 & -1 & 3 \\ 1 & -1 & -1 \end{bmatrix} \begin{bmatrix} x \\ y \\ z \end{bmatrix} = \begin{bmatrix} 2 \\ 5 \\ -2 \end{bmatrix}$ (11.) $\begin{bmatrix} 1 & 5 & -3 \\ 1 & 1 & 1 \\ 2 & -3 & 1 \end{bmatrix} \begin{bmatrix} x \\ y \\ z \end{bmatrix} = \begin{bmatrix} 0 \\ 0 \\ 0 \end{bmatrix}$

(12.) $\begin{bmatrix} 1 & -1 & 1 & -1 \\ 1 & 1 & 1 & 1 \\ 2 & -1 & 1 & -1 \\ -4 & 1 & -2 & 4 \end{bmatrix} \begin{bmatrix} w \\ x \\ y \\ z \end{bmatrix} = \begin{bmatrix} 0 \\ 6 \\ 1 \\ 1 \end{bmatrix}$ (13.) $\begin{bmatrix} 1 & 1 & 1 & 1 & 1 \\ 1 & 0 & 0 & 0 & 1 \\ 2 & 1 & 1 & 0 & 0 \\ 0 & 1 & 1 & 1 & 0 \\ 0 & 0 & 1 & 1 & 1 \end{bmatrix} \begin{bmatrix} x_1 \\ x_2 \\ x_3 \\ x_4 \\ x_5 \end{bmatrix} = \begin{bmatrix} 3 \\ 0 \\ 2 \\ 3 \\ 0 \end{bmatrix}$

(14.) $\begin{bmatrix} 2 & 1 & 3 \\ 1 & 0 & 2 \end{bmatrix} \begin{bmatrix} x_1 \\ x_2 \\ x_3 \end{bmatrix} = \begin{bmatrix} 1 \\ 1 \end{bmatrix}$

PAGES 554-555   Exercises

1. $\begin{bmatrix} 1 & 2 \\ 4 & 3 \end{bmatrix} \rightarrow \begin{bmatrix} 1 & 2 \\ 0 & -5 \end{bmatrix} \rightarrow \begin{bmatrix} 1 & 2 \\ 0 & 1 \end{bmatrix}$ row echelon (re) $\rightarrow \begin{bmatrix} 1 & 0 \\ 0 & 1 \end{bmatrix}$ reduced row echelon (rre)

3. $\begin{bmatrix} 1 & 2 & 4 \\ 3 & 1 & 2 \end{bmatrix} \rightarrow \begin{bmatrix} 1 & 2 & 4 \\ 0 & -5 & -10 \end{bmatrix} \rightarrow \begin{bmatrix} 1 & 2 & 4 \\ 0 & 1 & 2 \end{bmatrix}$ (re) $\rightarrow \begin{bmatrix} 1 & 0 & 0 \\ 0 & 1 & 2 \end{bmatrix}$ (rre)   5. $\begin{bmatrix} 1 & 1 & 1 & 1 \\ 1 & 0 & 0 & 1 \\ 1 & 2 & 1 & 0 \end{bmatrix} \rightarrow$

$\begin{bmatrix} 1 & 1 & 1 & 1 \\ 0 & -1 & -1 & 0 \\ 0 & 1 & 0 & -1 \end{bmatrix} \rightarrow \begin{bmatrix} 1 & 1 & 1 & 1 \\ 0 & 1 & 1 & 0 \\ 0 & 0 & -1 & -1 \end{bmatrix} \rightarrow \begin{bmatrix} 1 & 1 & 1 & 1 \\ 0 & 1 & 1 & 0 \\ 0 & 0 & 1 & 1 \end{bmatrix}$ (re) $\rightarrow \begin{bmatrix} 1 & 0 & 0 & 1 \\ 0 & 1 & 0 & -1 \\ 0 & 0 & 1 & 1 \end{bmatrix}$ (rre)

7. $(3, -1)$ 9. $(1, -1)$ 11. $(1, 1, -3)$ 13. $(0, 0, 0)$ 15. $(0, 0, 0)$

17. If $0_1, 0_2, 0_3, \cdots 0_n$ is the finite sequence of elementary row operations performed on A which result in B, then the set of elementary row operations which

SYSTEMS OF LINEAR EQUATIONS USING MATRICES   S-69

undo O_n, O_{n-1}, $\cdots$ O_2, O_1 performed on B will result in A. Thus B is row equi-

valent to A.   19.
$$\begin{array}{l} x_1 + x_2 = 3 \\ x_1 + (a^2 - 8)x_2 = a \end{array} \quad : \quad \begin{bmatrix} 1 & 1 & : & 3 \\ 1 & a^2 - 8 & : & a \end{bmatrix} \rightarrow \begin{bmatrix} 1 & 1 & : & 3 \\ 0 & a^2 - 9 & : & a - 3 \end{bmatrix}$$

a. For there to be no solution $a^2 - 9$ must be zero, and $a - 3$ must not be zero.

$a = -3$ will ensure this.   b. For a unique solution neither $a^2 - 9$ nor $a - 3$ can

be zero. $a \in R$ and $a \neq 3$, or -3 will ensure this.   c. For infinitely many solu-

tions both $a^2 - 9$ and $a - 3$ must be zero. $a = 3$ will ensure this.

PAGES 559-560   Exercises

1. $\begin{bmatrix} 3 & 2 & -1 & : & 0 \\ 2 & -1 & 2 & : & 0 \end{bmatrix} \rightarrow \begin{bmatrix} 1 & \frac{2}{3} & -\frac{1}{3} & : & 0 \\ 0 & -\frac{7}{3} & \frac{8}{3} & : & 0 \end{bmatrix} \rightarrow \begin{bmatrix} 1 & 0 & \frac{3}{7} & : & 0 \\ 0 & 1 & -\frac{8}{7} & : & 0 \end{bmatrix}$ Thus $\begin{bmatrix} x_1 \\ x_2 \\ x_3 \end{bmatrix} = x_3 \begin{bmatrix} -\frac{3}{7} \\ \frac{8}{7} \\ 1 \end{bmatrix}$

3. $\begin{bmatrix} x_1 \\ x_2 \end{bmatrix} = \begin{bmatrix} 0 \\ 0 \end{bmatrix}$ 5. $\begin{bmatrix} x_1 \\ x_2 \\ x_3 \end{bmatrix} = x_3 \begin{bmatrix} 0 \\ \frac{7}{2} \\ 1 \end{bmatrix}$ 7. $\begin{bmatrix} x_1 \\ x_2 \\ x_3 \end{bmatrix} = \begin{bmatrix} 0 \\ 0 \\ 0 \end{bmatrix}$ 9. $\begin{bmatrix} x_1 \\ x_2 \\ x_3 \end{bmatrix} = \begin{bmatrix} \frac{2}{3}x_2 - \frac{1}{3}x_3 \\ x_2 \\ x_3 \end{bmatrix} =$

$x_2 \begin{bmatrix} \frac{2}{3} \\ 1 \\ 0 \end{bmatrix} + x_3 \begin{bmatrix} -\frac{1}{3} \\ 0 \\ 1 \end{bmatrix}$ 11. $\begin{bmatrix} x_1 \\ x_2 \\ x_3 \\ x_4 \\ x_5 \\ x_6 \end{bmatrix} = x_4 \begin{bmatrix} \frac{9}{5} \\ \frac{6}{5} \\ -\frac{4}{5} \\ 1 \\ 0 \\ 0 \end{bmatrix} + x_6 \begin{bmatrix} -\frac{1}{2} \\ 0 \\ \frac{1}{2} \\ 0 \\ -\frac{1}{2} \\ 1 \end{bmatrix}$ 13. $\begin{bmatrix} x_1 \\ x_2 \\ x_3 \end{bmatrix} = x_3 \begin{bmatrix} \frac{1}{3} \\ \frac{5}{6}(i - 1) \\ 1 \end{bmatrix}$

15.   Let x be, successively, 1, 0, -1, 2.

$$\begin{cases} c_3 + c_2 + c_1 + c_0 = 0 \\ \qquad\qquad\quad c_0 = 0 \\ -c_3 + c_2 - c_1 + c_0 = 0 \\ 8c_3 + 4c_2 + 2c_1 + c_0 = 0 \end{cases}$$
It follows that $c_0 = 0$ solve the remaining three equations.

$\begin{bmatrix} 1 & 1 & 1 & : & 0 \\ -1 & 1 & -1 & : & 0 \\ 8 & 4 & 2 & : & 0 \end{bmatrix} \rightarrow \begin{bmatrix} 1 & 1 & 1 & : & 0 \\ 0 & 2 & 0 & : & 0 \\ 0 & -4 & -6 & : & 0 \end{bmatrix} \rightarrow \begin{bmatrix} 1 & 0 & 1 & : & 0 \\ 0 & 1 & 0 & : & 0 \\ 0 & 0 & 1 & : & 0 \end{bmatrix} \rightarrow \begin{bmatrix} 1 & 0 & 0 & : & 0 \\ 0 & 1 & 0 & : & 0 \\ 0 & 0 & 1 & : & 0 \end{bmatrix}$

Thus the unique solution is (0, 0, 0) and $c_3 = c_2 = c_1 = c_0 = 0$.

17. $\begin{bmatrix} 1 & 3 \\ 3 & k^2 \end{bmatrix} \rightarrow \begin{bmatrix} 1 & 3 & : & 0 \\ 0 & k^2 - 9 & : & 0 \end{bmatrix}$ Thus any $k \in R$ and $k \neq \pm 3$ will produce only

the trivial solution. $k = \pm 3$ will produce infinite solutions.

1. Solution. 3. Solution. 5. Solution. 7. Not a solution 9. Not a

solution. 11. Solution. 13. Only solution is $(\frac{11}{5}, \frac{2}{5})$ 15. $\begin{bmatrix} 1 & 1 & 2 & : & 2 \\ 2 & 1 & 4 & : & 3 \\ 3 & 1 & 6 & : & 6 \end{bmatrix} \rightarrow$

$\begin{bmatrix} 1 & 1 & 2 & : & 2 \\ 0 & -1 & 0 & : & -1 \\ 0 & -2 & 0 & : & 0 \end{bmatrix} \rightarrow \begin{bmatrix} 1 & 1 & 2 & : & 2 \\ 0 & 1 & 0 & : & 1 \\ 0 & 0 & 0 & : & 2 \end{bmatrix}$ No solution. 17. No solution.

19. $(1, 2, -2, 0, 1, 3)$ 21. $\begin{bmatrix} x_1 \\ x_2 \\ x_3 \\ x_4 \\ x_5 \end{bmatrix} = \begin{bmatrix} 1 \\ -1 \\ 1 \\ -1 \\ 1 \end{bmatrix} + x_4 \begin{bmatrix} -\frac{3}{2} \\ -4 \\ 2 \\ 1 \\ 0 \end{bmatrix} + x_5 \begin{bmatrix} -\frac{1}{2} \\ -2 \\ 1 \\ 0 \\ 1 \end{bmatrix}, \begin{bmatrix} 1 \\ -1 \\ 1 \\ -1 \\ 1 \end{bmatrix}, \begin{bmatrix} -\frac{1}{2} \\ -5 \\ 3 \\ 0 \\ 1 \end{bmatrix}, \begin{bmatrix} 0 \\ -3 \\ 2 \\ 0 \\ 0 \end{bmatrix}$

23. $k = \pm \sqrt{3}$, no solution. $k \neq \pm \sqrt{3}$, one solution. 25. $k = 3$, no solution.
$k = -3$, infinite solution, $k \neq \pm 3$, one solution.

1. $\begin{bmatrix} 1 & 0 & 0 & 0 \\ 0 & 0 & 0 & 1 \\ 0 & 0 & 1 & 0 \\ 0 & 1 & 0 & 0 \end{bmatrix}$ 3. $\begin{bmatrix} 1 & 0 & 0 & 0 \\ 0 & 1 & 0 & 0 \\ 0 & 0 & -\frac{2}{3} & 0 \\ 0 & 0 & 0 & 1 \end{bmatrix}$ 5. $\begin{bmatrix} 1 & 0 & 0 & 0 \\ 0 & 1 & 0 & 0 \\ 0 & 3 & 1 & 0 \\ 0 & 0 & 0 & 1 \end{bmatrix}$ 7. $\begin{bmatrix} 1 & 0 & 0 & 0 \\ 0 & 1 & 0 & 0 \\ 0 & 0 & 1 & 0 \\ 0 & 0 & \frac{2}{3} & 1 \end{bmatrix}$

9. $\begin{bmatrix} 1 & 0 & 0 & 0 \\ -1 & 1 & 0 & 0 \\ -1 & 0 & 1 & 0 \\ -1 & 0 & 0 & 1 \end{bmatrix}$ 11. (1.) $\begin{bmatrix} 1 & 0 & 0 & 0 \\ 0 & 0 & 0 & 1 \\ 0 & 0 & 1 & 0 \\ 0 & 1 & 0 & 0 \end{bmatrix}$ (2.) $\begin{bmatrix} 0 & 0 & 0 & 1 \\ 0 & 1 & 0 & 0 \\ 0 & 0 & 1 & 0 \\ 1 & 0 & 0 & 0 \end{bmatrix}$ (3.) $\begin{bmatrix} 1 & 0 & 0 & 0 \\ 0 & 1 & 0 & 0 \\ 0 & 0 & -\frac{3}{2} & 0 \\ 0 & 0 & 0 & 1 \end{bmatrix}$

(4.) $\begin{bmatrix} \frac{1}{100} & 0 & 0 & 0 \\ 0 & 1 & 0 & 0 \\ 0 & 0 & 1 & 0 \\ 0 & 0 & 0 & 1 \end{bmatrix}$ (5.) $\begin{bmatrix} 1 & 0 & 0 & 0 \\ 0 & 1 & 0 & 0 \\ 0 & -3 & 1 & 0 \\ 0 & 0 & 0 & 1 \end{bmatrix}$ (6.) $\begin{bmatrix} 1 & 0 & 0 & 0 \\ 1 & 1 & 0 & 0 \\ 0 & 0 & 1 & 0 \\ 0 & 0 & 0 & 1 \end{bmatrix}$ (7.) $\begin{bmatrix} 1 & 0 & 0 & 0 \\ 0 & 1 & 0 & 0 \\ 0 & 0 & 1 & 0 \\ 0 & 0 & -\frac{2}{3} & 1 \end{bmatrix}$

13. $\frac{1}{2} \begin{bmatrix} 3 & -2 & 1 \\ 1 & 0 & -1 \\ -3 & 2 & 1 \end{bmatrix}$ 15. $\begin{bmatrix} 3 & 2 & -4 \\ -1 & 0 & 1 \\ 0 & -1 & 1 \end{bmatrix}$ 17. $\begin{bmatrix} \frac{7}{3} & -\frac{1}{3} & -\frac{1}{3} & \frac{2}{3} \\ \frac{4}{9} & -\frac{1}{9} & -\frac{4}{9} & \frac{1}{9} \\ \frac{1}{9} & -\frac{2}{9} & \frac{1}{9} & \frac{2}{9} \\ \frac{5}{3} & \frac{2}{3} & \frac{2}{3} & \frac{1}{3} \end{bmatrix}$

19. $\begin{bmatrix} 1 & -1 & 0 & -1 \\ 0 & -\frac{1}{2} & 0 & 0 \\ -\frac{1}{5} & 1 & \frac{1}{5} & \frac{3}{5} \\ \frac{2}{5} & -\frac{1}{2} & \frac{2}{5} & -\frac{1}{5} \end{bmatrix}$ 21. $X = \begin{bmatrix} 8 \\ 2 \\ -7 \end{bmatrix}$ 23. $X = \begin{bmatrix} -1 \\ 0 \\ 0 \\ 0 \end{bmatrix}$ 25. $X = \begin{bmatrix} -3 \\ 2 \\ -3 \\ \frac{2}{3} \\ 3 \end{bmatrix}$

27. $(A_1 A_2 A_3 \cdots A_k)(A_k^{-1} A_{k-1}^{-1} \cdots A_1^{-1}) = A_1 A_2 \cdots A_{k-1} I A_{k-1}^{-1} \cdots A_1^{-1} = \cdots = I.$

Thus $(A_k^{-1} A_{k-1}^{-1} \cdots A_1^{-1})$ is the unique inverse.   29. A and B are row equivalent

if B may be obtained from A by a sequence of elementary row operations. Each

elementary row operation may be accomplished by premultiplication by an elementary

matrix E_i. If E_1, $E_2 \cdots E_k$ are the k elementary matrices which correspond to the

sequence of elementary row operations, then $B = E_k E_{k-1} \cdots E_1 A$. Similarly if

$B = E_k \cdots E_1 A$ and E_i are elementary, then B is row equivalent to A.   31. "only if"

If A is invertible then $A = E_k E_{k-1} \cdots E_2 E_1$ by Theorem 11-17 where the E_i are

elementary matrices. By Theorem 11-13 each E_i is invertible and $(E_k \cdots E_1)^{-1}$

$= E_1^{-1} E_2^{-1} \cdots E_{k-1}^{-1} E_k^{-1}$. Thus $E_1^{-1} E_2^{-1} \cdots E_{k-1}^{-1} E_k^{-1} A = (E_1^{-1} E_2^{-1} \cdots E_k^{-1})$

$(E_k E_{k-1} \cdots E_2 E_1) = I_n$ Thus A is row equivalent to I_n. "if" If A is row equi-

valent to I_n, then there are elementary matrices such that $A = E_k E_{k-1} \cdots E_2 E_1 I_n$

$= E_k E_{k-1} \cdots E_2 E_1$. Thus A is invertible by Theorem 11-17.   33.   Let A be an

n x n matrix with row i all zeros. Assume A is invertible. Thus there is an

n x n matrix B by Exercise 30 and 31 such that $AB = BA = I_n$. Consider AB and its

i^{th} row. Since the ith row of A is all zeros, every element of the ith row of

AB is all zeros because each element in the ith row of AB is the product of the

i^{th} row of A and a column of B. Thus AB has i^{th} row all zeros, but $AB = I_n$ with

i^{th} row 0 0 $\cdots$ 1 0 0. This is a contradiction.

PAGES 575-578 Chapter Objectives and Review

1. See definitions in text.   3. $\begin{bmatrix} -8 & -4 & -6 \end{bmatrix}$ 5. $\begin{bmatrix} 2 & 3 & 4 & 5 & 1 \\ -6 & -9 & -12 & -15 & -3 \\ 4 & 6 & 8 & 10 & 2 \\ 10 & 15 & 20 & 25 & 5 \end{bmatrix}$

7. $\begin{bmatrix} -1 & 1 & 6 \\ 3 & 6 & -1 \\ 9 & 0 & 0 \end{bmatrix}$ 9. $\begin{bmatrix} 2 & 0 \\ 0 & 2 \\ 0 & 1 \\ 1 & 0 \end{bmatrix}$ 11. The set of constant terms are all zeros for

the homogeneous systems. 13. Interchange 2 rows, multiply a row by a constant,

add a multiple of one row to another row. 15. $\begin{bmatrix} 8 & 3 & 5 & \vdots & 5 \\ 2 & -1 & 9 & \vdots & 3 \end{bmatrix}$ 17. A, B, C

are in row echelon form and A, C are in reduced row echelon form.

19. $\begin{bmatrix} 1 & 2 & -3 & 4 \\ 2 & 4 & 5 & 6 \end{bmatrix} \rightarrow \begin{bmatrix} 1 & 2 & -3 & 4 \\ 0 & 0 & 11 & -2 \end{bmatrix} \rightarrow \begin{bmatrix} 1 & 2 & 0 & 3\frac{5}{11} \\ 0 & 0 & 1 & -\frac{2}{11} \end{bmatrix}$ 21. $\begin{bmatrix} x_1 \\ x_2 \\ x_3 \end{bmatrix} = \begin{bmatrix} 0 \\ 1 \\ 1 \end{bmatrix} + x_3 \begin{bmatrix} 1 \\ -\frac{1}{2} \\ -\frac{1}{2} \\ 1 \end{bmatrix}$

23. $\begin{bmatrix} x_1 \\ x_2 \\ x_3 \\ x_4 \end{bmatrix} = \begin{bmatrix} 1 \\ -5 \\ 0 \\ 5 \end{bmatrix} + x_4 \begin{bmatrix} 0 \\ 0 \\ -1 \\ 1 \end{bmatrix}$ 25. $\begin{bmatrix} x_1 \\ x_2 \\ x_3 \end{bmatrix} = \begin{bmatrix} 0 \\ 1 \\ 1 \end{bmatrix} + x_3 \begin{bmatrix} 1 \\ -\frac{1}{2} \\ \frac{1}{2} \\ -\frac{1}{2} \\ 1 \end{bmatrix}$ 27. $\begin{bmatrix} x_1 \\ x_2 \\ x_3 \\ x_4 \end{bmatrix} = x_3 \begin{bmatrix} 1 \\ 0 \\ 1 \\ 0 \end{bmatrix} + x_4 \begin{bmatrix} 1 \\ -\frac{1}{2} \\ \frac{1}{2} \\ 1 \end{bmatrix}$

$\begin{bmatrix} 0 \\ 1 \\ 0 \\ 1 \end{bmatrix}$ 29. No inverse. 31. $\frac{1}{25} \begin{bmatrix} -39 & 40 & -17 \\ 19 & -15 & 7 \\ -8 & 5 & 1 \end{bmatrix}$

PAGES 578-579 Chapter Test

1. $\begin{bmatrix} 1 & 5 & 0 \\ -3 & 5 & -2 \end{bmatrix}$ 3. When the number of columns of the first matrix equals to

the number of rows of the second one. 5. $k = -4$ 7. $\begin{cases} 3x_1 + 2x_2 - x_3 = 0 \\ 4x_1 + 5x_2 - 7x_3 = 0 \end{cases}$

9. Interchange two rows, multiply a row by a number, add a multiple of one row

to another. 11. $\begin{bmatrix} 2 & -3 & 5 \\ 1 & 7 & 3 \end{bmatrix} \rightarrow \begin{bmatrix} 1 & 7 & 3 \\ 0 & 1 & \frac{1}{17} \end{bmatrix}$ (re)$\rightarrow \begin{bmatrix} 1 & 0 & 2\frac{10}{17} \\ 0 & 1 & \frac{1}{17} \end{bmatrix}$ (rre)

13. $\begin{bmatrix} x_1 \\ x_2 \end{bmatrix} = \frac{1}{11} \begin{bmatrix} 20 \\ 19 \end{bmatrix}$ 15. $\begin{bmatrix} x_1 \\ x_2 \\ x_3 \end{bmatrix} = x_3 \begin{bmatrix} \frac{7}{3} \\ \frac{1}{3} \\ 1 \end{bmatrix}$ 17. $\frac{1}{5} \begin{bmatrix} -3 & 2 & 4 \\ -5 & 0 & 5 \\ 1 & 1 & -3 \end{bmatrix}$

PAGE 583 Exercises

1. Answers will vary.

PAGES 588-589 Exercises

1. Semimajor: 4, semiminor: 2, $(\pm 2\sqrt{3}, 0)$. 3. Semimajor: 6, semiminor: 2, $(0, \pm 4\sqrt{2})$. 5. Semimajor: 6, semiminor: 4, $(\pm 2\sqrt{5}, 0)$. 7. Semimajor: 4, semiminor: $2\sqrt{2}$, $(0, \pm 2\sqrt{2})$. 9. $c = 3$, $a = 5$ implies $b = 4$: $\dfrac{x^2}{25} + \dfrac{y^2}{16} = 1$

11. $c = 2$, $b = \dfrac{3}{2}$ implies $a = \dfrac{5}{2}$: $\dfrac{4x^2}{25} + \dfrac{4y^2}{9} = 1$ 13. $c = 3$, $a = 6$ implies $b = 3\sqrt{3}$: $\dfrac{x^2}{27} + \dfrac{y^2}{36} = 1$ 15. $c = 2$, $a = 4$ implies $b = 2\sqrt{3}$: $\dfrac{x^2}{12} + \dfrac{y^2}{16} = 1$

17. $4x^2 + 9y^2 = 25$ 19. Slope $\overleftrightarrow{AC} = \dfrac{y - 0}{x - 2}$, slope $\overleftrightarrow{BC} = \dfrac{y - 0}{x + 2}$, $\dfrac{y}{x - 2} \cdot \dfrac{y}{x + 2}$

$= -4 \Rightarrow y^2 = -4(x^2 - 4) \Rightarrow y^2 + 4x^2 = 16 \Rightarrow \dfrac{x^2}{4} + \dfrac{y^2}{16} = 1.$ 21. By Equation 3, $a\sqrt{(x - c)^2 + y^2} = a^2 - cx$ or $\sqrt{(x - c)^2 + y^2} = a + \dfrac{c}{a}x$. Since $F(c, 0)$ and $P(x, y)$, $\sqrt{(x - c)^2 + y^2} = FP$, thus $FP = a - \dfrac{cx}{a}$.

PAGES 591-592 Exercises

1. $a = 4$, $b = 2$, $c = 2\sqrt{3}$, $e = \dfrac{\sqrt{3}}{2}$, 2, $x = \pm\dfrac{16}{2\sqrt{3}} = \pm\dfrac{8\sqrt{3}}{3}$ 3. $a = 6$, $b = 2$, $c = 4\sqrt{2}$, $e = \dfrac{2\sqrt{2}}{3}$, $\dfrac{4}{3}$, $y = \pm\dfrac{9\sqrt{2}}{2}$ 5. $a = 6$, $b = 4$, $c = 2\sqrt{5}$, $e = \dfrac{1}{3}\sqrt{5}$, $\dfrac{16}{3}$, $x = \pm\dfrac{18\sqrt{5}}{5}$ 7. $a = 4$, $b = 2\sqrt{2}$, $c = 2\sqrt{2}$, $e = \dfrac{\sqrt{2}}{2}$, 4, $y = \pm 4\sqrt{2}$ 9. $a = 9.45 \times 10^7$, $c = .15 \times 10^7$ $\therefore e = \dfrac{.15 \times 10^7}{9.45 \times 10^7} = \dfrac{15}{945} = \dfrac{3}{189}$ 11. The set of

ellipses such that as $e \rightarrow 0$, the ellipse approaches a circle. As $e \rightarrow 1$ the ellipse approaches a straight line. 13. $\overleftrightarrow{BP}$ is $y - b = \dfrac{s - b}{r}x$, x intercept M: $-b \cdot \dfrac{r}{s - b}$, $\overleftrightarrow{B'P}$ is $y + b = \dfrac{s + b}{r}x$, x intercept N: $b \cdot \dfrac{r}{s + b}$, OM $\cdot$ ON $= \dfrac{-br}{s - b} \cdot \dfrac{br}{s + b} = \dfrac{-b^2r^2}{s^2 - b^2}$, but $b^2r^2 + a^2s^2 = a^2b^2$ because $P(r, s)$ is on the ellipse. Thus $+b^2r^2 = a^2b^2 - a^2s^2$ OM $\cdot$ ON $= \dfrac{a^2s^2 - a^2b^2}{s^2 - b^2} = \dfrac{a^2(s^2 - b^2)}{s^2 - b^2} = a^2$

when $s \neq \pm b$. 15. Let A have coordinates (a, 0) a < r. Let P have coordinates

(x, y). AP $= \sqrt{(x - a)^2 + y^2}$. PT $= r - PO = r -\sqrt{x^2 + y^2}$. $\therefore \sqrt{(x - a)^2 + y^2}$

$= r - \sqrt{x^2 + y^2}$. $(x - a)^2 + y^2 = r^2 - 2r\sqrt{x^2 + y^2} + x^2 + y^2$. $-2ax + a^2 =$

$r^2 - 2r\sqrt{x^2 + y^2}$. $r^2 - a^2 + 2ax = 2r\sqrt{x^2 + y^2}$. $4ar^2x - 4a^3x + 4a^2x^2 + a^4$

$- 2a^2r^2 + r^4 = 4r^2x^2 + 4r^2y^2$. $-4x^2(r^2 - a^2) + 4a(r^2 - a^2)x + (r^2 - a^2)^2 = 4r^2y^2$.

$-4x^2 + 4ax + r^2 - a^2 = \dfrac{4r^2}{r^2 - a^2} y^2$. $-4(x - \dfrac{a}{2})^2 + r^2 = \dfrac{4r^2}{r^2 - a^2} y^2$. $4(x - \dfrac{a}{2})^2$

$+ \dfrac{4r^2}{r^2 - a^2} y^2 = r^2$.

This is an ellipse.

PAGE 596 Exercises

1. a $= 4$, b $= 3$, c $= 5$, hyperbola, vertices: a(-4, 0), A'(-4, 0), foci: F(± 5, 0)

latera recta: $(5, \pm \dfrac{9}{4})$, $(-5, \pm \dfrac{9}{4})$, e $= \dfrac{5}{4}$ 3. a = 3, b = 2, c $= \sqrt{13}$, hyperbola,

vertices: (0, ± 3), foci: (0, $\pm\sqrt{13}$), latera recta: $(\pm\dfrac{4}{3}, \sqrt{13})$, $(\pm\dfrac{4}{3}, -\sqrt{13})$, e $= \dfrac{\sqrt{13}}{3}$

5. a $= 1$, b $= \dfrac{1}{2}$, c $= \dfrac{\sqrt{5}}{2}$, hyperbola, vertices: (0, ± 1), foci: (0, $\pm \dfrac{\sqrt{5}}{2}$),

latera recta: $(\pm\dfrac{1}{4}, \dfrac{\sqrt{5}}{2})$, $(\pm\dfrac{1}{4}, -\dfrac{\sqrt{5}}{2})$, e $= \dfrac{\sqrt{5}}{2}$ 7. a $= 6$, b $= 6$, c $= 6\sqrt{2}$,

hyperbola, vertices: (0, ± 6), foci: (0, $\pm 6\sqrt{2}$), latera recta: (± 6, $6\sqrt{2}$),

(± 6, $-6\sqrt{2}$), e $= \sqrt{2}$ 9. a $= 2$, b $= \sqrt{21}$, c $= 5$, hyperbola, vertices: (± 2, 0),

foci: (± 5, 0), latera recta: $(5, \pm\dfrac{21}{2})$, $(-5, \pm\dfrac{21}{2})$, e $= \dfrac{5}{2}$ 11. a $= 2$, b $= 3$,

c $= \sqrt{13}$, hyperbola, vertices: (0, ± 2), foci: (0, $\pm \sqrt{13}$), latera recta:

$(\pm\dfrac{9}{2}, \sqrt{13})$, $(\pm\dfrac{9}{2}, -\sqrt{13})$, e $= \dfrac{\sqrt{13}}{2}$ 13. a $= 4$, b $= 3$, c $= 5$: $\dfrac{x^2}{16} - \dfrac{y^2}{9} = 1$

15. a $= 2$, b $= \sqrt{5}$, c $= 3$: $\dfrac{x^2}{4} - \dfrac{y^2}{5} = 1$ 17. a $= 3$, b $= 4$, c $= 5$: $\dfrac{x^2}{9} - \dfrac{y^2}{16} = 1$

19. a $= 4$, b $= 3$, c $= 5$: $\dfrac{y^2}{16} - \dfrac{x^2}{9} = 1$

PAGES 600-601 Exercises

1. $\dfrac{x}{4} \pm \dfrac{y}{3} = 0$ 3. $\dfrac{y}{3} \pm \dfrac{x}{2} = 0$ 5. $2x \pm y = 0$ 7. $y \pm x = 0$ 9. $\sqrt{21}x - 2y = 0$

11. $3y \pm 2x = 0$ 13. The equations of the asymptotes of $\dfrac{x^2}{a^2} - \dfrac{y^2}{b^2} = 1$ are

$bx - ay = 0$ and $bx + ay = 0$ or $y = \dfrac{b}{a}x$ and $y = -\dfrac{b}{a}x$. Thus the product of the slopes is $-\dfrac{b^2}{a^2}$ which is -1 if and only if $b^2 = a^2$. But since a > 0 and b > 0 $a^2 = b^2$

is equivalent to a = b.   15. Yes.   17. a = 6, b = 12, $\dfrac{x^2}{36} - \dfrac{y^2}{144} = 1$

19. $\dfrac{10x^2}{16} - \dfrac{10y^2}{144} = 1$ 21. Let P(x, y) be a point on $x^2 - 4y^2 = 4$. The equations

of the asymptotes are x + 2y = 0 and x - 2y = 0. The distance from P to x + 2y

= 0 is $\dfrac{|x + 2y|}{\sqrt{5}}$. The distance from P to x - 2y = 0 is $\dfrac{|x - 2y|}{\sqrt{5}}$. The product is

$\dfrac{|x^2 - 4y^2|}{5} = \dfrac{4}{5}$, a constant.   23. Foci of ellipse are (±8, 0): $\dfrac{x^2}{100} + \dfrac{y^2}{36} = 1$.

Foci of hyperbola are (±8, 0): $\dfrac{x^2}{36} - \dfrac{y^2}{28} = 1$.   25. $81x^2 - 144y^2 + 1065y = 13{,}600$

27. Calculate the slopes of $\overleftrightarrow{FN}$ and $\overleftrightarrow{FM}$. Show that their product is -1.   29. Slope

of $\overleftrightarrow{A'D} = \dfrac{r}{p + a}$. Slope of $\overrightarrow{DA} = \dfrac{r}{p - a}$. Thus slope of $\overleftrightarrow{TA} = \dfrac{p - a}{r}$. Equa-

tion of $\overleftrightarrow{A'D}$ is $y = \dfrac{r}{p + a}(x + a)$ (1.) Equation of $\overleftrightarrow{TA}$ is $y = \dfrac{p - a}{r}(x - a)$

(2.) Eliminate r between equations (1.) and (2.).   (1.) $r = \dfrac{y(p + a)}{x + a}$

(2.) $r = \dfrac{-(p - a)(x - a)}{y}$ $\therefore \dfrac{y(p + a)}{x + a} = \dfrac{-(p - a)(x - a)}{y} \Rightarrow y^2 = \dfrac{-(p - a)}{p + a}(x^2 - a^2) \Rightarrow$

$y^2 + \dfrac{p - a}{p + a}x^2 = \dfrac{(p - a)a^2}{p + a}$ This is a hyperbola since $|p| < |a|$.

PAGES 604-606 Exercises

1. p = 1. Focus (1, 0), x = -1, latus rectum (1, ± 2).   3. $p = -\dfrac{11}{4}$. Focus

$(-\dfrac{11}{4}, 0)$, $x = \dfrac{11}{4}$, latus rectum $(-\dfrac{11}{4}, \pm \dfrac{11}{2})$.   5. $p = -\dfrac{3}{2}$. Focus $(-\dfrac{3}{2}, 0)$, $x = \dfrac{3}{2}$,

latus rectum $(-\dfrac{3}{2}, \pm 3)$.   7. $p = \dfrac{3}{4}$. Focus $(\dfrac{3}{4}, 0)$, $x = -\dfrac{3}{4}$, latus rectum

$(\dfrac{3}{4}, \pm \dfrac{3}{2})$.   9. $p = \dfrac{9}{16}$. Focus $(0, \dfrac{9}{16})$, $y = -\dfrac{9}{16}$, latus rectum $(\pm \dfrac{9}{8}, \dfrac{9}{16})$.

11. $y^2 = -6x$ 13. $y^2 = -16x$ 15. $x^2 = -\dfrac{7}{2}y$ 17. $x^2 = -12y$ 19. $x^2 = \dfrac{9}{2}y$

21. $x^2 = -12y$ 23. Vertex is (0, 0). The slopes of the lines are $\dfrac{2}{1}$ and $-\dfrac{1}{2}$.

Thus the angle is a right angle.   25. $y^2 = 12(x - 1)$ 27. $x^2 = -16(y + 2)$

29. Let d = distance from P(x, y) to the circle. Then $d = OP - r = \sqrt{x^2 + y^2} - r$.

Let $\overleftrightarrow{AB}$ be the x axis. Then the distance from P to $\overleftrightarrow{AB}$ is y. Under the

conditions $y = d = \sqrt{x^2 + y^2} - r$. Thus $y + r = \sqrt{x^2 + y^2}$ and $(y + r)^2$

$= x^2 + y^2$ or $2yr + r^2 = x^2$ or $x^2 = 2r(y + \frac{r}{2})$. This is a parabola. 31. $\angle P_2AQ_2$ has its vertex at the origin. Thus the vectors $\overrightarrow{AP_2} = 4pi + 4pj$ and $\overrightarrow{AQ_2} = 4pi - 4pj$. Thus $\cos \Theta = 4p \cdot 4p - 4p \cdot 4p = 0$. The angle is right. 33. The product of the slopes calculated using points $x = \frac{2p}{m^2}(2m^2 + 1 \pm \sqrt{1 + 4m^2})$, $y = \frac{2p}{m}(1 \pm \sqrt{1 + 4m^2})$ from Exercise 32 is

$$\frac{\frac{2p}{m}(1 + \sqrt{1 + 4m^2})}{\frac{2p}{m^2}(2m^2 + 1 + \sqrt{1 + 4m^2})} \cdot \frac{\frac{2p}{m}(1 - \sqrt{1 + 4m^2})}{\frac{2p}{m^2}(2m^2 + 1 - \sqrt{1 + 4m^2})}$$ which reduces to -1. Thus the

angle is a right angle.

PAGE 611 Exercises

1. $a = 3$, $b = 2$, $c = \sqrt{13}$: $\frac{(x - 1)^2}{9} - \frac{(y - 3)^2}{4} = 1$ 3. $a = \sqrt{7}$, $b = 3$, $c = 4$: $\frac{(x - 3)^2}{7} - \frac{(y - 2)^2}{9} = 1$ 5. $a = 6$, $b = 8$, $c = 10$: $\frac{(x - 6)^2}{36} - \frac{y^2}{64} = 1$

7. $a = 6$, $b = 2\sqrt{5}$, $c = 4$: $\frac{x^2}{36} + \frac{(y - 3)^2}{20} = 1$ 9. $a = 3$, $b = 2$, $c = \sqrt{5}$: $\frac{(x - 2)^2}{9} + \frac{(y - 3)^2}{4} = 1$ 11. $p = 4$, $(y - 3)^2 = 16(x - 2)$ 13. $p = 3$, $(x - 3)^2 = 12(y + 2)$ 15. $p = -2$, $(y + 1)^2 = -8(x - 4)$ 17. Consider in each case the y coordinates of the intersection of line $x = h \pm c$ where c is $\sqrt{a^2 + b^2}$ for the hyperbola and $\sqrt{a^2 - b^2}$ for the ellipse. For the hyperbola the details are, $b^2(c)^2 - a^2(y - k)^2 = a^2b^2 \Longrightarrow -a^2(y - k)^2 = a^2b^2 - b^2c^2 \Longrightarrow (y - k)^2 = \frac{b^2c^2 - a^2b^2}{a^2}$ $y = k \pm \frac{b}{a}\sqrt{c^2 - a^2} = k \pm \frac{b^2}{a}$. Thus latus rectum has length $\frac{2b^2}{a}$.

The derivation for the ellipse is similar. 19. $x = h \pm \frac{a^2}{c}$

PAGE 616 Exercises

1. $(x' - h)^2 + (y' - k)^2 - 2(x' - h) - 4(y' - k) - 20 = 0 \Longrightarrow x'^2 - 2x'h + h^2 + y'^2 - 2y'k + k^2 - 2x' + 2h - 4y' + 4k - 20 = 0 \Longrightarrow x'^2 + y'^2 + (-2h - 2)x' + (-2k - 4)y' + h^2 + k^2 + 2h + 4k - 20 = 0$. Let $h = -1$, $k = -2$. $x^2 + y^2 + 1 + 4 - 2 - 8 - 20 = 0 \Longrightarrow x^2 + y^2 = 25$. 3. $x^2 - 4y^2 = 0$ 5. $y^2 = 6x$

7. $9x^2 + y^2 = 9$ 9. $16x^2 - 4y^2 = 64$ 11. $y^2 + x^2 = 25$ 13. $9x^2 + 4y^2 = 36$

PAGE 621 Exercises

1. $2(x - h)^2 + 4(x - h)(y - k) + 5(y - k)^2 - 8(x - h) - 14(y - k) + 5 = 0 \Rightarrow$

$2x^2 - 4xh + 2h^2 + 4xy - 4hy - 4xk + 4hk + 5y^2 - 10yk + 5k^2 - 8x + 8h - 14y + 14k$

$+ 5 = 0 \Rightarrow 2x^2 + 4xy + 5y^2 + (-4h - 4k - 8)x + (-4h - 10k - 14)y + 2h^2 + 4hk +$

$5k^2 + 8h + 14k + 5 = 0$ $(h = -1, k = -1) \Rightarrow 2x^2 + 4xy + 5y^2 + 2 + 4 + 5 - 8 - 14$

$+ 5 = 0 \Rightarrow 2x^2 + 4xy + 5y^2 - 6 = 0$ $\cot 2\theta = \frac{5 - 2}{4} = \frac{3}{4} \therefore \cos 2\theta = \frac{3}{5}, \sin\theta =$

$\frac{\sqrt5}{5}, \cos\theta = \frac{2\sqrt5}{5}, x = \frac{\sqrt5}{5}(2x' + y'), y = \frac{\sqrt5}{5}(-x' + 2y').\ 2\left[\frac{\sqrt5}{5}(2x + y)\right]^2 +$

$4(\frac{\sqrt5}{5} \cdot \frac{\sqrt5}{5})(2x + y)(-x + 2y) + 5(\frac{\sqrt5}{5})^2(-x + 2y)^2 = 6 \Rightarrow 2 \cdot \frac{5}{25}(4x^2 + 4xy + y^2)$

$+ 4 \cdot \frac{5}{25}(-2x^2 + 4xy - xy + 2y^2) + \frac{25}{25}(x^2 - 4xy + 4y^2) = 6 \Rightarrow \frac{5}{25}\left[8x^2 + 8xy + 2y^2\right.$

$- 8x^2 + 16xy - 4xy + 8y^2 + 5x^2 - 20xy + 20y^2\right] = 6 \Rightarrow \frac{5}{25}(20y^2 + 5x^2) = 6 \Rightarrow 20y^2$

$+ 5x^2 = 30.$ 3. $\frac{x^2}{16} - \frac{3y^2}{4} = 1$ 5. $\frac{x^2}{12} + \frac{y^2}{2} = 1$ 7. $\frac{10y^2}{9} - \frac{x^2}{3} = 1$

9. $25x^2 - 25y^2 = 12$

PAGES 622-624 Chapter Objectives and Review

3. See page 593. 5. a. $\frac{x^2}{a^2} + \frac{y^2}{b^2} = 1, a > b$ b. $\frac{x^2}{b^2} + \frac{y^2}{a^2} = 1, a > b$

c. $\frac{(x - 3)^2}{a^2} + \frac{(y - 5)^2}{b^2} = 1, a > b$ d. $\frac{(x - 3)^2}{b^2} + \frac{(y - 5)^2}{a^2} = 1, a > b$

e. $\frac{(x)^2}{b^2} + \frac{(y - 2)^2}{a^2} = 1, a > b$ f. $\frac{x^2}{a^2} + \frac{(y - 2)^2}{b^2} = 1, a > b$ 7. a. $y^2 = \pm 4px$

b. $x^2 = \pm 4py$ c. $(y - 5)^2 = \pm 4p(x - 3)$ d. $(x - 3)^2 = \pm 4p(y - 5)$ 9. a. Para-

bola. b. Latus rectum: 12, vertex (3, -2), focus (3, 1), e = 1. 11. a. El-

lipse. b. Major axis: 10, minor axis: 6, latus rectum $\frac{18}{5}$, center: (1, -5),

vertices: (-4, -5), (6, -5), minor: (1, -2) (1, -8), foci: (-3, -5), (5, -5),

e = $\frac{4}{5}$, directrix: $x = \pm \frac{25}{4}$. 13. a. Hyperbola. b. Major axis: 16, minor axis:

12, latus rectum: 9, center: (2, -3), vertices: (2, 5), (2, -11) minor:

(-4, -3), (8, -3), foci: (2, 7), (2, -13), e = $\frac{5}{4}$, directrices: $y = \pm \frac{32}{5}$, asymptotes: $6(y - 2) \pm 8(x + 3) = 0$. 15. $4AC - B^2 = 4(3)(1) - 16 = -4$:

Hyperbola. 17. $4AC - B^2 = 4(2)(1) - 4 = 4$: Ellipse. 19. $4AC - B^2 = 4(-3)(-3)$

$- 0 = 36$: Ellipse. 21. $4AC - B^2 = 4(9)(0) - 0 = 0$: Parabola. 23. (h, k)

$= (2, -1) : x^2 - \frac{y^2}{4} = 1$. 25. $(h, k) = (1, -2) : 9y^2 - 16x^2 = -225$ 27. $\cot 2\Theta$

$= \frac{3}{4}$, $\cos 2\Theta = -\frac{3}{5}$, $\sin \Theta = \frac{2}{\sqrt{5}}$, $\cos \Theta = \frac{1}{\sqrt{5}}$, $4y^2 - 6x^2 = 7$ 29. $\cot 2\Theta = \frac{4}{3}$,

$\cos 2\Theta = \frac{4}{5}$, $\sin \Theta = \frac{1}{\sqrt{10}}$, $\cos \Theta = \frac{3}{\sqrt{10}}$, $10x^2 + \frac{1}{\sqrt{10}}(30x + 30y) + \frac{40}{10} = 0 \Rightarrow x^2$

$+ \frac{1}{\sqrt{10}}(3x + 3y) + \frac{4}{10} = 0$. $h = \frac{3}{2\sqrt{10}}$, $k = \frac{7}{12\sqrt{10}}$, $x^2 = -\frac{3}{\sqrt{10}}(y)$

PAGES 624-625 Chapter Test

1. $(y - \frac{3}{2})^2 = -3(x - \frac{49}{12})$ 3. a. $\frac{y^2}{25} - \frac{x^2}{24} = 1$ b. $\frac{(x - 2)^2}{9} - \frac{(y + 2)^2}{7} = 1$

c. $\frac{x^2}{64} - \frac{y^2}{36} = 1$ 5. $\frac{8}{9}$ 7. $6, 2\sqrt{5}$ 9. $4AC - B^2 = 4 \cdot 4 \cdot 3 - 0 > 0$: Ellipse.

11. $4AC - B^2 = 4 \cdot 0 \cdot 3 - 0 = 0$: Parabola. 13. $\cot 2\Theta = \frac{5}{12}$, $\cos 2\Theta = \frac{5}{13}$,

$\sin \Theta = \frac{2}{\sqrt{13}}$, $\cos \Theta = \frac{3}{\sqrt{13}}$, $13x^2 - 4 = 0$

CHAPTER 13 GRAPHS IN THREE SPACE

PAGE 631 Exercises

1. Circular cylinder, center at $(2, 0, 0)$, elements parallel to z axis.

3. Circular cylinder, center at $(0, 2, 0)$, elements parallel to x axis.

5. Sphere with center $(0, 0, 0)$, radius 2. 7. Parabolic cylinder, elements

parallel to x axis. 9. Elliptic cylinder, elements parallel to y axis.

11. Elliptic cylinder, center $(2, 4, 0)$, elements parallel to z axis. 13. Cy-

lindric surface with directrix as the sine curve, elements parallel to z axis.

15. a. $x^2 + 4y^2 = 16$ is an elliptical cylinder, elements parallel to the z axis.

b. $x^2 + 4y^2 = 16$ and $z = 2$ is an ellipse in the plane $z = 2$. It can be obtained

from (a.) by passing a plane parallel to xy plane through the point $(0, 0, 2)$.

17. Circle in plane $z = 3$. Cut the sphere with center $(0, 0, 0)$ and radius 4 in

Exercise 16 with the plane $z = 3$. 19. Parabola cut from the parabolic cylinder in Exercise 18 with the plane $x = -2$. 21. Ellipse cut from the Elliptical

cylinder with center $(2, 0, 0)$ in Exercise 20 with the plane $y = 1$.

23. $d_1 = \sqrt{(x-1)^2 + (y-2)^2 + (z-7)^2}$, $d_2 = \sqrt{(x-1)^2 + (y-5)^2 + (z-7)^2}$

$\therefore (x-1)^2 + (y-2)^2 + (z-7)^2 = (x-1)^2 + (y-5)^2 + (z-7)^2$ or $y^2 - 4y + 4$

$= y^2 - 10y + 25$ or $6y = 21 \Rightarrow 2y = 7 \Rightarrow y = \frac{7}{2}$. The graph is the plane $y = \frac{7}{2}$.

PAGE 635   Exercises

1. $\frac{1}{4}(x^2 + z^2) = 0$, $\frac{1}{4}x^2 = y$, $\frac{1}{4}z^2 = y$. Surface of revolution about y axis since

$\frac{1}{4}(x^2 + z^2) = k$ is the empty set for $k < 0$, one point for $k = 0$, a circle for $k > 0$.

3. $9z^2 + 16y^2 = 144$, $9z^2 + 16x^2 = 144$, $16(x^2 + y^2) = 144$. z axis is axis of re-

volution. $16(x^2 + y^2) = 144 - 9k^2 = 9(16 - k^2)$ or $x^2 + y^2 = \frac{9}{16}(16 - k^2)$. For

$-4 < k < 4$ the intersection is a circle, for $-4 = k$ or $k = 4$ the intersection is

one point, for $k < -4$ or $k > 4$ the intersection is empty. 5. $x^2 + 4y^2 = 36$,

$x^2 + 9z^2 = 36$, $4y^2 + 9z^2 = 36$. No axis of revolution. 7. $x^2 + z^2 = 0$,

$x^2 + y^2 - 6y = 0$, $z^2 + y^2 - 6y = 0$. y axis is axis of revolution. Note that any

plane perpendicular to the z axis or the x axis also intersects the surface

$x^2 + y^2 + z^2 - 6y = 0$ in a circle, a point, or the empty set. 9. $x^2 - 16y^2 = 0$,

$x^2 + z^2 = 0$, $-16y^2 + z^2 = 0$. y axis is axis of revolution. 11. Whenever a pair

of the coefficients A, B, and C are identical.

PAGES 641-642   Exercises

1. Symmetric with respect to yz and xz planes. Traces: $\frac{x^2}{a^2} + \frac{y^2}{b^2} = 0$, $\frac{x^2}{a^2} = cz$,

$\frac{y^2}{b^2} = cz$. z = k: $\frac{x^2}{a^2} + \frac{y^2}{b^2} = ck$, ellipse for $k > 0$, point for $k = 0$, null set for

$k < 0$. y = k: $\frac{x^2}{a^2} = cz - \frac{k^2}{b^2} = c(z - \frac{k^2}{b^2 c})$, parabola for all $k \in \mathbb{R}$. x = k: $\frac{y^2}{b^2}$

$= cz - \frac{k^2}{a^2}$, parabola $\forall\, k \in \mathbb{R}$. 3. Symmetry with respect to the xy, yz, and xz

planes. Traces: $\frac{x^2}{a^2} + \frac{y^2}{b^2} = 0$, $\frac{x^2}{a^2} - \frac{z^2}{c^2} = 0$, $\frac{y^2}{b^2} - \frac{z^2}{c^2} = 0$. z = k: $\frac{x^2}{a^2} + \frac{y^2}{b^2} = \frac{k^2}{c^2}$, ellipse for $k \neq 0$, single point for $k = 0$. $y = k$: $\dfrac{x^2}{a^2} - \dfrac{z^2}{c^2} = \dfrac{k^2}{b^2}$, hyperbola for

$k \neq 0$, two lines for $k = 0$. $x = k$: $\dfrac{y^2}{b^2} - \dfrac{z^2}{c} = -\dfrac{k^2}{a^2}$, hyperbola for $k \neq 0$, two lines

for $k = 0$. 5. Symmetry with respect to xy, xz, and yz planes. Traces:

$\dfrac{x^2}{a^2} - \dfrac{y^2}{b^2} = 1$, $\dfrac{x^2}{a^2} - \dfrac{z^2}{c^2} = 1$, $\dfrac{y^2}{b^2} + \dfrac{z^2}{c^2} = -1$. $z = k$: $\dfrac{x^2}{a^2} - \dfrac{y^2}{b^2} = 1 + \dfrac{k^2}{c^2}$, hyperbola for

all k. $y = k$: $\dfrac{x^2}{a^2} - \dfrac{z^2}{c^2} = 1 + \dfrac{k^2}{b^2}$, hyperbola for all k. $x = k$: $\dfrac{y^2}{b^2} + \dfrac{z^2}{c^2} = -1 + \dfrac{k^2}{a^2}$,

ellipse for $k < -a$, $k > a$, for $k = \pm a$ a single point, for $-a < k < a$, null set.

7. Ellipsoid. 9. Hyperboloid, one sheet. 11. Hyperboloid, two sheets. 13. Elliptic

Cone. 15. Elliptic Paraboloid. 17. Hyperbolic Paraboloid. 19. Sphere.

21. Circular cylinder. 23. Elliptic Cone. 25. Circular cylinder.

27. z axis. 29. Ellipsoid. 31. Hyperboloid of one sheet. 33. Circular

Paraboloid. 35. Elliptical cylinder. 37. Hyperbolic cylinder. 39. Hyper-

boloid of one sheet.

PAGES 646-647 Exercises

1. $(3, 0, 2)$ $\therefore$ $x = 3 \cos 0 = 3$, $y = 3 \sin 0 = 0$, $z = 2$. 3. $(0, 7, 4)$

5. $(-1, -\sqrt{3}, 3)$ 7. $x = 7 \cos \left(\dfrac{\pi}{4}\right) \sin 0 = 0$, $y = 7 \sin \left(\dfrac{\pi}{4}\right) \sin 0 = 0$, $z = 7$

$\cos 0 = 7$. 9. $x = 7 \cos(\pi) \sin \dfrac{\pi}{2} = -7$, $y = 7 \sin \pi \sin \dfrac{\pi}{2} = 0$, $z = 7 \cos \dfrac{\pi}{2}$

$= 0$. 11. $x = 8 \cos \dfrac{\pi}{13} \sin \pi = 0$, $y = 8 \sin \dfrac{\pi}{13} \sin \pi = 0$, $z = 8 \cos \pi = -8$.

13. $\rho^2 = z^2 + r^2 = z^2 + x^2 + y^2$, $\rho = \sqrt{z^2 + x^2 + y^2}$. 15. $\tan \Theta = \dfrac{y}{x}$

17. $r = \sqrt{x^2 + y^2}$ 19. $x^2 + y^2 + z^2 = 9$, c: $r^2 + z^2 = 9$, s: $\rho^2 = 9$ or $\rho = 3$

21. $z^2 = r^2 \Rightarrow z^2 = x^2 + y^2$ or $x^2 + y^2 - z^2 = 0$ in rectangular. s: $\phi = \dfrac{\pi}{4}$

or $\phi = \dfrac{3\pi}{4}$. 23. $\rho = 8 \cos \phi \Rightarrow \dfrac{\rho}{8} = \cos \phi \Rightarrow \dfrac{\rho}{8} = \dfrac{z}{\rho} \Rightarrow \rho^2 = 8z$. r: $\Rightarrow x^2 + y^2$

$+ z^2 = 8z$, c: $\Rightarrow r^2 + z^2 = 8z$. 25. $4x^2 = (x^2 + y^2)(x^2 + y^2 + z^2)$, $r^2 + z^2 =$

$16 \sin^2 \theta$

PAGES 649-650 Exercises

1. The curve is a helix. In the first quadrant some points it passes through are:

$(0, 6, 0)$, $(3, 3\sqrt{3}, \frac{5\pi}{6})$, $(3\sqrt{2}, 3\sqrt{2}, \frac{5\pi}{4})$, $(3\sqrt{3}, 3, \frac{5\pi}{3})$, $(6, 0, \frac{5\pi}{2})$

3. This is an elliptic cone. Some points in the first quadrant are:

$(0, 0, 0)$, $(\frac{\pi\sqrt{3}}{4}, \frac{\pi}{4}, \frac{2\pi}{3})$, $(\frac{3\sqrt{2}\pi}{8}, \frac{3\sqrt{2}\pi}{8}, \pi)$, $(\frac{\pi}{2}, \frac{\sqrt{3}\pi}{2}, \frac{4\pi}{3})$, $(0, \frac{3\pi}{2}, 2\pi)$.

5. In the first quadrant some points the curve passes through are: $(0, 0, 0)$,

$(\frac{\pi}{6}, \frac{\pi}{6}, \frac{2}{3}(\frac{\pi}{6})^{\frac{2}{3}})$, $(\frac{\pi}{4}, \frac{\pi}{4}, \frac{2}{3}(\frac{\pi}{4})^{\frac{2}{3}})$, $(\frac{\pi}{3}, \frac{\pi}{3}, \frac{2}{3}(\frac{\pi}{3})^{\frac{2}{3}})$. All points on the curve in

the first quadrant are equidistant from the xz and yz planes. 7. Plane curve.

Draw the circular cylinder with directrix $x^2 + y^2 = 25$ in the xy plane. Cut the

cylinder with the plane $x - z = 0$. Some points the curve passes through in the

first quadrant are: $(0, 5, 0)$, $(1, \sqrt{24}, 1)$, $(2, \sqrt{21}, 2)$, $(3, 4, 3)$, $(4, 3, 4)$,

$(5, 0, 5)$. 9. Plane curve. Draw the circular cylinder with directrix $x^2 + y^2$

$- 4y = 0$ in the xy plane. (Circle with center $(0, 2)$ and radius 2.) Cut the cylin-

der with the plane $y = 2x$. The curve is an element of the cylinder. 11. In the

first quadrant some points the curve passes through are: $(0, 0, 0)$, $(1, \frac{\sqrt{2}}{2}, \frac{1}{3})$,

$(2, 2\sqrt{2}, \frac{8}{3})$, $(3, \frac{9\sqrt{2}}{2}, 9)$, $(4, 8\sqrt{2}, \frac{64}{3})$.

PAGES 650-651 Chapter Objectives and Review

3. Parabolic cylinder. 5. Hyperbolic cylinder. 7. Hyperbolic cylinder.

9. Traces: $9x^2 + 4y^2 = 36$, $9x^2 + 9z^2 = 36$, $4y^2 + 9z^2 = 36$. y axis is axis of

revolution. 11. Traces: $x^2 + 4y^2 = 4$, $x^2 + z^2 = 4$, $4y^2 + z^2 = 4$. y axis is

axis of revolution. 13. Traces: $x^2 - 16y^2 = 0$, $x^2 + z^2 = 0$, $-16y^2 + z^2 = 0$.

y axis is axis of revolution. 15. Elliptic Paraboloid. 17. Sphere.

19. Hyperboloid of 2 sheets. 21. $(r \cos\Theta, r \sin\Theta, z)$ 23. $(\rho\cos\Theta \sin\phi,$

$\rho \sin\Theta \cos\phi, \rho \cos\phi)$ 25. Some points the curve passes through in the first

quadrant are: $(0, 3, 0)$, $(\frac{3}{2}, \frac{3\sqrt{3}}{2}, \frac{\pi}{12})$, $(\frac{3\sqrt{2}}{2}, \frac{3\sqrt{2}}{2}, \frac{\pi}{8})$, $(\frac{3\sqrt{3}}{2}, \frac{3}{2}, \frac{\pi}{6})$, $(3, 0, \frac{\pi}{4})$

PAGE 651 Chapter Test

1. Parabolic cylinder. 3. $4x^2 + y^2 = 4$, $4x^2 - 4z^2 = 4$, $y^2 - 4z^2 = 4$. No. No

circular sections when cut by planes perpendicular to the axes. 5. Hyperboloid of one sheet.

CHAPTER 14 INTRODUCTION TO CALCULUS

PAGES 656-657 Exercises

1. $-4x + 3$ 3. 0 5. $\frac{-21}{x^8}$ 7. $\frac{1}{x} + e^x - 12x^2$ 9. $3x^2 - 4x - 3$ 11. $x^2 e^x$ $+ xe^x + 4x - e^x - 2$ 13. e^x. $(\frac{1}{x} - x^2 - \frac{1}{x^2} - 2x)$ 15. $f'(x) = e^x \cdot e^x +$ $e^x e^x = 2e^{2x}$ 17. $4e^{4x}$ 19. ne^{nx}

21. Note: To avoid confusion, let $r(x) = h(x)$.

$$f'(x) = \lim_{h \to 0} \frac{\frac{r(x + h)}{g(x + h)} - \frac{r(x)}{g(x)}}{h} = \lim_{h \to 0} \frac{\frac{g(x)r(x + h) - r(x)g(x + h)}{g(x + h)g(x)}}{h}$$

$$= \lim_{h \to 0} \frac{g(x)r(x + h) - g(x)r(x) + g(x)r(x) - r(x)g(x + h)}{g(x + h)g(x)h}$$

$$= \lim_{h \to 0} \frac{g(x)\left[r(x + h) - r(x)\right]}{g(x + h)g(x)h} - \lim_{h \to 0} \frac{r(x)\left[g(x + h) - g(x)\right]}{g(x + h)g(x)h}$$

$$= \lim_{h \to 0} \frac{g(x)}{g(x + h)g(x)} \lim_{h \to 0} \frac{r(x + h) - r(x)}{h} - \lim_{h \to 0} \frac{r(x)}{g(x + h)g(x)} \lim_{h \to 0} \frac{g(x + h) - g(x)}{h}$$

$$= \frac{g(x)}{g^2(x)} r'(x) - \frac{r(x)g'(x)}{g^2(x)} = \frac{g(x)r'(x) - r(x)g'(x)}{g^2(x)}$$

PAGE 661 Exercises

1. Since $S(3) = 9 - 25 = -16$ and $S(5) = 25 - 25 = 0$, the average velocity is $\frac{0 - (-16)}{5 - 3} = \frac{16}{2} = 8$ 3. 6.1 5. $\frac{S(3 + h) - S(3)}{h} = \frac{(3 + h)^2 - 25 - (-16)}{h}$ $= \frac{9 + 6h + h^2 - 25 + 16}{h} = 6 + h$ 7. -12 9. -15.96 11. $4, 1, -1.7, -1.97,$ $3h - 2$ 13. $a(t) = 6$, $a(0) = 6$ 15. $v(t) = 4$, $a(t) = 0$ $v(t) = 4$ for all t, $a(t) = 0$ for all t. 17. $v(t) = 8t + 12$, $a(t) = 8$, $v(0) = 12$, $v(1) = 20$, $v(2)$ $= 28$, $v(3) = 36$, $v(4) = 44$, $a(t) = 8$ for all t. 19. $v(t) = 64 - 32t$, $a(t) = -32$, $v(0) = 64$, $v(1) = 32$, $v(2) = 0$, $v(3) = -32$, $v(4) = -64$, $a(t) = -32$ for all t. 21. $v(t) = 6t^2 - 18t$, $a(t) = 12t - 18$, $v(0) = 0$, $v(1) = -12$, $v(2) = -12$, $v(3) = 0$,

$v(4) = 24$, $a(0) = -18$, $a(1) = -6$, $a(2) = 6$, $a(3) = 18$, $a(4) = 30$ 23. $v(2) = 64$,

$v(4) = 0$, $v(6) = -64$ 25. $v(t) = 0$ when $t = 4$, $S(4) = 256$. Yes.   27. Since

$v(t) = 32 - 32t$ and $v(t) = 0$, when $t = 1$, the ball reaches its maximum height

at 1 second.   29. $S(t) = 0$ when $t = 2$

PAGES 665-666 Exercises

1. $\Delta x = \frac{2 - 0}{2} = 1$, $y_i = \frac{3}{2}i\Delta x = \frac{3}{2}i$, therefore, $A_2 = \sum\limits_{i=1}^{2} y_i \Delta x = \sum\limits_{i=1}^{2} \frac{3}{2}i =$

$\frac{3}{2}(3) = \frac{9}{2}$ 3. $A_{16} = \frac{51}{16}$ 5. $A_2 = 8$, $A_4 = 7$, $A_{16} = 6\frac{1}{4}$, $A = 6$ 7. $A_2 = 4$,

$A_4 = 5$, $A_{16} = 5\frac{3}{4}$, $A = 6$ 9. $A_8 = \frac{51}{16}$ 11. $A_{16} = \frac{1}{8}\sum\limits_{i=1}^{16} \sqrt{i} \approx \frac{44.47}{8}$ 13. A_4

$= \frac{25}{4}$ 15. If $n = 4$, $\Delta x = \frac{4 - 2}{4} = \frac{1}{2}$

PAGES 668-669 Exercises

1. $\Delta x = \frac{1}{2}$, $x_0 = 0$, $y_0 = 0$, $x_1 = \frac{1}{2}$, $y_1 = \frac{1}{2}$, $x_2 = 1$, $y_2 = \frac{2}{2}$, $x_3 = \frac{3}{2}$, $y_3 = \frac{3}{2}$,

$x_4 = 2$, $y_4 = 2$, $T = \frac{1}{2}(\frac{1}{2} + \frac{2}{2} + \frac{3}{2} + \frac{2}{2}) = \frac{1}{2}(4) = 2$ 3. $\Delta x = \frac{1}{4}$, $x_0 = 1$, $y_0 = 1$,

$x_1 = 1 + \frac{1}{4} = \frac{5}{4}$, $y_1 = (\frac{5}{4})^3 = \frac{125}{64}$, $x_2 = 1 + \frac{2}{4} = \frac{6}{4}$, $y_2 = (\frac{6}{4})^3 = \frac{216}{64}$, $x_3 = 1 + \frac{3}{4} = \frac{7}{4}$,

$y_3 = (\frac{7}{4})^3 = \frac{343}{64}$, $x_4 = 2$, $y_4 = (\frac{8}{4})^3 = \frac{512}{64}$, $\frac{1}{2}y_0 = \frac{1}{2} = \frac{32}{64}$, $\frac{1}{2}y_4 = \frac{256}{64}$, $T =$

$\frac{1}{4}(\frac{32}{64} + \frac{125}{64} + \frac{216}{64} + \frac{343}{64} + \frac{256}{64}) = \frac{1}{4}(\frac{972}{64}) = \frac{243}{64} \approx 3.80$ 5. 3.45   7. 3.832

9. 732.00   11. 32.78

13. $\Delta x = \frac{b - a}{4}$, $x_0 = a$, $y_0 = ma$, $x_1 = a + \frac{b - a}{4}$, $y_1 = m(a + \frac{b - a}{4})$, $x_2 =$

$a + \frac{2(b - a)}{4}$, $y_2 = m(a + \frac{2(b - a)}{4})$, $x_3 = a + \frac{3(b - a)}{4}$, $y_3 = m(a + \frac{3(b - a)}{4})$,

$x_4 = a + \frac{4(b - a)}{4} = b$, $y_4 = mb$, $\frac{1}{2}y_0 = \frac{ma}{2}$, $\frac{1}{2}y_4 = \frac{mb}{2}$, $T_4 = \frac{b - a}{4}\left[\frac{ma}{2} + m(a + \frac{b - a}{4})\right.$

$+ m(a + \frac{2(b - a)}{4}) + m(a + \frac{3(b - a)}{4}) + \frac{mb}{2}\right] = \frac{m(b - a)}{4}(\frac{a}{2} + a + \frac{b - a}{4} + a + \frac{2(b - a)}{4}$

$+ a + \frac{3(b - a)}{4} + \frac{b}{2}) = \frac{m(b - a)(b + a)}{2} = \frac{m(b^2 - a^2)}{2}$, $T_8 = \frac{(b - a)}{8}\left[\frac{ma}{2} + m(a + \frac{b - a}{8}\right.$

$+ m(a + \frac{2(b - a)}{8}) + m(a + \frac{3(b - a)}{8}) + m(a + \frac{4(b - a)}{8}) + m(a + \frac{5(b - a)}{8})$

$+ m(a + \frac{6(b - a)}{8}) + m(a + \frac{7(b - a)}{8}) + \frac{mb}{2}\right] = \frac{m(b - a)(b + a)}{2} = \frac{m(b^2 - a^2)}{2}$

S-84 CHAPTER 14

$T_4 = T_8$ since the region is a trapezoid and therefore $T_4 = T_8 =$ area of the region.

PAGE 673 Exercises

1. $A_2^5(2x) = \frac{2}{2}(5^2 - 2^2) = 25 - 4 = 21$ 3. $\frac{63}{2}$ 5. 18.75   7. $A_0^3(x^2)$

$= \frac{3^3 - 0^3}{3} = 9$ 9. $\frac{91}{3}$ 11. 24   13. Since $m < 0$, $A_2^4(-x) = \frac{(-1)}{2}(4^2 - 2^2) = 6$

15. $A_{-2}^0(x) = \frac{1}{2}(0^2 - (-2)^2) = -2$. This is true since $f(x) < 0$ for all $x \in [-2, 0]$.
Therefore, $A_{-2}^0 = |-2| = 2$.

17. $\Delta x = \frac{b - a}{n}$, $y_i = p(a + \frac{i(b - a)}{n})^2$, $A_n = \sum_{i=1}^{n} p(a + \frac{i(b - a)}{n})^2 \frac{(b - a)}{n} =$

$= \frac{p(b - a)}{n} \cdot \sum_{i=1}^{n}(a + \frac{i(b - a)}{n})^2 = \frac{p(b - a)}{n} \cdot \sum_{i=1}^{n}\left[a^2 + \frac{2ai(b - a)}{n} + \frac{i^2(b - a)^2}{n^2}\right]$

$= \frac{p(b - a)}{n}\left[na^2 + \frac{2a(b - a)(n + 1)n}{2n} + \frac{(b - a)^2(n(n + 1)(2n + 1))}{6n^2}\right]$

$= \frac{p(b - a)}{n}\left[na^2 + (ab - a^2)(n + 1) + \frac{(b - a)^2(2n^3 + 3n^2 + n)}{6n^2}\right]$

$A_a^b(px^2) = \lim_{n \to \infty}\left[p(b - a)a^2 + p(b - a)(ab - a^2) + \frac{p(b - a)(ab - a^2)}{n}\right.$

$\left. + \frac{p(b - a)(b - a)^2(2n^2 + 3n + 1)}{6n^2}\right] = pa^2b - pa^3 + pab^2 - pa^2b - pa^2b + pa^3$

$+ \lim_{n \to \infty} \frac{p(b - a)(b - a)^2(1 + \frac{3}{2n} + \frac{1}{2n^2})}{3}$

$= pab^2 - pa^2b + \left[\frac{pb^3 - 2pab^2 + pa^2b - pab^2 + 2pa^2b - pa^3}{3}\right]$

$= \frac{3pab^2 - 3pa^2b + pb^3 - 2pab^2 + pa^2b - pab^2 + 2pa^2b - pa^3}{3} = \frac{p(b^3 - a^3)}{3}$

19. $\frac{1}{4}(b^4 - a^4)$

21. $y_i = \left[a + \dfrac{i(b-a)}{n}\right]^2 + 1$, $A_n = \displaystyle\sum_{i=1}^{n}\left(\left[a + \dfrac{i(b-a)}{n}\right]^2 + 1\right)\dfrac{b-a}{n}$

$= \dfrac{b-a}{n}\left[\displaystyle\sum_{i=1}^{n}\left(a^2 + \dfrac{2ai(b-a)}{n} + \dfrac{i^2(b-a)^2}{n^2}\right) + \displaystyle\sum_{i=1}^{n}1\right]$

$= \dfrac{b-a}{n}\left[na^2 + \dfrac{(2ab - 2a^2)n(n+1)}{2n} + \dfrac{(b-a)^2\left(\dfrac{n(n+1)(2n+1)}{6}\right)}{n^2} + n\right]$

$= a^2b - a^3 + (ab^2 - 2a^2b + a^3)(1 + \dfrac{1}{n}) + \dfrac{b^3 - 2ab^2 + a^2b - ab^2 + 2a^2b - a^3}{6}(1 + \dfrac{1}{n}) \cdot$

$(2 + \dfrac{1}{n}) + b - a$, $A_a^b(x^2 + 1) = \displaystyle\lim_{n\to\infty} A_n = a^2b - a^3 + ab^2 - 2a^2b + a^3 +$

$\dfrac{b^3 - 2ab^2 + a^2b - ab^2 + 2a^2b - a^3}{3} + b - a = \dfrac{b^3 - a^3}{3} + b - a$

23. $\dfrac{b^4 - a^4}{4} + 3(b - a)$

PAGES 677-678 Exercises

1. $\displaystyle\int_0^3 3x^2 dx = 3\int_0^3 x^2 dx = 3\dfrac{3^3 - 0^3}{3} = 27$ 3. $-\dfrac{7}{6}$ 5. $\dfrac{40}{3}$ 7. $\dfrac{8}{3}$ 9. 25

11. $\dfrac{-4}{21}$ 13. $\displaystyle\int_1^2 x\,dx = \dfrac{2^2 - 1^2}{2} = \dfrac{3}{2}$ and $\displaystyle\int_2^1 x\,dx = \dfrac{1^2 - 2^2}{2} = \dfrac{-3}{2}$ hence

$\displaystyle\int_2^1 x\,dx = -\int_1^2 x\,dx$ 15. $\displaystyle\int_{-1}^3 x^4 dx = \dfrac{244}{5}$ and $\displaystyle\int_3^{-1} x^4 dx = -\dfrac{244}{5}$ hence $\displaystyle\int_3^{-1} x^4 dx$

$= -\displaystyle\int_{-1}^3 x^4 dx$ 17. $\displaystyle\int_{-2}^0 x^3 dx = -4$ and $\displaystyle\int_0^{-2} x^3 dx = 4$ hence $\displaystyle\int_0^{-2} x^3 dx = -\int_{-2}^0 x^3 dx$

19. In each case, $\displaystyle\int_b^a f(x)dx = -\int_a^b f(x)dx$. That is, the integral from x = b to

x = a of f(x) is equal to the negative of the integral from x = a to x = b of f(x)

21. $\displaystyle\int_1^2 2x^2 dx + \int_2^5 2x^2 dx = \dfrac{248}{3}$, $\displaystyle\int_1^5 2x^2 dx = \dfrac{248}{3}$ hence $\displaystyle\int_1^2 2x^2 dx + \int_2^5 2x^2 dx$

$= \displaystyle\int_1^5 2x^2 dx$ 23. $\displaystyle\int_a^c 3x^2 dx + \int_c^b 3x^2 dx = b^3 - a^3$, $\displaystyle\int_a^b 3x^2 dx = b^3 - a^3$ hence

$$\int_a^c 3x^2 dx + \int_c^b 3x^2 dx = \int_a^b 3x^2 dx \quad 25. \quad G'(x) = 6x^2 - 1 \quad 27. \quad G(b) - G(a)$$

$$= 2b^3 - b + 2 - (2a^3 - a + 2) = 2(b^3 - a^3) - (b - a) \quad 29. \quad G'(x) = 1, \int_a^b$$

$$G'(x)dx = \int_a^b 1 dx = b - a = G(b) - G(a) \quad 31. \quad \int_a^b G'(x) \, dx = \int_a^b 3x^2 dx = b^3 - a^3$$

$$= G(b) - G(a) \quad 33. \quad \int_a^b G'(x)dx = \int_a^b 2x dx = b^2 - a^2 = (b^2 - 1) - (a^2 - 1)$$

$$= G(b) - G(a)$$

PAGES 683-684 Exercises

1. The curve of $y = 2x - x^2$ intersects x axis at 0 and 2. $\therefore \int_0^2 (2x - x^2)dx$

$= \dfrac{2(2)^2}{2} - \dfrac{2^3}{3} - 0 = 4 - \dfrac{8}{3} = \dfrac{4}{3}$ 3. The curve of $y = x^2 - 9$ intersects x axis at 3.

$\therefore \int_1^4 (x^2 - 9)dx = \left| \int_1^3 (x^2 - 9)dx \right| + \int_3^4 (x^2 - 9)dx = \dfrac{38}{3} = \left| 9 - 27 - \dfrac{1}{3} + 9 \right|$

$+ \dfrac{64}{3} - 36 - 9 + 27 = \dfrac{38}{3}$ 5. The curve of $y = 2x - x^2$ intersects $y = -3$ at

$x = -1$ and $x = 3$. $\therefore \int_{-1}^3 \left[2x - x^2 - (-3) \right] dx = \dfrac{32}{3}$. 7. Two curves intersect at

$(-2, 8)$ and $(2, 8)$. $\therefore \int_{-2}^2 2x^2 dx - \int_{-2}^2 (x^4 - 2x^2)dx = \int_{-2}^2 \left[2x^2 - (x^4 - 2x^2) \right] dx$

$= \dfrac{128}{15}$ 9. The curve $y = x^3 - x^2 - 2x$ intersects y axis at -1, 0, and 2.

$\therefore \int_{-1}^0 (x^3 - x^2 - 2x)dx + \left| \int_0^2 (x^3 - x^2 - 2x)dx \right| = \dfrac{37}{12}$ 11. Two curves intersect

at $(-2, -6)$, $(0, 0)$, and $(2, 6)$. $\therefore \int_{-2}^0 (x^3 - x - 3x)dx + \int_0^2 \left[3x - (x^3 - x) \right] dx$

$= 8$ 13. $\int_0^1 x^n dx (n \in W)$ is the area of the region bounded by $y = x^n$, $x = 0$,

$x = 1$, and the x axis.   15. Decreases.   17. $\int_0^2 (x^2 + x - x)dx = \frac{8}{3}$ 19. No.

21. Yes. No.

PAGES 687-688 Exercises

1. $\int_0^3 \pi(2x + 1)^2 dx = \pi\int_0^3 (4x^2 + 4x + 1)dx = \pi(4\frac{(3)^3}{3} + 4 \cdot \frac{3^2}{2} + 3) = 57\pi$

3. $\int_0^2 \pi(x^2 + 1)^2 dx = \frac{206}{15}\pi$ 5. $\int_0^1 \pi(x - x^2)^2 dx = \frac{\pi}{30}$

7. $\int_0^4 \pi\left[(5x - x^2)^2 - x^2\right]dx = \frac{384}{5}\pi$ 9. $\int_0^2 \pi\left[8^2 - (x^3)^2\right]dx = \frac{768}{7}\pi$

11. $x^2 = y$, $h = \Delta y$, $\int_0^2 \pi y\, dy = 2\pi$ 13. $\int_0^1 \pi(y - y^2)dy = \frac{1}{6}\pi$

15. $\int_0^4 \pi y\, dy = 8\pi$ 17. Since the axis is the line $y = 4$, the interval is

$\left[0, 2\right]$. Use the translation equation $y = y' + 4$, or $y' = x^2 - 4$, then $\int_0^2 \pi$

$(x^2 - 4)^2 dx = \frac{256}{15}\pi$ 19. $\int_0^4 \pi\left[(-4)^2 - (\sqrt{y} - 2)^2\right]dy = \frac{184}{3}\pi$

21. $2\int_0^a \pi(\frac{b}{a}\sqrt{a^2 - x^2})^2 dx = \frac{4}{3}\pi b^2 a$

PAGES 688-689 Chapter Objectives and Review

1. See the text.   3. $3x^2$ 5. $\frac{2}{x}$ 7. $\frac{-35}{x^6}$ 9. $5x^4 - 6x^2 - 3$ 11. a. 23

b. 37   13. a. $v(t) = 1280 - 32t$ b. 640, 0, -640   c. -32   d. $t = 80$ e. -1280

15. Area $= \sum_{i=1}^{16} 4 \cdot i^2 \cdot (\frac{3}{16})^3 = 4 \cdot (\frac{3}{16})^3 \cdot \frac{16(16 + 1)(32 + 1)}{6} = \frac{3^2}{4 \cdot 16}$

$\cdot \frac{(17)(33)}{2} = 39\frac{57}{128}$ 17. Answers will vary.   19. 18.75   21. $\int_3^9 3x^2 dx$

$= 9 \cdot 78 = 702$ 23. $\displaystyle\int_0^1 (x^3 - x^4)dx + \int_1^2 (x^4 - x^3)dx = \frac{1}{20} + 2\frac{9}{20} = 2\frac{1}{2}$

25. $\displaystyle\int_{-\sqrt{2}}^{\sqrt{2}} (2 - x^2)dx = \frac{8\sqrt{2}}{3}$ 27. $\displaystyle\int_0^4 \pi x^2 dy = \pi \int_0^4 y\, dy = 8\pi$

29. $\displaystyle\int_0^8 \pi x^2 dy = \pi \int_0^8 y^{\frac{2}{3}}dy = \frac{3\pi}{5}(8^{\frac{5}{3}} - 0^{\frac{5}{3}}) = \frac{3\pi}{5}(32) = \frac{96\pi}{5}$

PAGE 691 Chapter Test

1. $2x - 3 + e^x$ 3. $\dfrac{e^x}{x} + e^x \ln x$ 5. $a(t) = 48 - 36t$ 7. $a(t) > 0$ when $0 <$

$t < \dfrac{4}{3}$ 9. $\dfrac{54 - 18}{3 - 1} = \dfrac{36}{2} = 18$ 11. $\displaystyle\int_0^2 x^3 dx = \frac{1}{4}(2^4 - 0^4) = 4$

13. $\displaystyle\int_0^5 (3x^2 + 5x^4)dx = 3250$ 15. $\displaystyle\int_0^5 (mx + b)dx = \frac{25m}{2} + 5b$